1992 Novel & Short Story Writer's Market

1992

Novel & Short Story Writer's Market

Editor: Robin Gee

Assistant Editor: Christine Martin

Writer's Digest Books

Cincinnati, Ohio

Distributed in Canada by McGraw-Hill Ryerson,
300 Water St.,
Whitby, Ontario L1N 9B6.
Distributed in Australia by Kirby Books, Private
Bag No. 19, P.O. Alexandria NSW 2015.
Distributed in New Zealand by David Bateman
Ltd., P.O. Box 100-242, North Shore Mail Cen-
tre, Auckland 10

Managing Editor, Market Books Department:
Constance J. Achabal; Assistant Managing Editor: Glenda Tennant Neff

1992 Novel & Short Story Writer's Market.

International Standard Serial Number
ISSN 0897-9812
International Standard Book Number
0-89879-486-2

Cover illustration by Tom Post

Contents

The Markets

From the Editors

Welcome to the 1992 *Novel & Short Story Writer's Market*. We think of this edition as the "community issue," because if there's one thing we've learned from talking with writers this year it's that they are part of a very strong and far-reaching support network.

Not only do writers come together to critique each others' work, but they also form groups to share mutual concerns and triumphs. Some writers meet to hear their peers read, while others organize in support of issues important to all. Some writers communicate through regular meetings, some use newsletters, others attend conferences and still others "talk" to each other on computer networks. While the act of writing is a solitary one, the writing life can be a very full one.

We've designed the book to be a part of this writing community—a place where we can share with you what we learn from other writers, as well as editors and publishers. This is a place where you can hear from Amy Tan about how important her own writing group has been to her career and from Ira Levin about how he finds extraordinary ideas in seemingly ordinary events. David Huddle shares with you what his writing has meant to him and Donna Levin reveals her tips for getting started on your novel.

You'll also find a variety of tips and advice from many other novelists and short story writers. From Nanci Kincaid, for example, you will learn how to handle dialect—Southern and otherwise—and from Laura Hendrie how to use criticism to improve your writing. You'll find articles from both editors and writers with answers to your questions on submitting manuscripts, plotting, developing characters and publishing.

Whether you're a new or experienced writer, you'll find helpful information on dealing with editors and publishers in The Business of Fiction Writing. This is the section covering all the basics and the "nitty-gritty" of manuscript submission—from preparation to mailing to approach.

You'll find, too, the market listings provide much more than just names and addresses. Each editor and publisher included in the listings has taken time to reflect upon their needs and make their policies available to writers. Often they've included advice on how to approach them or how a writer can "make it" in their field. Every listing, therefore, is a personal message.

Close-up interviews also add to our community. This year writers Frank Chin, Sue Grafton, Robert Pope and C.J. Cherryh share with us their views on writing and give you a few helpful tips along the way. In this collection of interviews we've also gathered together editors from around the world, including Hawaii, New York, Saskatchewan and Paris.

We've also initiated four new sections under the title Resources. The first section offers information on conferences and workshops held in almost every state and province in North America—and a few overseas. Following this are retreats and writers colonies for those who need some concentrated time to work. We've included a section on organizations and other resources for writers, including gathering places and writers "rooms." Finally there's a selection of magazines to help you keep in touch with what other writers are doing, as well as help you learn more about your field.

Writers of popular fiction have long known the value of networking and sharing ideas with others interested in the same work. We went to a number of those writers and asked for names of people in the industry they felt were on top of changes and trends in the field. From this list we contacted writers, editors, publishers, agents and booksellers. The result is our "Popular Fiction Report" on page 36. Here you'll find out how western novels are changing, what types of mysteries sell best and, generally, what's happening in fantasy, horror, romance and science fiction as well.

Our book is a group effort. We gather information from editors and publishers and visit writers groups to talk about the market for fiction, but we also rely on your comments, questions and suggestions.

Feedback from our readers and from the readers of our other books for writers, artists and photographers led us to an important decision this year. So many of you had questions and concerns about working with agents that we developed a new book devoted to the subject, *The Guide to Literary Agents & Art/Photo Reps*. This book enables us to answer many more questions and in greater depth than ever before. You will find most of the agents previously listed in our book now listed in this new volume along with others not previously listed here.

While many of the markets listed in our book also accept poetry—and this year we've indicated this in the listings—you will find more detailed information on poetry markets in *Poet's Market*. If you write fiction for children or if you write humorous fiction, you will find markets in our book, but you may also want to see *Children's Writer's & Illustrator's Market* or *Humor & Cartoon Markets* if you specialize in these areas.

At *Novel & Short Story Writer's Market* we're pleased to be able to pass on a wealth of information from writers, editors and publishers. We hope, too, you will share your knowledge with us. In the meantime, we wish you the best of luck with your writing and, remember, you're not alone.

Robin Gee

Editor

Christine Martin

Assistant Editor

Writing
Techniques

An Interview with Amy Tan

by Perri Weinberg-Schenker

That Amy Tan even attempted to be a writer is a major victory of tenacity and perseverance. Her parents urged her to embrace a medical career. Standardized test scores throughout school indicated that her worst skills were in writing. And when, despite such odds, she finally took a job as a professional writer, her boss informed her that she would be better suited to project management.

"Fine," she responded. "I quit. I'm going to go off to be a freelance writer."

"Fat chance," was his retort. "You'll be lucky if you make a dime."

Many dimes later, Tan is the bestselling author of *The Joy Luck Club* and *The Kitchen God's Wife*. At the time of this interview, she had just completed a screenplay of *The Joy Luck Club* and was enthusiastically researching her third book, whose working title is *The Year of No Flood*. Her almost meteoric rise from her start in 1985 as a successful but anonymous freelance business writer to her status today as a celebrated author has been, by all accounts including her own, charmed. Her work has been published without ever having been submitted; agents and publishers have, in effect, come knocking on her door.

"I had people believe in me as a fiction writer before I ever believed in myself," she says. "I began to feel at some point that there was something beyond myself that was pushing me to be a writer."

This statement hints at the same mystical qualities that imbue Tan's books, both of which explore the Chinese culture that is her heritage. Born in 1952 in Oakland, California, she is first-generation Chinese-American, the daughter of a minister who captivated her with his sermons and a mother who had a knack for telling fascinating tales. Hailed not only as a brilliant novelist but as a pioneer in a new genre of American literature, her success has been both exhilarating and burdensome; yet she proves to be unaffected and straightforward, giving unhurried, thoughtful responses to all questions about her work.

PW-S: You were a successful business writer — a workaholic, I understand — before turning to fiction. What prompted the decision? Was it a difficult transition to make?

AT: I didn't really know why people hired me as a freelance writer for such a long time. I didn't necessarily think I was the greatest writer in the world; I thought it was because I was so accommodating. I literally would take phone calls at 2 a.m. and have a presentation written for someone by 9 a.m. It was a big leap of faith for me to say "No, I'm sorry, I don't work on weekends" or "I'm sorry, I'm booked. I have as many projects as I can handle."

That leap of faith for me came in part because I needed time to live a life that was meaningful to me, that would include something more important than this fear I have that I would somehow fail if I didn't work 90 hours a week. I took jazz piano and started to read fiction and write fiction so I began to have all these interests in my life that required my time. As part of a deal with myself that I would take it seriously and not be this dilettante — which I had been a lot of my life — I made a commitment not to work more than 50 hours a week. During those times, to reward myself, I would play the piano and write fiction.

Perri Weinberg-Schenker *is a freelance book editor and has written for a variety of publications.*

At first I mostly read. I made half-starts at some writing, and it was around that time, in 1985 or 1986, that I went to my first writer's workshop.

PW-S: That must have been the Squaw Valley Community of Writers workshop. Can you tell me what that was like and how it was a turning point for you?

AT: I sent in a manuscript that was terrible. It was a frightening experience for me because I arrived there thinking I was the worst writer at the conference and they would laugh me right out of there. It seemed everybody had been writing for years and years and had an agent interested, an editor interested, and I was the most inexperienced fiction writer there. There was terminology bantered around that I didn't understand. I didn't even know at the time what "point of view" meant for a writer. I'd ask myself, "What does she mean by voice? What is pathetic fallacy?"

Actually, it was wonderful. It was like somebody turning on the lights and showing me everything that I had been stumbling over and saying, "This is why you're stumbling."

I showed my manuscript to Molly Giles; she wasn't my teacher, but you could get a second opinion from another teacher. She was great. She circled things in my manuscript and said, "There's no consistent voice here. Here's the beginning of a story, here's the beginning of a story, here's the beginning of a story. What you should do is take one of these beginnings and try to focus on what that story is and the voice that tells the story."

And I thought, "This is great. There are all of these questions: What is the story? What is the voice? How do you know what a story is? Is it defined by the ending?" Instead of being crushed—because I did see a lot of people crushed when they didn't get a contract right on the spot—I was elated. And I knew right then, that week, that this was what I wanted to do the rest of my life. That it would be worthwhile for my lifetime to look at these questions and to use fiction as a way to answer them.

PW-S: You're in a writer's group now with Molly Giles, aren't you? How important has that group been to you? What do you think a writer should look for in such a group?

AT: I was in another group briefly and we had somebody who was not a teacher but just another unpublished writer, whose philosophy was: "We don't need to bash each other; we need to support one another." I decided that was not the group for me. My motivation was to *improve* my writing; I needed to hear people tell me what wasn't working. So I think a writer should understand what he or she wants to get out of it. If what they want is effusive support, I'm not sure their writing would improve, but maybe all they need is that encouragement. And that's important, too.

I wanted to be in a group where somebody was in charge, a leader, a teacher—that authority that controls the group and determines how things would be run. And it should be somebody whose work I really admired. That's where Molly came in. We met once a week and would read our work aloud—say 10 or 15 pages. It's amazing what you discover when you read your work aloud. You trip over the very things you worked the hardest on, those things that you think are so clever, so brilliantly executed. You don't even need anybody to tell you they're false; you hear it.

I advocate reading work aloud, whether you read it to yourself or to a group. A group is much more painful, and that's why it's a good experience. Because if you're really serious about getting your work read, well, somebody's going to read it someday, and you might as well have the pain of knowing what works and what doesn't work in the beginning, before it's out there.

I think a group is a wonderful way to get feedback because, if you're able to accept that kind of criticism, it opens up better possibilities for the story.

PW-S: Do you still participate in the group?

AT: I do, although my schedule makes it impossible to attend weekly. I have Molly read everything and give incisive comments, as well as my editor. I don't listen to everybody's opinions; it's important to know who your readers are, whose sensibilities are closest to yours. You can have somebody saying, "I'd like it to be more mystical here" or "Why don't we have a love affair going on there," and that kind of advice is not helpful. That's the voice of a reader who really wants to be the writer of that story.

PW-S: I understand that when you first were contemplating writing fiction, you found it helpful to read interviews with writers. Did any in particular influence you?

AT: I don't recall exactly which ones, but I certainly read those in your publication. I also bought back issues of *The Paris Review* interviews and the one I liked best was a volume devoted just to women writers. When I was in college, all of my professors seemed to assign male writers and that was one of the reasons, I think, why I didn't seriously consider becoming a fiction writer. There was something in me that realized I didn't have the sensibilities to write as they were writing. So I was always fascinated to read any interviews with women about what writing meant to them. I remember in particular that I was very encouraged by women who said that as they wrote they weren't always sure of, for example, endings. That you could end up discovering the story just as a reader would.

PW-S: I read that Louise Erdrich's *Love Medicine* had a tremendous effect on you. Have there been other major influences on you and your writing?

AT: I would have to say that the most profound influences are the storytelling qualities of my mother and father. I say that because I think it's important for people to know that writers don't simply take on the great literature of our time as models. There are other influences that are more true than reading a book and saying, "Gosh, I love *Jane Eyre*."

Those certainly had influences on me, as well: *Jane Eyre*, and from very early times, the fairy tale. Then when I started to read fiction again, I fell in love with what I discovered was a very strong voice, the voice of characters and narrators that controlled that voice. And that's where Louise Erdrich came in. I read the book *Love Medicine* and was astounded by the diversity of voices and yet how absolutely true each one was, and what control this writer had over each of those voices. And I thought to myself at the time that this was what it was to be a writer: to discover one's own voice. Not take this voice that I loved so much, Louise Erdrich's, and try to imitate it, but to find a voice that was as unique and as true to the things I wanted to write about, and make that my own.

PW-S: The voice sounds like a somewhat vague quality—sort of related to style, but different. Can you define it?

AT: I've always felt that finding a voice is like embarking on a journey. I had asked a question rich enough that it would take me a lifetime to find the full answer. What I've discovered so far—and I think it will change over time—is that the voice is what determines which stories will be told. Maybe other writers find it's different, but I don't have a story until I have a voice. It seems very strange to me that you could have a story first and then go out and try to seek the voice.

I hear in this voice a sensibility and where that sensibility comes from in terms of life experience. Was this a voice imbued with pain? With humor? With a certain sensitivity toward language? How were emotions conveyed in that language? Within the voice there can be a style in the way language is used, and I think the aspects of style are much more in the control of the author, giving it an additional spin—because my voices spin out of control, leading the story where they want and rambling a lot. The style is what I put into it. But the voice always surprises me.

Whenever I speak about it, I feel like I'm talking about something mystical, and it's not really mystical. It's an enlargement of imagination, in believing so much in these characters that I have to give them qualities very much like a real person. With *The Kitchen God's*

Wife, it was much easier because the qualities of that voice were pretty much from my mother. I knew from a single word whether it was true to the voice. *Terror*. She would never use a word like that. She would use a completely different word.

PW-S: So the character of Winnie in *The Kitchen God's Wife* shares much in common with your mother. And in your other works, *The Joy Luck Club* and the short story "Fish Cheeks," you also deal with Chinese mothers and their Chinese-American daughters. Will you ever write about characters who aren't Chinese?

AT: My next book has two main characters, one of whom isn't Chinese. It uses the backdrop of history. Set in the 1890s, it's a story about a young boy and a missionary. It's my opportunity to look at questions I have about one's intentions, and consequences, and where your responsibilities lie in both those directions.

PW-S: Multiculturalism is a major focus in literature today. Do you think it's important to focus on different cultures as a learning device, or is it best to look beyond those differences and find the common ground?

AT: I think what enriches American literature is a diversity of voices. What people are beginning to recognize – and this is wonderful – is that all these different voices *are* American literature. We're not categorizing anymore, which is what people did in the beginning. When *The Joy Luck Club* came out, I was Amy Tan, writer of ethnic literature, Amy Tan, writer of Asian-American literature, Chinese-American literature, immigrant literature. That stopped happening after the book became a mainstream success. Once a piece of work achieves a certain amount of commercial success, it gets accepted as part of all American experience.

I give as much support as I can to writers, Asian-American writers especially. One practice I think is not good is the policy of assigning reviews of those books only to Asian-American reviewers. It happened a lot with *The Joy Luck Club* and happened less with *The Kitchen God's Wife*. But the newly published writers – Gish Jen and Gus Lee and David Wong Louie – end up getting reviewed by Asian-American reviewers. It worries me that people who read those reviews might say, "Yes, this is good from an Asian-American standpoint, but it isn't for me." I think that's the time to take it into the public and say, "This is literature for everybody."

PW-S: A lot has been written about you as being the first Asian-American since Maxine Hong Kingston to find your literary voice. And now other Asian-American writers are being published. Do you find that being in the forefront is a burden, or is there something liberating about being able to create a new literary niche?

AT: I'm conflicted. On one hand, I do as much as I can to support any new voice, whether it's Asian-American or Hispanic or whatever. And I think that's an exciting position to be in. But I think being hailed as some sort of pioneer is a burden. It's unfair mostly to new writers, because we end up being compared like so many brands of soap. And there's also the burden of responsibility of having to point out that this is not a fad, that there have been people writing for a long time; they're not doing it because it's suddenly in vogue.

PW-S: I've read the story of how seemingly effortless it was for you to get published. Was it really that charmed? Or were there hidden difficulties that no one knows about?

AT: Unfortunately, you're not far from wrong. It was charmed. It was the most incredible amount of luck. And I say it's unfortunate because now certain unpublished writers take this as a model of what can happen typically, and I know this does not happen typically. I doubted it all the way. I kept saying, "This will never happen" – and it kept happening. I went to Squaw Valley and I had that awful story, which I rewrote. Then Molly mentioned it to somebody, and somebody from a little magazine called, and the third rewrite got published. Then somebody from *Seventeen* saw it, and they published it.

PW-S: Did that story eventually end up in *The Joy Luck Club*?

AT: Yes, it was "Rules of the Game."

I had this vision of sending stuff off to *The New Yorker* and gleefully decorating my bulletin board and then my wall with mimeographed rejections. I was going to take this with such grace and pragmatism, that this is the life of the writer. And suddenly I had this agent who came to me and said, "I've read this story and I'd like to be your agent."

PW-S: And this agent sold *The Joy Luck Club*?

AT: I had three stories that she took to New York. And I never really paid attention to the fact that she was going to New York to sell these stories. I still did not believe that could happen, because everything I heard was that if you sell a collection of short stories, you'd better be published in *The New Yorker* and *The Atlantic* and several other good small literary magazines and have a novel waiting in the wings. And I had three short stories. Who's going to buy a book from an unknown writer with three stories?

My husband and I were on vacation when all these events were happening — I had just gotten this agent and things were being published without my even sending them out — and I said to him, "I want us to remember this conversation. I don't know what's happening, and it's kind of scary. I feel like somebody's pushing me." It was as if I had a guardian angel. It was just magic.

PW-S: Did you ever have to worry about anything being rejected?

AT: I did get maybe two or three rejection letters from *The New Yorker*. But what's amazing is that I'd get a little penned note at the bottom, or I'd actually get a personal response typed out telling me why the story didn't work. I never had to bite my lips, wondering if someone was going to buy what I had written.

I wish I could say there was a lot more that went into trying to get published. There was a lot more that went into the writing, and I would emphasize that. There was a lot that went into the pain in my life from childhood and other experiences.

It was reported back to me once after I had left a conference where I had given an opening talk that another writer said about me, "She doesn't deserve this. She hasn't paid her dues." And I thought, "That's a mistaken notion." The process of publishing is not that you stand in line and wait your turn. That's a communistic notion, that everything gets apportioned equally. Publishing is much more democratic. You get elected. You get chosen.

PW-S: Did the experience of being so easily chosen with *The Joy Luck Club* make approaching your second book especially difficult?

AT: It made it terrorizing. I didn't know what people responded to. Was it the novelty of my being the first popular Chinese-American writer in a long time? Was it the fairy tale of being discovered that generated some publicity? I had a lot of doubts about who I was as a writer.

PW-S: Do you still?

AT: Not as great as I did back then. The doubts had to do with whether I had to write according to what people expected. Would they be disappointed if I wrote something different? And if so, would that mean I'm less of a writer? I discovered in that process — and it was such a painful experience to me — that I had to find again what was important to me about writing. Once I found that, I knew that no matter what happened, I wouldn't completely lose myself and be devastated. The reviews could be bad, the sales could be bad, and I would still have a sense of accomplishment, because I had learned something about writing. This was, after all, my first novel, because I had written *The Joy Luck Club* as a collection of short stories. So I learned something about the story and about pulling the story through. And I learned more about the voice; the voice had gotten stronger. And I learned something about myself and my mother and my family, about this quality of hope and strength that runs through my family. And that was the most important discovery.

PW-S: So *The Joy Luck Club* was conceived as a collection of short stories, although some have called it a novel or, more commonly, a "work of fiction." But *The Kitchen God's Wife* was written as a traditional novel. Will you go back to writing short stories?

AT: I have ideas for short stories, but the novel is more interesting to me because there's greater risk involved. At the same time, there's greater freedom: freedom to go off in different directions and then later, with the luxury of time, tying up those pieces. There can also be a bit of chaos and untrimmed edges to a novel that you cannot afford to have in a short story. A short story is a gem, and the facets have to be nearly perfect. You can't have extraneous characters and dialogue that don't advance the scene.

This is my notion for a novel, what I've discovered for myself: In the novel, you can create the world, and the world is not a neat and tidy place. You have scenes that are not hugely important, but they are part of the world in that novel. I can indulge myself a little bit by permitting those scenes. At the same time, I cannot indulge myself too much, or I'm at fault as the craftsperson.

I like to discover what pulls the story ahead, and the short story is more about what closes the story.

PW-S: I read that you were a rigorous editor, that you edited each page you wrote about a dozen times. Is that correct?

AT: I would say at least a dozen times. I have an idea of how much I've rewritten because when I wrote *The Joy Luck Club*, I went through at least 6,000 pages of paper. That was just from printing out and doing edits on the page. At the same time, I was reading out loud and doing edits on the screen, so there were many more versions that never made it to the page.

When I was writing *The Joy Luck Club* I would sometimes write a story in one day, and then I would spend the next month revising it over and over again. I did that with a chapter in *The Kitchen God's Wife*, called "Heaven's Breath." I liked the spontaneity of just writing, of getting carried away with the scene. I wrote it in a day, and then I had to spend a lot of time revising it. The original just spewed of emotions and words—I usually err on the side of excess in my writing. So when I edit I remove things, but I also read it out loud and look at every word. There has to be a certain rhythm to the language so that, for example, the emotions and tone of the voice match. I would say a lot has to do with the whole rhythm of what is being said, the rhythm of the whole structure of that chapter, and the rhythm of each sentence, especially in dialogue.

And it changes from day to day. One day I could read something and it sounds fine, and the next morning I read it and say, "I must have gremlins in my computer. This is really stilted and awkward." So I don't have that complete mastery as an editor, when I know exactly what's right and wrong. It's still a guessing game.

PW-S: How much time per day do you spend writing?

AT: It depends. I'm much more relaxed writing this screenplay than I am when I write fiction. When I'm writing fiction, it occupies my mind during all my waking hours. I usually start writing around 9 in the morning. If I have lunch, it's at home—probably a bowl of Cheerios and milk so I don't faint. Then I write until my husband comes home from work, which is 7:30 or 8. Then at night I read items related to what I'm writing about. So it's pretty constant and intense.

PW-S: Is it a struggle to discipline yourself to keep such a demanding schedule?

AT: For the most part, it's not difficult. I wouldn't want to be doing anything else. I love being in that world: It's going places and doing things and seeing people. Certainly there are points when it gets boring, when I'm rewriting something and I just want to go to sleep.

What's more difficult for me is trying to figure out how to write while I'm still doing publicity from the last book. I did a European tour and a paperback tour at the same time I was trying to write my second book. It's awful to be talking about an old book that you no longer are in love with, and being in love with a new book that you can't devote proper attention to. It's like talking about somebody you're divorced from when you're in love with somebody else and you just want to say, "I want to go be with this person that I love and not hark back to this old relationship."

PW-S: Are you beginning to have periods between books, or does one still blend into the next?

AT: Right now they blend together. I'm hoping to be able to save three months out of the year when I do nothing but the writing, and I can get out the most important part of the book. Three months would get me solidly into the book, so I wouldn't be flailing back and forth between doing publicity for one book and having to start over and over again on the next.

PW-S: What's your workspace like?

AT: I've always had an office in my house. Now I live in a condominium, and it's the first time I've been able to design my space according to the way I lead my life. I have three offices—most people have a guest bedroom; we have a guest office. My main office used to be a dressing room, but it looks out over San Francisco Bay and a bunch of rooftops and eucalyptus forest. I have a clock suspended in front of the window by the bay so I know that it's not just boats passing by; it's time passing by. I have this tendency, like everybody else, to drift off.

I put on a headset that blocks distractions, and I play the same music over and over again when I'm working on a particular scene or chapter. I associate that music with the scene. It's very hypnotic and helps me to get back into the same world I was in the day before, when I quit writing.

PW-S: Do you have other techniques or rituals that help you work?

AT: I love the feel of books and the look of pages, so I like to print out what I've written the way it will look when it's published, in Times Roman. Then I mark it all up.

I've always written by computer, so I have a portable laptop to use when I'm on an airplane. This is not to say writers should write on computers—they should use whatever they're most comfortable with—but I've always used computers, to the point where I cannot write a coherent sentence longhand. It's so painful to write thank-you letters: "I shall never forget the wonderful stew that you made." It's the most clichéd, bad writing. I pick up a pen and become self-conscious, revert back to what I was taught in grammar school about how I should write.

PW-S: I read that you like to burn incense when you work.

AT: That was sort of tongue-in-cheek. I was talking about the Muse and I said jokingly, "Oh, yes, I have this little wind chime and I burn incense." I do have, I have to say, a Chinese altar in my office. There's a woman there who serves as a reminder to me of why I write. I nicknamed her Lady Sorrowfree, and then I used her name at the end of my second book as a tribute to her. She has offerings of Johnnie Walker Black and Lucky Strike cigarettes and an urn of incense. It's done with a little bit of humor, and sometimes I light the incense just because I like the smell. But it's not as ritualistic as people would like to believe.

PW-S: What about writing exercises? Are there any particular methods or techniques you use to get yourself going?

AT: I usually remind myself that I can't wait for inspiration to catch up with me; I have to run after it myself. So I just have to start writing. I try to think of an image. It may be one object, such as a vase, or a certain kind of pen, or the look of a cracked cup sitting on a table. I'll look at that image, and from that image the world expands out a little and I see a scene. I create a world around the image, and I start to write about the world.

I'll give you an example: In *The Kitchen God's Wife*, there are these chopsticks. My mother had once told me about her dowry, and that she'd received these chopsticks with chains connecting them. The chain was so the chopsticks would never be separated. And she described how they were made out of pure silver, very heavy, very expensive. Then she said to me, "That whole set, never used, never touched." And that image always stayed in my mind; it was connected to an emotion. I didn't know whether the emotion was regret, or anger, or hope that they'd still be used. I started imagining those chopsticks being used by a whole banquet room full of people, and what each of those people might have been thinking. I was in the scene, and I had to get to know each of the people.

That, in a very simplified way, is how I use my imagination—often picking an image that comes from memory, which usually has a very strong emotional edge to it. And from there I build upon the imaginary world that this image resides in. I've always, since childhood, been quite adept at creating imaginary worlds. I'm able to think of a door, open it and go inside, look to the left and say, "This is what I see," look to the right and say, "This is what I see," look down and notice what shoes I'm wearing. It's like a movie reel. A lot of it is worthless junk, but I keep writing it, and I edit out. There might be only one paragraph that I save.

PW-S: Is there any specific advice you'd like to pass on to new or mid-career fiction writers who are trying to be published?

AT: My advice has more to do with how to be the best writer you can be. If you approach your writing with the idea, "How can I get published?" it'll make it that much harder to get published. From what I've learned in the publishing world—now that I've had a chance to meet some writers and editors and publishers—they're looking for something that's unique, not someone who writes just like Ray Carver or Anne Beattie or Anne Tyler. They have those people.

If you're committed to being the best writer you can be, to drawing from all those experiences that have made you who you are, the questions you've asked in your life from childhood—if you're honest enough to write about that without the self-consciousness of "Will I be published?"—the chances are much, much greater that somebody will notice. If it's good, if it's different, if it's honest, the match will be made.

It's also important for writers to think about the questions they ask themselves in their writing. I think writers who really push themselves are asking themselves questions about life: What is the meaning of life? What is the quality of hope? What is the responsibility between one's intentions and the consequences? Those don't have to be directly expressed in the story, but something should be there that you're exploring beyond just the story. I don't think a story has to completely resolve the question—at least, not from a plot point of view—but there should be an emotional resolution. For me, the purpose of fiction is not to provide answers, but to stir up questions that often disturb us and make us want to keep thinking more about our own lives.

An Interview with Ira Levin

by Anne Bowling

Mention the name of novelist Ira Levin and you're likely to draw a polite stare, unless you've stumbled across one of his avid readers. But mention the titles of some of his novels—*Rosemary's Baby, The Boys from Brazil, The Stepford Wives*—and you're likely to get instant recognition. His novels of macabre intrigue, which plunge ordinary protagonists into sinister and deadly circumstances, have become part of the American lexicon.

Publishers and filmmakers know Levin as a bankable craftsman of psychological thrillers. His 41-year career spans stage, novel and television writing. Four of his six novels have been bestsellers and have been made into films. His books have sold millions of copies and have been translated into several languages. His work also includes the blockbuster mystery/comedy "Deathtrap," which enjoyed a record-breaking run on Broadway.

Levin's career began in the early 1950s. He wrote scripts for some of the top television programs of the period: "Lights Out," "Clock" and the "U.S. Steel Hour." It was scriptwriting that he spent his college career preparing to do. Having studied short story, radio and screen writing, he entered a script competition for seniors at New York University.

"I entered that with a half-hour thriller, which was a runner-up," he says. "Someone at CBS suggested that I take it to an agent, that it was salable, and suggested an agent who was also just starting out. I brought the script to her, and she sold it to NBC. Before that, all I had done was the homework for my classes. I had been studying radio and screen writing, but television was new and so it was easier to break into."

The sale of that first script, he says, gave his parents the confidence to let him stay home after college for a year to write. And write he did. "I (wrote) a few more television plays while I was in this grace period with my parents before they kicked me out and made me earn a living," he recalls. "A couple of them sold, and a couple of them didn't. I still had some time left, so I thought I'd take a shot at a novel."

A Kiss Before Dying, which the *New York Herald Tribune* Book Review called "the most striking debut of the year," was the result of Levin's first "shot" at novel writing. It was completed on his twenty-third birthday ("I shudder to think of that now," he says.) This first novel was the tightly-crafted story of a college student whose hunger for wealth and power leads him into unspeakably vicious crimes against a prominent family with no shortage of eligible heiresses. Purchased by the first publisher his agent approached, *A Kiss Before Dying* quickly became a bestseller and earned Levin an Edgar Allan Poe Award as best first novel of 1953. Film rights were purchased shortly after its publication. Perhaps as remarkable as the critical acclaim for the novel and its public reception was the maturity of its craftsmanship. As Anthony Boucher of *The New York Times* wrote: "Levin combines great talent for pure novel writing—full-bodied characterization, subtle psychological exploration, vivid evocation of locale—with strict whodunit tricks as dazzling as anything ever brought off by Carr, Rawson, Queen or Christie."

While *A Kiss Before Dying* was his first novel, it did not mark his entrance to the suspense/mystery genre. His scriptwriting had already given him some schooling in the area—he describes "Clock" and "Lights Out" as "sort of like the 'Twilight Zone,' without the super-

Freelance writer and editor **Anne Bowling** *interviewed Allan Gurganus for the 1991* NSSWM *and is a frequent contributor to Writer's Digest Books.*

natural elements." He also credits the masters of the genre: "I think at that point I was very much influenced by the mysteries I had read in my early teens. Because I was—and still am—a great fan of classical mysteries by writers such as Ellery Queen, Agatha Christie and John Dickson Carr. They really are marvelously plotted. So I think *A Kiss Before Dying* reflects traditional mystery plotting to a certain degree."

The success of that first novel convinced Levin to begin a career as a fulltime writer, but the U.S. Army had other ideas. Shortly after Simon & Schuster bought *A Kiss Before Dying*, his draft notice arrived. His next novel, *Rosemary's Baby*, would not come until 14 years later. But this fluke of fate got Levin the chance to write for his other love, the theater. He was contacted by the "U.S. Steel Hour" to write the television adaptation of Mac Hyman's *No Time for Sergeants* (at that time a bestselling novel). Based on his success with the television adaptation, Levin was asked to write the stage adaptation. "So there I was right where I originally wanted to be, with a chance to write a play," he recalls. "I guess I've always been seduced by the theater. It's hard to say which was my primary ambition, because I've always wanted to write both books and plays. I stayed with the theater for the next 10 years or so. *Sergeants* was a hit, and then I wrote a couple of plays that weren't hits, and then I had one disaster. It was a musical (*Drat! The Cat*) which folded in a week. I said, 'I've had enough of this theater nonsense. I'm going to write another book.' And that was *Rosemary's Baby*."

Levin's return to the novel was a happy reunion. *Rosemary's Baby* was a bestseller, with more than 5 million copies sold, and was credited in some circles with setting a trend in the early 1970s for occult thrillers. It also marked Levin's departure from traditional mysteries and his establishment as a topflight writer of psychological thrillers. It is the element of the fantastic that sets his later novels apart from *Kiss*, and in those novels he combines his skills in traditional plotting and suspense with an ability to make plausible the most fantastic of premises. Barbara Nelson of *Library Journal* compared *Rosemary's Baby* to the work of Shirley Jackson: "The veneer of normality with hideous evil forces busy just beneath the surface is reminiscent of her work. Mr. Levin suspends disbelief so effectively that the unwary reader may well be converted to belief in the supernatural."

How does an author convince his readers that devil worshippers are at work in New York City; that Hitler could have been cloned and reproduced to create a Fourth Reich; that contemporary women could be transformed into robot housewives; that residents of a New York apartment building could become embroiled in a grisly series of slayings unwittingly by a young man with an elaborate surveillance system?

"I remember thinking when I began *Rosemary's Baby*, that because this is so unreal I've got to make it as believable as possible," says Levin. "And that's why I think I may have bent over backwards a little, because I tied it in with real events that were happening (in New York City) at the time. There's a transit strike that figures in the book, and a mayoral election." This juxtaposition of the banal with the fantastic is critical to a credible story, says Levin. "I think particularly if you're dealing with material that's supernatural or unreal, more than ever you have to keep those details real to make it believable. I like to try to show different aspects of the characters' lives. I like to find a moment when they're eating, or paying bills, and doing all the ordinary things, calling the folks back home, or whatever."

Levin also employs visualization to keep his writing realistic and accurate. "I think that is an important aspect of fiction," he says, "that you really visualize things clearly, and think things through, and remember the little things that make writing convincing. You know: When does she buy groceries, and does she remember to put them in the refrigerator? Sometimes, I do little sketches of floor plans of rooms to keep the movement straight, to know where people are going and to keep the windows in the same place."

It is the movement and pacing of his novels that critics almost universally applaud. The plots move swiftly and the writing is lean, with an economy of style that reflects his experience in writing for the stage. Levin doesn't linger on character development or meander into subplots with his stories—in fact, the whole of *Stepford Wives* spans 110 pages. Wrote *Newsweek*'s Alex Keneas of Levin's third novel, *This Perfect Day*: "Levin shows . . . that he knows how to handle a plot, twisting here and turning there, so that his story breezes along at 'top speed, no friction' . . . for a couple of hours it takes you away."

According to Levin, his ability to plot has become "instinctive," and as he writes a sort of sixth sense guides his building of suspense and story line. Levin says he attained his instinct "by reading, and seeing a lot of movies, which I did as a kid, and going to plays. When something works for you, and pleases you, you have to stop and analyze why does this work, and why do I like this moment? Then you do what you can to duplicate it."

Levin says the movement of his plots has its roots in the conflict and likens the conflict to "a good baseball game or a good prizefight. The good ones are always where the teams are evenly matched . . . and I also somehow find that with everything I write I'm in a way writing two stories at once—one that's seemingly going on on the surface, and the one I really know is going on underneath. A typical example being *Rosemary's Baby*, where I was well aware from page one what was really going on with the neighbors, and her husband, and I think somehow that comes through. The reader gets the sense that there's something that they're not aware of that they should be, and that creates a tension."

His ability to squeeze a lot of story into a little space came first through poet E.L. Mayo at Drake University, where Levin studied short story writing. "He was a great believer in clarity, in paring things down and in stripping away unnecessary words," he says. "In the theater, there's no room for wasted words. As soon as you start filling, the audience starts coughing, so you get accustomed to making everything as spare and to the point. At the same time, it leads to perhaps excessive spareness, because certainly one advantage to novel writing is that you do have room to spread things out a little . . . I'm very rigorous in asking, 'Is this necessary?' and, 'Is that invisible audience going to start coughing? So I do have this habit of keeping things very tight and structured."

The ideas for his fantastic tales have come from some not-so-fantastic sources. The idea for *Rosemary's Baby* came to him while he was listening to a lecture, "and I think maybe I got bored and my mind wandered," he recalls. *The Stepford Wives* was sparked by a chapter in Alvin Toffler's *Future Shock. The Boys from Brazil*, he says, was inspired by an article on cloning in *The New York Times*. "The article was bordered with a checkerboard of pictures of Hitler and Mozart, and of course I didn't think about Mozart, I thought about Hitler. It takes me a long time to develop an idea, and I thought, 'Well, this is such a natural idea for some kind of thriller, that somebody's going to have the book out before I can even start page one.' So I just clipped the article and put it in my file of interesting articles. A couple of years later I stumbled on it and thought, 'No, I haven't heard of any books on cloning and little Hitlers,' so I gave it more thought."

As for many novelists, it is a long journey from idea to publication for Levin—*Rosemary's Baby* was six years in the works. In the concept development stage, he says, it's not unusual for him to juggle the story line around, reach a dead end and put the whole thing aside to work on something else. If the idea's a good one, it comes back. "I always think of it as being the way an oyster develops a pearl," he says. "Each time the idea crops up, it's gotten a little more complex and larger, and I put it away again. Six months later, there's more to it, and suddenly somehow, it reaches the point where it really is a usable idea." From that point, the process accelerates, with note-making on character and plot development, which he says work together. "When I'm working, I really become a workaholic," he says. "With *Sliver*, I was really working up to 15 or 16 hours a day."

As a novelist, Levin has been quoted as saying his primary goal is to entertain. There is a litmus test he applies to each idea to determine its worthiness as entertainment. "I ask myself, 'If this really happened, would it at least rate a paragraph in the *Times*?' Because I believe that you shouldn't ask a reader to give his or her time unless you've got a really out-of-the-ordinary story to tell. I think certainly a great writer can deal with any kind of material and make it worth reading, but I feel writers who write about their conflicts with their parents or their first love—unless they're really terrific writers—are by and large imposing on the reader. Because while it may be of great interest to them and their close friends and family, I don't think it's of major interest to anyone else.

"If you can reflect morality in your work, fine. I guess in a way *The Boys from Brazil* does reflect certain basic values that I have. But that's a by-product, really. I think unless a writer entertains first and foremost, there's no chance of making a moral point. Because I think the reader will tune out on you. If I'm reading a book and I'm not enjoying it, I don't care how good it's supposed to be, I just stop reading."

It is perhaps the entertainment value of his novels that keeps the filmmaking industry coming back for contracts. Most recently, the rights to *Sliver* were purchased by Paramount Pictures. *A Kiss Before Dying* has reached the screen twice: First in 1956 and again in 1991, when it was redone by Universal Pictures. To Levin, certain novels do lend themselves more to film adaptation than others, although he does not go so far as to claim that his work for the stage has given his novels an advantage. "I don't conciously set out to write a book that's going to be filmable," he says, "but I do think there are certain things that they look for out there. Part of it is good conflict and good characters that can be cast interestingly. I think if you've got a good conflict with fully rounded characters, they become attractive roles for actors to play."

Levin sold all rights "in perpetuity" for the first film version of *A Kiss Before Dying* so when it was resold to Universal Pictures he did not benefit. Since then his film contracts all contain provisions which give him compensation for sequels and remakes "where usually you get half of what you were paid originally. Although that doesn't make sense," he adds. "If they're going to remake a film, that means the first one was successful, and if anything you should get more."

Creative control is much more elusive, he says. "I was very lucky with *Rosemary's Baby*, because Roman Polanski ... was very faithful to the book. But with *Sliver*, while I was writing it I thought, 'Well, I'm really going to retain control over this,' but somehow when it comes to the reality of the situation, there's just no way that you can, without getting an ulcer. And I finally got to the point where I said, 'Okay, I'm just going to sell it and keep my fingers crossed.' So far, the producer has been very nice."

The business of Levin's writing has been handled by an agent since before he graduated from New York University, dating back to his first script sale to NBC. Levin suggests young writers looking for their first manuscript sale can benefit from an agent: "While it seems there are still publishers who are willing to read unsolicited manuscripts, they are few and far between," he says. "So it helps to have an agent, but I don't think it's 100% essential.

"The biggest challenge for young writers today is just getting the work read. Today I think it's much harder than it was, because publishing is so much more a big business now. I remember with *Rosemary's Baby*, Random House was certainly a big publisher, but there was very much a family feeling, a warmth; the writer was welcome. And that just isn't the case today. You're dealing with large conglomerates, and you're just another product."

What You Get for Good Writing

by David Huddle

Good writing is a calling. Whoever answers it should not do so naively. One of my first "mature" stories, "Poison Oak," went through 25 drafts to reach its final 28 pages. I composed it on a typewriter, so I typed approximately 700 pages of words to produce the story—at about 15 minutes a page, or some 175 hours of typing. Back then, the going rate for typing was $1 a page. So if I'd typed all those pages for somebody else, I'd have made $700. Even if I'd typed only the 28 pages of the final draft for somebody else, I'd have made more than the $25 *The New England Review* paid me for it.

For all the writing I've published and that I count as "my own work"—eight books counting those forthcoming in 1992, 40 stories, a couple hundred poems and maybe a dozen essays—my pay probably works out to a little more than $1 an hour. In spite of, or maybe even because of, the lousy pay, I've turned out to be a better writer than I first envisioned myself as becoming. A commercial hack is what I first aspired to be.

My quick definition of an artist as "someone whose primary aim is to produce original work of the highest quality" suggests high-mindedness, nobility, integrity by choice. But my experience has demonstrated to me that it's much more a matter of inclination than choice. When I encounter unlikely people who happen to be artists, I have to remind myself of what I know quite intimately, that the inclination toward artistry is common, human and random. It's mostly a matter of dissatisfaction—of feeling vaguely askew with the universe and wanting to *construct* something—some magical object or talisman—that we hope will correct our cosmic alignment. Then it's a matter of being unable to leave that constructed something alone until we have pestered it into being exactly the way we want it to be. Choosing to be an artist won't help you become one if you're not inclined that way. Choosing *not* to be an artist may not save you from becoming one if you *are* inclined that way.

Around the age of 19, I was enormously impressed by Herman Wouk's *Youngblood Hawke*, a popular novel based loosely and sensationally on the life of Thomas Wolfe. That book was what set me to thinking about trying to become a writer. Since then my education has taught me about its inaccurate portrayal of the life of a writer, along with its esthetic failures; even so, I remember *Youngblood Hawke* with a kind of wistful pleasure.

The blessing or the curse

I'd like to write books that lots of people would read and love. If I could write like Stephen King, I'd be sorely tempted to do it; whereas if I could write like Marcel Proust or James Joyce or William Gass, I wouldn't. Given a choice, I expect I'd take the low road.

But blessed or cursed—whichever, it all comes to the same thing—I have no choice but to write like myself.

I write the way I write because that's how the language and I work it out. The act of

A version of this piece will appear in **David Huddle***'s latest book,* The Writing Habit: Essays on Writing, *due out May 1992. It appears with permission of Gibbs, Smith, Publisher. Huddle teaches at the University of Vermont and the Bread Loaf School of English. His other work includes* Stopping By Home, Only the Little Bone *and* The High Spirits.

composition, for me, is a gradual working toward a certain way for my writing to seem *right*. That intuitively-determined "certain way" — down to the length and the tone of my sentences, the number of conjunctions I'll allow myself in a given paragraph, the way I use dashes — is the truth of things, as I am able to locate it in my work.

My personal inclination is to fuss with my writing over a period of time, to ask my writer-pals to criticize it, to try one thing and another, to cut and add and change and combine and separate and move the parts around this way and that in an effort to move it closer to that "certain way." Fussing is the method that suits my abilities; I'm not good at fast thinking or off-the-top-of-my-head composing; I need to write a thing over and over again to be able to understand it and to get it right.

Along with fussing, what I write about is also a basic impulse of my personality. Given crayons and paper, my oldest daughter, at around the age of seven, used to draw elaborate bunny palaces. Given the same materials at the same age, my youngest daughter drew rows of ballerinas. Given language, there are certain patterns I am similarly inclined to pursue — for reasons deeply embedded in my brain and body cells.

When I'm working on "my own writing," though I rarely pay attention to it, I experience a sense of physical "rightness" — very much like eating when I'm hungry, drinking when I'm thirsty, sleeping when I'm tired. My body's signals are that I'm doing exactly what I ought to be doing.

The spark that ignites

The most important aspects of "my own writing" are beyond (or beneath or above) my conscious will. I think I have a general idea about where I'm going when I begin a piece of writing, and in terms of the piece I end up producing, that general idea may be entirely correct or all wrong. But the good stuff of my writing, the part that continues to interest me through the years, is what has come unexpectedly. It's what my intuition rather than my planning has brought onto the page.

Discovery is the spark that ignites the essential energy of a work of art. When I sit down to write, I don't have a thing to say, not even the beginning of a message, but I usually have a great deal that I have begun to feel the need to find out. When revelation begins to emerge from a story as I work on it, that's when I feel the thing taking on its own life.

What do I mean by "discovery" and "finding out something"? Usually the kind of discovery I make is a connection — or an understanding of the connection — between certain elements that present themselves in my writing. "Poison Oak" is as good an example as any: It's a story about a young boy's partial understanding of a hired man's dangerous and harmful sexual obsession with his mother. The insight I gained from writing that story is suggested in the passage about the dangerous man's replacement:

> I liked [the new hired man] because he was very nice to me . . . , but I was becoming less and less interested in him. The only time he seemed at all dangerous was when he went into the barn to pray . . .

Through writing "Poison Oak," I made a connection between my feelings toward two hired men I vividly remembered from my childhood, one diabolical and the other angelic; in the process of writing about characters based on them, I was able to think about these men and how they influenced me. I learned something — or I came to acknowledge something — about my attraction to the dangerous, the forbidden, the harmful.

Here are some basic principles I believe about writing and art:

● Essential to the making of literary art is the artist's pursuit through writing of the deepest patterns of his or her personality.

• The aim of this pursuit for the artist is a written work that embodies significant personal discovery. The artist may pursue those patterns, but if the artist doesn't find out anything in the writing, what he or she produces will lack the crucial energy of art.

• Revision is the refining of a piece of writing to such an extent that the discovered pattern yields an exact revelation. Revision is the artist's struggle to achieve a precise understanding of what has been generally discovered in drafting a piece of writing.

• Usually what the artist finds out is "hard knowledge," something perhaps unattractive or difficult to accept, e.g., the fact that one is attracted to what is dangerous and harmful.

• The discoveries made through writing are liberating to the artist. If they are "hard knowledge," these discoveries may grant the artist a permanent unburdening. Thus personal liberation is the basic incentive for trying to write as well as one can. Through writing—the process itself must produce the discovery—the literary artist seeks to work through the confining forces of his or her life toward freedom.

My subscription to these principles has emerged from my writing life. They weren't the ideas I had in mind when I began. What I had in mind then was more in the line of *Youngblood Hawke*, both in terms of the kind of book I wanted to write and in terms of the kind of life I thought I wanted to live. I had in mind work that would come easy to me and for which I would receive a good deal of money and adoration. I did not have in mind typing 700 pages to get a 28-page story. I did not have in mind having to come to terms with unpleasant facts about myself. I had in mind quickly becoming a beloved genius. What I have gotten to be over almost a quarter of a century is a more or less respected writer.

The most important thing

I know that I'm lucky to have gotten what I have. I'm acquainted with more gifted people who've worked harder on their writing than I have and haven't gotten anything.

Luck has everything to do with an artist's being able to take possession of his or her given work. For one thing, an artist needs a number of years to understand in personal terms how the process of making art works and to establish the working habits that will produce art. In my own case, flunking out of the University of Virginia and joining the Army gave me three extra years of growing up before I had to graduate; then I was granted an additional three years of graduate study in which writing had first claims on my time, energy and attention. So I got six "free" years to try to realize my dreams of becoming a writer, to discover my artistic inclinations and to establish the habits that would enable me to be productive. I also had the benefit of advice and counsel from older writers who knew what I needed. Had I proceeded on track and on schedule, I would have taken my B.A. after four or five years, gone to law school or gotten a job, and forever after, I'd have been trying to squeeze out an hour or two to give my writing. Worse and more likely, when things got bad at the office, I'd have simply daydreamed about giving it all up and running away to become a writer.

An obvious necessity for the artist is the ability and the circumstance of giving first priority to your artistic work: In spirit and in fact, your own work must be the most important thing in your life or you can't produce art. Why is this case? Because works of art only come out of the artist's wholehearted effort, out of the artist's being able to give the work everything—knowledge, feeling, energy, passion. The artist must be able to give him- or herself to the work again and again, day in and day out.

Please note I'm not saying an artist must forget or disregard his or her family. The artist builds his or her life on the belief that an hour of writing time is more important than grocery shopping, but in my view it's possible to write for a couple of hours and then do the grocery shopping, possible to try to write well *and* to keep fresh produce in the refrigerator. You may have to pay with sleep or a lousy social life, but it is possible.

So what do you get out of such labor and sacrifice? Mostly what you get is the privilege of doing something that makes such extreme demands of you, that asks you for everything you've got. If you're lucky enough to be able to give art what it wants, even occasionally, you should bow your head and say thanks.

The spiritual checkbook

Perhaps the basic discoveries of my writing life have been that in order to tell a good story, I have to carry out a spiritual struggle and that making narratives is my method of spiritual inquiry. If I'd had my choice years ago, I'd have picked another approach to writing. In this regard, I've taken comfort from these lines from Franz Kafka's "The Hunger Artist": " . . . I couldn't find the food I liked. If I had found it, believe me, I should have made no fuss and stuffed myself like you or anyone else."

A valuable by-product of the way I have been forced to write—or the one way that I have discovered it to be possible for me to write—is that I live in the world as a known person. I'm not talking about fame or reputation here; I'm talking about the fact that my spiritual checkbook is out there in the open for you or anybody else to have a look at. My work enables me to examine my life, and the struggles of that examination are a matter of public record. I can be "straight" with the world.

Difficulties go with making yourself so available. In the process of reckoning with yourself, you can hurt family members and friends, who might not wish to be revealed to the world or who might prefer to reveal themselves in their own terms. Instead of love and admiration, you could win anger and alienation. You can show yourself to be stupid, obtuse, insensitive, ignorant, treacherous and generally despicable. And you can't take it back.

This ongoing nakedness, in my opinion, is one reason why some very fine writers get nervous about discussing their work. We admire their writing so much we can't imagine why they'd feel weird talking about it. But it's one thing to walk around naked in a world where most people are very well dressed; most of the time, nobody says anything about it. It's something else when you're called upon to try to account for why you choose to live this way; that's when you begin to seem a little freakish even to yourself.

The true value of art

In spite of these liabilities, it seems to me that living in the world as a known person is a privilege. It is perhaps the ultimate incentive for trying to practice an art form. The opposite circumstance, living within reticence or a permanent disguise, must be a severe form of suffering.

If trying to write the best you can is what is most important to you, your pay may be lousy, your family may have disowned you, your enemies may be suing you and the lettuce in your refrigerator may be turning brown and mushy around the edges, but for better or for worse, you've taken possession of your life.

Getting Around to Plot

by Gabby Hyman

When you're constructing a story, the last thing you should have to worry about is plot. I'm convinced, and would like to convince you, that if you pay loving attention to all the other necessary aspects of crafting a story—setting, deep characterization, language—you can't help but work out a well-plotted narrative. Your first line will mail a message to the final line; the first page will lean across all that prose and shake hands with the last. Of course, you'll have to listen for clues when your story speaks to you.

Let's cut through some hocus-pocus: There are but a few classical turns of plot and they've already been handled by Homer and Hawthorne and Katherine Anne Porter and Elmore Leonard. You can mail away for software disks which, by their makers' claims, computerize every conceivable plot for you. They probably do. If you've been a reader as well as a writer, you've already internalized a majority of these plots in your subconscious. What you want to do is take that tried and true plot, hang upon its skeleton the musculature of language and power the beast with your character's unique heartbeat.

I've had many a student tell me, "It's going fine, but I can't come up with an end to my story." I know better than to ask, "What's it about?" A story is a sum of its parts, of which plot is but one aspect. Instead I ask, "How much work have you put into the beginning and middle?"

Flannery O'Connor wrote that the huge impetus of narrative that you accrue in the beginning and middle sections of a story will hurtle you toward a climax. There may come several options, narrative forks in the road, but one will likely suggest itself to you in a way that surpasses all others as an inevitable, unique way to complete your story. It's learning by doing.

Some writers believe it's absolutely necessary to construct an outline for your story, to block out each dramatic moment, to determine what materials should be skimmed in expository prose and which details should be turned into full dramatic treatment. If this works for you, make maps, then sail ahead into your story and keep writing.

For others, and I'm one of them, rigid adherence to a strict manner of plotting can keep you from reaching into the depth of your material. You can blunder past too many doors this way, bypassing surprise scenes and dramatic actions that can transform your story. Working without maps means you have to reinvent your story each time out, and I believe it's by working in this organic manner that the plot of your story grows directly out of its most vital parts. I support the equation that plot grows from the interaction of character and event. (Plot = character + intervention of people, places and things.)

Many beginning writers insist on knowing the ending and then spend most of their creative time trying to wrestle a manuscript to comply with some idea they have. It gets ugly; coffee cups shatter; pets hide under beds and so forth. Fastening your story to an idea is counterproductive. The idea can birth your story, but then you must be willing to part with it.

Gabby Hyman *has written a book of short stories,* The Infinite Nearby, *and is working on a novel,* Natural Inclinations. *He has taught creative writing at the University of Illinois and the University of Alaska-Fairbanks. He now lives in a cabin on Washington's Olympic Peninsula.*

Walking through your plot

The surest means of plotting require patience and the willingness to revise. Don't wince at the prospect of hard work. I know one writer who wrote a thousand pages of narrative to discover what his novel was about. Now he's sure of its direction and is starting over. Next time, he thinks, it won't take so much time. Maybe. I have heard, and perhaps it's but folklore, that Philip Roth wrote several hundred pages of prose until he found the paragraph that stylistically suggested a novel to him.

I think the lesson here is that if you're willing to cut, add and reshape your narrative, then you can let your story discover its own plot. And one way to do that is by building and observing your main characters.

Let's agree that plot is the arrangement of events that show a movement in character over time. The length of time that transpires in a story is related to your main character; for your protagonist, time may extend over several minutes to a period of many years. If you have an idea of plot, the "what happens" in a story, then you have to decide how much time it will take for that "what" to transpire. And as long as you're doing that, you might as well consider the "why" of the behavior in character over time. Stories must move sideways *while* they speed forward. Think how a river takes its bank.

There are a limited number of "whats", so you'll have to create your own "whys." The "whys" may be limited too, since most of us want similar things, though at different times. What happens to your character in a story is a direct result of what sort of human being you've put down on the page in the first place. In this way, characterization and plot are inextricably linked.

The best advice I could give is to walk through your story as you'd walk through a baroque mansion. The story-as-architecture idea is not new. Your growing narrative is a ripe habitation of images, colors, objects and personages. Meander with a keen eye and open arms as you rework a draft, picking up pieces, observing the force of what you've already set down. Borrow from yourself.

What I discovered

Let me give you an example of how a plot came together for me. While stopping for a week in a rustic seaport on the Japanese island of Kyushu, I was startled by the view outside my dormer window. In the bay below Kagoshima lay a smoldering volcano. Nearly 80 years had passed since the last full-scale eruption of the volcano, yet the city streets were streaked gray and the azaleas outside my window were dusted with ash. What was it like to live so close to death? I saw people in the streets and talked with many in my *ryokan*, and though I spoke some Japanese, I began to realize I could only know life here as an outsider.

A few years later I began to write about it. I thought I would create a kind of ultimate outsider and land him in this place. But I knew very little. I opened the story with a view of the bay (because that's what stayed with me) and pulled the camera of my inner eye back through the dormer window to imagine someone, a man who had decided to live here, far from home, far from himself.

That's all I had, then, was this vision of a volcano, a room and the shadow of a man. I had no way of knowing on page one that the shadow would turn into an American language teacher named Horton, that in the final scene as he lay in bed with his fiancee, a jilted bar girl would leap onto the skylight above and shatter his dreams. To get there it would take 30 pages, and perhaps an additional 10 pages I never used. I was trying to remain flexible and some of the materials did not fit into the final picture.

As plots go, this was a conventional story of betrayal. But the story grew first because of that volcano and the knowledge that it lay steaming ominously in the harbor. Then I had to see this fellow Horton. Who goes over to Japan to teach English anyway? He could be someone in love with the culture or in love with the yen. But *my* character had tried to escape an America where his wife had an affair and was leaving him. He was already moody, isolated, bitter, dishonest. Kagoshima seemed an appropriate setting in which such a man could stew.

If he is lonely, he might seek out the provinces of nightclubs to palliate his spiritual bankruptcy. There he finds a bar girl to fill his hours, and she hopes Horton will take her to America. Usury cuts both ways.

Horton eventually pursues another woman whom he finds more acceptable. He likes how he wants to clean up his life for her. So later, having reconstructed his idea of himself on a series of lies, only weeks away from yet another marriage based on images, Horton has to fail. Because I had already woven into my opening the tale of the bar girl, it seemed inevitable that she should reappear in the finale.

I had not planned these things. In generating a buzzing field of interactions between Horton and the minor characters, I had already set in motion events that would prompt the necessary ending. As I wrote along, I realized that I had the setting and I had established its resident American alien, but I knew nothing about him. Once I had located Horton in Kagoshima, given a taste of his present life and treated it scenically, I could use exposition to detail in shorthand his history in the States.

After I had filled in his past, I then allowed the story to progress forward as he met the woman, Kimiko, who would become his fiancee. She was a student from his language class. It's a pretty despicable gesture, I think, wooing a student, made more desperate by Horton's having fallen in love with her. I decided during my revisions to have him fall in love. It would up the ante. Raising stakes for your protagonist is a large part of plotting.

Successive scenes traced Horton's effort to clean up his past, to quit his nightly bar stints, to become someone on surface that he'd like to be, someone that he hoped Kimiko would want to see. Some of these scenes I added in revisions. I had discovered in one draft that his efforts to change would take time and that the story needed to show this in a convincing way. What seemed right was that Horton was attempting to convince himself he'd gotten beyond his past without having come to terms with it.

By now I had written several drafts of the story and had not discovered an ending. It seemed clear to me that his wedding plans with Kimiko could not succeed. For one thing, he was an outsider in a land where even on his best days he'd never be accepted. There might have been several alternative endings and stock plots, but I knew from what had happened so far that at least on this occasion, Horton would not turn his life around.

I had in an early scene placed a skylight in Horton's apartment so the reader could observe the continuous stream of smoke from the volcano. Of course the skylight was there for setting, but it could suggest symbolic implications, and now it worked for me in generating plot. On the very evening Horton spends nested in a futon with Kimiko, the plot comes due. In the first light of morning the bar girl lands like a heavy bird in the skylight. From there, I knew I had to get out of the story quickly, within a few paragraphs.

What I learned

All this came to me by watching the story come together, by not *assuming* an outcome from the beginning, but by listening to the lies my character had made up for himself.

There was a need for the ending to arise from the complications created by the character, but it didn't happen all at once. I had to return to the story many times to add additional materials to Horton's past to make him the kind of character who would lose this misdirected effort to change himself. Having the image of the bar girl in the skylight got the story moving again, but it wasn't enough yet. I had to rework the center of the story to make the ending I selected appear even more inevitable:

Horton and Kimiko walk through a Kagoshima park. They have never really communicated very well. There's been this language barrier, for one thing. For another, Horton has his own barriers. There's an incredible pressure on Kimiko from her family to leave Horton. But she'd be willing to sacrifice her family standing (which is near soul-suicide in Japan) for their marriage. Above all, she says, Horton must be honest. It's all she has to go on.

Once I had written that section, I prepared the story for the skylight scene with the scorned bar girl. The story was over but for the short finale, Horton sitting on a pier, drinking, watching the volcano. I presume he left the island and is still on his way to another lesson in life. Does the plot sound familiar? Of course it does, but this is uniquely my story, Horton's story.

It seems to me that every scene grew from Horton's character. The minor characters serve as adjuncts, really, to draw out his dishonesty, to chart a morality to which he aspires, albeit superficially. The skylight is the narrow window Horton has on a world of smoke that he hurtles through without understanding. The elements of setting and characterization drive the plot, and the story gains its angular momentum out of Horton's needs. As it reads on the page, Horton's story seems inevitable, each event cresting toward the next one. But it did not spin out that way except by successive drafting.

A few years after I wrote this story I read Fitzgerald's "Babylon Revisited" for the first time. I don't know why I had missed it before. It's a terrific story about a drinker and his race to escape the past. The protagonist Charlie Wales has changed his behavior, but it is by his encounter with old drinking companions early in the story that his scheme to recover his daughter is brought to failure. This is what really matters: Structurally, the disaster of the climax is seeded in the initial scenes of the story. Two drunks from Charlie's past intrude on what Charlie hopes is his moment of triumph. "Babylon Revisited" bears repeated study for Fitzgerald's precision in plotting and scenic management. The story is told in numbered sections, and you can map out the plot. Each early section lays a direct path into its successor, and each late scene gazes back on its materials.

Getting unstuck

When you're stuck with your own plot, type out the first draft and then answer the following questions:

How does each scene reflect the specific movement of the protagonist toward, or away from, his particular desire?

If you've really created a character in your story, you've built that person up within a world of conflict. Everyone has needs, and characters have a way of forcing issues to meet those needs. You create blocks for them: Other people, strange places and intangible cravings which stand in your protagonist's way. One of those blocks is surely the protagonist himself. In reviewing all the scenes you've constructed, what happens to your main character? How does the scene help define his issues? Remember that the scene does this dramatically, not through windy explanations. Is the scene you've just read necessary?

Which characters, objects, settings point a path through the story?

Often when your piece bogs down, it's because you haven't been following a thread through the story, following the conflict or the story's original coloring as expressed through landscape. Maybe you've lost track of the character's voiceprint of speech or of the details which contribute to characterization such as clothing, furnishings or physical gestures. A bar of soap travels in Leo Bloom's pocket as he wanders the city of Dublin in *Ulysses*.

The consistent use of these details not only provides structural and character integrity, but gives your reader a sense of the inevitable. When you force a character to suffer his self-destructive behavioral tics or condemn that character to endure a severe, unchanging physical or psychic environment, you create plot.

In Flannery O'Connor's "A Good Man is Hard to Find" the protagonist's insatiable fantasies and her emotional neediness drive the plot with a vengeance. The grandmother in the story wants to return to her mythic past, and she is willing to connive her way into its terrain at the expense of her life and the lives of her immediate family members. She is brutally ignorant, unrelenting and hypocritical. She hides the cat in the backseat of the family car; she imagines a plantation house and manipulates her son into driving a back road to reach it. Once the cat is out of the bag—it leaps onto the son's neck while he's driving—the car flips into a ditch. Seeking help, the grandmother waves her arms to flag down an approaching sedan. It's a carload of killers. Finally, in her divine innocence, she recognizes the ringleader as one of her own children; when she touches him, which she does both physically and metaphorically, he shoots her. These are but a few examples of how the protagonist powers the plot, and you can find a half-dozen more in that story.

If you're having trouble with action, maybe you need to amplify the setting. By this, of course, I include the inner landscape of your characters. Raise the ante; turbocharge the psychic environment; don't let up.

Which materials have been summarized that would reveal more in scenes? Which scenes require additional background?

You can fill in as much motivation and characterization as you need once you've got the story moving. Begin in the middle of significant action, or certainly close to action. Once the reader has a sense of characters moving against a brightly-lit backdrop, you can take time to back-fill the narrative. As you revise, can you find scenes which duplicate each other? Are there dramatic moments that overlap? Are there sections you've flown right past in summary which need dramatic treatment? Or have you told too much in a scene, blabbed out theme instead of observing the action? A story may be strengthened by the cutting of excessive dialogue. What if you shuffled the order of the scenes within the story? Don't throw away your drafts; you may want to retrieve things you've cut from them. Stay loose on your feet.

What if your protagonist took a divergent path from the one imagined for her? What if she did something you had not planned on?

If you're able to wander from the map and keep your eyes peeled for details, plot will help itself along. I am often saddened by the things my characters say and do. I can't help them out of the mess they're in. I don't want to.

I'm willing to introduce additional characters into my stories and remove the ones that don't add much to the overall tension. Sometimes I find that several characters are performing roles (heavies usually) that may be combined easily into a composite character. This means I'll require fewer scenes to achieve the same effects. I'll have cuts to make.

What takes the place of the excised material? I'm ready to write out several scenes where only one might ordinarily suffice. I'm curious to find out what happens if the character acts a certain way or acts out its opposite gesture, and I'll work down both forks in the road until I discover the outcome. Eventually the reader will follow the final path I've selected and will never know about the one that led me into a dead end. What if Horton and Kimiko got married? I had imagined two possible outcomes, one of which ended in an abrupt annulment with Horton angry, lonely and as confused as ever. Why bother going there? I already wrote this ending. The other possibility presented for them an excruciating, lingering hell, a plot that would consume a novel-length stack of paper. Perhaps I'll take them down that path someday.

Finding your way out of the maze

When it comes to plot, you have to read broadly, borrow liberally and find your own best way out of the maze. I hate to sound arcane, but your story already knows where it's headed.

Right now I'm writing a novel I'm calling *Natural Inclinations*. Seems to me that those words, "natural inclinations," comprise both a working title and a plot manifesto. My protagonist, Evan, has just had his ponytail sheared off by a drunken barber and for the first time we see his birthmark, a reddish streak of lightning that darts behind his left ear. Can't you see Evan, later in the novel, spluttering across the Texas desert in his '68 Triumph coupe? There's an awful storm, heat lightning everywhere. Something will come up. I'm not unduly worried. Plot happens.

> 66 Meander with a keen eye and open arms as you rework a draft, picking up pieces, observing the force of what you put down. Borrow from yourself. 99
>
> —Gabby Hyman

From the Ground Up: The Importance of Setting

by Renée Manfredi

I am a collector of maps, something I hadn't realized until unpacking cartons after a recent move. Road Atlases, street maps of cities I've lived in or visited, campus maps, even hastily scrawled directions on the back of an envelope showing the way to a friend's house.

Coming from a family of eccentric collectors—my sister, for instance, has a collection of nearly 500 bags from places near and far—my motto has always been: When in doubt, throw it out. It makes moving and housecleaning easier. Still, I have all these maps, and for whatever reason, they've survived four moves in as many years. I am especially fond of the ones from the auto club, those Triptiks that point you in the right direction with cheery yellow highlighter and big, blocky arrows. Maps for the directionally dyslexic, I think of them. As anyone who's ever driven with me knows, I never take North for granted. Direction is something I want obviated.

Mapping it out

The instructor of one of the first writing classes I took as an undergraduate had us draw imaginary maps of the places our characters lived. It is during this semester of map-drawing that I date my beginnings as a writer. There is something about knowing where the bank is in an imaginary town, how far away the YMCA is from the church and the size of the library that lends factuality to the fiction. If you know a place, know the kind of people who live there—the instructor's theory went—then you should never suffer from that nebulous thing called Writer's Block—which, thankfully, I was taught not to believe in and still don't. Having those maps took away a lot of anxiety about knowing what to write. If I was stuck for material, all I had to do was visit this imaginary town and see what a given character in this place was doing on a Saturday afternoon in July.

I once read an article in a decorating magazine that said if one was on a limited budget or had to remodel gradually, one should work from the bottom up—that is, having impeccably finished floors and baseboards was more important visually than a perfectly painted ceiling or fetching wallcoverings. People automatically look down upon entering a room, the article claimed. It's an instinctive thing, having to do with the part of the brain that regulates balance, firm footing.

The same is true in a story or novel, I think: Readers need to know fairly early in a work where they are. Bringing on characters without some detail about the setting in which they exist is like having a room full of invited guests and not turning on the lights. And the richer the details of setting, the more recognizable the things on the fictional map, the more at ease your readers will feel.

I don't mean to suggest that one should pack every scene like a Japanese commuter train, only that the carefully chosen detail illuminates character in a way that more direct methods, such as dialogue, can't. A character who has lava lamps in his apartment is a

Renée Manfredi's work has appeared in The Georgia Review, The Iowa Review, Mississippi Review and other publications. She recently completed a collection of short stories.

different personality than one who has lamps by Tiffany or track lighting. Or, to use a more geographic example, someone who has a bottle tree in his backyard in the heart of Mississippi will be a different kind of person than one who has this same tree in downtown Chicago. What is accepted as traditional legend in one part of the country is just plain eccentric in another. So, if my character is living on the north side of Pittsburgh and each morning before he goes to work puts a folding chair in the space his car just vacated, the neighbors understand and respect this gesture and the chair and parking place will be there at 5:30 p.m. when he returns. (Try doing this in New York City).

Setting can be the story

Setting provides qualitative and subtle differences in a way that no other fictional device can. It is the background that harmonizes or is discordant with what's in the foreground. Think a moment of the Mona Lisa, one of the most recognizable faces in the world. But how many people remember what's in the background of the painting? And how important are those dark, menacing mountains? Would we interpret the smile as mysterious if, say, Da Vinci had put her against a background of light-dappled oak trees and daisies? Or what if there was nothing at all in the background, if it was merely a portrait painting? What we interpret about the woman's expression is in large part shaped by what's around her.

Of course, if a particular place or setting influences a character, the opposite is true as well: Landscapes are also shaped narratively by individual perception.

Marlow's struggles in *Heart of Darkness* are mirrored in the sea and sky and savages; in many ways, the setting *is* the story. Or, to look at a more contemporary model, the short stories of Charles Baxter are excellent examples of ordinary settings and places becoming strange and unfamiliar through the point-of-view character.

In the story "Saul and Patsy are Pregnant," Saul, like many of Baxter's people, defines himself by the things he owns—a stretch of land, collections of German philosophy, a motorcycle—and is forced to reexamine their meaning and thus himself when an outsider challenges their value. For Saul, as for many of Baxter's characters, what starts as an internal tension becomes externally configured: He becomes obsessed with his newlywed neighbors—simple, happy people—and their house becomes emblematic of all that's missing in Saul's life: "As usual, it looked like something out of an American genre painting. Happiness lived in such houses, where people like Saul had never been permitted." Setting in this story is fluid, an aspect of characterization.

Not all stories need to have a strongly established setting. Sometimes a generic backdrop is part of the story's intention. Anonymity of place is one of the hallmarks of what's known as minimalism: A reduction of everything to an equal weight or importance. Characters are defined by the car they drive rather than where they drive it.

In general, though, I think it's a good idea for beginning writers to start firmly rooted in place. It's tempting to try to imitate writers like Raymond Carver and Ann Beattie, but it's difficult to achieve their kind of resonance, much the same way it takes more, not less, skill on the part of the playwright to stage a work without props or scenery.

A place to begin

Setting can also be the germ of the story. More often than not, I know nothing about a story I want to write other than where it takes place. I have to "see" the place before I see the characters moving around and talking and brushing their teeth. With a few exceptions, I've never imagined a character and followed him or her home. Usually I'm already there looking around when they walk in. This is just my way of working—not necessarily the best way, but it seems to me that the more a writer knows about the details of an imagined life, the better the writer knows, finally, the life itself. (Take a look at the contents of the Glass's medicine cabinet in Salinger's *Franny and Zooey*, as an example of this.)

Good stories happen anywhere. The years I spent editing a literary magazine helped teach me this. I was always surprised at the places writers went in their stories that I would have never thought to go. Tattoo shops were a big trend for a while—I saw three or four stories a month set in one skin palace or another. (This trend followed directly on the heels of the dead dog story, and stories of characters with missing body parts. As of last April, if anybody is interested, the most popular setting was health clinics.)

In fiction, travel is circumscribed only by the imagination. Just follow the map and you're there.

66 **Bringing on characters without some detail about the setting in which they exist is like having a room full of invited guests and not turning on the lights.** 99

—Renée Manfredi

Handling Southern Dialect

by Nanci Kincaid

A psychology teacher suggested: "Men fall in love through their eyes. Women fall in love through their ears." A startled class fell into hot debate. I have no idea whether the statement is true—but I'm suspicious. It's an interesting idea that the door to love is unlocked primarily by one sense for one group and another sense for the other. In that case falling in love is not unlike writing fiction.

We all know of writers who enter their fiction eyes first, intent on the visual, on making the reader *see*. This "seeing is knowing" idea has some illustrious practitioners, among them Herman Melville, Charles Dickens, George Elliot, James Joyce, Emily Bronte, James Salter and Toni Morrison. Theirs is a landscape of well-chosen adjectives, detailed descriptions, colorful, textural language—a painterly fiction.

Visual fiction elevates the power of observation, magnifies the significance of detail. Whether the woman wears a white dress or red dress becomes important, as does whether she pins her hair back with a rusty bobby pin or a silver engraved barrette. Maybe she allows it to hang in her face. The tiny scar beneath her eye matters, as do the 14 gray hairs in her dyed blue-black hair. No detail is too tiny to bear weight. Each detail is a stroke of the brush. It is the blending of visual detail that makes the picture—that tells the story.

This visual approach to fiction is highly successful, but there is another, equally legitimate, approach based on the idea that "hearing is knowing." Here, voice—not visualization—powers the story. This is my own approach to writing and I have some very distinguished predecessors, such as Eudora Welty, Mark Twain, William Faulkner, Harriet Beecher Stowe, Thomas Hardy and Alice Walker.

Years ago after one of my stories was read at a workshop, I was startled when asked "What do these characters look like? Are they black or white? Do they wear clothes?" It had never occurred to me that this was something that needed to be spelled out. I guess I thought readers would be able to visualize the characters by listening to their dialogue—with some assistance from the narrative voice. It was the first I was made aware of my inattention to visual description. I've worked on it since—and improved. But the legitimacy of these comments made me understand something about myself as a writer.

Sometimes hearing is seeing

I write because I hear—and hearing makes me see. Stories come to me by listening, first to some internal voice, then to the voices of the characters who overtake me once the story begins. Like many writers, I reveal characters less by the details of their physical appearance or the space they inhabit, than by what they say—and how they say it. It is the speech of the narrator and of the characters that give the story its color, texture and detail.

The two sentences, "Zat your dog, boy?" and "Whose dog is that, son?" conjure up different visual images of the speaker. We can make a reasonable guess as to which of the characters wears the business suit and which one mows his grass in his undershirt. Later, we see the characters again having drinks. One says to a woman seated at the bar, "I beg

Nanci Kincaid's short stories have appeared in several periodicals including Story, Missouri Review, Ontario Review and the anthology, New Stories from the South. Her first novel, Crossing Blood, is forthcoming from Putnam.

your pardon. Is this seat taken?" After the woman nods no, slides her briefcase off the barstool and looks away from him, he seats himself and orders a Scotch. In a bar across town the other character says to a woman seated alone in a booth, "Hey, babe, you looking for company?" The woman answers, "What if I am? What are you going to do about it?" He slides into the booth next to her. "To start with I'm going to buy you an ice cold beer." Already we know quite a bit about these characters, although we have yet to learn their problem or the color of their eyes. As the story builds we will know more and more about them by what they say and what is said to them.

When a character operates in his own world, and it's a world we recognize, the writer needn't describe the dimly lit bar and the pictures hanging on the wall—unless, of course, one of them is a recent nude of the character's ex-wife, something pertinent and unusual outside the visual image the reader himself will provide. When a writer creates a real and intriguing character the reader can readily assume much of the setting and physical detail, although it is good not to overwork the reader by asking him to bring more to the story than the writer does.

Venturing into unfamiliar territory

When a fictional character operates in less familiar territory—say, Ivana Trump falls in love with a handsome young plumber and goes with him to Little Horse, West Virginia, to visit his grandmother, the evangelist—then the reader needs all the visual aid he or she can get because the character (therefore the reader) is in unfamiliar terrain. If the story is from Ivana's point of view we need to see the grandmother's storefront church from Ivana's eyes. While the reader might already know there is a piano in the corner and the collection is taken up in tin pie plates, we need to be told again so that we share Ivana's first time experience and learn something from her response. The unfamiliar requires more effort on the writer's part to make a character (therefore the reader) see what he has not seen— or hear and understand what he is not accustomed to hearing and understanding.

Writers whose characters speak a derivative language are especially challenged. When a character fails to speak standard English he ceases on a certain level to be the generic "everyman." This is fine. But dialect brings with it the burdens of stereotype. This is particularly true of Southern dialect.

In recent years this has not been as big a problem with other American dialects. In fact, Hispanic, Oriental or urban Black dialect seems fresh and energetic by contrast. Minority writers are giving voice to cultures and characters that we are excited about. To many of us the particularized language seems new, refreshing and bold. Their dialect seems charming and efficient. The American culture is not as saturated with literature from these groups as it is from "Southern writers," so readers bring less preconceived notion to it, less "ho-hum." Amy Tan, Terry McMillan, Earl Lovelace and Sandra Cisneros are examples of current writers whose use of dialect produces high-energy fiction. Unfortunately Southern dialect often seems to do the opposite. If overdone it becomes exhausting and can slow the reader to a stop.

In 1930 Zora Neal Hurston allowed her Florida characters a complete freedom of speech in *Their Eyes Were Watching God*:

> Ah'm gointuh tell yuh. Ah'm gointuh run dis conversation from uh gnat heel to uh lice. It's nature dat keeps un man off of uh red-hot stove.

The language is a joy for me, because it is familiar. But I've known other people to put the book down over it. Fifty years later Terry McMillan in *Disappearing Acts* maintains a Black dialect for only one character, Franklin. Dialect divides her characters by class, illustrating and complicating the issues of the book. Her middle-class character, Zora, says:

> Franklin was broke on my birthday. He called me from a phone booth and said he had to work overtime and wasn't able to cash his check. For some reason I didn't believe him, but I didn't tell him that.

And Franklin says:

> What time is it? Shit, I better get my ass up. Daydreaming ain't gon' get it. I ain't felt this good since . . . I hit the Lotto for four numbers and won $306. Naw, even that shit can't compare to this.

McMillan's use of dialect makes us love Franklin and at the same time represents his dilemma as one set apart from the larger, empowered group. Her use of dialect is double-edged. It becomes a political statement.

In 1884 Mark Twain charmed readers with Huckleberry Finn's first few sentences:

> You don't know me without you have read a book by the name of *The Adventures of Tom Sawyer*; but that ain't no matter. That book was made by Mr. Mark Twain, and he told the truth, mainly.

While today there are still plenty of Southerners who speak like Huckleberry, readers are far less tolerant of them. Current Southern writers maintain sense of place with less emphasis on dialect.

Understanding the power of language

It was only when I began to write that I understood I operated outside the realm of standard English and realized how Southern I really am. The language of my fiction was as real as if I had tape-recorded it—I could hear it perfectly—but when I committed it to the page it was awkward and embarrassed there.

Like many other groups, Southerners have separate standards for spoken and written language. The two are not necessarily interchangeable. Nonetheless, for the longest time I remained totally faithful to the idiom. Who did I ever know in my life that actually put an ing on the end of a word? Who ever spoke one measly sentence if he could get away with a whole paragraph? Part of the thrill of Southern language is the illustration in it. "The man is tight as Dick's hatband." "Does he think I was born yesterday?" "Don't listen to his usual excuse—that dog won't hunt." Nowhere is language richer than in the South. There are whole stories inside sentences.

As a beginning writer I felt it was absolutely crucial that I be faithful to the spoken language I'd heard all my life. I still feel that way, although I've learned more effective ways to do it than my earlier tape-recorder method.

Did you ever wonder why so many country songs are about Mississippi, Alabama, Texas, Georgia and Louisiana? I thought it was because love of place was so powerful. I felt sorry for people who came from some unsung place. Ray Charles' "Georgia on my Mind," Charley Pride's "Missing Mississippi," Alabama's "Sweet Home Alabama." There is an apology in these songs for ever having left the South. They absorb place with exuberance. Eventually it seems they love their place so much they aren't interested in seeing anywhere else. Hank Williams Jr. sings, "If Heaven ain't a lot like Dixie I don't want to go."

What is this all about? Why aren't there more songs about Iowa or Minnesota or Rhode Island? Don't those people love their place too? Don't they have mamas and granddaddies and ex-wives to sing about? Don't they have mountains and rivers and trains on the track? Perhaps it is because Southerners are frequently less traveled than people of other regions. They make up for this with a celebration of home.

It has taken me a while to understand that country music is not simply about love of place. It is about the power of language — the need to apply language to circumstance. The South believes — more than any place I know — that a thing is what you name it. It is the label that empowers and determines worth — not the thing itself. We believe language can elevate and/or destroy. It is more powerful than the people who speak it.

Language is the salve smeared over our wounded history, people and land. It comforts and unites and entertains. My late mother-in-law was a woman who refused to speak an ill word — ever — about anything. This was the way she controlled her world and let only the good in. By refusing to apply negative words, even to negative circumstances, she was expressing her faith in the power of language. If you don't say it, it's not true. Don't name it and it won't exist. She rejoiced in her right to name things. If we came in the kitchen and found her at work and said, "What you doing, Granny?" She'd say, "I call myself making a pineapple upside-down cake."

I call myself. This is a common Southern usage which allows room for friendly disagreement and declares the right of the individual to name his own deed — to apply language of his or her own choosing to an activity. "You might think I'm in here tearing this kitchen apart, but I call myself making a pineapple upside-down cake."

I had a grandfather who often prefaced his remarks with, "If you let me tell it." This too suggests that there are always multiple versions and he is simply claiming the right to his own version in his own words. "If you let me tell it, that woman didn't have a bit of business inside the locker room with 95 naked men. Does she call herself getting a story? I call her getting an eyeful."

Don't add too much of a good thing

Excess dialect exhausts the reader whose ear isn't trained to hear it. You don't want readers pausing at each line of dialogue as if it were a riddle to be solved. Too much dialect causes the reader to stumble, fix too heavily on unfamiliar usage and puzzle over the mentality of the speaker. We can thank Gomer Pyle, Boss Hogg, Daisy Mae and, I hate to say it, even Aunt Bea, Opie and Barney, for this correlation between Southern language and dim-wittedness. Too strong a dialect implies an ignorance no matter how wise a thing the character might be saying. The idea being, "If they're so smart, why can't they talk right?"

When I began to send stories out for publication I got polite notes that, "This isn't right for our magazine." I realize now that a story comfortable to my ears often overworked other ears. While I wasn't exactly writing Uncle Remus, I was writing, "Shoot, the girl ain't had time to miss me yet. When she does she's gon be eat up with misery. Ima laugh too. You hear me? Ima laugh my head off."

Slowly, by the process of literary rejection, I realized that although I did want to establish my characters as members of a particular region and distinctive group, I didn't want to isolate them through use of heavy dialect, stressing their foreignness. In the end, I wanted to establish characters representative of the universal human condition. If I had to add water and stir a bit I'd do it. I have learned, and continue to learn, how to moderate the regionality of my fiction. It was the swarm of rejections I received early on, and the increase of acceptances that came when I homogenized the Southern dialect a bit — that taught me to compromise.

Tips on using dialect

As a writer who has learned some hard lessons the hard way I offer the following advice to beginners writing dialect. The advice is practical—not ideal.

● *Dialect is like salt. A small amount flavors; too much ruins.*

● *When introducing a character, his first few spoken lines should suggest, but not declare, his regional or ethnic background. The middle of a story is a better place to turn him loose a bit. Reign him back in toward the end of the story.*

● *A character need only speak one "ain't" to establish him as an "ain't" user. The reader will continue to hear ain't even if you don't write it again.*

● *Don't use apostrophe in place of g at the end of ing words. If you occasionally leave off the g (occasionally, I said) also leave off the apostrophe. A page full of apostrophes is unappealing to the eye (visually suggests a foreign language), and it makes the words themselves more powerful than their meaning.*

● *Use y'all (as well as youse, you guys, you'uns, etc.) rarely. This is a hard one.*

● *Minimize phonetic spellings. I'm occasionally forced to give into* Ima, mize, spoze, *etc. But one* spoze *teaches the reader how to hear* supposed.

● *Beware of exhausted ethnic or regional names. One character (or two at the most) with conspicuous names is more than plenty.*

● *Tighten dialogue. Repetition is a wonderfully poetic aspect of some speech, but it can become heavy and slow on the page. For example:*

> *"That boy is making me crazy. Crazy as a bat. If I get any crazier I'm gon have to check myself in at Chattahoochie."*
>
> *"You don't seem any crazier than you ever were."*
>
> *"Well, thank you for your two cents. It'll come in handy when I get to the crazy house."*

Beginning writers are often startled to find that editors enjoy circling repeated words. Southerners learn to say everything three times for emphasis. Editors only want to hear it once. The above example might be rewritten as:

> *"That boy is driving me crazy."*
>
> *"You don't seem any crazier than you ever were."*
>
> *"Thank you for your two cents."*

Amazingly I've found that tightening the language doesn't have to damage the story. It's easier to condense without losing authenticity, once you believe in it.

● *Go easy on the conspicuously ethnic or regional expressions. Choose only one character to speak in parables. Don't have a whole cast of characters spouting "sayings."*

● *Go easy on symbols, such as cornbread, hounddogs, preachers, biscuits, fried chicken, etc. Be selective in your choice of images. Aim for a fresh angle.*

● *Don't overdo the number of relatives/characters. Many a story has been buried beneath the vast number of aunts, uncles, cousins, grandmothers and neighbors.*

● *Urbanize your stories when you can. It is an increasingly urban world we live in. Only the most powerful rural stories get good response from editors.*

Popular Fiction Report

by Robin Gee and Christine Martin

Like all facets of the industry, popular fiction publishing (both trade and mass market) was hurt some by the Persian Gulf War and the recession. Sales in some areas were down and returns from retail outlets, always a problem in mass market publishing, were up. The result of this has been a tightening of the market.

Depending on how you look at it, this can be bad news or good news. The bad news first: Publishers may not be as willing to take risks on new writers. More are relying on agents and on writers who already have proven sales records. On the other hand, some experts say a periodic downturn in the market helps "weed out" mediocre books. And even though the competition is keen, publishers are still eager to find fresh new voices. Finally, fewer titles published means more money and effort will be spent on the lucky few.

There are trends in popular fiction publishing, but they can be deceiving. The popularity of certain subjects tends to run in cycles in this business. Gothics are a good example of this. In the late 1960s and early 1970s, gothic romances, mysteries and horror were very popular. Walk into any bookstore and you'd find several books with covers featuring young women in distress, murky houses, dark swirling skies. Ten years later this type of novel had all but disappeared. Editors say, however, that they're starting to look for gothics and you may be seeing them on the shelves again very soon.

One important but gradual change in popular fiction has been a move away from "the formula." While we would not venture to say formula fiction is dead, a category novel today is much more than that. Certain aspects continue to define each genre—the love story is still the essential element of romance, for example—but books being written today have more interesting and well-drawn characters, unusual or exotic settings and deal more directly with contemporary issues than they have ever done in the past.

In general women characters reflect the gains made by women in the last 20 years. There are more women protagonists in the traditional "male" categories and heroines now tend to save themselves. Settings have changed too. You are now as likely to find a private eye roaming the streets of Philadelphia, Seattle or San Diego as you would New York City or Chicago.

While publishers continue to have strict word requirements for many category novels, there's a growing market for longer works of popular fiction and more development of secondary characters and subplots. Mixed genres continue to be a growth area with more novels (and short stories) crossing the boundaries between horror and mystery, mystery and romance, romance and fantasy. Most importantly, it is the well-crafted story that is a little bit different, slightly quirky even, that will make it in today's competitive market.

Keeping a watchful eye

Market watching can be risky business. It's important to be aware that publishers are buying books one to two years in advance. Saturation is a problem. It takes a keen eye to watch for signs of what is really new and what has become passé. For example, right now there are hundreds of fiction and nonfiction books on serial killers. It would seem even a quickly-done novel about such a killer would be a good bet, but booksellers are starting to complain there are just too many books of this type out there—so many, in fact, readers are either turned off completely or they're overwhelmed with too many choices. Publishers may have already decided to pull back on the number of books about slashers and stalkers they will buy for next year.

On the other hand, there will always be a market for serial killer novels, if they are top quality thrillers. Even when a "trend" seems to have peaked, if you have a book that you believe in, that you've spent great care crafting, by all means send it out—there's *always* room for well-done fiction regardless of trends.

Writers can only benefit from haunting their local bookstores. It's good business to know the competition and to know what your customers—your readers—want. Yet there are many other ways to keep an eye on the market. Talk to booksellers—after all they are the ones on the front lines.

Networking is very important in the popular fiction field and nowhere else is communication between writers so well established. There are national and regional organizations across the U.S. and Canada and throughout Europe devoted to particular types of writing. These groups usually have local chapters and provide market newsletters, conferences, workshops and even computer bulletin boards devoted to their interests. Joining one of these groups may well be the most important step you take toward marketing your work. You will find the addresses to many of these groups in the new Organizations and Resources section starting on page 589. Magazines featuring market and other information about specific fields can be found in the section titled Publications of Interest to Fiction Writers on page 597.

Some things ring true for all categories of popular fiction. Writers, editors, publishers, agents and booksellers agree, without exception, that the books that do well in any given field (and hold their own despite the ebb and flow of the market) are those written by people who love the field in which they write, who respect the genre and who also read the classics and the work of their peers.

Fantasy

Fantasy crosses over into horror, science fiction and now even romance, but it is a field that deserves separate standing from the fields in which it still plays a crucial role. Fantasies are actually outselling science fiction novels these days and a number have made it to the bestseller lists. In a 1991 *The New York Times* Book Review article, David G. Hartwell, editor of TOR's *The World Treasure of Science Fiction*, said fantasy "accounts for nearly 10% of all fiction sales in the United States."

The market for fantasy is very good right now and it is holding its own despite—or perhaps because of—the recession. One of the purest forms of escapism, the fantasy novel helps take us away from the pressures of everyday living.

Few have taken us away from it all as cleverly as J.R.R. Tolkien, father of the fantasy trilogy. January 3 marked his 100th birthday. Look for special Tolkien-style stories in many of the small fiction journals that feature fantasy and for special editions of *Lord of the Rings* and his other works. If you haven't read Tolkien's work since you were a kid, now might be a good time to read it again.

Fantasy novels often come in twos and threes and many writers are being asked to write with this in mind. Yet individual, longer works of fantasy seem to be gaining ground.

Peter Heck, science fiction editor for Berkley/Ace, said there is no one type of science fiction or fantasy doing better than any other, but he noted a growing interest in "funny fantasy." While the inclusion of humor in fantasy is not new, the emphasis on books that are primarily written for laughs is a fairly new one.

Fantasy is still about magic, but beyond this, look for a variety of protagonists and situations. The unicorn and the dragon have been unofficial mascots for the genre, but cats, dogs, horses, even dinosaurs are gaining ground. In fact several publishers have come out with animal-themed anthologies this year.

With a few notable exceptions such as the *Magazine of Fantasy and Science Fiction*, the market for short fantasy fiction is limited to small circulation magazines and anthologies. If you don't mind being paid modestly or in copies, however, there are a number of publications in the small press devoted to or open to fantasy including *Magic Realism, Lost Worlds, Once Upon a World, The Mage* and *Beyond . . . Science Fiction and Fantasy*.

Many of the anthologies for original fantasy are by invitation only, but editors say it's not too hard to get on the invitation lists. Publication in small magazines helps writers get noticed as does meeting editors at conventions. If you are active in any science fiction or fantasy writing organizations or subscribe to science fiction/fantasy/horror field publications such as *Locus* or *Science Fiction Chronicle* you have a good chance to see calls for submissions.

Horror

With apologies ahead of time for the bad pun—1991 was a grim year for horror. This may be an unfair assessment because horror has been doing so well in recent years that a bottoming out or settling down of the market can't help but look like a slump. Yet despite a sluggish spring sales record, horror editors and writers are looking to the future with optimism.

One of the major happenings in the horror market in 1991 was the launching of the new Abyss line from Dell. The publisher went against the odds—started a new line at a time when others were cutting back—and so far it looks like a very smart move. The line was created to attract the best new writers in the field and Editor Jeanne Cavelos has been very successful finding new and worthy talent. The line has garnered much praise, including an endorsement from Stephen King. Two of the early books in the line are especially worth noting: Kathe Koja's *Cipher* and Melanie Tem's *Prodigal*.

Nearly every large commercial publisher has a horror line these days but several are cutting back on the number of new books. The word is caution, so this may be a particularly hard market to break into this year if you are a new writer. Horror Writers of America, fully aware of the low ebb and the problems writers face within the field, has expanded its services and networking expertise available to writers interested in the field.

The horror field can be divided very loosely into two areas—psychological horror/dark suspense and supernatural horror/dark fantasy. The incredible success of Thomas Harris' books *Red Dragon* and *Silence of the Lambs* and the subsequent movie based on the latter has led to a deluge of books about serial killers, some in nonfiction, some in fiction.

These books and other reality-based, psychological horror titles, are no longer carrying the "horror" label. Publishers instead are referring to them as "dark suspense" and "psychological thrillers." This may be a reaction to the overabundance of slasher books and movies termed "horror" in the 1980s and the mostly media-created "splatterpunk" movement of a few years ago.

There will always be an interest in this type of thriller but, insiders say, it better be an exceptional book to break ahead of what is already out there. Look for less interest in this area from publishers in the coming year.

On the other hand, interest in supernatural or dark fantasy horror is on the rise. Traditional characters—especially vampires and ghosts—are doing very well and may be a part of the return of gothic horror. In fact, Dell just published *The Ultimate Dracula Book*, *The*

Ultimate Werewolf Book and *The Ultimate Frankenstein Book*. Add to this the popularity of Anne Rice's books and you've got the start of something big.

As with most other types of popular fiction, there are few commercial magazine markets for the horror short story. In this field anthologies are the best place for reprint and original short fiction. There are so many out there, it's hard to keep track. Almost every publisher has one or two horror anthologies going and many of these are open to original fiction. Ellen Datlow, fiction editor for *Omni* magazine (known for publishing topnotch science fiction *and* horror), has edited a number of anthologies including the *Year's Best Fantasy and Horror* for St. Martin's Press and with Terri Windling, *Whisper of Blood*, an anthology of vampirism stories, for Morrow. Ramsey Campbell and Stephen Jones edit *Best New Horror* for Carroll & Graf and J.N. Williamson edits the anthology series *Masques* for St. Martin's.

Again, the best way to get on an invitation-to-submit list for original horror anthologies is to get published in the small press and watch for announcements at conferences and through the HWA newsletter. Another newsletter worth mentioning here is Kathy Ptacek's *Gila Queen's Guide to the Markets* which lists quite a few anthology announcements. Ptacek covers all genres in her newsletter, but she started with markets for the HWA and is a horror writer herself. *Mystery Scene*, a magazine primarily for mystery fiction, also includes a sizable section on horror writing and book reviews well worth a look.

While commercial markets for short fiction other than anthologies are few, the small press includes several magazines devoted to horror and dark fantasy. A sampling of these include *Plots*, *Aberations*, *Bloodreams*, *Deathrealm* and *Haunts*. *Pulphouse*, both a magazine and a small press, features horror, fantasy, science fiction and even some mystery.

Mystery

Unlike horror, the market for mystery fiction is booming. Ed Gorman, mystery writer and editor of *Mystery Scene* magazine, says mystery sales, in general, are very good. As for quality, Gorman says, "This is the true golden age—with more good writers than ever before."

In the past few years women writers have dominated the field and continue to do so, but this year sales for books by men are doing better than they have been. Until about six or seven years ago women writers tended to write what has become known as English cozy novels, those novels set in small towns and featuring amateur sleuths. Yet, perhaps the biggest change in more recent years has been the number of women writing private investigator and detective fiction.

Today, many of the "superstars" of detective fiction are women—Sue Grafton, Marcia Muller and Sara Paretsky, to name a few. Paretsky's detective, V.I. Warshawski, made it to the screen last year. "Many people were already enamored of Paretsky's heroine, and now the movie has caused the other half of the population to start buying Paretsky's books," says John Douglas, owner of the bookstore Foul Play: Books of Mystery and Suspense, located in New York City.

Despite the solid interest in all types of mysteries, there are a few trends or changes in the field worth noting. In hardboiled or detective fiction, the protagonists are a little more human these days. Writers are paying more attention to character and the heroes (or heroines) are definitely three-dimensional people complete with eccentricities and faults. The people writing these novels have changed, too. Now, more than ever before, doctors, lawyers, professional detectives and academics are trying their hand at the mystery novel— some with enormous success.

Douglas has one word of caution for writers breaking into the market. It's not enough to go with the tried-and-true, he says. Editors, as well as readers, are becoming bored with the same old stories and formulas. New mysteries must be different; something has to distinguish the story. Many writers, he says, are taking this challenge by "staking out unusual new turf either in time, expertise or orientation of the hero or heroine."

This "new turf" may come as a change of scenery. Location has become increasingly important in detective fiction and regionalism within the genre has caused a boomlet of sorts. While only a few years ago most protagonists lived and worked in the big cities of the Northeast or West Coast, today you are just as likely to find them in New Orleans, Cincinnati, Seattle, the Ozarks or in a remote town in the Pacific Northwest.

Another new twist is in the background or orientation of the detective. Of course, the biggest change has been the emergence of the strong, independent, female detective. You'll find detectives who are also gourmands, priests and Navaho policemen.

Sometimes a different time is the key. There is a growing interest in mysteries set in the Victorian era, the early 1940s, the Jazz Age and even ancient Rome and medieval Europe.

As mentioned earlier, protagonists are becoming more well-drawn and many writers have taken the opportunity to include some interesting facets to their characters. You'll find more detectives (amateur and professional) who also have training or careers in archaeology, anthropology, medicine, law. Many have interesting hobbies such as buying and selling antiques or collecting rare coins.

Douglas calls this information the "salt and pepper of arcana" and says, as with spices, writers should use extraneous detail sparingly. "As long as this information is folded into the story, I think people welcome it, but you can not add too much weight, or it will cease to be a mystery."

Practically every commercial publisher has a mystery line. Penquin's Onyx line and Bantam's Crime Line are doing exceptionally well. In the independent and small press the genre is equally popular, including Pulphouse, which recently announced its new Mystery Scene Press line.

The market for short stories is better for mystery than for many of the other popular fiction categories. There are a number of "old faithful" markets such as *Ellery Queen's Mystery Magazine* and *Alfred Hitchcock's Mystery Magazine* and fairly new markets such as *New Mystery*. Even *Playboy*, *Esquire* and many of the mainstream magazine markets publish some good mystery as well.

Romance

By now, if you're in the field of romance, you have probably devoured the industry's best kept secret: *Scarlett: The Sequel to Margaret Mitchell's Gone With the Wind*, by Alexandra Ripley. Whether readers loved or hated it, this long-awaited sequel was reported to have had more advance book reservations from customers than any novel ever published. It was released in 40 countries and 20 languages simultaneously—causing excitment for romance readers everywhere.

Although one agent reports that romance is down, most say the industry is actually booming. "We've doubled our business within the last year," says Denise Little, B. Dalton's Romance Buyer, adding that the "great resurgence" in romance shows in the number and duration of books on *The New York Times* Bestseller List. One very good sign is that many publishers are adding lines rather than closing them.

Yet, even if there is question about the state of the industry, no one can deny romances are changing. Heroines, for instance, have grown up right along with the Baby Boomer generation. Gone are the 18-year-old virgins of yesterday. Heroines today are older and have more life experience, says Linda Cajio, president of Romance Writers of America. "They are also extremely independent," notes Little, who writes *Heart to Heart*, a bimonthly romance newsletter available free from B. Dalton bookstores.

With the emergence of ethnic romances, heroines are also becoming more representative of the nation's diversity. Both Odyssey Books and Marron Publishers are producing romances featuring African-American characters and even characters of African descent in other countries. Look for similar books from Holloway House in California. Also, Silhouette will bring out a new ethnic romance this August: *Unforgivable*, by Joyce McGill.

As far as changes in today's heroes, "We used to have the rich playboy, but you really don't see him around anymore," says Cajio, noting that the playboy's demise probably resulted from the need for safer sex in this age of AIDS. Romances of today are also more likely to feature a Prince Charming who shares the household chores and is good with children.

It's not surprising that most publishers are seeking romances that, as Cajio says, "reflect trends in society with a fictional twist." The main focus is still the relationship between the hero and heroine, but now children — or the lack of them — are a consideration. There is indeed a "real rise in popularity of plots involving children," says Leslie Wainger, senior editor and editorial coordinator in charge of Silhouette's Intimate Moments. "There is also a willingness to accept contemporary issues such as recovery from alcoholism or drug addiction, surrogate motherhood and hostage releases," she says. As always, however, the prerequisite is a happy ending.

More realistic portrayals of women and issues have prompted romance novels by the genre's top writers to cross over into mainstream women's fiction. Such books are often released in hardcover — without the picture of the embracing hero and heroine. These books are occasionally reviewed and may make it to *The New York Times* Bestseller List. Judith McNaught's *Paradise* even gained the distinction of being the first romance to be offered as a main selection for the Book-of-the-Month Club.

For many, however, the most exciting trend is the blending of the romance genre with fantasy and/or science fiction, resulting in books which publishers hope will appeal to all concerned. These books include New Age aspects of the paranormal such as reincarnation, clairvoyance and telepathy. Also, watch for more ghosts and time travels, which feature a person who by some twist of fate finds him or herself in another era. In many ways, time travels are a combination of a contemporary and historical. One example is Jack Finney's *Time and Again*. Perhaps best known for time travels is Constance O'Day-Flannery, whose latest work, *Once in a Lifetime*, features a ghost. Romance stories are tending toward the futuristic and some are being set in completely different worlds, such as Rebecca Brandewyne's *Passion Moon Rising* and Johanna Lindsey's *Warrior's Woman*. Look for more paranormal and/or futuristic romances in the coming months from Avon and Leisure Books, among others.

As for historical romances, "they will always be a mainstay," says Cajio. But American readers are preferring American settings, Wainger says. Western settings and Native American heroes are particularly popular, she adds. Proof of this might be Berkley's new Wildflower line, which will feature historicals with western settings written by new authors. And recently, *Thunder on the Plains*, by Rosanne Bittner, was released by Doubleday.

Some say that gothics — or gothic elements — are increasing in popularity. Silhouette, for one, is developing a new line for 1993, tentatively called Silhouette Shadows, focusing on women-in-jeopardy. "These are contemporary romances ranging from traditional gothic plots to paranormal to soft horror," explains Wainger, who will oversee the line. The heroine will find love and face her fears, internal and external, whereas the hero may be part of the threat or outside of it. "But he will not be the knight on the white horse," Wainger says. "The heroine may be helped by him, but not rescued."

In the area of short stories, the number of anthologies, especially ones with holiday themes, continues to grow—although these tend to include only the field's top writers. Avon published the *Haunting Love Story Anthology* last October and Avon, Harlequin, Signet, Silhouette and Zebra all had offerings for Christmas. On the other hand, commercial magazines accepting short romances range from *Cosmopolitan* to *Woman's World*. And both literary and commercial periodicals are more willing to accept contemporary short stories with romance elements.

Science fiction

Science fiction publishers agree: Sales have been sluggish and they are cutting back on print runs, especially of books by new authors. This year no type of science fiction is doing better than any other; all categories are selling, but not with the gusto of a few years ago. On the other hand, a number of science fiction books have made it to the mainstream bestseller lists in recent years.

Saga science fiction is doing particularly well. Many editors are looking for series books in this area. Author Michael Banks agrees: "What I see my friends selling regularly are series books; it's almost a prerequisite for writers to have at least the possibility of a sequel."

Part of the popularity of series science fiction can be attributed to other media. Although it's been several years since the first of the Star Wars series hit the big screen, books based on the characters continue to be very big sellers. In fact, in 1991 Bantam's *Heir to the Empire* made number one on *The New York Times* Bestseller List.

In addition to two television series and several movies, the Star Trek series has also spawned several popular books. While it is certain the series will continue its popularity on all fronts, the death of series creator Gene Roddenberry ended last year on a sorrowful note for fans, as well as industry insiders.

Hard science fiction is making a comeback, with editors and readers alike interested in military science and high tech novels. Interest in cyberpunk, science fiction featuring individuals on the edge of society, is waning in favor of a more societal approach. Yet, again, well-written science fiction novels seem to have a place, no matter what the orientation.

Berkley/Ace Editor Peter Heck agrees: "I've seen material all over the map—funny fantasy, comic wizards, future cops, military fiction. I tend to look more for something that distinguishes a manuscript from the rest—a strong individual voice or character."

Betsy Mitchell, associate publisher for Bantam Spectra, adds that science fiction writers today should write to a wide audience. Write material that would appeal to young adults, as well as older people, she says, because readers tend to get interested in science fiction at a young age. This does not mean juvenile fiction, although there is a market for science fiction geared directly to young people. It means, rather, keeping a broad appeal in mind when writing.

Writers of short science fiction are more fortunate than their counterparts in other popular fiction categories because of the number of fine commercial markets for the genre, including *Isaac Asimov's Science Fiction Magazine, Analog Science Fiction/Science Fact, Aboriginal Science Fiction, Amazing Stories*, and, of course, *Omni*. There's an equally long list of small press magazines and publishers interested in science fiction as well. Anthologies, both open and invitational, are also fertile markets for the science fiction writer.

A lot has been said about science fiction conventions, or "cons" as they are called in this field. They remain an excellent opportunity to meet science fiction editors, writers, artists, publishers and fans. A newer form of networking is going on in the science fiction world, however. Science fiction writers are among the first large group of fiction writers to use computer bulletin boards and on-line services. The cost of modems has gone down in recent years and subsequently the number of writers using on-line services has soared. Writers have been using bulletin boards to exchange information and critique each other's work. Professional writers groups have their own bulletin boards and now editors and publishers are taking advantage of this by using them as a way to narrow in on new and established writers. Science Fiction Writers of America maintains its own members services on line, passing on marketing and trade information and special interest material. Banks, chairman of the on-line committee for SFWA, says he often submits directly to editors using an on-line system.

Western

Contrary to what some folks might have expected, interest in western fiction did not cease with the death of Louis L'Amour. In fact, westerns are doing quite well for some publishers. "As far as Berkley is concerned, the western is as strong as ever," says Gary Goldstein, Berkley's westerns editor. Wallach Exman, senior editor at Zebra Books, also feels the western fiction market is very healthy right now. Most agree.

One reason western fiction might now be the "the bread and butter of category publishing," as Goldstein puts it, is that the definition of novels under the "westerns" classification is changing—actually expanding. No longer are westerns strictly set in the period between 1865 and 1890. And no longer are writers of westerns relegated to approximately 60,000 words. Such "traditional" westerns are still being released by major publishers, both as originals and reprints, but other western fiction books are making a mark in the field.

These are not "adult westerns," those spicy western novels where a man's love for his horse is often second to his love for a woman (or women), although these, too, cannot be ignored. Many traditional western writers wrote adult westerns under a "house name" when the market for traditional westerns was soft. These books continue to sell well, if not always in the same large numbers.

The books that are expanding the category, however, are most commonly called "novels of the West." These are longer, bigger books—typically 100,000 words or more—with stories that take place prior to 1865. They are usually set against a western backdrop and have many of the elements of the traditional western novel, but they are more realistic. Characters are more developed, as are plots and subplots, and settings and events are more historically accurate. An early example of this type of novel is the late A.B. Guthrie's *The Big Sky*, a realistic portrayal of the life of a mountain man in the 1830s. Sometimes these longer books are called frontier novels, especially when they are set in "nonwestern" places such as Florida or East Tennessee.

Perhaps the primary example of a novel of the West, however, is Larry McMurtry's *Lonesome Dove*, which won a number of awards including the Pulitzer Prize. As western novelist Doris Meredith says, "*Lonesome Dove* really woke up the public to the possibilities of the western. We generally think of westerns as cowboys and Indians, outlaws and sheriffs. At the same time, there were railroads, mining and cattle raising." More and more such novels of the West enter the market as mainstream books, such as *The Snowblind Moon* written by John Byrne Cooke and first released by Simon & Schuster.

Now that the trend toward longer, more historical western novels is well established, it's time to take a closer look at what's happening within such books. "More of these novels focus on women in the West and their interaction with the environment," says Meredith, who also writes a "West in Print" column for *Roundup*, a publication of the Western Writers of America. Women in traditional westerns, with a few notable exceptions "were rather generic helpless characters needing male protection or rescuing," she says.

Historical western novels, however, portray women in quite different roles. They feature "ordinary women in the West," Meredith says, and they are serious books with serious female characters. It's not surprising to discover that those now writing most about women in the West are women themselves. A good example is Jeanne Williams, who offered a different perspective in *Lady of No Man's Land*, the story of a seamstress who traveled through the Oklahoma Panhandle selling clothes to other women.

Women are not the only ones portrayed differently today in western fiction writing. "There is a tendency to portray minorities more sympathetically, especially in case of Indians. You rarely see them as villains," says Elmer Kelton, one of today's most respected western writers. Goldstein attributes this more sympathetic treatment to the nation's feelings of guilt regarding how Native Americans were treated both in real life and in fiction. Exman emphasizes that the portrayal is more realistic "in terms of the framework of their life and times." All mention Don Coldsmith's Spanish Bit Series, which focuses on the life of Native Americans just after the arrival of the Spaniards, as an excellent example of realistic portrayal.

Of course, no discussion of western fiction is complete without mentioning the "series." Both traditional and historical western fiction is subject to serialization. A series based on the former tends to limit the characters. They can move around over a lot of the country, but they don't have much room to grow, says Kelton. Characters in novels of the West, on the other hand, do grow and age. A series of such historical books may feature the same protagonist until he or she ages to the point where an offspring becomes the main focus of the book — or some other individual connected to the original protagonist takes center stage. Sometimes this prompts a whole new series. Recently, Zebra's The Mountain Man Series gave way to a whole new series, The First Mountain Man Series, where the stories actually take place prior to — and feature a character that appears in — the first series.

As with other genres, western series fiction remains quite popular. "Series characters are attractive to the reader because one can get involved with them," says Meredith. Such being the case, it's important to note publishers and writers alike believe the way for aspiring western fiction writers to start is to write a "one-shot." Series writing develops later.

Overall, folks say we will be seeing more mountain man books in the coming year centered around the beaver trappers in the Rocky Mountains of the 1820s and 1830s. Terry Johnston is one of those currently writing about fur traders. The Civil War is also hot now, due to the success of the PBS television series, says Goldstein. And look for more frontier fiction — those longer books — as "people want more for their money nowadays," he says. Another possible subject area is the Gold Rush, says Meredith, as the 150th anniversary of the Gold Rush in California is less than a decade away.

As Kelton points out, today there is almost no short story market for westerns and competition for publication in western fiction writing is heavy. That's why it is important to have "believable characters in believable situations," he says, adding that writers should "look for new material, yet stay within the genre."

Putting Humor in Your Horror

by J. N. Williamson

Because—just as Steve Allen once said—"Nothing is quite as funny as the unintended humor of reality," watching readers meet horror writers is great fun to me. As nearly as I can judge, people who have never seen any of us in person tend to be shocked into silence.

They don't expect writers of horror to appear even remotely normal!

Worse, if we seem to an unfamiliar interviewer no more or less sinister than, say, Tom Clancy, Danielle Steel or Andrew Greeley, we're bound to be deeply probed in the hope of locating our latent strain of madness. I have always thought the suspicion of horror writers' secret strangeness was behind an oft-quoted quip by the author of *The Scarf* and *Psycho*, Robert Bloch. "I have the heart of a boy," Bloch declared. "I keep it at home in a drawer."

The truth is one would have to travel far to find a more gracious couple than Mr. and Mrs. Robert R. McCammon, a gentler man than Dean Koontz; Peter Straub is the definition of dignity; Rambo creator David Morrell is an affable ex-literature instructor; F. Paul Wilson is a cordial baby doctor. Most of us are married, on average, longer than those in the general population, and, if we have children—my wife and I had six—we're usually crazy only about them!

So Steve Allen's remark is apt because few of us in horror/dark fantasy shock anybody *away* from the printed page.

And *on* it, we're often wittier than most people out of the field ever seem to notice. Just as Jerry Lewis was correct when he said, "Funny had better be sad somewhere," topnotch horror fiction is sometimes so grim that it had better be *funny* somewhere!

I found this was so in 1985 when I wrote *The New Devil's Dictionary* (W. Paul Ganley, publisher) with this subtitle: "Creepy Clichés and Sinister Synonyms." It was there that I collected overworked words, defined them and estimated the percentage of pro writers guilty of periodically working a bit hastily. I also had the temerity to identify by initials those writers I caught at the vile practice. A few examples follow:

"*Blood froze.* Mercifully, not an epidemic problem. (Alternate, *blood boiled*, 7%.) SK. 13%."

" '*He knew they were gone now.*' They weren't. 83.9%."

"*Throat had been ripped open.* Throats are never sewn shut even when in need. They are ripped, torn, carved or cut—open. FPW. 94.3%. *Suggestion*: Why not, for variety, *Ears had been ripped off*?"

There's a closer kinship between humor and horror than meets the bulging eye. In fact about one-third of my own short fiction utterly belies my image as a solemn, rather moralistic horror author. For example:

"Hellter-Shelter" (*The Naked Flesh of Feeling*, Pulphouse, 1991) is gravely serious at first. It concerns a man with advance warning of a nuclear attack who's so selfish he builds a bomb shelter for himself alone. Gleeful when he leaves his family (and boss) outside on

J.N. Williamson *is the author of more than 40 novels, including* The Black School *and* Hellstorm *from Dell. His short stories (more than 100) have appeared in numerous anthologies and he is also the editor of the anthology* Masques IV *(St. Martin's) and* How to Write Tales of Horror, Fantasy and Science Fiction *(Writer's Digest Books).*

the ground, he discovers someone entering the shelter—from *below*. The devil, and a team of demons. Easily overpowering Mr. Me-First, they let him watch while they gather his possessions on the scorched earth and the denizens of Hell clamber to the surface for a combination picnic and yard sale.

A twist on a favorite horrific legend and a fantastic serves-him-right, sardonic tale: "One Look at You and the Earth Moves Beneath My Feet," published in *Doppelganger*, is a yarn about a Californian who has survived the devastating earthquake everybody predicted—because the *rest* of the country broke off and fell into the *Atlantic* Ocean!

"Turning 40 for Fun and Prophet" (*Nevermore!*, Maclay, 1983) involves a man so fearful of becoming 40 that he learns how to have an out-of-body experience on the eve of his birthday so he can delay the inevitable. Unfortunately, his wife was having an affair, they *moved* his body and he couldn't get back into it at all.

Novices beware

Clearly, some stories published under the ever-widening horror "umbrella" are intended from concept to be at least amusing, present some fresh idea (or twist), set up a moral viewpoint or solution painlessly or to be a sort of "in joke." For the most part, previously unpublished novelists won't sell either books of humor or humorous horror the first time out.

However, new *short* fiction that utilizes the iconography of horror (vampires, werewolves, end-of-the-world themes, child-in-peril, feral children or psychopaths) in an amusingly sassy fashion often does find its way into anthologies and magazines. Then, it calls for a good working knowledge of the field in order to be sure one is really being original. The most recent anthology I edited (*Masques IV*) features a half-dozen humorous-horror stories—involving angels, roadkill, a demon, rock music promotion and intelligent birds.

Among horror-hands of the past few decades who placed at least a few notable yarns of this kind are Ray Russell, the late Roald Dahl, James Kisner, R.C. Matheson, the late Charles Beaumont, Harlan Ellison, Joe R. Lansdale, Skipp and Spector, the late Fredric (no second "E") Brown, Bloch, and the brilliant cartoonist-writer, Gahan Wilson. Researching their work would scarcely hurt your own creation of lighter yarns.

Just us

It's possible for one who knows the contemporary horror/supernatural milieu very well to believe that *most* published writers in the genre occasionally write short and full-length fiction alike that is *primarily* funny! So much depends on the question of whether the reader is familiar enough with such yarns that he or she is aware—at a glance—of the writer's *intention*. By that I mean that an experienced horror reader fondly smiles when Dahl's "The Rat-Catcher" or Stephen King's "The Mist," or Kisner's "The Stoner" is mentioned.

Why? I think the answer is that we identify with a certain youthful abandon, possess an understanding that the author was having great fun in writing it—and that we are reminded of something essential in the crafting of good horror fiction:

Unlike those who cringe at the hint of the "h"-word, people who have a deep-down affection for horror always know that we are dealing with make-believe—fantasy of the sort we know will not come true (we *hope!*), just as there is a make-believe fantasy fiction which we yearn for but cannot become "real" either! A certain element of writing horror successfully involves quite nearly the same shared smart-alecks-together-against-the-world give-and-take that thrives between a sharp stand-up comic and his audience.

Here are some examples of how it works in recent or especially well-known horror short stories: In James Kisner's "Moose Oysters" (*Night Visions 9*, Dark Harvest, 1991), four men go on a moose hunt. Smart-alecks all the way, they talk of spoors, a rut pit and preferring different parts of the animal with no regard for the moose's feelings in the matter—particularly young Kurt, who seeks its private parts in the belief that consuming them will replenish his own virility. What none of the mighty hunters know is that the moose, a female, is the mate of the mythical Bigfoot—who sharply resents it when they kill the cow.

Comedy is replaced by horror when all the men but Kurt are slaughtered by the Bigfoot. And the horror is relieved, strangely, by Kurt's outrageous discovery that he is to *replace* the moose they shot. Beyond that—at the close of "Moose Oysters"—the tension of wondering what will happen to young Kurt is shattered by the ridiculous but seemingly apt image of a heartbroken Bigfoot.

Readers of the yarn are together against the world, momentarily remade by the writer-as-stand-up-comic, laughing at the unfeeling hunters so wholeheartedly that the story more effectively criticizes wanton hunting—as well as "male bonding"—than any right-minded public speech could possibly do.

One of the very best writers of this century in terms of injecting humor in his stories of horror, science fiction and mystery was Fredric Brown, who often took bus rides of several days just to clear his head and devise clever and often hilarious new ideas. As Robert Bloch wrote in his introduction to *The Best of Fredric Brown* (Doubleday, 1976), "There was [in Fred's writing] a *leavening element of playfulness* [emphasis added] which adds an extra dimension to his most savage satire or scarring cynicism. Add to this his gift for the realistic rendering of dialogue and accurate observation of character traits and the result is as impressive as it is entertaining."

In Brown's often-dramatized (and -plagiarized) "Arena," astronaut Carson finds himself coming to on a planet of blue sand, naked and unarmed, confronted by a legless horror of an adversary who rolls toward him with deadly intent—until it is stopped by a force-field. Soon, it becomes clear that he must kill the Roller or it will somehow kill him; its telepathic messages alone are almost enough to unhinge him. The two of them hurl make-shift weapons *over* the barrier while the heat and need for water add to the tension. When Carson's leg is struck with a projectile and begins to bleed, readers identify strongly with the character's awful plight. Sitting in the sand, helpless, the astronaut notices a blue lizard crawling out from under a bush and, because he is human, Carson grins and says, "Hello, there."

The lizard says "Hello" right back to him!

The impact on the reader is tremendous; a talking lizard is completely unsuspected in a serious tale of two beings in mortal combat. Brown's character laughs it off as a case of his mind wandering. The story, and the combat, resume, become more deadly—and Carson certainly seems doomed: The Roller has nearly completed a wooden catapult. But the lizard returns and again says hello. "Go away," Carson grunts at it: "I'm imagining things again."

The little blue 10-legged creature runs along the edge of the barrier, looks back and says to Carson, "Kill. Hurt—kill. Come."

So we see a master storyteller not only relieving tension with humor, but also using the object of humor as a plot device with which his protagonist may escape! Amazingly, that lizard ultimately enables Carson to survive. And, even then, Brown isn't through—because his twist-ending discloses that the Roller and Carson, without knowing it, were the representatives of two great civilizations *chosen* to fight for millions—without the need for millions to perish!

In horror and comedy alike, we sometimes make faces, poke fun at and laugh at the atrociously callow, evil or incredibly stupid circumstances that confront us—instead of crying or blowing something or someone to kingdom come.

It's in that particular and peculiar realm of writing that most short horror stories and many scary novels consistently utilize a sort of *companionable humor*—not actual gags and funny situations necessarily, but shared humor injected within the well-plotted texture of the work. And it is from that mutuality of outlook on the absurd, vile, hurtful or vindictive aspect of life that devotion to the Kings and Koontzes has sprung, along with any defense that might appear to be required of those who like this fiction.

Outsiders are generally the ones who take it all *too* seriously.

Permission granted

In Ray Bradbury's *Zen in the Art of Writing*, subtitled "Essays on Creativity" (Capra Press, 1989), that genre-straddling, gentle genius wrote that authors "build tensions toward laughter, then give permission, and laughter comes." Hence, we smile when Jim Kisner's Bigfoot wins out; Kisner gives us permission to see the human hunters as interlopers, the much-rumored beast as the outraged, invaded party. Hence, we accept the lizard because we've *identified with* Carson and we're willing to suspend our critical judgments.

This quality is easily recognized if you'll imagine yourself watching a movie in a theater and recall how you jump, then laugh, when a director only *seems ready* to show you the next shocker. Then, working as does a skilled writer, he *re*builds the tension. You're lulled into the notion that the shocker may never come—and then it *does*, then you're *helpless* in your seat, possessed by silent laughter! In fact, however terrifying your instant of mutuality with the director (or writer) has been—regardless of how horrific the shock—you'll grimace, at least. And if the creative hand behind it all was sufficiently skillful and has not mistaken mere revulsion for horror—even though you may well wind up having nightmares about it—your mouth and your mind must twist up at the corners.

Bradbury wrote in his same, marvelous book, "Each tension seeks its own proper end, release and relaxation." An author who knows her or his own stuff senses this and gives the reader that opportunity, even when it amounts to no more than *ending* the scene.

The truth of the matter is, in the hands of a remarkably inventive writer (or director) the tension can become nearly unendurable. I do not mean by this the amount of action or violence; I refer to the fact the reader (or viewer) must be able to *relate to* the problems of the character presently on the scene. This does not mean all the characters must be personable, engaging people. Even if the character currently present is a cruel and malicious *thing* with no redeeming qualities, if it is threatened by "things" that are *more* monstrous—if it is about to die in agonizing pain, losing its sight or its limbs or plummeting 100 stories to a noisy "splat" on the sidewalk, we can relate to and empathize with it if we have ever been afraid of that sort of agony, blindness, mutilation, or of falling. And of course, all of us have been!

That is precisely the point when a writer with skill can relieve his or her reader's tension with a quip that is suitable: "One down and forty-seven thousand to go," perhaps; "I haven't heard a sound like that since I dropped Grandma's watermelon"; or "Y'know, I think it looks *better* without a face."

Do observe, however, I urged upon you a *suitable* quip. Such lines have no business being written about a dying mother of five, the hero's beloved brother, or children (except possibly when a writer is working in the "splatterpunk" school of horror). In such instances a more suitable moment of warm "humor" might find an unknowing child of two seeing what happened and inquiring, without malice, "Uncle Eddie go boom?"

It's only make-believe

Why do we find ourselves smiling at the most terrible moment in the life of a fictitious character? In Allen's *Funny People* (Stein and Day, 1981), Steve said Plato described the "pleasure of laughter" as recognizing others' misfortune and suddenly feeling aware of our superiority, "in that we ourselves are not in the predicament observed." It might be in this connection that most people would see the kinship of humor and horror, if they wanted to be honest about it. Competent horror writers utilize self-superiority two ways:

1. The characters are developed in such a way that we come to see they're not so much unlike ourselves, whereupon we respond with a sense of good old guilt and therefore identify with as well as root for them;

2. The characters are proved to be the monsters we *suspected* they were, and we're free now to root for the writer to annihilate them.

Frankly, I don't believe there's much truth to Plato's perception.

It's my view that the healthy reader (in company with the healthy writer) has a capacity for believing absolutely the frightening things that are happening . . . *just as long as he or she is reading or writing it*. We smile because the character *is* make-believe. Audiences at burlesque and silent films laughed when the comic slipped on a banana peel. I find no references in print anywhere to the theatergoer running outside and promptly giggling at the misfortunes of real people.

And I have read no persuasive evidence that healthy horror readers (or those who write it) use the laugh or the grimace, shudder or titillation (the word's definition includes tickling and "pleasurable excitement") derived from an imaginative work to become vampires, serial killers or other actual monsters of the night.

We *want* to believe monsters exist in a let's-pretend world, and the best of modern horror fiction permits us to think that for awhile—to burrow into ourselves and pretend the Bad Guys will be defeated, inevitably, at the end. It's there that this genre is much more conservative than one might imagine, and democratizing: Readers often discover they were in error to dislike certain kinds of characters and are reminded of how unwise it remains to judge a book by its cover. In the majority of horror novels today lives may be lost, but the *status quo* stays intact and is rarely permanently disturbed by the threat of awful change.

Many varieties

Because (as Allen wrote) humor comes in "too many varieties to be adequately encompassed by any one definition," it may be helpful to examine a few more examples of humor I've put to work in my own novels of horror but with no attempt toward guiding your own choices:

While writing my fourth novel (*Premonition*, 1981) I sensed that so much was getting grim due to the presence of a cancer-giving mythical horror called an *aloqua* that a lighter note was needed. A sort of second-banana bad guy improbably named Morley Sinoway— I didn't possess the self-discipline I have now—wanted to show off his expertise in genetics and cloning so I decided he'd grow a living pterodactyl! Then the impulse to create a virtual "sight gag" overcame me. Mentioning that the bird last existed 135 million years ago, I wrote that it was a "sort of feathered Dracula" with wings "roughly the length of a vampire's cape." I had huge fun explaining how it had "clattered like the passage of a mighty night train" through skies "predating incomparable Rome," and that its claws were capable of "picking out the spine as a man might break a chicken's breastbone for luck." And Sinoway whispers, "It's only a baby . . . scarcely out of its egg."

My *Dead to the World* is crammed with one-liners and wordplay exchanged by two footloose ad-space salesmen. And my eleventh novel (*The Evil One*, 1982), otherwise a grave story of psychic possession and telepathy, contains a character (and scene) for whom I still have a soft spot:

Michael is in love with Sandy Willis, they are 14, and he accidentally—more or less—catches a glimpse of her emerging from a shower. I'd wanted to create a shower scene very different from those in movies, explore the psychology of two nice kids at a second of great embarrassment and do those things with insight and warmth. "In any man's life," I wrote, "if he is lucky, it is possible he will see perhaps two or three major fantasies come to life before his eyes." Michael was waiting in Sandy's bedroom for her to finish showering and is stunned when she enters and shouts "Get out! Get out!" and backtracks into the corridor. Michael replies (not unreasonably), "How can I get out with you standing there in the hall?" He adds, "I will if you *want* me to!"

Sandy retorts, "Count five and then go; I'll wait in the bathroom." Then when Michael has blundered his way to the stairs, she senses he's clumping up and down on the *same step*! "Go down some more," Sandy orders him. "Still more!"

Looking ahead

Is horror getting too scary to be funny? Some predict that dark fiction may become increasingly violent. I think not. I think it will become—never while sacrificing plot—more clever, funnier (if only as the characters become more genuine and fully-fleshed).

In the immediate future, though, works of horror may well deal more than they have in the past with realistic and contemporary concerns—Richard Pryor noted that "Everyone carries around his own monsters," after all—I believe we'll see developments in this genre that will astonish many people.

And they'll emerge with a deeper understanding of the nature of a fiction that is often bloody, grim, emotional and violent but has the potential (and allows the latitude) for saying a great deal about the human condition.

As Mel Brooks expresses it, "Humor is just another defense against the universe." Since the darker fantasy is frequently concerned with inexplicable cosmic or supernatural infiltration and attack, the aptness of Brooks' remark to horror is obvious.

Life has never been more complicated and we search unconsciously for those who agree with us, identify the nature of the roadblocks (and suggest ways of skirting them) and remind us that it could be considerably worse. If we appear sometimes to have little choice but to conclude that brilliant success or heartbreaking loss are mere matters of whim and caprice, we want to be "let in" on the gag so that our ability to appreciate the joke—even laugh at it—can be restored. The difference between a comedian slipping on a banana peel and a similarly not-real character who is too dumb to know a vampire when he or she meets one is very slight.

The skill in evoking the laugh depends upon the comic's timing and the writer's very similar need to make us suspend credulity. There's no performing art that calls for greater talent and hard work than comedy. There is no writing art that demands greater ability to make the reader *believe in* the set-up and the suspense than fantasy.

And in fantasy, there's no genre more difficult or rewarding to create with credibility than horror.

Are We Writing Yet?

by Donna Levin

If you are a novelist, even if you are just starting to practice your craft, you will have already noticed that it is not a writer-friendly world out there. People conspire against you at every opportunity: They drop by when they know you are writing, because they figure it's the best time to catch you at home; then they tell you how impossible it is to sell anything unless your mother has her own publishing house.

Meanwhile, you are torturing yourself with doubts about whether you have "enough talent" to be a writer in the first place. That, however, is the wrong question to ponder. Kurt Vonnegut wisely observed, "Talent is extremely common. What is rare is the willingness to endure the life of a writer."

The life of a writer, unfortunately, involves more than just hanging out in cafés smoking thin brown cigarettes: Living the life of a writer demands persistence, self-discipline, patience and a dollop of insanity. It means you must ignore the discouragement of supposedly well-meaning friends; it means working on a book. This article is about ways to do just that—to go from planning to be a writer to *being* a writer.

The balancing act

To write a book, one must first find the time to write. Yet many of us juggle the competing demands of family, friends, jobs, dates, volunteer commitments, home maintenance, hobbies, schoolwork—and we have the temerity to dream of an occasional day at the beach on top of that.

We'd have trouble writing an extra Christmas card—and we say we want to write *novels*?

Some changes have to be made. But you really don't have to quit your job, leave your family and go live in the woods. In fact, I'd recommend against making immediate, drastic lifestyle changes, so you can stop worrying about whether or not your local monastery will accept your application.

Writing is a lot like exercising. If you wanted to run a marathon (and a novel is definitely the marathon run of fiction writing), you wouldn't simply enter yourself in the Boston marathon, show up on the day of the race and expect your natural talent to take you to the finish. Rather, knowing that you had set yourself an admirable and difficult goal, you would begin by training: Eating right, running short distances and getting in shape to endure the 26-plus miles the race requires.

Similarly, it would be asking a lot of yourself, on Day One of your writing career, to sit down for four hours and churn out 30 pages, just as it would be asking a lot of yourself to bench press 300 pounds your first day in the gym.

Instead, what you need to do is to find ways to write a little bit each day, then gradually expand that time into a longer period that you can live with on a regular basis.

Recognize at the outset that writing a book is a long-term project. It's probably not realistic to expect to knock off a saleable novel in six months, unless you are both fairly experienced and writing formula fiction. And realistic expectations are a good armor

Novelist **Donna Levin** is the author of Extraordinary Means and California Streets. *This piece is adapted from her upcoming book on writing,* Get That Novel Started, *to be published by Writer's Digest Books in Spring 1993.*

against the kind of disappointment that leads to giving up. The novel will not be written in a few days, but it will be written.

Here's how:

You can hang by your thumbs

Start by writing 10 minutes a day. That's right, just 10 minutes a day. For the first few weeks, that's enough.

You say you don't have 10 minutes a day? Su-u-ure you do.

You can get up 10 minutes earlier and write before your day begins, or stay up 10 minutes later and write when it's all over.

If you work in an office, you can trim 10 minutes from your lunch hour (maybe you were taking an hour and 10 minutes anyway). You can stay at the office for an extra 10 minutes and write at your desk (your boss will just think you're working extra hard). You can stop at the library for 10 minutes on your way home or write on the commuter train or ferry.

If you are at home with children, then postpone your errands and housework for 10 minutes after they leave for school. Summer vacation? Be firm: Make a deal with the kids that you have a short time each day during which they are not to interrupt you. If that becomes the most likely time for them to fall off their bikes or set the cat's tail on fire, then contract with your partner that he or she is responsible for them for even just a short time after dinner. You can do the same for him or her during another part of the day.

In every situation, there are always alternatives. With a little effort, you can find a regular time to write. Even if the time you choose is not your most creative, you can probably tolerate some discomfort for 10 minutes. Hey, if you had to, you could hang by your thumbs for 10 minutes a day.

If you are wondering how a novel can be written in 10-minute increments, you are right to wonder. The important thing is to get started. My "10 minutes a day" prescription is meant to be a wedge to get writing into your life and to start collecting some pages. Once you take that first step and have a book underway, it becomes much easier to get up half an hour, or even an hour, earlier or to stay up later or to eat lunch at your desk instead of going to a restaurant.

If you can build up to an hour a day of writing, and use that hour faithfully, that will be enough. Many novels have been written in an hour a day. Obviously, more is better. If you are able to work part-time, and/or your children are grown or in school, or you happen to win the lottery, then you are fortunate. If not, then that's still no excuse not to write.

What is absolutely crucial at this stage is that you do it *every day*—yes, seven days a week. Your mind, just like your body, has to be trained to perform certain tasks. If you wait until Saturday—"I'll have the whole afternoon!"—I can almost guarantee that will be the day that the pipes in the basement burst, or the dog starts throwing up, or you do. If nothing else, the big screen television you've been wanting to buy for two years will go on sale (for one day only) and you'll *just have* to drive 30 miles to the warehouse to get it.

Daily work, on the other hand, will stimulate your unconscious to keep simmering over the novel during nonwriting hours, so you are really making maximum use of your time. Continuity is very important in a novel; you need to be able to hold a lot of information in your head, so you need to constantly remind yourself of what you are doing. If you work regularly during the week, then you *will* be able to use a long block of time if it comes your way over the weekend or on a day off.

Same time tomorrow

Just waking up with the determination to get 10 minutes of writing done "sometime" during the day isn't quite enough. A surprisingly large amount of writing is simply habit. Find the time that works best for you and stick to it.

You'll be tempted to bargain with your sacrosanct time. ("I haven't seen Janine for so long, I must have lunch with her — I'll write later" or "I'm catching a cold, maybe I'll skip today.") Resist temptation. Get the habit. Open that notebook — for 10 minutes.

The determination factor

I heard about one writer so starved for privacy (he had a small apartment full of young children) that he would go out to his car for an hour in the evening and work under the dome light. While it didn't do the battery of his car a lot of good, he did manage to get some work done.

One much-published novelist told me how he got his start: He was working in telemarketing, selling magazine subscriptions. Between phone calls he would jot down a few sentences at a time on the index cards that were supposed to be used to keep records of the calls. Later, after work, he would sit in a coffee shop and expand upon this cryptic writing.

Legend has it that Jean Genet, the French novelist and playwright who started writing while in prison, began his first novel with a stolen pencil, writing on the brown paper that the prisoners were using to make paper bags.

We can admire the heroism and determination of these people and still know that they were ordinary people who simply wanted to do something badly enough. What have you wanted to do badly? Learn to play the guitar? Save for a Camaro? Backpack through Europe? What you've wanted to do badly you have probably made the time, and found the resources, to do.

Set priorities

Let's say you've set aside your 10 minutes, and you are as regular as a metronome about using them. Now you can start making some accommodations in the rest of your life so that you can expand those minutes to an hour — or more if possible. At this point, it will be easier, because you will be starting to feel your writing muscles grow stronger. You will see the evidence of your work unfold before you. You will have pages collecting in a box or notebook, and this will be something worth fighting for.

Once again, that doesn't mean that you have to go from 10 minutes to 10 hours a day overnight. Rather, see how you can gradually phase out other commitments. If the novel is important to you, you will be willing to give up some other things.

Novelists tend to be hard workers and overachievers — who else would tackle a novel in the first place? But that may mean that you've also taken on a lot of other projects, all of which you do better than anyone else. You may feel that you are the only mom who can run the school bake sale or the only dad who can coach Little League. You may indeed be the only one on your bowling team who can score over 100, or you may be the best volunteer at the crisis hotline.

Giving up some of these extracurricular activities will be difficult, and not just because *they* need *you*. If you are a good bowler or hotline volunteer, for example, you are getting regular feedback on your performance. You are able to measure your progress as you go and see the results of your actions while enjoying the immediate gratification of being out with your friends or helping a worthy cause.

By contrast, the work you do on your novel may not have any impact on anyone for as long as several years. At the very least you are not going to get the same instant response to it. When you sit alone at your desk and come up with a marvelously profound insight, no one applauds the way they would when you bowl your third consecutive strike. To choose to give up some evenings out to engage in solitary relationship with a piece of paper or a computer screen is a tough choice. Only you can decide if you want to do it.

Recognize that a novelist needs a streak of selfishness. Some of us have streaks as wide as the interstate, but if you are more the caretaker-to-the-world, can't-say-no type, you may have to cultivate a little self-centeredness, at least when it comes to your book.

In *The Writing Life*, Annie Dillard describes how she let all her houseplants die while she was finishing a novel. Annie Dillard has dead plants but she also has a Pulitzer Prize.

Take my job—please

You may be able to "downscale" your job. Some writers find that working three or four days a week, sometimes for longer hours, works better for them. Depending on what you do, perhaps you can take on fewer clients, patients or accounts, or become a freelancer or consultant. In some professions, and some locations, a consultant can make as much or more money in fewer hours.

If you have the choice to make, remember that a job which does not require you to do much writing, or even much reading, has some definite advantages. If you are driving a cab, selling cosmetics, waiting tables or building houses, you are moving your body and using a different part of your brain than you do as a novelist. During your off-hours, you will have more energy for fiction than the lawyer who writes appellate briefs, the public relations person who writes press releases or the journalist who writes news stories.

One way of giving yourself more time to write is to pay someone else to do the things that are keeping you from writing. There are plenty of people who would love to earn money doing your gardening, housework, bookkeeping, child care, even your personal errands. Obviously, this only makes sense up to the point that you can afford it. Don't engage a staff of servants on the theory that you'll recoup the investment on your first advance. That may indeed happen; but most first advances are relatively small, so it's not a very effective way to manage your finances in the meantime.

Otherwise, let the dust collect and the laundry pile up.

Too much time on your hands

If you are one of those who has to scrape writing hours together, you may not believe it's possible to have *too* much time to write. *Au contraire, mes amis*!

Consider the case of Annabelle, a young woman who has recently inherited enough money to quit her job for a year and write that novel she's always wanted to write.

Annabelle worked for the past several years as a sales representative for a medical supply company. She used to arrive at the office at 9 a.m., make a series of phone calls to set up appointments, then hit the road to see customers. She checked in for messages, stopped for lunch, ran a few errands between sales calls. At 5 p.m., she stopped by her office again, then headed home for the evening.

This morning, on her first day of liberty, she awakens as usual at 7:30. She can spend the whole day on that novel! What? The whole day?

Annabelle hides under the covers, trying to go back to sleep. Being chained to a typewriter until bedtime seems a Promethean fate, to put it kindly. When she didn't have time to write, Annabelle's ideas seemed to be bubbling just under the surface. Suddenly they have evaporated.

Sure, having the leisure to work is clearly the optimum situation for a budding novelist. But here are the pitfalls: There's no boss to overhear your personal phone calls, and therefore to stop you from making them. There are no appointments to keep, except your appointment with a very inhospitable and stubborn typewriter. You work alone, without coworkers to snitch pencils off your desk and remind you that you are alive. The day is not easily divisible into particular tasks. Faced with long, intimidating hours, one easily becomes overwhelmed.

My advice to Annabelle and to those in similar, albeit enviable situations, is *also* to start with 10 minutes a day and build up gradually. The analogy of writing to physical exercise applies equally to all writers: No matter how much time you had to work out, you still wouldn't bench press those 300 pounds on your first day in the gym.

Once you've done your 10 minutes, then go ahead and enjoy the rest of your day. Ten minutes isn't a lot, but it is 10 minutes *spent writing*, 10 minutes of honest effort, be it in front of ruled pad or computer. If all you do during those 10 minutes is type the words to "The Star Spangled Banner," you are entitled to feel that you have accomplished something, besides being a patriot.

It will take a few weeks, maybe even a month or more, to learn to become your own time manager. Meanwhile, experiment with some of these techniques:
- Make two or three writing appointments for yourself, for example, at 9 a.m., 11 a.m. and 2 p.m. If you'd rather do it all at one stretch, then firmly commit to beginning at a certain time of day, be it 8 a.m. or at 12:30 a.m. (Some writers prefer the morning, others are at their most creative when everyone else is asleep.)
- Schedule other events for the day — not so many that you won't have time to write — but activities that will bracket your writing time and make those work sessions both manageable and harder to postpone. For example, plan to swim or jog or even take a walk at some point during the day. Exercise is marvelous for loosening ideas from where they lie plastered inside your head. Meet someone for lunch, especially someone who must get back to work, so that your lunch date won't extend too late into your afternoon.
- Reward yourself for a segment of writing time, or a certain number of pages, completed. "When I finish this section I can call my friend Sheila," or "I'll write until 4 p.m., and then I get to watch Oprah." Treat yourself to something you enjoy. The more mindless and unconstructive the reward is, the better, but nonfood and nonsubstance rewards are preferable. Yet, going to the grocery store may seem like a reward after a few tough hours pounding those keys.
- The at-home writer with all day to write might benefit more than others from going out to work at the library or a café. Going somewhere else simulates going to a job. Perhaps you will befriend a kindhearted librarian, waiter or waitress who will take an interest in your work, and ask you how it's going. Then, you have to show up; you can't let this good person down.

As weeks and months go by, you won't have to be so vigilant with yourself. As writing becomes a routine, distractions will lose some of their power.

Finally, don't isolate yourself too much. Certainly it's more common to find would-be writers in the situation described at the beginning of this article, in which the company softball team and keeping up with Grandpa's stamp collection eclipse all writing hours. But the other extreme isn't good, either. If you don't have contact with other people, if you don't have some activities and social events to look forward to — a reason to get dressed up and out of the house occasionally — then not only will it be difficult to write productively, but you will have less material to write about.

How much is enough?

If you can write three hours a day, you are doing as much as most fulltime, published novelists (though note that this means three hours, seven days a week). Once you have been writing for awhile taking Sundays or even weekends off is hardly fatal, but I must repeat how strongly I recommend you write daily during the first year.

It's an extremely rare writer who can work more than five hours a day over any extended period of time. The most notable exceptions occur when a novelist is nearing the end of a project and doing fine-tuning that doesn't require as much deep thought. Then he or she may be up for a weekend marathon.

If, however, you *are* one of those writers who can do five-plus hours at a stretch, then please do so, with my admiration. I would never discourage anyone from time he or she wants to spend writing. But three to four hours a day is enough time to do some fairly serious work. Remember, I'm not only talking about three hours a day, seven days, *this week*—I'm talking about three hours a day, five to seven days a week, every week for a couple of years or more. It adds up.

Hard time

As I said at the outset, a novelist must be prepared for a certain lack of understanding on the part of nonwriting humans. If you are a fulltime writer and you tell people that you work three or four hours, you will often be asked, "What do you do the rest of the day?" You might reply, with a dramatic roll of the eyes, "Recuperate from the draining creative process." Then pass your hand wearily over your forehead.

There would be some truth to your answer. When you talk about writing three hours, you're talking about some of the most concentrated work there is. At a regular job, chances are you spend a certain amount of time brewing coffee or calling home or reading the paper and calling it work.

Some of the rest of your day, as a fulltime writer, might be spent on research for the novel or reading the manuscripts of other people in your writing group. But if you spend three hours a day writing and the rest of the day watching the lawn grow, you are a writer, and don't let anyone on this planet tell you otherwise.

I don't know what to write yet!

"All right," you say. "I've cut down my hours at work; I've bribed my partner to clean up the yard; I've bought the kids enough Nintendo games to keep them in their rooms until they leave for college. What if I don't even know what my novel is about yet?"

No problem. All you need is the desire to write. Let's assume you don't even have the germ of a seed of an idea. Just start writing about *anything*. An excellent writing teacher, Leonard Bishop, always said, "Writing begets writing," and he was correct.

So get yourself a journal. This can be a $1.49 spiral from the five-and-dime or the needlepoint-covered blank book you bought at a crafts fair. (Or you can use your computer.) Then *start*. Try these ideas:

• *Write about some unusual thing you saw the day before*: The other day at the variety store the woman ahead of me was checking out with a package of Raisinets, a box of Velveeta cheese, a large bottle of mineral water and Tylenol. I tried to imagine what she was planning to do with this stuff. Was she filling requests from roommates who had headaches and sugar cravings? Was she pregnant and getting an urge for Velveeta melted over Raisinets?

• *Write about the first time you did something*: "The bike felt so wobbly, as I stood next to it, I couldn't imagine how anyone could ever ride one. My older brother had been riding a bike for two years, but then he could do many things I couldn't, including talk to girls."

• *Try to imagine how your parents met*: (Our families provide us with unlimited material.) "They were young then, younger than I am now. From the pictures I've seen, my father was unusually handsome, with a long, straight nose and curly black hair, and even the suggestion of a cleft chin."

• *Write about the worst date you ever had*: "My aunt gave him my phone number without asking me if she could. What could I do when he called? I wasn't seeing anyone else; I didn't have an excuse. I guess I could have pretended to be seeing someone else, but Aunt Betty had pretty much told him everything about me, and I admit I was a tiny bit curious, too. Except that I knew that anyone Aunt Betty gave my number to would be the greatest dork of the 20th century."

• *Write about something you love to do*: "The first rush of water when I dive in the pool is so cold, I feel it chill even my lungs. But then I'm stroking hard against the water, blowing out bubbles and raising my head to suck in more air, and I feel alive, conscious of every muscle, my mind joined with my body."

• *More ideas*: Describe the view from your window; write a letter to a friend; imagine what your life would be like if it were perfect.

• *If you just want to be putting words down on paper, try*: Summarizing the plot of your favorite novel or movie or writing the words to as many Broadway (or Beatles, or Elvis or Talking Heads) songs as you can remember. Yes, this counts. You're writing, aren't you?

Copy these "jump-starters" down and keep them near your typewriter, or set aside the first few pages of your notebook for the list, so you won't waste precious time trying to remember them.

You will have your own ideas for similar topics to pursue, so carry a small notebook (or index cards) in your purse, pocket or briefcase. Keep a pad by your bedside. When you do get an idea, write it down and later transfer it to your master list.

Avoid the "journal pit" by not using your journal to obsess about your life. By obsessing I mean repeating abstract concerns, questions with no answers, over and over. A journal can be helpful as a therapeutic tool, certainly, but that's not really what we're doing here.

Rather, use the journal to begin to acquire a novelist's skills of observation. Identify specific objects, numbers and colors in the outside world. Describe how people look or how they move. Create dialogues or recreate them from memory. Experiment. Stretch. No one ever has to see what you've written but you.

Beware the saboteur

Novelists are always vulnerable about their work, no matter how much they've published. (Just try talking to an author after he or she reads a bad review of his or her latest novel.) But you are at your most vulnerable when you are starting out.

Most writers like to encourage beginners, but a few feel the need to lessen the competition. And even more commonly, nonwriting acquaintances will have discouraging reactions without meaning to. They just don't understand that wrinkling their noses or telling you about a novel with a similar story line will seem like a death knell to your entire writing career.

So be careful with whom you discuss your material, especially at this early stage. If you tell someone that you are writing a novel and they want to know what it's about, you are entitled to explain politely that you don't discuss works-in-progress. (Most people have heard that one.) If it feels more comfortable, you can always give a brief, vague answer like, "Oh, it's this romance thing." Leave it at that. You should take the excitement you feel about your work to the work itself. If you casually discuss what you plan to write about, you lessen some of your drive to do the actual writing.

You *do* want to get feedback on your work-in-progress. For that, though, you will be going to your writing group or to a few trusted folks whom you have cultivated as critics.

Your personal fan club

Although writers are often surrounded by voices of doom, you may in fact be blessed with a partner and/or a few close friends who fully support your literary ambitions. If that is the case, then I hope you show them how very much you appreciate them, every single day of your life. These significant others who encourage you—who tolerate your absences and introspective moods—are doing so primarily on faith, because no one who doesn't write fiction will have a complete understanding of the rigors and risks of the craft.

As time goes by, and you continue to work, people around you will accept that this is something you do. As you set priorities and cut down on your television watching and card playing, you will be sending a signal to them that writing is worth some sacrifices to you.

A place for you

Virginia Woolf is well-known for saying that one must have a room of one's own in order to write. But it is not crucial to have a private office with the latest in word-processing technology. That can easily become another excuse. People say, "Well, I have to go out and rent a space with *ambiance*," or "I have to wait 'til Johnny goes to Yale so I can use his room," or "I have to save up for that AKA 989 voice-activated laser jet combination modem and coffeemaker." Watch out for anything that lets you postpone writing.

Still, creating some separate space for yourself does make what you are doing easier, especially as you begin to collect notes, chapters and completed drafts. See what you can carve out of your existing quarters.

If you live alone it won't be hard. There's always the dining room table—in modern America, probably more dining room tables are used as desks than for entertaining anyway. Even if you just have a studio apartment, you can use the coffee table that goes with your sleeper couch. A walk-in closet can become an office.

If you prefer to write on buses, in cafés or at work, your corner at home can simply become the place where you keep your accumulating material. You can put a bulletin board on the wall, to tack up inspirational sayings or favorite snapshots or reminders to yourself ("Mention Celia's age somewhere in the first chapter").

It's good to be flexible about where you write, so that if you travel a lot or have to be away from home for any reason, you can adapt. But it's worth investing some time and energy in personalizing a writing area, in no small part because it reinforces the message you want to send to yourself and others: *I am a writer. This is important to me.*

No matter how humble your space, you can look with pride at the orange crate desk and peeling paint and the spider on the ceiling who seems to smile when you come in.

Only the beginning

Sure, there's still a long road ahead. Even after you publish, the daily process of working will often be tedious; you will often wonder why you bother in this world where people recognize game-show hosts, but not novelists, in the street.

But getting started is the biggest hurdle. Now you *are* living the life of a writer. If you are willing to continue, publication will certainly follow.

What to do about Criticism

by Laura Hendrie

I'm sitting at a bar with a young man who's recently taken to calling himself a writer. After throwing back a shot of whiskey, he turns to me and says "I think the greatest thing about writing is the honesty of the response you get back. Nobody hedges. Nobody tries to be polite. It's exhilarating. Know what I mean?"

I look at him with curiosity. We've just spent an hour together in a class where he was told by several writers, including me, that his novel—despite interesting characters, sharp-paced dialogue and a real eye-opener of a plot—doesn't work. As far as I could tell from his reaction at the time, he wasn't all *that* thrilled by honesty, and now, though he smiles warmly at me before he turns to motion for another drink, I notice a tic in the muscle at the side of his neck.

A negative response from your readers—especially when they've taken the time to be conscientious about it—is always a shock. It's like getting kicked in the behind while bending over to pick up the penny. It's not the kick that hurts, it's the humiliation of having bent over for the penny. True, your voice may not quiver when you're thanking them for their honesty. Your hands may be steady when you're opening that letter of advice from the editor you've always admired. You may even be able to agree with your favorite author when he tells you that he thinks your new book isn't half as interesting as the last one you wrote. But your whole face is on fire, there's a roaring in your ears and behind that pleasant, puppet-strung "uh-huh" of yours stands an infuriated, tic-faced little dictator demanding to know this instant one of three things: A) how you could allow these half-wits near your best work; B) why you *ever* thought you could get away with calling yourself a writer; or C) how you're ever going to write again. And this may be where you stop. But it shouldn't be. In fact, the difference between the writer who's going to add up to something in a few years and the writer who's not may have less to do with the quality of the work than with the way each one handles criticism.

Using criticism to your advantage

Some writers *use* criticism. Experienced writers do it all the time. They selectively choose whom to listen to, selectively listen for what they need to hear and selectively use the information they're given. They do this with the same skill and concentration they use in their writing. Some writers will panic and toss out everything readers didn't like while embalming for worship everything they praised. Either that or balk at the very idea of changing a word or comma. A successful writer will panic too, but then he will flounder onward, pondering this criticism and sweating out that compliment, trying all the wrong advice and being thoroughly disgusted with himself when he can't seem to make it work, until somewhere along the line, if he's open enough, he turns almost by accident to the advice he needed to hear in the first place—the advice he was too biased or nervous or green to understand before—and wham! he's invented something new. Not only that, but he's learned things *not* to invent along the way as well.

Laura Hendrie's work has appeared in The Missouri Review, Taos Review, Writers' Forum *and in various anthologies including* Best of the West I *and* III, Into the Silence *and* Ten American Signatures. *Her stories have also aired on National Public Radio as part of the PEN Syndicated Fiction Project.*

Writers who realize that feedback can be a valuable tool use it often and with growing dexterity and gratitude. And why not? Writing is a lonely enough experience without summarily refusing all help and input from outsiders. To do so simply because the reader may be wrong, the advice might upset you or you don't like to be told what you didn't think up yourself is not only stubborn but ultimately foolhardy.

If you're thinking, "Yes, but writers who can jump at a chance to receive feedback don't get the kind of feedback I get; they don't have to put up with the grunting manuscript-eaters I've got to deal with," you're wrong. Everybody gets their share of negative feedback and everybody gets their share of nonobjective, incompetent criticism. So don't think you're being unfairly picked on when even the most unskilled reader you know calls to tell you how to fix your story or poem, when even the silliest little free pamphlet-magazine sends you a rejection. It comes with the territory.

Writers who use critical feedback are not less egocentric or thicker-skinned or more flexible than writers who can't. Writers are by definition egocentric, thin-skinned and highly sensitive to criticism. They write to be understood and when they are not, no matter how they may try to hide it, it hurts.

But while one writer may walk off from a negative response to his work looking like a suicide headed for the bridge, another writer can leave the same situation with a sense of excitement, even eagerness. Why? Not because he enjoys humiliation. And not because he is, in John Wayne's words, a damn fool. He just hasn't lost sight of his priority in the process. His priority is and always should be, even at the cost of pride and temporary pleasures, *to improve the writing*.

Okay, so you want to improve your writing, too. So you want to be able to learn from readers even when they start sucking the air out of the room. How do you manage it?

Step one: Ask yourself why

The way to handle criticism is to know *why* you're asking for it. You should know the answer to this *before* you ever send out a piece of work to be read.

This is not as easy as you might first suppose. Writers may be notoriously honest, but when it comes to the question of why they're sending out their work to be read, they tend to hold their hands over their mouths when they speak. Or as Logan Pearsall Smith explained it: "Every author, however modest, keeps a most outrageous vanity chained like a madman in the padded cell of his breast."

So the first question you should answer has two parts, one for the writer in you and one for the madman: What do you think you want? What do you *really* want? "I know!" you chirp like the good child. *"To improve the writing!"* But to do that you must be as honest about your weaknesses as you are about your strengths. This can be extremely difficult when your weaknesses are being pointed out to you by someone else. Honest readers know this. That's why there are so few of them. They know how likely it is that when you say you want honesty, your preference is praise. Yet the irony is, you know you have to have that dose of honesty once in a while. You can't live without it, not if you're to become any sort of "real" writer.

The best way to get honesty from your readers is by asking for honesty from yourself. This is why *before* I send off a story or poem, I clear a place on my desk and sit down with a clean sheet of paper and a thick, black felt-tip pen to work out the reasons *why* I'm about to send out my work to whatever reader(s) I've chosen. I start at the top with the word:

Priorities

Some days this in itself is enough to make me feel virtuous. Below that, I write:

Why do I need to send out this piece?

Priorities are more like eternal laws than personal decisions. They do not change much and they are as easy to remember as the memory of your mother's voice telling you to sit up straight or that brussels sprouts are good for you. I have two priorities: "To improve the writing" and "to get honest feedback." My only other priority is when I'm sending my manuscript out to be published, and then I'll naturally include "to have the story published."

Notice how I avoid using personal pronouns in priorities. I like to keep them sounding as noble and unselfish and thoroughly martyred for the sake of the writing as the mother who offers to crawl to Bethlehem for the sake of her children.

When I'm done with that, I move down to the middle of the page. There I draw a heavy black line similar to the River Styx and below that I take a breath and write:

Preferences

Then, I write

What else do I want?

This is where it gets tricky. You'll do anything but admit what you *really* want, right? To get around this, write your answers in the form of questions.

What else do I want?

To show my readers that:

- I'm a living treasure?
- I've led a fascinating life? (had fascinating parents? children? dogs?)
- I'm not afraid of a little criticism?
- I should be published soon in some magazine their mother works for?
- I'm nothing like them?
- I'm just as good as them?
- I'm 10 times better than them?

I try to put the preferences that sound most vulgar right at the top of the list. That way I offer myself the chance to be honest from the start. I also think it's helpful to go over each item and ask yourself "If I could ever be *so* grossly self-centered as to want that and then the opposite actually happened, I wonder how I'd feel?" Then close your eyes and imagine it. If you feel anything like nausea or dizziness, you're probably close to the truth. Keep going. When it comes to preferences — i.e., vanity-driven motives that have absolutely nothing to do with good writing — still waters run deep. And what do you do with all this truth? Examine your options:

Options:

- Forget about sending out the story.
- Forget about getting honest feedback and send the story to your aunt who "always loves anything" you write.
- Send it out to honest readers but ask them to read only for grammar and spelling errors. Or better yet, tell them to read it "only for enjoyment." (Don't worry, they'll get the point.)
- Send it out and prepare yourself for the possibility of seeing every one of your preferences shot for the sake of improving the work.

If you choose the last option, remember two things. One is that the reason you're asking for feedback is that you are still learning to write (if you're smart, you'll spend your entire life learning and still never be able to admit you know how.) The other is Marcus Aurelius' quote: "It is not death that a man should fear, but he should fear never beginning to live." Which in my neck of the woods translates to mean that if I'm fully prepared to get bucked off my horse in a negative critique, and then I actually *get* bucked off, I'm a lot less stunned about it than if I assumed my horse wasn't the bucking type. Plus I'll be able to get back on faster and decide which direction to go in next with a great deal more clarity and eagerness.

The surprising thing is this little pre-game self-exam can make a big difference. Let's say, for example, that I've given my fiction to my most honest reader who then informs me that she thinks the main character is insipid. If I'm not aware of my preferences, if I've deluded myself into thinking that honest feedback was my *only* expectation, I may get the desire to, let's say, snap off her head at the neck. Why? Because the story was so *obviously* all about me and my incredible childhood! Granted, I *called* it fiction instead of autobiography, granted I *asked* for her honest opinion — but *really!*

But if on the other hand, after admitting to myself that my desire to send out my poem about Miami was influenced not only by my desire to improve the work but also because the reader I chose just happens to edit a magazine called *Miami Monthly*, I can't be all that upset with her if she spends her time talking about the heavy-handedness of the setting. After all, she's kept her priorities straight — to give honest feedback. I'm the one who bent the rules, who tried to submit to her magazine without her realizing it. But I can forgive myself — wanting love is only human, right? I'll look at the poem some more, try to see what she saw, maybe even change the setting to something I know more about. And in the meantime I've discovered a gem: The reader who insists on being honest.

Step two: Ask your readers questions

Contrary to what many people believe, giving a manuscript to readers for a critical discussion does not mean the writer gives up control of it. Far from it. In most cases, readers look to the writer for direction. If they sense the writer's priority is to improve the work, they'll try to deliver; but if they sense the writer is fishing for compliments or expecting a browbeating, they're likely to do that, too. It's hard not to. So if you don't want to leave your next critique feeling duped, take charge. Teach your readers how to teach you.

One way to do this is to come to the discussion with a carefully planned set of what I call writing-oriented questions about your work. Asking writing-oriented questions accomplishes several things. It makes you an active participant in the feedback process, provides a framework for you and your readers to address particular concerns about the work and helps organize your readers' discussion into themes which are easier for you to grasp, understand and later use.

But most important, writing-oriented questions clarify for everyone concerned why the critique is taking place. Not because the writer is hoping to be coddled and not because the readers want to toot their horns about how much they know. No, this discussion is taking place for one reason and one reason only: *To improve the writing.* Most readers appreciate being reminded of this.

Which is why, if you want your questions to be writing-oriented instead of self-oriented, they should be written down *before* you enter the critique, before that little madman imprisoned in your breast, your ego, starts shrieking and rattling his chains too loudly for you to think.

A writing-oriented question sounds exactly like what it is. It's the same kind of open-ended question English teachers pose for their students on a piece of literature, and it demands the same sort of response from readers, i.e.:

- Clearly stated ideas about the piece backed by concrete examples;
- Objectivity in arguments;
- A strong sense of respect for and deference to the work (i.e., a writing-oriented question asks the reader for a clear description of what *is* on the page, not a prescription of what to

put there next);
- Examination based on two bigger issues: What works? What doesn't work?

Now let's put this to the test. Suppose that as the author, you're curious to know if the complexity of your main character translates onto the page. If you ask something like "Did you like the main character?" or "Didn't you think that ending was confusing?" the reader feels trapped. The questions are close-ended and ego-oriented. They plead not for an honest response from the reader but an ego-mollifying, uninformed and uninformative, knee-jerk response like "yeah" or "sure."

A writing-oriented question, however, might be "Can you describe the kind of person the main character is?" Now you are asking an open-ended question that demands objective information based not on opinion but on what is on the page. *You* as author know the answer. You know it because it's your work, but see if your readers know it, too. If they don't, and you know they're careful readers, then the character is obviously not as fully realized on paper as he is in your head.

Here are some other examples of writing-oriented questions:
- Can you tell me why the man does what he does?
- Can you tell me why or why not the point of view (the pace/voice/setting/dialogue/ whatever you're concerned about) works for this particular piece?
- Can you tell me what the strongest images were in the piece and why? The weakest? Why?
- Can you explain why I changed from third person to first at the end?

Adapt questions to your specific needs, your specific style and your specific readers. Then make sure to open your ears. Good listening begins with respect. Write down everything, even if you don't agree with it (if your critique occurs through the mail, copy down the comments from your reader(s) in your own hand). Listen not only to what is said, but also to what is not said. Be courteous. Be sure you understand. Encourage them if you think they are holding back. And *never* argue. You are there to improve the writing, and no matter how far off the mark they are in this regard, they are trying to help. Remember this. The more you're able to hear what they're saying and why they're saying it, the more you'll understand the worth of it later.

Step three: What to do with feedback

After you come out of a critique of your work, you've got, as you know, several choices. If you don't believe what you hear, you can throw a fit and send the story to someone else. If you believe it, you can throw a fit and destroy the piece. Or you can throw a fit and then hide the piece in the back of your closet for a while.

But most writers — even the ones who don't throw fits — end up wanting to rewrite. The question is how to do it when every voice is yammering at you except the original one that told you to write the piece in the first place. Here are some methods that have helped me:

Pace problems: I learned this method from Andre Dubus and I still use it, especially when I think my work may need to be heavily edited. I clear out the furniture in my living room and then lay out my manuscript, page by page, on the floor, like tiles. I then get down on my hands and knees and, starting at page one, skim the content and then paraphrase it in one short sentence. I do this with every page, using ditto marks and arrows where the idea doesn't change from one page to the next. It is much like dismantling and cataloging a skeleton, studying the shape and weight of each bone so as to better understand the body and how it works. When I'm done, my list can tell me how much space each idea/character/ scene takes up and how they fit and move (or don't fit and move) together. This has, at times, clearly mirrored for me what my manuscript as a whole needs in terms of trimming here and fattening there.

Story development problems: I prefer free-form writing. The purpose is to suspend critical judgment by writing down whatever comes into your head, whether it's related to the subject or not. Be silly. Be crazy. Write fast and judge nothing. This can lead you to stumble over your subconscious memory and onto the missing key which will once again unlock the sound of the story you want.

Character development problems: Any long-married person will tell you that after you've grown accustomed to someone, no matter how much you love them, you can lose sight of who they are sometimes until you take a break from your regular surroundings, when that person becomes suddenly strange and wonderful all over again. Therefore, if you're having trouble getting interested in or understanding one of your characters after a critique, remove the character from the situation you had him in and try him out in something else. Describe him in front of the mirror brushing his teeth. Put him to bed, or if he's already there, put him in the kitchen in his pajamas staring into the refrigerator for something to eat. Use any small, mundane act (new action is not what you're looking for, it's new insight into personality) and see how he does it. Study movements, look for revealing details, listen to what he thinks. Whole new personality quirks for characters have come to me in this way, sometimes even whole new characters. And even when they don't, it's a good exercise anyway.

Morale problems in general: When I get really bogged down by negative feedback so that I don't know where to begin, I sometimes give myself an absolute three-week deadline to finish the story *and* an absolute order to stop writing anything but random notes to myself for a week.

This may sound crazy and it certainly can make you feel crazy, but it's like turning on the heat under a pot of water and then putting a tight lid on it so the pressure builds, making the water boil faster. In my case, it makes me both acutely aware of and eager to foster the idea that everything I do and see and feel is related to what I'm going to write, whether or not I'm writing it at the time. What I see happening around me, what I read, the way I talk, what I eat, what people say to me, sometimes even what I dream—if I believe all of it holds messages for my writing in all sorts of mysterious and coincidental ways, when I am truly focused on that, it works. I'll pick up a magazine in the local laundry with a quote in it that is exactly what I was trying to get at; I'll hear a conversation at the store that is stunningly like what my fictional character wants to say; I'll sit down to write a letter to the editor of a newspaper and suddenly know how the story which is in my bottom drawer will end.

The more aware I can make myself of the possibility of the answer coming to me unannounced, the more it does. This is not magic. It has nothing to do with New Age affirmations. It is simply allowing the mind to imagine what it wants while keeping tabs on the priority of improving the writing.

You'll have more success with a holistic, work-oriented approach to rewriting than the simplistic types of problem-shooting the how-to books suggest. A story is a living, breathing organism with all kinds of angles and textures and private, changeable moods to it, and it should be viewed as such, from a cubist's vision, seeing all different sides at once. This doesn't apply just to writing it. You can dictate it to a tape recorder. Read it in a voice other than your own. Shout it at the wall. Whisper it to your cat. Make it into a poem. Draw a picture of it if you can. Anything, anything that will *let the story speak*.

Because in the end, that is exactly what will happen. The story will speak. It will make your decisions for you, either by becoming too awful to work on another moment or by becoming too interesting not to. You can count on it. No matter how badly it's written in its first draft, no matter how much negative and/or uninformed criticism it gets buried under, no matter how cruel and barbaric your ego behaves when left alone to rewrite it, if the story has something worthwhile in it, it is indestructible. Throw a good idea away and it will emerge in the next story you write. Hide a good character in your closet and sooner or later you will hear him telling you to take him out again, whether you want to or not. You can't stop it.

Writers in the critiquing process too often forget this. They think they're in charge of the story or the readers are in charge of the story, but the truth is *the writing is in charge*. It is the top priority. Treat it as such, listen to it as such, honor it as such, and from the day you get back the results of your first critique to the day you sit down to rework the final draft, you will be better able to make wise decisions.

Dealing with Small Magazines: One Editor's View

by Alicia Griswold

I probably don't need to remind you that many of our finest and most successful writers published their first stories in the category known as the "little/literary magazines" and that it is more than likely you will submit your work to one of us, if you haven't already.

Unlike the commercial markets or even some of the more venerable literary magazines such as *The Paris Review* or *The North American Review*, staffed by professionals, there is another group of small, but well-established magazines such as *The Black Warrior Review* staffed solely by graduate students for whom working on the magazine is a cherished learning experience, but where much of their wisdom is gained from the mistakes made establishing a workable schedule, living within a budget and meeting production deadlines. Student-run literary magazines have one built-in disadvantage: Every year the new editor gets to make the same mistakes the previous editor made.

What I'd like to do here is describe some of the ways writers and editors go wrong and focus on how the writer, in preparing a submission, can help us avoid them. While my experience has been with student-run magazines, much of the information here applies to the writer/editor relationship at many small publications.

Your reasons for wanting to be helpful are simple. In publishing, writers are the ones who live longest with somebody else's mistakes. The easier you make it for us, the better we can make it for you.

Correct address and current editor

Of course, all responsible writers know how to find the correct address and the name of a reasonably current editor. You've discovered us in your local or university library or bookstore, or, using the address in this market book, have read a sample copy and think we might be interested in your work. Because student editorial staffs change appreciably every three years—new editor, fiction and poetry editors are chosen every spring from among the reading staff—this should be your yardstick. If you address yourself to someone further back than three years, you're telling us two things: You haven't read the magazine and you picked our name off an old list and probably don't know what we're looking for. Granted, we don't always know what we're looking for until we've found it, but if we've just published two incest stories, it's a good bet we aren't looking for a third.

It's not us you need to know so much as the trends in publishing. The year I was fiction editor at *The Black Warrior Review*, it seemed like every fifth story detailed a woman in her 30s running away from a nonabusive, yet unsatisfying husband only to have her car break down on some flat stretch of highway where she then met a recovering alcoholic minister who bought her and her small child a dinner at Denny's. Jim Jones got a lot of incest and AIDS stories, and two years ago Alan Holmes kept a scorecard on the wall of stories about unpopular young men who had trouble fitting in at school.

We have tended to like stories that are a little on the weird side, but so well written you

Alicia Griswold *is a former editor and fiction editor for* The Black Warrior Review. *She is currently a freelance writer based in Atlanta, Georgia.*

can't always tell just how weird the mind behind them is. We've also liked stories set in other cultures. My issues had two stories set in France, one in China, three in Vietnam and a collection of poems from the Philippines. We also seemed to favor stories with death in them. But that was then. If you submit a story on the basis of this article, you will need to first read the latest issue because the staff is new. (But this is to your advantage: If I didn't like it or Jim sent it back with a note, try Nikki; her taste is different.)

Postage

Although most writers send SASEs or, regrettably, stamped reply cards (It's a personal thing, but why should we do your recycling?), I was surprised to discover how often (more than once a week) I would have to reject manuscripts at the post office because paying for a steady stream of insufficiently stamped manuscripts just wasn't in our budget. Occasionally, my curiosity would get the better of my pocket and I'd fork over the 15¢ but we never accepted one manuscript that wasn't appropriately stamped. You might think this is a coincidence, but I think writers who are careless about their postage are just as careless about their manuscripts and their writing.

Of course, no magazine returns unstamped manuscripts (and we have the pile to prove it) but what you may not realize is that SASEs which aren't sufficiently stamped don't go anywhere either. I used to just dump the rejected manuscripts in a mailbox, but one day I turned them over to the postal clerk and he weighed all of them and tried to make me take back the ones without enough postage. About a dozen!

The envelope

Less than once a week, but often enough to mention here, we would receive the remains of a manuscript, its flimsy envelope shredded, sodden, footprints visible, swaddled in plastic and accompanied by a cautiously apologetic note from our friendly post office. Easy to read? No. Easy to reject? Yes.

Please use the best quality envelopes you can find, especially for thick manuscripts. If submitting more than four pages go with a 9 × 12 envelope. Nothing is more frustrating or easy to lose than a story stuffed into an envelope half its size. It tells us you care more about postage than you do about the story. Yes, mass mailing is expensive, but why not save money by carefully selecting your markets and spending the amount necessary on the magazines most likely to respond? We tend to respect your manuscripts about as much as you do, though we may not love them as much.

Mechanics

Neatness does count but too slick a presentation just makes us wonder where your priorities are. Use the cleanest paper, the sharpest printer, and retype your manuscript until you know it by heart. Only amateurs (and some prisoners) who aren't really interested in publishing submit handwritten work. Alternatively, those high gloss, laser printed "jobs" that advertise the variety of your fonts and skills with a mouse appear as juvenile as the lavender ink and pink stationery. It's my belief, having personally typeset four issues of fiction and two of poetry and reviews, that a story that can hold up to repeated typings is a story worth submitting.

Be clean! We'd get some manuscripts that were so grimy I'd shift them immediately into their return envelopes. I didn't know where they'd been and I didn't want to!

Vitals

Your real name, address, telephone and Social Security numbers should appear in the brief cover letter and on the first page of your short story or review. Your name and page number should appear on every page. Your title and pen name should appear on the first page about a third of the way down.

If you're submitting poetry, put everything on every page. I'll tell you why. In my first issue, we accepted a poem very early in the cycle, put the cover letter in the Contract Pending file (I was very organized) and the poem in the typesetter's box. The typesetter was a darling undergraduate who typed the poem, which had a title, a subtitle and a line from a David Byrne lyric. No author. Unfamiliar with Talking Heads, the typesetter credited the poem to David Byrne and it wasn't until the galleys were staring me in the face one dark night close to deadline that I said, "Gee, I didn't know David Byrne wrote poetry."

"He doesn't, you idiot," said the fiction editor, reading over my shoulder.

"Then who wrote this poem?"

A cross-check with my contracts failed, unaccountably, to reveal the author and so we pulled the poem. Amusingly enough (though not at the time) the contract was there and the contributor's list, which is typeset from the contracts at the same time the contributor's notes are compiled, appeared, with her brief biography, in the fall issue. The poem appeared the following spring.

We all learn from our mistakes. There is one poet who puts her name on every page she sends out and one editor who has learned to think ahead. Now, if the writer's name isn't on the poem, I put it there. This fail-safe worked for me in my second issue and should work for the current editor and maybe the one after him, but holes like this have a way of appearing at magazines where the staff changes as frequently as ours.

Things get lost. Spread your name around.

By the same token, be sure to secure the pages of your story. While many magazines ask that you paperclip pages together, we prefer you staple your story rather than paperclip it so that the pages won't spill apart when the story is separated from its cover letter and envelope. Up to 10 people handle a manuscript under consideration and you might not believe what some readers do to a manuscript. (Or maybe you would.)

Submission

Although we do read simultaneous submissions, it is *our* policy at *BWR* that by its submission to us your work is considered to be under contract. This means we can publish the story even if you haven't signed a contract *unless you tell us you've submitted it elsewhere*. In which case, we'll hold off publishing it until we've received your signed contract or the pitiful phone call that tells us your agent sent it to *The North American Review* and they want it too, and oh, gosh, what a tough choice. This happened to us twice with one writer! Don't send us stories if you're not serious about our publishing them. And keep track of what your agent is doing too.

A less forgivable instance of this practice (because a third party wasn't involved) was the writer who signed her contract and then informed us, mid-production, that an annual she'd sent the story to had responded with an offer to publish and a $500 award. Neither the *BWR* nor the annual wanted the story as a reprint so the author had to choose. You can guess who got it. Our favorite, however, was the poet whose poems made it to the finals of a pricey contest, pulled his simultaneous submission to us and then, after losing the big prize, resubmitted his work. I'm not going to tell you what we did with it.

Cover letter

We sometimes use your cover letter in lieu of a contract and as a way of keeping track of what has been accepted and typeset. It was my practice to compile the contributor's notes and the payroll from the contract file as well and this is why you should always list your real name and your most reliable address. You want to be paid, don't you? It often seemed publication was the impetus for writers to move because every time University Payroll sent out the contributors' checks, at least three writers had moved, leaving no forwarding address. We've still got contributors' copies floating around in postal space.

Just in case we accept your manuscript two days before going to press, don't forget your telephone number(s), Social Security number and a brief (three to five sentences) biographical statement that includes previous publications and whatever toney literary affiliations you want to see in eight point print. Last minute acceptances are supposed to be rare, but sometimes an extra signature will open up (a signature is eight pages) and if we have poems ready, we take them.

While simultaneous submissions are an accepted fact of life, multiple submissions are intolerable. Except for poetry (and then limit yourself to five), the rule is one story at a time, or they all go home—unless the editor has solicited more than one story from you and wants to pick and choose. Or unless they're really, really great. This happened once and, in defense of this writer, each story was so short that I needed to see all of them. We published three. We've also published parts of long stories and urged mandatory cuts in others. The average literary magazine in our tier publishes 144 pages each issue and we prefer a range of six or seven short stories (under 25 pages) and 25 poems. The selection of work often becomes very partisan and the more stories we can publish, the more peace we can keep on staff.

The only other thing your submission might want to include is what interests you about our magazine. If you are familiar with your market, here's the chance to prove it with a reference to a previous issue or the work of a current contributor. We like to hear where you've been published before or if you're in a writing program (since we're in a program too) but we get very dubious when you list *Harper*'s and *The New Yorker* among your credits and then send us a story we can't even read. We think you're lying, or worse, using us for feedback on stories you know aren't finished.

Some editors find it embarrassing to receive manuscripts from friends and friends of friends and people they haven't heard from in years, but basically this kind of networking comes with the territory and we do it ourselves. Just don't lie or imply that our mutual friend has any voice in our decision to accept your manuscript.

Attachments

While we're on the subject, here is a list of "attachments" it is unnecessary (and prejudicial) to include in your submission:

- Testimonials from your professors or psychiatrist.
- Swanky photographs of yourself surrounded by vanity press editions of your work and public relations bilge.
- The same computer-generated letter in which you compare your work to Edna St. Vincent Millay (or anyone else) with every submission.
- Complicated forms that rely on our administrative and secretarial acumen. We don't have any acumen, nor do we have time to cultivate it. Try not to give the impression that you spend more time at your computer devising ways to get noticed than you do making art.

- Descriptions of the story, the story's origins or the writer's mother's biography. Ditto names of cats.
- Ditto your thoughts and feelings about the work.

As you might have guessed by now, there are always exceptions. On one occasion a description of the writer's country and family (the work was based on both) included in her cover letter was so compelling we used it as an introduction to the poetry. Another time, a solicited review was so disappointingly dull that I thought we'd have to reject it. Fortunately, in her cover letter the writer revealed her affection for the book and her discoveries about the culture it described so fluently that we wound up editing (and publishing) that work instead of the intended review.

Another exception has to do with visual art. We don't get too much and we'd like to get more. A Brooklyn poet included half a dozen wonderful postcards of her paintings and drawings which made such a hit with the staff that we selected one for our fall cover and T-shirt. "The Blue Nun" was one of our most successful images and a tough one to beat.

In spite, or despite, these rare exceptions, a submission should give the editor everything she needs to publish your work without having to chase you down—but not too much more. If we do have to chase you down (and sometimes your work is just that good), consider the purchase of an answering machine or train your children to take messages.

Mistakes editors make

Okay, now that I've told you how to do your job, so that I can do mine, here are some of the mistakes editors make that can make your life a living hell. There is nothing you can do about these except call up and complain.

- Some editors don't have dinnerware of their own and use your manuscript.
- Some editors are so inexperienced or disorganized that they remove your manuscript from the office and lose it in the trunk of their car.
- Some editors neglect to log their submissions, then lie to you when you call up asking about your work.
- Some editors can't type. Or spell. Or proofread. Or hire anyone else to do it either.
- Baby editors need at least one issue to know how much is enough and how not to find themselves with an extra, accepted story, too few poems or no room for the exchange ads they promised the other small, literary magazines they'd run.
- The first thing a student editor does is write a budget. The last thing she learns is how to live with it.

Please remember that student editors are also writers and teachers. We're doing this because we love it. Every new editor wants to make her issues the best and while we start off thinking we can, we end up satisfied if the typos are minimal, the work provocative and the staff still speaking.

We appreciate your willingness to trust us with your work and are never happier than on those two days a year when our magazine arrives from the printer, with your name spelled correctly, and the issue is ready to sell.

The Business of Fiction Writing

by Robin Gee

It's true there's no substitute for talent and hard work. A writer's first concern must always be attention to craft. No matter how well presented, a poorly written story or novel has little chance of being published. Yet, on the other hand, a well-written piece may be equally hard to sell in today's competitive publishing market. Talent alone is just not enough.

To be successful, writers need to study the field and pay careful attention to finding the right market. While the hours spend perfecting your writing are usually hours spent alone, you're not alone when it comes to developing your marketing plan. *Novel & Short Story Writer's Market* provides you with detailed listings containing the essential information you'll need to locate and contact the markets most suitable for your work.

Yet once you've determined where to send your work, you must turn your attention to presentation. We can help here, too. Over the years we've made our listings as concise as possible in order to leave more space for new listings. In this effort, however, we took out some of the very basics of manuscript preparation—the things we like to call the "givens." We've included these basics below along with a compilation of information on submission procedures, approaching markets and the basics of manuscript mechanics—the "business" of fiction.

Approaching magazine markets: While it is essential for nonfiction markets, a query letter by itself is usually not needed by most magazine fiction editors. If you are approaching a magazine to find out if fiction is accepted, a query is fine, but editors looking for short fiction want to see *how* you write. Many editors don't even read queries—they want to go right to the story. A cover letter, however, can be useful as a letter of introduction, but it must be accompanied by the actual piece. Include basic information in your cover letter— name, address, a brief list of previous publications—if you have any—and two or three sentences about the piece (why you are sending it to *this* magazine or how your experience influenced your story). Keep it to one page and remember to include a self-addressed, stamped envelope for reply. See "Short Story Cover Letter" included on page 75.

Approaching book publishers: Some book publishers do ask for queries first, but most want a query plus sample chapters or an outline or, occasionally, the complete manuscript. Again, make your letter brief. Include the essentials about yourself—name, address, phone number and publishing experience. Include only the personal information related to your story. For example, if your story takes place in Tokyo and you lived there 10 years, mention it—it adds credibility. Show that you have researched the market with a few sentences about why you chose this publisher. For example, if you chose the publisher because you feel your book would fit nicely into their young adult mystery line, let them know.

Book proposals: A book proposal is a package sent to a publisher that includes a cover letter and one or more of the following: sample chapters, outline, synopsis, author bio, publications list. When asked to send sample chapters, send up to three *consecutive* chapters. An outline covers the highlights of your book chapter by chapter. Be sure to include details on main characters, the plot and subplots. Outlines can run up to 30 pages, depending on the length of your novel. The object is to tell what happens in a concise, but clear, manner. A synopsis is a very brief description of what happens in the story. Keep it to two or three pages. The terms synopsis and outline are sometimes used interchangeably, so be sure to find out exactly what each publisher wants.

Agents: Agents are not usually needed for short fiction and most do not handle it unless they already have a working relationship with you. For novels, you may want to consider working with an agent, especially if you are interested in marketing to publishers who do not look at unsolicited submissions. For more on approaching agents see *The Guide to Literary Agents & Art/Photo Reps* (Writer's Digest Books, 1507 Dana Ave., Cincinnati OH 45207).

Approaching markets outside your own country: When sending return postage to another country, do not send stamps. You must purchase International Reply Coupons (IRCs). The publisher can use the IRCs to buy stamps from his/her own country. IRCs cost 95 cents each and can be purchased at the main branch of your local post office. This rule applies between countries in North America—US writers without access to Canadian postage (and vice versa) may use IRCs.

Main branches of local banks will cash foreign checks, but keep in mind payment quoted in our listings by publishers in other countries, is usually payment in their currency. Also note reporting time is longer in most overseas markets. To save time and money, you may want to include a return postcard (and IRC) with your submission and forego asking for a manuscript to be returned.

Some mailing tips: Manuscripts under five pages long can be folded into thirds and sent in a business-size (#10) envelope. For submissions of five pages or more, however, mail it flat in a 9×12 or 10×13 envelope. Your manuscript will look best if it is mailed in an envelope only slightly larger. For the return envelope, fold it in half, address it to yourself and add a stamp (or clip IRCs to it with a paper clip).

Mark both of your envelopes in all caps, FIRST CLASS MAIL or SPECIAL FOURTH CLASS MANUSCRIPT RATE. The second method is cheaper, but it is handled the same as Parcel Post (Third Class) and is only for manuscripts weighing more than one pound and mailed within the US First Class mailing assures fastest delivery and better handling.

Book manuscripts should be mailed in a sturdy box (a ream-size typing paper box works well). Tape the box shut and tape corners to reinforce them. To ensure your manuscript's safe return, enclose a self-addressed and stamped insulated bag mailer. You may want to check with the United Parcel Service (UPS) or other mailing services for rates when mailing large manuscript packages.

If you use an office or personal postage meter, do not date the return envelope—it could cause problems if the manuscript is held too long before being returned. First Class mail is forwarded or returned automatically. Mark Third or Fourth Class return envelopes with "Return Postage Guaranteed" to have them returned.

If you send a cover letter with a Fourth Class manuscript, you must indicate this on the envelope (FIRST CLASS LETTER ENCLOSED) and include First Class postage.

It is not necessary to insure or certify your submission. In fact, many publishers do not appreciate receiving unsolicited manuscripts in this manner. Your best insurance is to always keep a copy of all submissions and letters.

Manuscript mechanics: A professionally presented manuscript will not guarantee publication. Yet on the other hand, a handwritten story in pencil on the back of your shopping list will almost always be rejected no matter how well written it is. A sloppy, hard-to-read manuscript will not be read—publishers simply do not have the time. Here's a list of suggested submission techniques for polished manuscript presentation:

• Use white, $8\frac{1}{2} \times 11$ bond paper, preferably 16 or 20 lb. weight. The paper should be heavy enough so that it will not show pages underneath it and strong enough to take handling by several people. Do not use onion skin or erasable paper.

● Type your manuscript on a typewriter with a dark ribbon. Make sure the letters are clean and crisp. You can also use a computer printer, but avoid hard-to-read dot matrix. Near-letter or letter quality is acceptable.

● Proofread carefully. Most editors will not mind an occasional white-out, but do not send a marked up manuscript or one with many typos. Also keep a dictionary, thesaurus and stylebook handy.

● Always double space and leave a 1¼ inch margin on all sides of the page. For a short story manuscript, your first page should include your name, address and phone number (single-spaced) in the upper left corner. In the upper right, indicate an approximate word count. Center the name of your story about one-third of the way down, skip two or three lines and center your byline (byline is optional). Skip three lines and begin your story.

● For subsequent pages, include your last name and page number in the upper right hand corner.

● For book manuscripts, use a separate cover sheet. Put your name, address and phone number in the upper left corner and word count in the upper right. Some writers list their agent's name and address in the upper right (word count is then placed at the bottom of the page). Center your title and byline about halfway down the page. Start your first chapter on the next page. Begin by centering the chapter number and chapter title (if there is one) about one-third of the way down the page. Be sure to include your last name and page number in the upper right of this page and each page to follow. Start each chapter with a new page.

● There are a number of ways to count the number of words in your piece. One way is to count the number of words in five lines and divide that number by five to find an average. Then count the number of lines and multiply to find the total words. For long pieces, you may want to count exactly how many words in the first three pages, divide by three and multiply by the number of pages you have.

● Always keep a copy. Manuscripts do get lost. To avoid expensive mailing costs, send only what is required. If a publisher asks for two sample chapters, only send two. If you are including artwork or photos, but you are not positive they will be used, send photocopies. Artwork is hard to replace.

● Most publishers do not expect you to provide artwork and some insist on selecting their own illustrators, but if you have suggestions, please let them know. Magazine publishers work in a very visual field and are usually open to ideas.

● If you want a reply or if you want your manuscript returned, enclose a self-addressed, stamped envelope (SASE). For most letters, a business-size (#10) envelope will do. Avoid using any envelope too small for an 8½×11 sheet of paper. For manuscripts, be sure to include enough postage and an envelope large enough to contain it. If you are requesting a magazine, send an envelope big enough to fit. When in doubt, you can send a label with your address and stamps.

● When sending electronic (disk or modem) submissions, contact the publisher first for specific information and follow the directions carefully.

● Keep accurate records. This can be done in a number of ways, but be sure to keep track of where your stories are and how long they have been "out." Write down submission dates. If you do not hear about your submission for a long time — about three weeks to one month longer than the reporting time stated in the listing — you may want to contact the publisher. When you do, you will need an accurate record for reference.

Rights: Know what rights you are selling. The Copyright Law states that writers are selling one-time rights (in almost all cases) unless they and the publisher have agreed otherwise. Below is a list of various rights. Be sure you know exactly what rights you are selling before you agree to the sale.

● **All Rights** allow a publisher to use the manuscript anywhere and in any form, including movie and book club sales, without further payment to the writer.

● **Copyright** is the legal right to exclusive publication, sale or distribution of a literary work. This right is that of the writer or creator of the piece and you need simply to include your name, date and the copyright symbol © on your piece in order to copyright it. You can also register your copyright with the Copyright Office for additional protection. Request information and forms from the Copyright Office, Library of Congress, Washington DC 20559. Publications listed in *Novel & Short Story Writer's Market* are copyrighted *unless* otherwise stated. In the case of magazines that are not copyrighted, be sure to keep a copy with your notice printed on it.

● **First Serial Rights** mean that the publisher has the right to publish your work for the first time in any periodical.

● **First North American Serial Rights** are the same as First Serial, but they are only for publication on the North American Continent.

● **One-time Rights** allow a publisher to publish a story one time.

● **Reprint Rights** are permission to print a piece that was first published somewhere else.

● **Second Serial Rights** allow a publisher to print a piece in another periodical after it appeared for the first time in book form or in a magazine.

● **Subsidiary Rights** are all rights other than book publishing rights included in a book contract such as book club rights, movie rights and paperback rights.

● **Work-for-hire** is work that does not belong to the creator. If you do work-for-hire, you do not own the copyright and cannot sell any rights. For example, if you write a pamphlet for your company as an employee, generally the rights to that material do not belong to you. Writers doing work-for-hire usually paid a flat fee for the work and do not collect royalties or other payments.

Samples

This year we're very pleased to include a sample cover letter by writer Don Feigert followed on page 76 by his comments on why he feels the letter has worked well for him. He answered our call in the 1991 edition for sample cover letters from our readers. If you have a successful cover letter, outline, summary or book proposal letter we might use for an example in our next edition, please send us a copy. We'd also like to hear from you about samples you'd like to see in future editions. For more on manuscript formats see *The Writer's Digest Guide to Manuscript Formats*, by Dian Dincin Buchman and Seli Groves (Writer's Digest Books).

Each year for your convenience we've included postal charge charts for the US and Canada. This year the charts follow the sample cover letter. A 7% Government Sales Tax is now required on postage in Canada. Since Canadian postage rates will be voted on in January (before this book is released), check for updated information from the Canada Post Corp. Customer Service Division office located in most cities in Canada.

For more information on the business of writing see *The Writer's Essential Desk Reference*, edited by Glenda Tennant Neff (also by Writer's Digest Books). This book contains a special chapter devoted to the business of writing in Canada.

The Short Story Cover Letter

Don Feigert
Address
Phone

May 20, 1991

Ms. Carolyn Page, Co-Editor
Potato Eyes
Nightshade Press
Box 76
Troy, ME 04987

Dear Ms. Page:

Please consider the enclosed short story "Killing the Waterdog" for publication. I think it will fit in well with your Appalachian themes.

I first became aware of Nightshade Press when I purchased The Wild Trout by Walt Franklin. Later I received my contributor's copy of Great Elm Press's Riveries and bought the 1991 edition of Novel and Short Story Writer's Market. You and Co-Editor Roy Zarucchi were featured in both. Finally, I sent for a sample copy of Potato Eyes and enjoyed it much. Hence this, my first submission to your magazine.

I am a lifelong outdoorsman, and I have spent twenty years in education, as a teacher and college recruiter. I write stories for outdoor magazines such as Gray's Sporting Journal and Pennsylvania Game News and poems and stories for literary magazines such as Hiram Poetry Review and Samisdat. My first book, Visiting the Pig Farm, a collection of outdoor stories and poems, was published in December, 1989, by Old Hickory Press, Jackson, TN.

Thanks for your consideration.

Sincerely,

Don Feigert

Why this letter works

Don Feigert is a part-time freelance writer with nearly 50 publication credits. This letter format has worked for him several times. He explains why he feels it has been so successful:

The first paragraph of this cover letter is characteristically brief. Writers should avoid "explaining" their stories. The significant thing here is the acknowledgement of the magazine's general theme.

The second paragraph makes very clear the fact that the writer has shown a serious and sincere interest in the press to which he is submitting. Without becoming obsequious, writers should relate that they respect their intended markets and that they are professional enough to subscribe or purchase sample copies and study them before submitting anything.

The "bio note" paragraph is alway a problem. Published writers tend to boast about past successes, while unpublished writers fear their lack of credits disadvantage them. Generally, a few brief but relevant remarks will do. In the example case, my "bio" paragraph is longer than usual, because so much of my background relates to this particular magazine's outdoor, rural, Appalachian emphasis. I believe, however, that I received a quick acceptance here not because of past credits but because I sent the editors a very good story that was right up their thematic alley.

U.S. Postage by the Page

by Carolyn Hardesty

Mailing costs can be an appreciable part of writing expenditures. The chart below can help save money as well as time by allowing you to figure the fees for sending your manuscripts to prospective publishers.

Postage rates are listed by numbers of pages (using 20 lb. paper) according to the most commonly used envelopes and their self-addressed, stamped envelopes (SASEs). While most writers prefer to send their work First Class, Third Class is becoming a choice for some. Third Class moves more slowly, but it costs less than First Class after the first 4 ounces. Also, it is permissible in Third Class to include a letter pertaining to the material inside.

First Class mail weighing more than 11 ounces is assessed according to weight plus geographical zone so it needs to be priced at the Post Office.

Postcards can be a bargain for writers. If the postage costs are higher than another computer printout or photocopied version of a manuscript, a postcard can be used for the editor's reply. The cost is 20¢.

For short manuscripts or long queries, use a #10 (business-size) envelope with a 29¢ stamp. Four pages is the limit if you are including a SASE. Another option is the 6×9 envelope. For 1-3 pages, postage is 29¢ in the U.S. For 1-7 pages with SASE, cost is 52¢ in the U.S.

Ounces	9×12 9×12 SASE number of pages	9×12 SASE (for return trips) number of pages	First Class Postage	Third Class Postage **	Postage from U.S. to Canada **
under 2	...	1 to 2	$ .39*	$ .39*	$ .63*
2	1 to 4	3 to 8	.52	.52	.73
3	5 to 10	9 to 12	.75	.75	.86
4	11 to 16	13 to 19	.98	.98	1.09
5	17 to 21	20 to 25	1.21	1.21	1.32
6	22 to 27	26 to 30	1.44	1.21	1.55
7	28 to 32	31 to 35	1.67	1.33	1.78
8	33 to 38	36 to 41	1.90	1.33	2.01
9	39 to 44	42 to 46	2.13	1.44	2.24
10	45 to 49	47 to 52	2.36	1.44	2.47
11	50 to 55	53 to 57	2.59	1.56	2.70

*This cost includes an assessment for oversized mail that is light in weight.
**Postage to other countries and increments for Third Class had not been determined at the time we went to press. Check with your post office for increases.

Carolyn Hardesty's *short fiction has appeared in* Four Minute Fictions, The North American Review *and the* Montana Review. *She is the editor of* Goldfinch, *a prizewinning history magazine for children.*

Canadian Postage by the Page

by Barbara Murrin

The following chart is for the convenience of Canadian writers sending domestic mail and American writers sending an envelope with International Reply Coupons (IRCs) or Canadian stamps for return of a manuscript from a Canadian publisher. Unfortunately these figures are approximate, because the Canadian Postal Service meets to determine new fees in January each year, after we go to press. Check your post office for changes.

Manuscripts returning from the U.S. to Canada will take a U.S. stamped envelope although the original manuscript was sent with Canadian postage. This applies to return envelopes sent by American writers to Canada, too, which must be accompanied with IRCs or Canadian postage.

In a #10 envelope, you can have up to five pages for 40¢ (on manuscripts within Canada) or 46¢ (on manuscripts going to the U.S.). If you enclose a SASE, four pages is the limit. If you use 10 × 13 envelopes, send one page less than indicated on the chart.

IRC's are worth 46¢ Canadian postage but cost 95¢ to buy in the U.S.

Canada Post has made major changes in designation of types of mail, as follows:

Standard Letter Mail   Minimum size: 9cm × 14cm (3⅝″ × 5½″); Maximum size: 14cm × 24.5cm (5½″ × 9⅝″); Maximum thickness: 5mm (³⁄₁₆″)

Oversize Letter Mail   Minimum size: 14cm × 24.5cm (5½″ × 9⅝″); Maximum size: 27cm × 38cm (10⅞″ × 15″); Maximum thickness: 2cm (¹³⁄₁₆″)

International Letter Mail   Minimum size: 9cm × 14cm (3⅝″ × 5½″); Maximum size: Length + width + depth 90cm (36″) Greatest dimension must not exceed 60cm (24″)

Insurance: To U.S. and within Canada — 45¢ for each $100 coverage to a maximum coverage of $1000. International — 65¢ for each $100 coverage to a maximum coverage of $1000.
Registered Mail: $2.70 plus postage (air or surface — any destination). Legal proof of mailing provided.

Weight up to	9×12 envelope, 9×12 SASE number of pages*	9×12 SASE (for return trips) number of pages	Canada Standard	Oversize	First Class to U.S. Standard	Oversize
30 g/1.07 oz.	. . .	1 to 3	$ .40	$ .50	$ .46	$ .80
50 g/1.78 oz.	1 to 4	4 to 7	.63	.63	.67	1.03
100 g/3.5 oz.	5 to 14	8 to 18	.80	.80	. . .	1.03
200 g/7.1 oz.	15 to 46	19 to 49	. . .	1.25		1.95
300 g/10.7 oz.	47 to 57	50 to 61	. . .	1.80		2.40
400 g/14.2 oz.	58 to 79	62 to 82	. . .	1.80		3.35
500 g/17.8 oz.	80 to 101	83 to 104	. . .	. . .		4.30
1.0 kg/2.2 lbs.	102 to 208	105 to 212	**	**(air pkt.)		7.50

*Based on 20 lb. paper and 2 adhesive labels per envelope.
**For Canadian residents mailing parcels 1 kg. and over within Canada (domestic mail), rates vary according to destination. Ask your Post Master for the chart for your area.

Barbara Murrin *owns and operates a desk-top publishing business in Williams Lake, British Columbia. She teaches music and business subjects at a nearby community college and, when there is time, writes romance. One of her short stories has been included in* Insight's Most Unforgettable Stories, *a compilation of stories from 20 years of publication.*

The Markets

Important Listing Information

- *Listings are* not *advertisements. Although the information here is as accurate as possible, the listings are not endorsed or guaranteed by the editor of* Novel & Short Story Writer's Market.
- Novel & Short Story Writer's Market *reserves the right to exclude any listing that does not meet its requirements.*

Key to Symbols and Abbreviations

How to Get the Most Out of the Markets

Finding the right market for your work requires careful research and planning. This book is designed to help you with that search by providing listings of magazine and book publishers looking for fiction submissions. To make your search easier, the markets section is divided into five areas: literary and small circulation magazines, commercial periodicals, small presses, commercial book publishers and contests and awards. Following each main section is a list of similar international markets (for more information on approaching publishers outside your own country, see The Business of Fiction Writing).

If you are not sure what category your work fits in or if you just want to explore the possibilities, start by browsing through the sections to find a market that interests you. The browsing method will also help you get an idea of what types of fiction are most needed, payment ranges and other general information about the magazine or book publishing industry. Read the section introductions to learn more about current trends and information specific to the type of listing featured in each section.

To help narrow your search, we've also included a Category Index located immediately preceding the Markets Index at the back of the book. The Category Index is divided into sections (i.e. literary and small circulation magazines, commercial magazines, etc.) and each section is divided by specific fiction categories or genres. For example, if you are looking for a small press publisher that accepts science fiction, look under "Small Press" in the category index and find the "Science Fiction" heading. There you will find an alphabetical list of all the small press publishers of science fiction listed in the book.

Once you've selected a listing, it is important to read it carefully. A dagger (‡) before a listing indicates a listing new to this edition. In the book publisher sections, a listing may also have an asterisk, indicating it is a subsidy publisher (*) or a square (■) indicating the listing is that of a book packager. For quick reference see the Key to Symbols and Abbreviations. Further explanation of these and other symbols and terms can be found in the section introductions and in the Glossary.

We've also ranked the magazine and book publishers with the following codes to help you select those markets most appropriate for your work.

I **Open to beginners. Especially encourages new writers to submit fiction.**

II **Accepts work both from beginning and established writers, depending on quality.**

III **Prestige market, generally hard to break into, usually accepting work only by established or agented writers and a very few outstanding new writers.**

IV **Specialized publication or press, limited to contributors from certain regions or within a specific age group or to those writing on specialized subjects or themes.**

We occasionally receive letters asking why a certain magazine, book publisher or contest is not in the book. Sometimes when we contact a listing, the editor does not want to be listed because they: do not use very much fiction; are overwhelmed or backlogged with submissions; are having financial difficulty or have been recently sold; use only solicited material; accept work from a select group of writers; do not have the staff or time for the many unsolicited manuscripts a listing may bring.

Some listings do not appear because we have chosen not to list them. We investigate complaints about misrepresentation by editors in the information they provide us or about unethical or unprofessional activities in a publisher's dealings with writers. If we find these reports to be true, after thorough investigation, we will delete a listing. See Important Listing Information for more about our listing policies.

If you feel you have not been treated fairly by a market listed in our book we advise you take the following steps:

● First, try to contact the listing. Sometimes one phone call or letter can quickly clear up the matter.

● Be sure to document all your correspondence with the listing. When you write to us with a complaint, we will ask for the name of your manuscript, the date of your submission and the dates and nature of your subsequent correspondence.

● We will write to the publisher or editor and ask them to resolve the problem. We will then enter your letter into our files.

● The number, frequency and severity of unresolved complaints will be considered in our decision whether or not to delete the listing from the book.

This year we've also included the names and addresses of certain well-known markets not listed in the book. You will find them in alphabetical order within the listing section. If these markets have given us a reason why they do not wish to be in, we've included this information as well. To find out what happened to other listings that appeared in the 1991 edition, but not in the 1992 edition, check "Other" markets at the end of each section.

Listings appearing in *Novel & Short Story Writer's Market* are compiled from detailed questionnaires, phone interviews and information provided by editors, publishers and awards directors. The publishing industry is volatile and changes of address, editor, policies and needs happen frequently. To keep up with the changes we suggest you check the monthly Markets column in *Writer's Digest* magazine.

We also rely on our readers for information on new markets and changes in the markets listed in the book. Write us if you have any new information or if you have suggestions on how to improve our listings to better suit your writing needs.

Sample listing

The following is a sample listing. Each element of the listing is numbered and numbers correspond to the explanations following the listing. For more information on specific terms, see the Glossary and the introductions to each section.

(1) CONCHO RIVER REVIEW, (I, II, IV), Fort Concho Museum Press, 213 East Avenue D, San Angelo TX 76903. (915)657-4441. **(2)** Editor: Terence A. Dalrymple. **(3)** Magazine: 6½×9; 100-125 pages; 60 lb. Ardor offset paper; Classic Laid Color cover stock; b&w drawings. **(4)** "We publish any fiction of high quality—no thematic specialties—contributors must be residents of Texas or the Southwest generally." **(5)** Semiannually. **(6)** Estab. 1987. **(7)** Circ. 300.

(8) Needs: Contemporary, ethnic, historical (general), humor/satire; literary, regional and western. No erotica; no science fiction. **(9)(10)** Receives 10-15 unsolicited mss/month. **(11)** Accepts 3-6 mss/issue, 8-10 mss/year. **(12)** Publishes ms an average of 4 months after acceptance. **(13)** Published work by Robert Flynn, Clay Reynolds, Roland Sodowsky. **(14)** Length: 3,500 words average; 1,500 words minimum; 5,000 words maximum. **(15)** Also publishes literary essays, poetry. **(16)** Sometimes critiques rejected mss and recommends other markets.

(17) How to Contact: Send complete ms with SASE, cover letter optional. **(18)** Reports in 3 weeks on queries; 3-8 weeks on mss. **(19)** SASE for mss. **(20)** Simultaneous and photocopied submissions OK. Accepts computer printout submissions. **(21)** Sample copy $4. Fiction guide-

lines for #10 SAE and 1 first class stamp. **(22)** Reviews novels and short story collections. Send books to Terence A. Dalrymple, c/o English Dept., Angelo State University, San Angelo TX 76909.
(23) Payment: Pays in contributor's copies; $4 charge for extras.
(24) Terms: Acquires first rights.
(25) Advice: "We prefer a clear sense of conflict, strong characterization and effective dialog."

(1) Symbols, names, addresses and phone numbers. One or more symbols may precede the name of the market. A dagger symbol (‡) indicates the listing is new. Other symbols include subsidy (*) or book packager (■).
(2) Contact name. Whenever possible send your query or submission to a specific person. Use the fiction editor's name, if available. If you are not sure of the gender, it is best to use the full name (e.g. Robin Jones). If no name is given in the listing, check the masthead, if it is a magazine or, for the book publishing industry, check the directory, *Literary Market Place*.
(3) Physical description. Listings for publications often include physical description—the number of pages, type of paper, binding, number of illustrations or photos. This information is provided to give you some idea of the quality and type of publication. Magazines with inexpensive paper and binding may be more open to the work of new writers.
(4) Descriptive quote. This is a quote from the publisher describing the magazine or book publisher. The statement sometimes focuses on the publisher's philosophy and often contains a description of the audience. In book publishers' listings this is followed by a description of the types of books published (e.g., hardbound originals, paperback reprints).
(5) Frequency of publication. Some literary magazines published by universities are not published in the summer; the listing will then include a line beginning with "Does not read manuscripts from . . . "
(6) Date established. New magazines are often receptive to new writers.
(7) Circulation. For the literary and small circulation magazines, circulation is under 10,000. In book publisher listings information is included on the number of titles and percentage of fiction titles published each year.
(8) Needs. This section lists the types of fiction needed. Sometimes a quote about what is most needed and what material should not be submitted is included.
(9) Themes. If a publication plans a special edition or specific themed issues, it will be mentioned here. When possible, we will include the deadlines for theme submissions or the date of the themed issue. Most magazines featuring themes will provide a list of upcoming themes for a SASE.
(10) Number of manuscripts received. This can give you an idea of the competition. If a publisher receives several hundred manuscripts each week, but only publishes two or three, response time will be slow and competition high.
(11) Number of manuscripts published. See number 10.
(12) Time between publication and acceptance. This is especially important if you will not be paid until publication. Some small journals may take up to one year to publish.
(13) Recently published. Names of authors and, if the listing is a book publisher, book titles will appear in this section.
(14) Length requirements. Minimum and maximum word lengths are often given. Short shorts are short pieces under 700 words, unless otherwise indicated.
(15) Also publishes. As a service to those of you who do other types of writing in addition to fiction writing, we've indicated if the magazine also accepts literary-type essays, literary criticism or poetry.
(16) Feedback. If the magazine comments on or will critique rejected manuscripts, we have

indicated this here.

(17) How to contact. This section gives details on how to contact the listing including whether it is necessary to query first or to send a complete manuscript. If sample chapters are required, send *consecutive* chapters, preferably starting with the first chapter. Cover letter and other submission requirements are listed here.

(18) Reporting time. This is a rough estimate of the time it will take for the publisher to respond to your query or submission. New publishers sometimes miscalculate the time needed to respond to the submissions generated by this book. Add three weeks to the time given, but if you have waited much longer, feel free to check the status of your submission with a letter, return postcard or a phone call.

(19) SASE. A self-addressed, stamped envelope in a size to fit your manuscript or letter is usually required.

(20) Acceptable submissions. If reprints, simultaneous or photocopied submissions are accepted, it will say so here. If not mentioned, they probably are not acceptable. When in doubt, call or write to obtain fiction guidelines. When sending computer printouts be sure your ribbon fairly new and send only submissions that are near-letter or letter quality. If computer disk submissions are accepted, contact the publisher to find out specifics.

(21) Sample copy and guidelines. To find out more about a publisher, it is best to obtain a sample copy, catalog or fiction guidelines.

(22) Reviews novels and short story collections. This information is provided for those writers interested in having their published books reviewed. If authors should send review copies to a different address or someone other than the editor, that information also is provided here.

(23) Payment. Some small and literary magazines only pay in copies; others pay excellent rates. Note whether payment is made on acceptance or on publication. For book publishers, advances are upfront payments, made in one or more installments against royalties. You will not receive royalties until the advance has been recovered by the publisher.

(24) Terms. This is an important section. Note what type of rights you are selling. If the publication is not copyrighted, all rights belong to the author. Often the rights will revert to the author upon publication. Both of these agreements are the same as one-time rights— the publisher acquires or buys the right to publish your piece one time only. For more information on rights, see The Business of Fiction Writing.

(25) Advice. Read the information in this section carefully. It is here where publishers and editors have the opportunity to pass on inside information on how to approach their magazine or publishing firm.

We include in the listings as much specific information as possible, but there are some items we do not mention because they are basically the same for all listings. See "The Business of Fiction Writing" for more on the basic requirements of all fiction markets.

Remember your market research should begin with a careful study of the listing but it should not end there. Whenever possible try to obtain a sample copy or catalog. For book publishers, check *Books in Print* at the library to find a publisher's titles and take a look a some of their books. The library also has publishing industry magazines such as *Publishers Weekly* as well as magazines for writers. Some magazines for writers are listed in the section Publications of Interest to Fiction Writers located later in this book. These can help you keep informed of new publishers and changes in the field.

Literary and Small Circulation Magazines

Each year we ask publishers of literary journals and small magazines how they got started and why. And every year, no matter who we ask, the answer is always the same—they want to provide more opportunities for readers to see the work of new writers. Many are themselves writers and know personally how difficult the road to publication can be.

Publishing a small journal is, therefore, a labor of love. It's no wonder, then, that despite the sluggish economy, rising postage and production costs, and even drastic funding cuts, many of these people continue to publish. This is good news for writers, especially those more interested in exposure and experience than monetary reward.

Long-term rewards

While a few of the more prestigious journals may offer several hundred dollars for a short story, many of these publications pay in copies, subscriptions or small honorariums. Yet publication in small magazines and journals can lead to important long-term rewards. For many writers, publication in these magazines is the first step on the road to a successful writing career.

Publishing in small magazines helps writers garner publication credits while they gain experience submitting their work and dealing with editors. For more experienced writers, publication in literary journals brings the added benefit of prestige. Many of the literaries are published by respected universities and writing programs. Commercial magazine editors and book publishers look to smaller publications for new talent. In other words, publication in small magazines and literary journals helps get you and your work noticed.

Hundreds of opportunities

For those writers interested in literary journals or small circulation magazines, there are indeed hundreds of opportunities listed in this section. From prestigious journals such as *The Paris Review* and *The Georgia Review* to publications especially for beginners including *Amateur Writers Journal* and *Chapter One*. Some are regional in slant and some feature particular types of writing such as science fiction, mystery or writing for children.

Basically, these magazines can be divided by type. University and state-supported journals often feature the work of well-respected writers along with that of talented newcomers. Fanzines, on the other hand, are tiny one- or two-person operations featuring the work mostly of friends and often highly experimental writing and graphics. In between are several small, single-subject publications devoted to everything from model railroading to life in Japan.

To narrow in on the magazines most likely to be interested in your work, either browse through the section or check the Category Index located just before the Markets Index at the back of the book. This index is divided into sections corresponding with those in the book and each section in turn is divided into lists of magazines focusing on particular subjects. It is there you will find a list of the magazines featuring science fiction, mystery, feminist topics and a variety of other subject areas.

Once you've selected some potential markets, read the listing and send for a sample copy. Additional guidelines are sometimes available as well. Some university and independent bookstores have good selections of small publications, but you may have to send away for the very small ones. Often you can obtain a back issue at a reduced price.

Things to consider

Before selecting a market, you may want to consider a few things about publication in small journals. It's important to note that while we add more than 100 new listings to this section each year, we also lose almost that many. Publishing a small journal can be a risky venture. Most of these failures are due to a lack of funding, poor subscription sales and more heart than business savvy on the part of the owner/publisher. Yet publishers who are taking risks on their magazine are also more likely to take a risk on a new writer.

With that in mind look carefully at the physical descriptions, establishment date and circulation figures in each listing. This information, while no substitute for looking at a sample copy, is helpful in determining the prestige and stability of the publication.

New editors will sometimes underestimate the number of submissions they will receive from their listing. Be patient. Give them an additional three weeks beyond their stated reporting time before checking on your submission. It may be they didn't anticipate the deluge of submissions.

New this year

This year we've added a few extra items to the listings in this section. Increasingly we've noticed more literary journals are publishing literary essays in addition to fiction and poetry. These essays are basically nonfiction, but many are written as stories with definite fiction elements. Often they are memoirs of some sort or a discussion of a particular issue of interest to the literary community. Since many of the writers whose fiction appears in these journals also write the essays, we decided to indicate if the publication is interested in literary essays.

Literary essays are not to be confused with editorials or essays on current events. For publications looking for this type of writing, see *Writer's Market* (Writer's Digest Books).

Since many of you also write poetry and literary criticism, we decided to include whether the publication is interested in these also. Yet, for details on poetry submissions, we suggest you look at our sister publication, *Poet's Market*.

For those of you who have a book published, we have included information on whether the magazine reviews novels and short story collections. If review copies are to be sent to someone other than the editor, we've included that information too. Keep in mind that sending a book is costly and does not guarantee a review. You may want to read the reviews already published in the magazine and send a query first briefly describing your book and asking if they'd like to see a review copy.

How to submit

The basics of submitting to magazine editors are outlined in "The Business of Fiction Writing" starting on page 71. As with commercial publications, a professional presentation gives you an extra edge over the competition. Even though some of these publications operate on a shoestring, the editors appreciate a clean, neat copy accompanied by a self-addressed, stamped envelope.

Unless otherwise noted, send the entire manuscript with a concise cover letter. If you want your manuscript returned, send enough return postage with an envelope large enough to contain it. Remember, too, when sending return postage to an editor outside your country, you must send International Reply Coupons instead of stamps. US and Canadian listings are included in this section, followed by a special section for international literary and small magazine markets.

If you are interested in learning more about fanzines and very small magazines, you may want to look at *Factsheet Five* (P.O. Box 1163, Cincinnati OH 45201-1163). For additional literary markets see *The International Directory of Little Magazines and Small Presses* (Dustbooks, Box 100, Paradise CA 95967). The following is the ranking system we have used to categorize the listings in this section:

I   **Publication encourages beginning writers or unpublished writers to submit work for consideration and publishes new writers regularly.**

II **Publication accepts work by established writers and by new writers of exceptional talent.**

III **Publication does not encourage beginning writers; prints mostly writers with previous publication credits and very few new writers.**

IV **Special-interest or regional publication, open only to writers in certain genres or on certain subjects or from certain geographical areas.**

‡ABERATIONS, (II), Experiences Unlimited, 544 Ygnacio Valley Rd., #13, or (POB 8040), Walnut Creek CA 94596. (415)942-5116. Editor: Jon L. Herron. Fiction Editor: J. Moretz. Magazine: Digest-sized, 5½ × 8½; 64 pages; 20 lb. bond; 80 lb. glossy cover; b&w illustrations and photographs. "Adult horror, science fiction and dark fantasy short stories and poems for an over-18 audience." Estab. 1992. Circ. 500.
Needs: Erotica, experimental, fantasy (dark), horror, humor/satire, prose poem, science fiction. No formula stories. Publishes annual special fiction issue. Receives 20-30 unsolicited mss/month. Buys 6-8 mss/issue and 25 for anthology; 120 mss/year. Publishes ms "within 3 issues." Recently published work by Jeff Vandermeer, Kevin J. Anderson, Brad Boucher. Length: 4,000 words preferred; 500 words minimum; 6,000 words maximum. "Always" critiques rejected mss and recommends other markets.
How to Contact: Send complete ms with cover letter that includes Social Security number, telephone number and bio. Reports in 1 month on queries; 2 weeks to 3 months on mss. SASE. Photocopied submissions OK. Accepts computer printout submissions. Accepts electronic submissions (MicroSoft Word 5 or Word Perfect). Sample copy for $3.50 and 4 first class stamps. Fiction guidelines for #10 SAE and 1 first class stamp.
Payment: Pays ¼-½¢/word, plus contributor's copy; extra contributor's copies for reduced charge.
Terms: Pays on acceptance. Purchases first North American serial rights or one-time rights. Sends galleys to author on request.
Advice: "With the advent of the personal computer the small press magazine market has boomed. I expect the market to continue growing into the next decade. Each December we publish an anthology 200 pages of stories and poems. We don't want erotica just for erotica sake, but we want good stories where the sex, gore, profanity is instrumental to the story not just thrown in for the sake of blood, guts, sex etc. We will print stories that other magazines might reject just because of the usage of certain words etc."

ABYSS MAGAZINE, "Games and the Imagination," (II, IV), Ragnarok Enterprises, P.O. Box 140333, Austin TX 78714-0333. (512)472-6535. Editor: David F. Nalle. Fiction Editor: Patricia Fitch. Magazine: 8½ × 11; 28 pages; bond paper; glossy cover; illustrations; photos. "Heroic fantasy fiction: some fantasy, horror, SF and adventure fiction, for college-age game players." Bimonthly. Plans special fiction issue. Estab. 1979. Circ. 1,500.
Needs: Adventure, fantasy, horror, psychic/supernatural/occult, cyberpunk, science fiction, heroic fantasy, sword and sorcery. "Game-based stories are not specifically desired." Receives 20-30 unsolicited mss/month. Buys 1 ms/issue; 7 mss/year. Publishes ms 1-12 months after acceptance. Published work by Antoine Sadel, Kevin Anderson, Alan Blount; published new writers within the last year. Length: 2,000 words average; 1,000 words minimum; 4,000 words maximum. Publishes short shorts

occasionally. Also publishes literary essays and literary criticism. Sometimes critiques rejected mss or recommends other markets.

How to Contact: Send for sample copy first. Reports in 1 month on queries; 2 months on mss. "Do send a cover letter, preferably entertaining. Include some biogaphical info and a precis of lengthy stories." SASE. Photocopied submissions OK. Accepts computer printout submissions. "Call IIBBS at (512)472-6905 for modem ASCII info." Sample copy and fiction guidelines $3. Reviews novels and short story collections (especially fantasy novels).

Payment: Pays 1-3¢/word or by arrangement, plus contributor's copies.

Terms: Pays on publication for first North American serial rights.

Advice: "We are particularly interested in new writers with mature and original style. Don't send us fiction which everyone else has sent back to you unless you think it has qualities which make it too strange for everyone else but which don't ruin the significance of the story. Make sure what you submit is appropriate to the magazine you send it to. More than half of what we get is completely inappropriate. We plan to include more and longer stories."

ACM, (ANOTHER CHICAGO MAGAZINE), (II), Left Field Press, 3709 N. Kenmore, Chicago IL 60613. (312)248-7665. Editor: Barry Silesky. Fiction Editor: Sharon Solwitz. Magazine: 5½×8½; 150-200 pages; "art folio each issue." Estab. 1977.

Needs: Contemporary, literary, experimental, feminist, gay/lesbian, ethnic, humor/satire, prose poem, translations and political/socio-historical. Receives 75-100 unsolicited fiction mss each month. Published work by David Michael Kaplan, Diane Wakoski, Gary Soto; published new writers in the last year. Also publishes literary essays. Sometimes recommends other markets.

How to Contact: Unsolicited mss acceptable with SASE. Accepts computer printout submissions. Publishes ms 6 months to 1 year after acceptance. Sample copies are available for $8 ppd. Reports in 2 months. Receives small press collections.

Payment: Small honorarium plus contributor's copy.

Terms: Acquires first North American serial rights.

Advice: "Get used to rejection slips, and don't get discouraged. Keep introductory letters short. Make sure ms has name and address on every page, and that it is clean, neat and proofread. We are looking for stories with freshness and originality in subject angle and style, and work that encounters the world and is not stuck in its own navel."

THE ACORN, (I,II), 1530 7th St., Rock Island IL 61201. (309)788-3980. Editor: Betty Mowery. Newsletter: 8½×11; 8-10 pages; illustrations. "Manuscripts of interest to K-12th grade audience or K-12th grade librarians and teachers." Bimonthly. Estab. 1989. Circ. 100.

Needs: Ethnic, juvenile, mainstream, prose poem, regional, religious/inspirational, romance (contemporary, historical, young adult), science fiction, suspense/mystery, young adult. "We use some adult manuscripts, if they are of interest to young people. No erotica or anything degrading to race or religion or background." Receives 50 unsolicited fiction mss/month. Accepts 10-12 mss/issue; 60-70 mss/year. Publishes ms within two months after acceptance. Length: 500 words preferred; 200 words minimum; 500 words maximum. Accepts short shorts. Length: 200 words. Sometimes critiques or comments on rejected mss and recommends other markets.

How to Contact: Send complete ms with cover letter. Reports in 1 week. SASE. Simultaneous, photocopied and reprints OK. Sample copy for $1. Fiction guidelines are contained in publication.

Payment: Pays in contributor's copies.

Terms: Acquires first rights.

Advice: Looks for "tight writing and a manuscript that has something to say and isn't preachy, but still gets the point across. I am open to all manuscripts from both published and unpublished writers. I'm eager to help a beginning author get into print. "

ADRIFT, Writing: Irish, Irish American and . . . , (II), #4D, 239 E. 5th St., New York NY 10003. Editor: Thomas McGonigle. Magazine: 8×11; 32 pages; 60 lb. paper stock; 65 lb. cover stock; illustrations; photos. "Irish-Irish American as a basis—though we are interested in advanced writing from anywhere." Semiannually. Estab. 1983. Circ. 1,000+.

The double dagger before a listing indicates that the listing is new in this edition. New markets are often the most receptive to freelance contributions.

Needs: Contemporary, erotica, ethnic, experimental, feminist, gay, lesbian, literary, translations. Receives 40 unsolicited mss/month. Buys 3 mss/issue. Recent issues have included work by Francis Stuart. Published new writers within the last year. Length: open. Also publishes literary criticism. Sometimes critiques rejected mss and recommends other markets.

How to Contact: Send complete ms. Reports as soon as possible. SASE for ms. Photocopied submissions OK. Accepts computer printout submissions. Sample copy $5. Reviews novels or short story collections.

Payment: Pays $7.50-300.

Terms: Pays on publication for first rights.

Advice: "The writing should argue with, among others, James Joyce, Flann O'Brien, Juan Goytisolo, Ingeborg Bachmann, E.M. Cioran, Max Stirner, Patrick Kavanagh."

‡**THE ADVOCATE, (I, II),** PKA Publications, 301A Rolling Hills Park, Prattsville NY 12468. (518)299-3103. Editor: Remington Wright. Tabloid: 11¼ × 13¾; 28 pages; newsprint paper; line drawings; b&w photographs. "Eclectic for a general audience." Bimonthly. Estab. 1987.

Needs: Adventure, contemporary, ethnic, experimental, fantasy, feminist, historical (general), humor/satire, juvenile (5-9 years), literary, mainstream, prose poem, regional, romance, science fiction, senior citizen/retirement, sports, suspense/mystery, western, young adult/teen (10-18 years). Nothing religious, pornographic, violent, erotic, pro-drug or anti-environment. Plans special issue or an anthology. Receives 6 unsolicited mss/month. Accepts 3-5 mss/issue; 40-50 mss/year. Publishes ms 2 months to 1 year after acceptance. Length: 1,000 words preferred; 2,500 words maximum. Sometimes critiques rejected mss and recommends other markets.

How to Contact: Send complete ms with cover letter. Reports in 2 weeks on queries; 2 months on mss. SASE. Photocopied submissions OK. Accepts computer printout submissions. Sample copy for $2 (US currency for inside US; $4.25 US currency for Canada). Fiction guidelines for SAE and 1 first class stamp.

Payment: Pays contributor's copies.

Terms: Acquires first rights.

Advice: "The highest criterion in selecting a work is its entertainment value. It must first be enjoyable reading. It must, of course, be original. To stand out, it must be thought provoking or strongly emotive, or very cleverly plotted. Will consider only previously unpublished works by writers wo do not earn their living principally through writing."

‡**AETHLON, (I,II,IV),** East Tennessee State University Press, Johnson City TN 37614-0002. Editor: Don Johnson (615)929-6675. Fiction Editor: Fred Boe (615)265-5184. Magazine: 6 × 9; 180-240 pages; illustrations and photographs. "Theme: Literary treatment of sport. We publish articles on that theme, critical studies of author's treatment of sport and original fiction and poetry with sport themes. Most of our audience are academics." Semiannually. Plans "possible" special fiction issue. Estab. 1983. Circ. 800.

Needs: Sport. "Stories must have a sport-related theme and subject; otherwise, we're wide open." No personal experience memoirs. Receives 10-15 fiction mss/month. Accepts 4-8 fiction mss/issue; 10-15 fiction mss/year. Publishes ms "about 6 months" after acceptance. Length: 2,500-5,000 words average; 500 words minumum; 7,500 words maximum. Also publishes literary essays, literary criticism, poetry. Sometimes critiques rejected mss.

How to Contact: Send complete ms with cover letter. Reports in 6 months. SASE. Simultaneous, photocopied and reprint submissions OK. Accepts computer printout submissions. Sample copy $12.50. Reviews novels and short story collections. Send books to Professor Brooke Horvath, Dept. of English, Kent State University, 6000 Frank Ave., Canton OH 44720.

Payment: Pays 1 contributor's copy and 5 offprints.

Terms: Sends pre-publication galleys to author.

Advice: "Too many people with no talent are writing. Too many people think a clever idea or an unusual experience is all it takes to make a story. We are looking for well-written, insightful stories. Don't be afraid to be experimental."

AGNI, (II), Creative Writing Program, Boston University, 236 Bay State Rd., Boston MA 02215. (617)353-5389. Editor-in-Chief: Askold Melnyczuk. Magazine: 5½ × 8½; 320 pages; 55 lb. booktext paper; recycled cover stock; occasional illustrations and photos. "Eclectic literary magazine publishing first-rate poems and stories." Semiannually. Estab. 1972.

Needs: Stories, excerpted novels, prose poems and translations. Receives 200 unsolicited fiction mss/month. Accepts 4-7 mss/issue, 8-12 mss/year. Reading period Oct. 1 to June 1 only. Recently published work by Joyce Carol Oates, Stephen Dixon, Andra Neiburga, Ha Jin. Rarely critiques rejected mss or recommends other markets.

How to Contact: Send complete ms with SASE and cover letter listing previous publications. Simultaneous and photocopied submissions OK. Accepts computer printout submissions. Reports in 1 month. Sample copy $7.

Payment: Pays $10/page up to $150; 2 contributor's copies; one-year subscription.

Terms: Pays on publication for first North American serial rights. Sends galleys to author. Copyright reverts to author upon publication.

Advice: "Read *Agni* carefully to understand the kinds of stories we publish. Read—everything, classics, literary journals, bestsellers."

AGORA, The Magazine for Gifted Students, (IV), AG Publications, P.O. Box 10975, Raleigh NC 27605. (919)787-6832. Editor: Thomas E. Humble. Magazine: 8½×11; 32 pages; illustrations and photographs. "We publish winners of our writing competitions for students in grades 7-12." Bimonthly (4 issues per school year). Estab. 1986. Circ. 3,200.

Needs: Ethnic, historical (general), humor/satire, literary, regional, religious, science fiction. Receives 2-4 unsolicited mss/month. Length: 450-1,500 words average. Publishes short shorts.

How to Contact: "Subscribe to magazine or attend a school that subscribes to a class set." Accepts electronic submissions via disk. Sample copy $4. Free fiction guidelines.

ALABAMA LITERARY REVIEW, (II), Smith 253, Troy State University, Troy AL 36082. (205)670-3286, ext. 330. Editor: Theron Montgomery. Fiction Editor: Jim Davis. Magazine: 6×11½; 100+ pages; top paper quality; some illustrations; photos. "National magazine for a broad range of the best contemporary fiction, poetry, essays and drama that we can find." Semiannually. Estab. 1987.

Needs: Condensed novel, contemporary, erotica, ethnic, experimental, fantasy, feminist, historical (general), humor/satire, literary, prose poem, regional, science fiction, serialized/excerpted novel, suspense/mystery, translations. "Serious writing." Receives 50 unsolicited fiction mss/month. Buys 2 fiction mss/issue. Publishes ms 5-6 months after acceptance. Published work by Manette Ansay, Ed Peaco, Peter Fromm and Rick Shelton; published new writers within the last year. Length: 2,000-3,000 words average. Publishes short shorts of 1,000 words. Also publishes literary essays, literary criticism, poetry. Sometimes comments on rejected mss and recommends other markets.

How to Contact: Send complete ms with cover letter or submit through agent. Reports on queries in 2 weeks; on mss in 2-4 weeks (except in summer). SASE. Simultaneous submissions OK. Accepts computer printouts. Sample copy for $4 plus 50¢ postage. Reviews novels or short story collections. Send to Steve Cooper.

Payment: Pays in contributor's copies.

Terms: First rights returned to author upon publication. Work published in *ALR* may be read on state-wide (nonprofit) public radio program.

Advice: "Read our publication first. Avoid negative qualities pertaining to gimmickry and a self-centered point of view. We are interested in any kind of writing if it is *serious* and *honest* in the sense of 'the human heart in conflict with itself.'"

ALASKA QUARTERLY REVIEW, (II), University of Alaska, Anchorage, 3211 Providence Dr., Anchorage AK 99508. (907)786-1327. Fiction Editor: Ronald Spatz. Magazine: 6×9; 146 pages; 60 lb. Glatfelter paper; 10 pt. C1S black ink varnish cover stock; photos on cover only. Magazine of "contemporary literary art and criticism for a general literary audience." Semiannually. Estab. 1982.

Needs: Contemporary, experimental, literary, prose poem and translations. Receives 100 unsolicited fiction mss/month. Accepts 5-11 mss/issue, 15-22 mss/year. Does not read mss May 15-August 15. Published new writers within the last year. Publishes short shorts. Occasionally critiques rejected mss.

How to Contact: Send complete ms with SASE. Photocopied submissions OK. Reports in 2 months. Publishes ms 6 months to 1 year after acceptance. Sample copy $4.

Payment: Pays 1 contributor's copy and a year's subscription.

Terms: Acquires first rights.

Advice: "We have made a significant investment in fiction. The reason is quality; serious fiction *needs* a market. Try to have everything build to a singleness of effect."

Each issue of Alabama Literary Review, "a state literary medium representing local and national submissions," is considered a collectible, says Chief Editor Theron Montgomery. Since its early days, covers have featured original calligraphy and drawings of well-known authors. "We also try to use a thought-provoking quote from the author that reflects our belief in writing and what writing should be about," he adds. This issue features a drawing of the late Walker Percy. It is one of many cover drawings contributed by Sergei L. Shillabeer, assistant professor of art at Troy State University, where the review is produced. The calligraphy is by Charles Orlofsky.

ALDEBARAN, (II), Roger Williams College, 1 Old Ferry Rd., Bristol RI 02809. (401)253-1040. Editor: Debra L. Malewicki. Magazine: 5½×8½; 60-100 pages; illustrations; photos. Literary publication of prose and poetry for a general audience. Published annually or twice a year. Estab. 1970.
Needs: Will consider all fiction. Does not read mss between April 2 and September 1, and November 2 and February 1. Preferred length: 3,500 words or shorter.
How to Contact: Send complete ms with SASE and cover letter, which should include "information for possible contributor's notes—but cover letters will not influence decision on publication." Accepts computer printout submissions. Reports in 6-12 weeks. Sample copy $4 with SASE.
Payment: Pays 2 contributor's copies.
Terms: Copyright reverts to author on publication.
Advice: Mss are rejected because of "incomplete stories, no live character, basic grammatical errors; usually returned with suggestions for revision and character change."

ALPHA BEAT SOUP, (IV), 12 N. Union St., , Lambertville NJ 08530. Editor: Dave Christy. Magazine: 7½×9; 95-125 pages; illustrations. "Beat and modern literature—prose, reviews and poetry." Semiannually. Estab. 1987. Circ. 475.
Needs: Erotica, experimental, literary and prose poem. Plans another magazine, supplementing *Alpha Beat Soup*, and an *ABC Anthology*. Published work by Charles Bukowski, Joy Walsh and Richard Nason; published new writers within the last year. Length: 600 words minimum; 1,000 words maximum. Also publishes literary essays, literary criticism, poetry. Sometimes recommends other markets.
How to Contact: Query first. Reports on queries ASAP. SASE. Simultaneous, photocopied and reprint submissions OK. Sample copy for $5. Reviews novels and short story collections.
Payment: Pays in contributor's copies.
Terms: Rights remain with author.
Advice: "*ABS* is the finest journal of its kind available today, having, with 9 issues, published the widest range of published and unpublished writers you'll find in the small press scene."

THE AMARANTH REVIEW, (I, II), Window Publications, P.O. Box 56235, Phoenix AZ 85079. Editor: Dana L. Yost. Magazine: 8½×11; 60-80 pages; 60 lb. offset paper; 90 lb. cover stock; illustrations and occasional photos. "Our theme is eclectic—we are interested in poetry and short fiction which deals

Market categories: (I) Beginning; (II) General; (III) Prestige; (IV) Specialized.

with the human condition in its broadest possible expression. For an educated, thinking audience of those who enjoy quality poetry and fiction." Estab. 1989. Circ. 1,500.

Needs: Literary, contemporary, experimental. Upcoming themes: Send #10 SASE for details. Receives 100+ unsolicited mss/month. Accepts 8-10 mss/issue; 20 mss/year. Publishes ms 2-6 months after acceptance. Published work by Susan Moon and Susan Roberts. Length: 2,500 words average; 5,000 words maximum. Publishes short shorts. Also publishes literary essays, literary criticism, poetry. Sometimes critiques rejected mss and recommends other markets.

How to Contact: Send complete ms with cover letter. "Include how the writer heard about us— brief bio is also welcome." Reports in 2 weeks on queries; 1 month on ms. SASE. Simultaneous and photocopied submissions OK. Accepts computer printout submissions. Accepts electronic submissions (IBM Word Perfect 5.0 only). Sample copy for $6.50. Writer's guidelines for #10 SAE and 1 first class stamp. Reviews novels and short story collections.

Payment: Pays in contributor's copies; charges for extras (40% discount.)

Terms: Acquires first North American serial rights.

Advice: "The one basic requirement is that the piece be good, quality fiction. But more specifically, we look for the piece to deal with some basic condition of human existence, and we look for the piece to hit hard and knock us into thinking—really thinking—about the issue or circumstances of the story. I also think that today's fiction writers need to take some chances—a lot of the stories we receive could have been written by a dozen other writers, and that almost always means that they will end up being rejected. Fiction is about voice, and it's about tone—quite simply, it's about the unique perspective of the author. Tell the story in the way that only you can tell it and forget about the rubber-stamp approach to writing fiction—it just doesn't cut it in today's highly competitive market."

‡**AMATEUR WRITERS JOURNAL, Four Seasons Poetry Club Magazine, (I)**, R.V. Gill Publishing Co., 3653 Harrison St., Bellaire OH 43906. (614)676-0881. Editor: Rosalind Gill. Magazine: 8½×11; 38 pages; 20 lb. paper; no cover; illustrations. "Stories, articles, essays and poetry on all subjects. No avant-garde or porno-type manuscripts of any kind accepted. Poetry, when seasonal, published only in the season for which it is appropriate. Same rule applies to stories. For a family audience." Quarterly. Estab. 1967. Circ. 700+.

Needs: Adventure, contemporary, fantasy, horror, humor/satire, mainstream, religious/inspirational, contemporary romance, science fiction, suspense/mystery, young adult/teen. Receives around 300 fiction mss/month. Accepts 8 fiction mss/issue; 48 mss/year. Publishes ms "within 3 months" after acceptance. Length: 1,200 words average; 1,500 words maximum. Also publishes literary essays, literary criticism, poetry. Sometimes critiques rejected mss and recommends other markets.

How to Contact: Send complete ms with cover letter. State whether you are offering first rights, or, if material has been published elsewhere, the name of the publication in which your work appeared. Reports on queries in 1 month; on mss in 1 week. SASE. Photocopied submissions OK. Accepts computer printout submissions. Sample copy available for $1.85 and 3 first class stamps. Fiction guidelines for #10 SAE and 2 first class stamps.

Payment: No payment.

Terms: Acquires one-time rights.

Advice: "I believe that all fiction writers should have a showplace for their work, and my magazine readers prefer fiction to nonfiction, although I accept both."

AMBERGRIS, (I, II), P.O. Box 29919, Cincinnati OH 45229. Editor: Mark Kissling. Magazine: 5×8; 80-128 pages; illustrations; photographs. "*Ambergris* is a non-profit magazine dedicated to the discovery and publication of quality art and literature." Annual. Estab. 1987. Circ. 500.

Needs: "Excellent short fiction showing stylistic distinction. Contemporary themes, any subject." *No simultaneous submissions accepted.* No genre fiction, strictly preschool, juvenile, romance, serialized/ excerpted novel or young adult. Plans special compilation issue. Receives 30-40 mss/month. Accepts 8-12 mss/issue. Publishes ms "up to one year" after acceptance. Recently published work by Bernard Cooper, Mark Richard and Jack Heffron. Word length open, prefers under 5,000 words. Also publishes literary essays.

How to Contact: Send complete ms with cover letter which should include a three-line biographical sketch. One work of fiction per submission. Please include computer disk specs and availability if applicable. Reports on mss in 3 months. Enclose SASE for return of mss. Sample copy $4; back issue $3. Fiction guidelines for #10 SASE.

Payment: Pays 2 contributor's copies, extras available at a discount.

Terms: Acquires first North American serial rights.

Advice: "We give special consideration to works by Ohio writers and about the Midwest in general. We attempt to foster the emerging writer, but encourage beginning writers and others unfamiliar with our format to look at a sample copy before submitting work." *Ambergris* is a consulting magazine to *The Best American Short Stories, The O. Henry Short Story Awards, The Pushcart Prize, Editor's Choice* and *Street Songs. Ambergris* is a member of the Council of Literary Magazines and Presses.

AMELIA, (II), 329 E St., Bakersfield CA 93304. (805)323-4064. Editor-in-Chief: Frederick A. Raborg, Jr. Magazine: 5½ × 8½; 124-136 pages; perfect-bound; 60 lb. high-quality moistrite matte paper; kromekote cover; four-color covers; original illustrations; b&w photos. "A general review using fine fiction, poetry, criticism, belles lettres, one-act plays, fine pen-and-ink sketches and line drawings, sophisticated cartoons, book reviews and translations of both fiction and poetry for general readers with catholic tastes for quality writing." Quarterly. Plans special fiction issue each July. Estab. 1984. Circ. 1,250.

Needs: Adventure, contemporary, erotica, ethnic, experimental, fantasy, feminist, gay, historical (general), humor/satire, lesbian, literary, mainstream, prose poem, regional, science fiction, senior citizen/retirement, sports, suspense/mystery, translations, western. Nothing "obviously pornographic or patently religious." Receives 160-180 unsolicited mss/month. Buys up to 9 mss/issue; 25-36 mss/year. Published 4 new writers within the last year. Published Judson Jerome, Jack Curtis, Maxine Kumin, Eugene Dubnov and Merrill Joan Gerber. Length: 3,000 words average; 1,000 words minimum; 5,000 words maximum. Usually critiques rejected ms. Sometimes recommends other markets.

How to Contact: Send complete manuscript. Cover letter with previous credits if applicable to *Amelia* and perhaps a brief personal comment to show personality and experience. Reports in 1 week on queries; 2 weeks-3 months on mss. SASE. Photocopied submissions OK. Accepts computer printout submissions. Sample copy for $7.95. Fiction guidelines free for #10 SAE and 1 first class stamp.

Payment: Pays $35-50 plus 2 contributor's copies; extras with 20% discount.

Terms: Pays on acceptance. Buys first North American serial rights. Sends galleys to author "when deadline permits."

Advice: "Write carefully and well, but have a strong story to relate. I look for depth of plot and uniqueness, and strong characterization. Study manuscript mechanics and submission procedures. Neatness does count. There is a sameness—a cloning process—among most magazines today that tends to dull the senses. Magazines like *Amelia* will awaken those senses while offering stories and poems of lasting value."

AMERICAN DANE, (II, IV), The Danish Brotherhood in America, 3717 Harney, Omaha NE 68131-3844. (402)341-5049. Editor: Jennifer C. Denning. Magazine: 8¼ × 11; 20-28 pages; 40 lb. paper; slick cover; illustrations and photos. "The *American Dane* is the official publication of the Danish Brotherhood. Corporate purpose of the Danish Brotherhood is to promote and perpetuate Danish culture and traditions and to provide fraternal benefits and family protection." Estab. 1916. Circ. 8,900.

Needs: Ethnic. "Danish!" Receives 4 unsolicited fiction mss/month. Accepts 1 ms/issue; 12 mss/year. Reads mss during August and September only. Publishes ms up to one year after acceptance. Length: 1,000 words average; 3,000 words maximum. Publishes short shorts. Also publishes literary essays, some literary criticism, poetry.

How to Contact: Query first. SASE. Simultaneous submissions OK. Accepts computer printout submissions. Sample copy for $1 and 9 × 12 SAE with 54¢ postage. Fiction guidelines for #10 SAE and 1 first class stamp. Reviews novels and short story collections.

Payment: Pays $15-50.

Terms: Pays on publication for first rights. Publication not copyrighted.

Advice: "Think Danish!"

AMERICAN FICTION, (II), English Dept., Springfield College, Springfield MA 01095. Editor: Michael C. White. Magazine: 5¾ × 8¼; 200-300 pages; Annually. "No themes, just a yearly open national contest." For "serious readers of fiction." Circ. 5,000.

Read the Business of Fiction section to learn the correct way to prepare and submit a manuscript.

Needs: Contemporary, experimental, traditional literary. Receives 700-800 mss/year. Buys or accepts 20-25 mss/year. "We accept stories *only* from February 1-March 31." Publishes ms within 12 months of acceptance. *Charges $7.50 reading fee.* Published work by Ursula Hegi, Florri·McMillan, Clint Mc-Cown, Perry Glasser, Antonya Nelson. Length: 5,000 words average 10,000 words maximum. Publishes short shorts. Sometimes critiques rejected mss.
How to Contact: "Send ms, cover/bio, *after* reading our ads in *AWP* and *Poets & Writers* each spring" SASE for query. "We don't return mss." Simultaneous and photocopied submissions OK. Accepts computer printout submissions. Fiction guidelines for #10 SAE and 1 first class stamp. For sample copy (strongly encouraged) write Birch Lane Press, 600 Madison Ave., New York, NY 10022.
Payment: Pays $50 maximum and contributor's copies. "$1,000, 500, 250 awards to top 3 stories based on guest judge's decision."
Terms: Pays on publication for first North American serial rights. "The *American Fiction* series is a contest. Top 20-25 stories published, with awards given to judge's top 3 stories. 1989 judge was Anne Tyler; 1990 Louise Erdrich."
Advice: Looks for "moving, interesting, engaging characters, action, language."

AMERICAN LITERARY REVIEW, A National Journal of Poems and Stories, (II), University of North Texas, P.O. Box 13615, Denton TX 76203. (817)565-4670, 565-2124. Editor: J.F. Kobler. Fiction Editor: Clay Reynolds. Magazine: 7×10; 128 pages; 60 lb. Glatfelter paper; 60 lb. Springhill Vellum cover. "Publishes poems and stories for a general audience." Semiannually. Estab. 1990. Circ. 200.
Needs: Mainstream and literary only. No genre works. Receives 25 unsolicited fiction mss/month. Accepts 7-10 mss/issue; 14-20 mss/year. Publishes ms within 2 years after acceptance. Recently published work by Gordon Weaver, Gerald Haslam and William Miller. Length: 3,500 words preferred; 5,000 words maximum. Critiques or comments on rejected mss and recommends other markets. Also accepts poetry.
How to Contact: Send complete ms with cover letter. Reports in 6-8 weeks. SASE. Simultaneous and photocopied submissions OK. Sample copy for $5. Fiction guidelines free.
Payment: Pays in contributor's copies.
Terms: Acquires one-time rights. Sends pre-publication galleys to author.
Advice: "We want to publish poems and stories that reflect the kinds of writing being done in various regions of America. We are not looking for a 'style' or an aesthetic to make us distinctive." Looks for "literary quality and careful preparation."

THE AMERICAS REVIEW, A Review of Hispanic Literature and Art of the USA, (II, IV), Arte Publico Press, 4800 Calhoun, University of Houston, Houston TX 77204-2090. (713)749-4768. Editors: Dr. Julian Olivares and Evangelina Vigil-Pinon. Magazine: 5½×8½; 128 pages; illustrations and photographs. "*The Americas Review* publishes contemporary fiction written by U.S. Hispanics—Mexican Americans, Puerto Ricans, Cuban Americans, etc." Quarterly. Estab. 1972.
Needs: Contemporary, ethnic, literary, women's, hispanic literature. No novels. Receives 12-15 fiction mss/month. Accepts 2-3 mss/issue; 8-12 mss/year. Publishes mss "6 months to 1 year" after acceptance. Length: 3,000-4,500 average number of words; 1,500 words minimum; 6,000 words maximum. Publishes short shorts. Sometimes critiques rejected mss and recommends other markets.
How to Contact: Send complete manuscript. Reports in 3 months. SASE. Photocopied submissions OK. Accepts computer printout submissions. Accepts electronic submissions via IBM compatible disk. Sample copy $5; $10 double issue.
Payment: Pays $50-200; 5 contributor's copies.
Terms: Pays on acceptance for first rights, and rights to 40% of fees if story is reprinted. Sponsors award for fiction writers.
Advice: "There has been a noticeable increase in quality in U.S. Hispanic literature."

THE AMHERST REVIEW, (II, IV), Box 1811, Amherst College, Amherst MA 01002. (413)542-2250. Editor: Mark Sadeghian. Fiction Editor: Bryant Rousseau. Magazine: 7½×8½; 60-70 pages; illustrations and photographs. "We are a college literary magazine publishing work by students, faculty and professionals. We seek submissions of poetry, fiction, and essay for the college community." Annually.
Needs: Adventure, confession, contemporary, ethnic, experimental, fantasy, feminist, gay, historical (general), horror, humor/satire, lesbian, mainstream, prose poem, psychic/supernatural/occult, regional, romance, science fiction, suspense/mystery, translations, western. "No sentimentality." Receives 10-20 unsolicited mss/month. Does not read mss March-August. Length: 4,500 words; 7,200 words maximum.

How to Contact: Send complete ms with cover letter. Reports in 4 months on mss. Accepts computer printout submissions. Sample copy for $5, SAE and $1 postage.
Payment: Pays 2 contributor's copies; $5 charge for extras.
Terms: Acquires first rights.

ANTAEUS, (III), The Ecco Press, 100 West Broad St., Hopewell NJ 08525. (609)466-4748. Editor-in-Chief: Daniel Halpern. Managing Editor: Cathy Jewell. Magazine: 6½×9; 275 pages; Warren old style paper; some illustrations and photographs. "Literary magazine of fiction and poetry, literary documents, and occasional essays for those seriously interested in contemporary writing." Quarterly. Estab. 1970. Circ. 5,000.
Needs: Contemporary, literary, prose poem, excerpted novel, and translations. No romance, science fiction. Receives 600 unsolicited fiction mss/month. Recently published fiction by Richard Ford, Donald Hall, Joyce Carol Oates; published new writers within the last year. Rarely critiques rejected mss. Also publishes poetry.
How to Contact: Send complete ms with SASE. Photocopied submissions OK; no multiple submissions. Accepts computer printout submissions. Reports in 6-8 weeks. Sample copy $5. Fiction guidelines for SASE.
Payment: Pays $10/page and 2 contributor's copies, 40% discount for extras.
Terms: Pays on publication for first North American serial rights and right to reprint in any anthology consisting of 75% or more material from *Antaeus*.
Advice: "Read the magazine before submitting. Most mss are solicited, but we do actively search the unsolicited mss for suitable material. Unless stories are extremely short (2-3 pages), send only one. Do not be angry if you get only a printed rejection note; we *have* read the manuscript. Always include an SASE. Keep cover letters short, cordial and to the point."

ANTIETAM REVIEW, (II, IV), Washington County Arts Council, 82 W. Washington St., Hagerstown MD 21740. (301)791-3132. Editor: Susanne Kass. Magazine: 8½×11; 42 pages; photos. A literary journal of short fiction, poetry and black-and-white photographs. Annually. Estab. 1982. Circ. 1,000.
Needs: Contemporary, ethnic, experimental, feminist, literary and prose poem. "We read manuscripts from our region—Delaware, Maryland, Pennsylvania, Virginia, West Virginia and Washington D.C. only. We read from October 1 to March 1." Receives about 100 unsolicited mss/month; accepts 7-9 stories/year. Published work by Rachel Simon, Elisavietta Ritchie, Philip Bufithis; published new writers within the last year. Length: 3,000 words average.
How to Contact: "Send ms and SASE with a cover letter. Let us know if you have published before and where." Photocopies OK. Accepts computer printouts. Reports in 1 to 2 months. "If we hold a story, we let the writer know. Occasionally we critique returned ms or ask for rewrites." Sample copy $5. Back issue $2.50.
Payment: "We believe it is a matter of dignity that writers and poets be paid. We have been able to give $100 a story and $25 a poem, but this depends on funding. Also 2 copies." Prizes: "We offer a $100 annual literary award in addition to the $100, for the best story."
Terms: Acquires first North American serial rights. Sends pre-publication galleys to author if requested.
Advice: "We look for well crafted work that shows attention to clarity and precision of language. We like relevant detail but want to see significant emotional movement within the course of the story—something happening to the central character. This journal was started in response to the absence of fiction markets for emerging writers. Its purpose is to give exposure to fiction writers, poets and photographers of high artistic quality who might otherwise have difficulty placing their work."

THE ANTIGONISH REVIEW, St. Francis Xavier University, Antigonish, Nova Scotia B2G 1C0 Canada. (902)867-3962. Editor: George Sanderson. Literary magazine for educated and creative readers. Quarterly. Estab. 1970. Circ. 800.
Needs: Literary, contemporary, prose poem and translations. No erotic or political material. Accepts 6 mss/issue. Receives 25 unsolicited fiction mss each month. Published work by Arnold Bloch, Richard Butts and Helen Barolini; published new writers within the last year. Length: 3,000-5,000 words. Sometimes comments briefly on rejected mss.
How to Contact: Send complete ms with cover letter. SASE or IRC. Accepts disk submissions compatible with Apple and Macintosh. Prefers hard copy with disk submission. Reports in 3 months. Publishes ms 3 months to 1 year after acceptance.

Payment: Pays 2 contributor's copies.
Terms: Authors retain copyright.
Advice: "Learn the fundamentals and do not deluge an editor."

ANTIOCH REVIEW, (II), Box 148, Yellow Springs OH 45387. (513)767-6389. Editor: Robert S. Fogarty. Associate Editor: Nolan Miller. Magazine: 6×9; 128 pages; 60 lb. book offset paper; coated cover stock; illustrations "seldom." "Literary and cultural review of contemporary issues in politics, American and international studies, and literature for general readership." Quarterly. Published special fiction issue last year; plans another. Estab. 1941. Circ. 4,000.
Needs: Literary, contemporary, translations and experimental. No children's, science fiction or popular market. Buys 3-4 mss/issue, 10-12 mss/year. Receives approximately 175 unsolicited fiction mss each month. Approximately 1-2% of fiction agented. Length: any length the story justifies.
How to Contact: Send complete ms with SASE, preferably mailed flat. Accepts computer printout submissions. Reports in 2 months. Publishes ms 6-9 months after acceptance. Sample copy $5; Guidelines for SASE.
Payment: Pays $15/page; 2 contributor's copies. $2.70 for extras.
Terms: Pays on publication for first and one-time rights (rights returned to author on request).
Advice: "Our best advice, always, is to *read* the *Antioch Review* to see what type of material we publish. Quality fiction requires an engagement of the reader's intellectual interest supported by mature emotional relevance, written in a style that is rich and rewarding without being freaky. The great number of stories submitted to us indicates that fiction apparently still has great appeal. We assume that if so many are writing fiction, many must be reading it."

‡ANYTHING THAT MOVES, Beyond The Myths of Bisexuality, (II, IV), Bay Area Bisexual Network, #24, 2404 California St., San Francisco CA 94115. (415)564-BABN. Editor: Karla Rossi. Fiction Editor: Marcy Sheiner. Magazine: 8½×11; 64 pages; newsprint paper; glossy cover; illustrations and photographs. "Of interest to bisexuals—priority given to bisexual writers and bisexual themes." Quarterly. Estab. 1991. Circ. 5,000.
Needs: Bisexual: erotica, ethnic, experimental, fantasy, feminist, gay, historical (general) humor/satire, lesbian, prose poem, psychic/supernatural/occult, science fiction. Plans special fiction issue or an anthology. Receives 100 unsolicited mss/month. Accepts 3-5 mss/issue; 20 ms/year. Publishes ms up to 1 year after acceptance. Length: 2,500 words maximum. Publishes short shorts. Also accepts poetry.
How to Contact: Query with clips of published work. Reports in 2 weeks on queries; 6-8 weeks on mss. SASE. Accepts computer printout submissions. Sample copy for $6. Fiction guidelines for SAE and 1 first class stamps.
Payment: Pays contributor's copies.
Terms: Acquires first rights.
Advice: Looks for "especially strong beginning, tight, non-rambling plot and dialogue. We are especially interested in writers w/themes regarding controversial topics or traditionally censored writers and topics. Erotica considered, but graphic sex or pornography rejected. Erotica is not a priority with us."

APPALACHIAN HERITAGE, (I, II), Hutchins Library, Berea College, Berea KY 40404. (606)986-9341. Editor: Sidney Farr. Magazine: 7×9½; 80 pages; 60 lb. stock; 10 pt. Warrenflo cover; drawings and b&w photos. "*Appalachian Heritage* is a southern Appalachian literary magazine. We try to keep a balance of fiction, poetry, essays, scholarly works, etc., for a general audience and/or those interested in the Appalachian mountains." Quarterly. Estab. 1973. Circ. 1,100.
Needs: Regional, literary, historical. Receives 20-25 unsolicited mss/month. Accepts 2 or 3 mss/issue; 10 or more mss/year. Published work by Robert Morgan, Richard Hague and James Still; published new writers within the last year. Length: 2,000-2,500 word average; 3,000 words maximum. Publishes short shorts. Length: 500 words. Occasionally critiques rejected mss and recommends other markets.
How to Contact: Send complete ms with cover letter. Reports in 1-2 weeks on queries; 3-4 weeks on mss. SASE for ms. Simultaneous, photocopied submissions OK "if clear and readable." Accepts computer printout submissions. Sample copy for $5.
Payment: Pays 3 contributor's copies; $5 charge for extras.
Terms: Acquires one-time rights. No reading fee, but "would prefer a subscription first."
Advice: "Trends in fiction change frequently. Right now the trend is toward slick, modern pieces with very little regional or ethnic material appearing in print. The pendulum will swing the other way again, and there will be a space for that kind of fiction. It seems to me there is always a chance to have really

good writing published, somewhere. Keep writing and keep trying the markets. Diligent writing and rewriting can perfect your art. Be sure to study the market. Do not send me a slick piece of writing set in New York City, for example, with no idea on your part of the kinds of things I am interested in seeing. It is a waste of your time and money. Get a sample copy, or subscribe to the publication, study it carefully, then send your material."

ARARAT QUARTERLY, (IV), Ararat Press, AGBU, 585 Saddle River Rd., Saddle Brook NJ 07662. (201)797-7600. Editor: Dr. Leo Hamalian. Magazine: 8½×11; 72 pages; illustrations and b&w photographs. "*Ararat* is a forum for the literary and historical works of Armenian intellectuals or non-Armenian writers writing about Armenian subjects."
Needs: Condensed/excerpted novel, contemporary, historical (general), humor/satire, literary, religious/inspirational, translations. Publishes special fiction issue. Receives 25 unsolicited mss/month. Buys 5 mss/issue; 20 mss/year. Length: 1,000 words average. Publishes short shorts. Length: 500 words. Also publishes literary essays, literary criticism, poetry. Sometimes critiques rejected mss and recommends other markets.
How to Contact: Send complete manuscript with cover letter. Reports in 1 month on queries; 3 weeks on mss. SASE. Simultaneous, photocopied and reprint submissions OK. Accepts computer printout submissions. Sample copy $7 and $1 postage. Free fiction guidelines. Reviews novels and short story collections.
Payment: Pays $40-75 plus 2 contributor's copies.
Terms: Pays on publication for one-time rights. Sends galleys to author.

ARCHAE, A Paleo-literary Review, (II), Cloud Mountain Press, 10 Troilus, Old Bridge NJ 08857-2724. (908)679-8373. Edtior: Alan Davis Drake. Magazine: 7×8½; 50-70 pages; illustrations. "For a literary, anthropological, general audience." Semiannually. Estab. 1990. Circ. 425.
Needs: Contemporary, experimental, historical, humor/satire, literary, mainstream, prose poem, translations. "No confessional material." Receives 8-10 unsolicited fiction mss/month. Accepts 1-2 mss/issue; 2-4 mss/year. Publishes mss 2-3 months after acceptance. Length: 3,000-6,000 words preferred; 8,000 words maximum. Publishes short shorts. Length: 500 words. Also publishes literary essays, criticism, poetry. Critiques or comments on rejected mss and recommends other markets.
How to Contact: Query first. Reports in 2 days on queries; in 3 weeks on mss. SASE. Simultaneous, photocopied and computer printout submissions OK. Accepts electronic submissions. Sample copy for $7, 8×9 SAE and 4 first-class stamps. Fiction guidelines for #10 SAE and 1 first-class stamp. Make checks payable to "Alan Drake." Reviews novels and short story collections.
Payment: Pays in contributor's copies.
Terms: Aquires first North American serial rights. Sends pre-publication galleys to author. Sponsors fiction contest—send for details.

ARGONAUT, (II), Box 4201, Austin TX 78765-4201. Editor: Michael Ambrose. Magazine: 5⅜×8½; 60 or more pages; 60 lb. paper; coated cover stock; illustrations. "*Argonaut* is a weird fantasy/science fiction magazine. Our readers want original, literate, unusual stories with a strong science fiction or weird element." Annually. Estab. 1972. Circ. 500.
Needs: Science fiction and weird fantasy. Upcoming themes: 20th anniversary issue (March); all science fiction issue. Receives 40-50 unsolicited fiction mss each month. Buys 5-8 mss/issue. Published work by Charles R. Saunders, Albert J. Manachino, John Alfred Taylor, Ardath Mayhar and Denis Tiani. Length: 2,500-10,000 words. Also publishes poetry. Sometimes recommends other markets.
How to Contact: Send complete ms with SASE. "Cover letter OK but not necessary." Reports in 1-2 months. "We do not consider simultaneous submissions or reprints." Sample copy for $5. Guidelines available for #10 SASE.

Market conditions are constantly changing! If you're still using this book and it is 1993 or later, buy the newest edition of Novel & Short Story Writer's Market at your favorite bookstore or order directly from Writer's Digest Books.

Payment: Pays 2 or more copies. Extras at 50% discount.
Terms: Acquires first North American serial rights.
Advice: "We are not interested in heroic or 'high' fantasy, horror, or media-derived stories. Our main focus is upon science fiction, particularly of the 'hard' variety, although we also publish weird fantasy of a highly original, unusual nature. If unsure about a story, try us."

‡THE ARMCHAIR DETECTIVE, (III, IV), 129 W. 56 St., New York NY 10019. (212)765-0902. Editor: Kathy Daniel. Magazine: 8½×11; 128 pages; 50 lb. paper; b&w illustrations and photographs. "Mystery and crime fiction for hardcore mystery fans." Quarterly. Estab. 1967. Circ. 4,500.
Needs: Suspense/mystery. Receives 25 unsolicited mss/month. Buys 2 mss/issue; 8 mss/year. Publishes ms 6 months after acceptance. Agented fiction 50%. Recently published work by Joe Gores, Jonathan Valen, John Gardner, Nancy Pickard. Sometimes comments on rejected mss and recommends other markets.
How to Contact: Send complete ms with cover letter. Reports in 3 months on mss. SASE. Simultaneous and photocopied submissions OK. Accepts computer printout submissions. Sample copy for $7.50. Fiction guidelines for #10 SAE.
Payment: Pays $100-1,000.
Terms: Pays on publication for all rights. Sends galleys to author.
Advice: "Quality of writing, characterization is more important than a twist ending. Make the best of location, character."

ARNAZELLA, (II), English Department, Bellevue Community College, Bellevue WA 98007. (206)641-2021. Advisor: Laura Burns. Magazine: 5×6; 104 pages, 70 lb. paper; heavy coated cover; illustrations and photos. "For those interested in quality fiction." Annually. Estab. 1976. Circ. 500.
Needs: Adventure, contemporary, ethnic, experimental, fantasy, feminist, gay, historical, humor/satire, lesbian, literary, mainstream, prose poem, regional, suspense/mystery, translations. Submit in fall and winter for issue to be published in spring. Published new writers within the last year. Publishes short shorts. Also publishes literary essays and poetry. *Preference may be given to local contributors.*
How to Contact: Send complete ms with cover letter. Reports on mss in spring. "The months of June through October are very hard for us to read mss because we have no staff at that time. The best times to submit are October through January." SASE. Photocopied submissions OK. Accepts computer printout submissions. Sample copy for $5. Guidelines for SASE.
Payment: Pays in contributor's copies.
Terms: Acquires first rights.
Advice: "Read this and similar magazines, reading critically and analytically."

ARTEMIS, An Art/Literary Publication from the Blue Ridge and Virginia, (IV), Box 8147, Roanoke VA 24014. (703)365-4326. Editor: Dan Gribbin. Magazine: 8×8; 85 pages; heavy/slick paper; colored cover stock; illustrations; photos. "We publish poetry, art and fiction of the highest quality and will consider any artist/writer who lives or has lived in the Blue Ridge or Virginia. General adult audience with literary interest." Annually. Estab. 1976. Circ. 2,000.
Needs: Literary. Wants to see "the best contemporary style." Receives 40 unsolicited fiction mss/year. Accepts 3-4 mss/issue. Does not read mss Jan.-Aug. Publishes ms 4-5 months after acceptance. Published works by Rosanne Coggeshall, Jeanne Larsen, Kurt Rheinheimer; published work by new writers within the last year. Length: 1,500 words average; 2,500 words maximum. Also publishes poetry.
How to Contact: Submit 2 copies of unpublished ms between Sept. 15-Nov. 15, name, address and phone on title page only. Reports in 2 months. SASE for ms. Photocopied submissions OK. Accepts computer printout submissions. Sample copy $6.50. "Ms not adhering to guidelines will be rejected."
Payment: Pays 1 complimentary copy.
Terms: Acquires first rights.
Advice: "We look for polished quality work that holds interest, has imagination, energy, voice."

ARTFUL DODGE, (II), Department of English, College of Wooster, Wooster OH 44691. Editor-in-Chief: Daniel Bourne. Magazine: 150-200 pages; illustrations; photos. "There is no theme in this magazine, except literary power. We also have an ongoing interest in translations from Eastern Europe and elsewhere." Annually. Estab. 1979. Circ. 1,000.
Needs: Experimental, literary, prose poem, translations. "We judge by literary quality, not by genre. We are especially interested in fine English translations of significant contemporary prose writers." Receives 40 unsolicited fiction mss/month. Accepts 5 mss/year. Recently published fiction by Edward Kleinschmidt, William S. Burroughs and Zbigniew Herbert; published 2 new writers within the last

year. Length: 10,000 words maximum; 2,500 words average. Also publishes literary essays, literary criticism, poetry. Occasionally critiques rejected mss.

How to Contact: Send complete ms with SASE. Do not send more than 30 pages at a time. Photocopied submissions OK. Reports in 3-4 months. Sample copies of older, single issues are $2.75 or five issues for $5; recent issues are double issues, available for $5.75. Fiction guidelines for #10 SAE and 1 first class stamp.

Payment: Pays 2 contributor's copies and small honorarium.

Terms: Acquires first North American serial rights.

Advice: "If we take time to offer criticism, do not subsequently flood us with other stories no better than the first. If starting out, get as many readers, good ones, as possible. Above all, read contemporary fiction and the magazine you are trying to publish in."

‡**ART:MAG, (II),** P.O. Box 70896, Las Vegas NV 89170. (702)597-0943. Editor: Peter Magliocco. Magazine: 5½ × 8½; 60 pages; 20 lb. bond paper; b&w pen and ink illustrations and photographs. Publishes "irreverent, literary-minded work by committed writers," for "small press, 'quasi-art-oriented' " audience. Estab. 1984. Circ. under 100.

Needs: Condensed/excerpted novel, confession, contemporary, erotica, ethnic, experimental, fantasy, feminist, gay, historical (general), horror, humor/satire, lesbian, literary, mainstream, prose poem, psychic/supernatural/occult, regional, science fiction, suspense/mystery, translations and arts. No "slick-oriented stuff published by major magazines." Receives 1 plus ms/month. Accepts 1-2 mss/issue; 4-5 mss/year. Publishes ms within 3-6 months of acceptance. Recently published work by James Purdy, Bethany Ericson and Robin Merle. "Collaborated with *Gypsy* magazine (90) to feature fiction from various authors; similar projects for the 90s are possible." Length: 2,000 words preferred; 250 words minimum; 10,000 words maximum. Also publishes literary essays "if relevant to aesthetic preferences," literary criticism "occasionally," poetry.Sometimes critiques rejected mss and recommends other markets.

How to Contact: Send complete ms with cover letter. Reports in 3 months. SASE for ms. Simultaneous and photocopied submissions OK. Sample copy for $2.50, 6 × 9 SAE and 79¢ postage. Fiction guidelines for #10 SAE and first class stamp.

Payment: Pays contributor's copies.

Terms: Acquires one-time rights.

Advice: "Seeking more novel and quality-oriented work, usually from solicited authors. Magazine fiction today needs to be concerned with the issues of fiction writing itself—not just with a desire to publish or please the largest audience. Think about things in the fine art world as well as the literary one and keep the hard core of life in between."

‡**ARTS INDIANA LITERARY SUPPLEMENT, (III, IV),** Arts Indiana, Inc., #701, 47 S. Pennsylvania St., Indianapolis IN 46204. (317)632-7894. Editor: Alison Jester. Magazine: 9 × 12; 32 pages; 80 lb. signature gloss paper; self-cover; illustrations. "The *Arts Indiana Literary Supplement* is an annual anthology of fiction and poetry published in a magazine format. The primary criterion for selection is high literary quality for well-educated, active patrons of the arts." Annually. Estab. 1989.

Needs: Condensed/excerpted novel, contemporary, experimental, humor/satire, literary, prose poem, regional, translations. "Writers must currently live in Indiana or have an extraordinary tie." Receives 1,200 unsolicited mss/year. Buys 4-6 mss/issue. Publishes ms 3-4 months after acceptance. Recently published work by Scott Russell Sanders, Maura Stanton and James Walton. Length: 4,000 words preferred. Sometimes critiques rejected mss.

How to Contact: Send complete ms with cover letter which should include brief biography. Reports in 2½ months on mss. SASE. Simultaneous submissions OK with nonfiction. Sample copy for $2.95 and $2 postage. Fiction guidelines for SAE and 1 first class stamp.

Payment: Pays $125-625 ($500 award of excellence); and 2 contributor's copies. Charges for extras.

Terms: Pays on publication for first rights, one-time rights.

Advice: "Fresh perspectives and use of the English language make a ms stand out."

The double dagger before a listing indicates that the listing is new in this edition. New markets are often the most receptive to freelance contributions.

ASYLUM, (II), P.O. Box 6203, Santa Maria CA 93456. Editor: Greg Boyd. Magazine: 5½ × 8½; 80-128 pages; 10 pt. C1S cover. "For a literary audience." Semiannually. Estab. 1985. Circ. 500.
Needs: Contemporary, erotica, experimental, literary, prose poem, translations. Publishes special fiction issue. "We have just published a 'best of' fiction collection entitled: *Unscheduled Departures: The Asylum Anthology of Short Fiction.*" Receives 20 unsolicited mss/month. Accepts 5 mss/issue; 25 mss/year. Publishes ms 6-18 months after acceptance. Agented fiction 1%. Publishes short shorts. Also publishes literary criticism, poetry. Rarely critiques rejected mss or recommends other markets.
How to Contact: Send complete ms with cover letter. Reports in 1-4 weeks on queries; 1-4 months on mss. SASE. Sample copy for $3. Reviews a limited number of novels and short story collections each year.
Payment: Pays contributor's copies.
Terms: Acquires first rights. Sends galleys to author.
Advice: "Short, tightly written prose fiction and prose poems stand the best chance of gaining acceptance in *Asylum*. Writers should read the magazine before submitting work."

ATALANTIK, (II, IV), 7630 Deer Creek Drive, Worthington OH 43085. (614)885-0550. Editor: Prabhat K. Dutta. Magazine: 8½ × 11; approx. 80 pages; paper quality and cover stock vary; illustrations and photos. "The publication is bilingual: Indian (Bengali) and English language. This was started to keep the Indian language alive to the Indian immigrants. This contains short stories, poems, essays, sketches, book reviews, cultural news, children's pages, etc." Quarterly. Estab. 1980. Circ. 400.
Needs: Adventure, condensed novel, contemporary, ethnic, experimental, historical (general), humor/satire, juvenile (5-9 years), literary, mainstream, psychic/supernatural/occult, romance, science fiction, suspense/mystery, translations, travelogue, especially to India. No politics and religion. Plans special issues, upcoming themes: "Fall of Marxism in USSR;" "Homelessness;" "Global Economic Downturn;" "Saving Mother Earth." Receives 15 unsolicited fiction mss/month. Publishes about 2-4 fiction mss/issue; about 20-50 mss/year. Publishes ms an average of at least 6 months after acceptance. Length: 2,000-5,000 words average. Publishes short shorts. Length: 1-2 pages. Also publishes literary essays, literary criticism, poetry. Sometimes comments on rejected mss and recommends other markets.
How to Contact: Query with clips of published work or send complete ms with cover letter; "author's bio data and a synopsis of the literary piece(s)." Reports on queries in 1 month; on mss in 4 months. SASE. Photocopied submissions OK. Computer laser printout submissions OK. Sample copy $6; fiction guidelines for #10 SASE. Reviews novels and short story collections.
Payment: Pays in contributor's copies; charge for extras.
Terms: Acquires all rights. Sponsors contests for fiction writers.
Advice: "A short story has to be short and should have a story too. A completely imaginative short story without any real life linkage is almost impossible. The language should be lucid and characters kept to a small number. A short story is not simply the description of an incident. It goes far beyond, far deeper. It should present the crisis of a single problem. Usually a successful short story contains a singular idea which is developed to its most probable conclusion in a uniquely charted path. A smaller version of *Atlantik* is managed by Keshab K. Dulta (36B, Bakul Bagan Rd., Calcutta 700025, India), for distribution in India and other Asian countries."

ATLANTIS, A Women's Studies Journal, (II), Institute for the Study of Women, Mt. St. Vincent University, Halifax, Nova Scotia B3M 2J6 Canada. (902)443-4450. Editors: Susan Clark, Deborah Poff. Magazine: 7½ × 9½; 170-200 pages; recycled paper; glossy cover stock; b&w illustrations and photos. "Interdisciplinary women's studies journal, accepts original research and some fiction in French and English for academics and researchers interested in feminism." Semiannually. Estab. 1975. Circ. 800.
Needs: Feminist research and creative work (short stories, poetry, etc.). Receives 15 unsolicited fiction mss/month. Accepts 1-2 mss/issue; 2-4 mss/year. Publishes ms 6-12 months after acceptance. Publishes short shorts. Also publishes literary criticism, poetry. Critiques rejected mss.
How to Contact: Send complete ms with cover letter. Photocopied submissions OK. Accepts computer printouts. Current issue for $10; back issue for $7.50 (Canadian). Occasionally reviews novels and short story collections. Send books to Managing Editor.
Payment: Pays 1 contributor's copy.
Advice: "We welcome and have published work by previously unpublished writers."

ATROCITY, Publication of the Absurd Sig of Mensa, (I), 2419 Greensburg Pike, Pittsburgh PA 15221. Editor: Hank Roll. Newsletter: 8½×11; 8 pages; offset 20 lb. paper and cover; illustrations; photographs occasionally. Humor and satire for "high IQ-Mensa" members. Monthly. Estab. 1976. Circ. 250.
Needs: Humor/satire. Liar's Club, parody, jokes, funny stories, comments on the absurdity of today's world. Receives 20 unsolicited mss/month. Accepts 2 mss/issue. Publishes ms 3-6 months after acceptance. Published 10 new writers within the last year. Length: 50-150 words preferred; 650 words maximum. Also publishes literary essays.
How to Contact: Send complete ms. "No cover letter necessary if ms states what rights (e.g. first North American serial/reprint, etc.) are offered." Reports in 1 month. SASE. Simultaneous, photocopied and reprint submissions OK. Accepts computer printout submissions. Sample copy for 50¢, #10 SAE and 2 first class stamps. Reviews novels and short story collections—"humor only."
Payment: Pays contributor's copies.
Terms: Acquires one-time rights.
Advice: Manuscript should be single spaced, copy ready. Horizontal format to fit on one 8½×11 sheet. "Be funny."

AURA Literary/Arts Review, (II), University of Alabama at Birmingham, Box 76, University Center, Birmingham AL 35294. (205)934-3216. Editor: Nan Smith. Magazine: 6×9; 150 pages; b&w illustrations and photos. "We publish various types of fiction with an emphasis on short stories. Our audience is college students, the university community and literary-minded adults, the arts community." Semiannually. Estab. 1974. Circ. 1,000.
Needs: Literary, contemporary, science fiction, regional, romance, men's, women's, feminist and ethnic. No mss longer than 7,000-8,000 words. Accepts 3-4 mss/issue. Receives 30-50 unsolicited fiction mss each month. Published works by Nickell Romjue, Josephine Marshall, Rodolfo Tomes; published new writers within the last year. Length: 2,000-8,000 words. Publishes short shorts; length according to editor's decision. Also publishes literary essays, literary criticism, poetry. Critiques rejected mss when there is time.
How to Contact: Send complete ms with SASE. No simultaneous submissions; please include biographical information. Reports in 3 months. Sample copy $2.50. "Occasionally" reviews novels and short story collections.
Payment: Pays 2 contributor's copies.
Terms: Acquires first North American serial rights.
Advice: "We welcome experimental or traditional literature on any subject."

THE AZOREAN EXPRESS, (I, IV), Seven Buffaloes Press, Box 249, Big Timber MT 59011. Editor: Art Cuelho. Magazine: 6¾×8¼; 32 pages; 60 lb. book paper; 3-6 illustrations/issue; photos rarely. "My overall theme is rural; I also focus on working people (the sweating professions); the American Indian and Hobo; the Dustbowl era; and I am also trying to expand with non-rural material. For rural and library and professor/student, blue collar workers, etc." Semiannually. Estab. 1985. Circ. 600.
Needs: Contemporary, ethnic, experimental, humor/satire, literary, regional, western, rural, working people. Receives 10-20 unsolicited mss/month. Accepts 2-3 mss/issue; 4-6 mss/year. Publishes ms 1-6 months after acceptance. Length: 1,000-3,000 words. Also publishes short shorts, 500-1,000 words. "I take what I like; length sometimes does not matter, even when longer than usual. I'm flexible." Sometimes recommends other markets.
How to Contact: "Send cover letter with ms; general information, but it can be personal, more in line with the submitted story. Not long rambling letters." Reports in 1-4 weeks on queries; 1-4 weeks on mss. SASE. Photocopied submissions OK. Accepts computer printouts. Sample copy for $4.75. Fiction guidelines for SASE.
Payment: Pays in contributor's copies. "Depends on the amount of support author gives my press."
Terms: Acquires first North American serial rights. "If I decide to use material in anthology form later, I have that right." Sends pre-publication galleys to the author upon request.
Advice: "There would not be magazines like mine if I was not optimistic. But literary optimism is a two-way street. Without young fiction writers supporting fiction magazines the future is bleak, because the commercial magazines allow only formula or name writers within their pages. My own publications receive no grants. Sole support is from writers, libraries and individuals."

BABY SUE, (I), Box 1111, Decatur GA 30031-1111. (404)875-8951. Editor: Don W. Seven. Magazine: 8½×11; 20 pages; illustrations and photos. *"Baby Sue* is a collection of music reviews, poetry, short fiction and cartoons," for "anyone who can think and is not easily offended." Bi-annually. Plans special fiction issue. Estab. 1983. Circ. 1,500.
Needs: Erotica, experimental and humor/satire. Receives 5-10 mss/month. Accepts 3-4 mss/year. Publishes ms within 3 months of acceptance. Publishes short shorts. Length: 1-2 single-spaced pages.
How to Contact: Query with clips of published work. SASE. Accepts computer printout submissions.
Payment: Pays 1 contributor's copy.
Advice: "If no one will print your work, start your own publication—it's easy and cheap. It's also a great way to make contact with other people all over the world who are doing the same."

BAD HAIRCUT (II), #4, 1055 Adams St. SE, Olympia WA 98501-1443. Editors: Ray Goforth, Kim Goforth. Magazine: 5½×8½; 30 pages; illustrations. Published irregularly. Estab. 1987. Circ. 1,000.
Needs: Experimental, humor/satire, prose poem, translations, political, world-conscious. Receives 20 fiction ms/month. Accepts 1-3 mss/issue; 4-12 mss/year. Publishes short shorts. Also publishes literary essays, poetry. Almost always critiques rejected mss and recommends other markets.
How to Contact: Query with or without clips of published work; send complete ms with cover letter; or "send by special messenger." Reports in 1 week on queries; 2 months on mss. SASE. Simultaneous, photocopied and reprint submissions OK. Accepts computer printout submissions. Sample copy for $4. Fiction guidelines for #10 SAE and 1 first class stamp.
Payment: Pays subscription to magazine or contributor's copies; charge for extras. Payment "depends on our financial state."
Terms: Acquires first North American serial rights. Rights revert to author.
Advice: "Keep on trying. You reap what you sow. Love is love. Enjoy your life. Always include a nice cover letter describing who you are and why you're sending your stuff to us."

BAHLASTI PAPERS, The Newsletter of the Kali Lodge, O.T.O., (I), P.O. Box 15038, New Orleans LA 70115. (504)899-7439. Editor: Chén. Newsletter: 8½×11; 12 pages; 20 lb. paper; 20 lb. cover; 2 illustrations; occasional photographs. "Mythological, artistic, alternative and political material for the lunatic fringe." Monthly. Estab. 1986. Circ. 200.
Needs: Condensed/excerpted novel, erotica, ethnic, experimental, fantasy, feminist, gay, horror, humor/satire, lesbian, literary, psychic/supernatural/occult, science fiction, serialized novel, suspense/mystery. "We do not publish poetry." Plans special compilation issues. Receives 5 unsolicited mss/month. Accepts 2 mss/issue; 24/year. Publishes mss approx. 1 month after acceptance. Published work by Steve Canon and Darius James. Publishes short shorts. Also publishes literary essays, literary criticism.
How to Contact: Send complete ms with cover letter telling "why author is interested in being published in *Bahlasti Papers*." Reports in 2 weeks on queries and 1 month on mss. SASE. Simultaneous, photocopied and reprint submissions OK. Accepts computer printout submissions. Sample copy for $2.25 with #10 envelope and 2 first class stamps. Occasionally reviews novels and short story collections.
Payment: Pays subscription to magazine.
Terms: Publication not copyrighted.
Advice: "We look for the odd point-of-view; the individual; independence of thought; work which breaks down established archetypes and so liberates us from social programming."

‡BAKUNIN, P.O. Box 1853, Simi Valley CA 93062-1853. Editor: Jordan Jones. Magazine: 5½×8½; 96 pages; acid-free paper; b&w high contrast illustrations; half-tone photographs. "A magazine for the dead Russian anarchist in all of us. We are looking for well-written stories and do not pre-judge themes or styles. For a literary, counter-culture audience." Semiannually. Estab. 1990. Circ. 300.
Needs: Confession, erotica, ethnic, experimental, feminist, gay, lesbian, literary, prose poem, serialized novel, translations (translators must submit proof of their right to translate that author's work.) "No formula fiction." Receives 15 unsolicited mss/month. Accepts 6-8 mss/issue; 12-16 mss/year. Usually publishes ms within 6 months after acceptance. Recently published work of Harold Jaffe, Mark Wisniewski, Barbara Jamison. Length: 2,000 words preferred; 4,000 words maximum. Publishes short shorts. Sometimes critiques rejected mss and recommends other markets.
How to Contact: Send complete ms with cover letter. Cover letter should include short biographical note. Reports in 2 weeks to 3 months on mss. SASE. Simultaneous submissions (if noted), photocopied submission (if legible) OK. Accepts computer printout submissions. Accepts electronic submissions

via disk (IBM-DOS format). Sample copy for $7. Fiction guidelines for #10 SAE and 1 first class stamp.
Payment: Pays 2 contributor's copies.
Terms: Acquires first North American serial rights.
Advice: "We are looking for well-written work. Much of the work we accept is humorous and/or anti-establishment."

‡BAMBOO RIDGE, The Hawaii Writers' Quarterly, (II, IV), P.O. Box 61781, Honolulu HI 96839-1781. (808)599-4823. Editors: Darrell Lum and Eric Chock. "Writing that reflects the multicultural diversity of Hawaii." Published 2-4 times/year. Estab. 1978.
Needs: Ethnic, literary, Hawaii interest. "Writers need not be from Hawaii, but must reflect Hawaiis' multicultural ethnic mix." Publishes annual special fiction issue. Publishes ms 6 months-1 year after acceptance. Length: up to 25 typed pages, double-spaced. Publishes short shorts.
How to Contact: Query first. Reports in 1 month on queries; 3-6 months on mss. SASE. Photocopied submissions OK. Fiction guidelines for #10 SAE and 1 first class stamp.
Payment: Pays 2 contributor's copies and small honorarium, depending on grant money. Charges for extras (40% discount).
Terms: Pays on publication. Acquires first North American serial rights.

BARDIC RUNES, (IV), 424 Cambridge St, Ottawa, Ontario K1S 4H5 Canada. (613)231-4311. Editor: Michael McKenny. Magazine. Estab. 1990.
Needs: Fantasy. "Traditional or high fantasy. Story should be set in pre-industrial society either historical or of author's invention." Length: 3,500 words or less.
Payment: Pays ½¢/word.
Terms: Pays on acceptance.

BEING, A Celebration of Spirit, Mind & Body, (I, II, IV), M. Talarico Publications, P.O. Box 417, Oceanside CA 92049-0417. (619)722-8829. Editor: Marjorie E. Talarico. Magazine: Digest-sized; 40-50 pages; "desk-top published;" vellum cover; black-and-white, pen-and-ink illustrations. "General and New Age short stories, poems and articles for those interested in the correlation of spirit, mind and body to the culmination of being." Quarterly. Estab. 1989. Circ. 300.
Needs: New Age, reincarnation, pagan. Also adventure, ethnic, experimental, fantasy, horror, literary, prose poem, psychic/supernatural/occult, religious/inspirational, science fiction. "Looking for New Age fairy tales/fantasy for children. Length: 500 to 2,500 words. Also need articles on tarot, astrology, magick for a better life, herbs, past and future lives, psychic/metaphysical experiences. No AIDS, drugs or porno stories." Upcoming themes: "Soulmates/Pure Love Issue." (Looking for short stories with "Lovers throughout eternity" theme. Up to 2,500 words. Deadline 4/25/92); "Fantasy" (In honor of mystic marriages—Venus/Adonis. Short stories with that magical feeling of the co-existence of fantasy/reality. Can be erotic, no porno. Up to 3,500 words. Deadline 8/20/92); "Mother of the Universal Stars Issue" (Short stories of Myth/Magick/Gods/Goddesses. Up to 2,500 words. Deadline 11/18/92). Receives 80 unsolicited fiction mss/month. Accepts 6-10 mss/issue; 60 mss/year. Publishes mss 2-4 months after acceptance. Recently published work by Antonia, Paul Truttman, Roy Howell, Jr. Length: 2,500 words preferred; 300 words minimum; 7,500 words maximum. Publishes short shorts. Length: 650 words. Also publishes literary essays, literary criticism, poetry. Critiques or comments on rejected mss and recommends other markets.
How to Contact: Send complete mss with cover letter. "I like to know a little bit about the author, credits (if any) and what prompted author to write this particular story." Reports in 8-10 weeks. SASE. Simultaneous, photocopied, reprint and computer printout submissions OK. Sample copy for $3, 7½×10¼ SAE and 3 first class stamps. Fiction guidelines for £10 SAE and 1 first class stamp. Reviews novels and short story collections.
Payment: Pays in contributor's copies; charges for extras.
Terms: Acquires one-time rights.
Advice: Looks for "Originality! I like to see an author really bend their imagination and keep me wanting to turn the pages. (if there is artwork to go along, I would like to see it.)"

LA BELLA FIGURA, (I, II, IV), Box 411223, San Francisco CA 94141-1223. Editor: Rose Romano. Magazine: 8½×11; 10 pages. Publishes "work by Italian-American women, mostly about us. We now publish men also." Quarterly. Estab. 1988. Circ. 150.

Needs: Ethnic, feminist, lesbian, literary, prose poem, translations and Italian-American culture and heritage. "It is the purpose of *LBF* to provide a space for a much-neglected group of people. It is our space to share ourselves with each other and to help others understand us." Receives 10-15 mss/month. Accepts 1-2 mss/issue; 4-8 mss/year. Publishes ms within 3-6 months of acceptance. Published work by Maria Mazziotti Gillan, Rina Ferrarelli, Jennifer Lagier and Anna Bart. Length: about 5 double-spaced pages preferred. Publishes short shorts. Also publishes literary essays, poetry. Sometimes critiques rejected mss and recommends other markets.

How to Contact: Send complete ms with cover letter, which should include previous publications and any other credits. Reports within 4 months. SASE. Photocopied and reprint submissions OK. Accepts computer printout submissions. Sample copy for $2. Reviews novels and short·story collections.

Payment: Pays 2 contributor's copies; charge for extras.

Terms: Acquires one-time rights.

Advice: "There's not enough work by and about Italian-Americans published yet. The writer must find that space between stereotyped and assimilated. Although any good writing is considered, I'm most interested in work about Italian-American culture."

‡**BELLES LETTRES, A Review of Books by Women, (II),** 11151 Captain's Walk Ct., N. Potomac MD 20878. Editor: Janet P. Mullaney. Fiction Editor: Suzanne Berne. Magazine: 8½ × 11; 64 pages; 50 lb. offset paper; 8 pt. glossy cover; illustrations and photographs. "General audience review of books by women; we publish 1 short story in each issue for a literary audience." Quarterly. Estab. 1985. Circ. 5,000.

Needs: Ethnic, feminist, humor/satire, lesbian, literary, science fiction, suspense/mystery, translations. Receives 10 unsolicited mss/month. Accepts 1 ms/issue; 4-6 mss/year. Publishes ms 6 months-1 year after acceptance. Recently published work by Fay Moskowitz, Maxine Rodburg, Lynne Sharon Schwartz. Length: 2,000 words preferred; 1,000 words minimum; 6,000 words maximum. Publishes short shorts.

How to Contact: Send fiction mss to Susan Berne, 120 Bellevue Rd., Watertown MA 02172. Send complete ms with cover letter. Reports in 2 months on mss. SASE. Simultaneous, photocopied submissions OK. Accepts computer printout submissions. Sample copy for $5. Fiction guidelines for #10 SAE and 1 first class stamps.

Payment: Pays free subscription to magazine and contributor's copies.

Terms: Acquires first rights.

‡**THE BELLETRIST REVIEW, (I, II),** Marmarc Publications, Suite 290, 17 Farmington Ave., Plainville CT 06062. (203)793-9509. Editor: Marlene Dube. Fiction Editor: Marc Saegaert. Magazine: 8½ × 11; 50 pages; heavy paper; 90 lb. cover stock; illustrations. "We are interested in compelling, well-crafted short fiction in a variety of genres. Our title *Belletrist*, means 'lover of literature.' This magazine will appeal to an educated, adult audience that appreciates quality fiction." Semiannually. *First issue to be published in September 1992.*

Needs: Adventure, contemporary, erotica, horror (psychological), humor/satire, literary, mainstream, regional, suspense/mystery. "To give writers an idea of our eclectic tastes in fiction, we are inspired by the masters such as Poe, Chekhov, and O'Henry, and contemporary authors such as Richard Selzer, Ray Bradbury and Isaac Bashevis Singer." No fantasy, juvenile, westerns, or overblown horror or confessional pieces. Will accept 10-12 mss/issue; approximately 25 mss/year. Publishes ms within 1 year after acceptance. Length: 2,500-5,000 words preferred; 1,000 words minimum; 5,000 words maximum. Comments on or critiques rejected mss when time permits and recommends other markets on occasion.

How to Contact: Send complete ms with cover which should include brief biographical note and any previous publications. Reports in 1 month on queries; 2 months on mss. SASE. Simultaneous and photocopied submissions OK. Fiction guidelines for 4 × 9 SAE and 1 first class stamp.

Payment: Pays contributor's copies.

Terms: Acquires one-time rights.

Advice: "Short story fiction writing, like letter writing, is almost a lost art in this age of high-tech media communications. We want fiction that we can climb into—that has that elusive, but unmistakable quality to elicit a reaction or a thought that is not easily forgotten. When you reread that fifth, sixth or seventh draft out loud and you know it sounds exactly right, submit it. Remember, there is a publication out there that will be your needle in that haystack of rejections."

THE BELLINGHAM REVIEW, (II), 1007 Queen St., Bellingham WA 98226. Editor: Susan Hilton. Magazine: 5½ × 8; 64 pages; 60 lb. white paper; varied cover stock; photos. "A literary magazine featuring original short stories, novel excerpts, short plays and poetry of palpable quality." Semiannually. Estab. 1977. Circ. 700.
Needs: All genres/subjects considered. Acquires 1-2 mss/issue. Publishes short shorts. Published new writers within the last year. Length: 5,000 words or less. Also publishes poetry. Critiques rejected mss when there is time.
How to Contact: Send complete ms. Reports in 2 weeks to 3 months. Publishes ms an average of 1 year after acceptance. Sample copy $2. Reviews novels and short story collections.
Payment: Pays 1 contributor's copy plus 2-issue subscription. Charges $2 for extras.
Terms: Acquires first North American serial and one-time rights.
Advice: Mss are rejected for various reasons, "but the most common problem is too much *telling* and not enough *showing* of crucial details and situations. We also look for something that is different or looks at life in a different way."

BELLOWING ARK, A Literary Tabloid, (II), Box 45637, Seattle WA 98145. (206)545-8302. Editor: R.R. Ward. Tabloid: 11½ × 16; 20 pages; electro-brite paper and cover stock; illustrations; photos. "We publish material which we feel addresses the human situation in an affirmative way. We do not publish academic fiction." Bimonthly. Estab. 1984. Circ. 500.
Needs: Contemporary, literary, mainstream, serialized/excerpted novel. "Anything we publish will be true." Receives 250-300 unsolicited fiction mss/year. Accepts 1-2 mss/issue; 7-12 mss/year. Time varies, but publishes ms not longer than 6 months after acceptance. Recently published work by Jon Remmerde, Grace Cash and Greg Cohen; published new writers within the last year. Length: 3,000-5,000 words average. Publishes short shorts. Also publishes literary essays, literary criticism, poetry. Sometimes critiques rejected mss and recommends other markets.
How to Contact: No queries. Send complete ms with cover letter and short bio. "I always cringe when I see letters listing 'credits' and stating the 'rights' offered! Such delights indicate the impossible amateur. Many beginners address me by first name—few of my close friends do." Reports in 6 weeks on mss. SASE. Sample copy for $2, 9 × 12 SAE and 85¢ postage.
Payment: Pays in contributor's copies.
Terms: Acquires first rights.
Advice: "*Bellowing Ark* began as (and remains) an alternative to the despair and negativity of the Workshop/Academic poetry scene; we believe that life has meaning and is worth living—the work we publish reflects that belief. Learn how to tell a story before submitting. Avoid 'trick' endings—they have all been done before and better."

BELOIT FICTION JOURNAL, (II), Box 11, Beloit College WI 53511. (608)363-2308. Editor: Clint McCown. Magazine: 6 × 9; 130 pages; 60 lb. paper; 10 pt. C1S cover stock; illustrations and photos on cover. "We are interested in publishing the best contemporary fiction and are open to all themes except those involving pornographic, religiously dogmatic or politically propagandistic representations. Our magazine is for general readership, though most of our readers will probably have a specific interest in literary magazines." Semiannually. Estab. 1985.
Needs: Contemporary, literary, mainstream, prose poem, spiritual and sports. No pornography, religious dogma, political propaganda. Receives 75 unsolicited fiction mss/month. Accepts 8-10 mss/issue; 16-20 mss/year. Replies take longer in summer. Publishes ms within 9 months after acceptance. Length: 5,000 words average; 250 words minimum; 10,000 words maximum. Sometimes critiques rejected mss and recommends other markets.
How to Contact: Send complete ms with cover letter. Reports in 1 week on queries; 1-6 weeks on mss. SASE for ms. Simultaneous and photocopied submissions OK, if identified as such. Accepts computer printouts. Sample copy $5. Fiction guidelines for #10 envelope and 1 first class stamp.
Advice: "Many of our contributors are writers whose work we have previously rejected. Don't let one rejection slip turn you away from our—or any—magazine."

Market categories: (I) Beginning; (II) General; (III) Prestige; (IV) Specialized.

BERKELEY FICTION REVIEW, (II), 700 Eshelman Hall, University of California, Berkeley CA 94720. Editor: Catherine Harris. Magazine: journal size; 200 pages; some visual art and photographs. "We publish fresh, inventive fiction and poetry, as well as non-academic essays." Annually. Estab. 1981. Circ. 500.

Needs: No "self-consciously trendy fiction." Receives up to 50 unsolicited mss/month. Accepts 8-20 mss/issue. Published work by new writers in the last year. Also publishes literary essays, literary criticism, poetry. Occasionally critiques rejected mss.

How to Contact: Send complete ms with short author's note. SASE. Photocopied submissions OK. Sample copy for $5.

Payment: Pays 1 contributor's copy.

Advice: "As time in our society becomes a more and more precious commodity it seems to me that short fiction collections and anthologies are gaining ground. However, I am not sure that the fiction itself has responded to this change. I have yet to see short fiction which attempts to be as encompassing and unifying as the novel. Our goal is to publish innovating new writing which, if it doesn't exemplify perfection, explores possibilities."

BEYOND . . . SCIENCE FICTION & FANTASY, (I, II, IV), Other Worlds Books, P.O. Box 136, New York NY 10024. (201)791-6721. Editor: Shirley Winston. Fiction Editor: Roberta Rogow. Magazine: 8½×11; 56 pages; illustrations. Science fiction and fantasy fiction, art and poetry. Audience is "mostly adults, some younger." Quarterly. Estab. 1985. Circ. 300.

Needs: Fantasy and science fiction. No pornography. Receives 100 unsolicited mss/month. Accepts 11 mss/issue; 44 mss/year. Publishes ms "up to 2 years after acceptance." Length: 5,000 words average; 500 words minimum; 12,000 words maximum. Publishes short shorts. Sometimes critiques rejected mss and recommends other markets.

How to Contact: Send complete ms with cover letter. Reports in 2 months. SASE. Photocopied submissions OK. Accepts computer printout submissions. Sample copy for $4.50; fiction guidelines for SASE.

Payment: Pays ⅓¢ per word and contributor's copies.

Terms: Pays on publication for first North American serial rights.

BILINGUAL REVIEW, (II, IV), Hispanic Research Center, Arizona State University, Tempe AZ 85287. (602)965-3867. Editor-in-Chief: Gary D. Keller. Scholarly/literary journal of US Hispanic life: poetry, short stories, other prose and theater. Magazine: 7×10; 96 pages; 55 lb. acid-free paper; coated cover stock. Published 3 times/year. Estab. 1974. Circ. 2,000.

Needs: US Hispanic creative literature. "We accept material in English or Spanish. We publish original work only—no translations." US Hispanic themes only. Receives 50 unsolicited fiction mss/month. Accepts 3 mss/issue; 9 mss/year. Publishes ms an average of 1 year after acceptance. Published work by Demetria Martinez, Alicia Gaspar de Alba, Tomás Rivera; published work of new writers within the last year. Also publishes literary criticism on US Hispanic themes and poetry. Often critiques rejected mss.

How to Contact: Send 2 copies of complete ms with SAE and loose stamps. Reports in 1 month. Simultaneous and high-quality photocopied submissions OK. Sample copy for $9. Reviews novels and short story collections.

Payment: Pays 2 contributor's copies. 30% discount for extras.

Terms: Acquires all rights (50% of reprint permission fee given to author as matter of policy).

Advice: "We do not publish literature about tourists in Latin America and their perceptions of the 'native culture.' We do not publish any fiction set in Latin America; we only publish works set in the United States."

THE BLACK HOLE LITERARY REVIEW, (I), 1312 Stonemill Court, Cincinnati OH 45215. (513)821-6670. Editor: Wm. E. Allendorf. Electronic Bulletin Board. "This is an attempt to revolutionize publishing—no paper, no rejection slips, no deadlines. For any person with access to a home computer and a modem." Estab. 1989. Circ. 900+.

Needs: "Any or all fiction and nonfiction categories are acceptable. Any size, topic, or inherent bias is acceptable. The only limitation is that the writer will not mind having his piece read, and an honest critique given directly by his readership." Plans future hardcopy anthology. Publishes ms 1-2 days after acceptance. Length: 2,000-10,000 words. Publishes short shorts, poetry, essays. "Critique given if not by editor, then by readers through Email."

How to Contact: Upload as EMAIL to the editor. Cover letter should include "titles, description (abstract), copyright notice." Reports in 1-2 days. Simultaneous submissions OK.
Payment: Pays in royalties, but charges fee for initial inputting (see below).
Terms: Charges $5 minimum subscription. Submissions cost $.50+ (deducted from subscription). Royalties are accrued each time the piece is read. Contact editor for details. Buys one-time rights.
Advice: "If the concept of the electronic magazine goes over with the public, then the market for fiction is limitless. Any piece that an author has taken the trouble to set to print is worth publishing. However, The Hole is looking for writers that want to be read—not ones that just want to write. The electronic magazine is an interactive medium, and pieces are judged on their ability to inspire a person to read them." Writers interested in submitting should: "Do it. You would be the first to be rejected by The Hole, if we did not use your piece; to make matters easier for all concerned, submit your piece as a ASCII text file via the modem. If you do not have access to a home computer with a modem, buy one, borrow one, steal one. This is the wave of the future for writers."

BLACK JACK, (I), Seven Buffaloes Press, Box 249, Big Timber MT 59011. Editor: Art Cuelho. "Main theme: Rural. Publishes material on the American Indian, farm and ranch, American hobo, the common working man, folklore, the Southwest, Okies, Montana, humor, Central California, etc. for people who make their living off the land. The writers write about their roots, experiences and values they receive from the American soil." Annually. Estab. 1973. Circ. 750.
Needs: Literary, contemporary, western, adventure, humor, American Indian, American hobo, and parts of novels and long short stories. "Anything that strikes me as being amateurish, without depth, without craft, I refuse. Actually, I'm not opposed to any kind of writing if the author is genuine and has spent his lifetime dedicated to the written word." Receives approximately 10-15 unsolicited fiction mss/month. Buys 5-10 mss/year. Length: 3,500-5,000 words (there can be exceptions).
How to Contact: Query for current theme with SASE. Reports in 1 week on queries; 2 weeks on mss. Sample copy for $4.75.
Payment: Pays 1-2 author's copies.
Terms: Acquires first North American serial rights and reserves the right to reprint material in an anthology or future *Black Jack* publications. Rights revert to author after publication.
Advice: "Enthusiasm should be matched with skill as a craftsman. That's not saying that we don't continue to learn, but every writer must have enough command of the language to compete with other proven writers. Save postage by writing first to the editor to find out his needs. A small press magazine always has specific needs at any given time. I sometimes accept material from country writers that aren't all that good at punctuation and grammar but make up for it with life's experience. This is not a highbrow publication; it belongs to the salt-of-the-earth people."

‡BLACK MOUNTAIN REVIEW, (IV), Lorien House, P.O. Box 1112, Black Mountain NC 28711-1112. (704)669-6211. Editor: David A. Wilson. Magazine: 5½×8½; 48 pages; 60 lb. offset paper; 65 lb. cover stock; occasionally illustrations and photographs. "Each issue covers an American writer and all material must fit the theme." Annually. Estab. 1987. Circ. 100-150.
Needs: Literary. "The category of fiction is not as important as meeting the requirements of the theme. Guidelines for SASE." Receives 10 unsolicited mss/month. Buys 1-2 mss/issue. Publishes ms 6 months to 1 year after acceptance. Recently published work by Maureen Williams. Length: 1,000 words preferred; 2,000 words maximum. Publishes short shorts. Comments on or critiques rejected mss and "encourages the writer."
How to Contact: Query first. Reports in 1 week. SASE. Photocopied submissions OK. Sample copy for $5. Fiction guidelines for #10 SAE and 1 first class stamp.
Payment: Pays $15 maximum.
Terms: Pays on publication for one-time rights.
Advice: "Wait! Hold it! Don't send that ms . . . until you have written for the guidelines. General material is not wanted. We are covering Ernest Hemingway, Tennessee Williams and Carl Sandburg in the near future. Submitted material is read carefully for content and (aagh!) spelling, but not the name/fame of the writers. There must be evidence of research within the story, and details must be accurate. There is still room for creativity. Do a good story, and you are welcome here."

BLACK RIVER REVIEW, (II), 855 Mildred Ave., Lorain OH 44052. (216)244-9654. Editor: Kaye Coller. Fiction Editor: Jack Smith. Magazine: 8½×11; 60 pages, recycled paper; mat card cover stock; b&w drawings. "Contemporary writing and contemporary American culture; poetry, book reviews, essays on contemporary literature, short stories." Annually. Estab. 1985. Circ. 400.

Needs: Contemporary, experimental, humor/satire and literary. No "erotica for its own sake, stories directed toward a juvenile audience." Accepts up to 5 ms/year. Does not read mss May 1-Dec. 31. Publishes ms no later than July of current year. Recently published work by David Shields, Jeanne M. Leiby, Louis Gallo. Length: up to 3,500 words but will consider up to 4,000 maximum. Publishes short shorts. Also publishes literary essays, literary criticism, poetry. Sometimes critiques rejected mss and recommends other markets.

How to Contact: Reports on mss no later than July. SASE. Photocopied submissions OK. Sample copy for $3 back issue; $3.50 current. Fiction guidelines for #10 SAE and 1 first class stamp. Reviews novels and short story collections.

Terms: Acquires one-time rights.

Payment: Pays in contributor's copies.

Advice: "Since it is so difficult to break in, much of the new writer's creative effort is spent trying to match trends in popular fiction, in the case of the slicks, or adapting to narrow themes ('Gay and Lesbian,' 'Vietnam War,' 'Women's Issues,' etc.) of little and literary journals. An unfortunate result, from the reader's standpoint, is that each story within a given category comes out sounding like all the rest. Among positive developments of the proliferation of small presses is the opportunity for writers to decide what to write and how to write it. My advice is support a little magazine that is both open to new writers and prints fiction you like. 'Support' doesn't necessarily mean 'buy all the back issues,' but, rather, direct involvement between contributor, magazine and reader needed to rebuild the sort of audience that was there for writers like Fitzgerald and Hemingway."

THE BLACK SCHOLAR, (II, IV), The Black World Foundation, Box 2869, Oakland CA 94609. (415)547-6633. Editor: Robert Chrisman. Magazine: 7×10; 56+ pages; newsprint paper; glossy, 24 lb. cover; illustrations; b&w photos. Magazine on black culture, research and black studies for Afro-Americans, college graduates and students. "We are also widely read by teachers, professionals and intellectuals, and are required reading for many black and Third World Studies courses." Bimonthly. Estab. 1969. Circ. 10,000.

Needs: Literary, contemporary, juvenile, young adult and ethnic. No religious/inspirational, psychic, etc. Receives approximately 75 unsolicited fiction mss each month. Published new writers within the last year. Length: 2,000-5,000 words. Also publishes poetry.

How to Contact: Query with clips of published work and SASE. Reports in 2 months on queries, 1 month on mss.

Payment: Pays 10 contributor's copies and 1 year's subscription.

Terms: Acquires all rights.

Advice: "Poetry and fiction appear almost exclusively in our annual culture issue (generally, Sept./Oct. of given year)."

BLACK WARRIOR REVIEW, (II), Box 2936, Tuscaloosa AL 35487. (205)348-4518. Editor-in-Chief: Glenn Mott. Fiction Editor: Nicola Williams. Magazine: 6×9; approx. 144 pages; illustrations and photos sometimes. "We publish contemporary fiction, poetry, reviews, essays and interviews for a literary audience." Semiannually. Estab. 1974. Circ. 1,300-2,000.

Needs: Contemporary, literary, mainstream and prose poem. No types that are clearly "types." Receives 100 unsolicited fiction mss/month. Accepts 5 mss/issue, 10 mss/year. Approximately 25% of fiction is agented. Published work by Scott Gould, Max Phillips and Lynda Sexson; published new writers within the last year. Length: 7,500 words maximum; 3,000-5,000 words average. Also publishes literary criticism, poetry. Occasionally critiques rejected mss.

How to Contact: Send complete ms with SASE. Photocopied submissions OK. Reports in 2-3 months. Publishes ms 2-5 months after acceptance. Sample copy $4. Fiction guidelines for SAE and 1 first class stamp. Reviews novels and short story collections.

Payment: Pays $5-10/page and 2 contributor's copies.

Terms: Pays on publication.

Advice: "Become familiar with the magazine(s) being submitted to; learn the editorial biases; accept rejection slips as part of the business; keep trying. We are not a good bet for 'commercial' fiction. Each year the *Black Warrior Review* will award $500 to a fiction writer whose work has been published in either the fall or spring issue, to be announced in the fall issue. Regular submission deadlines are August 1 for fall issue, January 1 for spring issue."

BLACK WRITER MAGAZINE, (II), Terrell Associates, Box 1030, Chicago IL 60690. (312)924-3818. Editor: Mable Terrell. Fiction Editor: Herman Gilbert. Magazine: 8½×11; 40 pages; glossy paper; glossy cover; illustrations. "To assist writers in publishing their work." For "all audiences, with a special emphasis on black writers." Quarterly. Estab. 1972.
Needs: Ethnic, historical, literary, religious/inspirational, prose poem. Plans annual anthology. Receives 20 unsolicited mss/month. Accepts 15 mss/issue. Publishes ms on average of 6 months after acceptance. Length: 3,000 words preferred; 2,500 words average; 1,500 words minimum. Also publishes literary essays. Sometimes critiques rejected mss and recommends other markets.
How to Contact: Send complete ms with cover letter, which should include "writer's opinion of the work, and rights offered." Reports in 3 weeks. SASE. Simultaneous submissions OK. Sample copy for 8½×11 SAE and 70¢ postage. Fiction guidelines for SASE. Reviews novels and short story collections. Send books to the editor.
Payment: Pays subscription to magazine.
Terms: Acquires one-time rights.
Advice: "Write the organization and ask for assistance." Sponsors awards for fiction writers. Contest deadline May 30.

BLATANT ARTIFICE, Hallwalls Annual Anthology of Short Fiction, (V), Hallwalls Contemporary Arts Center, 700 Main St., Buffalo NY 14202. (716)854-5828. Editor: Edmund Cardoni. Magazine: 7×9; 150 pages; high-quality paper; glossy 2-color cover; illustrations; photos. "Innovative contemporary short fiction by visitors to our reading series. Fiction writers may submit work to be considered for inclusion in the reading series, but all contributors to the publication must first have been readers in the series." Audience is readers of contemporary fiction, writers, artists. Annually. Estab. 1986. Circ. 1,000.
Needs: Contemporary, erotica, ethnic, feminist, gay, humor/satire, lesbian, literary, excerpted novel, translations only if submitted by the original author, not by the translator, political fiction. No "genre fiction, so-called 'minimalist' fiction, Iowa-style fiction, realistic fiction, yuppie fiction." Receives 2-4 unsolicited mss/month. Buys 30 mss/year. Length: 1,500 words preferred; 1,250 words minimum; 2,500 words maximum. Publishes short shorts. Sometimes critiques rejected mss and recommends other markets.
How to Contact: Submit a résumé, list of publications, readings, awards, etc., and samples of writing to be considered for inclusion in the reading series. All writers invited to do readings will subsequently be invited to submit work to the annual anthology. Reports in 3 months on mss. SASE. Simultaneous and photocopied submissions OK. Published work may be submitted for consideration for inclusion in the reading series. Accepts computer printout submissions. Sample copy for SAE and $10.
Payment: Pays $35. "This is the payment for publication only, but publication ensues from first doing a reading, for which there is a separate, negotiable payment."
Terms: Pays on publication for first or one-time rights. One 3-month writer's residency *for fiction writers only* is occasionally offered, depending on availability of funding in any given year.
Advice: "Be daring or forget it, which means write as only you can write, and not as you perceive others around you (or *out there*) writing; take my word for it, most of them are wrong. Submit work and a résumé to be considered for inclusion in our reading series; if invited to give reading, subsequent publication in *Blatant Artifice* is automatic. Women writers as well as black, hispanic, and other minority writers are particularly encouraged to apply for readings and residencies at Hallwalls."

‡BLIND IGUANA PRESS, (I, II), 513 Corby Ave., South Bend IN 46617. (219)234-3330. Editor: Daniel Breen. Fiction Editor: Darren Jackson. Tabloid: 10¾×16¾; 8 pages; newsprint paper; b&w illustrations and photographs. "We publish all types of stories, but stories of gutsy and energetic satire and humor desired most. We are trying to reach the 'common person' the roofer, the waitress, the student. But remember, these people are intelligent too." Quarterly. Estab. 1990. Circ. 3,000.
Needs: Adventure, contemporary, erotica, ethnic, experimental, horror, humor/satire, literary, mainstream, prose poem, science fiction, suspense/mystery. No fantasy, gay or feminist. Receives 5 unsolicited mss/month. Buys 3-5 mss/issue; 20 mss/year. Publishes ms 4 months after acceptance. Recently published work by Peter Sniegowski, Dannon Kingsly. Length: 5,000 words preferred; 1,000 words minimum; 20,000 words maximum. Publishes short shorts. Length: 500 words. Sometimes critiques rejected mss.
How to Contact: Send complete ms with cover letter. Reports in 1 month on mss. SASE. Simultaneous, photocopied and reprint submissions OK. Accepts computer printout submissions. Sample copy for 1 first class stamp. Fiction guidelines for #10 SAE and 1 first class stamp.

Payment: Pays $25 maximum and contributor's copies.
Terms: Pays on publication for one-time rights.
Advice: "We want to publish stories that are fun and interesting. *Blind Inquana Press* is not targeted at the scholar, but it is also not targeted at idiots or teenagers. We are looking for mature writers with confidence and control. I have always perceived *BIP* as a quick and thought provoking read. Think about what you like to read in the bathroom. Approach your idea like a craftsman and with confidence. Be sure your story is whole in all of its parts. And please, have a good time with it."

‡BLOODREAMS, A Magazine of Vampires & Werewolves, (II, IV), 1312 W. 43rd St., North Little Rock AR 72118. (501)771-2047. Editor: Kelly Gunter Atlas. Magazine: 8½×11; 40-50 pages; 20 lb. paper; 60 lb. stock cover; b&w drawings. "*Bloodreams* is dedicated exclusively to the preservation, continuance, and enhancement of the vampire and the werewolf legends for adult fans of the genre." Quarterly. Estab. 1991. Circ. 60.
Needs: Vampires and werewolves. "We do not want to see gore, unnecessary violence, or pornography." Receives 10-12 unsolicited mss/month. Buys 4-6 mss/issue; 16-24 mss/year. Does not read mss in April, July, October, January. Publishes ms 2 months after acceptance. Recently published work by Gregory L. Norris and Deidra Cox. Length: 1,500 words preferred; 250 words minimum; 2,500 words maximum. Publishes short shorts. Length: 250-500 words. Also publishes poetry. Sometimes critiques rejected mss and recommends other markets.
How to Contact: Send complete ms with cover letter. Include a brief introduction and past credits if any. Reports in 1 week on queries; 2-4 weeks on mss. SASE. Simultaneous, photocopied and reprint submissions OK. Accepts computer printout submissions. Sample copy for $3. Fiction guidelines for #10 SAE and 1 first class stamp.
Payment: Pays in contributor's copies. Charges for extras.
Terms: Acquires one-time rights.
Advice: "We look for well-written, concise short stories which are complete within themselves. We like writers who have their own sense of style and imagination who write with their own 'voice' and do not try to copy others' work. We are open to a variety of interpretations of the vampire and werewolf legends. For example, we like anything ranging from Stephen King to Anne Rice to Robert R. McCammon to Brian Lumley."

BLUE LIGHT RED LIGHT, A Periodical of Speculative Fiction & the Arts, (III), Suite F-42, 496A Hudson St., New York NY 10014. (201)432-3245. Publisher: Alma Rodriguez. Magazine: 6×9; 170 pages. Semiannually. Estab. 1989.
Needs: Ethnic, experimental, fantasy, literary, prose poem. No horror, cyber punk. Agented fiction 20%. Publishes short shorts. Length 6-8 pages. Recommends other markets.
How to Contact: Send manuscript up to 15 pages with cover letter. Reports in 3 weeks on queries; 2 months on mss. SASE. Simultaneous and photocopied submissions OK. Accepts computer printout submissions. Sample copy $5.50.
Payment: Pays contributor's copies.
Terms: Acquires first rights.
Advice: "*Blue Light Red Light* is open to any nationality or ethnicity. We accept the finest works of new and established writers, fusing mainstream writing, magic realism and surrealism together with speculative fiction. As an interdiciplinary periodical, we seek not to isolate these genres but to discover the points of contact between them and mainstream writing itself. As contemporary life becomes fragmented, the search for meaning, for personal myths becomes all the more intense. We want to participate in this search for meaning. Everyone interested in *BLRL* should read a copy before submitting their work."

‡BLUE RYDER, (I, II), (formerly *Heathenzine, Storyzine,* and *Temm Poetry Magazine*), Box 587, Olean NY 14760. Editor: Ken Wagner. Magazine: 8½×11; 40-48 pages; 50 lb. paper; 60 lb. color cover; many illustrations and photographs. "Publishes excerpts from underground, alternative, small and micropress publications for an educated audience with an interest in alternative politics, humor and art." Bimonthly. Estab. 1990. Circ. 750.

Read the Business of Fiction section to learn the correct way to prepare and submit a manuscript.

Needs: Contemporary, ethnic, experimental, feminist, gay, historical (general), humor/satire, lesbian, literary, prose poem. "*Blue Ryder* usually reprints fiction after it has appeared in another magazine. Writers should submit clear photocopies or tearsheets of the piece the way it originally appeared." Receives 6-15 unsolicited mss/month. Buys 1-2 mss/issue; 6-12 mss/year. Publishes mss 6-18 months after acceptance. Recently published work by Richard Kostelanetz. Length: 1,000 words preferred; 1,500 words maximum. Publishes short shorts. Sometimes critiques rejected mss and recommends other markets.
How to Contact: Query with clips of published work. Reports in 2 months on queries; 3 months on mss. SASE. Sample copy for $2. Free fiction guidelines.
Payment: Pays in contributor's copies.
Terms: Acquires one-time rights. Not copyrighted.

BLUELINE, (II, IV), English Dept., SUNY, Potsdam NY 13676. Editor-in-Chief: Anthony Tyler. Magazine: 6 × 9; 112 pages; 70 lb. white stock paper; 65 lb. smooth cover stock; illustrations; photos. "*Blueline* is interested in quality writing about the Adirondacks or other places similar in geography and spirit. We publish fiction, poetry, personal essays, book reviews and oral history for those interested in the Adirondacks, nature in general, and well-crafted writing." Annually. Estab. 1979. Circ. 700.
Needs: Adventure, contemporary, humor/satire, literary, prose poem, regional, reminiscences, oral history and nature/outdoors. Receives 8-10 unsolicited fiction mss/month. Accepts 6-8 mss/issue. Does not read January-August. Publishes ms 3-6 months after acceptance. Published fiction by Jeffrey Clapp. Published new writers within the last year. Length: 500 words minimum; 3,000 words maximum; 2,500 words average. Also publishes literary essays, poetry. Occasionally critiques rejected mss. Sometimes recommends other markets.
How to Contact: Send complete ms with SASE and brief bio. Submit mss Aug. 1-Nov. 30. Reports in 2-10 weeks. Photocopied submissions OK. Accepts computer printout submissions. Reports in 2-10 weeks. Sample copy for $5.75. Fiction guidelines for 5 × 10 SAE with 1 first class stamp.
Payment: Pays 1 contributor's copy. Charges $3 each for 3 or more extra copies.
Terms: Acquires first rights.
Advice: "We look for concise, clear, concrete prose that tells a story and touches upon a universal theme or situation. We prefer realism to romanticism but will consider nostalgia if well done. Pay attention to grammar and syntax. Avoid murky language, sentimentality, cuteness or folksiness. We would like to see more good fiction related to the Adirondacks. Please include short biography and word count. If manuscript has potential, we work with author to improve and reconsider for publication. Our readers prefer fiction to poetry (in general) or reviews. Write from your own experience, be specific and factual (within the bounds of your story) and if you write about universal features such as love, death, change, etc., write about them in a fresh way. Triteness and mediocracy are the hallmarks of the majority of stories seen today."

‡BLUFF CITY, A Magazine of Poetry and Fiction, (II), Bluff City Press, P.O. Box 7697, Elgin IL 60121. (708)741-5620. Editor: Carol A. Morrison. Magazine: 5½ × 8½; 86 pages; 70 lb. paper; glossy heavy cover; occasionally illustrations and photographs. "Finely crafted poetry and short stories for a small press literary audience." Semiannually. Estab. 1990. Circ. 350.
Needs: Experimental, literary, prose poem. "No didactic, religious, special interest or unrevised drafts." Receives 20 unsolicited mss/month. Accepts 5-8 mss/issue; 10-16 mss/year. Publishes ms 3-6 months after acceptance. Recently published work by Thomas E. Kennedy, Elias Papadimitrakopoulos, Rebecca Rule. Length: 2,500 words maximum. Publishes short shorts. Comments on or critiques rejected mss and recommends other markets.
How to Contact: Send complete ms with cover letter which should include previous publication credits, affiliations, a brief bio. Reports in 2-8 weeks on mss. SASE for ms. Photocopied submissions OK. Accepts computer printout submissions. Sample copy for $4.50. Fiction guidelines for #10 SAE and 1 first class stamp.
Payment: Pays in contributor's copies.
Terms: Pays on publication. Acquires first North American serial rights.
Advice: "Quite simply, we choose the best fiction we receive, from reactionary to dangerously experimental. We look for tension, surprise, and careful command of language. We like tightly constructed stories with fully developed characters, written by contributors with an ear for language, rhythms, and sound. This is not a market for hastily written first drafts. Revise and polish your work and read previous issues of *Bluff City* to form an eye for our market."

BLUR, Boston Literary Review, (II), Box 357, W. Somerville MA 02144. (617)625-6087. Editor: Gloria Mindock. Magazine: 5¼ × 13; 24 pages; 70 lb. offset paper; 80 lb. cover. Contemporary poetry and fiction. Semiannually. Estab. 1985. Circ. 500.
Needs: Contemporary, experimental. "Non-mainstream work that has a strong and unique voice and that takes risks with form or content." Receives 50 unsolicited mss/month. Accepts 1-2 mss/issue; 2-4 mss/year. Publishes ms 6 months-1 year after acceptance. Length: 2,500 words maximum. Publishes short shorts. Sometimes critiques rejected mss.
How to Contact: Send complete ms with cover letter. Reports in 2-4 weeks on queries. SASE. Photocopied submissions OK. Sample copy for $4.
Payment: Pays 2 contributor's copies.
Terms: Acquires first North American serial rights. Sends galleys to author.

BOGG, A Magazine of British & North American Writing, (II), Bogg Publications, 422 N. Cleveland St., Arlington VA 22201. (703)243-6019. U.S. Editor: John Elsberg. Magazine: 9 × 16; 64-68 pages; 60 lb. white paper; 60 lb. cover stock; line illustrations. "American and British poetry, prose poems and other experimental short 'fictions,' reviews, and essays on small press." Published 3 times a year. Estab. 1968. Circ. 750.
Needs: Very short experimental and prose poem. "We are always looking for work with British/ Commonwealth themes and/or references." Receives 25 unsolicited fiction mss/month. Accepts 1-2 mss/issue; 3-6 mss/year. Publishes ms 3-12 months after acceptance. Published 50% new writers within the last year. Also publishes literary essays, literary criticism, poetry. Occasionally critiques rejected mss.
How to Contact: Query first or send ms (2-6 pieces) with SASE. Reports in 1 week on queries; 2 weeks on mss. Photocopied submissions OK. Accepts computer printout submissions. Length: 300 words maximum. Sample copy for $3.50 or $4.50 (current issue). Reviews novels and short story collections.
Payment: Pays 2 contributor's copies. Reduced charge for extras.
Terms: Acquires one-time rights.
Advice: "Read magazine first. We are most interested in prose work of experimental or wry nature to supplement poetry."

BONE SAW, (II), (formerly *Brain Dead*), P.O. Box 1492, Taylor MI 48180. Editors: James O'Barr, John Bergin. Magazine: 6¾ × 10¼; 144 pages; 60 lb. bond paper; 60 lb. cover stock; illustrations and photographs; comics. "All kinds of people read *Bone Saw.*"
Needs: Experimental, science fiction, horror, weird stuff, poetry, essays, politics. Receives 15 unsolicited mss/month. Accepts 5-6 mss/issue. Publishes ms 3-7 months after acceptance. Length: 1,500 words average; up to 9,000 words maximum. Also publishes poetry.
How to Contact: Send mss. Reports in 1 month on mss. SASE. Photocopied and reprint submissions OK. Accepts computer printout submissions. Include word count.
Payment: Pays 7-10¢/word.
Terms: Buys one-time rights.
Advice: "I don't really have a set of criteria. I'll print it if it moves me . . . if it's a good work, honest, revealing, well-written, different . . . or just interesting. The manuscripts that seem to stand out are the vicious ones. Pieces that bite. And the experimental work. . . ."

‡BOTH SIDES NOW, An Alternative Journal of New Age/Aquarian Transformations, (II), Free People Press, Rt. 6, Box 28, Tyler TX 75704. (903)592-4263. Editor-in-Chief: Elihu Edelson. Magazine: 8½ × 11; 8-10 pages; bond paper and cover; b&w line illustrations; photos (screened for newsprint). Estab. 1969.
Needs: Material with new-age slant, including fantasy, feminist, humor/satire ("including political"), psychic/supernatural, spiritual, religious/inspirational, ecological fables, parables. "No violence (including S/M), prurience (pornography), or fascistic views." Length: "about 4 magazine pages at most." Also publishes some poetry. Occasionally critiques rejected mss with "brief note."
How to Contact: Send complete ms with SASE. Simultaneous submissions, photocopied submissions and previously published work OK. Reports in 3 months on mss. Sample copy for $1. Reviews "New Age and counterculture fiction."
Payment: Pays 6 contributor's copies. Charges $1 each for extra copies.
Terms: "Authors retain rights."
Advice: "Heed our editorial interests."

BOULEVARD, (III), Opojaz Inc., Suite 2208, 2400 Chestnut St., Philadelphia PA 19103. (215)561-1723. Editor: Richard Burgin. Magazine: 5½ × 8½; 150-220 pages; excellent paper; high-quality cover stock; illustrations; photos. *"Boulevard* aspires to publish the best contemporary fiction, poetry and essays we can print." Published 3 times/year. Estab. 1986. Circ. about 2,500.
Needs: Contemporary, experimental, literary, prose poem. Does not want to see "anything whose first purpose is not literary." Receives over 400 mss/month. Buys about 6 mss/issue. Publishes ms less than 1 year after acceptance. Agented fiction ⅓-¼. Length: 5,000 words average; 10,000 words maximum. Publishes short shorts. Published work by Madison Smartt Bell, Francine Prose, Alice Adams. Sometimes critiques rejected mss and recommends other markets.
How to Contact: Send complete ms with cover letter. Reports in 2 weeks on queries; 2 months or less on mss. SASE. Simultaneous and photocopied submissions OK. Accepts computer printout submissions. Sample copy for $6 and SAE with 5 first class stamps.
Payment: Pays $50-200; contributor's copies; charges for extras.
Terms: Pays on publication for first North American serial rights. Does not send galleys to author unless requested.
Advice: "Master your own piece of emotional real estate. Be patient and persistent."

MARION ZIMMER BRADLEY'S FANTASY MAGAZINE, Box 249, Berkeley CA 94701. (415)601-9000. Editor and Publisher: Marion Zimmer Bradley. Magazine: 8½ × 11; 64 pages; 60 lb. text paper; 10 lb. cover stock; b&w interior and 4 color cover illustrations. "Fantasy only; strictly family oriented." Quarterly.
Needs: Adventure, contemporary, fantasy, humor/satire, suspense/mystery and young adult/teen (10-18) (all with fantasy elements). "No avant garde or romantic fantasy. No computer games!" Receives 50-60 unsolicited mss/week. Buys 8-10 mss/issue; 36-40 mss/year. Publishes 3-12 months after acceptance. Agented fiction 5%. Length: 3,000-4,000 words average; 7,000 words maximum. Publishes short shorts.
How to Contact: Send complete ms. SASE. Photocopied submissions OK. Accepts computer printout submissions. Sample copy $3.50. Fiction guidelines for #10 SASE.
Payment: Pays 3-10¢/word; contributor's copies.
Terms: Pays on acceptance. $25 kill fee "if held 12 months or more." Buys first North American serial rights.
Advice: "If I want to finish reading it—I figure other people will too. A manuscript stands out if I care whether the characters do well, if it has a rythm. Make sure it has characters I will know *you* care about. If you don't care about them, how do you expect me to?"

‡BRAVO MUNDO NUEVO, Alternative Literature for a Brave New World, (I, II), La Sombra Publishing, P.O. Box 285, Hondo TX 78861. (512)426-5453. Editor: E.D. Santos. Newsletter: 8½ × 11; 8 pages; 70 lb. paper; illustrations. Lesser known fiction writers are encouraged to submit to *BMN*. Fantasy, science fiction, social awareness type material are most welcome." Quarterly. Estab. 1990.
Needs: Fantasy, science fiction, "social awareness" material. No "how-to; editorials; any racist material; any socially or environmentally flammable material." Publishes annual special fiction issue. Receives 5 unsolicited mss/month. Accepts 5 mss/issue; 20 mss/year. Publishes ms 3-6 after acceptance. Recently published work by Angela deHoyos. Length: 600 words preferred; 20 words minimum; 1,200 words maximum. Publishes short shorts. Sometimes critiques rejected mss and recommends other markets.
How to Contact: Send complete ms with cover letter. Cover letter should include previous publications, if any, length of experience in writing, preferred genre of writing, current address and phone number. Reports in 2 months on mss. SASE. Simultaneous, photocopied and reprint submissions OK. Accepts computer printout submissions. Sample copy free. Fiction guidelines for #10 SAE and 1 first class stamp.
Payment: Pays subscription to magazine.
Terms: Acquires one-time rights.
Advice: Looks for "originality and a gift for spontaneous storytelling as the principal criteria in choosing fiction for this publication. A manuscript need not be 'polished' to stand out; in point of fact, the more unrefined, the more authentic and genuinely appealing it is."

BREAKTHROUGH!, (II), Aardvark Enterprises, 204 Millbank Dr. S.W., Calgary, Alberta T2Y 2H9 Canada. (403)256-4639. Editor: J. Alvin Speers. Magazine: 5½ × 8½; 52 pages; bond paper; color cardstock cover; illustrations. "Up-beat, informative and entertaining reading for general audience— articles, short stories, poetry, fillers and cartoons. General interest—popular with writers and readers

Close-up

Richard Burgin
Editor
Boulevard

"Originality" is what Richard Burgin looks for when he reads manuscripts for *Boulevard*. As editor of this highly respected magazine—winner of numerous awards for poetry, essays and stories—he is also dedicated to publishing fiction of literary merit.

Burgin defines originality *not* as "stylistic tricks where the writer is intently trying to write every sentence in an odd, bizarre, catchy or so-called avant-garde way." That, he says, becomes stale in a short time. Rather, he explains, "Originality is really the character or vision of the writer, the tone of voice of the writer, as it shines through in the totality of his or her work. It's an outlook on life and the power to express that singular, unique outlook."

Original writers, he says, always have their own "emotional real estate"—a territory that is uniquely their own and that they are uniquely qualified to write about by virtue of its coming from their own experience. "And I would advise writers who submit to *Boulevard* or to any magazine to discover that territory that is their own, to cultivate it, to perfect it and then to share it."

Writers must first realize what they have to say and contribute to literature is not that which is merely a carbon copy of Raymond Carver or Bobbie Ann Mason or whoever may be in vogue at the time, Burgin adds. They must recognize their strengths and know what they can and can't do. "Once they recognize their limitations and focus on what they can do, then they're on their way to being original."

Burgin, who is also an associate professor of humanities at Drexel University, has obviously found his own "emotional real estate." Winner of two Pushcart Prizes for fiction, he is the author of two collections of short fiction published by University of Illinois Press, *Man without Memory* (1989) and *Private Fame* (1991). His stories have appeared in *TriQuarterly*, *Kansas Quarterly*, *Mississippi Review* and numerous other literary magazines. Burgin also reviews contemporary fiction for several publications including *The New York Times* Book Review and *The Philadelphia Inquirer* and has won critical acclaim for his nonfiction books as well, *Conversations with Jorge Luis Borges* and *Conversations with Isaac Bashevis Singer*.

Speaking as an editor, Burgin discusses the process by which he selects manuscripts: "It's subjective, of course. I'm astonished sometimes at material being published by big commercial publishers and work that's submitted to me that I don't think is literature, and yet obviously there are other people who do. So this is not a science. This is where you get into the always subjective reactions of an editor."

Burgin sees this subjectivity as a limitation in one sense, but he still thinks it's preferable to "art by committee where you don't get a reflection of anybody's sensibilities, where anything that takes a chance or is an emotional extreme gets thrown away and everything becomes a compromise and the least effective thing is rewarded. So, basically, *Boulevard* does reflect the work that I like, that touches me, that I identify with."

A typical issue of the magazine contains a mix of about eight or nine stories, an interview, two essays and 25-30 poems. Each year they receive well over 5,000 submissions and Burgin, of course, isn't the only person who reads manuscripts. But those that are passed along to him receive his careful attention. "Sometimes I take longer than I really want to or should because I agonize over pieces trying to figure out whether they fit or not." Sometimes he gets involved in a story and makes suggestions for revisions, but a lot of factors are involved in that decision. "Some writers I feel more comfortable doing that with than others. Editors have suggested revisions to me and sometimes it hurts initially, but I'm grateful later. Sometimes I see a better way, but on some pieces I might be more reticent about making suggestions."

Boulevard doesn't publish theme issues because Burgin feels they shut out too many readers and writers. Also, he feels that theme issues can become a form of pseudocreativity on the part of editors. "There are some exceptions, of course," he says.

His first concern is to publish "the best contemporary fiction whose first purpose is literary," Burgin says. "If something is good and interesting and moving and serious in intent—it can be hilariously funny—it will find its way into our pages. We try to be eclectic in the best sense of the word. We're not trying to promote any particular school of poetry or fiction."

Boulevard has published works by such contemporary authors as Joyce Carol Oates, John Updike, Isaac Bashevis Singer and Octavio Paz. However, Burgin says, they are "absolutely" interested in publishing new writers. Although quite a few of *Boulevard's* fiction manuscripts come through agents, many writers published in the magazine submitted their own work.

Burgin doesn't have a fixed quota for manuscripts so he doesn't feel compelled to take a certain number of submissions. He always has enough material on hand for another issue beyond what's already been accepted, so it's more a case of trying to catch up with the backlog yet he doesn't like to make writers wait too long. "Having that backlog, however, gives me security," he says, "so I don't get into a situation, which I never have, of feeling I have to accept something to fill up a certain number of pages. We don't have an exact number of pages and I would never do that. I have to believe that each thing is worthy of publication."

—Pat Beusterien

❝I would advise writers . . . to discover that territory that is their own, to cultivate it, to perfect it and then to share it. ❞

—Richard Burgin

for information and entertainment." Quarterly. Estab. 1982. Circ. 200+.

Needs: Adventure, historical (general), humor/satire, literary, regional, religious/inspirational, romance (contemporary, historical, young adult), suspense/mystery. "No pornography, uncouth language, crudely suggestive, gay or lesbian." Receives 25 mss/month. Accepts 8-10 mss/issue; 30-40 mss/year. "Publication time varies with available space, held for season, etc." Length: 1,500 words; 500 words minimum; 2,500 words maximum. Publishes short shorts. Also publishes literary essays, literary criticism, poetry. Sometimes critiques rejected mss.

How to Contact: Subscribe, or buy sample and submit ms. Include brief bio. Reports in 1 week on queries. SASE. Simultaneous, photocopied and reprint submissions OK. Accepts computer printouts. Sample copy $5. Fiction guidelines for #10 SAE, IRC, Canadian 46¢ stamp, or $1 U.S. quite acceptable. Reviews novels or short story collections by subscribers only.

Payment: By readers' vote small cash honorarium for best 3 items each issue, plus 4th place Honorable Mention Certificate.

Terms: Acquires one-time rights.

Advice: "We look for quality in line with editorial guidelines, clarity of presentation of story or information message. Be familiar with our style and theme—do not submit inappropriate material. We treat submittors with respect and courtesy."

THE BRIDGE, A Journal of Fiction & Poetry, (II), The Bridge, 14050 Vernon St., Oak Park MI 48237. Editor: Jack Zucker. Fiction Editor: Helen Zucker. Magazine: 5½ × 8½; 120 pages; 60 lb. paper; heavy cover. "Fiction and poetry for a literary audience." Semiannually. Estab. 1990.

Needs: Ethnic, feminist, humor/satire, mainstream, regional. Receives 40 unsolicited mss/month. Buys 5-7 mss/issue; 10-14 mss/year. Publishes ms within one year of acceptance. Length: 3,000 words average; 7,500 words maximum. Publishes short shorts. Length: 1,000 words. Also publishes some short essays, some criticism, poetry.

How to Contact: Send complete manuscript with cover letter. Reports in 1 week on queries; 2 months on mss. SASE. Photocopied submissions OK. Accepts computer printout submissions. Sample copy for $4 ($5 for 2). Reviews novels and short story collections.

Payment: Pays in contributor's copies.

Terms: Acquires first North American serial rights.

Advice: "Don't give us fiction intended for a popular/commercial market—we'd like to get 'real literature.'"

BROOMSTICK, A National, Feminist Periodical by, for, and About Women Over Forty, (II, IV), 3543 18th St. #3, San Francisco CA 94110. (415)552-7460. Editors: Mickey Spencer and Polly Taylor. Magazine: 8½ × 11; 40 pages; line drawings. "Our first priority in selecting and editing material is that it convey clear images of women over 40 that are positive, that it show the author's commitment against the denigration of midlife and long-living women which pervades our culture, and that it offer us alternatives which will make our lives better." For "women over 40 interested in being part of a network which will help us all develop understanding of our life situations and acquire the skills to improve them." Quarterly. Estab. 1978. Circ. 3,000.

Needs: Feminist experience in political context, old women, age, and agism, humor, ethnic. No mss of "romantic love, nostalgic, saccharine acceptance, by or about men or young women." Receives 10 unsolicited fiction mss/month. Accepts 2-3 mss/issue; 20 mss/year. Published work by Astra, Wilma Elizabeth McDaniel, Ruth Harriet Jacobs; published new writers within the last year. Recommends magazine subscription before sending ms. Critiques rejected mss.

How to Contact: Send complete mss with 2 SASEs. Simultaneous, photocopied and previously published submissions OK. Accepts computer printout submissions. Reports in 3 months on queries and mss. Sample copy for $5. Writer's guidelines for 50¢ or SASE.

Market conditions are constantly changing! If you're still using this book and it is 1993 or later, buy the newest edition of Novel & Short Story Writer's Market at your favorite bookstore or order directly from Writer's Digest Books.

Payment: Pays 2 contributor's copies; $5 charge for extras.
Advice: "Don't use stereotypes to establish character. Give protagonists names, not just roles (e.g. 'mother'). Avoid using "you," which sounds preachy. Read our editorials."

‡**BROWNBAG PRESS, (II)**, Hyacinth House Publications, 290 Wiles St., Morgantown WV 26505. Editors: Shannon Frach, Randal Seyler. Magazine: Digest-sized; 30-40 pages; 20 lb. paper; cardstock cover; black & white illustrations. "*Brownbag Press* is a digest of poetry, fiction, and experimental writing that is seeking avant-garde, forceful, and often bizarre literature for a literate, adult audience that is bored to death with the standard offerings of modern mainstream fiction." Semiannually. Estab. 1989. Circ. 150.
Needs: Condensed/excerpted novels, contemporary, erotica, ethnic, experimental, feminist, gay, horror, humor/satire, lesbian, literary, mainstream, prose poem, psychic/supernatural/occult, translations, "Punk, psychedelia, fringe culture, Dada, surrealism, postmodern. A sense of dark humor is definitely a plus. No religious, romance, or criminally boring mainstream. No tedious formula fiction. No yuppie angst. Nothing saccharine. No obvious limitations—don't write like Bukowski unless, of course, you happen to be Bukowski." Receives 15-25 unsolicited ms/month. Buys 2-4 ms/issue. Publishes ms 3-6 months after acceptance. Recently published work by Brooks Caruthers, Bob Black, and Gregory Nymon. Length: 100-5,000 words. Publishes short shorts. Length: 100 words or longer. Sometimes critiques rejected mss and recommends other markets.
How to Contact: Send complete ms with or without cover letter. "Cover letter not necessary—we often find them pompous and annoying. Don't use a cover letter to brag about how great you are; if you're that good, I guarantee we'll have heard of you." Reports in 2 weeks on queries; 1-4 months on ms. SASE. Simultaneous, photocopied and reprint submissions OK. Accepts computer prinout submissions. Sample copy for $3. Fiction guidelines for #10 SAE and 1 first class stamp.
Payment: Pays in contributor's copies; charges for extras.
Terms: Acquires one-time rights.
Advice: "A manuscript stands out when it is well-executed in both narrative content and grammatical precision. Simple errors mar the bulk of the mss we receive; this hardly speaks well for the individuals who submit them. This is not to suggest that we're elitist grammarians; we're not. Even the most subversive, bomb-hurling radical should know the difference between too/to, it's/its, and your/you're, not to mention other cloying habits like using "alot" when there is no such word. Other problems include bungling, inept dialogue, wretchedly handled dialect pieces, and plain misspelling. If you submit here, we presume that you are already a writer; we have neither the time nor the inclination to teach you the basics of your craft. In short, brush up your dialogue and grammar, write straight from the heart, and send your work our way! We really are quite open to beginning writers as well as 'name' writers."

BVI-PACIFICA NEWSLETTER, (I), Tahuti/Quetzlcoatl Press, Box 45792, Seattle WA 98145-0792. (206)547-2364 or 547-2202. Editor: Yael Dragwyla. Magazine: 5½ × 8½; 32-36 pages; 20 lb. paper; 60 lb. cover; illustrations; some photographs. "Theme: Breaking new trails in the Inner Planes (world of the mind)." Quarterly. Plans special fiction issue. Estab. 1985. Circ. 200+.
Needs: Erotica, experimental, fantasy, horror, humor/satire, psychic/supernatural/occult, science fiction, dementia, serialized/excerpted novel, suspense/mystery, SubGenius. "No romance, children's, New Ager or Norman Vincent Peale-type inspirational, anything saccharine." Receives 1-2 unsolicited mss/month. Accepts 6-12 mss/issue; 6-24 mss/year. Publishes ms 3 months-1 year after acceptance. Length: 450 words preferred; 100 words minimum; 1,000 words maximum. Also publishes poetry. Sometimes critiques rejected mss and recommends other markets.
How to Contact: Send complete ms with cover letter. Reports in 1-4 weeks. SASE. Simultaneous, photocopied and reprint submissions OK. Accepts computer printout submissions. Sample copy for $3.50. All checks, M.O.s *must* be made out to "Yael Dragwyla."
Payment: Pays in contributor's copies.
Terms: Acquires first North American serial rights.
Advice: "Write with your heart as well as your head. As the state of the world today is both horrifying and disgusting in many places and respects, often the most honest and gripping fiction and the best humor deals with the terror and anger this provokes, head-on. We want fiction, humor, poetry and graphics that free up and change the mind, so that the actions underlaid by mind will change, and in the changing, maybe open up new cracks in the Cosmic Egg."

BYLINE, (II), Box 130596, Edmond OK 73013. (405)348-5591. Editor-in-Chief: Marcia Preston. Managing Editor: Kathryn Fanning. Monthly magazine "aimed at encouraging and motivating all writers toward success, with special information to help new writers." Estab. 1981.
Needs: Literary, suspense/mystery and general fiction. Especially like stories with a literary or writing twist. Receives 75-100 unsolicited fiction mss/month. Accepts 1 ms/issue, 12 mss/year. Recently published work by Kathleen Larson Woodall and Michael Bugeja. Published many new writers within the last year. Length: 4,000 words maximum; 1,000 words minimum. Also publishes poetry.
How to Contact: Send complete ms with SASE. Photocopied submissions OK. "For us, no cover letter is needed." Reports in 2-6 weeks. Publishes ms an average of 3 months after acceptance. Sample copy, guidelines and contest list for $3.
Payment: Pays $50 and 2 contributor's copies.
Terms: Pays on acceptance for first North American rights.
Advice: "We're very open to new writers. Submit a well-written, professionally prepared ms with SASE. No erotica or senseles violence; otherwise, we'll consider most any theme. We also sponsor short story and poetry contests."

CALLALOO, A Journal of Afro-American and African Arts and Letters, (II, IV), Dept. of English, University of Virginia, Charlottesville VA 22903. (804)924-6637. Editor: Charles H. Rowell. Magazine: 7×10; 200 pages. Scholarly magazine. Quarterly. Plans special fiction issue in future. Estab. 1976. Circ. 1,000.
Needs: Contemporary, ethnic (black culture), feminist, historical (general), humor/satire, literary, prose poem, regional, science fiction, serialized/excerpted novel, translations. Accepts 3-5 mss/issue; 10-20 mss/year. Length: no restrictions.
How to Contact: Submit complete ms and cover letter with name and address. Reports on queries in 2 weeks; 2-3 months on mss. Simultaneous and photocopied submissions OK. Previously published work accepted "occasionally." Accepts computer printout submissions. Sample copy $5.
Payment: Pays in contributor's copies.
Terms: Acquires all rights. Sends galleys to author.

CALLIOPE, (II, IV), Creative Writing Program, Roger Williams College, Bristol RI 02809. (401)254-3217. Co-ordinating Editor: Martha Christina. Magazine: $5\frac{1}{2} \times 8\frac{1}{2}$; 40-56 pages; 50 lb. offset paper; vellum or 60 lb. cover stock; occasional illustrations and photos. "We are an eclectic little magazine publishing contemporary poetry, fiction, and occasionally interviews." Semiannually. Estab. 1977. Circ. 300.
Needs: Literary, contemporary, experimental/innovative. "We try to include at least 2 pieces of fiction in each issue." Receives approximately 10-20 unsolicited fiction mss each month. Does not read mss mid-March to mid-August. Published new writers within the last year. Length: 3,750 words. Publishes short shorts under 20 pages. Critiques rejected mss when there is time.
How to Contact: Send complete ms with SASE. Reports immediately or up to 3 months on mss. Sample copy $1.
Payment: Pays 2 contributor's copies and one year's subscription beginning with following issue.
Terms: Rights revert to author on publication.
Advice: "We are not interested in reading anyone's very first story. If the piece is good, it will be given careful consideration. Reading a sample copy of *Calliope* is recommended. Let the characters of the story tell their own story; we're very often (painfully) aware of the writer's presence. Episodic is fine; story need not (for our publication) have traditional beginning, middle and end."

‡**CALYX, A Journal of Art & Literature by Women, (II)**, Calyx, Inc., P.O. Box B, Corvallis OR 97339. (503)753-9384. Managing Editor: Margarita Donnelly. Editors: Rebecca Gordon, Cheryl McLean, Catherine Holdorf, Linda Varsell Smith, Beverly McFarland. Magazine: 7×8; 128 pages per single issue, 250 per double; 60 lb. coated matte stock paper; 10 pt. chrome coat cover; original art. Publishes prose, poetry, art, essays, interviews and critical and review articles. "*Calyx* editors are seeking innovative and literary works of exceptional quality." Biannually. Estab. 1976. Circ. 3,000.
Needs: Accepts 3-5 fiction mss/issue, 9-15 mss/year. Receives approximately 300 unsolicited fiction mss each month. Published works by Ruthann Robson, Shirley Sikes, S.C. Wisenberg; published new writers within the last year. Length: 5,000 words maximum. Also publishes literary essays, literary criticism, poetry.

How to Contact: Send ms with SASE and biographical notes. Reads mss only from March 1-April 15 and October 1-November 15 each year. Submit only during these periods. Reports in up to 6 months on mss. Publishes ms an average of 4 months after acceptance. Sample copy $8 plus $1.25 postage. Reviews novels and short story collections.
Payment: Pays in copies.
Advice: Most mss are rejected because "the writers are not familiar with *Calyx*—writers should read *Calyx* and be familiar with the publication."

CANADIAN AUTHOR & BOOKMAN, (II), Canadian Authors Association, Suite 500, 275 Slater St., Ottawa, Ontario K1P 5H9 Canada. (613)233-2846. FAX: (613)235-8237. Editor: Gordon Symons. Magazine: 8½×11; 32 pages; illustrations; photos. "Craft magazine for Canadian writers, publishing articles that tell how to write and where to sell. We publish half a dozen poems and one short story per issue as well as the craft articles. We aim at the beginning or newly emerging writer." Quarterly. Estab. 1921. Circ. 4,000.
Needs: Contemporary, humor/satire, literary. "Will not accept writing for children or 'young' adult market." Receives 100-200 unsolicited mss/year. Buys 8-10 mss/issue, 30-40 mss/year. Publishes ms 3-6 months after acceptance. Published new writers within the last year. Length: 2,500 words average; 2,000 words minimum; 3,000 words maximum. Also publishes poetry. Occasionally recommends other markets.
How to Contact: Send complete ms with cover letter, which should include introduction and brief bio. Reports in 1-2 weeks on queries; 1-2 months on mss. SASE. Photocopied submissions OK. Accepts computer printout submissions. Sample copy $5.50, 9×12 SAE and IRC. Fiction guidelines #10 SAE and IRC.
Payment: "Our magazine publishes one short-fiction piece per issue, which receives the Okanagan Short Fiction Award of $125 Canadian funds." Pays 1 contributor's copy.
Terms: Pays on publication for first North American serial rights.
Advice: "We are looking for originality, flair and imaginative work. The writer's strategy is examined from the overall structure, to the rise and fall of the sentences to the placement of the punctuation."

CANADIAN FICTION MAGAZINE, (II,IV), Box 946, Station F, Toronto, Ontario M4Y 2N9 Canada. Editor: Geoffrey Hancock. Magazine: 6×9; 148-300 pages; book paper; overweight cover stock; 16-32 page portfolio. "This magazine is a quarterly anthology devoted exclusively to the contemporary creative writing of writers and artists in Canada and Canadians living abroad. Fiction only, no poetry. The ideal reader of *CFM* is a writer or somebody interested in all the modes, manners, voices, and conventions of contemporary fiction." Quarterly. Estab. 1971. Circ. 1,800.
Needs: Literary. "Theme, style, length and subject matter are at the discretion of the author. The only requirement is that the work be of the highest possible literary standard." Buys 10 mss/issue, 35 mss/year. Publishes short shorts. Published new writers within the last year.
How to Contact: *Canadian authors only.* Send complete ms with SASE or IRC. Reports in 6 weeks on mss. Publishes ms up to 18 months after acceptance. "It is absolutely crucial that three or four issues be read. We sell back issues up to 1976 for $3; current issue $9.95 (postage included). Some double issues are $15. CFM Writers Kit: Guidelines, reading list and selected back issues available ($60 resource) for only $30 and $2.10 GST." (Canadian funds.)
Payment: Pays $10/page (Canadian) plus one-year subscription.
Terms: Pays on publication for first North American serial rights. Sends galleys to author.
Advice: "*CFM* publishes Canada's leading writers as well as those in early stages of their careers. A wide knowledge of contemporary literature (in English and in translation) plus expertise in creative writing, modern fiction theories, current Canadian literature, and the innovative short story would be of great help to a potential contributor. *CFM* is an independent journal not associated with any academic institution. Each issue includes French-Canadian fiction in translation, interviews with well-known Canadian writers on the techniques of their fiction, forums and manifestoes on the future of fiction, as well as art work and reviews. $500 annual prize for the best story submitted in either French or English. Contributors might study anthology spin-offs, such as *Magic Realism; Illusion: Fables, Fantasies* and *Metafictions; Shoes and Shit: Stories for Pedestrians; Canadian Writers at Work: Interviews* or *Singularities: Physics and Fiction.*"

‡**THE CAPILANO REVIEW, (II),** 2055 Purcell Way, North Vancouver, British Columbia V7J 3H5 Canada. (604)984-1712. Editor: Robert Sherrin. Magazine: 6×9; 80-100 pages. Magazine of "fresh, innovative art and literature for literary/artistic audience." Three issues yearly. Estab. 1972. Circ. 1,000.

Needs: Contemporary, experimental, literary and prose poem. Receives 30 unsolicited mss/month. Accepts 1-2 mss/issue; 4 mss/year. Recently published works by Bill Gaston, Sharon Thesen and Myrna Kostash. Published "lots" of new writers within the last three years. Length: 2,000-6,000 words. Publishes short shorts. Also publishes literary essays. Occasionally recommends other markets.
How to Contact: Send complete ms with cover letter. Photocopied submissions OK. Sample copy for $8 (Canadian).
Payment: Pays $120 maximum ($30/page), 2 contributor's copies and one year subscription.
Terms: Pays on publication.

THE CARIBBEAN WRITER, (IV), The University of the Virgin Islands, RR 02, Box 10,000—Kingshill, St. Croix, Virgin Islands 00850. (809)778-0246. Editor: Erika Smilowitz-Waters. Magazine: 6×9; 130 pages; 60 lb. paper; glossy cover stock; illustrations and photos. "*The Caribbean Writer* is an international magazine with a Caribbean focus. The Caribbean should be central to the work, or the work should reflect a Caribbean heritage, experience or perspective." Annually. Estab. 1987. Circ. 1,500.
Needs: Contemporary, historical (general), humor/satire, literary, mainstream and prose poem. Receives 300 unsolicited mss/year. Accepts 10 mss/issue. Length: 300 words minimum; 3,750 words maximum. Also accepts poetry.
How to Contact: Send complete ms with cover letter. "Blind submissions only. Send name, address and title of ms on separate sheet. Title only on ms. Mss will not be considered unless this procedure is followed." Reports "once a year." SASE. Simultaneous and photocopied submissions OK. Accepts computer printout submissions. Sample copy for $7 and $2 postage. Fiction guidelines for SASE.
Payment: Pays 1 contributor's copy. Annual prizes for best story ($400); for best poem ($250).
Terms: Acquires one-time rights.

CAROLINA QUARTERLY, (II), Greenlaw Hall CB #3520, University of North Carolina, Chapel Hill NC 27599-3520. (919)962-0244. Editor-in-Chief: David Kellogg. Fiction Editor: Joshua Pate. Literary journal: 90-100 pages; illustrations; photos. "Fiction, poetry, graphics and some reviews, for that audience—whether academic or not—with an interest in the best in poetry and short fiction." Triannually. Estab. 1948. Circ. 1,000.
Needs: No pornography. Receives 150-200 unsolicited fiction mss/month. Buys 5-7 mss/issue; 15-20 mss/year. Publishes ms an average of 10 weeks after acceptance. Published work by Ian MacMillan, Jessica Weber, Rick Bass. Published new writers within the last year. Length: 7,000 words maximum; no minimum. Also publishes short shorts, literary essays, poetry. Occasionally critiques rejected mss.
How to Contact: Send complete ms with cover letter (no synopsis of story) and SASE to fiction editor. Photocopied submissions OK. Reports in 2-4 months. Sample copy for $4; Writer's guidelines for SASE and $1 postage. Reviews novels and short story collections.
Payment: Pays $15/printed page; 2 contributor's copies.
Terms: Pays on publication for first North American serial rights.
Advice: "We publish a good many unsolicited stories and yes, I love publishing a new writer for the first time; *CQ* is a market for newcomer and professional alike. Write 'Fiction Editor' on envelope of submitted manuscript. Keep story to decent length—it's hard to publish very long stories. Also—read what gets published in the journal/magazine you're interested in. Write the kind of story you would like to read. Make your packet look professional yet modest."

CAROUSEL LITERARY ARTS MAGAZINE, (II), Room 217, University Centre, University of Guelph, Guelph, Ontario N1G 2W1 Canada. Editors: Michael Carbert, Shirley Senoff. Magazine: 5½×8½; 80 pages; illustrations and photographs. Annually. Estab. 1985. Circ. 500.
Needs: Adventure, contemporary, ethnic, experimental, fantasy, feminist, gay, horror, humor/satire, lesbian, literary, prose poem, religious/inspirational, romance, science fiction, sports, suspense/mystery and western. Receives 5 unsolicited mss each month. Accepts 5-6 mss per issue. Publishes ms 1-2 months after acceptance. Published work by Leon Rooke and J.J. Steinfield. Length: 3,000 words maximum. Also publishes literary essays, literary criticism, poetry.
How to Contact: Send complete ms. Include bio with manuscript. Reports in 2 weeks on queries; 2 months on mss. SASE. Simultaneous and photocopied submission OK. Accepts computer printout submissions. Sample copy $3.50 (Canadian) and 2 first class stamps. Fiction guidelines for SAE.
Payment: Pays in contributor's copies.
Terms: Acquires one-time rights.
Advice: "We want work which takes chances in style, point of view, characterization. We are open to new writers."

‡**CATALYST, A Magazine of Heart & Mind, (II, IV)**, Catalyst, Inc. #2330, 34 Peachtree St., Atlanta GA 30303. (404)730-5785. Editor: Pearl Cleage. Magazine: 8 × 11; 130 pages; newsprint; photographs. "Seeks to stimulate the worldwide flow of ideas. Publishes fiction, drama, short stories, poetry and criticism for a general audience." Semiannually. Estab. 1986. Circ. 5,000.
Needs: Open. Publishes annual special fiction issue. Receives 100-200 unsolicited mss/month. Buys 75-100 mss/issue. Publishes ms 6 months after acceptance. Agented fiction 1%. Recently published work by Lois Lyles, Zaron Burnett, Jr. Length: 3,000 words maximum. Publishes short shorts. Recommends other markets.
How to Contact: Query first. Reports in 1 week on queries; 6 months on mss. SASE. Simultaneous submissions OK. Sample copy for $2.50 and 9 × 12 SAE. Fiction guidelines for #10 SAE.
Payment: Pays $10-200, contributor's copies. Charges for extras.
Terms: Pays on publication. Rights remain with author.
Advice: "Attend workshops; join a writing organization; read a variety of different writers' works; learn good writing skills; and seek advice from established writers."

CATHEDRAL OF INSANITY, (II), 514 10th Ave., Lancaster CA 93534. Editor: Julie Luce. Magazine: 5½ × 8½; 120 pages; illustrations. "The theme is mainly humor with a bit of seriousness. Publishes short stories and poetry for underground intellectuals." Published irregularly. Estab. 1988. Circ. 50.
Needs: Contemporary, experimental, humor/satire, psychic/supernatural/occult, serialized/excerpted novel and strange personal experiences. "I would like something with an underground feel. Nothing mainstream." Accepts 1 ms/issue; 2 mss/year. Publishes ms within 1-2 months of acceptance. Publishes short shorts. Sometimes critiques rejected mss.
How to Contact: Query with clips of published work. Reports in 2 weeks. Simultaneous and reprint submissions OK. Accepts computer printout submissions. Sample copy for $2 — cash or check payable to Julie Luce. Fiction guidelines free.
Payment: No payment.
Advice: "Send some work. My magazine is eager for material. Short-shorts are best, nothing over 3 pages. Something humorous/satirical (I am fond of word play) or unnatural (drug experiences) is a good thing to send."

CEILIDH, An Informal Gathering for Story & Song, (II), Box 6367, San Mateo CA 94403. (415)591-9902. Editors: Patrick S. Sullivan and Perry Oei. Associate Editor: Denise E. Sullivan. Magazine: 5½ × 8½; 32-64 pages; illustrations. "We are a growing literary magazine looking for literary fiction, drama and poetry." Quarterly. Two issues annually devoted to fiction. Estab. 1981. Circ. 500.
Needs: Experimental, literary, prose poem, science fiction, serialized/excerpted novel and translations. No romance, juvenile, erotica, preschool or young adult. Receives 25 unsolicited mss/month. Accepts 5 mss/issue; 10-12 mss/year. Published work by Karlton Kelm and Anne Brashler; published new writers within the last year. Length: 3,000 words average; 6,000 words maximum. Also publishes short shorts. Will consider literary essays. Sometimes recommends other markets.
How to Contact: Send complete ms with SASE. Reports in 6-8 weeks. Photocopied submissions OK. Accepts computer printout submissions. Publishes ms 2-3 months after acceptance. Sample copy $5. Fiction guidelines for #10 SAE and 1 first class stamp.
Payment: Pays 2 contributor's copies; $3 charge for extras.
Terms: "At this point we cannot pay for every piece, but we occasionally sponsor a contest." Acquires one-time rights.
Advice: "We lean toward experimental, more serious fiction, with a strong sense of voice. Send a neat manuscript with a descriptive cover letter, SASE. Fiction is a good voice for our times. Poetry is also, but people seem to enjoy a short story over a long poem."

‡**CENTER MAGAZINE, For Innovative Writing**, 307 Johnson St., Santa Fe NM 87501. (505)986-1774. Editor: Carol Bergé. Magazine: 8½ × 11. "Innovative fiction only for a highly well-read and literate; avant garde audience." Published irregularly. "Depends on grants; 13 issues published so far." Estab. 1970. Circ. 4,000.
Needs: Condensed/excerpted novel; contemporary (but not "new age"), erotica, experimental, humor/satire, prose poem, translations. "No crystals, gurdjieff, mythos, first-person narratives (unless clearly not from point of view of the writer). No journals, poetry or kid-lit of any kind." Publishes annual special fiction issue. Receives 3-10 unsolicited mss/month. Publishes ms 4 months-1 year after acceptance. Recently published work by Miriam Sagan and Carl Ginsburg. Publishes short shorts. Length: ½-1 page. Sometimes critiques rejected mss (if paid $25).

How to Contact: Send complete manuscript with cover letter. Reading fee of $10 for longer works (5 pages or more), $5 for 2 pages. Reports in 2 weeks on queries; 3 weeks on mss. SASE. Sample copy for $6, 9×12 SAE and $1.05 (book rate) postage.
Payment: Pays in contributor's copies; charges for extras.
Terms: Acquires one-time rights. Sends galleys to author.
Advice: Looks for "brilliant, sharp, careful writing-which shows experience and wisdom. A sense of humor and wryness. Very few beginners accepted. Will read and critique. I have taught writing since 1970 and have 21 books of my own published."

CENTRAL PARK, A Journal of the Arts and Social Theory, (II), Neword Productions, Inc. Box 1446, New York NY 10023. (212)362-9151. Editor: Stephen-Paul Martin. Magazine: 7½×10, 100 pages; glossy cover stock; illustrations; photos. Magazine of theoretical essays, poetry, fiction, photos and graphics for intellectual audience. Semiannually. Estab. 1981. Circ. 1,000.
Needs: Contemporary, erotica, ethnic, experimental, feminist, gay, historical (general), lesbian, literary, prose poem, serialized/excerpted novel and translations. Approximately 10% of fiction is agented. Receives 50 unsolicited mss/month. Publishes short shorts of 5-10 pages. Accepts 5 mss/issue; 10 mss/year. Published works by Ron Sukenick, Clarence Major, Dick Higgins. Published new writers within the last year. Usually critiques rejected mss. Sometimes recommends other markets.
How to Contact: "Prospective contributors should order a sample copy before asking us to consider their work." Reports in 2 months. SASE. Simultaneous and photocopied submissions OK. Accepts computer printout submissions. Publishes ms an average of 3 months after acceptance. Sample copy for $7.50.
Payment: Pays 2 contributor's copies; $5 for extras.
Terms: Acquires first rights.
Advice: "Almost all the fiction we publish is formally innovative."

CHAKRA, (I, II), Box 8551, FDR Station, New York NY 10022. Editor: Liz Camps. Magazine; 7×8½; 16-32 pages; illustrations. "Erotica, mysticism, magick, speculative nonfiction/fiction, psychedelia, sf/ fantasy, QBL, philosophy for a new Aeon, cybershamanism, esoteric sociopolitics. Erotica and way-out art especially encouraged." Published irregularly—2 or 3 times/year. Estab. 1988. Circ. "several hundred."
Needs: Condensed/excerpted novel, erotica, experimental, fantasy, feminist, gay, horror, lesbian, literary, prose poem, psychic/supernatural/occult, religious, science fiction, philosophy and socio politics. Receives 12 unsolicited mss/week. Accepts 2-4 mss/issue; 5-15 mss/year. Time between acceptance and publication varies. Published work by George Smyth, Richard Behrens, Lorraine Schein. Length: 4,000 words maximum. Publishes short shorts. Also considers literary essays; publishes poetry. Occasionally critiques rejected mss.
How to Contact: Send complete ms with cover letter. Reports in 3 months. SASE. Simultaneous, photocopied and reprint submissions OK. Accepts computer printout submissions. Sample copy for $2. Fiction guidelines for #10 SAE and 1 first class stamp. Reviews novels and short story collections.
Payment: Pays $5/page plus 1 contributor's copy.
Advice: "Please submit all queries, manuscripts, etc. on *used paper* to encourage amateur recycling. I am seeking *very* original material."

CHALK TALK, (IV), 1550 Mills Road, RR2, Sidney, British Columbia V8L 3S1 Canada. (604)656-1858. Editor: Virginia Lee. Magazine: Pony tabloid-sized; 24 pages; recycled newsprint paper. "Writing by children only for children, ages 5-14." Monthly. Estab. 1988. Circ. 3,600.
Needs: *Children writers only.* Juvenile, young adult. "No war or violence." Publishes mss 1-4 months after acceptance. Length: 200 words preferred. Publishes short shorts. Critiques or comments on rejected mss and recommends other markets.
How to Contact: Send complete ms with cover letter. Reports in 3 months. SASE. (IRCs) Sample copy and fiction guidelines free.
Payment: Pays in contributor's copies.
Terms: Acquires one-time rights. Sponsors occasional contests for children only.

CHAMINADE LITERARY REVIEW, (II), Chaminade Press, 3140 Waialae Ave., Honolulu HI 96816. (808)735-4723. Editor: Loretta Petrie. Magazine: 6×9; 175 pages; 50 lb. white paper; 10 pt. C1S cover; photographs. "Multicultural, particularly Hawaii—poetry, fiction, artwork, criticism, photos, translations for all English-speaking internationals, but primarily Hawaii." Semiannually. Estab. 1987. Circ. 350.

Needs: Excerpted novel, ethnic, experimental, humor/satire, literary, religious/inspirational, translations. "We have published a variety including translations of Japanese writers, a fishing story set in Hawaii, fantasy set along the Amazon, but the major point is they are all 'literary.' No erotica, horror, children's or young adult, confession, lesbian, gay." Receives 8 unsolicited mss/month. Accepts 5-8 mss/issue. Publishes ms 3-6 months after acceptance. "We haven't published short shorts yet, but would depending on quality." Sometimes critiques rejected ms.
How to Contact: Send complete ms with cover letter. Include short contributor's note. Reporting time depends on how long before deadlines of May 15 and December 15. SASE. Photocopied and reprint submissions OK. Accepts computer printout submissions. Sample copy for $3.50.
Payment: Pays subscription to magazine.
Terms: Acquires one-time rights.
Advice: "We look for good writing; appeal for Hawaii audience and writers everywhere. *CLR* was founded to give added exposure to Hawaii's writers, both here and on the mainland, and to juxtapose Hawaii writing, with mainland and international work."

CHAMPAGNE HORROR, Champagne Productions, 2419 Klein Place, Regina, Saskatchewan S4V 1M4 Canada. (306)789-2419. Art Editor: Randy Nakoneshny. Fiction Editor: Cathy Buburuz. Magazine: 8½×11; 60 pages; semi-gloss cover stock; illustrations; photographs. "Psychological, thought-provoking horror fiction, poetry, artwork and photographs for horror fans." Annually. Estab. 1990. Circ. 500+.
Needs: Horror. Receives 50 unsolicited mss/month. Buys approximately 20 mss/issue. Does not read mss January-June. Publishes ms within 6 months after acceptance. Published work by Cliff Burns, Alan Catlin, John-Ivan Palmer, Diana Kemp-Jones. Length: 1,000 average; 300 words minimum; 2,000 words maximum. Publishes short shorts. Length: 500 words. Sometimes critiques rejected mss and recommends other markets.
How to Contact: Send complete manuscript with cover letter and biography. Reports in 3 weeks. SASE. "Send loose (unaffixed) postage or International Reply Coupons as US postage cannot be used in Canada." Photocopied submissions OK. Accepts computer printout submissions. Sample copy $5.95. Fiction guidelines for SAE and 50¢ (unaffixed postage stamps).
Payment: Pays $5-40 (Canadian) and contributor's copies.
Terms: Pays on publication for first rights.
Advice: "If your work contains one or more of the following elements, we want to see it: psychological or thought provoking horror, chilling mystery, a touch of morbid humor, unique situations or locations. Especially interested in the work of established and upcoming artists, writers and poets."

‡CHANGING MEN, Issues in Gender, Sex, & Politics, (II), Feminist Men's Publications, Inc., 306 N. Brooks, Madison WI 53715. (608)246-8006. Editor: Michael Biernbaum. Fiction Editor: Pat Matalucci. Magazine: 8½×11; 60 pages; bond paper; card stock cover; illustrations and photographs. "Issues in gender, sex and politics for pro-feminist men (largely)." Biannual. Estab. 1979. Circ. 5,000.
Needs: Contemporary, erotica, experimental, feminist, gay, humor/satire, lesbian, literary, sports. "Fiction should be pro-feminist or pro-gay/lesbian or deal with issues in leftist/radical politics." Receives 5-10 unsolicited mss/month. Buys 1-2 mss/issue. Publishes ms 6 months to 1 year after acceptance. Recently published work by Bob Shelby, S. Kolankiewicz, Keith Kelly. Length: 1,500-2,000 words preferred; 1,000 words minimum; 4,000 words maximum. Sometimes critiques rejected mss.
How to Contact: Send complete ms with cover letter. Include brief description of work enclosed. Reports in 6 months on mss. SASE. Simultaneous, photocopied submissions OK. Accepts computer printout submissions. Sample copy for $6. Fiction guidelines for SASE.
Payment: Pays contributor's copies.
Terms: Acquires first North American serial rights. Sends galleys to author.
Advice: "Fresh perspectives on feminist, gay/lesbian and political issues. Writer should ideally be familiar with our magazine, know our spheres of interest and know what we have recently published to avoid excessive similarity/duplication."

CHAPTER ONE, For the Unpublished Writer in All of Us, (I), JAB Publishing, Box 4086, Cary NC 27519-4086. Editor: Belinda J. Puchajda. Magazine: 5¼×8; 100-200 pages. "For short stories and poems." Bimonthly. Estab. 1989.
Needs: Adventure, confession, contemporary, erotica, ethnic, experimental, fantasy, feminist, historical (general), horror, humor/satire, juvenile (5-9 years), literary, mainstream, preschool (1-4 years), prose poem, psychic/supernatural/occult, regional, religious/inspirational, romance (contemporary, historical, young adult), science fiction, senior citizen/retirement, sports, suspense/mystery, western,

young adult/teen (10-18 years). "No pornography." Publishes annual special fiction issue. Receives 150-300 unsolicited mss/week. Buys 25-35 mss/issue. Publishes ms 8 months after acceptance. Length: 4,500 words; 100 words minimum; 6,000 maximum. Publishes annual children's special issue. Publishes short shorts. Length: 100 words. Sometimes critiques rejected mss and recommends other markets.

How to Contact: Send complete ms with cover letter. Include biographical information. Reports in 1 month on queries; 2 months on ms. Simultaneous, photocopied submissions OK. Accepts computer printout submissions. Sample copy $1. Fiction guidelines for #10 SAE and 1 first class stamp.

Payment: Pays $30 maximum; contributor's copies.

Terms: Pays on publication for one-time rights.

Advice: "We feel that there is a lot of talent out there, and we want to see it. Whether it be a story from a housewife who never wrote anything before, or a writer who has been writing for years and has never got published. We want to get you in print."

THE CHARITON REVIEW, (II), Northeast Missouri State University, Kirksville MO 63501. (816)785-4499. Editor: Jim Barnes. Magazine: 6×9; 100+ pages; 60 lb. paper; 65 lb. cover stock; photographs on cover. "We demand only excellence in fiction and fiction translation for a general and college readership." Semiannually. Estab. 1975. Circ. 700+.

Needs: Literary, contemporary and translations. Buys 3-5 mss/issue; 6-10 mss/year. Published work by Steve Heller, John Deming, Eve Shelnutt; published new writers within the last year. Length: 3,000-6,000 words. Also publishes literary essays, poetry. Critiques rejected mss when there is time. Sometimes recommends other markets.

How to Contact: Send complete ms with SASE. No book-length mss. Reports in less than 1 month on mss. Publishes ms an average of 6 months after acceptance. Sample copy for $3 with SASE. Reviews novels and short story collections.

Payment: Pays $5/page up to $50 maximum; contributor's copy; $2.50 for extras.

Terms: Pays on publication for first North American serial rights; rights returned on request.

Advice: "Do not ask us for guidelines: the only guidelines are excellence in all matters. Write well and study the publication you are submitting to. We are interested only in the very best fiction and fiction translation. We are not interested in slick material. We do not read photocopies or carbon copies. Know the simple mechanics of submission—SASE, no paper clips, no odd-sized SASE, etc. Know the genre (short story, novella, etc.). Know the unwritten laws."

THE CHATTAHOOCHEE REVIEW, (II), DeKalb College, 2101 Womack Rd., Dunwoody GA 30338. (404)551-3166. Editor: Lamar York. Magazine: 6×9; 150 pages; 70 lb. paper; 80 lb. cover stock; illustrations; photographs. Quarterly. Estab. 1980. Circ. 1,250.

Needs: Contemporary, erotica, experimental, feminist, gay, humor/satire, literary, mainstream, regional and translation. No juvenile, romance, sci-fi. Receives 500 unsolicited mss/month. Accepts 5 mss/issue. Recently published work by Leon Rooke, R.T. Smith; published new writers within the last year. Length: 2,500 words average. Also publishes literary essays, literary criticism, poetry. Sometimes critiques rejected mss and recommends other markets.

How to Contact: Send complete ms with cover letter, which should include sufficient bio for notes on contributors' page. Reports in 6 months. SASE. Photocopied submissions OK. Accepts computer printout submissions. Sample copy for $4. Fiction guidelines printed in magazine. Reviews novels and short story collections.

Payment: Pays in contributor's copies.

Terms: Acquires first rights.

Advice: "Arrange to read magazine before you submit to it."

CHICAGO REVIEW, 5801 S. Kenwood Ave., Chicago IL 60637. Fiction Editor: Andy Winston. Magazine for a highly literate general audience: 6½×9; 96 pages; offset white 60 lb. paper; illustrations; photos. Quarterly. Estab. 1946. Circ. 2,000.

Needs: Literary, contemporary, and especially experimental. Accepts up to 5 mss/issue; 20 mss/year. Receives 80-100 unsolicited fiction mss each month. No preferred length, except will not accept book-length mss. Also publishes literary essays, literary criticism, poetry. Critiques rejected mss "upon request." Sometimes recommends other markets.

How to Contact: Send complete ms with cover letter. SASE. Simultaneous submissions OK. Accepts computer printout submissions. Reports in 4-5 months on mss. Sample copy for $5. Guidelines with SASE. Reviews novels and short story collections. Send books to Book Review Editor.

Payment: Pays 3 contributor's copies and subscription.
Advice: "We look with interest at fiction that addresses subjects inventively, work that steers clear of clichéd treatments of themes. We're always eager to read writing that experiments with language, whether it be with characters' viewpoints, tone or style."

CHIPS OFF THE WRITER'S BLOCK, (I), Box 83371, Los Angeles CA 90083. Editor: Wanda Windham. Newsletter. "Freelancer's forum, the beginner's chance to be published." Bimonthly.
Needs: "We will consider all categories of fiction, as our publication gives writers a chance to be 'critiqued' by fellow writers." No pornographic or offensive material. Published new writers within the last year. "Always" critiques rejected mss.
How to Contact: Submit complete ms. "Cover letters are not necessary. Please note the word count on the first page of the story." Reports in 3 weeks on queries; 1 month on mss. SASE. Considers simultaneous submissions; "prefers" photocopies. Accepts computer printout submissions. Sample copy for $2. Fiction guidelines for #10 SAE and 1 first class stamp.
Payment: Pays in contributor's copies.
Advice: "The editor works directly with the author if editing is necessary or if the story needs to be reworked. The writer's peer group also sends in comments, suggestions, etc., once the story is in print. The comments are discussed in later issues."

‡CHIRICÚ, (IV), Ballantine Hall 849, Indiana University, Bloomington IN 47405. Editor: Edith Báez-Baéz. Fiction Editor: Sean T. Dwyer. "We publish essays, translations, poetry, fiction, reviews, interviews and artwork (illustrations and photos) that are either by or about Hispanics. We have no barriers on style, content or ideology, but would like to see well-written material." Annually. Estab. 1976. Circ. 500.
Needs: Contemporary, ethnic, experimental, fantasy, feminist, humor/satire, literary, mainstream, prose poem, science fiction, serialized/excerpted novel, translations. No fiction that has nothing to do with Hispanics (when not written by one). Recently published work by Ricardo Lindo, Eduardo Galeano; published new writers within the last year. Length: 7,000 words maximum; 3,000 words average. Occasionally critiques rejected mss. Sometimes recommends other markets.
How to Contact: Send complete ms with cover letter. "Include some personal information along with information about your story." SASE. Photocopied submissions OK. Reports in 5 weeks. Publishes ms 6-12 months after acceptance. Sample copy for $5. Guidelines for #10 SASE.
Advice: "Realize that we are an Hispanic literary review so that if you are not Hispanic, then your work must reflect an interest in Hispanic issues or have an Hispanic bent to it in literature." Mss rejected "because beginning writers force their language instead of writing from genuine sentiment, because of multiple grammatical errors and because writers think that naming a character José gives their story a Hispanic slant."

CHIRON REVIEW, (I), 1514 Stone, Great Bend KS 67530-4027. (316)792-5025. Editor: Michael Hathaway. Tabloid: 10×13; 24+ pages; newsprint; illustrations; photos. Publishes "all types of material, no particular theme; traditional and off-beat, no taboos." Estab. 1982. Circ. 1,200.
Needs: Contemporary, experimental, humor/satire, literary. Receives 6 mss/month. Accepts 1 ms/issue; 4 mss/year. Publishes ms within 6-18 months of acceptance. Length: 3,500 words preferred. Publishes short shorts. Sometimes recommends other markets to writers of rejected mss.
How to Contact: Query. Reports in 1-2 months. SASE. Photocopied submissions OK. Accepts computer printout submissions. Sample copy $2 ($4 overseas). Fiction guidelines for #10 SAE and 1 first class stamp.
Payment: Pays 1 contributor's copy. Charge for extra copies, 50% discount.
Terms: Acquires first rights.

CHRYSALIS, Journal of the Swedenborg Foundation, (II), The Swedenborg Foundation, 139 E. 23rd St., New York NY 10010. (212)673-7310. Send mss to: Rt. 1, Box 184, Dillwyn VA 23936. (804)983-3021. Editor-in-Chief: Carol S. Lawson. Fiction Editor: Phoebe Loughrey. Magazine: 7½×10; 80 pages; archival paper; coated cover stock; illustrations; photos. "A literary magazine centered around one theme per issue. Publishes fiction, articles, poetry, book and film reviews for intellectually curious readers interested in spiritual topics." Triannually. Estab. 1985. Circ. 2,000.
Needs: Adventure (leading to insight), contemporary, experimental, historical (general), literary, mainstream, science fiction, spiritual, sports, suspense/mystery. No religious, juvenile, preschool. Upcoming themes: "Science & Spirituality" (Spring 1992); "The Future of Human Nature" (Summer 1992); "Crossroads" (Autumn 1992); "Time" (Spring 1993); "Work" (Summer 1993). Receives 40

mss/month. Buys 2-3 mss/issue; 6-9 mss/year. Publishes ms within 9 months of acceptance. Published work by Stephen Larsen, Robert Beum, Julia Randall; published new writers within the last year. Length: 1,500 words minimum; 2,500 words maximum. Publishes short shorts. Also publishes literary essays, literary criticism, poetry. Sometimes critiques rejected mss and recommends other markets. Does not accept reprinted or inpress material.

How to Contact: Query first and send SASE for guidelines. Reports in 1 month on queries; in 2 months on mss. SASE. Photocopied submissions OK. Accepts computer printout submissions. Sample copy for $5. Fiction guidelines for #10 SAE and 1 first class stamp.

Payment: Pays $75-250, free subscription to magazine and 5 contributor's copies.

Terms: Pays on publication for one-time rights. Sends galleys to author.

Advice: Looking for "1. *Quality*; 2. appeal for our audience; 3. relevance to/illumination of an aspect of issue's theme."

CICADA, (II, IV), 329 "E" St., Bakersfield CA 93304. (805)323-4064. Editor: Frederick A. Raborg, Jr. Magazine: 5½×8¼; 24 pages; Matte cover stock; illustrations and photos. "Oriental poetry and fiction related to the Orient for general readership and haiku enthusiasts." Quarterly. Estab. 1985. Circ. 600.

Needs: *All with Oriental slant*: Adventure, contemporary, erotica, ethnic, experimental, fantasy, feminist, historical (general), horror, humor/satire, lesbian, literary, mainstream, psychic/supernatural/occult, regional, contemporary romance, historical romance, young adult romance, science fiction, senior citizen/retirement, suspense/mystery and translations. "We look for strong fiction with Oriental (especially Japanese) content or flavor. Stories need not have 'happy' endings, and we are open to the experimental and/or avant-garde. Erotica is fine (the Japanese love their erotica); pornography, no." Receives 30+ unsolicited mss/month. Buys 1 ms/issue; 4 mss/year. Publishes ms 6 months-1 year after acceptance. Agented fiction 5%. Published work by Gilbert Garand and Jim Mastro. Length: 2,000 words average; 500 words minimum; 3,000 words maximum. Critiques rejected ms when appropriate. Always recommends other markets. Also publishes poetry.

How to Contact: Send complete ms with cover letter. Include Social Security number and appropriate information about the writer in relationship to the Orient. Reports in 2 weeks on queries; 3 months on mss (if seriously considered). SASE. Photocopied submissions OK. Accepts computer printout submissions. Sample copy $4.50. Fiction guidelines for #10 SAE and 1 first class stamp.

Payment: Pays $10-25 plus contributor's copies; charge for extras.

Terms: Pays on publication for first North American serial rights. $5 kill fee.

Advice: Looks for "excellence and appropriate storyline. Strong characterization and knowledge of the Orient are musts. Neatness counts high on my list for first impressions. A writer should demonstrate a high degree of professionalism."

CIMARRON REVIEW, (II), Oklahoma State University, 205 Morrill, Stillwater OK 74078-0135. (405)744-9476. Editor: Gordon Weaver. Managing Editor: Deborah Bransford. Magazine: 6×9; 100 pages; illustrations on cover. "Poetry and fiction on contemporary themes; personal essays on contemporary issues that cope with life in the 20th century, for educated literary readers. We work hard to reflect quality." Quarterly. Estab. 1967. Circ. 500.

Needs: Literary and contemporary. No collegiate reminiscences or juvenilia. Plans 25th-year Anniversay issue (Oct. 1992). Accepts 6-7 mss/issue, 24-28 mss/year. Published works by Peter Makuck, Mary Lee Settle, W. D. Wetherell, John Timmerman; published new writers within the last year. Also publishes literary essays, literary criticism, poetry. Sometimes recommends other markets.

How to Contact: Send complete ms with SASE. "Short cover letters are appropriate but not essential, except for providing *CR* with the most recent mailing address available." Accepts computer printout submissions. Reports in 4-6 weeks on mss. Publishes ms 6-9 months after acceptance. Sample copy with SASE. Reviews novels and short story collections.

Payment: Pays one year subscription to author.

Terms: Acquires all rights on publication. "Permission to reprint granted freely."

Advice: "Short fiction is a genre uniquely suited to the modern world. *CR* seeks an individual, innovative style that focuses on contemporary themes."

‡CIMMERIAN JOURNAL, Tales of the Weird & Unusual, (I, II), RBH Agency, P.O. Box 1022, Northampton MA 01061. Editor: Robert Heath. Magazine: 5½×8½; 80 pages; 20 lb. paper; card stock cover; b&w illustrations. "Thoughtful suspense, weird or horror, but not gory and graphic for readers of the weird or unusual who think about what they read." Bimonthly. Estab. 1990. Circ. 50±.

Needs: Condensed/excerpted novel, experimental, fantasy, horror, science fiction, suspense. "No porn, gay/lesbian, erotica, grue and gore/psychic/occult. Nothing anti-Judeo/Christian." Receives 5 unsolicited mss/month. Buys 3-5 mss/issue. Publishes mss within 4 months after acceptance. Length: 2,000 words preferred; 250 words minimum; 7,300 words maximum. Publishes short shorts. Sometimes critiques rejected mss.

How to Contact: Send complete ms with cover letter. Include *brief* bio, any credits. Reports in 1 month. SASE. Photocopied submissions OK. Accepts computer printout submissions. Sample copy for $2.50 and #10 SAE with 5 first class stamps. Fiction guidelines for #10 SAE and 1 first class stamp.

Payment: Pays 5 contributor's copies.

Terms: Acquires one-time rights.

Advice: "I want a story to make me smile because of a new twist, an original idea, because it provokes thought or even self-examination. I'd like the reader (myself) to be changed (for the better hopefully), even in a tiny way, by a story. I like a story that digs below the superficiality of the human condition, but in an original way. Should provoke thought more than raw emotion, seek to stimulate reader through careful style rather than graphic depictions of grue and gore, not interested in technical sci-fi, but future settings fine. No standard mysteries, but suspense (non-detection) OK. No porn of any sort—no abuse of persons for sake of gratification. No victims for simple sake of victimization."

Editor Robert B. Heath chose to title his magazine The Cimmerian Journal *because "the mythical Land of the Cimmerians was said to be characterized by starkness and gloominess," he says. "When I found this drawing, I immediately saw it as a graphic realization of the land I had pictured in my mind. Additionally, many of the stories I have published so far would best be described in the same terms: simple, almost stark, with a certain sense of gloom, or despair," he adds. "In spite of its simplicity, the drawing is thought-provoking, just what I hope the magazine itself to be for its readers." The artist is Elizabeth Spencer.*

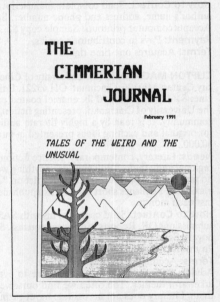

THE CIMMERIAN JOURNAL

February 1991

TALES OF THE WEIRD AND THE UNUSUAL

CIPHER, (II), 5415 Connecticut Ave., NW, #819, Washington DC 20015. (202)966-3583. Editor: James Heynderickx. Magazine: 5½×8½; 62 pages; 24 lb. paper; vellum cover, 5 illustrations/issue. "We present contemporary art, fiction, poetry and critical essays to an open-minded, educated audience." Quarterly. Estab. 1990.

Needs: Contemporary, experimental, literary, mainstream, prose poem, translations. "We also have a 'Works in Progress' section in each issue. In this section, excerpts from developing and yet-to-be-published novels, books of poetry and major works of criticism will be presented." Does not want to see "anything that is imitative. We can also pass on adventure, fantasy, science fiction and romance." Plans special fiction issue. Receives 30-40 unsolicited fiction mss/month. Accepts 3-4 mss/issue; 12-16 mss/year. Publishes mss 4-6 months after acceptance. Published work by Sarah Freligh. Length: 2,000 words preferred; 300 words minimum; 4,000 words maximum. Publishes short shorts. Length: 300-500 words. Critiques or comments on rejected mss and recommends other markets.

How to Contact: Send complete ms with cover letter. "Include name, address, phone number, but no publishing history or background on the specific piece." Reports in 2 months. SASE. Photocopied submissions are OK. Sample copy for $4. Fiction guidelines for #10 SAE and 1 first-class stamp.

Payment: Pays in contributor's copies.
Terms: Acquires first North American serial rights.
Advice: "More than anything else, we are looking for a clarity of voice in the fiction we publish. This clarity is usually achieved by writers who are conscious of their purpose and use of language. We admire stories in which both content and form attempt to offer insight...Our editors believe that 'a lack of revision' is the number one reason that fiction from beginning writers is often passed over...Our main recommendation is that writers should investigate and revise a piece of fiction as much as possible if they are interested in discovering its true potential."

CITY SCRIPTUM, (I, II), City College of San Francisco, 50 Phelan Ave., San Francisco CA 94112. (415)239-3000. Editor: H. Brown Miller. Magazine: 8½ × 11; 50-60 pages. "Our publication is a college literary magazine that publishes short fiction, essays and poetry for a college/general audience." Semi-annually. Revived 1989. Circ. 1,000.
Needs: Adventure, condensed/excerpted novel, confession, contemporary, ethnic, experimental, fantasy, feminist, gay, historical (general), horror, humor/satire, lesbian, literary, mainstream, prose poem, psychic/supernatural/occult, science fiction, suspense/mystery, western. We accept manuscript *only* two times per year: September 1-October 31 and February 1-March 31. Length: 2,000 words average for prose. Publishes short shorts. Length: No preference. Also publishes poetry.
How to Contact: Send complete manuscript with cover letter. Request writers guidelines including author's name, address and phone number. SASE. Simultaneous and photocopied submissions OK. Accepts computer printouts. Sample copy $2. Fiction guidelines for #10 SAE and 1 first class stamp.
Payment: Pays in contributor's copies.
Terms: Acquires one-time rights.

CLIFTON MAGAZINE , (II), University of Cincinnati Communications Board, 204 Tangeman University Center, ML 136, Cincinnati OH 45221. Editor: Eden Casteel. Fiction Editor: Steve Libbey. Magazine: 8 × 11; 48 pages; 70 lb. enamel coated paper; illustrations; photos. "*Clifton* is the magazine of the University of Cincinnati, presenting fiction, poetry and feature articles of interest to the University community. It is read by a highly literate audience of students, academics and professionals looking for original and exciting ideas presented in our award-winning format." Quarterly. Estab. 1972. Circ. 30,000.
Needs: Literary, contemporary, science fiction, fantasy, feminist, erotica, horror, humor, prose poem, regional and ethnic. "Will consider anything we haven't read a thousand times before. We try to have no preconceptions when approaching fiction." Accepts 1-2 mss/issue, 5 mss/year. Length: 5,000 words maximum. Publishes short shorts. Also publishes poetry. Receives approximately 30 unsolicited fiction mss each month.
How to Contact: Send complete ms with SASE. Photocopied, computer printout and simultaneous submissions OK. Reports in 6-8 weeks on mss. Sample copy $1.75. Guidelines with #10 SASE. Reviews novels. Send books to Fiction Editor.
Payment: Pays 3 free author's copies.
Terms: Acquires first rights.
Advice: "There is a trend in literature to overglorify the mundane, resulting in bland stories with lukewarm themes. Too often we find ourselves rejecting well-written stories that have no punch to them. Literary does not necessitate navel gazing. Literature is a mirror (usually the funhouse variety) to the world, and is just as dirty, ugly and sweaty, if not more so. Good writing feels right, like an expensive steak, and takes as long to eat. Don't be afraid to be different. Don't be different for the sake of being different. We read manuscripts first as readers, then as editors. If we as readers are bored, we as editors don't waste our time. A story should be mechanically sound, intricate, concise and lyrical. New and young writers are encouraged to submit. Work by UC students, grads and faculty is especially welcome."

CLOCKWATCH REVIEW, A Journal of the Arts, (II), Dept. of English, Illinois Wesleyan University, Bloomington IL 61702. (309)556-3352. Editor: James Plath. Magazine: 5½ × 8½; 64-80 pages; coated stock paper; glossy cover stock; illustrations; photos. "We publish stories which are *literary* as well as alive, colorful, enjoyable — stories which linger like shadows," for a general audience. Semiannually. Estab. 1983. Circ. 1,500.
Needs: Contemporary, experimental, humor/satire, literary, mainstream, prose poem and regional. Receives 50-60 unsolicited mss/month. Accepts 2 mss/issue; 4 mss/year. Recently published work by Ellen Hunnicutt, Beth Brandt, Charlotte Mandel; published new writers within the last year. Length:

2,500 words average; 1,200 words minimum; 4,000 words maximum. Occasionally critiques rejected mss if requested.

How to Contact: Send complete ms. Reports in 2 months. SASE. Photocopied submissions OK. Accepts computer printout submissions. Publishes ms 3-12 months after acceptance. Sample copy for $4.

Payment: Pays 3 contributor's copies and small cash stipend. (Currently $50, but may vary).

Terms: Buys first serial rights.

Advice: "*Clockwatch* has always tried to expand the audience for quality contemporary poetry and fiction by publishing a highly visual magazine that is thin enough to invite reading. We've included interviews with popular musicians and artists in order to further interest a general, as well as academic, public and show the interrelationship of the arts. Give us characters with meat on their bones, colorful but not clichéd; give us natural plots, not contrived or melodramatic. Above all, give us your *best* work."

COCHRAN'S CORNER, (I), Box 2036, Waldorf, MD 20601. (301)843-0485. Editor: Debra G. Tompkins. Magazine: 5½×8; 52 pages. "We publish fiction, nonfiction and poetry. Our only requirement is no strong language." For a "family" audience. Quarterly. Estab. 1986. Circ. 500.

Needs: Adventure, historical (general), horror, humor/satire, juvenile (5-9 years), preschool (1-4 years), prose poem, religious/inspirational, romance, science fiction, suspense/mystery and young adult/teen (10-18 years). "Mss must be free from language you wouldn't want your/our children to read." Plans a special fiction issue. Receives 50 mss/month. Accepts 4 mss/issue; 8 mss/year. Publishes ms by the next issue after acceptance. Published work by Juni Dunkin, Ruth Cox Anderson, Becky Knight. Length: 500 words preferred; 300 words minimum; 1,000 words maximum. Also publishes literary essays, literary criticism, poetry. Sometimes critiques unsolicited mss and recommends other markets.

How to Contact: "Right now we are forced to limit acceptance to *subscribers only*." Send complete ms with cover letter. Reports in 3 weeks on queries; 3 months on mss. SASE for manuscript. Simultaneous, photocopied and reprint submissions OK. Accepts computer printout submissions. Sample copy for $5, 9×12 SAE and 90¢ postage. Fiction guidelines for #10 SAE and 1 first class stamp. Reviews novels and short stories. Send books to Ada Cochran, president.

Payment: Pays in contributor's copies.

Terms: Acquires one-time rights.

Advice: "I feel the quality of fiction is getting better. The public is demanding a good read, instead of having sex or violence carry the story. I predict that fiction has a good future. We like to print the story as the writer submits it if possible. This way writers can compare their work with their peers and take the necessary steps to improve and go on to sell to bigger magazines. Stories from the heart desire a place to be published. We try to fill that need."

THE COE REVIEW, (II), Student Senate of Coe College, 1220 1st St., Cedar Rapids IA 52402. Contact: Jack Nulick. Magazine: 8½×5½; 100-150 pages; illustrations; photos. Annual anthology of "quality experimental writing in both poetry and fiction. Especially directed to an academic or experimental literary audience that is concerned with current literature." Annually. Estab. 1972. Circ. 500.

Needs: Literary, contemporary, psychic/supernatural, science fiction, fantasy, feminist, gay/lesbian, erotica, quality ethnic, regional, serialized and condensed novels, translations. "We publish students, unsolicited professional and solicited professional mss. *The Coe Review* is growing and it is our goal to become nationally acknowledged in literary circles as a forerunner in the publication of experimental writing. We support writing workshops and invite both writing professors and student writers to submit." No "religious propaganda, gothic, romance, western, mystery or adventure." Length: 500-4,000 words.

How to Contact: Send complete ms with SASE. "Mss sent in summer will possibly not be returned until fall depending on availability of a fiction editor in summer." Accepts computer printout submissions. Sample copy $4.

Payment: Pays $25-100 for solicitations and 1 contributor's copy; $4 charge for extras.

Terms: Pays on publication "but possibly sooner with solicited mss. Upon request we will reassign rights to the author." Buys all rights.

Advice: "We desire material that seeks to explore the vast imaginative landscape and expand the boundaries thereof. Study experimental writers such as Borges, Vonnegut, Brautigan, J. Baumbach and Manual Puig. Avoid sentimentalism. Do not be afraid to experiment or to write intelligent fiction."

COLD-DRILL MAGAZINE, (IV), English Dept., Boise State University, 1910 University Dr., Boise ID 83725. (208)385-1999. Editor: Leiann Burton. Magazine: 6×9; 150 pages; Beckett text paper; illustrations; photos. Material submitted *must be by Idaho authors or deal with Idaho.* For adult audiences. Annually. Estab. 1970. Circ. 500.
Needs: "For our 1992-93 issue we are looking for poems, short stories, nonfiction, essays, artwork relating to 'America's Work Force.' We want material about the sweat and frustration, anger and satisfaction of a day's work."
How to Contact: Query first. SASE.
Payment: Pays in contributor's copies.
Terms: Acquires first rights.

COLLAGES AND BRICOLAGES, The Journal of International Writing, (II), Office of International Programs, 212 Founders Hall, Clarion University of Pennsylvania, Clarion PA 16214. (814)226-2340. Editor: Marie-José Fortis. Magazine: 8×11; 100-150 pages; illustrations. "The theme, if there is any, is international post-modern/avant-gardist culture. The magazine may include essays, short stories, short plays, poems that show innovative promise." Annually. Estab. 1987. Plans special fiction issue.
Needs: Contemporary, ethnic, experimental, feminist, humor/satire, literary, mainstream, philosophical, prose poem and science fiction. "Also post-modern, surrealist designs/illustrations are welcome." Upcoming themes: "Voices From Prison"—written by prisoners (1992); "Camille-Paglia," "Deconstructionism," "Feminism" (1993). Receives about 10 unsolicited fiction mss/month. Publishes ms 6-9 months after acceptance. Recently published work by Marilou Awiakta, Boris Vian, Aisha Eshe; published new writers within the last year. Publishes short shorts. Also publishes literary essays, literary criticism, poetry. Sometimes critiques rejected ms; recommends other markets when there is time.
How to Contact: Send complete ms with cover letter. Reports in 2-3 months. SASE. Simultaneous submissions OK. Accepts computer printout submissions. Sample copy $5. Reviews novels and short story collections. "How often and how many per issue depends on reviewers available."
Payment: Pays 2 contributor's copies.
Terms: Acquires first rights.
Advice: "As far as fiction is concerned, it seems that everything has been said before. Hence, the writer's despair. This literary despair should be an asset to today's young writer. It should be his motif. The only innovation that can still be done is language innovation, playfulness, humor (with a sense of doom). We are now living in a neo-dada age, in a 'post-modern aura.' Hence, the writer's input should concentrate on these premises. Writing about the decadence of inspiration can bring us to a new age in literature. (The Dadaist despair was, after all, answered with surrealism.)We encourage experimental and literary writers that do not shy away from reading the classics."

COLORADO REVIEW, (II), English Department, Colorado State University, Fort Collins CO 80523. (303)491-7251. General Editor: William Tremblay. Fiction Editor: David Milofsky. Translations Editor: Mary Crow. Literary journal: 160 pages; 70 lb. book weight paper. Semiannually. Estab. as *Colorado State Review* 1966. Circ. 1,100.
Needs: Contemporary, ethnic, experimental, literary, mainstream, translations. Receives 200 unsolicited fiction mss/month. Accepts 3-4 mss/issue. Recently published work by Reginald Gibbons, T. Alan Broughton, Gladys Swan; published new writers within the last year. Length: under 6,000 words. Does not read mss May-August. Also publishes literary essays, literary criticism, poetry. Occasionally critiques rejected mss and recommends other markets.
How to Contact: Send complete ms with SASE and brief bio with previous publications. Accepts computer printout submissions. Reports in 3 months. Publishes ms 3-6 months after acceptance. Sample copy for $5. Reviews novels or short story collections.

Market conditions are constantly changing! If you're still using this book and it is 1993 or later, buy the newest edition of Novel & Short Story Writer's Market at your favorite bookstore or order directly from Writer's Digest Books.

Payment: Pays $20/printed page; 1 year subscription to magazine; 2 free contributor's copies; extras for $5.
Terms: Pays on publication for first North American serial rights. "We assign copyright to author on request." Sends galleys to author.
Advice: "We are interested in manuscripts which show craft, imagination and a convincing voice. If a story has reached a level of technical competence, we are receptive to the fiction working on its own terms. The oldest advice is still the best: persistence. Approach every aspect of the writing process with pride, conscientiousness—from word choice to manuscript appearance."

COLORADO-NORTH REVIEW, (I, II), University of Northern Colorado, Greeley CO 80639. (303)351-1350. Editor: Martin Schaefer. Magazine: 5½×8½; 64 pages; 70 lb. paper; 80 lb. cover stock; illustrations; photos. "Magazine of poetry, short fiction, translations, photography, interviews and graphic arts for writers or those interested in contemporary creativity." Published in winter and spring. Estab. 1968. Circ. 2,500.
Needs: Contemporary, literary and prose poem. Receives 100 unsolicited fiction mss/month. Accepts 70 mss/issue (including poetry), 140 mss/year. Published work by James Lentestey and Dennis Vannatta. Length: 1,000 words maximum. Critiques rejected mss by request. Also publishes poetry.
How to Contact: Send complete ms with SASE and brief biographical info for contributor's section. Photocopied submissions OK. Reports in 3 months. Publishes ms 2-3 months after acceptance. Sample copy $3.50; free guidelines with SASE.
Payment: Pays in contributor's copies.
Advice: "We print poetry, art, and short fiction, so space is limited for short fiction, averaging three to four stories an issue. Obviously we must be very selective so send your best work. We are looking for stories whose form is dictated by its content. Innovative work is welcome as long as the innovation meets its own standards for quality. Work with insight is always appreciated. Please do not send simultaneous submissions."

COLUMBIA: A MAGAZINE OF POETRY & PROSE, (II), 404 Dodge Hall, Columbia University, New York NY 10027. (212)854-4391. Editors: Rotating. Magazine: 5¼×8¼; approximately 200 pages; coated cover stock; illustrations, photos. "We accept short stories, novel excerpts, translations, interviews, nonfiction and poetry." Semiannually.
Needs: Literary and translations. Accepts 3-10 mss/issue. Receives approximately 125 unsolicited fiction mss each month. Does not read mss April 1 to August 31. Published work by Philip Lopate, Amy Hempel, Madison Smartt Bell, John McNally; published 5-8 unpublished writers within the year. Length: 25 pages maximum. Publishes short shorts.
How to Contact: Send complete ms with SASE. Accepts computer printout submissions. Reports in 1-2 months. Sample copy $5.
Payment: Pays contributor's copies. $3 charge for extras. Offers annual fiction awards.
Advice: "Don't overwhelm editors. Send work that's not longer than 20 pages."

COMMON LIVES/LESBIAN LIVES, A Lesbian Quarterly, (IV), Box 1553, Iowa City IA 52244. "*CL/LL* seeks to document the experiences and thoughts of lesbians for lesbian audience." Magazine: 5×8½; 112-128 pages; illustrations; photos. Quarterly.
Needs: *All pertaining to lesbian culture*: Adventure, comics, contemporary, erotica, ethnic, experimental, fantasy, feminist, historical (general), humor/satire, juvenile, lesbian, prose poem, psychic/supernatural/occult, regional, romance, science fiction, senior citizen/retirement, suspense/mystery, western and young adult/teen. Length: 4-10 pages. Also publishes literary essays, literary criticism, poetry. Occasionally critiques rejected mss.
How to Contact: Send complete ms with cover letter; a short bio sketch is required. Reports in 4 months. SASE. Photocopied submissions OK. Accepts computer printout submissions. Publishes ms up to 4 months after acceptance. Published "many" new writers within the last year. Sample copy $5. Reviews novels and short story collections.
Payment: Pays 2 contributor's copies.
Advice: "Readers relate stories to their lives; fiction is an interesting and accessible way for lesbians to document their experience and express their opinions."

‡COMMUNITIES: JOURNAL OF COOPERATION, (II), Communities Publications Cooperative, 105 Sun St., Stelle IL 60919. (815)256-2252. Editor: Charles Betterton. "Features articles on intentional communities, urban collectives, rural communes, politics, health, alternative culture and workplace democracy for people involved in cooperative ventures." Quarterly. Estab. 1973. Circ. 4,000.

Needs: Feminist, science fiction, utopian and cooperative. Accepts "maybe 1 manuscript in 2 years (would do more if we got them)." Length: 1,000 words minimum; 5,000 words maximum. Occasionally critiques rejected ms.
How to Contact: Query first or send complete ms. Reports in 4 weeks on queries; 6 weeks on mss. Simultaneous, photocopied and previously published submissions OK. Accepts computer printout submissions. Sample copy for $4.
Payment: Pays 1 year subscription and 3 contributor's copies.
Terms: Acquires one-time rights.

A COMPANION IN ZEOR, (I, II, IV), 17 Ashland Ave., RR 5, R Box 82, Cardiff NJ 08232. Editor: Karen Litman. Fanzine: 8½×11; 60 pages; "letter" paper; heavy blue cover; b&w line illustrations; occasional b&w photographs. Publishes science fiction based on the various Universe creations of Jacqueline Lichtenberg. Occasional features on Star Trek, and other interests, convention reports, reviews of movies and books, recordings, etc. Published irregularly. Estab. 1978. Circ. 300.
Needs: Fantasy, humor/satire, prose poem, science fiction. "No vicious satire. Nothing X-rated. Homosexuality prohibited unless *essential* in story. We run a clean publication that anyone should be able to read without fear." Occasionally receives one manuscript a month. Accepts "as much as can afford to print." Publication of an accepted ms "can take years, due to limit of finances available for publication." Occasionally critiques rejected mss and recommends other markets.
How to Contact: Query first or send complete ms with cover letter. "Prefer cover letters about any writing experience prior, or related interests toward writing aims." Reports in 1 month. SASE. Simultaneous and photocopied submissions OK. Accepts computer printout submissions. Sample copy price depends on individual circumstances. Fiction guidelines for #10 SAE and 1 first class stamp. "I write individual letters to all queries. No form letter at present." SASE for guidelines required. Reviews sf/fantasy collections or titles.
Payment: Pays in contributor's copies.
Terms: Acquires first rights.
Advice: "We take fiction based on any and all of Jacqueline Lichtenberg's published novels. The contributor should be familiar with these works before contributing material to my fanzine. Also accepts manuscripts on cassette from visually handicapped if submitted. 'Zines also on tape for those individuals."

COMPOST NEWSLETTER, (IV), Compost Coven, 729 Fifth Ave., San Francisco CA 94118. (415)751-9466. Editor: Valerie Walker. Newsletter: 7×8½; 20 pages; bond paper; illustrations and scanned photographs. Publishes "humor/satire from a pagan/punk perspective." Published 8 times/year. Estab. 1981. Circ. under 100.
Needs: Experimental, fantasy, feminist, gay, humor/satire, lesbian, psychic/supernatural/occult, science fiction, serialized novel, pagan. No Christian. Publishes ms within 3 or 4 issues after acceptance. Length: 500 words minimum; 2,000 words maximum.
How to Contact: Query with clips of published work. Reports in 2 months. SASE. Simultaneous, photocopied and reprint submissions OK. Accepts laser print computer printouts; accepts electronic submissions via Macintosh disk. Sample copy $2. (Make checks/MO's out to Valerie Walker; mark "for CNL".)
Payment: Pays in contributor's copies.
Terms: Acquires one-time rights. Publication not copyrighted.
Advice: "If you don't like the magazine market, go out and make one of your own. Type single space on white paper, or send a Macintosh disk in MacWrite or Microsoft Word. Don't bother to format unless it's essential for the feel of the piece. Entertain us, even if you're serious. Get strange." Publishes ms "if it is funny, bizarre, or we agree with its politics."

CONCHO RIVER REVIEW, (I, II, IV), Fort Concho Museum Press, 213 East Avenue D, San Angelo TX 76903. (915)657-4441. Editor: Terence A. Dalrymple. Magazine: 6½×9; 100-125 pages; 60 lb. Ardor offset paper; Classic Laid Color cover stock; b&w drawings. "We publish any fiction of high quality—no thematic specialties—contributors must be residents of Texas or the Southwest generally." Semiannually. Estab. 1987. Circ. 300.
Needs: Contemporary, ethnic, historical (general), humor/satire, literary, regional and western. No erotica; no science fiction. Receives 10-15 unsolicited mss/month. Accepts 3-6 mss/issue; 8-10 mss/year. Publishes ms 4 months after acceptance. Published work by Robert Flynn, Clay Reynolds, Roland Sodowsky. Length: 3,500 words average; 1,500 words minimum; 5,000 words maximum. Also publishes literary essays, poetry. Sometimes critiques rejected mss and recommends other markets.

How to Contact: Send complete ms with SASE; cover letter optional. Reports in 3 weeks on queries; 3-8 weeks on mss. SASE for ms. Simultaneous and photocopied submissions OK. Accepts computer printout submissions. Sample copy $4. Fiction guidelines for #10 SAE and 1 first class stamp. Reviews novels and short story collections. Send books to Terence A. Dalrymple, % English Dept., Angelo State University, San Angelo TX 76909.
Payment: Pays in contributor's copies; $4 charge for extras.
Terms: Acquires first rights.
Advice: "We prefer a clear sense of conflict, strong characterization and effective dialogue."

CONFRONTATION, (II), English Dept., C.W. Post of Long Island University, Greenvale NY 11548. (516)299-2391. Editor: Martin Tucker. Magazine: 6×9; 190-250 pages; 70 lb. paper; 80 lb. cover; illustrations; photos. "We like to have a 'range' of subjects, form and style in each issue and are open to all forms. Quality is our major concern. Our audience is literate, thinking people; formally or self-educated." Semiannually. Estab. 1968. Circ. 2,000.
Needs: Literary, contemporary, prose poem, regional and translations. No "proselytizing" literature. Plans special fiction issue on new South African literature. Buys 30 mss/issue; 60 mss/year. Receives 400 unsolicited fiction mss each month. Does not read June-Sept. Approximately 10-15% of fiction is agented. Recently published work by Jerzy Kosinski, Irvin Faust, Lore Segal; published new writers within the last year. Length: 500-4,000 words. Publishes short shorts. Also publishes literary essays, poetry. Critiques rejected mss when there is time. Sometimes recommends other markets.
How to Contact: Send complete ms with SASE. "Cover letters acceptable, not necessary. We accept simultaneous submissions but do not like it." Accepts computer printout submissions. Accepts diskettes if accompanied by computer printout submissions. Reports in 6-8 weeks on mss. Publishes ms 6-12 months after acceptance. Sample copy for $3. Reviews novels and short story collections.
Payment: Pays $10-$100; 1 contributor's copy; half price for extras.
Terms: Pays on publication for all rights "with transfer on request to author."
Advice: "Keep trying."

CONJUNCTIONS (II), 33 W. 9th St., New York NY 10011. Editor: Bradford Morrow. Magazine: 6×9; 294 pages; 55 lb. woven paper; heavy cream laid paper cover stock; illustrations; photos. "*Conjunctions*: a conjoining of texts by many diverse writers: a forum of work-in-progress by both well-known and new writers. We represent no clique but are concerned solely with publishing works of high artistic and technical calibre." Semiannually. Estab. 1981. Circ. 5,500.
Needs: Experimental, literary and translations. Receives 200 unsolicited fiction mss/month. Accepts 65 mss/year. "Recent issues have included new work by John Hawkes, William T. Vollman and Mary Caponegro." Published new writers within the last year. No preferred length.
How to Contact: Send complete ms with SASE. Reports in 8-12 weeks on mss.
Payment: Pays 3 contributor's copies; extra copies available at 40% discount to contributors.
Terms: Acquires one-time rights. Sends galleys to author.
Advice: "Gain a far wider personal experience than that which is possible in writing schools. A broader reading base than is evident in most of the unsolicited work we receive would be useful. So much has already been accomplished, and it seems to us the literacy rate among writers is only barely higher than any other community or profession."

CORONA, Marking the Edges of Many Circles, (II), Department of History and Philosophy, Montana State University, Bozeman MT 59717. (406)994-5200. Magazine: 7×10; 130 pages; 60 lb. "mountre matte" paper; 65 lb. Hammermill cover stock; illustrations; photos. "Interdisciplinary magazine—essays, poetry, fiction, imagery, science, history, recipes, humor, etc., for those educated, curious, with a profound interest in the arts and contemporary thought." Annually. Estab. 1980. Circ. 2,000.
Needs: Comics, contemporary, experimental, fantasy, feminist, gay, lesbian, humor/satire, literary, preschool, prose poem, psychic/supernatural/occult, regional, romance and senior citizen/retirement. "Our fiction ranges from the traditional Talmudic tale to fiction engendered by speculative science, from the extended joke to regional reflection—if it isn't accessible and original, please don't send it." Receives varying number of unsolicited fiction mss/month. Accepts 6 mss/issue. Published work by Rhoda Lerman and Stephen Dixon; published new writers within the last year. Publishes short shorts. Also publishes literary essays, poetry. Occasionally critiques rejected mss. Sometimes recommends other markets.

How to Contact: Query. *Not reading unsolicited mss until 1993.* Accepts computer printout submissions. Reports in 6 months on mss. Sample copy $7.
Payment: Pays minimal honorarium; 2 free contributor's copies; discounted charge for extras.
Terms: Acquires first rights. Sends galleys to author upon request.
Advice: "Be knowledgeable of contents other than fiction in *Corona*; one must know the journal."

COSMIC LANDSCAPES, An Alternative Science Fiction Magazine, (I), % Dan Petitpas, 6 Edson St., Hyde Park MA 02136. (617)361-0622. Editor: Dan Petitpas. Magazine: 7×8½; 32-56 pages; white bond paper and cover stock; illustrations; photos occasionally. "A magazine which publishes science fiction for science-fiction readers; also articles and news of interest to writers and SF fans. Occasionally prints works of horror and fantasy." Annually. Estab. 1983. Circ. 100.
Needs: Science fiction. Receives 10-15 unsolicited mss/month. Accepts 8 mss/issue. Published new writers in the last year. Length: 2,500 words average; 25 words minimum. Will consider all lengths. "Every manuscript receives a personal evaluation by the editor." Sometimes recommends other markets.
How to Contact: Send complete ms with info about the author. Reports usually in 1 week-3 months. SASE. Photocopied submissions preferred. Accepts computer printout submissions. Sample copy for $3.50. Fiction guidelines with SASE.
Payment: Pays 2 contributor's copies; $2 for extras.
Terms: Acquires one-time rights.
Advice: "Writers should send a cover letter; include SASE and a return address. I like to know a little about them. Please give some background, and how the story pertains to their experience. Learn manuscript formats. Get E. B. White's *Elements of Style*. Don't get all your ideas from TV shows or movies. Try to know the basics."

CRAZYHORSE, (III), Dept. of English, Univ. of Arkansas, Little Rock, AR 72204. (501)569-3160. Managing Editor: Zabelle Stodola. Fiction Editor: Judy Troy. Magazine: 6×9; 140 pages; cover and front page illustrations only. "Publishes original, quality literary fiction." Biannually. Estab. 1960. Circ. 1,000.
Needs: Literary. No formula (science-fiction, gothic, detective, etc.) fiction. Receives 100-150 unsolicited mss/month. Buys 3-5 mss/issue; 8-10 mss/year. Does not read mss in summer. Past contributors include Lee K. Abbott, Frederick Busch, Andre Dubus, Pam Durban, H.E. Francis, James Hannah, Gordon Lish, Bobbie Ann Mason and Maura Stanton; published new writers within the last year. Publishes short shorts. Also publishes literary essays, literary criticism, poetry. "Rarely" critiques rejected mss.
How to Contact: Send complete ms with cover letter. Reports in 1 week to 1 month. SASE. Photocopied submissions OK. Accepts computer printout submissions. Sample copy $4. Reviews novels and short story collections. Send books to fiction editor.
Payment: Pays $10/page and contributor's copies.
Terms: Pays on publicaton for first North American serial rights. *Crazyhorse* awards $500 to the author of the best work of fiction published in a given year.
Advice: "Read a sample issue and submit work that you believe is as good as or better than the fiction we've published."

CRAZYQUILT (II), P.O. Box 632729, San Diego CA 92163-2729. (619)688-1023. Editor: Jim Kitchen. Magazine: 5½×8½; 92 pages; illustrations and photos. "We publish short fiction, poems, nonfiction about writing and writers, one-act plays and b&w illustrations and photos." Quarterly. Estab. 1986. Circ. 175.
Needs: Contemporary, ethnic, fantasy, gay, historical, humor/satire, literary, mainstream, science fiction, excerpted novel, suspense/mystery. "Shorter pieces are preferred." Receives 85-100 unsolicited mss/quarter. Accepts 1-3 mss/issue; 4-12 mss/year. Publishes 1 year after acceptance. Published work by Louis Phillips, Geraldine Little, David Mouat; published new writers within the last year. Length: 1,500 words minimum; 5,000 words maximum. Also publishes literary essays, literary criticism, poetry. Occasionally critiques rejected mss.

Read the Business of Fiction section to learn the correct way to prepare and submit a manuscript.

How to Contact: Send complete ms with cover letter. Reports in 3 weeks on mss. Simultaneous and photocopied submissions OK. Accepts computer printout submissions. Sample copy $4.50 ($2.50 for back issue). Fiction guidelines for SAE and 1 first class stamp. "Sometimes" reviews novels and short story collections.
Payment: Pays 2 contributor's copies.
Terms: Acquires first North American serial rights or one-time rights. Holds annual poetry and fiction contest ($100, $50 and $25 prizes) and annual chapbook contest.
Advice: "Write a story that is well constructed, develops characters and maintains interest."

THE CREAM CITY REVIEW, (II), University of Wisconsin-Milwaukee, Box 413, Milwaukee WI 53201. (414)229-9708. Editors: Kathlene Postma, Sandra Nelson. Fiction Editor: Mary Jeane Smoller. Magazine: 5½ × 8½; 120-200 pages; 70 lb. offset/perfect-bound paper; 80 lb. cover stock; illustrations; photos. "General literary publication—an electric selection of the best we receive." Semiannually. Plans to publish special fiction issue. Semiannually. Estab. 1975. Circ. 1,000-1,500.
Needs: Ethnic, experimental, humor/satire, literary, prose poem, regional and translations. Receives approximately 100-200 unsolicited fiction mss each month. Accepts 6-10 mss/issue. Published work by Eve Shelnutt, Ellen Hunnicut and F.D. Reeve; published new writers within the last year. Length: 1,000-10,000 words. Publishes short shorts. Also publishes literary essays, literary criticism, poetry. Critiques rejected mss when there is time. Recommends other markets "when we have time."
How to Contact: Send complete ms with SASE. Photocopied submissions OK. Reports in 2 months. Sample copy $4.50. Reviews novels and short story collections.
Payment: Pays 2 contributor's copies.
Terms: Acquires first rights. Sends galleys to author. Rights revert to author after publication.
Advice: "Read as much as you write so that you can examine your own work in relation to where fiction has been and where fiction is going."

CREATIVE KIDS, (I, IV), GCT, Inc., Box 6448, Mobile AL 36660. (205)478-4700. Editor: Fay L. Gold. Magazine: 8½×11; 32 pages; illustrations; photos. Material by children for children. Published 8 times/year. Estab. 1980. Circ: 10,000.
Needs: "We publish work by children ages 5-18." Juvenile (5-9 years); young adult/teen (10-18 years). No sexist, racist or violent fiction. Accepts 8-10 mss/issue; 60-80 mss/year. Publishes ms up to one year after acceptance. Published new writers within the last year. Publishes short shorts.
How to Contact: Send complete ms with cover letter, which should include name, age, home address, school name and address, statement of originality signed by teacher or parent. Reports in 2 weeks on queries; 1 month on mss. SASE. Accepts computer printout submissions. Sample copy for $3.
Payment: Pays contributor's copy only.
Terms: Acquires all rights.
Advice: "Ours is a magazine to encourage young creative writers to use their imaginations, talent and writing skills. Type the manuscript—double space. Include all vital information about author. Send to one magazine at a time."

THE CRESCENT REVIEW, (II), The Crescent Review, Inc., 1445 Old Town Rd., Winston-Salem NC 27106-3143. (919)924-1851. Editor: Guy Nancekeville. Magazine: 6×9; 128 pages. Estab. 1983.
Needs: "All kinds of stories." Does not read submissions May-June; Nov.-Dec.
How to Contact: Reports in 2 weeks-4 months. SASE. Sample issue for $5.
Payment: Pays 2 contributor's copies; discount for contributors.
Terms: Acquires first North American serial rights.

‡CRIME CLUB, (I), Suite 5, 1929 The Alameda, San Jose CA 95126. (408)249-5689. Editors: Rob Oxoby and Marc Oxoby. Magazine. "Journal of poetry, prose and visual arts." Quarterly. Estab. 1991. Circ. 400.
Needs: Any genre. Adventure, experimental, fantasy, historical, humor/satire, literary, mainstream, psychic/supernatural/occult, regional, religious, science fiction, serialized novel, suspense/mystery, prose poem. Length: 200 words minimum; 5,000 words maximum. Publishes short shorts. Length: 200-500 words. Also accepts poetry.
How to Contact: Query first or send complete ms with cover letter.
Payment: Pays free subscription.
Terms: Acquires first North American serial rights.
Advice: "Be honest, be smart and have fun with it. We are serious but do this because we enjoy it. We'll publish anything of quality."

CROSSCURRENTS, (III), 2200 Glastonbury Rd., Westlake Village CA 91361. Editor: Linda Brown Michelson. Magazine: 6×9; 176 pages; 60 lb. paper stock; laminated cover; line drawings and halftone photos. "*Crosscurrents* is a literary magazine offering another corner for today's artistry. We publish short fiction, poetry, graphic arts and nonfiction. We direct our publication toward an educated audience who appreciate good writing and good art and who enjoy a periodic sampling of current trends in these fields." Quarterly. Estab. 1980. Circ. 3,000.
Needs: Most categories except heavy erotica, juvenile, science fiction and young adult. "Good writing is what we look for and consider first. We want high quality literary fiction." Buys 7-12 mss/issue, 45 mss/year. Approximately 10% of fiction is agented. Published fiction by Alvin Greenberg, Joyce Carol Oates and Alice Adams; published new writers in the last year. Length: 6,000 words maximum. Critiques rejected mss when there is time.
How to Contact: Send complete ms with SASE. Reviews material June 1-Nov 30 each year. No simultaneous submissions. Accepts computer printout submissions. Reports in 6 weeks on mss. Publishes ms 2-12 months after acceptance. Sample copy $6.
Payment: Pays $35 minimum. Offers 50% kill fee for assigned ms not published.
Terms: Pays on publication for first North American serial rights.
Advice: "Look at a sample issue to see what we publish. Include a short letter with your manuscript to let us know who you are. If given encouragement, submit three or four times each year, not every week. Study the awards collections and make sure your work measures up. Even small publications receive submissions from Nobel winners, and so self-monitoring will, in the long run, save postage."

‡CRUCIBLE, (I, II), English Dept., Barton College, College Station, Wilson NC 27893. (919)399-6456. Editor: Terrence L. Grimes. Magazine of fiction and poetry for a general, literary audience. Annually. Estab. 1964. Circ. 500.
Needs: Contemporary, ethnic, experimental, feminist, gay, lesbian, literary, regional. Receives 5 unsolicited mss/month. Accepts 5-6 mss/year. Publishes ms 4-5 months after acceptance. Recently published work by William Hutchins, Guy Nancekeville. Length: 8,000 words maximum. Publishes short shorts.
How to Contact: Send complete ms with cover letter which should include a brief biography, "in case we publish." Reports in 2 weeks on queries; 1 month on mss. SASE. Photocopied submissions OK. Accepts computer printout submissions. Sample copy for $4. Fiction guidelines free.
Payment: Pays contributor's copies.
Terms: Pays on publication for first rights.
Advice: "Write about what you know. Experimentation is fine as long as the experiences portrayed come across as authentic, that is to say, plausible."

‡CULTURE CONCRETE, (II), Suite 133, 2141-C Mission St., San Francisco CA 94110. Editor: Carlos Petroni. Magazine. Quarterly.
Needs: Open. Publishes short shorts.
How to Contact: Send complete manuscript with cover letter. SASE. Sample copy for $5.
Payment: No payment.

CUTBANK, (II), English Department, University of Montana, Missoula MT 59812. Editors-in-Chief: Peter Fong, Dennis Held. Fiction Editor: Claire Davis. Magazine: 5½×8½; 115-130 pages. "Publishes highest quality fiction, poetry, artwork, for a general, literary audience." Two issues/year. Estab. 1973. Circ. 400.
Needs: Receives 200 unsolicited mss/month. Accepts 6-12 mss/year. Does not read mss from February 28-August 15. Publishes ms up to 6 months after acceptance. Published new writers within the last year. Length: 40 pages maximum. Also publishes literary essays, literary criticism, poetry. Occasionally critiques rejected mss.
How to Contact: Send complete ms with cover letter, which should include "name, address, publications." Reports in 1-4 months on mss. SASE. Sample copy $4 (current issue $6.95). Fiction guidelines for SASE. Reviews novels and short story collections. Send books to fiction editor.
Payment: Pays 2 contributor's copies.
Terms: Rights revert to author upon publication, with provision that *Cutbank* receives publication credit.
Advice: "Strongly suggest contributors read an issue. We have published stories by David Long, William Kittredge, Rick DeMarinis, Patricia Henley, Melanie Rae Thon and Michael Dorris in recent issues, and like to feature new writers alongside more well-known names. Send only your best work."

CWM, (II, III, IV), 1300 Kicker Rd., Tuscaloosa AL 35404. (205)553-2284. Editor: David C. Kopaska-Merkel. Co-editor: Geof Huth, 317 Princeton Rd., Apt. 451, Schenectady NY 12306. (518)374-7143. Magazine: Variable size; pages, paper quality, cover variable; ink drawings or others possible. "Each issue has a theme; that of the 2nd issue is: 'What Lies Beneath the Surface.' We publish fiction, art and poetry for anyone interested in something a little bit different." Estab. 1990.
Needs: "Any submission fitting the theme." Receives 5-10 mss/months. Accepts 1-5 mss/issue; 2-10 mss/year. Publishes ms 1-11 months after acceptance. Length: 10,000 words maximum. Publishes short shorts; any length is acceptable. Also publishes poetry. Sometimes comments on rejected mss and recommends other markets.
How to Contact: Query first or send complete manuscript with cover letter. Reports in 1-4 weeks on queries; 1-8 weeks on mss. SASE. Photocopied submissions OK. Accepts computer printout submissions. Accepts electronic submissions via disk. Fiction guidelines for #10 SAE and 1 first class stamp.
Payment: Pays contributor's copies.
Terms: Acquires one-time rights.
Advice: "A manuscript must meet our theme for the issue in question. It stands out if it begins well and is neatly and clearly prepared. Given a good beginning, the story must hold the reader's interest all the way to the end and not let go. It helps if a story haunts the reader even after it is put aside."

D.C., (I), K3, 18 Taylor Ave., Earlville NY 13332. (315)691-9431. Editor: Katrina Kelly. Newsletter: 8½×11; 10-12 pages; illustrations. "*D.C.* is interested in funny and/or interesting materials, sick humor is good, too. Our audience is people of the punk genre and the sarcastically morbid." Monthly. Estab. 1988. Circ. 150.
Needs: Confession, ethnic, experimental, horror, humor/satire, prose poem, psychic/supernatural/occult. Receives 2-6 unsolicited mss/month. Acquires 3 (depending on length) mss/issue. Publishes ms soon after acceptance. Published work by Katrina Kelly, Jenn Nixon, Ben White. Publishes short shorts. Also publishes literary essays, poetry. Length: less than one page typed.
How to Contact: Query first. Reports in 1 week. Simultaneous and photocopied submissions OK. Accepts computer printout submissions. Sample copy for $1. Fiction guidelines for SAE and 1 first class stamp. Reviews novels and short story collections.
Payment: Pays subscription to magazine. Must write often to stay on mailing list.
Advice: "I like submissions that are well written, are *somewhat* logical and interest or amuse."

DAGGER OF THE MIND, Beyond The Realms Of Imagination, (II), K'yi-Lih Productions (a division of Breach Enterprises), 1317 Hookridge Dr., El Paso TX 79925. (915)591-0541. Editor: Arthur William Lloyd Breach. Magazine. 8½×11; 62-86 pages; hibright paper; high glossy cover; from 5-12 illustrations. Quarterly. Estab. 1990. Circ. 5,000.
Needs: Lovecraftian. Adventure, experimental, fantasy, horror, prose poem, science fiction, suspense/mystery. Nothing sick and blasphemous, vulgar, obscene, racist, sexist, profane, humorous, weak, exploited women stories and those with idiotic puns. Plans special paperback anthologies. Receives 120 unsolicited mss/month. Publishes 8-15 mss/issue; 90-100 mss/year depending upon length. Publishes ms 1 year after acceptance. Agented fiction 30%. Published work by Sidney Williams, Jessica Amanda Salmonson, Donald R. Burleson. Length: 4,500 words average; 5,000 minimum; 10,000 words maximum. Publishes short shorts. Length: Under 1,000 words. Also publishes literary essays, literary criticism, poetry. Sometimes comments on rejected mss.
How to Contact: Send complete manuscript with cover letter. "Include a bio and list of previously published credits with tearsheets. I also expect a brief synopsis of the story." Reports in 2 weeks on queries; 2 months on mss. SASE. Photocopied submissions OK. Accepts computer printout submissions. Accepts electronic submissions. Sample copy for $3.50, 9×12 SAE and 5 first class stamps. Fiction guidelines for #10 SAE and 1 first class stamp.
Payment: Pays ½-1¢/word plus 1 contributor's copy.
Terms: Pays on publication for first rights (possibly anthology rights as well).
Advice: "I'm a big fan of the late H.P. Lovecraft. I love reading through Dunsanian and Cthulhu Mythus tales. I'm constantly on the lookout for this special brand of fiction. If you want to grab my attention immediately, write on the outside of the envelope. 'Lovecratian submission enclosed.' There are a number of things which make submissions stand out for me. Is there any sensitivity to the tale? I like sensitive material, so long as it doesn't become mushy. Another thing that grabs my attention is characters which leap out of the pages and grab you. Then there are those old standards for accepting a manuscript: good imagery, story plot and originality. Move me, bring a tear to my eye; make me stop and think about the world and people around me. Frighten me with little spoken of truths about the human condition. In short, bring out all my emotions (except humor, I detest humor) and show me

that you can move me in such a way as I have never been moved before."

THE DALHOUSIE REVIEW, (II), Room 314, Dunn Building, Dalhousie University, Halifax, Nova Scotia B3H 3J5 Canada. Editor: Dr. Alan Andrews. Magazine: 14cm×23cm; approximately 140 pages; photographs sometimes. Publishes articles, short stories and poetry. Quarterly. Circ. 800.
Needs: Literary. Length: 5,000 words maximum. Also publishes literary essays, literary criticism, poetry.
How to Contact: Send complete ms with cover letter. SASE (Canadian stamps). Sample copy $5.50 (Canadian) plus postage. Occasionally reviews novels and short story collections.

DAN RIVER ANTHOLOGY, (I), Box 123, South Thomaston ME 04858. (207)354-6550. Editor: R. S. Danbury III. Book: 5½×8½; 156 pages; 60 lb. paper; gloss 65 lb. full-color cover; b&w illustrations. For general/adult audience. Annually. Estab. 1984. Circ. 1,200.
Needs: Adventure, contemporary, ethnic, experimental, fantasy, historical (general), horror, humor/satire, literary, mainstream, prose poem, psychic/supernatural/occult, regional, romance (contemporary and historical), science fiction, senior citizen/retirement, suspense/mystery and western. No "evangelical Christian, pornography or sentimentality." Receives 20-30 unsolicited mss/month. Accepts about 8-10 mss/year. Reads "mostly in March." Length: 2,000-2,400 words average; 800 words minumum; 4,000 words maximum. Also publishes poetry.
How to Contact: *Charges reading fee: $1 for poetry; $3 for prose.* Send complete ms with SASE. Reports in April each year. Accepts computer printout submissions. Sample copy for $9.95 paperback, $19.95 cloth, plus $2.50 shipping. Fiction guidelines for #10 SASE.
Payment: Pays $5/page, minimum *cash advance on acceptance* against royalties of 10% of all sales attributable to writer's influence: readings, mailings, autograph parties, etc., plus up to 50% discount on copies, plus other discounts to make total as high as 73%.
Terms: Acquires first rights.
Advice: "Also: The CAL Anthology—Same Guidelines. Acceptance/Rejection—November."

DANCE CONNECTION, A Canadian Dance Journal, (II, IV), 603, 815 1st St. SW, Calgary, Alberta, T2P 1N3 Canada. (403)237-7327. Editor: Heather Elton. Magazine: 8½×11; 56 pages; recycled bond paper; illustrations and b&w photographs. "Dance: Interview, essay, commentary, reviews for dance lovers, academics, educators, professionals, artists." Published 5 times per year. Estab. 1983. Circ. 5,000.
Needs: Dance. "Do not send anything not related to dance or poems about ballet." Plans special fiction issue. Receives 10 unsolicited mss/month. Accepts 1 mss/issue; 3 mss/year. Publishes ms 3 months after acceptance. Length: 1,100 words average; 400 words minimum; 2,500 words maximum. Publishes short shorts. Length: 800 words.
How to Contact: Query with clips of published work or send complete manuscript with cover letter. Reports in 6 weeks. SASE. Simultaneous, photocopied and reprint submissions OK. Accepts computer printout submissions. Accepts electronic submissions; prefers Macintosh disc (Microsoft Word). Sample copy for 9×12 SAE. Fiction guidelines for #10 SAE.
Payment: Pays $25-250 (Canadian), free subscription to magazine and contributor's copies.
Terms: Pays on publication. Buys first rights or one-time rights.

‡DANDELION MAGAZINE, (II), Dandelion Magazine Society, 922 9th Ave., Calgary, Alberta T2C 0S4 Canada. (403)265-0524. Fiction Editor: Flora Malteure. Magazine: 100 pages. Semiannually. Estab. 1972. Circ. 700.
Needs: Literary. Receives 50 unsolicited mss/month. Accepts 5 mss/issue; 10 mss/year. Publishes ms 6 months after acceptance. Pubilshes short shorts. Sometimes critiques rejected mss.
How to Contact: Send complete ms with cover letter. Reports in 6 months on mss. SASE. Reviews novels and short story collections by Alberta authors. Sample copy for $6. Fiction guidelines for SAE.
Payment: No payment.
Terms: Acquires one-time rights.
Advice: "The best way to understand what we publish is by reading *Dandelion*. We invite you to subscribe. We publish reviews of books by Alberta authors, poetry, visual arts, short fiction and the occasional article. We try to be eclectic in what we publish. Please remember that since we only publish

Market categories: (I) Beginning; (II) General; (III) Prestige; (IV) Specialized.

twice a year this sometimes gives rise to a delay in returning manuscripts. For our June issue we consider manuscripts during January through to the end of March. For our December issue we consider manuscripts during July through to the end of September. Manuscripts without a SASE, or without sufficient postage will not be returned."

DARK TOME, (I, IV), P.O. Box 705, Salem OR 97308. Editor: Michelle Marr. Magazine: 5½ × 8½; 30-80 pages; 20 lb. paper; 60 lb. cover; illustrations. "We publish horror fiction for mature readers who are not easily offended." Bimonthly. Estab. 1990. Circ. 125.
Needs: Horror, psychic/supernatural/occult. "I want original stories, not classic ghost stories. I also tend to stay away from purely gothic material." Receives 30 unsolicited mss/month. Acquires 6-10 mss/issue; 30-60 mss/year. Publishes manuscript 2 months after acceptance. Length: 1,500 words average; 3,000 words maximum. Always comments on rejected mss.
How to Contact: Send complete manuscript with cover letter. Include something about the author. Reports in 1 week on queries; 3 weeks on mss. SASE. Photocopied submissions OK. Accepts computer printout submissions. Sample copy for $2 payable to Michelle Marr. Fiction guidelines for #10 SAE and 1 first class stamp.
Payment: Pays in contributor's copies and small cash payment.
Terms: Buys first North American serial rights.
Advice: "I am looking for *horror* fiction *only*. What makes a manuscript stand out is originality, a believable plot, stories that leave a lasting image in the mind of the reader. Check for inconsistencies in plot; do something original; if an editor suggests a change that you strongly disagree with, *don't* do it (even if it means not selling the story). AND DON'T GIVE UP! I'm trying to expand the types of fiction I use, staying within the realms of horror, fantasy and speculative fiction. *Dark Tome* is a very active market I *need* good stories."

DAUGHTERS OF SARAH, (II, IV), 3801 N. Keeler, Box 411179, Chicago IL 60618. (312)736-3399. Editor: Reta Finger. Magazine: 5½ × 8½; 64 pages; illustrations and photos. "Christian feminist publication dealing with Christian theology, history, women and social issues from a feminist point of view." Quarterly. Estab. 1974. Circ. 5,000.
Needs: Historical, religious/inspirational, feminist and spiritual (Christian feminist). "No subjects unrelated to feminism from Christian viewpoint." Upcoming themes: "Women and War," "Feminism on Prophecy," "Birth, Adoption, Abortion," "Prostitution," "Women in Ministry." Receives 6-8 unsolicited fiction mss/month. Buys 4-6 mss/year. Published work by Mary Cartledge-Hayes. Length: 1,800 words maximum. Publishes short shorts. Also publishes poetry. Occasionally critiques rejected mss "if related and close to acceptance."
How to Contact: Query first with description of ms and SASE. Include cover letter stating why ms was written; biography of author. Simultaneous, photocopied and previously published submissions OK "but won't pay." Accepts computer printout submissions. Reports in 2 weeks on queries. Publishes "most" ms 3 months to 1 year after acceptance. Sample copy for $2.50. Reviews novels and short story collections. Send books to Dulcie Gannett.
Payment: Pays $15/printed page; 3 free contributor's copies. Offers kill fee of one-half stated fee.
Terms: Pays upon publication for first North American serial or one-time rights.
Advice: "Make sure topic of story fits with publication. We get many stories that are either Christian stories, women's stories, Christian women's stories, but not necessarily feminist. We believe that the Christian gospel was meant to be radically egalitarian and we try to integrate it with the feminist insights and analysis available today."

‡DEAD TREE PRODUCT, (I, II), 2-3 Humanities Bldg., University of Alberta, Edmonton, Alberta T5H 2E5 Canada. (403)491-7193. Editor: Kyle Loranger. Fiction Editor: Jason Kapalka. Tabloid: 11 × 17; 16-24 pages; newsprint; illustrations and photos. *Dead Tree Product* prints short stories, poems, comics and essays generally for students. Monthly. Estab. 1990. Circ. 5,000.
Needs: Adventure, contemporary, ethnic, experimental, fantasy, feminist, gay, historical, horror, humor/satire, lesbian, literary, mainstream, prose poem, psychic/supernatural/occult, science fiction, suspense/mystery, western. No "Vietnam war epics." Receives 20 unsolicited mss/month. Buys 3-5 mss/issue; 25-35 mss/year. Publishes ms 1-2 months after acceptance. Recently published Jon Ward, D.Q. Domber and Thomas Whorton. Length: 2,000 words preferred; 3,000 words maximum. Publishes short shorts. Sometimes critiques rejected mss.
How to Contact: Send complete ms with cover letter. Reports in 3-4 weeks. SASE. Simultaneous and photocopied submissions OK. Accepts computer printout submissions. Sample copy for 7 × 11 SAE with IRC (or $1 American).

Payment: Pays contributor's copies.

Terms: Acquires first North American serial rights.

Advice: Looks for "comfortable and accessible introduction to capture interest; expressive and vivid characters or action. The shorter the better, but longer quality pieces are OK. Most submissions are applicable to whatever contest we have running at the time. We have three categories: short story, poem and photo. The first prize is always $100 cash and whatever else."

DEATHREALM, (II), 3223-F Regents Park, Greensboro NC 27405. (919)288-9138. Editor: Mark Rainey. Magazine: 8½×11; 50-60 pages; 20 lb. bond paper; 8 pt. glossy coated cover stock; pen & ink, screened illustrations; b&w photos. Publishes "fantasy/horror," for a "mature" audience. Quarterly. Estab. 1987. Circ. 1,200.

Needs: Experimental, fantasy, horror, psychic/supernatural/occult and science fiction. "Sci-fi tales should have a horror slant. *Do not* send tales that are not in the realm of dark fantasy. *Strongly* recommend contributor buy a sample copy of *Deathrealm* before submitting." Receives 200-300 mss/month. Buys 6-8 mss/issue; 30 mss/year. Publishes ms within 1 year of acceptance. Published work by Joe R. Lansdale, Fred Chappell, Kevin J. Anderson, Jessica Amanda Salmonson. Length: 5,000 words average; 10,000 words maximum. Publishes short shorts. Also publishes literary criticism, poetry. Sometimes critiques rejected mss and recommends other markets.

How to Contact: Send complete ms with cover letter, which should include "publishing credits, some bio info, where they heard about *Deathrealm*. Never reveal plot in cover letter." Reports in 1 week on queries; 2-6 weeks on ms. SASE. Photocopied submissions OK. Accepts computer printout submissions. Sample copy for $4 and 65¢ postage. Fiction guidelines for #10 SAE and 1 first class stamp. Reviews novels and short story collections. Send books to Mike Newland, 1030 Carriagehouse Lane, Garland TX 75040 or Randy Johnston, 3114 NW 41, Oklahoma City OK 73112.

Payment: Pays $5 minimum; higher rates for established professionals; contributor's copies.

Advice: "Concentrate on characterization; development of ideas; strong atmosphere, with an important setting. I frown on gratuitous sex and violence unless it is a mere side effect of a more sophisticated story line. Stay away from overdone themes – foreboding dreams come true; being a frustrated writer; using lots of profanity and having a main character so detestable you don't care what happens to him."

DENVER QUARTERLY, (II, III), University of Denver, Denver CO 80208. (303)871-2892. Editor: Donald Revell. Magazine: 6×9; 144-160 pages; occasional illustrations. "We publish fiction, articles and poetry for a generally well-educated audience, primarily interested in literature and the literary experience. They read *DQ* to find something a little different from a strictly academic quarterly or a creative writing outlet." Quarterly. Estab. 1966. Circ. 1,200.

Needs: "We are now interested in experimental fiction (minimalism, magic realism, etc.) as well as in realistic fiction." Also publishes poetry.

How to Contact: Send complete ms with SASE. Does not read mss May-September 15. Do not query. Reports in 1-2 months on mss. Publishes ms within a year after acceptance. Published work by Joyce Carol Oates, Jay Clayton, Charles Baxter; published new writers within the last year. No simultaneous submissions. Sample copy $5 with SASE.

Payment: Pays $5/page for fiction and poetry, 2 free author's copies plus 3 tear sheets.

Terms: Buys first North American serial rights.

Advice: "We'll be looking for serious, realistic and experimental fiction. Nothing so quickly disqualifies a manuscript as sloppy proofreading and mechanics. Read the magazine before submitting to it. Send clean copy and a *brief* cover letter. We try to remain eclectic and I think we do, but the odds for beginners are bound to be long considering the fact that we receive nearly 8,000 mss per year and publish only about 16 short stories."

DESCANT, (II), Box 314, Station P, Toronto, Ontario M5S 2S8 Canada. (416)927-7059. Editor: Karen Mulhallen. Magazine: 5¾×8¾; 100-300 pages; heavy paper; good cover stock; illustrations and photos. "High quality poetry and prose for an intelligent audience who wants to see a broad range of literature." Quarterly. Estab. 1970. Circ. 1,000.

Needs: Literary, contemporary, translations. "Although most themes are acceptable, all works must have literary merit." Upcoming themes: "Space" (Inner and Outer, Spring 1992); "First Nations" (not yet scheduled). Receives 100-200 unsolicited mss/month. Published work by Tim Lilburn, Douglas Glover, George Bowering. Publishes short shorts. Also publishes literary essays, poetry. Critiques rejected mss when there is time.

How to Contact: Send complete ms with cover letter. SAE, IRC. Reports in 4 months on mss. Sample copy for $7.50 plus $2 for postage to U.S.
Payment: Pays a modest honorarium and 1 year subscription. Extra author's copies at discount.
Advice: *"Descant* has plans for several special issues in the next two years. Unsolicited work is less likely to be accepted in the coming months, and will be kept on file for longer before it appears."

DESCANT, (II), Department of English, Texas Christian University, Fort Worth TX 76129. (817)921-7240. Editors: Betsy Colquitt, Stanley Trachtenberg, Harry Opperman. *"Descant* uses fiction and poetry. No restriction on style, content or theme. *Descant* is a 'little' literary magazine, and its readers are those who have interest in such publications." Semiannually. Estab. 1955. Circ. 500.
Needs: Literary, contemporary and regional. No genre or category fiction. Receives approximately 50 unsolicited fiction mss each month. Does not read mss in summer. Published new writers within the last year. Length: 1,500-5,000 words. Publishes short shorts. Sometimes recommends other markets. Also publishes poetry.
How to Contact: Send complete ms with SASE. Accepts computer printout submissions. Reports usually within 6 weeks on ms. Sample copy $4.50 (old copy).
Payment: Pays 2 free author's copies. (Pays $4.50 charge/extra copy.)
Advice: "Submit good material. Even though a small publication, *Descant* receives many submissions, and acceptances are few compared to the total number of mss received." Mss are rejected because they "are badly written, careless in style and development, shallow in characterization, trite in handling and in conception. We offer a $500 annual prize for fiction—the Frank O'Connor Prize. Award is made to the story considered (by a judge not connected to the magazine) to be the best published in a given volume of the journal."

‡DEUTERIUM, A Digest of Poems, Prose, and Art, (I), P.O. Box 20013, Dayton OH 45420-0013. (513)252-5784. Editor: Randy Watts. Magazine: 5½ × 8½; 16 pages; some illustrations. "For beginning, thought provoking writers." Semiannually. Estab. 1991. Circ. 100.
Needs: Confession, contemporary, experimental, fantasy, gay, historical (general), mainstream, prose poem, regional, romance (contemporary, historical), science fiction, suspense/mystery. Length: Open. Publishes short shorts. Also accepts poetry. Recommends other markets.
How to Contact: Query first. Simultaneous, photocopied and reprint submissions OK. Accepts computer printout submissions. Sample copy free.
Payment: Pays contributor's copies.
Terms: Acquires one-time rights.
Advice: "I personaly like down-to-earth writers. Don't write over the average American head."

DREAM INTERNATIONAL/QUARTERLY, (II, IV), U.S. Address: Charles I. Jones, 121 N. Ramona St. #27, Ramona CA 92065. Australia address: Dr. Les Jones, 256 Berserker St., No. Rockhampton, Queensland 4701, Australia. Editors: Les and Chuck Jones. Magazine: 5 × 7; 60-80 pages; photocopied; parchment cover stock; some illustrations and photos. Publishes fiction and nonfiction that is dream-related or clearly inspired by a dream. Quarterly. Estab. 1981. Circ. 200.
Needs: Adventure, confession, contemporary, erotica, ethnic, experimental, fantasy, historical (general), horror, humor/satire, juvenile (5-9 years), literary, mainstream, prose poem, psychic/supernatural/occult, romance, science fiction, senior citizen/retirement, serialized/excerpted novel, spiritual, suspense/mystery, translations, western, young adult/teen (10-18). Receives 20-40 unsolicited mss/month. Publishes ms 6-8 months after acceptance. Length: 1,500 words minimum; 2,000 words maximum. Published new writers within the last year. Publishes short shorts. Length: 1,000 words. Also publishes literary essays, poetry. Occasionally critiques rejected mss. Sometimes recommends other markets.
How to Contact: Reports in 6 weeks on queries; 3 months on mss. SASE. Photocopied and reprint submissions OK. Accepts computer printout submissions. Sample copy for $4 (add $1.50 to single copy purchases and $4.50 to subscriptions to cover postage and handling), SAE and 2 first class stamps. Guidelines for $1, SAE and 1 first class stamp. "Accepted mss will not be returned unless requested at time of submission."
Payment: Pays in contributor's copies; sometimes offers free magazine subscription.
Terms: Acquires one-time rights.
Advice: "Use your nightly dreams to inspire you to literary flights. Avoid stereotypes and clichés. Avoid Twilight Zone type stories. When contacting U.S. editor, make all checks, money orders, and overseas drafts payable to *Charles Jones.*"

DREAMS & NIGHTMARES, The Magazine of Fantastic Poetry, (IV), 1300 Kicker Rd., Tuscaloosa AL 35404. (205)553-2284. Editor: David C. Kopaska-Merkel. Magazine: 5½×8½; 20 pages; ink drawing illustrations. "*DN* is mainly a poetry magazine, but I *am* looking for short-short stories. They should be either fantasy, science fiction, or horror." Estab. 1986. Circ. 200.
Needs: Experimental, fantasy, horror, humor/satire, science fiction. "Try me with anything *except*: senseless violence, misogyny or hatred (unreasoning) of any kind of people, sappiness." Receives 4-8 unsolicited mss/month. Buys 0-1 ms/issue; 0-2 mss/year. Publishes ms 1-9 months after acceptance. Published work by Ron McDowell. Length: 500 words average; 1,000 words maximum. Publishes short shorts. Length: 500 or fewer words. Sometimes critiques rejected mss and recommends other markets. Also publishes poetry.
How to Contact: Query first, then send complete manuscript. Reports in 1-3 weeks on queries; 1-6 weeks on mss. SASE. Photocopied submissions OK. Accepts computer printout submissions. Accepts electronic submissions. Sample copy for $1.25 in stamps. Fiction guidelines for #10 SAE and 1 first class stamp.
Payment: Pays $2 and one contributor's copy.
Terms: Pays on acceptance for one-time rights.
Advice: "A story must grab the reader and hold on to the end. I want to be *involved*. Start with a good first line, lead the reader where you want him/her to go and end with something that causes a reaction or provokes thought."

DREAMS & VISIONS, New Frontiers in Christian Fiction, (II), Skysong Press, RR1, Washago, Ontario L0K 2B0 Canada. Editor: Steve Stanton. Fiction Editor: Wendy Stanton. Magazine: 5½×8½; 48 pages; 20 lb. bond paper; Mayfair Fancy cover; illustrations on cover. "Contemporary Christian fiction in a variety of styles for adult Christians." Quarterly. Estab. 1989. Circ. 500.
Needs: Contemporary, experimental, fantasy, humor/satire, literary, religious/inspirational. "All stories should portray a Christian world view or expand upon Biblical themes or ethics in an entertaining or enlightening manner." Receives 20 unsolicited mss/month. Accepts 7 mss/issue; 30 mss/year. Publishes ms 2-6 months after acceptance. Length: 2,500 words; 1,500 words minimum; 7,500 words maximum. Sometimes critiques rejected mss.
How to Contact: Send complete ms with cover letter. "Bio is optional: degrees held and in what specialties, publishing credits, service in the church, etc." Reports in 2 weeks on queries; 6-8 weeks on mss. SASE. Photocopied submissions OK. Accepts computer printout submissions. Sample copy for $3. Fiction guidelines for SAE and 1 IRC.
Payment: Pays in contributor's copies; extras at ⅓ discount.
Terms: Acquires first North American serial rights and one-time, non-exclusive reprint rights.
Advice: "In general we look for work that has some literary value, that is in some way unique and relevant to Christian readers today. Our first priority is technical adequacy, though we will occasionally work with a beginning writer to polish a manuscript. Ultimately, we look for stories that glorify the Lord Jesus Christ, stories that build up rather than tear down, that exalt the sanctity of life, the holiness of God, and the value of the family."

EAGLE'S FLIGHT, A Literary Magazine, (I), 2501 Hunters Hill Dr., #822, Enid OK 73703. Editor: Shyamkant Kulkarni. Fiction Editor: Rekha Kulkarni. Tabloid: 8½×11; 2-4 pages; bond paper; broad sheet cover. Publication includes "fiction and poetry for a general audience." Quarterly.
Needs: Literary, mainstream, romance, suspense/mystery. Plans to publish special fiction issue in future. Accepts 1-2 mss/year. Does not read mss June-December. Recently published work by Dr. Leroy Thomas, Laura Dawson, Chad Born, Branley Branson. Length: 1,500 words preferred; 1,000 words minimum; 2,000 maximum. Publishes short shorts. Also Publishes literary criticism, poetry.
How to Contact: Query first. Reports in 6 weeks on queries; 3 months on mss. Combine SASE. Photocopied submissions OK. Accepts computer printout submissions. Sample copy or fiction guidelines for $1 and #10 SAE and 1 first class stamp. Reviews novels and short story collections.
Payment: Pays $5-20 or free subscription to magazine, contributor's copies; charge for extras.
Terms: Pays on publication for first North American serial rights or one-time rights.
Advice: "We look for form, substance and quality. Read and study what one wants to write and work at."

EARTH'S DAUGHTERS (II), A Feminist Arts Periodical, Box 41, Central Park Station, Buffalo NY 14215. (716)835-8719. Collective editorship. Business Manager: Bonnie Johnson. Magazine: usually 5½×8½; 50 pages; 60 lb. paper; coated cover; 2-4 illustrations; 2-4 photos. "We publish poetry and short fiction; also graphics, art work and photos; our focus is the experience and creative expression of women." For a general/women/feminist audience. Quarterly. Published special topical issues last year; plans more this year. Estab. 1971. Circ. 1,000.

Needs: Contemporary, erotica, ethnic, experimental, fantasy, feminist, humor/satire, literary, prose poem. "Keep the fiction short." Receives 25-50 unsolicited fiction mss/month. Accepts 2-4 mss/issue; 8-12 mss/year. Published work by Gabrielle Burton, Mary Jane Markell, Meredith Sue Willis and Julia Alvarez; published several new writers within the last year. Length: 400 words minimum; 1,000 words maximum; 800 words average. Occasionally critiques rejected mss and recommends other markets.

How to Contact: Send complete ms. SASE. Simultaneous and photocopied submissions OK. Accepts computer printout submissions, "must be clearly legible." Reports in 3 weeks on queries; 3 weeks to 3 months on mss. Publishes ms an average of 1 year after acceptance. Sample copy for $4.

Payment: Pays 2 contributor's copies, additional copies half price.

Terms: Acquires first rights. Copyright reverts to author upon publication.

Advice: "We require work of technical skill and artistic intensity; we welcome submissions from unknown writers. Send SASE in April of each year for themes of upcoming issues. Please do not inquire as to the status of your work too soon or too often—the US Mail is dependable, and we have yet to lose a manuscript."

ECHOES, (II), The Hudson Valley Writers Association, Box 365, Wappingers Falls NY 12590. Editor: Marcia Grant. Fiction Editor: Don Monaco. Magazine: 5½ × 8½; 44 pages; illustrations. Quarterly. Estab. 1985. Circ. 300.

Needs: "We do not categorize material—we consider material of *all* types." Receives 15-30 unsolicited mss/month. Accepts 2-5 mss/issue; 8-20 mss/year. Publishes ms 8-12 weeks after acceptance. Published work by Arnold Lipkind, C.C. Doucette; "often encourages promising authors." Length: 1,500 words preferred; 750 words minimum; 3,000 words maximum. Publishes short shorts. Sometimes critiques rejected mss and recommends other markets.

How to Contact: Send complete manuscript with cover letter. Reports in 6-8 weeks. SASE. Simultaneous, photocopied submissions; reprints OK, if author owns rights. Accepts computer printout submissions OK. Sample copy for $4.50. Back issues $3. Fiction guidelines for SAE.

Payment: Pays 1 contributor's copy.

Terms: Acquires one-time rights.

Advice: "Suggest reading a sample copy. We look for quality writing, engaging ideas and writing that we can get excited about."

THE ECPHORIZER, A Mensa Magazine of Literature and Ideas, (II), American Mensa Ltd., Region 8, 481 Century Dr., Campbell CA 95008. (408)378-8820. Editor: Michael J. Eager. Magazine: 7 × 8½; 36 pages; 60 lb. offset paper; Astrobrite cover; 5-8 line art illustrations and limited photographs. "Eclectic magazine for Mensa members and friends." Bimonthly. Estab. 1981.

Needs: Adventure, contemporary, erotica, experimental, fantasy, historical (general), humor/satire, literary, mainstream, prose poem, psychic/supernatural/occult, regional, science fiction, serialized novel, suspense/mystery, translations. Receives 4-5 unsolicited mss/month. Accepts 2-3 mss/issue; 18-25 mss/year. Publishes ms 2-4 months after acceptance. Published work by Redge Mahaffey, Albert Russo. Length: 3,000 words average; 500 words minimum; 6,000 words maximum. Publishes short shorts. Sometimes critiques rejected mss.

How to Contact: Send complete manuscript with cover letter. Reports in 2-4 weeks. SASE. Simultaneous, photocopied and reprint submissions OK. Accepts computer printout submissions. Accepts electronic submissions (preferred method). Sample copy $2.

Payment: Pays contributor's copies.

Terms: Acquires first North American serial or one-time rights.

Advice: Looks for "interesting presentation, well-thought-out, unique approach to situation. Have clear idea of what you are trying to say and who you are saying it to. Too many articles received which are technically well written but appear to have no point or purpose. One gets to the end and says 'So? What next?' "

EIDOS: Sexual Freedom and Erotic Entertainment for Women, Men & Couples, (IV), Box 96, Boston MA 02137-0096. (617)262-0096. Editor: Brenda Loew Tatelbaum. Tabloid: 10 × 14; 60 pages; web offset printing; illustrations; photos. Magazine of erotica for women, men and couples of all sexual orientations, preferences and lifestyles. "Explicit material regarding language and behavior formed in relationships, intimacy, moment of satisfaction—sensual, sexy, honest. For an energetic, well informed, international erotica readership." Quarterly. Estab. 1984. Circ. 7,000.

Needs: Erotica. Humorous or tongue-in-cheek erotic fiction is especially wanted. Publishes at least 4 pieces of fiction/year. Published new writers within the last year. Length: 1,000 words average; 500 words minimum; 2,000 words maximum. Also publishes literary criticism, poetry. Occasionally critiques rejected mss and recommends other markets.
How to Contact: Send complete ms with SASE. "Cover letter with history of publication or short bio is welcome." Reports in 1 month on queries; 2 months on mss. Simultaneous and photocopied submissions OK. Accepts computer printout submissions. Sample copy $10. Fiction guidelines for #10 envelope with 1 first class stamp. Reviews novels and short story collections, "if related to subject of erotica (sex, politics, religion, etc.)."
Payment: Pays in contributor's copies.
Terms: Acquires first North American serial rights.
Advice: "We receive more erotic fiction manuscripts now than in the past. Most likely because both men and women are more comfortable with the notion of submitting these manuscripts for publication as well as the desire to see alternative sexually explicit fiction in print. Therefore we can publish more erotic fiction because we have more material to choose from. There is still a lot of debate as to what erotic fiction consists of. This is a tough market to break into. Manuscripts must fit our editorial needs and it is best to order a sample issue prior to writing or submitting material. Honest, explicitly pro-sex, mutually consensual erotica is void of unwanted power, control and degradation—no rape or coercion of any kind."

ELDRITCH SCIENCE, (II,IV), Greater Medford Science Fiction Society, 87-6 Park, Worcester MA 01605. Editor: George Phillies. Magazine: 8½×11; 30 pages; 20 lb. paper; 60 lb. cover; illustrations. Science fiction and fantasy for adults. Semiannually. Estab. 1988.
Needs: Adventure, fantasy, literary, science fiction. "No horror, contemporary, erotica." Receives 5-10 unsolicited mss/month. Accepts 4 mss/issue; 8 mss/year. Publishes mss 4-6 months after acceptance. Published work by Cabot, Moxley, Reedman. Length: 8,000 words; 5,000 words minimum; 15,000 words maximum. Also publishes literary essays. Sometimes critiques rejected mss and recommends other markets.
How to Contact: Send complete ms with cover letter. Reports in 2 weeks on queries; 6-8 weeks on mss. SASE for mss. Photocopied submissions OK. Accepts computer printout submissions. Prefers electronic submissions via disk (MS-DOS, low density). Sample copy for 9×12 SAE and 5 first class stamps. Free fiction guidelines.
Payment: Pays in contributor's copies.
Terms: Acquires one-time rights. Publication not copyrighted.
Advice: "Clear plots, heroes who think and solve their problems, and sparkling, literary prose. Make a manuscript stand out. Read the guidelines!"

11TH STREET RUSE, (II), 322 E. 11th St., #23, New York NY 10003. Editor: Violet Snow. Newsletter: 8½×11; 4 pages; bond paper. "Mythical travel; goddess religion; the homeless; for young intellectuals with poor spelling." Bimonthly. Estab. 1988. Circ. 150.
Needs: "We need humorous writers, who can *hear* what they write—preferably have studied poetry. Accepts all types of fiction." No "Romance or genre that's dumb and obvious." Receives 5 unsolicited mss/month. Accepts 1 ms/year. Publishes ms 2 months after acceptance. Published work by RLS, Violet Snow and Lucid. Length: 500 words average; 6 words minimum; 1,000 words maximum. Publishes short shorts. Length: 300 words. Also publishes literary essays, poetry. Sometimes comments on rejected mss.
How to Contact: Send complete manuscript with cover letter. Include "bio, hatsize." Reports in 3 months. SASE. Simultaneous and photocopied submissions OK. Accepts computer printout submissions. Sample copy for $1, #10 SAE and 1 first class stamp. Fiction guidelines for #10 SAE and 1 first class stamp.
Payment: Pays contributor's copies.
Terms: Acquires one-time rights. Publication not copyrighted.

 The double dagger before a listing indicates that the listing is new in this edition. New markets are often the most receptive to freelance contributions.

‡**ELF: ECLECTIC LITERARY FORUM, (II)**, P.O. Box 392, Tonawanda NY 14150. (716)693-7006. Editor: C.K. Erbes. Magazine: 8½×11; 56 pages; 60 lb. white offset paper; coated cover; 2-3 illustrations; 2-3 photographs. "Well-crafted short stories, poetry, essays or literary themes for a sophisticated audience." Quarterly. Estab. 1991. Circ. 1,000.

Needs: Adventure, contemporary, ethnic, fantasy, feminism, historical (general), humor/satire, literary, mainstream, prose poem, regional, science fiction, sports. No violence and obscenity (horror/erotica). Accepts 4-6 mss/issue; 16-24 mss/year. Publishes ms up to 1 year after acceptance. Recently published work by Annie Dawid, Janis Wick, W. Edwin Ver Becke. Length: 2,500 words average. Publishes short shorts. Length: 500 words. Sometimes critiques rejected mss and recommends other markets.

How to Contact: Send complete ms with optional cover letter. Reports in 4-6 weeks on mss. SASE. Simultaneous submissions OK (if so indicated). Sample copy for $4.50 ($6 foreign). Fiction guidelines for #10 SAE and 1 first class stamp.

Payment: Pays contributor's copies.

Terms: Acquires first North American serial rights.

Advice: "Short stories stand out when dialogue, plot, character, point of view and language usage work together to create a unified whole on a significant theme, one relevant to most of our readers. We also look for writers whose works demonstrate a knowledge of grammar and how to manipulate it effectively in a story. Each story is read by an Editorial Board comprised of English professors who teach creative writing and are published authors."

EMRYS JOURNAL, (II), The Emrys Foundation, Box 8813, Greenville SC 29604. (803)288-5154. Editor: Linda Julian. Magazine: 6×9; 96 pages; 60 lb. paper and cover stock; calligraphy illustrations. "We publish short fiction, poetry, essays and book reviews. We are particularly interested in hearing from women and other minorities. We are mindful of the southeast but not limited to it." Annually. Estab. 1984. Circ. 300.

Needs: Contemporary, feminist, literary, mainstream and regional. "We read only during September 1-February 15. During reading periods we receive around 800 manuscripts." Accepts 3-7 stories per issue. Publishes ms 2 months after acceptance. Length: 3,500 words average; 2,500 word minimum; 6,000 word maximum. Publishes short shorts. Length: 1,600 words. Sometimes recommends other markets. Also publishes poetry.

How To Contact: Send complete ms with cover letter. Put no identification on manuscript; include separate sheet with title, name, address and phone. "No queries." Reports in 2 months. SASE. Photocopied submissions OK. Accepts computer printout submissions. Sample copy $4 and 7×10 SAE with 4 first class stamps. Fiction guidelines for #10 SAE and 1 first class stamp.

Payment: Pays in contributor's copies.

Terms: Acquires first rights. "Send to managing editor for guidelines."

‡**ENCOUNTERS MAGAZINE, (I, II, IV)**, Black Matrix Press, Box 5737, Grants Pass OR 97527. (503)476-7039. Editor: Guy Kenyon. Tabloid/Newspaper: 16-20 pages; b&w illustrations. "Action/adventure and suspense, with a dash of humor welcome, sf, fantasy and horror for a general audience in a wide age group that enjoys imaginative fiction." Bimonthly. Estab. 1989. Circ. 2,000.

Needs: Fantasy, horror, science fiction. "No erotica or experimental fiction and no poetry." Receives 30-35 unsolicited mss/month. Accepts 8-10 mss/issue; 40-60 mss/year. Publishes 3-9 months after acceptance. Recently published Donald R. Burleson, K.D. Wentworth, Ken Wismen and J.E. Deegan. Length: 5,000 words; 1,000 words minimum; 10,000 words maximum.

How to Contact: Send complete ms with coverletter, include a short bio about the author. Reports in 2 weeks on queries; 4-6 weeks on mss. SASE. Photocopied and reprint submissions OK. Accepts computer printout submissions. Sample copy for $1. Fiction guidelines for #10 SAE and 1 first class stamp.

Payment: Pays ⅛ of a cent per word on acceptance plus 1 copy ($2 minimum payment).

Terms: Buys first North American serial rights.

Advice: "We lean toward those stories that have characters who are believable. Nomatter how exotic the setting, or how unusual the situation, the characterin the story must be someone the reader can relate to. A story is about people—the rest is a tapestry on which they play out their lives. Concentrate on telling a good story. Try to involve the reader in your characters' lives, make them interested in how they resolve their conflicts. Remember, as a writer you are an entertainer."

EOTU, Magazine of Experimental Fiction, (I, II), 1810 W. State, #115, Boise ID 83702. Editor: Larry D. Dennis. Magazine 5½ × 8½; 70-80 pages; 20 lb. paper; illustrations. "We publish short stories that try to say or do something new in literature, in prose. New style, new story structures, new voice, whatever." Bimonthly. Estab. 1988. Circ. 500.
Needs: Experimental, prose poem. For upcoming themes, send SASE for newsletter, *The Clam City News*. Receives 150-200 unsolicited fiction mss/month; accepts 10-12 mss/issue; 60-70 mss/year. Publishes ms 4-6 months after acceptance. Published work by Don Webb, Bruce Boston, H. Andrew Lynch; published new writers within the last year. Length: 2,500 words average; 2 words minimum; 5,000 words maximum. Sometimes comments on rejected mss or recommends other markets.
How to Contact: Send complete ms. "Cover letter isn't really necessary, but it's nice to know where they heard of us." Reports on queries in 1 week; on mss in 6-8 weeks. SASE. Photocopied submissions OK. Accepts computer printouts. Sample copy for $4; fiction guidelines for #10 SAE and 1 first class stamp.
Payment: Pays $5 minimum; $25 maximum and contributor's copies.
Terms: Pays on acceptance for first North American serial rights. Sends pre-publication galleys to author "only when a story has been edited and a writer's approval of the changes is needed."
Advice: "I've got this time and money and want to invest it in something. So, do I buy a Jiffy Lube or start a new Wendy's burger place? Or do I choose to create a business that caters to my strengths, my loves and desires? Well, that's what I'm doing. I always wanted to publish a magazine, and I've always loved short stories. I urge beginning writers to keep sending stories out. You'll never sell the one in your drawer. If a story comes back with a handwritten note, if it looks like someone really read it, send that editor another. When an editor takes time to critique, it means he's interested and he's trying to help."

‡EPIPHANY, A Journal of Literature, (II), P.O. Box 2699, University of Arkansas, Fayetteville AR 72701. (501)524-3326. Editor: Sandra Reyes. Fiction Editor: Dora Rainey. Newspaper: 8½ × 11 (folded); 86-120 pages; 24 lb. paper; leatherette paper cover. "Liberal 20th century—Modernism and Postmodernism for a general as well as academic audience." Quarterly. Estab. 1990. Circ. 300.
Needs: Confession, contemporary, ethnic, fantasy, feminist, literary, psychic/supernatural/occult, romance (contemporary), science fiction, suspense/mystery, translations. No religious, gay, lesbian, horror, dualistic fiction. Plans special fiction issue. Receives 200 unsolicited mss/month. Buys 5-10 mss/issue; 20-40 mss/year. Does not read mss in August. Publishes ms 6 months to 1 year after acceptance. Recently published work by Norman Lavers; Barbara Shoup; Barbara Hope. Length: 1,500 words preferred; 500 words minimum; 10,000 words maximum. Publishes short shorts. Length: 300-500 words. Sometimes recommends other markets "especially if the story is good but not suitable for our magazine."
How to Contact: Query first. Query with clips of published work or a partial listing of published work. Include biographical and publication info. Reports in 2 weeks on queries; 2 months on mss. SASE. Photocopied submissions OK. Sample copy for $4. Fiction guidelines for #10 SAE and 1 first class stamp.
Payment: *Charges a $3 reading fee.* Pays $4-25; contributor's copies.
Terms: Pays on publication for one-time rights. Sends galleys to author.
Advice: "A manuscript stands out if it is based on narrative voice. We prefer this to dualistic contrived plots based on conflict. Story should show a person's illusion of truth with great intensity. Have a friend, writer's group or teacher critique your story. Be sincere. Readers want to know what happened behind the facade that most people put up. Be natural and have something to say of interest."

EPOCH MAGAZINE, (II), 251 Goldwin Smith Hall, Cornell University, Ithaca NY 14853. (607)255-3385. Editor: Michael Koch. Magazine: 6 × 9; 80-100 pages; good quality paper; good cover stock. "Top level fiction and poetry for people who are interested in and capable of being entertained by good literature." Published 3 times a year. Estab. 1947. Circ. 1,000.
Needs: Literary, contemporary and ethnic. Buys 4-5 mss/issue. Receives approximately 100 unsolicited fiction mss each month. Does not read in summer. Published work by Dallas Wiebe, Harriet Doerr, Darrell Spencer; published new writers in the last year. Length: 10-30 typed, double-spaced pages. Also publishes literary essays (usually solicited), poetry. Critiques rejected mss when there is time. Sometimes recommends other markets.
How to Contact: Send complete ms with SASE. Accepts computer printout submissions. Reports in 2-8 weeks on mss. Publishes ms an average of 3 months after acceptance. Sample copy for $4.
Terms: Pays on publication for first North American serial rights.
Advice: "Read and be interested in the journals you're sending work to."

ERGO!, The Bumbershoot Literary Magazine, (II), Bumbershoot, Box 9750, Seattle WA 98109-0750. (206)622-5123. Editor: Judith Roche. Magazine: 6×9; 100 pages; 60 lb. offset stock; gloss cover; illustrations; photos. "Magazine publishes poems and prose by competition winners and invited writers who read at the Bumbershoot Festival." Annually. Circ. 1,500.
Needs: Literary. Accepts approximately 4 mss/issue. Agented fiction 4%. Publishes short shorts.
How to Contact: Query first. Reports in 2 weeks on queries; 2 months on mss. SASE for ms. Simultaneous, photocopied and reprint submissions OK. Accepts computer printout submissions. Sample copy for $6 and 9×12 SAE.
Payment: Pays $150 award honoraria for Bumbershoot writers; contributor's copies.
Terms: Pays on acceptance for one-time rights.
Advice: Request application for annual contest.

EROTIC FICTION QUARTERLY, (I, II, IV), EFQ Publications, Box 424958, San Francisco CA 94142. Editor: Richard Hiller. Magazine: 5×8; 186 pages; perfect-bound; 50 lb. offset paper; 65 lb. cover stock. "Small literary magazine for thoughtful people interested in a variety of highly original and creative short fiction with sexual themes. Irregularly published."
Needs: Any style heartfelt, intelligent erotica. Also, stories not necessarily erotic whose subject is some aspect of authentic sexual experience. No standard pornography; no "men's magazine" stories; no contrived plots or gimmicks; no broad satire, parody or obscure "literary" writing. Length: 500 words minimum; 5,000 words maximum; 1,500 words average. Occasionally critiques rejected ms.
How to Contact: Send complete ms only. Photocopied submissions, non-returnable copy OK with SASE for reply. Fiction guidelines free with SASE.
Payment: Pays $50.
Terms: Pays on acceptance for first rights.
Advice: "I specifically encourage unpublished as well as published writers who have something to say regarding sexual attitudes, emotions, roles, etc. Story ideas should come from real life, not media; characters should be real people. There are essentially no restrictions regarding content, style, explicitness, etc.; *originality*, *clarity* and *integrity* are most important. The philosophy is this: *EFQ* publishes stories *about* sex by persons who have something, grand vision or small insight, to say. We try not to publish anything that could easily be printed somewhere else, and what we need is original viewpoints not really describable in advance."

THE ESCAPIST, A Biannual Literary Journal for Fans of C.S. Lewis, (I), 6861 Catlett Rd., St. Augustine FL 32095. Editor: T.M. Spell. Magazine: 8½×11; 4-16 pages; 20-50 lb. paper; 20-50 lb. cover. "Escapism is viewed in a very positive light here, and stories in some way related to this theme are welcome. Looking for stories in the Lewisian tradition, or work that evokes what Lewis defined as 'Joy.' For teens to seniors who enjoy Christian fiction without the didactics, and who aren't afraid to ask themselves the tough questions about reality." Estab. 1990. Circ. 100+.
Needs: Adventure, ethnic, experimental, fantasy, humor/satire, literary, prose poem, religious/inspirational, science fiction, suspense/mystery, translations. Receives 15-25 unsolicited mss/month. Accepts 4-10 mss/issue; 8-20 mss/year. Publishes ms 6 months to 1 year after acceptance. Recently published work by Linda Foss, Timothy Scott, Don Hornbostel, Ron Blizzard. Length: 2,500 words average; 25 words minimum; 3,000 words maximum. Publishes short shorts. Sometimes critiques rejected mss and recommends other markets.
How to Contact: "Tell me a little about what you're submitting (is it a story, poem(s), or essay?), and where you saw *The Escapist* listed. If you would like me to comment on or critique your submission, just ask." Reports in 1-3 weeks on queries; 2-8 weeks on mss. SASE. Simultaneous, photocopied and reprint submissions OK. Accepts computer printout submissions. Sample copy for $2. Fiction guidelines for #10 SAE and 1 first class stamp.
Payment: Pays 2 contributor's copies.
Terms: Acquires first North American serial rights or one-time rights (if a reprint).
Advice: "Whether your story deals with global warming, space travel, or an alternate world adventure, strive through the use of imagery and the development of ideas to make the reader feel that sudden stab of Joy or unnameable longing that characterizes the effect that C.S. Lewis's work has had on you in the past. One story might be the feature piece of an entire issue, so I'm looking for especially excellent, vividly rendered, thought provoking writing."

EVENT, (II), Douglas College, Box 2503, New Westminster, British Columbia V3L 5B2 Canada. Editor: Dale Zieroth. Fiction Editor: Maurice Hodgson. Managing Editor: Bonnie Bauder. Magazine: 6×9; 120 pages; quality paper and cover stock; illustrations; photos. "Primarily a literary magazine, publishing poetry, fiction, reviews, occasionally plays and graphics; for creative writers, artists, anyone interested in contemporary literature." Published 3 times/year. Estab. 1970. Circ. 1,000.

Needs: Literary, contemporary, feminist, adventure, humor, regional. No technically poor or unoriginal pieces. Buys 6-8 mss/issue. Receives approximately 50+unsolicited fiction mss/month. Recently published work by Tom Wayman, Sandra Birdsell, Richard Lemm; published new writers within the last year. Length: 5,000 words maximum. Also publishes poetry. Critiques rejected mss "when there is time."

How to Contact: Send complete ms with SASE and bio (*must* be Canadian postage or IRC). Accepts computer printout submissions. Reports in 4 months on mss. Publishes ms an average of 6-12 months after acceptance. Sample copy $5.

Payment: Pays $20/page and 2 contributor's copies.

Terms: Pays on publication for first North American serial rights.

Advice: "A good narrative arc is hard to find."

‡**THE EVERGREEN CHRONICLES, A Journal of Gay & Lesbian Literature, (II),** Box 8939, Minneapolis MN 55408. Managing Editors: Jim Berg and Betty Mihelich. Magazine: 5½×8½; 80 pages; linen bond paper; b&w line drawings and photos. "No one theme, other than works must have a lesbian or gay appeal. Works sensual and erotic are considered, but must be handled well and have a purpose beyond just sexuality. We look for poetry and prose, but are open to well-crafted pieces of nearly any genre." Semi-annually. Estab. 1985. Circ. 300.

Needs: Adventure, confession, contemporary, ethnic, experimental, fantasy, feminist, gay, humor/satire, lesbian, literary, romance (contemporary), science fiction, serialized/excerpted novel, suspense/mystery. "We are interested in works by gay/lesbian artists in a wide variety of genres. The subject matter need not be specifically lesbian or gay-themed, but we do look for a deep sensitivity to that experience. No hardcore sex or porno; no unnecessary violence; nothing homophobic." Accepts 3-4 mss/issue; 12-15 mss/year. Publishes ms approx. 2 months after acceptance. Published work by Terri Jewel, Lev Raphael and Ruthann Robson; published new writers in the last year. Length: 3,500-4,500 words average; no minimum; 5,200 words maximum. 25 pages double-spaced maximum on prose. Publishes short shorts. Sometimes comments on rejected mss.

How to Contact: Send 4 copies of complete ms with cover letter. "It helps to have some biographical info included." Reports on queries in 3 weeks; on mss in 3-4 months. SASE. Photocopied and reprint submissions OK. Accepts computer printouts. Sample copy for $8, 6×9 SAE and 95¢ postage. Fiction guidelines for #10 SAE and 1 first class stamp.

Payment: Pays in contributor's copies.

Terms: Acquires one-time rights.

Advice: "Perseverance is on a par with skill at the craft."

EXPLORATIONS '92, University of Alaska Southeast, 11120 Glacier Highway, Juneau AK 99801. (907)789-4418. Editor: Art Petersen. Magazine: 5½×8¼; 44 pages; heavy cover stock; illustrations and photographs. "Poetry, prose and art—we strive for artistic excellence." Annually. Estab. 1980. Circ. 250.

Needs: Experimental, humor/satire. Receives 1,700 mss/year.

How to Contact: Send complete ms with cover letter, which should include bio. All submissions entered in contest. Reading/entry fee $4/story required. Submission deadline is March 21. Reports in 2-3 months. SASE. Simultaneous, photocopied and reprint submissions OK. Accepts computer printout submissions. Sample copy $4 ($3 for back issues).

Payment: Pays 2 contributor's copies. *Charges $4 reading fee for non-UAS fiction contributors.* Also awards two annual prizes of $100 each: one for poetry, one for fiction. Write for information.

Terms: Acquires one-time rights (rights remain with the author).

EXPLORER MAGAZINE, (I), Flory Publishing Co., Box 210, Notre Dame IN 46556. (219)277-3465. Editor: Ray Flory. Magazine: 5½×8½; 20-32 pages; 20 lb. paper; 60 lb. or stock cover; illustrations. Magazine with "basically an inspirational theme including love stories in good taste." Christian writing audience. Semiannually. Estab. 1960. Circ. 200+.

Needs: Literary, mainstream, prose poem, religious/inspirational, romance (contemporary, historical, young adult) and science fiction. No pornography. Buys 2-3 mss/issue; 5 mss/year. Length: 600 words average; 300 words minimum; 900 words maximum. Also publishes literary essays. Occasionally critiques rejected mss.

How to Contact: Send complete ms with SASE. Reports in 1 week. Publishes ms up to 3 years after acceptance. Photocopied submissions OK. Sample copy $3. Fiction guidelines for SAE and 1 first class stamp.
Payment: Pays up to $25; $3 charge for extras.
Terms: Cash prizes of $25, $20, $15 and $10 based on subscribers' votes. A plaque is also awarded to first place winner.
Advice: "See a copy of magazine first; have a good story to tell—in *good* taste! Most fiction sent in is too *long*! Be yourself! Be honest and sincere in your style. Write what you know about. Our philosophy is to reach the world with Christian literature, drawing others closer to God and nature."

‡EYES, (I), Apt. 301, 2715 S. Jefferson Ave., Saginaw MI 48601. (517)752-5202. Editor: Frank J. Mueller, III. Magazine: 8½×11; 25 pages; 20 lb. paper; Gilbert Laid 65 lb. cover. "No specific theme yet. Hopefully, horror-related surreal, SM most welcome. For a general, educated, not necessarily literary audience." Estab. 1991. Circ. 30-40.
Needs: Contemporary, experimental, fantasy (dark), horror, mainstream, prose poem. Nothing pornographic; no preachiness; no children's fiction. Receives 1-6 unsolicited mss/month. Accepts 2-3 mss/issue. Publishes ms 6 months to 1 year after acceptance. Length: 3,500 words preferred; 5,000 words maximum. Sometimes critiques rejected mss.
How to Contact: Query first or send complete ms. Reports in 1 month (or less) on queries; 4-6 weeks on mss. SASE. Photocopied submissions OK. Sample copy for $3. Fiction guidelines for #10 SAE and 1 first class stamp.
Payment: No payment.
Terms: Acquires one-time rights.
Advice: "Write and write again. If rejected, try again. If you have a manuscript you like and would like to see it in *Eyes*, send it to me. I may agree with you. Try to have your manuscript say something."

FAG RAG, Box 15331, Kenmore Station, Boston MA 02215. (617)661-7534. Editor: E. Carlotta. Magazine of gay male liberation. Annually. Estab. 1970. Circ. 5,000.
Needs: Gay male material only: adventure, comics, confession, erotica, fantasy, historical, men's, prose poem. Receives 5 unsolicited fiction mss/month. Accepts 5 mss/issue. Length: 1-10,000 words.
How to Contact: Query first. Reports in 2 months on queries; 9 months on mss. SASE for query. Photocopied submissions OK. Accepts computer printout submissions. Accepts disk submissions compatible with IBM-PC/Macintosh. Sample copy $5.
Payment: Pays in 2 contributor's copies.
Terms: Acquires first North American serial rights.

THE FARMER'S MARKET, (II), Midwestern Farmer's Market, Inc., Box 1272, Galesburg IL 61402. Editor: Jean C. Lee. Magazine: 5½×8½; 100-140 pages; 60 lb. offset paper; 65 lb. cover; b&w illustrations and photos. Magazine publishing "quality fiction, poetry, nonfiction, plays, etc., with a Midwestern theme and/or sensibility for an adult, literate audience." Semiannually. Estab. 1982. Circ. 500.
Needs: Contemporary, feminist, humor/satire, literary, regional and excerpted novel. "We prefer material of clarity, depth and strength; strong plots, good character development." No "romance, avant-garde, juvenile, teen." Accepts 6-12 mss/year. Published work by Donn Irving, Mary Maddox, David Williams; published new writers within the last year. Also publishes literary essays, poetry. Occasionally critiques rejected mss or recommends other markets.
How to Contact: Send complete ms with SASE. Reports in 1-2 months. Photocopied submissions OK. Accepts computer printout submissions. Publishes ms 4-8 months after acceptance. Sample copy for $4.50 and $1 postage and handling.
Payment: Pays 1 contributor's copy. (Other payment dependent upon grants).
Terms: Authors retain rights.
Advice: "We're always interested in regional fiction. We are trying to publish more fiction and we are looking for exceptional manuscripts. Read the magazines before submitting. If you don't want to buy it, ask your library. We receive numerous mss that are clearly unsuitable."

FAT TUESDAY, (II), 8125 Jonestown Road, Harrisburg PA 17112. Editor-in-Chief: F.M. Cotolo. Editors: B. Lyle Tabor and Thom Savion. Associate Editors: Lionel Stevroid and Kristen vonOehrke. Journal: 8½×11 or 5×8; 27-36 pages; good to excellent paper; heavy cover stock; b&w illustrations; photos. "Generally, we are an eclectic journal of fiction, poetry and visual treats. Our issues to date have featured artists like Patrick Kelly, Cheryl Townsend, Joi Cook, Chuck Taylor and many more who have focused on an individualistic nature with fiery elements. We are a literary mardi gras—as the title indicates—and irreverancy is as acceptable to us as profundity as long as there is fire! Our audience is anyone who can praise literature and condemn it at the same time. Anyone too serious about it on either level will not like *Fat Tuesday.*" Annually. Estab. 1981. Circ. 700.

Needs: Comics, erotica, experimental, humor/satire, literary, prose poem, psychic/supernatural/occult, serialized/excerpted novel and dada. "Although we list categories, we are open to feeling out various fields if they are delivered with the mark of an individual and not just in the format of the particular field." Receives 10 unsolicited fiction mss/month. Accepts 4-5 mss/issue. Published new writers within the last year. Length: 1,000 words maximum. Publishes short shorts. Occasionally critiques rejected mss.

How to Contact: Send complete ms with SASE. Photocopied submissions OK. Accepts computer printout submissions. "No previously published material considered." Reports in 1 month. Publishes ms 3-10 months after acceptance. Sample copy for $5.

Payment: Pays 1 contributor's copy.

Terms: Acquires one-time rights.

Advice: "As *Fat Tuesday* enters its second decade, we find that publishing small press editions is more difficult than ever. Money remains a problem, mostly because small press seems to play to the very people who wish to be published in it. In other words, the cast is the audience, and more people want to be in *Fat Tuesday* than want to buy it. It is through sales that our magazine supports itself. This is why we emphasize buying a sample issue ($5) before submitting. We have calculated that if only 25% of the submissions we received in the last year had bought sample issues, we could have published four or five issues in 1990 as opposed to the one we struggled to release. As far as what we want to publish—send us shorter works. 'Crystals of thought and emotion which reflect your individual experiences. As long as you dig into your guts and pull out pieces of yourself. Your work is your signature . . . Like time itself, it should emerge from the penetralia of your being and recede into the infinite region of the cosmos,' to coin a phrase, and remember *Fat Tuesday* is mardi gras—so fill up before you fast. Bon soir."

FELICITY, (I), Weems Concepts, Star Route, Box 21AA, Artemas PA 17211. (814)458-3102. Editor: Kay Weems-Winter. Newsletter: 8½ × 11; 20 lb. bond paper; illustrations. "Publishes articles, poetry and short stories. Poetry has different theme each month. No theme for stories." Monthly. Estab. 1988. Circ. 200.

Needs: Open. Short stories, any genre in good taste. No erotica, translations. All submissions treated as contest entries. Entry fee is $5 and the deadline is the 30th of each month. Length: 800-2,500 words. Publishes short shorts. Length up to 800 words; entry fee $2. Editor will consider stories that do not win for *My Legacy* or recommends other markets. Publishes ms 3-4 months after acceptance.

How to Contact: Send complete ms with cover letter or enter our monthly contests. "Send SASE for return of ms or tell me to destroy it if not accepted." Reports in 3-4 months. SASE. Simultaneous, photocopied and reprint submissions OK as long as author still retains rights. Accepts computer printout submissions. Sample copy for $2, #10 SAE and 65¢ postage. Fiction guidelines for #10 SAE and 1 first class stamp or check *The Bottom Line*, market listing for contests.

Payment: Pays in contributor's copies and ½ of entry fee collected for Short Story Contest. All entries receive copy of the issue.

Terms: Acquires one-time rights. "We will be" copyrighted. "We sponsor monthly contests. Winner receives half of entry fees collected for the short story contest. Submit ms along with entry fee and you will be entered in the contest. Deadline is the 30th of each month. Read both of our publications— *Felicity* and *The Bottom Line Publications*. Our contests are listed there."

Advice: Looks for "good opening sentence, realistic characters, nice descriptions, strong plot with believable ending. Use natural conversations. Let me *feel* your story. Keep me interested until the end. Keep trying. A lot of mss I read are from new writers. Personally I enjoy stories and articles which will create a particular emotion, build suspense, or offer excitement or entertainment. Don't spell out everything in detail—keep me guessing."

FICTION, (II), % Dept. of English, City College, 138th St. & Convent Ave., New York NY 10031. (212)650-6319/650-6317. Editor: Mark Jay Mirsky. Managing Editor: Allan Aycock. Magazine: 6 × 9; 150-250 pages; illustrations and occasionally photos. "As the name implies, we publish *only* fiction; we are looking for the best new writing available, leaning toward the unconventional. *Fiction* has traditionally attempted to make accessible the unaccessible, to bring the experimental to a broader audience." Biannually. Estab. 1972. Circ. 2,000.

Needs: Contemporary, experimental, feminist, humor/satire, literary and translations. No romance, science-fiction, etc. Receives 50-100 unsolicited mss/month. Accepts 12-20 mss/issue; 24-40 mss/year. Does not read mss May-October. Publishes ms 1-6 months after acceptance. Agented fiction 10-20%. Recently published work by Harold Brodkey, Joyce Carol Oates, Peter Handke, Max Frisch and Adolfo Bioy-Casares. Length: Open. Publishes short shorts. Sometimes critiques rejected mss and recommends other markets.

How to Contact: Send complete ms with cover letter. Reports in 1-3 months on mss. SASE. Simultaneous submissions OK, but please advise. Photocopied submissions OK. Accepts computer printout submissions. Sample copy $5. Fiction guidelines free.

Payment: Pays in contributor's copies.

Terms: Acquires first rights.

Advice: Submit "something different, off-the-wall—we would favor a less-polished but stylistically adventurous piece over a more-polished formulaic piece."

FICTION INTERNATIONAL, (II), English Dept., San Diego State University, San Diego CA 92182. (619)594-6220. Editors: Harold Jaffe and Larry McCaffery. "Serious literary magazine of fiction, extended reviews, essays." Magazine: 200 pages; illustrations; photos. "Our twin biases are progressive politics and post-modernism." Biannually. Estab. 1973. Circ. 2,500.

Needs: Literary, political and innovative forms. Receives approximately 300 unsolicited fiction mss each month. Unsolicited mss will be considered only from September 1 through December 15 of each year. Published new writers within the last year. No length limitations but rarely use manuscripts over 25 pages. Portions of novels acceptable if self-contained enough for independent publication.

How to Contact: Send complete ms with SASE. Reports in 1-3 months on mss. Sample copy for $9: query Ed Gordon, managing editor.

Payment: Payment varies.

Terms: Pays on publication for first rights and first North American serial rights.

Advice: "Study the magazine. We're highly selective. A difficult market for unsophisticated writers."

THE FIDDLEHEAD, (II), University of New Brunswick, Campus House, Box 4400 Fredericton, New Brunswick E3B 5A3 Canada. (506)453-3501. Editor: Don McKay. Fiction Editors: Bill Gaston, Diana Austin, Banny Belyea, Ted Colson and Linda McNutt. Magazine: 6×9; 104-128 pages; ink illustrations; photos. "No criteria for publication except quality. For a general audience, including many poets and writers." Quarterly. Estab. 1945. Circ. 1,000.

Needs: Literary. No non-literary fiction. Receives 100-150 unsolicited mss/month. Buys 4-5 mss/issue; 20-40 mss/year. Publishes ms up to 4 months after acceptance. Small percent agented fiction. Published work by Carol Edelstein; published new writers within the last year. Length: 50-3,000 words average. Publishes short shorts. Occasionally critiques rejected mss.

How to Contact: Send complete ms with cover letter. SASE. "Canadian stamps or international coupons!" for mss. Photocopied and reprint submissions OK. Accepts computer printout submissions. Sample copy for $5.50 (Canadian). Reviews novels and short story collections—*Canadian only*.

Payment: Pays $10-12 (Canadian)/published page and 1 contributor's copy.

Terms: Pays on publication for first or one-time rights.

Advice: "Less than 5% of the material received is published."

‡FIGHTING WOMAN NEWS, (IV), 6741 Tung Ave. West, Theodore AL 36582. Editor: Debra Pettis. Magazine: 8½×11; 16-32 pages; 60 lb. offset bond paper; slick cover; illustrations; photos. "Women's martial arts, self defense, combative sports. Articles, reviews, etc., related to these subjects. Well-educated adult women who are actually involved with martial arts read us because we're there and we're good." Quaterly. Estab. 1975. Circ. 3,500.

Needs: Science fiction, fantasy, feminist, adventure and translations. "No material that shows women as victims, incompetents, stereotypes; no 'fight scenes' written by people who don't know anything about fighting skills." Receives very few unsolicited fiction mss. Published work by Phyllis Ann Karr, Lauren Wright Douglas and Janrae Frank. Length: 2,500 words.

How to Contact: Query with clips of published work with SASE. Enclose cover letter with ms. Accepts computer printout submissions. "We must know if it is a simultaneous submission." Reports as soon as possible on queries and mss. Sample copy $3.50. Specify "fiction" when asking for samples. Free guidelines with #10 SASE.

Payment: Pays contributor's copies and subscription or $10 honorarium.
Terms: Pays on publication for one-time rights. Will print author's copyright if desired.
Advice: "We are now getting unsolicited mss from published writers who have what we want; i.e., a good, competent story that's just a bit too martial-arts oriented for their regular markets. Our readers have expressed a strong preference for more technique and theory with a few specific complaints about too much fiction or poetry. So even with a more regular publication schedule and corredsponding increase in total pages, we are not likely to use more fiction. Read the magazine before submitting. I also think the theme of death in combat can do with a rest. We published no fiction last year."

FIGMENT MAGAZINE, Tales from the Imagination, (I, II, IV), P.O. Box 3128, Moscow ID 83843-0477. Editors: Barb & J.C. Hendee. Magazine: 5½×8½; 56-60 pages; slick stock cover; illustrations. "Poetry/stories/vignettes/novelettes in genres of sf, fantasy, and sf/f related horror, for adults." Quarterly. Estab. 1989.
Needs: Fantasy, science fiction. "We're open to standard plotting through slightly experimental, as long as the story is interesting, comprehensible and always entertaining." Receives 300+ mss/month. Buys 8-12 mss/issue; 32-48 mss/year. Publishes ms within 6 months after acceptance. Recently published work by Dean Wesley Smith, Kristine Kathryn Rusch, Kevin J. Anderson, K.D. Wentworth. Length: 500-7,500 words; 3,000 words preferred. Also publishes poetry. Sometimes critiques rejected manuscripts and recommends other markets.
How to Contact: Send complete ms with cover letter; include Social Security number, bio, SASE and listing of publishing credits (year to date only) including where and when. Reports in 2 weeks on queries; 1 month average on mss. Photocopied submissions OK. Accepts computer printout submissions. Encourages disk submissions. Sample copy for $4. Fiction guidelines for #10 SASE. Reviews novels and short story collections. Send to J.P. McLaughlin, reviewer.
Payment: Pays ½-1¢/word (for fiction).
Terms: Pays within 30 days of acceptance for first North American serial rights only. Sends galleys to author.
Advice: "Looks for original ideas or original methods used with old ideas. Cutting edge material that is entertaining, fantastical, and far-reaching. Don't tell us what your story is about in your cover letter; if we can't figure it out from the manuscript, then some more work needs to be done before your submit. We expect professional submissions in the proper format."

FINE MADNESS, (II), Box 31138, Seattle WA 98103-1138. Magazine: 5×8; 80 pages; 65 lb. paper; 60 lb. cover stock. Estab. 1981. Circ. 800.
Needs: Contemporary, experimental, literary, prose poem and translations. Receives 10 unsolicited mss/month. Accepts 1-2 mss/issue; 2-4 mss/year. Publishes ms no more than 1 year after acceptance. Published work by Naomi Nye, David Downing, Hillel Schwarz and Michael Novak. Length: "approx. 12 pages max." Publishes short shorts. Also "would like to see" literary essays.
How to Contact: Query first or send complete ms with cover letter. Reports in 3 weeks on queries; 3 months on mss. Sample copy $4. Fiction guidelines free.
Payment: Pays free subscription to magazine and contributor's copies.
Terms: Acquires first North American serial rights.

FISH DRUM MAGAZINE, (II), % 626 Kathryn Ave., Santa Fe NM 87501. Editor: Robert Winson. Magazine: 5½×8½; 40-odd pages; glossy cover; illustrations and photographs. "Lively, emotional vernacular modern fiction, art and poetry." Published 2-4 times a year. Estab. 1988. Circ. 500.
Needs: Contemporary, erotica, ethnic, experimental, fantasy, gay, lesbian, literary, prose poem, regional, science fiction. "We're interested in material by New Mexican writers; also on the practice of Zen. Most of the fiction we've published is in the form of short, heightened prose-pieces." Receives 6-10 unsolicited mss/month. Accepts 1-2 mss/issue; 2-8 mss/year. Publishes ms 6 months-1 year after acceptance. Also publishes literary essays, literary criticism, poetry. Recommends other markets.
How to Contact: Send complete manuscript. Reports on mss in 1-3 months. SASE. Sample copy for $3. Reviews novels and short story collections.
Payment: Pays in contributor's copies. Charges for extras.
Terms: Acquires first North American serial rights. Sends galleys to author.

FIVE FINGERS REVIEW, (II), Box 15426, San Francisco CA 94115. (415)255-2159. Editor: Julia Ward. Magazine: 6×9; 125-150 pages; photographs on cover. "*Five Fingers* is dedicated to publishing well wrought poetry and prose from various aesthetic viewpoints. The magazine provides a forum from which talented writers (new and known, traditional and experimental) act as conscientious objectors, as creative witnesses to the passions and possibilities of our time." Semiannually. Estab. 1984. Circ. 1,000.

Needs: Ethnic, experimental, feminist, gay, humor/satire, lesbian, literary, regional, prose poems, prose vignettes and works that move between the genres. Receives 15-20 unsolicited mss/month. Accepts 2-5 mss/issue. Published work by Molly Giles, W.A. Smith and Peter Johnson; published new writers in the last year. Publishes short shorts. Also publishes poetry.

How to Contact: Query with clips of published work. SASE. Simultaneous, photocopied and reprint submissions OK. Sample copy for $6.

Payment: Pays in contributor's copies.

Advice: "We are particularly looking for short-short stories, prose poems, prose vignettes and works of translations."

‡**FLIPSIDE, (II)**, Professional Writing Program, Dixon 110, California University, California PA 15419. (412)938-4082. Editors: Jim Black, Jonathan Bagamery. Tabloid: 11½×17; 45-60 pages; illustrations; photos. "Emphasis on 'new journalism.' Fiction, nonfiction, poetry, humor." Semiannually. Estab. 1987. Circ. 2,000.

Needs: Contemporary, experimental, literary. No genre fiction. Receives 5-6 unsolicited mss/month. Accepts 2-3 mss/issue; 6-8 mss/year. Does not read June-August. Publishes ms 1-6 months after acceptance. Length: 1,000-5,000 words average; 10,000 words maximum. Also publishes literary essays, literary criticism, some poetry.

How to Contact: Send complete manuscript with or without cover letter. Reports in 2-4 weeks on queries; 1-2 months on mss. SASE. Simultaneous and photocopied submissions OK. Accepts computer printouts. Sample copy and fiction guidelines for 9×12 SAE and $1.24 postage.

Payment: Pays 3 contributor's copies.

Terms: Acquires first North American serial rights.

Advice: "Experimental and alternative fiction are always welcome here. Traditional fiction, darkly executed, is also encouraged. Read all you can, buy lots of envelopes."

THE FLORIDA REVIEW, (II), Dept. of English, University of Central Florida, Orlando FL 32816. (407)823-2038. Contact: Russell Kesler. Magazine: 5½×8½; 128 pages. Semiannually. Estab. 1972. Circ. 1,000.

Needs: Contemporary, experimental and literary. "We welcome experimental fiction, so long as it doesn't make us feel lost or stupid. We aren't especially interested in genre fiction (science fiction, romance, adventure, etc.), though a good story can transcend any genre." Receives 120 mss/month. Buys 8-10 mss/issue; 16-20 mss/year. Publishes ms within 3-6 months of acceptance. Published work by Stephen Dixon, Richard Grayson and Liz Rosenberg. Publishes short shorts. Also publishes literary criticism, poetry.

How to Contact: Send complete ms with cover letter. Reports in 2-4 months. SASE. Simultaneous and photocopied submissions OK. Accepts computer printout submissions. Sample copy for $4.50; free fiction guidelines. Reviews novels and short story collections.

Payment: Pays in contributor's copies. Small honorarium occasionally available.

Terms: "Copyright held by U.C.F.; reverts to author after publication. (In cases of reprints, we ask that a credit line indicate that the work first appeared in the *F.R.*)"

Advice: "We publish fiction of high 'literary' quality—stories that delight, instruct, and aren't afraid to take risks."

FOLIO: A LITERARY JOURNAL, (II), Literature Department, American University, Washington DC 20016. (202)885-2971. Editor changes yearly. Magazine: 6×9; 64 pages. "Fiction is published if it is well written. We look for language control, skilled plot and character development." For a scholarly audience. Semiannually. Estab. 1984. Circ. 400.

Needs: Contemporary, literary, mainstream, prose poem, sports, suspense/mystery, translations, essay, b&w art or photography. No pornography. Occasional theme-based issues. See guidelines for info. Receives 150 unsolicited mss/month. Accepts 3-5 mss/issue; 6-10 mss/year. Does not read mss during May-August or December-January. Published work by Henry Taylor, Kermit Moyer, Linda Pastan; publishes new writers. Length: 2,500 words average; 4,500 words maximum. Publishes short shorts. Occasionally critiques rejected mss.

How to Contact: Send complete ms with cover letter, which should include a brief biography. Reports in 1-2 weeks on queries; 1-2 months on mss. SASE. Simultaneous, photocopied and reprint submissions OK. Accepts computer printout submissions. Sample copy for $5. Guidelines for #10 SAE and 1 first class stamp.

Payment: Pays in contributor's copies.
Terms: Acquires first North American rights. "$75 award for best fiction and poetry. Query for guidelines."

FOOTWORK, The Paterson Literary Review, (I, II), Passaic County Community College, College Blvd., Paterson NJ 07509. (201)684-6555. Editor: Maria Gillan. Magazine: 8×11; 120 pages; 60 lb. paper; 70 lb. cover; illustrations; photos. Plans fiction issue in future.
Needs: Contemporary, ethnic, experimental. "We are interested in quality short stories, with no taboos on subject matter." Receives about 60 unsolicited mss/month. Accepts 4 mss/issue. Publishes ms about 6 months to a year after acceptance. Published new writers within the last year. Length: 2,500-3,000 words. Also publishes literary essays, literary criticism, poetry.
How to Contact: Reports in 3 months on mss. SASE. No simultaneous submissions or reprints. Accepts computer printouts. Sample copy $5. Reviews novels and short story collections.
Payment: Pays in contributor's copies.
Terms: Acquires first North American rights.
Advice: "We look for original, vital, powerful work. The short story is—when successful—a major achievement. Because we publish relatively little work, we cannot consider stories which are slight, however charming."

‡FORBIDDEN LINES, (I, IV), The Science Fiction Writers' Group, P.O. Box 23, Chapel Hill NC 27514. (919)942-3194. Managing Editor: Charles Overbeck. Magazine: 8×11; 64 pages; newsprint; 50 lb. white cover; illustrations and photographs. "We publish the strange, the awful, the wonderful (science fiction, horror, fantasy). Our readers are mostly college-aged to mid 30s, well educated, equal numbers m/f." Bimonthly. Estab. 1990. Circ. 500.
Needs: Condensed/excerpted novel, erotica, experimental, fantasy, horror, humor/satire, psychic/supernatural/occult, science fiction."No juvenile, no romance, no religious." Publishes annual special fiction issue. Receives 10-30 mss/month (varies widely). Accepts 6/7 mss/issue; 30-40 mss/year. Publishes ms 2-4 weeks after acceptance. Recently published work by Paul Thompson, Tonya Carter, Lawrence Barker. Length: open. Publishes short shorts. Also publishes poetry. Sometimes critiques rejected mss and recommends other markets.
How to Contact: Send complete ms with cover letter. "Please don't bore us with previous credits. We'll consider every story equally." Reports in 1 week on queries; 2 weeks-1 month on mss. SASE for queries "We do not return mss!!" Photocopied and reprint submissions OK. Accepts computer printout submissions. Accepts electronic submissions via disk or modem (on Apple MacIntosh *only*). Sample copy for $2.50. Fiction guidelines for #10 SAE and 1 first class stamp.
Payment: Pays 2 contributor's copies. Charges for extras at cost, $1 each.
Terms: Acquires one-time rights.
Advice: "We ask is it original? Is it strange? How does reading it make us (the staff) *feel*? Stories are chosen by majority vote of the staff. The editor has veto power, but rarely disagrees with the majority. Send us a professionally prepared ms, too weird or wild for the pro zines. Be fresh. Be *real*, while being *unreal*."

‡FRICTION, Wampus Multimedia, 6130 Calico Pool Lane, Burke VA 22015. (703)250-6010. Editor: Mark W. Doyon. Newsletter: 8½×11; 12-16 pages; 70 lb. diamond ultrafelt cover; line art only. "Thematically linked fiction . . . ." Quarterly. Estab. 1989.
Needs: Contemporary, humor/satire, literary. "*No genre fiction.*" Upcoming themes: send for 1992 editorial calendar. Receives 5-10 unsolicited mss/month. Accepts 3-5 mss/issue; 12-20 mss/year. Publishes ms 2-6 months after acceptance. Recently published work by Stephen Gerard, Paul Golder, Keith Donohue and Kevin Kerr. Length: 1,500-2,000 words average; 500 words minimum; 2,500 words maximum. Publishes short shorts. Sometimes critiques rejected mss and recommends other markets.
How to Contact: Send complete ms with cover letter. Reports in 2 weeks on queries; 6 weeks on mss. SASE. Simultaneous submissions OK. Accepts electronic submissions via disk. (PC-formatted). Sample copy for $2, 9×12 SAE and 3 first class stamps. Fiction guidelines free.
Payment: Pays subscription to magazine.
Terms: Acquires one-time rights.
Advice: "We look for mss with strong thematic and editorial content. The writing should be concise and essentially linear, but ultimately it's a strong point-of-view that makes or breaks a piece. If a submission reflects a strong vision, we'll often edit the language as necessary. Ultimately a ms must complement the issue's stated THEME (e.g. 1991 themes were: Enlightened Self-Interest; Mob Rules; Desperate Men; Dog Eat Dog). Make sure that you have *something to say*. And then say it as concisely

and elegantly as possible. Stay away from 'cute' or 'wacky' characterizations. Avoid 'clever' language. Present complex themes in a simple way."

The theme for this issue of Friction, admittedly a "quasi-quarterly" magazine, was "Mob Rules," says Editor Mark W. Doyon. "The line of doe-eyed, identically dressed 'businessmen' represents the threat of conformity in a declining culture," he explains. "The soot-puffing factories in the background suggest the fruits of conformism or 'majoritarianism.' " The four stories inside all reflect aspects of this theme. In general, the magazine accepts three to five thematically-linked pieces for each issue. The cover artist is Alisa Mullins. The masthead is the design of Valerie Larson and Laura Jensen.

‡**FRITZ, (II),** 3907 26th St., San Francisco CA 94131. Editors: Lisa McElroy and Richie Unterberger. Magazine: 8½×11; 24 pages; 60 lb. paper; vellum cover; illustrations and photographs. "A format for short stories, prose, poetry, photos, comics, nonfiction articles and some reviews for artists and writers who are absorbed by and/or objectify pop culture. Also, classic forms of writing as well as experimental." Annually. Estab. 1991. Circ. 700.
Needs: Erotica, ethnic, experimental, feminist, gay, historical (general), humor/satire, lesbian, literary, prose poem. No gore, sexist/racist for the sake of being sexist/racist. No formula genres. Receives 4-6 unsolicited mss/month. Accepts 3-4 mss/issue. Publishes ms 6 months (possibly more) after acceptance. Length: 2,500 words maximum. Publishes short shorts. Also accepts poetry.
How to Contact: Send complete ms with cover letter. Reports in 2 weeks on queries; 2-4 months on mss. SASE. Photocopied and reprint submissions OK. Accepts computer printout submissions. Sample copy for $2. Fiction guidelines for #10 SAE and 1 first class stamp.
Payment: Pays contributor's copies.
Terms: Acquires one-time rights.
Advice: Looks for "intelligent observation of human behavior. A new way of expressing an opinion. An ability to create a rhythmic flow of words. A heart-felt opinion. A sense of humor. A sense of pathos."

THE G.W. REVIEW, (II), The George Washington University, Box 20, The Marvin Center, 800 21st St., N.W., Washington DC 20052. (202)994-7288. Editor: April M. Robbins. Magazine: 6×9; 64 pages; 60 lb. white offset paper; 65 lb. Patina cover; cover photo. "The G.W. Review is a literary magazine that publishes poetry, short fiction and essays for the university community, the Washington, DC, metropolitan area and an increasing number of national subscribers." Semiannually. Estab. 1980. Circ. 4,000 (annually).
Needs: Condensed/excerpted novel, contemporary, experimental, humor/satire, literary, mainstream, prose poem, translations. "The G.W. Review does not accept previously published material. No pornography or proselytizing religious manuscripts." Does not read mss May 15-August 15. Publishes ms up to 6 months after acceptance. Recently published work by Julia Alvarez and Richard McCann. Length: 2,500 words average; 6,000 words maximum. Publishes short shorts. Also publishes literary essays, poetry. Sometimes critiques rejected mss.

How to Contact: Send complete manuscript with cover letter. Include biographical information, places previously published, previous books, etc. Reports in 3-6 weeks on queries; 4-10 weeks on mss. SASE. Simultaneous and photocopied submissions OK. Accepts computer printout submissions. Sample copy for $3. Fiction guidelines for 9×12 SASE.
Payment: Pays in contributor's copies.
Terms: Acquires one-time rights.
Advice: "The G.W. Review seeks to publish the best contemporary writing from outside the University community as well as the best from within. Initially intended for distribution to university students and the surrounding Washington D.C. metropolitan area, *The G.W. Review* has since begun to attain a more widespread national distribution and readership."

THE GAMUT, A Journal of Ideas and Information, (II), Cleveland State University, 1983 E. 24th St., FT 1218, Cleveland OH 44115-2440. (216)687-4679. Editor: Louis T. Milic. Managing Editor: Susan Dumbrys. Magazine: 7×10; 96 pages; 70 lb. Patina Matte paper; Patina Matte cover stock; illustrations; photos. *"The Gamut* is a general-interest magazine that *mainly* publishes well-researched, interesting articles; however, we like to publish one or two pieces of fiction per issue, if we find something suitable." For the college-educated audience. Triannually. Estab. 1980. Circ. 1,200.
Needs: Contemporary, experimental, feminist, humor/satire, literary, mainstream, prose poem, regional, translations. "Our only requirement is high quality fiction." No genre fiction, no fiction for specific age groups. Receives 100 unsolicited mss/month. Accepts 1-2 mss/issue; 4-6 mss/year. Publishes mss usually 3 months, certainly 1 year after acceptance. Reading fee "only when we have contest, then $5." Published work by Margot Livesey, Nancy Potter, John Gerlach; published new writers within the last year. Length: 3,000 words average; 1,000 words minimum; 6,000 words maximum. Also publishes literary essays, poetry. Occasionally publishes literary criticism.
How to Contact: Send complete ms with cover letter. Reports in 1 month on queries; 3 months on mss. SASE for ms. Simultaneous and photocopied submissions OK. Accepts computer printouts. Sample copy $2.50. Fiction guidelines for #10 SAE and 1 first class stamp.
Payment: Pays $25-150, depending on length; contributor's copies; charges reduced rate for extras.
Terms: Pays on publication for first North American serial rights.
Advice: "The best advice we have for writers who wish to be published in our magazine is that they should care about the quality of their writing. Further, we are interested neither in stale approaches to fictional situations nor in avant-garde experiments that have lost touch with the purpose of literature."

THE GEORGIA REVIEW, (II, III), The University of Georgia, Athens GA 30602. (404)542-3481. Editor-in-Chief: Stanley W. Lindberg. Associate Editor: Stephen Corey. Journal: 7×10; 208 pages (average); 50 lb. woven old style paper; 80 lb. cover stock; illustrations; photos. *"The Georgia Review,* winner of the 1986 National Magazine Award in Fiction, is a journal of arts and letters, featuring a blend of the best in contemporary thought and literature—essays, fiction, poetry, graphics and book reviews—for the intelligent nonspecialist as well as the specialist reader. We seek material that appeals across disciplinary lines by drawing from a wide range of interests." Quarterly. Estab. 1947. Circ. 5,300.
Needs: Experimental and literary. "We're looking for the highest quality fiction—work that is capable of sustaining subsequent readings, not throw-away pulp magazine entertainment. Nothing that fits too easily into a 'category.'" Receives about 300 unsolicited fiction mss/month. Buys 3-4 mss/issue; 12-15 mss/year. Does not accept unsolicited mss in June, July or August. Would prefer *not* to see novel excerpts. Published work by Lee K. Abbott, Marjorie Sandor, John Edgar Wideman; published new writers within the last year. Length: Open. Also publishes literary essays, literary criticism, poetry. Occasionally critiques rejected mss.
How to Contact: Send complete ms with SASE. Photocopied submissions OK; no multiple submissions. Accepts computer printout submissions. Reports in 2-3 months. Sample copy $4; free guidelines for #10 SAE with 1 first class stamp. Reviews short story collections.

Market conditions are constantly changing! If you're still using this book and it is 1993 or later, buy the newest edition of Novel & Short Story Writer's Market at your favorite bookstore or order directly from Writer's Digest Books.

Payment: Pays minimum: $35/printed page; 1 year complimentary subscription; 1 contributor's copy, reduced charge for extra.
Terms: Pays on publication for first North American serial rights. Sends galleys to author.

THE GETTYSBURG REVIEW, (II), Gettysburg College, Gettysburg PA 17325. (717)337-6770. Editor: Peter Stitt. Assistant Editor: Jeff Mock. Magazine: 6¾×10; approx. 170 pages; acid free paper; full color illustrations and photos. "Quality of writing is our only criterion; we publish fiction, poetry and essays." Quarterly. Estab. 1988. Circ. 2,000.
Needs: Contemporary, experimental, historical(general), humor/satire, literary, mainstream, regional and serialized novel. "We require that fiction be intelligent, and aesthetically written." Receives approx. 60 mss/month. Buys approx. 4-6 mss/issue; 16-24 mss/year. Publishes ms within 3-6 months of acceptance. Published work by Frederick Busch, William Hoffman, Beth Nugent. Length: 3,000 words average; 1,000 words minimum; 20,000 words maximum. Occasionally publishes short shorts. Also publishes literary essays, some literary criticism, poetry. Sometimes critiques rejected mss.
How to Contact: Send complete mss with cover letter, which should include "education, credits." Reports in 3-6 months. SASE. Photocopied submissions OK. Accepts computer printout submissions. Sample copy for $6 (postage paid). Does not review books per se. "We do essay-reviews, treating several books around a central theme." Send books to editor.
Payment: Pays $25/printed page plus free subscription to magazine, contributor's copy. Charge for extra copies.
Terms: Pays on publication for first North American serial rights.
Advice: "Reporting time can take three months. It is helpful to look at a sample copy of *The Gettysburg Review* to see what kinds of fiction we publish before submitting."

‡THE GINGERBREAD DIARY, Alternative Lifestyles in Interracial Love, (I, IV), Box 3333, New York NY 10185. (212)904-0512. Editor: Gary David. Fiction Editors: Gary David, Julie David. Magazine: 8½×11; 40-50 pages; bond paper; color bond paper cover; illustrations; photos. "We feature essays, stories, poems on the theme of interracial love and relating, as well as material embracing other 'human interest' topics, basically for those who are involved in, or who have thought about, interracial relationships; also those who are the products of interracial unions." Published 5 times/year. Plans special fiction issue. Estab. 1986. Circ. 50.
Needs: Erotica, ethnic, experimental, fantasy, gay, historical (general), humor/satire, lesbian, literary, mainstream, prose poem, spiritual, regional, romance (contemporary, historical, young adult). "As noted above, we accept for consideration material dealing with a broad range of subjects; bear in mind that we do not restrict ourselves to black/white issues, but include all other 'races' as well, the object being, of course, to illuminate the emotional and intellectual interplay between people of different racial and cultural backgrounds within the context of their relationship." Accepts 1-2 mss/issue; 8-9 mss/year. Publishes ms "2 issues hence" after acceptance. Length: 4,000 words average; 550 words minimum; 5,000 words maximum. Publishes short shorts. Also publishes literary essays, poetry. Sometimes critiques rejected mss and recommends other markets.
How to Contact: Send complete ms with cover letter, which should include "some personal information about the author, a brief genesis of his/her work and why the author chose us." Reports in 1-2 months on queries; 3-4 months on mss. No SASE. Simultaneous and photocopied submissions OK. Accepts computer printout submissions. Sample copy for $1. Fiction guidelines for #10 SAE and 1 first class stamp.
Payment: Pays in contributor's copies, charges for extras, voluntary donations.
Terms: Acquires all rights.
Advice: "Anyone interested in being published in the *Diary* would have to keep in mind that we are a new enterprise and, as such, are testing the waters of 'special-interest' literature in the hopes of building a readership of open-minded and intelligent people. Translation: You won't get rich and famous with us, if that is your aim. But . . . if you have a good imagination and are willing to tackle subject matter 'beyond your ken' (as interracial loving will most likely be) then we will be more than happy to consider your work. We like to think of ourselves as one of the few publications willing to take a chance on raw, undiscovered talent."

GOLDEN ISIS MAGAZINE, (I, IV), Suite 137, 23233 Saticoy St., Bldg. 105, West Hills CA 91304. Editor: Gerina Dunwich. Magazine: Digest-sized; approx. 8 pages; 20 lb. stock; paper cover; illustrations. "*Golden Isis* is a mystical New Age literary magazine of occult fiction, Goddess-inspired poetry, Pagan artwork, Wiccan news, letters, occasional book reviews and classified ads." Quarterly. Estab. 1980. Circ. 4,000 (including 2 libraries).

Needs: Psychic/supernatural/occult, bizarre humor, fantasy and mystical Egyptian themes. "Please do not send us pornographic, religious, racist or sexist material. We will not consider stories written in present tense." Receives 100+ mss/month. Buys 1-2 mss/issue; 4-8 mss/year. Published fiction by Rod R. Vick, Cary G. Osborne and Gypsy Electra; published many new writers within the last year. Length: 1,500 words maximum. Publishes short shorts. Also publishes poetry. Occasionally critiques rejected mss and often recommends other markets.

How to Contact: Send complete ms. SASE. Sample copy $2. Fiction guidelines for #10 SAE and 1 first class stamp.

Payment: Payment varies from 1 free contributor's copy to $5.

Terms: Pays on publication for first North American serial rights.

Advice: "Submit short fiction that is well-written, atmospheric and equipped with a good surprise ending. Originality is important. Quality writing is a must. Avoid clichés, poor grammar, predictable endings, unnecessary obscenity and run-on sentences, for these things will only bring you a fast rejection slip. Also publishes chapbooks: $5 reading fee; length up to 50 pages; query first or send complete ms. Sample chapbook $5."

GOTTA WRITE NETWORK LITMAG, (I), Maren Publications, 612 Cobblestone Circle, Glenview IL 60025. Editor: Denise Fleischer. Magazine: 8½×11; 48 pages; saddle-stapled ordinary paper; matte card or lighter weight cover stock; illustrations. Magazine "serves as an open forum to discuss new markets, victories and difficulties. Gives beginning writers their first break into print." Distributed through the US, Canada and England. Quarterly. Estab. 1988. Circ. 200.

Needs: Adventure, contemporary, fantasy, historical, humor/satire, literary, mainstream, prose poem, romance, science fiction and young adult/teen. Receives 75-150 unsolicited ms per month; accepts 3-5 mss per issue; up to 20 mss a year. Publishes mss 6-12 months after acceptance. Published work by Don Stockard, Chuck Howland, Carol Vinci and Jeff VanderMeer. Length: 4 pages maximum for short stories. Also publishes poetry. Recommends other markets.

How to Contact: Send complete ms with cover letter and query letter. Include "who the writer is, type of work submitted, previous publications and the writer's focused area of writing." Reports in 1 month. SASE. Photocopied submissions OK; reprints considered "at times." Accepts computer print-outs and electronic submissions via Macintosh disks. Sample copy for $3.75. Fiction guidelines for SASE.

Payment: Pays in contributor's copies; charge for extras.

Terms: Acquires first North American serial rights.

Advice: "If I still think about the direction of the story after I've read it, I know it's good. Organize your thoughts on the plot and character development (qualities, emotions) before enduring 10 drafts. Make your characters come alive by giving them a personality and a background and then give them a little freedom. Let them take you through the story."

GRAIN, (I, II), Saskatchewan Writers' Guild, Box 1154, Regina, Saskatchewan S4P 3B4 Canada. Editor: Geoffrey Ursell. Fiction Editor: Edna Alford. Literary magazine: 5½×8½; 128 pages; Chinook offset printing; chrome-coated stock; illustrations; some photos. "Fiction and poetry for people who enjoy high quality writing." Quarterly. Estab. 1973. Circ. 1,000-1,300.

Needs: Contemporary, experimental, literary, mainstream and prose poem. "No propaganda—only artistic/literary writing." No mss "that stay *within* the limits of conventions such as women's magazine type stories, science fiction; none that push a message." Upcoming theme: "Rural Issue," work dealing with small towns, farms, ranches, reservations; deadline: February 29, 1992. Receives 80 unsolicited fiction mss/month. Buys 8-12 mss/issue; 16-28 mss/year. Agented fiction approximately 1%. Recently published 2 short stories by emerging writers selected for the third *Journey Prize Anthology*. Length: "No more than 50 pages." Also publishes poetry. Occasionally critiques rejected mss.

How to Contact: Send complete ms with SAE, IRC and brief of one-two sentences. "Let us know if you're just beginning to send out." Reports within 6 months on ms. Publishes ms an average of 4 months after acceptance. Sample copy $5.

Payment: Pays $30-100; 2 contributor's copies.

Terms: Pays on publication for one-time rights. "We expect acknowledgment if the piece is republished elsewhere."

Advice: "Submit a story to us that will deepen the imaginative experience of our readers. *Grain* has established itself as a first-class magazine of serious fiction. We receive submissions from around the world. If Canada is a foreign country to you, we ask that you *do not* enclose US postage stamps on your return envelope. If you live outside Canada and neglect the International Reply Coupons, we *will not* read or reply to your submission."

The main focus of Grain, a quarterly published by the Saskatchewan Writers Guild, is to present its readers with both new writing and art of high quality, says Steven Smith, business manager. The cover illustration shown here was selected because it is "an extraordinary piece of art by a young artist living in our province," he says. "It is extraordinary because of its imaginative rendering and lively, colorful tone." The artist is Miranda Jones, whose work has been included in exhibitions in Saskatchewan, Newfoundland and Australia. This oil and mixed media piece is titled "Mother Supports the Rainbow."

GRASSLANDS REVIEW, (I), Mini-Course—University of North Texas, N.T. Box 13706, Denton TX 76203. Editor: Laura B. Kennelly. Magazine: 6×9; 55 pages. *Grasslands Review* prints creative writing of all types; poetry; fiction,essays for a general audience. Semiannually. Estab. 1989. Circ. 200.
Needs: Adventure, contemporary, ethnic, experimental, fantasy, horror, humor/satire, literary, prose poem, regional, science fiction, suspense/mystery and western. Nothing pornographic or overtly political or religious. Accepts 4-5 mss/issue. Reads only in October and March. Publishes ms 6 months after acceptance. Recently published work by Annie Dawid, James Hoggard, Gerald Locklin, Jendi Reiter, Carole Bellacera. Length: 1,500 words average; 100-3,500 words. Publishes short shorts (100-150 words). Also publishes poetry. Sometimes critiques rejected mss and recommends other markets.
How to Contact: Send complete ms in October or March *only* with cover letter. Reports on mss in 2 months. SASE. Sample copy for $1. May review novels or short story collections.
Payment: Pays in contributor's copies.
Terms: Acquires one-time rights. Publication not copyrighted.
Advice: "We are looking for fiction which leaves the reader with a strong feeling or impression—or a new perspective on life. The Review began as an in-class exercise to allow experienced creative writing students to learn how a little magazine is produced. We now wish to open it up to outside submissions so that our students can gain an understanding of how large the writing community is in the United States and so that they may have experience in working with other writers."

GREAT STREAM REVIEW, (II), Lycoming College, Box 66, Williamsport PA 17701. Editor: Penelope Wilkerson Austin. Fiction Editor: G.W. Hawkes. Magazine: 6×9; 100+ pages. "The best fiction, nonfiction and poetry we can find for an educated adult audience." Estab. 1989.
Needs: Contemporary, literary, mainstream, regional. Buys 2-4 mss/issue; 4-8 mss/year. Publishes ms within year of acceptance. Published work by Moses, Gridley, Barber, Paul. Length: 6,000-9,000 words average. Publishes short shorts. Length open. Sometimes critiques rejected mss and recommends other markets.
How to Contact: Send complete manuscript with cover letter including "name, address, phone number, brief bio." Reports in 1 week on queries; 2 months on mss. SASE. Simultaneous and photocopied submissions OK. Accepts computer printout submissions. Sample copy $4.
Payment: Pays $10/published page maximum $100 and contributor's copies.
Terms: Buys first North American serial rights. "Contests are announced."

GREEN MOUNTAINS REVIEW, (II), Johnson State College, Box A-58, Johnson VT 05656. (802)635-2356, ext. 339. Editor: Neil Shepard. Editor: Tony Whedon. Magazine: Digest-sized; 100-125 pages. Semiannually. Estab. 1975 (new series, 1987). Circ. 1,000.
Needs: Adventure, contemporary, experimental, humor/satire, literary, mainstream, regional (New England), serialized/excerpted novel, translations. Receives 30 unsolicited mss/month. Accepts 5 mss/issue; 10 mss/year. Publishes ms 1-2 months after acceptance. Length: 25 pages maximum. Publishes short shorts. Also publishes literary criticism, poetry. Sometimes critiques rejected mss.
How to Contact: Send complete ms with cover letter. Reports in 1 month on queries; 2 months on mss. SASE. Simultaneous and photocopied submissions OK. Accepts computer printout submissions. Sample copy for $4.
Payment: Pays in contributor's copies.
Terms: Acquires first North American serial rights. Sends galleys to author upon request.

GREEN'S MAGAZINE, Fiction for the Family, (II), Green's Educational Publications, Box 3236, Regina, Saskatchewan S4P 3H1 Canada. Editor: David Green. Magazine: 5¼×8; 100 pages; 20 lb. bond paper; matte cover stock; line illustrations. Publishes "solid short fiction suitable for family reading." Quarterly. Estab. 1972.
Needs: Adventure, fantasy, humor/satire, literary, mainstream, science fiction and suspense/mystery. No erotic or sexually explicit fiction. Receives 20-30 mss/month. Accepts 10-12 mss/issue; 40-50 mss/year. Publishes ms within 3-6 months of acceptance. Agented fiction 2%. Published work by Solomon Pogarsky, Ann Beacham, Hélène Scheffler-Mason. Length: 2,500 words preferred; 1,500 words minimum; 4,000 words maximum. Also publishes poetry. Sometimes critiques rejected mss and recommends other markets.
How to Contact: Send complete ms. "Cover letters welcome but not necessary." Reports in 2 months. SASE. "Must include international reply coupons." Photocopied submissions OK. Accepts computer printout submissions. No simultaneous submissions. Sample copy for $4. Fiction guidelines for #10 SAE and international reply coupon. Reviews novels and short story collections.
Payment: Pays in contributor's copies.
Terms: Acquires first North American serial rights.

GREENSBORO REVIEW, (II), University of North Carolina at Greensboro, Dept. of English, Greensboro NC 27412. (919)334-5459. Editor: Jim Clark. Fiction Editor: Sharon Krauss. Magazine: 6×9; approximately 136 pages; 60 lb. paper; 65 lb. cover. Literary magazine featuring fiction and poetry for readers interested in contemporary literature. Semiannually. Circ. 500.
Needs: Contemporary and experimental. Accepts 6-8 mss/issue, 12-16 mss/year. Published work by Julia Alvarez, Larry Brown and Madison Smartt Bell; published new writers within the last year. Length: 7,500 words maximum.
How to Contact: Send complete ms with SASE. Unsolicited manuscripts must arrive by September 15 to be considered for the winter issue and by February 15 to be considered for the summer issue. Manuscripts arriving after those dates may be held for the next consideration. Photocopied submissions OK. Sample copy for $2.50.
Payment: Pays in contributor's copies.
Terms: Acquires first North American serial rights.
Advice: "We want to see the best being written regardless of theme, subject or style. Recent stories from *The Greensboro Review* have been included in *The Best American Short Stories, Prize Stories: The O. Henry Awards, New Stories from the South* and *Best of the West,* anthologies recognizing the finest short stories being published."

GROUNDSWELL, A Literary Review, (II), P.O. Box 12093, Albany NY 12212-2093. (518)449-8069. Fiction Editor: F.R. Lewis. Magazine. 5½×8½; 100 pages; 70 lb. paper; occasional line drawings/graphics. "Variable themes; fiction, poetry reviews of small press publications, critical essays, interviews." Annually. Estab. 1984.
Needs: Contemporary, ethnic, experimental, fantasy, feminist, gay, humor/satire, lesbian, literary, mainstream, regional, excerpted novel, suspense/mystery, translations. "We are open to any high quality, significant, honest fictions." No formula stories; stories that are racist, sexist; stories that ignore craft and clarity. Reads mss from mid-October to mid-May. Accepts up to 5 mss/issue; 4-10 mss/year. Recently published work by Ginnah Howard, Lisa Kroger; published new writers within the last year. Length: 25 pages maximum. Publishes short shorts. Length 1-6 pages. Also publishes literary essays, poetry. Sometimes critiques rejected ms.

How to Contact: Send complete ms with brief bio note. "We want something that can be used as a contributor's note if the story is accepted." Reports in 3 months (varies). SASE. Photocopied submissions OK. Accepts computer printout submissions. Sample copy $6 and 6×9 SAE with 6 first class stamps.

Payment: Pays 2 contributor's copies; other payment depends on funding.

Terms: Acquires first North American serial rights. Copyright reverts to author.

Advice: "Read the magazine in which you want to publish. Polish your work. No onion skin."

GULF COAST, A Journal of Literature & Art, (II), Dept. of English, University of Houston, 4800 Calhoun Rd., Houston TX 77204-5641. (713)749-3431. Editors: Stewart James and Randall Watson. Fiction Editors: Mark O'Connor and Randy Brieger. Magazine: 6×9; 108 pages; stock paper, gloss cover; illustrations and photographs. "Fiction on the cusp for the literary-minded." Estab. 1984. Circ. 1,000.

Needs: Condensed/excerpted novel, contemporary, ethnic, experimental, humor/satire, literary, regional, translations, special interest: *translations* from emerging literatures, South America, Africa, China, etc. No children's, religious/inspirational. Plans special fiction issue. Receives 40 unsolicited mss/month. Accepts 3-4 mss/issue; 6-8 mss/year. Publishes ms 6 months to 1 year after acceptance. Agented fiction 5%. Published work by Larry Woiwode, John Hawkes and Oscar Hijuelos. Length: No limit. Publishes short shorts. Sometimes critiques rejected mss.

How to Contact: Send complete manuscript with cover letter. "As few words as possible; please notify us if the submission is being considered elsewhere." Reports in 3 weeks to 6 months. Simultaneous and photocopied submissions OK. Sample copy for $4, 9×12 SAE and 4 first class stamps. Fiction guidelines for #10 SAE and 1 first class stamp.

Payment: Pays contributor's copies.

Terms: Acquires one-time rights. Also sponsors fiction contest. "Write for guidelines."

Advice: "We are most intrigued by those who take risks, experiment with language."

GULF STREAM MAGAZINE, (II), Florida International University, English Dept., North Miami Campus, N. Miami FL 33181. (305)940-5599. Editor: Lynne Barrett. Associate Editors: Pamela Gross, Virginia Oesterle. Magazine: 5½×8½; 96 pages; bond paper; laminate (1 color, b&w) cover; cover illustrations only; cover photographs only. "We publish all *good quality*—fiction nonfiction and poetry for a predominantly literary market." Semiannually. Estab. 1989. Circ. 500.

Needs: Contemporary, humor/satire, literary, mainstream, regional, suspense/mystery. Nothing "radically experimental." Plans special issues. Receives 80 unsolicited mss/month. Acquires 5 mss/issue; 10 mss/year. Does not read mss during the summer. Publishes ms 6 weeks to 3 months after acceptance. Published work by Alan Cheuse, Ann Hood. Length: 5,000 words average; 7,500 words maximum. Publishes short shorts. Also publishes poetry. Sometimes critiques rejected mss.

How to Contact: Send complete manuscript with cover letter including "previous publications/short bio." Reports in 2 months. SASE. Photocopied submissions OK. Sample copy $4. Free fiction guidelines.

Payment: Pays 2 free subscriptions and contributor's copies.

Terms: Acquires first North American serial rights.

Advice: "Looks for good concise writing—well plotted; interesting characters."

GYPSY, Die Sympathische Alternative, (II), Vergin Press, 10708 Gay Brewer, El Paso TX 79935. (915)592-3701. Editors: Belinda Subraman and S. Ramnath. Magazine: 8½×11; 84 pages; 20-60 lb. offset paper; 60 lb. card cover; drawings; sometimes photographs. "Quality writing, not limited to theme, for the literary and artistic community." Semiannually. Estab. 1990. Circ. 1,000.

Needs: Experimental, feminist, literary, serialized novel, translations. Receives 100 unsolicited fiction mss/month. Accepts 2-4 mss/issue; 6-10 mss/year. Publishes ms 1-8 months after acceptance. Length: "open, but short is better—perhaps 500-2,500 words." Publishes short shorts. Also publishes literary essays, literary criticism, poetry. Sometimes critiques or comments on rejected mss. Sometimes recommends other markets.

Read the Business of Fiction section to learn the correct way to prepare and submit a manuscript.

How to Contact: Query first or send complete ms with cover letter. Reports in 2 weeks. SASE. Photocopied submissions OK. Reprint submissions sometimes OK. Sample copies for $5. Fiction guidelines for #10 SAE and 1 first-class stamp.
Payment: Pays in contributor's copies.
Terms: Acquires one-time rights.

‡HABERSHAM REVIEW, (I, II), Piedmont College, P.O. Box 10, Demorest GA 30535. (404)778-2215. Editors: David L. Greene, Lisa Hodgens Lumpkin. Magazine. "General literary magazine with a regional (Southeastern U.S.) focus for a literate audience." Semiannually. Estab. 1991.
Needs: Contemporary, experimental, literary, mainstream, regional. Publishes biannual fiction and poetry issue. Receives 20-25 unsolicited mss/month. Accepts 6-10 mss/issue. Publishes ms 6 month-1 year after acceptance. Publishes short shorts. Sometimes critiques rejected mss and recommends other markets.
How to Contact: Send complete ms with cover letter. Reports in 3 months on mss. SASE. Accepts electronic submissions via disk or modem. Sample copy for $4.
Payment: Pays in contributor's copies.
Terms: Acquires first rights. Sends galleys to author.

HALF TONES TO JUBILEE, (II), English Dept. Pensacola Junior College, 1000 College Blvd., Pensacola FL 32504. (904)484-1416. Editors: Allan Peterson and Walter Spara. Magazine: 6×9; approx. 100 pages; 70 lb. laid stock; 80 lb. cover. "No theme, all types published." Annually. Estab. 1985. Circ. 500.
Needs: Open. Receives 4-6 unsolicited mss/month. Accepts approx. 6 mss/issue. "We publish in September." Recently published work by Rachel Cann, Dusty Sklar, Johnathan Gillman, Mark Spencer. Length: 1,500 words average. Publishes short shorts. Also publishes poetry. Sometimes critiques rejected mss and recommends other markets.
How to Contact: Send complete manuscript with cover letter. SASE. Photocopied submissions OK. Accepts computer printout submissions. Sample copy $4. Free fiction guidelines.
Payment: Pays 2 contributor's copies.
Terms: Acquires one-time rights.

HARDBOILED, (I,II,IV), Gryphon Publications, Box 209, Brooklyn NY 11228-0209. Editor: Gary Lovisi. Magazine: Digest-sized; more than 80 pages; offset paper; card stock cover; illustrations. Publishes "cutting edge, hard, noir fiction with impact! Query on nonfiction and reviews." Quarterly. Estab. 1988.
Needs: Receives 20-30 mss/month. Accepts 20-30 mss/year. Publishes ms within 6 months to 2 years of acceptance. Recently published work by Andrew Vachss, Richard Lupoff, Frank Grubber; published new writers within the last year. Length: 2,000 words minimum; 4,000 words maximum. Sometimes critiques rejected mss and recommends other markets.
How to Contact: Query first or send complete ms with cover letter. Reports in 2 weeks on queries; 1 month on mss. SASE. Photocopied submissions OK. Accepts computer printout submissions. Sample copy $4.
Payment: Pays $5-25 and 2 contributor's copies.
Terms: Pays on publication for first North American serial rights. Copyright reverts to author.

HAUNTS, Tales of Unexpected Horror and the Supernatural, (II, IV), Nightshade Publications, Box 3342, Providence RI 02906. (401)781-9438. Editor: Joseph K. Cherkes. Magazine: 6×9 digest; 80-100 pages; 50 lb. offset paper; perfect-bound; pen and ink illustrations. "We are committed to publishing only the finest fiction in the genres of horror, fantasy and the supernatural from both semi-pro and established writers. We are targeted towards the 18-35 age bracket interested in tales of horror and the unknown." Quarterly. Plans special fiction issue. Estab. 1984. Circ. 1,200.
Needs: Fantasy, horror, psychic/supernatural/occult. No pure adventure, explicit sex, or blow-by-blow dismemberment. Receives 400-450 unsolicited fiction mss/month. Accepts 10-12 mss/issue; 50-75 mss/year. Publishes ms 6-9 months after acceptance. Published work by Mike Hurley, Kevin J. Anderson, Frank Ward; published new writers within the last year. Length: 3,500 words average; 1,000 words minimum; 8,500 words maximum. Critiques rejected mss and recommends other markets.
How to Contact: Query first. "Cover letters are a nice way to introduce oneself to a new editor." Open to submissions June 1 to December 1, inclusive. Reports in 2-3 weeks on queries; 2-3 months on mss. SASE for query. Photocopied submissions OK. Accepts computer printouts. Accepts magnetic

media (IBM PC-MS/DOS Ver 2.0 or higher). Sample copy $3.95 plus $1 postage and handling. Fiction guidelines for #10 SASE.
Payment: Pays $5-50 (subject to change), contributor's copies, charge for extras.
Terms: Pays on publication for first North American serial rights.
Advice: "Follow writers' guidelines closely. They are a good outline of what your publisher looks for in fiction. If you think you've got the 'perfect' manuscript, go over it again — carefully. Check to make sure you've left no loose ends before sending it out. Keep your writing concise. If your story is rejected, don't give up. Try to see where the story failed. This way you can learn from your mistakes. Remember, success comes to those who persist. We plan to open to advertising on a limited basis, also plan a media campaign to increase subscriptions and distributed sales."

HAWAII PACIFIC REVIEW, (II), Hawaii Pacific University, 1060 Bishop St., Honolulu HI 96813. (808)544-0259. Editor: Frederick Hohing. Magazine: 6×9; 100-150 pages; quality paper; glossy cover; illustrations and photos. "As a literary magazine located in Hawaii, we are interested in material that concerns or is set in the Pacific Rim and Asia. However, we are open to *quality* writing on any theme. Categories: fiction, poetry, essays and scholarly writing." Annually. Estab. "nationwide in 1988."
Needs: Adventure, contemporary, ethnic, experimental, fantasy, humor/satire, literary, mainstream, regional, science fiction, suspense/mystery, translations. No romance, confessions, religious or juvenile. Receives approx. 50 unsolicited fiction mss/month. Accepts 4-8 mss/issue. Deadline for the Spring annual issue is January 1. Does not read in summer. Publishes ms 3-12 months after acceptance. Published new writers within the last year. Length: 5,000 words maximum. Publishes short shorts. Also publishes literary essays, literary criticism, poetry. Sometimes critiques rejected mss or recommends other markets.
How to Contact: Send complete manuscript with cover letter, which should include a brief bio. Reports in 3 months. SASE. Simultaneous and photocopied submissions OK. Accepts computer printouts. Fiction guidelines for #10 SAE and 1 first class stamp.
Payment: Pays in contributor's copies.
Terms: Acquires first North American serial rights. Rights revert to author upon publication.
Advice: "A beginning writer should take pride in his work. Professional appearance of the manuscript, therefore, is a must."

HAWAII REVIEW, (II), University of Hawaii English Dept., 1733 Donaghho Rd., Honolulu HI 96822. (808)956-8548. Editor: Jeanne Tsutsui. Magazine: 6½×9½; 150-170 pages; illustrations; photos. "We publish short stories as well as poetry and reviews by new and experienced writers. As an international literary journal, we hope to reflect the idea that cultural diversity is of universal interest." For residents of Hawaii and non-residents from the continental US and abroad. Triannually. Plans special fiction issue on environmental concerns. Estab. 1972. Circ. 5,000.
Needs: Contemporary, ethnic, experimental, humor/satire, literary, prose poem, regional and translations. Receives 40-50 mss/month. Accepts no more than 40 mss/issue; 130 mss/year. Published work by William Pitt Root, Ursule Molinaro and Ian Macmillan; published new writers within the last year. Length: 4,000 words average; no minimum; 8,000 words maximum. Occasionally critiques mss. Also publishes poetry. Recommends other markets.
How to Contact: Send complete manuscript with SASE. Reports in 3-4 months on mss. Photocopied submissions OK. Accepts computer printout submissions. Sample copy for $5. Fiction guidelines free.
Payment: Payment "varies depending upon funds budgeted. Last year, we paid $35-70 per story;" 2 contributor's copies.
Terms: Pays on publication for all rights. Sends galleys to author upon request. After publication, copyright reverts to author upon request.

HAYDEN'S FERRY REVIEW, (II), Arizona State University, Matthews Center A.S.U., Tempe AZ 85287-1502. (602)965-1243. Managing Editor: Salima Keegan. Magazine: 6×9; 128 pages; fine paper; illustrations and photographs. "Contemporary material by new and established writers for a varied audience." Semiannually. Estab. 1986. Circ. 600.
Needs: Contemporary, ethnic, experimental, fantasy, feminist, gay, historical (general), humor/satire, literary, mainstream, prose poem, psychic/supernatural/occult, regional, romance (contemporary), science fiction, senior citizen/retirement. Possible special fiction issue. Receives 150 unsolicited mss/month. Accepts 5 mss/issue; 10 per year. Does not read mss in the summer. Publishes mss 3-4 months after acceptance. Published work by Chuck Rosenthal and Rick Bass. Length: No preference. Publishes short shorts. Also publishes literary essays.

How to Contact: Send complete manuscript with cover letter that includes bio. Reports in 8-10 weeks from deadline on mss. SASE. Photocopied submissions OK. Accepts computer printout submissions. Sample copy for $6. Fiction guidelines for SAE.
Payment: Pays $25 and contributor's copies.
Terms: Buys first North American serial rights. Sends galleys to author.

‡**THE HEARTLANDS TODAY, (II),** The Firelands Writing Center, Firelands College of BGSU, Huron OH 44839. (419)433-5560. Editors: Larry Smith and Nancy Dunham. Magazine: 6×9; 160 pages; b&w illustrations; 25-30 photographs. Material must be set in the Midwest . . . prefer material that reveals life in the Midwest today for a general, literate audience. Annually. Estab. 1991.
Needs: Ethnic, humor, literary, mainstream, regional (Midwest). Receives 10 unsolicited mss/month. Buys 6 mss/issue. Does not read mss August-December. Publishes ms 6 months after acceptance. Recently published work of Wendell Mayo, Tony Tomassi, Gloria Bowman. Length: 4,500 words maximum. Also publishes literary essays, poetry. Sometimes critiques rejected mss and recommends other markets.
How to Contact: Send complete ms with cover letter. Reports in 1 month on mss. SASE for ms, not needed for query. Simultaneous and photocopied submissions OK. Sample copy for $5.
Payment: Pays $20-25 and 2 contributor's copies.
Terms: Pays on publication. Buys first rights.
Advice: "We look for writing that connects on a real and human level, one thatmoves us with its truth and opens our vision of the world. If writing is a great escape for you, don't bother with us.We're in it for the joy, beauty or truth of the art. We look for a straight, honest voice dealing with human experiences. We do not define the Midwest, we hope to be a document of the Midwest. If you feel you are writing from the Midwest, send. We look first at the quality of the writing."

HEAVEN BONE, (IV), Heaven Bone Press, Box 486, Chester NY 10918. (914)469-9018. Editors: Steven Hirsch, Kirpal Gordon. Magazine: 8½×11; 49-78 pages; 60 lb. recycled offset paper; recycled C1S cover; computer clip art, graphics, line art, cartoons, halftones and photos scanned in tiff format. "New consciousness, expansive, fine literary, earth and nature, spiritual path. We use current reviews, essays on spiritual and esoteric topics, creative stories and fantasy. Also: reviews of current poetry releases and expansive literature." Readers are "spiritual seekers, healers, poets, artists, musicians, students." Semiannually. Estab. 1987. Circ. 1,200.
Needs: Experimental, fantasy, psychic/supernatural/occult, esoteric/scholarly, regional, religious/inspirational, spiritual. "No violent, thoughtless or exploitive fiction." Receives 45-110 unsolicited mss/month. Accepts 5-15 mss/issue; 12-30 mss/year. Publishes ms 2 weeks to 6 months after acceptance. Recently published work by Fielding Dawson, Joe Richey, Jeanine Pommy-Vega; published new writers within the last year. Length: 3,500 words average; 1,200 words minimum; 6,000 words maximum. Publishes short shorts. Also publishes literary essays, literary criticism, poetry. Sometimes critiques rejected mss and may recommend other markets.
How to Contact: Send complete ms with cover letter, which should include short bio of recent activities. Reports in 2 weeks on queries; 2 weeks-6 months on mss. SASE. Reprint submissions OK. Accepts computer printout submissions. Accepts electronic submissions via "Apple Mac SE/30 versions of Macwrite, Microsoft Word v. 4.0 or Writenow v. 2.0." Sample copy $5. Fiction guidelines free. Reviews novels and short story collections.
Payment: Pays in contributor's copies; charges for extras.
Terms: Acquires first North American serial rights. Sends galleys to author, if requested.
Advice: "Our fiction needs are tempermental, so please query first before submitting. We prefer shorter fiction. Do not send first drafts to test them on us. Please refine and polish your work before sending. Always include SASE. We are looking for the unique, unusual and excellent."

‡**HELTER SKELTER, (II),** Scream Press, 509 Enterprise Dr., Rohnert Park CA 94928. (707)585-1436. Editor: Anthony Boyd. Magazine: 8½×11; 14 pages; 20 lb. paper; 60 lb. cover; illustrations and photographs. "Horror is *not* a theme. *Helter Skelter* is general interest. Audience: youngest reader 15, oldest reader 74—all ages, all professions." Semiannually. Estab. 1987. Circ. 250.
Needs: Adventure, contemporary, fantasy, humor/satire, literary, mainstream, religious/inspirational, romance (contemporary), science fiction, suspense/mystery."No gore, no porn." Receives 2 unsolicited mss/month. Accepts 1 ms/issue; 2 mss/year. Publishes ms up to 11 months after acceptance. Length: 1,000 words average; 500 words minimum; 1,200 words maximum. Also publishes short literary essays (100-300 words).

How to Contact: Send complete ms with cover letter. Include "a short bio, a few publication credits, and anything else I may find interesting. Tell me a joke so I'm in a good mood to read your story." Reports in 1 week on queries; 1 month on mss. SASE. Photocopied and reprint submissions OK, if stated. Accepts computer printout submissions. Sample copy for $2.
Payment: Pays in contributor's copies.
Terms: Acquires one-time rights.
Advice: "I like a lot of what *Pandora* publishes, and I like what college students are sending; good plot, and some strong twists. Looks for neatness, a good cover letter, and appropriateness—I don't even look at stories obviously over 1,000 words, and when I skim it, if I see violence, lewdness, or if the first 2 paragraphs don't get my attention, I send it back."

HERESIES: A Feminist Publication on Art & Politics, (IV), Box 1306, Canal St. Station, New York NY 10013. Magazine: 8½×11; 96 pages; non-coated paper; b&w illustrations and photos. "We believe that what is commonly called art can have a political impact and that in the making of art and all cultural artifacts our identities as women play a distinct role . . . A place where diversity can be articulated. International and North American-wide readership; carried by many libraries, alternative bookshops, and art schools." Published 2 times/year. Estab. 1977. Circ. 8,000.
Needs: Feminist and lesbian. Upcoming themes: "Women on Men"; "Viva Latina"; "Crime and Transgression." "Due to reliance on volunteer editors and the extensive cuts in arts funding, notification for acceptance or rejection may take up to 1 year, particularly for nonthematic submissions." Published new writers within the last year. Publishes stories up to 25 typed pages maximum. Also publishes poetry.
How to Contact: Query. Guidelines with SASE.
Payment: Small payment post publication and several contributor's copies.
Advice: "Try not to imitate what you think is a successful, saleable style. Try to stick to concrete stuff you've experienced yourself so as to sharpen your narrative/dialogue skills on a foundation of familiarity."

‡HERSPECTIVES, The Dialogue of the Common Woman, (II, IV), Box 2047, Squamish, British Columbia V0N 3G0 Canada. (604)892-5723. Editor: Mary E. Billy. Newsletter: 8½×11; 30-40 pages; bond paper; b&w illustrations and photographs. "Feminist; ecology; spirituality; poetry; articles; cartoons; graphics; letters; short short fiction for women. Quarterly. Estab. 1989. Circ. 200.
Needs: Condensed/excerpted novel, confession, contemporary, erotica, ethnic, experimental, fantasy, feminist, gay, humor/satire, juvenile, lesbian, mainstream, prose poem, senior citizen/retirement, young adult/teen (10-18 years) (for women). "No sexist, racist, homophobic; prefer positive perspective." Receives 1 unsolicited mss/month. Accepts 1-2 mss/issue; 6 mss/year. Publishes ms 3-24 months after acceptance. Recently published work by Louise Allin, Gina Dergamino. Length: 1,000-2,000 words average; 200 words minimum; 3,000 words maximum. Publishes short shorts. Sometimes critiques rejected mss.
How to Contact: Send complete ms with cover letter. Include "where you heard or read about *Herspectives*, international coupons for ms return if outside of Canada. Reports in 2-6 weeks. SASE. Simultaneous, photocopied and reprint submissions OK. Accepts computer printout submissions. Sample copy for $5. Fiction guidelines for #10 SAE and 1 first class Canadian stamp or IRC.
Payment: Pays 1 contributor's copy.
Terms: Acquires first rights. Not copyrighted.
Advice: Looks for "clean tight writing, ring of honesty and guts, humor, a positive attitude without sounding Pollyanaish. Absolutely no violence."

HIGH PLAINS LITERARY REVIEW, (II), Suite 250, 180 Adams Street, Denver CO 80206. (303)320-6828. Editor-in-Chief: Robert O. Greer, Jr. Magazine: 6×9; 135 pages; 70 lb. paper; heavy cover stock. "The *High Plains Literary Review* publishes poetry, fiction, essays, book reviews and interviews. The publication is designed to bridge the gap between high-caliber academic quarterlies and successful commercial reviews." Triannually. Estab. 1986. Circ. 950.
Needs: Most pressing need: outstanding essays, serious fiction, contemporary, humor/satire, literary, mainstream, regional. No true confessions, romance, pornographic, excessive violence. Receives approximately 200 unsolicited mss/month. Buys 4-6 mss/issue; 12-18 mss/year. Publishes ms usually 6 months after acceptance. Published work by Richard Currey, Joyce Carol Oates, Nancy Lord and Rita Dove; published new writers within the last year. Length: 4,200 words average; 1,500 words minimum; 8,000 words maximum; prefers 3,000-6,000 words. Also publishes literary essays, literary criticism, poetry. Occasionally critiques rejected mss. Sometimes recommends other markets.

How to Contact: Send complete ms with cover letter, which should include brief publishing history. Reports in 6 weeks. SASE. Simultaneous and photocopied submissions OK. Accepts computer print-out submissions. Sample copy for $4. Reviews novels and short story collections.

Payment: Pays $5/page for prose and 2 contributor's copies.

Terms: Pays on publication for first North American serial rights. "Copyright reverts to author upon publication." Sends copy-edited proofs to the author.

Advice: "*HPLR* publishes *quality* writing. Send us your very best material. We will read it carefully and either accept it promptly, recommend changes or return it promptly. Do not start submitting your work until you learn the basic tenants of the game including some general knowledge about how to develop characters and plot and how to submit a manuscript. I think the most important thing for any new writer interested in the short story form is to have a voracious appetite for short fiction, to see who and what is being published, and to develop a personal style."

HILL AND HOLLER: Southern Appalachian Mountains, Seven Buffaloes Press, Box 249, Big Timber MT 59011. Editor: Art Cuelho. Magazine: 5½ × 8½; 80 pages; 70 lb. offset paper; 80 lb. cover stock; illustrations; photos rarely. "I use mostly rural Appalachian material: poems and stories. Some folklore and humor. I am interested in heritage, especially in connection with the farm." Annually. Published special fiction issue. Estab. 1983. Circ. 750.

Needs: Contemporary, ethnic, humor/satire, literary, regional, rural America farm. "I don't have any prejudices in style, but I don't like sentimental slant. Deep feelings in literature are fine, but they should be portrayed with tact and skill." Receives 10 unsolicited mss/month. Accepts 4-6 mss/issue. Publishes ms 6 months to a year after acceptance. Length: 2,000-3,000 words average. Also publishes short shorts of 500-1,000 words.

How to Contact: Query first. Reports in 2 weeks on queries. SASE. Accepts computer printouts. Sample copy $4.75.

Payment: Pays in contributor's copies; charge for extras.

Terms: Acquires first North American serial rights "and permission to reprint if my press publishes a special anthology." Sometimes sends galleys to author.

Advice: "In this Southern Appalachian rural series I can be optimistic about fiction. Appalachians are very responsive to their region's literature. I have taken work by beginners that had not been previously published. Be sure to send a double-spaced clean manuscript and SASE. I have the only rural press in North America; maybe even in the world. So perhaps we have a bond in common if your roots are rural."

HIPPO, (II), Chautauqua Press, 28834 Boniface Dr., Malibu CA 90265. (213)457-7871. Editor: Karl Heiss. Magazine: 5½ × 8½; 42-48 pages; 20 lb. bond paper; card cover; hi-contrast b&w illustrations. "Surreal and Hyper-real writing—writing that is honest and unpretentious—has a good chance of being considered. For open-minded, artistic, optimistic, cynical, paradoxical and all encompassing minds of all ages etc." Semiannually. Estab. 1988. Circ. 150.

Needs: Adventure, confessions, contemporary, erotica, experimental, fantasy, horror, humor/satire, literary, mainstream, prose poem, psychic/supernatural/occult, regional, science fiction, western and surreality. "No pure genre fiction, but love the inclusion of genre style and content elements. No pretentious stuff that could only possibly live within the confines of academia." Receives 30 unsolicited mss/month. Accepts 5-9 mss/issue; 10-18 mss/year. Publishes ms "up to 6 months" after acceptance. Recently published work by Stephen-Paul Martin, Lyn Lifshin, Greg Boyd and Christopher Woods. Length: 500-3,000 words average; 4,000 words maximum. Publishes short shorts. Sometimes critiques rejected mss and recommends other markets.

How to Contact: Send complete ms with cover letter. Reporting time varies. SASE. Photocopied and reprint submissions OK. Accepts computer printout submissions. Sample copy $2.50. "The magazine itself is the best guide for the submitter."

Payment: Pays in contributor's copies.

Terms: Acquires first or first North American serial rights.

Advice: "Be real, be unafraid, be spontaneous, tell me whatever you want."

HOBO JUNGLE, A Quarterly Journal of New Writing, (II), 33 Rucum Rd., Roxbury CT 06783. (203)354-4359. Editors: Marc Erdrich and Ruth Boerger. Magazine: 8 × 10½; 64 pages; newsprint; Groove cover; illustrations. "Magazine of new writing, considering poetry, fiction, essays, artwork and musical scores—works of high quality by serious writers for a general audience." Quarterly. Estab. 1987. Circ. 11,000.

Needs: Adventure, condensed/excerpted novel, contemporary, erotica, ethnic, experimental, fantasy, feminist, historical, humor/satire, literary, mainstream, prose poem, regional, science fiction, serialized novel, suspense/mystery, translations. "Young Hobos' section publishes work of young people through high school. No special requirements." Receives 25 unsolicited fiction mss/month. Buys 2-3 mss/issue; 10-12 mss/year. Publishes ms 1 month after acceptance. Agented fiction 5%. Length: Open. Publishes short shorts. Always comments on or critiques rejected mss. Also publishes poetry.
How to Contact: Send complete ms with cover letter. If pseudonym is being used, please include real name. Reports in 3-6 months. SASE. Simultaneous, photocopied and computer printout submissions OK. Accepts electronic submissions. Sample copy and fiction guidelines free.
Payment: Pays $10 plus 2 contributor's copies.
Terms: Pays on publication for one-time rights.
Advice: "We seek tightly written prose, displaying a command of the language. The beginning writer should read work aloud; read it to others who can offer constructive criticism; make sure the piece is accurate in terms of sentence construction, punctuation and spelling. Avoid clichés (unless relevant to work)."

HOBSON'S CHOICE (I), Starwind Press, Box 98, Ripley OH 45167. (513)392-4549. Editor: Susannah West. Magazine: 8½×11; 16 pages; 60 lb offset paper and cover; b&w illustrations; line shot photos. "Science fiction and fantasy for young adults (teen to 25 or so) with interest in science, technology, science fiction and fantasy." Monthly. Estab. 1974. Circ. 2,000.
Needs: Fantasy, humor/satire, science fiction. "We like SF that shows hope for the future and protagonists who interact with their environment rather than let themselves be manipulated by it." No horror, pastiches of other authors, stories featuring characters created by others (i.e. Captain Kirk and crew, Dr. Who, etc.). Receives 50+ unsolicited mss/month. Buys 4-6 mss/issue; 16-24 mss/year. Publishes ms between 4 months-2 years after acceptance. Published work by Barbara Myers, Allen Byerle, Kurt Hyatt; published new writers within the last year. Length: 3,000-8,000 words average; 1,000 words minimum; 8,000 words maximum. Also publishes literary criticism and "occasionally" literary essays. Occasionally critiques rejected mss.
How to Contact: Send complete ms. Reports in 6-8 weeks. SASE for ms. Photocopied submissions OK. Accepts computer printouts. Accepts electronic submissions via disk for the IBM PC or PC compatible; MacIntosh; word processors: Multimate, WordStar, MacWrite, or ASCII. Sample copy $3.50; issue #2-4 $2.50. Fiction guidelines free for #10 SAE and 1 first class stamp. Sometimes reviews novels and short story collections. Send books to Susannah West or Dave Powell.
Payment: Pays 1-4¢/word and contributor's copies.
Terms: Pays 25% on acceptance; 75% on publication. "25% payment is kill fee if we decide not to publish story." Rights negotiable. Sends galleys to the author.
Advice: "I certainly think a beginning writer can be successful if he/she studies the publication *before* submitting, and matches the submission with the magazine's needs. Get our guidelines and study them *before* submitting. Don't submit something *way over* or *way under* our word length requirements. Be understanding of editors; they can get swamped very easily, *especially* if there's only one editor handling all submissions. You don't need to write a synopsis of your story in your cover letter—the story should be able to stand on its own."

HOR-TASY, (II, IV), Ansuda Publications, Box 158-J, Harris IA 51345. Editor/Publisher: Daniel R. Betz. Magazine: 5½×8½; 72 pages; mimeo paper; index stock cover; illustrations on cover. "*Hor-Tasy* is bringing back actual *horror* to horror lovers tired of seeing so much science fiction and SF passed off as horror. We're also very much interested in true, poetic, pure fantasy."
Needs: Fantasy and horror. "Pure fantasy: Examples are trolls, fairies and mythology. The horror we're looking for comes from the human mind—the ultimate form of horror. It must sound real—so real that in fact it could very possibly happen at any time and place. We must be able to feel the diseased mind behind the personality. No science fiction in any way, shape or form. We don't want stories in which the main character spends half his time talking to a shrink. We don't want stories that start out with: 'You're crazy,' said so and so." Accepts 6 mss/issue. Receives 15-20 unsolicited fiction mss each month. Published work by Charmaine Parsons, M. C. Salemme, Jude Howell; published new writers within the last year. Critiques rejected mss "unless it's way off from what we're looking for." Sometimes recommends other markets.
How to Contact: Query or send complete ms with SASE. Accepts computer printout submissions. Reports in 1 day on queries. "If not interested (in ms), we return immediately. If interested, we may keep it as long as 6 months." Publishes ms an average of 1 year after acceptance. Sample copy for $2.95. Guidelines for #10 SASE.

Payment: Pays 2 contributor's copies. Extras at cover price less special discount rates.
Terms: Acquires first North American serial rights.
Advice: "Most stories rejected are about spooks, monsters, haunted houses, spacemen, etc. Because *Hor-Tasy* is a unique publication, I suggest the potential writer get a sample copy. Only unpublished work will be considered."

HOUSEWIFE-WRITER'S FORUM, (I), P.O. Box 780, Lyman WY 82937. (307)786-4513. Editor: Diane Wolverton. Fiction Editor: Bob Haynie. Magazine: 6½×10; 32-40 pages; glossy cover; illustrations. "Support for the woman who juggles writing with family life. We publish short fiction, poetry, essays, nonfiction, line drawings, humor and hints. For women of all ages; house husbands who write." Bimonthly. Estab. 1988. Circ. over 1,200.
Needs: Contemporary, experimental, historical (general), humor/satire, literary, mainstream, romance (contemporary, historical), suspense/mystery—with writing theme, preferably. No pornographic material. Receives 50-100 mss/month. Buys 1-2 mss/issue; 6-12 mss/year. Publishes ms within 6 months to 1 year after acceptance. Recently published work by Elaine McCormick, Carol Shenold and Carole Bellacera. Length: 1,500 words preferred; 500 words minimum; 2,000 words maximum. Publishes short shorts. Sometimes critiques rejected mss and if possible recommends other markets.
How to Contact: Send complete ms with cover letter. Cover letter should include "the basics." Reports in 1 month on queries; 3 months on mss. SASE. Simultaneous, photocopied and reprint submissions OK. Accepts computer printout submissions. Sample copy for $4. Fiction guidelines for #10 SAE and 1 first class stamp.
Payment: Pays 1¢/word, plus one contributor's copy. Half price for extra copies.
Terms: Pays on acceptance for first North American rights. Sponsors awards for fiction writers. "We sponsor occasional contests geared to the interests of housewife-writers. First place winners are published in the magazine. Entry fees: $4. Prize: $30. Send #10 SAE with 1 first class stamp for guidelines and further information."
Advice: "Fiction Editor Bob Haynie reads all mss and often offers suggestions on the rejections. All published materials are printed with Mr. Haynie's critiques. Here are a few samples to show you what he's looking for: 'Life is made up of small details. Writing often consists of finding the right ones out of the thousands that make up even the briefest moment and using them to convey information to the reader. There's more to this than just a bunch of required items and small details, though. There is also believable dialogue, controlled pacing, and a fine ending that fits the tone and the action and the narrator just right. I look for the overall effect of the story—the product of its theme, its narrative skill, its handling of detail and pace and dialogue, its felicity of beginning, transition and ending. The degree to which all these things mesh and contribute to a whole meaning that surpasses the mere sum of the constituents is the degree to which a story succeeds.' "

HOWLING DOG, (II), 8419 Rhode, Utica MI 48317. Magazine: 6×9; 64 pages; 65 lb. paper; some illustrations; some photographs. "A wild and crazy literary magazine for a diverse audience." Estab. 1985. Circ. 500.
Needs: Contemporary, experimental, humor/satire, literary and mainstream. Upcoming theme: "Music issue," stories and interviews of musicians. Receives 40 unsolicited mss/month. Accepts 2 mss/issue. Publishes ms 6 months after acceptance. Recently published work by M.L. Liebler and Gregory Burnham. Length: 800 words average; 300 words minimum; 1,000 words maximum. Publishes short shorts. Also publishes literary essays, literary criticism, poetry. Sometimes critiques rejected mss and recommends other markets.
How to Contact: Send complete ms. No cover letter. Reports in 1 year. Sample copy for $4. Reviews novels and short story collections.
Payment: Pays in contributor copies; discount charge for extras.
Terms: Acquires one-time rights.
Advice: "We look for crazy, *provocative*, quick, detailed, memorable, smooth reading, emotional or otherwise interesting. Keep it *less than* 1,000 words."

‡HUMERUS, A Magazine of Art and Satire, Foolscap Press, Box 222, Piermont NY 10968. Editor: W.S. Wyatt. Magazine: 8½×11; 78 pages; 60 lb. coated paper; 80 lb. coated cover; b&w illustrations and photographs. Publishes "literary-art-humor: pictures, prose, poetry and photos." Triannually. Estab. 1988.
Needs: Condensed/excerpted novel, experimental, fantasy, historical (general), humor/satire, literary, psychic/supernatural/occult, science fiction. No blasphemy, obscenity. Receives 10-12 unsolicited mss/month. Accepts 5-10 mss/year. Publishes ms 3-6 months after acceptance. Publishes short shorts.

How to Contact: Send complete ms with cover letter. No queries. Reports in 10 weeks on mss. SASE. Photocopied and reprint submissions OK. Accepts computer printout submissions. Sample copy for $3 and 9×12 SAE.
Payment: Pays "A work of my art for a work of theirs"; 2 contributor's copies.
Terms: Pays on publication. Acquires one-time rights.

HURRICANE ALICE, A Feminist Quarterly, (II), Hurricane Alice Fn., Inc., 207 Church St. SE, Minneapolis MN 55455. Executive Editors: Martha Roth, Patricia Cumbie. Fiction is collectively edited. Tabloid: 11×17; 12-16 pages; newsprint stock; illustrations and photos. "We look for feminist fictions with a certain analytic snap, for serious readers, seriously interested in emerging forms of feminist art/artists." Quarterly. Estab. 1983. Circ. 600-700.
Needs: Erotica, experimental, feminist, gay, humor/satire, lesbian, science fiction, translations. No coming-out stories, defloration stories, abortion stories. Receives 80 unsolicited mss/month. Publishes 4-6 stories annually. Publishes ms up to 1 year after acceptance. Recently published work by Beth Brant, Nona Caspers, Toni McNaron; published new writers within the last year. Length: up to 3,000 words maximum. Publishes short shorts. Occasionally critiques rejected mss.
How to Contact: Send complete ms with cover letter. "A brief biographical statement is never amiss. Writers should be sure to tell us if a piece was commissioned by one of the editors." Reports in 3 months. SASE for ms. Simultaneous and photocopied submissions OK. Accepts computer printout submissions. Sample copy for $2.50, 11×14 SAE and 2 first class stamps.
Payment: Pays 5 contributor's copies.
Terms: Acquires one-time rights.
Advice: "Fiction is a craft. Just because something happened, it isn't a story; it becomes a story when you transform it through your art, your craft."

‡HYPERBOLE, An Eclectic Hypermedia Entertainment, (I, II), King's Gambit, #2, 2402 Yoakum, Houston TX 77006. (713)522-0383. Editor: Greg Roach. Fiction Editor: Paul Wayne Hiaumet. Computer disk magazine: illustrations and photographs. "Published on computer disks—no general theme—fiction, poetry, graphics." Bimonthly. Estab. 1990. Circ. 350.
Needs: Adventure, condensed/excerpted novel, contemporary, erotica, experimental, fantasy, historical (general), horror, humor/satire, literary, mainstream, prose poem, science fiction, serialized novel, suspense/mystery, translations. Plans special fiction issue. Receives 4 unsolicited mss/month. Buys 1-3 mss/issue; 10-20 mss/year. Publishes ms 2-4 months after acceptance. Recently published work by Michael Banks, Christopher Woods, Hanz Doppler. Length: Open. Publishes short shorts. Also publishes poetry. Sometimes critiques rejected mss and recommends other markets.
How to Contact: Send complete ms with cover letter. Include Social Security number. Reports in 2 weeks on queries; 1 month on mss. SASE. Photocopied and reprint submissions OK. Accepts computer printout submissions. Accepts electronic submissions. Sample copy for $3. Fiction guidelines for #10 SAE and 1 first class stamp.
Payment: Pays $5 flat or $1/page and contributor's copies.
Terms: Pays on publication for first rights.
Advice: "Hypermedia opens up new doors for fiction writers—it's a whole new genre. *Hyperbole* is a disk based publication—no printed paper is involved. While *Hyperbole* runs on computers (Apple Macintosh & IIGS) it is not about computers. We are dedicated to exploring hypermedia (the integration of text, graphics, music, animation and sound on a computer) as a legitmate mode of communication and a viable opportunity for artists and writers."

‡IMAGINE!, (I, II), 1667 Atlantic Blvd., Jacksonville FL 32207. (904)724-1839. Senior Editor: Vickie L. Swindling. Managing Editor: Lisa Knappe-Croghan. Magazine: 8½×11; 50 pages; 65 lb. paper; 80 lb. matte; b&w illustrations. "Short fiction of most genre and sizes for fiction readers." Monthly. Estab. 1992. Circ. 3,000.
Needs: Adventure, confession, contemporary, ethnic, experimental, fantasy, historical (general), horror, humor/satire, literary, mainstream, prose poem, psychic/supernatural/occult, regional, romance, science fiction, serialized novel, sports, suspense/mystery, translations, western. "Open minded toward most things." No "gay/lesbian and erotica." Publishes annual special fiction issue. Receives 70 unsolic-

Market categories: (I) Beginning; (II) General; (III) Prestige; (IV) Specialized.

ited mss/month. Buys 8-10 mss/issue; 100-150 mss/year. Publishes ms an average of 2 months after acceptance. Length: 3,000 words average; 10,000 words maximum. Publishes short shorts. Sometimes critiques rejected mss and recommends other markets.

How to Contact: Send complete ms with cover letter; include social security number, published credits, writer's groups, other writing experience. Reports in 1 month. SASE. Simultaneous, photocopied and reprint submissions OK. Accepts computer printout submissions. Accepts electronic submissions via disk, in ASCII form. Sample copy for $3. Fiction guidelines for #10 SAE and 1 first class stamp.

Payment: Pays in contributor's copies.

Terms: Acquires first rights, first North American serial rights, or one-time rights. Sends galleys to author.

Advice: "The senior editor is interested in working with talented writers, but they must first show the desire and professionalism to follow the rules of submission. Manuscripts must be in correct format, spell checked, and grammatically correct. Grab my attention with the first word and don't let go before the last. Know your characters! Discover the traits that make people unique and develop them in what you write. Let their personalities determine the means by which they resolve the conflict of the plot."

‡IMMANENT FACE MAGAZINE, (II), P.O. Box 492, New Town Branch, Boston MA 02258. Editor: Carl Quesnel. Magazine: 8½×11; 20-25 pages; 25 lb. paper; 60 lb. cover; illustrations and photographs. "Theme: The expression of personal and global concerns of individuals. Types: From writing for the common people to the esoteric for anyone age 12-100 who really care about our reality." Quarterly. Estab. 1987. Circ. 250.

Needs: Condensed/excerpted novel, contemporary, experimental, fantasy, literary, prose poem, science fiction, serialized novel, translations. "We do *not* want to see material that is not final-draft quality, nor do we want to see material that is impossible to comprehend unless it has a stated, worthy purpose." Receives 5 unsolicited mss/month. Accepts 2 mss/issue; 10 mss/year. Publishes ms 2-5 months after acceptance. Recently published work by Ian MacKinnon, Mat Czaplinski. Length: 1,750 words preferred; 3,000 words maximum. Publishes short shorts. Sometimes comments on rejected mss and recommends other markets.

How to Contact: Send complete ms with cover letter. Include "name, address, greeting, how the writer heard of our magazine, biographical tidbit maybe, *not* a list of previous publications." Reports in 1 month on queries; 2 months on mss. SASE. Simultaneous, photocopied and reprint submissions OK. Accepts computer printout submissions. Accepts electronic submissions via disk or modem. Sample copy for $1.50. Fiction guidelines for #10 SAE and 1 first class stamp.

Payment: Pays contributor's copies.

Terms: Not copyrighted.

Advice: "Fiction either has to truly capture reality and make the reader feel it, or it has to create a different reality altogether. If a piece does one of these things, and it's well written, then I'll probably accept it. Manuscripts that stand out make me feel strongly—either positive or negative—or else they capture an atmosphere really well. Description is very important."

INDIAN YOUTH OF AMERICA NEWSLETTER, (II, IV), Indian Youth of America, Inc., P.O. Box 2786, Sioux City IA 51106. (712)252-3230. Contact: Paige Gordon. Newsletter: 8½×11; 12 or more pages; 100 lb. lustre paper; illustrations and photographs. "We are looking for Native American authors who write on a variety of themes for a broad audience, from children (former campers and others) through adults; nationwide, international." Quarterly. Estab. 1987.

Needs: Adventure, condensed/excerpted novel, contemporary, historical, literary, western, Native American. "Unsolicited manuscripts are welcome, and should be about 5-6 pages typed, double-spaced. Author should include biographical information and a photo (returnable) of himself/herself. Illustrations for the story can also be used, provided space is available. The author should also include tribal affiliation. All authors should be of Native American descent." Does not want to see "extremely abstract themes; extreme violence; sexual situations." Unsolicited mss received each month "varies greatly." Acquires one ms/issue; 4 mss/year. Publishes ms usually within a year after acceptance. Agented fiction 50%. Published work by Joseph Bruchac, Mary Tall Mountain, Louis Littlecoon Oliver, Virginia Driving Hawk Sneve. Length: 800 words average; 650-700 words minimum; 1,200 words maximum Recommends other markets.

How to Contact: Send complete manuscript with cover letter that includes information about the author, tribal affiliation, other published works and awards, if applicable. Reports in 2-4 weeks on queries; 4-6 weeks on mss. Simultaneous, photocopied and reprint submissions OK. Accepts computer printout submissions. Sample copy and fiction guidelines free.
Payment: Pays free subscription to magazine and contributor's copies.

INDIANA REVIEW, (II), 316 N. Jordan Ave., Indiana University, Bloomington IN 47405. (812)855-3439. Editor: Allison Joseph. Associate Editor: Dorian Gossy. Magazine: 6×9; 224 pages; 60 lb. paper; Glatfelter cover stock. "Magazine of contemporary fiction and poetry in which there is a zest for language, some relationship between form and content, and awareness of the world. For fiction writers/readers, followers of lively contemporary poetry." Biannually. Estab. 1976. Circ. 650.
Needs: Literary, contemporary, experimental, mainstream. "We are interested in innovation, logic, unity, a social context, a sense of humanity. All genres that meet some of these criteria are welcome. We would also consider novellas, novel excerpts and 'suites' of 3 related stories." Accepts 3-4 mss/issue. Recently published work by Ursula LeGuin, David Michael Kaplan, Ann Packer; published new writers within the last year. Length: 1-35 magazine pages. Also publishes literary essays, poetry.
How to Contact: Send complete ms with cover letter. "Don't describe or summarize the story." SASE. Accepts computer printout submissions. Reports in 3 months. Publishes ms an average of 2-10 months after acceptance. Sample copy $7.
Payment: Pays $5/page.
Terms: Buys North American serial rights.
Advice: "Refrain from the chatty cover letter. Send one story at a time (unless they're really short), and no simultaneous submissions."

INLET, (II), Virginia Wesleyan College, Norfolk VA 23502. Editor: Joseph Harkey. Magazine: 7×8½; 32-38 pages. "Poetry and short fiction for people of all ages." Annually. Estab. 1970. Circ. 700.
Needs: Literary, contemporary, mainstream, fantasy and humor. "Our main interest is well written fiction." Accepts 2-5 mss/issue. Receives 10-20 unsolicited fiction mss each month. Published work by Myron Taube and John H. Timmerman. Length: 750-2,000 words but "will consider up to 3,500." Sometimes recommends other markets.
How to Contact: "Manuscripts are read September through March only." Does not read in summer. Send complete ms to fiction editor with SASE. Reports in 2 months. Sample copy for 75¢ postage (Do not send personal checks.)
Payment: Pays contributor's copies.
Advice: "Write carefully and present a neatly typed manuscript with SASE. Send an example of your best work; short shorts preferred. Some rejected manuscripts are poorly written. Some lack imaginative treatments of the problems they raise."

INNISFREE, (I, II), Box 277, Manhattan Beach CA 90266. (310)545-2607. FAX (310)546-5862. Editor: Rex Winn. Magazine: 8½×11; 50+ pages; 90 lb. cover stock; illustrations and photos. Publishes "fiction, poetry, essays—open forum." Bimonthly. Estab. 1981. Circ. 350.
Needs: Adventure, contemporary, ethnic, fantasy, literary, mainstream, regional, science fiction and suspense/mystery. "No political or religious sensationalism." Accepts 12-15 mss/issue; approx. 80 mss/year. Publishes ms within 12 months of acceptance. Published work by Ron Fleshman, Peter McGinn, Clem Portman and John Birchler. Length: 3,000 words average. Publishes short shorts. Also publishes literary essays. Sometimes critiques rejected mss.
How to Contact: Send complete mss with cover letter. Reports in 1 month. SASE. Accepts electronic submissions via IBM disk. Sample copy for $4. Free fiction guidelines.
Payment: No payment. Prizes offered.
Terms: Acquires one-time rights.
Advice: "Fiction market is on the decline. This is an attempt to publish new writers who take pride in their work and have some talent."

INTERIM, (II), Dept. of English, University of Nevada, Las Vegas NV 89154. (702)739-3172. Editor and Founder: A. Wilber Stevens. Magazine: 6×9; 48-64 pages; heavy paper; glossy cover; cover illustrations. Publishes "poetry and short fiction for a serious, sophisticated, educated audience." Semiannually. Estab. 1944; revived 1986. Circ. 600-800.
Needs: Contemporary, experimental, literary and prose poem. Accepts 2-3 mss/issue. Publishes ms within 6 months to 1 year of acceptance. Recently published work by Peter Parsons and James B. Hall. Length: 4,000 words preferred; 7,500 words maximum. Also publishes poetry.

How to Contact: Send complete ms with cover letter. Reports on mss in 2 months. SASE. Photocopied submissions OK. Accepts computer printout submissions. Sample copy $3.

Payment: Pays in contributor's copies and free subscription to magazine.

THE IOWA REVIEW, (II), University of Iowa, 308 EPB, Iowa City IA 52242. (319)335-0462. Editor: David Hamilton. Magazine: 6×9; 200 pages; first grade offset paper; Carolina C1S-10 pt. cover stock. "Stories, essays, poems for a general readership interested in contemporary literature." Published triannually. Estab. 1970. Circ. 1,200.

Needs: Receives 150-200 unsolicited fiction mss/month. Agented fiction less than 10%. Buys 4-5 mss/ issue, 12-16 mss/year. Does not read mss May-August. Published work by Mary Swander, Charles Baxter and Donald Hall; published new writers within the last year. Also publishes literary essays, literary criticism, poetry.

How to Contact: Send complete ms with SASE. "Don't bother with queries." Simultaneous and photocopied submissions OK. Accepts computer printout submissions. Reports in 4 months on mss. Publishes ms an average of 4-12 months after acceptance. Sample copy $5. Reviews novels and short story collections (3-6 books/year).

Payment: Pays $10/page; 2 contributor's copies; charge for extras: 30% off cover price.

Terms: Pays on publication for first North American serial rights. Hardly ever buys reprints.

Advice: In cover letters, "be moderate. Be decent. Be brief."

IOWA WOMAN, P.O. Box 680, Iowa City IA 52244. Contact: Editor. Nonprofit magazine "dedicated to encouraging and publishing women writers and artists internationally." Quarterly. Estab. 1979. Circ. 2,500.

Needs: Historical, literary, regional, women's. Upcoming theme: "Crafts," broad concept of crafts for 1993 will be the Year of American Craft. Receives 10-15 unsolicited mss/month. Accepts 3 mss/issue; 12 mss/year. Length: 5,000 words maximum. Also publishes literary essays, literary criticism.

How to Contact: Send complete ms. Reports in 3 months. SASE. Sample copy for $5. Fiction or contest guidelines for SAE with 1 first class stamp. Reviews novels and short story collections. Send books to Natalie Pearson (Books Editor).

Payment: Pays 2 contributor's copies; $3 charge for extras.

Terms: Acquires first serial rights.

Advice: "Our editorial collective often responds critically with rejections. Our guidelines are clear, but we still get stories without women or women's experience as the center. New writers have a better chance with regular submissions than with our annual writing contest which is quite competitive. We rarely publish work written by men (once in 10 years, so far), and consider only insightful essays about relationships with women."

‡ipsissima verba/the very words, (I), Haypenny Press, 211 New St., West Paterson NJ 07424-3329. Editor: P.D. Jordan. Magazine: 5½×8½; b&w illustrations. "Short fiction, poetry, essays *written in the first person singular* for an adult/literary/general audience." Semiannually (soon to be triannually). Estab. 1989.

Needs: Adventure, contemporary, ethnic, experimental, fantasy, feminist, historical (general), humor/ satire, literary, mainstream, prose poem, psychic/supernatural/occult, regional, romance (contemporary), science fiction, senior citizen/retirement, serialized novel, sports, suspense/mystery, translations, western. "Will consider any type or genre of story, as long as the 'first person' rule is met . . . . Prefer suspense over true horror. No pornography." Publishes annual special fiction issue. Receives 50-75 unsolicited mss/month. Accepts up to 10 mss/issue. Publishes ms within 6 months after acceptance. Recently published work by Jim Adams, Tommy Lee Curtis. Length: varies. Publishes short shorts. Length: 1-4 pages. Sometimes critiques rejected mss and recommends other markets.

How to Contact: Send complete ms with cover letter. Reports in 2 weeks on queries; 1 month on mss. SASE. Simultaneous, photocopied and reprint submissions OK. Sample copy for 4 first class stamps. Fiction guidelines for #10 SAE.

Payment: Pays contributor's copies.

Terms: Acquires one-time rights.

Advice: "Remember the 'first person' rule. The single factor is the *ease* with which the writer 'speaks.' The more natural the 'voice,' the more likely it will be accepted. Read Barry Yourgrau, Tom DeHaven, P.D. Jordan . . . get a sample copy of the magazine. Write from your own self. First-person writing isn't for everyone, but if you can write as if you are talking you are on the right track."

‡IRIS: A Journal About Women, (II, IV), Box 323 HSC, University of Virginia, Charlottesville VA 22908. (804)924-4500. Editor: Jennifer Shepherd. Fiction Editor: Kristen Staby Rembold. Magazine: 8½×11; 72 pages; glossy paper; heavy cover; illustrations and photographs. "Material of particular interest to women. For a feminist audience, college educated and above." Semiannually. Estab. 1980. Circ. 2,000.

Needs: Experimental, feminist, lesbian, literary, mainstream. "I don't think what we're looking for particularly falls into the 'mainstream' category—we're just looking for well-written stories of interest to women (particularly feminist women)." Receives 300 unsolicited mss/year. Accepts 5 mss/year. Publishes ms within 1 year after acceptance. Length: 4,000 words average. Sometimes critiques rejected mss.

How to Contact: Send complete ms with cover letter. Include "previous publications, vocation, other points that pertain. Make it brief!" Reports in 3 months on mss. SASE. Simultaneous submissions OK. Accepts electronic submissions via disk or modem. Sample copy for $5. Fiction guidelines for #10 SAE and 1 first class stamp.

Payment: Pays in contributor's copies.

Terms: Acquires one-time rights.

Advice: "I select mss which are lively imagistically as well as in the here-and-now; I select for writing which challenges the reader. My major complaint is with stories that don't elevate the language above the bland sameness we hear on the television and everyday. Read the work of the outstanding women writers, such as Alice Munro and Louise Erdrich."

JACARANDA REVIEW, (II), Dept. of English, UCLA, Los Angeles CA 90024. (213) 825-4173. Editors: Bruce Kijewski, Katherine Swiggert. Fiction Editor: Cornel Bonca. Magazine: 5½×8; 200 pages; high quality paper; Archer cover stock; cover illustrations. "We publish anything that we think is high quality, for serious readers of fiction and poetry." Semiannually. Estab. 1984. Circ. 2,000.

Needs: Condensed/excerpted novel, contemporary, experimental, literary, mainstream, prose poem and translations. "We're not particularly interested in what people call 'genre' fiction. We're interested in fiction that reflects contemporary sensibilities about contemporary life." Receives 25 mss/month. Accepts 3 mss/issue; 6 mss/year. Does not read mss July-September. Publishes ms within 1-2 months of acceptance. Published work by Jorge Luis Borges, Ed Minus and Charles Bukowski; published new writers within the last year. Length: 2,500-5,000 words preferred; 500 words minimum; 10,000 words maximum. "For Spring, 1992 we are planning a 'short short' fiction section. We will be looking for fiction of 500 words and less, and will be offering a cash prize to the winner of our short fiction contest." Also publishes literary essays, poetry. Sometimes critiques rejected mss and recommends other markets.

How to Contact: Send complete mss with cover letter. Cover letter should include "contributor's note." Reports on queries in 2 weeks; on mss in 2 months. SASE. Simultaneous and photocopied submissions OK. Accepts computer printout submissions. Sample copy for $5, 6x9 SAE and 3 first class stamps. Reviews novels or short story collections. Send books to Book Review editor.

Payment: Pays in contributor's copies. Discount for extra copies.

Terms: Acquires one-time rights.

Advice: Sees "too much *unexamined* minimalist fiction; that is, fiction that dwells in passivity and is almost ashamed of passion. Not enough fiction inspired by Garcià Marquez or Kundera. Lately we tend to like fiction that avoids minimalist mannerisms (though we do publish work in the Robison-F. Barthelme mode), that has an energetic sense of humor, and which aspires to be psychologically fearless. We're interested in good experimental fiction, too, if we can find some, and fiction about and by women. A lot of the fiction we receive seems inspired in conception but underdeveloped and unrealized in execution. Care—deeply—about the reader, and care deeply about your work."

JAPANOPHILE, (II, IV), Box 223, Okemos MI 48864. (517)349-1795. Editor-in-Chief: Earl Snodgrass. Magazine: 5¼×8½; 50 pages; illustrations; photos. Magazine of "articles, photos, poetry, humor, short stories about Japanese culture, not necessarily set in Japan, for an adult audience, most with college background; travelers." Publishes 3 times/year. Estab. 1974. Circ. 600.

Needs: Adventure, historical (general), humor/satire, literary, mainstream, and suspense/mystery. Published special fiction issue last year; plans another. Receives 40-100 unsolicited fiction mss/month. Buys 1 ms/issue, 4-10 mss/year. Recently published work by Mimi Hinman, Bobbi Crudup, Joan Van De Moortel; published new writers within the last year. Length: 2,000 words minimum; 9,000 words maximum; 4,000 words average. Also publishes literary essays, literary criticism, poetry. Sometimes recommends other markets.

How to Contact: Send complete ms with SASE and cover letter with author bio and information about story. Photocopied and previously published submissions OK. Accepts computer printout submissions. Reports in 2 months on mss. Sample copy for $4; guidelines for #10 SAE and 1 first class stamp.

Payment: Pays $20 on publication, for short stories.

Terms: Pays on publication for all rights, first North American serial rights or one-time rights (depends on situation).

Advice: "Short stories usually involve Japanese and 'foreign' (non-Japanese) characters in a way that contributes to understanding of Japanese culture and the Japanese people. However, a *good* story dealing with Japan or Japanese cultural aspects anywhere in the world will be considered, even if it does not involve this encounter or meeting of Japanese and foreign characters. Some stories may also be published in an anthology." Annual contest pays $100 plus publication for the best short story. Deadline December 31. Entry fee is $5.

JEOPARDY, Literary Arts Magazine, (II), CH 132, Western Washington University, Bellingham WA 98225. (206)676-3118. Contact: Editors. Magazine: 6×9; 108 pages; 70 lb. paper; Springhill 215 cover stock; illustrations and photographs. Material published: fiction, nonfiction, poetry, photographed artwork (slide form) for "all inclusive" audience. Annually. Estab. 1965. Circ. 3,000-4,000.

Needs: Adventure, contemporary, ethnic, experimental, fantasy, feminist, humor/satire, literary, mainstream, prose poem, regional, contemporary romance, science fiction and translations. No long stories. Accepts 7-10 mss/year. Length: 4 pages (average 800-1,000 words). Also publishes literary essays, literary criticism, poetry.

How to Contact: Submissions accepted between September and February. Mss sent during summer months may not be read immediately. Send complete ms. SASE. Simultaneous and previously published submissions OK. Accepts computer printout submissions. Sample copy $2.

Payment: Pays 2 contributor's copies. "Sometimes *Jeopardy* awards cash prizes or special recognition to winners in various categories."

Advice: "We are a student-run university literary publication. We are happy to look at any fiction. Sometimes, if staff is large enough, at writer's request we will comment on the work."

‡JEWISH CURRENTS MAGAZINE, (IV), 22 E. 17th St., New York NY 10003. (212)924-5740. Editor-in-Chief: Morris U. Schappes. Magazine: 5½×8½; 48 pages. "We are a progressive monthly, broad in our interests, printing feature articles on political and cultural aspects of Jewish life in the US and elsewhere, reviews of books and film, poetry and fiction, Yiddish translations; regular columns on Israel, US Jewish community, current events, Jewish women today, secular Jewish life. Monthly themes include Holocaust and Resistance, Black-Jewish relations, Jewish Book Month, Jewish Music Month, etc. National audience, literate and politically left, well educated." Monthly. Estab. 1946. Circ. 3,000.

Needs: Contemporary, ethnic, feminist, historical (general), humor/satire, literary, senior citizen/retirement, translations. "We are interested in *authentic* experience and readable prose; Jewish themes; humanistic orientation. No religious, political sectarian; no porn or hard sex, no escapist stuff. Go easy on experimentation, but we're interested." Upcoming themes: Two quincentennials: "Columbus;" "The explusion of the Jews from Spain."Receives 6-10 unsolicited fiction mss/month. Accepts 0-1 ms/issue; 8-10 mss/year. Recently published work by Maurice Isserman, Jesse Zel Lurie; published new writers within the last year. Length: 1,000 words minimum; 3,000 words maximum; 1,800 words average. Also publishes literary essays, literary criticism, poetry.

How to Contact: Send complete ms with cover letter. "Writers should include brief biographical information, especially their publishing histories." SASE. Reports in 2 months on mss. Publishes ms 2 months to 2 years after acceptance. Sample copy for $2 with SASE and 3 first class stamps. Reviews novels and short story collections.

Payment: Pays complimentary one-year subscription; 6 contributor's copies.

Terms: "We readily give reprint permission at no charge." Sends galleys to author.

Advice: "Family themes are good, but avoid sentimentality; keep the prose tight, not sprawling; matters of character and moral dilemma, maturing into pain and joy, dealing with Jewish conflicts OK. Space is increasingly a problem. Tell the truth, as sparely as possible."

THE JOURNAL, (II), Dept of English, Ohio State University, 164 W. 17th St., Columbus OH 43210. (614)292-4076. Editors: Kathy Fagan (poetry); Michelle Herman (fiction). Magazine: 6×9; 80 pages. "We are open to all forms of quality fiction." For an educated, general adult audience. Semiannually. Estab. 1973. Circ. 1,300.

Needs: "Interested in all literary forms." No romance or religious/devotional. Accepts 2 mss/issue. Receives approximately 100 unsolicited fiction mss each month. "Usually" publishes ms within 1 year of acceptance. Agented fiction 10%. Recently published work by Liza Wieland, M.V. Clayton; published new writers within the last year. Length: Open. Also accepts poetry. Critiques rejected mss when there is time.

How to Contact: Send complete ms with cover letter. Reports "as soon as possible," usually 3 months. SASE. Photocopied submissions OK. Accepts computer printout submissions. Sample copy $5.50; fiction guidelines for SASE.

Payment: Pays $25 stipend when funds are available; contributor's copies; $5.50 charge for extras.

Terms: Acquires First North American serial rights. Sends galleys to author.

Advice: Mss are rejected because of "lack of understanding of the short story form, shallow plots, undeveloped characters. Cure: read as much well-written fiction as possible. Our readers prefer 'psychological' fiction rather than stories with intricate plots. Take care to present a clean, well-typed submission."

‡**THE JOURNAL, (II),** Poetry Forum, 5713 Larchmont Dr., Erie PA 16509. (814)866-2543. FAX: (814)866-2543 (Faxing hours: 8-10 a.m. and 5-8 p.m.) Editor: Gunvor Skogsholm. Newspaper: 7 × 8½; 18-20 pages; card cover; photographs. "Good writing—material on writing for late teens to full adulthood." Quarterly. Estab. 1989. Circ. 200.

Needs: Mainstream. Plans annual special fiction issue. Receives 25-30 unsolicited mss/month. Accepts 1 ms/issue; 7-10 mss/year. Publishes mss 2 weeks-7 months after acceptance. Agented fiction 1% . Length: 500 words preferred; 300 words average; 150 words minimum. Publishes short shorts. Length: 400 words.

How to Contact: Send complete ms. Reports in 2 weeks to 7 months on mss. SASE. Simultaneous submissions OK. Accepts electronic submission via disk. Sample copy for $3. Fiction guidelines for SASE.

Payment: No payment.

Terms: Acquires one-time rights. Not copyrighted.

Advice: "Subscribers come first!" Looks for "a good lead stating a theme, support of the theme throughout and an ending that rounds out the story or article. 1.) Let it be believable; 2.) Please don't preach; 3.) Avoid propaganda; 4.) Don't say: 'This is a story about a retarded person.' Instead prove it by your writing."

JOURNAL OF POLYMORPHOUS PERVERSITY, (II), Wry-Bred Press, Inc., Suite 20-B, 10 Waterside Plaza, New York NY 10010. (212)689-5473. Editor: Glenn Ellenbogen. Magazine: 6¾ × 10; 24 pages; 60 lb. paper; antique india cover stock; illustrations with some articles. "*JPP* is a humorous and satirical journal of psychology, psychiatry, and the closely allied mental health disciplines." For "psychologists, psychiatrists, social workers, psychiatric nurses, *and* the psychologically sophisticated layman." Semiannually. Estab. 1984.

Needs: Humor/satire. "We only consider materials that are 1) funny, 2) relate to psychology *or* behavior." Receives 10 unsolicited mss/month. Accepts 8 mss/issue; 16 mss/year. Published work by Kathleen Donald, Ph.D. Most writers published last year were previously unpublished writers. Length: 1,500 words average; 4,000 words maximum. Comments on rejected ms.

How to Contact: Send complete ms *in triplicate*. Reports in 1-3 months on mss. SASE. Photocopied submissions OK. Accepts computer printout submissions. Sample copy for $5. Fiction guidelines for #10 SAE and 1 first class stamp.

Payment: Pays 2 contributor's copies; charge for extras: $5.

Advice: "We will *not* look at poetry or short stories. We only want to see intelligent spoofs of scholarly psychology and psychiatry articles written in scholarly scientific languages. Take a look at *real* journals of psychology and try to lampoon their *style* as much as their content. There are few places to showcase satire of the social sciences, thus we provide one vehicle for injecting a dose of humor into this often too serious area. Occasionally, we will accept a piece of creative writing written in the first person, e.g. 'A Subjective Assessment of the Oral Doctoral Defense Process: I Don't Want to Talk About It, If You Want to Know the Truth' (the latter being a piece in which Holden Caulfield shares his

***The double dagger before a listing indicates that
the listing is new in this edition. New markets are
often the most receptive to freelance contributions.***

experiences relating to obtaining his Ph.D. in Psychology). Other creative pieces have involved a psychodiagnostic evaluation of The Little Prince (as a psychiatric patient) and God being refused tenure (after having created the world) because of insufficient publications and teaching experience."

JOURNAL OF REGIONAL CRITICISM, (II), Arjuna Library Press, 1025 Garner St. D, Space 18, Colorado Springs CO 80905. Editor: Joseph A. Uphoff, Jr. Pamphlet: size variable; number of pages variable; bond paper; Bristol cover stock; b&w illustrations and photos. "Surrealist and dreamlike prose poetry and very short surrealist stories to illustrate accompanying mathematical, theoretical material in the fine arts for a wide ranging audience interested in philosophical sophistication and erudite language." Variable frequency. Estab. 1979.

Needs: Adventure, contemporary, ethnic, experimental, fantasy, historical (general), horror, humor/satire, literary, mainstream, prose poem, psychic/supernatural/occult, regional, religious/inspirational, contemporary romance, science fiction. Upcoming theme: "The Myth of Pegasus as It Relates to a Modern Conception of the Supernatural." Receives 0-1 unsolicited fiction ms/month. Accepts 1-5 mss/issue. Recently published work by Simon Perchik, B.Z. Niditch, Michael Rawn. Short short stories preferred. Also publishes literary criticism, poetry. Sometimes critiques rejected mss and recommends other markets.

How to Contact: Send complete ms with cover letter. Manuscript will *not* be returned. Cover letter should include goals, behind-the-scenes explanation, and biographical material or résumé, date of birth, degrees, awards, offices and publications. SASE for query. Simultaneous, photocopied and reprint submissions OK. Accepts computer printouts. Sample copy, if and when available, for $1 postage. Reviews novels and short story collections.

Payment: Pays by contract after profit; contributor's copies.

Terms: Acquires "prototype presentation rights." Publication copyrighted—limited edition procedure copyrights.

Advice: "Relevance is determined in part by visionary patience. This does not necessarily mean artistic presence. The artistic product can be and often must be projected to stand alone without the defense of argumentation, debate, or discussion. This is particularly true where irony is involved. A work has many interpretations some literal and some metaphorical. The author can only be in control of literal factors by a conventional idiom. Thus, the most effective message is delivered in the context of relevance to literary history. The most potent vision is awareness of past. The most useful vision is also designed to serve the future; such literature is often considered as being ahead of its time."

‡JOYEUX EROTIQUE, A Journal of Literate, Happy Sex, Limelight Publishing Company, P.O. Box 11618, Denver CO 80211. Editor: Paul H. Wigton. Fiction Editor: Harry Lime. Magazine: 8×11; 60-80 pages; 30 lb. bond paper; 100 lb. card cover stock; occasional pen and ink illustrations. "A literate journal of happy sexual encounter." Quarterly. Estab. 1989. Circ. under 300.

Needs: "Erotica fiction only. Fiction can be presented in sci/fi, fantasy, western, contemporary, mystery, straight, lesbian, gay or gray. Eroticism must be part of and essential to the supporting story." No S&M or confession. Receives 5 mss/month; accepts 5-8 mss/issue. Publishes ms 1-6 months after acceptance. Length: 400-3,500 words preferred. "Will publish under 500 words if ms meets other criteria." Also publishes literary essays.

How to Contact: "Do not send ms without first sending #10 SASE for guidelines! Then send ms that conforms to the guidelines." Reports on ms in less than 1 month. SASE. Accepts any typed, clearly legible, clean copy. No simultaneous submissions. Sample copy for $3.95. Fiction guidelines for #10 SAE and 1 first class stamp.

Payment: Pays in contributor's copies.

Terms: Acquires one-time rights. Publication not copyrighted.

Advice: "We find that many people in recent years do not read novels. They have not developed the habit and do not wish to take the time. They prefer short fiction. Writing for this genre, erotica, is no different than any other literary effort. Proper use of language is the framework that supports your story. Without that the story is not acceptable. Do not write for shock effect; do let yourself go, turn the readers on and leave them with a tear, a smile or laugh, a fond reminiscence and possibly a change of outlook."

K, (II), 351 Dalhousie St., Brantford, Ontario N3S 3V9 Canada. Editor: G.J. McFarlane. Magazine: 8½×11; 50 pages. Has an "open theme that provides a forum for writers whose contemporary ideas establish a voice for turbulent times." Published as funds permit. Estab. 1985.

Needs: Condensed novel, confession, contemporary, erotica, experimental, feminist, humor/satire, literary, mainstream, science fiction, serialized/excerpted novel. Accepts mss "as quality and space permit." Mss published an undetermined time after acceptance. Publishes short shorts. Occasionally critiques rejected mss and recommends other markets.
How to Contact: Send complete ms with cover letter. Reports in 1 month on queries. SASE. Simultaneous, photocopied and reprint submissions OK. Accepts computer printout submissions. Sample copy for $4.
Payment: Pays in contributor's copies.

KALEIDOSCOPE, International Magazine of Literature, Fine Arts, and Disability, (II, IV), 326 Locust St., Akron OH 44302. (216)762-9755, ext. 27. Editor-in-Chief: Darshan Perusek, Ph.D. Magazine: 8½×11; 56-64 pages; non-coated paper; coated cover stock; illustrations (all media); photos. Semiannually. Estab. 1979. Circ. 1,500.
Needs: Personal experience, drama, fiction, essay, humor/satire, prose poem. Upcoming themes: "Disability and the Family" (July 1992); "Disability and Education" (January 1993). Receives 20-25 unsolicited fiction mss/month. Accepts 10 mss/year. Approximately 1% of fiction is agented. Recently published work by Ellen Hunnicutt, Douglas P. Lathrop, Beverly Sheresh, Richard Gardiner. Published new writers within the last year. Length: 3,000 words minimum; 5,000 words maximum. Also publishes literary criticism, poetry.
How to Contact: Query first or send complete ms and cover letter, which should include author's educational and writing background; if author has a disablity, how the disability has influenced the writing. SASE. Accepts computer printout submissions. Reports in 1 month on queries; 6 months on mss. Sample copy for $2. Guidelines for #10 SAE and 1 first class stamp. Reviews novels and short story collections. Send books to Gail Willmott, senior editor.
Payment: Pays cash ranging from $25-75; 2 contributor's copies; charge for extras: $4.50.
Terms: Pays on publication for first rights. Reprints are permitted with credit given to original publication.
Advice: "Read the magazine and get fiction guidelines. Writers with disablties may write on any topic; non-disabled writers must limit themselves to the theme of disability. *Kaleidoscope* seeks work that challenges stereotypical images of people with disabilities by presenting balanced, realistic images of those who have disabilities.

KALLIOPE, A Journal of Women's Art, (II), Florida Community College at Jacksonville, 3939 Roosevelt Blvd., Jacksonville FL 32205. (904)387-8211. Editor: Mary Sue Koeppel. Magazine: 7¼×8¼; 76-88 pages; 70 lb. coated matte paper; Bristol cover; 16-18 halftones per issue. "A literary and visual arts journal for women, *Kalliope* celebrates women in the arts by publishing their work and by providing a forum for their ideas and opinions." Short stories, poems, plays, essays, reviews and visual art. Published 3 times/year. Estab. 1978. Circ. 1,000.
Needs: "Quality short fiction by women writers." Upcoming themes: "Body Images" (April 1992). Accepts 2-4 mss/issue. Receives approximately 100 unsolicited fiction mss each month. Published work by Layle Silbert, Robin Merle, Claudia Brinson Smith, Colette; published new writers within the last year. Preferred length: 750-3,000 words, but occasionally publishes longer (and shorter) pieces. Also publishes poetry. Critiques rejected mss "when there is time and if requested."
How to Contact: Send complete ms with SASE and short contributor's note. Reports in 2-3 months on ms. Publishes ms an average of 1-6 months after acceptance. Sample copy: $7 for current issue; $4 for issues from '78-'88. Reviews novels and short story collections. Send books to Ruthann Robson, P.O. Box 489, Port Washington NY 11050.
Payment: Pays 3 contributor's copies or year's subscription. $7 charge for extras, discount for large orders.
Terms: Acquires first rights. "We accept only unpublished work. Copyright returned to author upon request."
Advice: "Read our magazine. The work we consider for publication will be well written and the characters and dialogue will be convincing and have strength and movement. We like a fresh approach and are interested in new or unusual forms. Make us believe your characters; give readers an insight which they might not have had if they had not read you. We would like to publish more work by minority writers." Manuscripts are rejected because "1) nothing *happens!*, 2) it is thinly disguised autobiography (richly disguised autobiography is OK), and 3) ending is either too pat or else just trails off."

KANSAS QUARTERLY, (I, II), Kansas Quarterly Association, 122 Denison Hall, English Dept., Kansas State University, Manhattan KS 66506-0703. (913)532-6716. Editors: Harold Schneider (emeritus), Ben Nyberg, John Rees, G.W. Clift and Jonathan Holden. Magazine: 6×9; 104-356 pages; 70 lb. offset paper; Frankcote 8 pt. coated cover stock; illustrations occasionally; unsolicited photos rarely. "A literary and cultural arts magazine publishing fiction and poetry. Special material on selected, announced topics in literary criticism, art history, folklore and regional history. For well-read, general and academic audiences." Quarterly. Published double and single fiction issues last year; plans repeat. Estab. 1968. Circ. 1,300.
Needs: "We consider most categories as long as the fiction is of sufficient literary quality to merit inclusion, though we have no interest in children's literature. We resist translations and parts of novels, but do not absolutely refuse them." Accepts 30-50 mss/year. Limited reading done in summer. Agented fiction approximately 1%. Recently published work by Stephen Dixon, D.E. Steward and Jerry Bumpus; published new writers within the last year. Length: 350-12,000 words. Sometimes recommends other markets.
How to Contact: Send complete ms with SASE. Reports in 3 months+ on mss. Publishes ms an average of 18-24 months after acceptance. Sample copy $6.
Payment: Pays 2 contributor's copies and annual awards to the best of the stories published.
Terms: Acquires all rights. Sends galleys to author. "We reassign rights on request at time of republication." Sponsors awards: *KQ*/KAC (national); Seaton awards (for Kansas natives or residents). Each offers 6-10 awards from $25-$250.
Advice: "Always check a sample copy of the magazine to which you send your stories—note its editors' likes and interests. Send your story with SASE—do not appear to devalue them by asking they be discarded rather than returned."

KARAMU, (II), English Dept., Eastern Illinois University, Charleston IL 61920. (217)581-5614. Editor: Peggy L. Brayfield. Magazine: 5×8; 60 pages; cover illustrations. "We like fiction that builds around real experiences, real images and real characters, that shows an awareness of current fiction and the types of experiments that are going on in it, and that avoids abstraction, sentimentality, over-philosophizing and fuzzy pontifications. For a literate, college-educated audience." Annually. Estab. 1967. Circ. 500.
Needs: Literary, contemporary. Upcoming theme: "Looking Back at the 60s" (deadline April 92). Receives approximately 20-30 unsolicited fiction mss/month. Accepts 4-5 mss/issue. Recently published work by Jonathan Hall, David Sims, James Crawford Story; published new writers within the last year. Length: 2,000-7,000 words. Also publishes literary essays, poetry. Critiques rejected mss when time permits.
How to Contact: Send complete ms with SASE. Accepts computer printout submissions. Reports in 2-3 months on mss. Publishes ms an average of 1 year after acceptance. Sample copy $3; 2 issues for $4.
Payment: Pays 1 contributor's copy; half price charge for extras.
Advice: "Send for a sample copy, read it, and send a complete ms if your stories seem to match our taste. Please be patient—we sometimes get behind in our reading, especially between May and September. Mss submitted between January and June have the best chance. We feel that much of the best writing today is being done in short fiction."

KENNESAW REVIEW, (II), Kennesaw State College, English Dept., P.O. Box 444, Marietta GA 30061. (404)423-6297. Editor: Dr. Robert W. Hill. Fiction Editors: Drs. Greg Johnson and Paula Yow. Magazine. "Just good fiction, all themes, for a general audience." Quarterly. Estab. 1987.
Needs: Condensed/excerpted novel, contemporary, ethnic, experimental, fantasy, feminist, gay, horror, humor/satire, literary, mainstream, psychic/supernatural/occult, regional. No romance. Plans special fiction issue. Receives 25-60 mss/month. Accepts 2-4 mss/issue. Publishes ms 6 months after acceptance. Published work by Lisa Koger, Michael Lee West, Eve Shelnutt, David Bottom. Length: 9-30 pages. Publishes short shorts. Length: 500 words. Often comments on or critiques rejected mss.
How to Contact: Send complete ms with cover letter. Include previous publications. Reports in 3 weeks on queries; in 2 months on mss. SASE. Simultaneous, photocopied and computer printout submissions OK. Sample copy and fiction guidelines free.
Payment: Pays in contributor's copies.
Terms: Acquires all rights.
Advice: "Use the language well and tell an interesting story. Send it on. Be open to suggestions."

THE KENYON REVIEW, (II), Kenyon College, Gambier OH 43022. (614)427-3339. Editor: Marilyn Hacker. "Fiction, poetry, essays, book reviews for primarily academic audience." Quarterly. Estab. 1939. Circ. 4,000.
Needs: Condensed/excerpted novel, contemporary, ethnic, experimental, fantasy, feminist, gay, historical, humor/satire, lesbian, literary, mainstream, prose poem, senior citizen/retirement, translations. Receives 300 unsolicited fiction mss/month. Accepts up to 3 mss/issue; up to 12 mss/year. Does not read mss April-August. Publishes ms 12-18 months after acceptance. 50% of fiction is agented. Length: 3-15 (typeset) pages preferred. Rarely publishes short shorts. Sometimes comments on rejected ms.
How to Contact: Send complete ms with cover letter. Reports on mss in 1 month. SASE. Simultaneous and photocopied submissions OK. Sample copy for $7.
Payment: $10/page for fiction.
Terms: Pays on publication for one-time rights and option on anthology rights. Sends copy-edited version to author for approval.
Advice: "Read several issues of our publication."

KINGS REVIEW, P.O. Box 1933, S. San Francisco CA 94083-1933. Editor: Larry Sparks. Magazine; illustrations. "We publish mostly poetry. However, we are open to prose; usually for an academic audience." Estab. 1987.
Needs: Experimental, literary, prose poem. "All work should come with SASE." Plans special edition in the future. Receives "several" unsolicited mss/month. Accepts "few" mss/issue. Publishing time after acceptance varies. Also publishes literary essays, poetry. Recommends other markets.
How to Contact: Send complete manuscript with cover letter and "some biographical information." Reports in 6 weeks on queries; 3 months on mss. SASE. Simultaneous, photocopied and reprint submissions OK. Accepts computer printout submissions. Accepts electronic submissions. Sample copy for $3.50. Fiction guidelines for SASE. Reviews novels and short story collections.
Payment: Usually.
Terms: Payment may be either on acceptance or publication for one-time rights.
Advice: "It helps everyone's chances of publication if they buy a copy of the magazine."

KIOSK, (II), English Department, S.U.N.Y. at Buffalo, 302 Clemens Hall, Buffalo NY 14260. (716)636-2570. Editor: N. Gillespie. Magazine: 5½ × 8½; 100 pages; card stock cover. "We seek innovative, non-formula fiction and poetry." Plans special fiction issue. Annually (may soon be Biannual). Estab. 1986. Circ. 750.
Needs: Excerpted novel, erotica, experimental, feminist, gay, humor/satire, lesbian, prose poem and translations. "No genre or formula fiction; we seek fiction that defies categorization—lush, quirky, flippant, subversive, etc." Receives 35 mss/month. Accepts 10-20 mss/issue. Publishes ms within 6 months of acceptance. Published work by Ray Federman, Carol Berge, James Sallis. Length: 3,000 words preferred; 7,500 words maximum. Publishes short shorts "the shorter the better." Also publishes poetry. Sometimes critiques rejected mss; rarely recommends other markets.
How to Contact: Send complete mss with cover letter. Does not read from May to September. Reports in 2-3 months on mss. "Most sooner; if we keep it longer, we're considering it seriously." SASE. Simultaneous, photocopied and reprint submissions OK. Accepts computer printout submissions. Sample copy for 9x6 or larger SAE and 2 first class stamps.
Payment: Pays in contributor's copies.
Terms: Acquires one-time rights.
Advice: "First and foremost *Kiosk* is interested in sharp writing. There's no need to be dogmatic in terms of pushing a particular style or form, and we aren't. At the same time, we get tired of reading the same old story, the same old poem. Make it new, but also make it worth the reader's effort. Style without substance is a bugaboo. No gratuitous obscurity, but don't be afraid to take real chances. Though we consider all types, we definitely lean towards the experimental. Literary magazine writing is exciting when editors take chances and offer a place for writers who find other avenues closed."

LACTUCA, (II), Box 621, Suffern NY 10901. Editor: Mike Selender. Magazine: Folded 8½ × 14; 72 pages; 24 lb. bond; soft cover; illustrations. Publishes "poetry, short fiction and b&w art, for a general literary audience." Published 2-3 times/year. Estab. 1986. Circ. 700.
Needs: Adventure, condensed/excerpted novel, confession, contemporary, erotica, literary, mainstream, prose poem and regional. No "self-indulgent writing or fiction about writing fiction." Receives 30 or more mss/month. Accepts 3-4 mss/issue; 10-12 mss/year. Publishes ms within 3-12 months of acceptance. Published work by Douglas Mendini, Tom Gidwitz, Ruthann Robson; published new

writers within the last year. Length: around 12-14 typewritten double-spaced pages. Publishes short shorts. Often critiques rejected mss and recommends other markets.

How to Contact: Query first or send complete ms with cover letter. Cover letter should include "just a few brief notes about yourself. Please no long 'literary' résumés or bios. The work will speak for itself." Reports in 2 weeks on queries; 6-8 weeks on mss. SASE. Photocopied submissions OK. No simultaneous or previously published work. Accepts computer printouts. Accepts electronic submissions via "MS DOS or Macintosh formatted disk. We can convert most word-processing formats." Sample copy for $4. Fiction guidelines for #10 SAE and 1 first class stamp.

Payment: Pays 2-5 contributor's copies, depending on the length of the work published.

Terms: Acquires first North American serial rights. Sends galleys to author if requested. Copyrights revert to authors.

Advice: "Too much of the poetry and fiction I have been reading over the past two years has been obsessed with the act of writing or life as a writer. We're not interested in this kind of writing. I place a strong emphasis on the readability of fiction. The dialogue should be clear, and the characters speaking readily discernible. It is worth making the extra revisions necessary to obtain this level of quality. We strongly suggest that writers send a SASE for our guidelines before submitting any fiction."

LAKE EFFECT, (II), Lake County Writers Group, Box 59, Oswego NY 13126. (315)635-5714. Editor: Jean O'Connor Fuller, M.E. Tabloid: 11½×17; 28 pages; newsprint paper and cover; illustrations; photos. "We publish short fiction, poetry, humor, reviews, b&w art and photographs and one nonfiction piece of interest to the area each issue. Our circulation is principally upstate NY." Quarterly. Estab. 1986. Circ. 10,000.

Needs: Contemporary, fantasy, historical (general), humor/satire, literary, mainstream, regional. "We want previously unpublished, honest stories." Accepts 2-3 mss/issue. Does not read mss in August. Publishes ms within 6 months after acceptance. Recently published work by Ron Robinson, Leslee Becker; published new writers within the last year. Length: 5,000 words maximum. Publishes short shorts. Also publishes literary essays, literary criticism, poetry. Occasionally critiques rejected mss and recommends other markets.

How to Contact: Send complete ms with cover letter, which should include biographical information on author. Reports in 2 months. SASE for ms. Photocopied submissions OK. No simultaneous submissions. Accepts computer printout submissions. Sample copy for $2. Fiction guidelines for #10 SAE and 1 first class stamp. Reviews novels and short story collections if author is regional resident.

Payment: Pays $25 and 1 contributor's copy; $2 charge for extras.

Terms: Acquires first North American serial rights.

Advice: "We exist primarily to give outlet to the writers of this region, but also will use good work from outside if we like it. Send us stories about human beings we can believe in, in neat, professional style. We prefer upbeat to downbeat work, but deplore sentimentality. Do not send us your death stories."

LANGUAGE BRIDGES QUARTERLY, Polish-English Literary Magazine, (II, IV), Box 850792, Richardson TX 75085-0792. (214)530-2782. Editor: Eva Ziem. Fiction Editor: Zofia Przebindowska-Tousty. Magazine: 8½×11; 20+ pages; 60 lb. paper; 65 lb. cover; illustrations. "Today's Poland and Polish spirit are the main subject; a picture of life in Poland, with emphasis on the recent Polish emigration wave problems, however topics of general nature are being accepted. For both English and Polish speaking readers." Quarterly. Estab. 1989. Circ. 300.

Needs: Condensed/excerpted novel, fantasy, historical (general), humor/satire, literary, prose poem, religious/inspirational, translations, young adult/teen (10-18 years). "No horror, no vulgar language." Receives 1 unsolicited ms/month. Accepts one fiction ms every second issue. Publishes ms 3-6 months after acceptance. "Length does not matter. The longer works are broken into parts." Publishes short shorts. Sometimes critiques rejected mss and recommends other markets.

How to Contact: Send complete ms with cover letter. Reports in 2-3 months on mss. Simultaneous, photocopied and reprint submissions OK. Accepts computer printouts. Accepts electronic submissions via disk. Free sample copy and fiction guidelines.

Payment: Pays contributor's copies.

Terms: Pays for one-time rights. Sends galleys to author.

Advice: "*LBQ* is the only fully bilingual Polish-English literary magazine in the U.S. It obviously helps Polish newcomers to learn English and Polish Americans to brush up on their Polish. Consequently, through translated Polish literary works, *LBQ* introduces the English-speaking reader to Polish culture and problems of Poles in Poland and abroad. *LBQ* creates a bridge between Polish and American writers as well as the readers. As the bilingual population of Polish Americans has recently grown in the U.S.A., *LBQ* also fulfills the increasing demand for crosscultural dialogue in seeking common roots and discovering differences."

‡**LATIN AMERICAN LITERARY REVIEW, (II, IV),** Department of Hispanic Languages and Literatures, 1309 Cathedral of Learning, University of Pittsburgh, Pittsburgh PA 15260. (412)351-1477. Magazine: 6×9; 112-272 pages; 60 lb. paper; 10 pt. C1S cover stock; occasional photos. "A journal in English devoted to the literature of Latin America. Our publication is directed primarily to an audience of young adults and adults with an interest in Latin American literature." Semiannually. Plans special fiction issue. Estab. 1972. Circ. 1,000.
Needs: Literary, contemporary and ethnic (Hispanic, Latin American, chicano). No "themes not pertaining to the focus of our journal." Publishes short shorts. Accepts 3-5 mss/issue. Published new writers within the last year. No preferred length. Critiques rejected mss "when requested."
How to Contact: Send complete ms and copy with SASE. Reports in 3 months. Sample copy if requested.
Terms: "Rights are relinquished by author upon publication of ms." Sends galleys to author.
Advice: "The fiction which appears in the *LALR* is usually translations of works originally written in Spanish by established authors. *LALR* is associated with the Latin American Literary Review Press (2300 Palmer St., Pittsburgh PA 15218) which publishes novels in Spanish and Portuguese in English translations. *Charges $100 reading fee for books.*"

THE LAUREL REVIEW, (II), Northwest Missouri State University, Dept. of English, Maryville MO 64468. (816)562-1265. Associate Editors: Craig Goad, David Slater and William Trowbridge. Associate Editors: Jim Simmerman, Randy Freisinger. Magazine: 6×9; 124-128 pages; good quality paper. "We publish poetry and fiction of high quality, from the traditional to the avant-garde. We are eclectic, open and flexible. Good writing is all we seek." Biannually. Estab. 1960. Circ. 700.
Needs: Literary and contemporary. Accepts 3-5 mss/issue, 6-10 mss/year. Receives approximately 60 unsolicited fiction mss each month. Approximately 1% of fiction is agented. Length: 2,000-10,000 words. Sometimes publishes literary essays; also publishes poetry. Critiques rejected mss "when there is time." Reads September to May.
How to Contact: Send complete ms with SASE. Accepts computer printout submissions. Reports in 1 week to 4 months on mss. Publishes ms an average of 1-12 months after acceptance. Sample copy for $3.50.
Payment: Pays 2 contributor's copies, 1 year subscription.
Terms: Acquires first rights. Copyright reverts to author upon request.
Advice: Send $3.50 for a back copy of the magazine.

THE LEADING EDGE, Magazine of Science Fiction and Fantasy, (II, IV), 3163 JKHB, Provo UT 84604. Editor: Marny Parkin. Fiction Editor: Lisa Curtis. Magazine: 5×8; 100-120 pages; 20 lb. bond paper; 40 lb. card stock; 15-20 illustrations. "We are a magazine dedicated to the new and upcoming author, poet, and artist involved in the field of science fiction and fantasy. We are for the upcoming professional." Published 3 times/year. Circ. 400.
Needs: Adventure, experimental, fantasy, humor/satire, prose poem, science fiction. "We are very interested in experimental sf and humorous stories, but all pieces should fall within the category of sf and fantasy. No graphic sex, violence, dismemberment, etc. No outrageous religious commentary. No fannish/media stories; i.e., no Star Wars, Star Trek, Dr. Who, etc." Receives 40 unsolicited mss/month. Buys 6-8 mss/issue; 20-30 mss/year. Publishes ms 1-4 months after acceptance. Recently published work by Michael R. Collings, Thomas Easton, David Brin, Dave Wolverton. Length: 5,000 words; 500 words minimum; 17,000 words maximum. Publishes short shorts. Also publishes literary essays, literary criticism, poetry. Critiques rejected mss.
How to Contact: Send complete ms with cover letter. Include name and address, phone number, title of story and classification of story (leave name off manuscript—put it on cover letter only). Reports in 3-4 months on mss. SASE. Simultaneous and photocopied submissions OK. Accepts computer printout submissions. Sample copy for $2.50. Fiction guidelines for #10 SAE and 1 first class stamp. Sometimes reviews novels and short story collections.
Payment: Pays $5-75 plus contributor's copies.
Terms: Pays on publication for first North American serial rights. Sends galleys to author.
Advice: "All fiction must be original, innovative and interesting. We are very familiar with the body of sf and fantasy work, and look for new stories. Too many writers of sf and fantasy rely on existing cliché and convention. Humor, hard science, and experimental fantasy have the best chance for publication. Accurate science, vivid imagery, and strong characterization will impress the editors. We want

stories about people with problems; the setting is there to illustrate the problem, not vice versa. Proofread!!! Please send clean, proofread copy. Just because we're small doesn't mean we're sloppy. Research! Be accurate. Our readers are *very* aware of science and history. We do not publish graphic violence or sex. Violence is okay if it is necessary to the story."

THE LEDGE POETRY AND FICTION MAGAZINE, (II), 64-65 Copper Ave., Glendale NY 11385. (718)366-5169. Editor: Timothy Monaghan. Magazine: 5½×7; 64+ pages; typeset and perfect-bound; gloss cover; cover art. "Our only criteria is material of high literary merit." Semi-annually. Estab. 1988. Circ. 450.
Needs: Condensed/excerpted novels, confession, contemporary, erotica, humor/satire, literary, mainstream, prose poem, romance. Receives approx. 24 unsolicited fiction mss/month. Accepts 3 mss/issue; 6 mss/year. Publishes mss 2 weeks-5 months after acceptance. Recently published work by George Held, Mitch Levenberg, Deb Hiett, Michael O'Brien. Length: "up to 10 pages, double-spaced." Publishes short shorts. Also publishes poetry. Comments on or critiques rejected mss occasionally, if warranted. Recommends other markets.
How to Contact: Send complete ms with cover letter (optional). Reports in 2-3 weeks on queries; 6-8 weeks on mss. SASE. Photocopied, reprint and computer printour submissions OK. Accepts electronic submissions. Sample copy for $6. Fiction guidelines for #10 SASE.
Payment: Pays in contributor's copies.
Terms: Acquires one-time rights.
Advice: "We tend to be partial to material that is both vivid and gritty in its theme, material with a strong sense of place and purpose. Clarity and craft are the keys to a successful piece. No workshop slop, we're looking for originality and individuality, stories that stand out."

LEFT CURVE, (II), Box 472, Oakland CA 94604. (415)763-7193. Editor: Csaba Polony. Magazine: 8½×11; 96 pages; 60 lb. paper; 100 pt. C1S Durosheen cover; illustrations; photos. "*Left Curve* is an artist-produced journal addressing the problem(s) of cultural forms emerging from the crises of modernity that strive to be independent from the control of dominant institutions, based on the recognition of the destructiveness of commodity (capitalist) systems to all life." Published irregularly. Estab. 1974. Circ. 1,000.
Needs: Contemporary, ethnic, experimental, historical, humor/satire, literary, prose poem, regional, science fiction, translations, political. Receives approx. 1 unsolicited fiction ms/month. Accepts approx. 1 ms/issue. Publishes ms a maximum of 6 months after acceptance. Length: 1,200 words average; 500 words minimum; 2,500 words maximum. Publishes short shorts. Sometimes comments on rejected mss or recommends other markets.
How to Contact: Send complete ms with cover letter, which should include "statement on writer's intent, brief bio, why submitting to *Left Curve*." Reports on queries in 1 month; on mss in 3 months. SASE. Accepts computer printouts. Sample copy for $5, 9×12 SAE and 90¢ postage. Fiction guidelines for 2 first class stamps.
Payment: Pays in contributor's copies.
Terms: Acquires first rights.
Advice: "Be honest, realistic and gorge out the truth you wish to say. Understand yourself and the world. Have writing be a means to achieve or realize what is real."

LEFT-FOOTED WOMBAT, Literary Eccentricity, (II), Vishnu-Ala Dav Press, M31 Jardine Terrace, Manhattan KS 66502-3369. (913)539-4629. Editor: David McGhee. Magazine: 5½×8½; 20-24 pages; bond paper; illustrations and photographs. "Unusual theme and/or writing style for an eccentric audience." Published 2 times a year. Estab. 1988.
Needs: Adventure, contemporary, erotica, ethnic, experimental, fantasy, feminist, gay, horror, humor/satire, lesbian, prose poem, psychic/supernatural/occult, regional, religious/inspirational, science fiction, senior citizen/retirement, suspense/mystery, translations. "No sap, bad science fiction, fantasies or same old stories." Receives 8 unsolicited mss/month. Accepts 1 ms/issue; 2 mss/year. Publishes ms 2-3 weeks after acceptance. Length: 2,000 words; 1,000 words minimum; 3,000 words maximum. Also publishes literary essays, poetry. Sometimes critiques rejected mss.
How to Contact: Send complete ms. Reports in 1 week on queries; 3-4 months on mss. SASE. Simultaneous, photocopied and reprint submissions OK. Sample copy for $1. Fiction guidelines for #10 SAE and 1 first class stamp.

Payment: Pays in contributor's copies; charges for extras.
Terms: "Author retains rights."
Advice: Looking for "writing that evokes an emotional response in a clever, subtle manner; original thoughts, plots, characters, and/or writing style; eccentric topics, themes, plots, characters; but especially written well. Keep writing as long as you enjoy. If you're writing for money, forget it. The Big Bucks are rare to find. It is about the love of the word, communicating a personal emotion, not cash. Practice and wading through dry spells are important, which is why enjoying it is a necessity."

LEGEND, A "Robin of Sherwood" Fanzine, (I, II, IV), 1036 Hampshire Rd., Victoria, British Columbia V85 4S9 Canada. (604)598-2197. Editor: Janet P. Reedman. Magazine: Size varies; 170+ pages; bond paper; color print cover; illustrations. "Fantasy: Based on TV series 'Robin of Sherwood.'" Annually. Estab. 1989. Circ. 200+.
Needs: Adventure, fantasy, historical, retold myths/legends. "Mostly need material based on 'Robin of Sherwood' in these genres. Nothing excessively violent/sexual, though adult themes are fine. Nothing sticky-sweet and saccharine, either!" Receives 2-3 unsolicited mss/month. Accepts 15-20 mss/issue; 15-20 mss/year. Publishes ms 4-18 months after acceptance. Length: 3,000 words preferred; 150 words minimum; 20,000 words maximum. Also publishes poetry. Sometimes critiques rejected mss and recommends other markets.
How to Contact: Query first. (I'll accept mss without queries, but it might be wise to write and ask if we're still open, overstocked, etc.). Reports in 2-3 weeks on queries; 5-6 weeks on mss. SASE. "Will accept loose stamps or IRCs, as I can use stamps from other countries." Photocopied submissions OK. Accepts computer printout submissions. Sample copy for $17. Fiction guidelines for #10 SAE and 1 loose first class stamp.
Payment: Pays in contributor's copies for material over 3 pages long.
Terms: Acquires first North American serial rights.
Advice: "Please support small publications, so they can *survive* to publish your work! *Read* a sample copy, so you don't waste postage and the editor's time! We have had handwritten mss, juveniles, no SASE, satires, experimental fiction, 5 stories crammed in one envelope . . . *despite explicit* guidelines!"

LIBIDO, The Journal of Sex and Sensibility, (II, IV), Libido, Inc. P.O. Box 146721, Chicago IL 60614. (312)281-5839. Editors: Jack Hafferkamp and Marianna Beck. Magazine: 5½×8½; 72 pages; 70 lb. non-coated; b&w illustrations and photographs. "Erotica is the focus. Fiction, poetry, essays, reviews for literate adults." Quarterly. Estab. 1988. Circ. 7,500.
Needs: Condensed/excerpted novel, confession, erotica, gay, lesbian. No "Dirty words for their own sake, violence, sexual exploitation." Receives 25-50 unsolicited mss/month. Buys about 5/issue; about 20 per year. Publishes ms up to 1 year after acceptance. Published work by Marco Vassi, Anne Rampling (Ann Rice), Larry Tritten. Length: 1,000-3,000 words; 300 words minimum; 3,000 words maximum. Also publishes literary essays, literary criticism. Sometimes critiques rejected ms and recommends other markets.
How to Contact: Send complete manuscript with cover letter including Social Security number and brief bio for contributor's page. Reports in 1-3 months on mss. SASE. Photocopied and reprint submissions OK. Accepts computer printout submissions. Accepts electronic submissions via disk. Sample copy for $7. Free fiction guidelines. Reviews novels and short story collections.
Payment: Pays $15-50 and 2 contributor's copies.
Terms: Pays on publication for one-time or anthology rights.
Advice: "Humor is a strong plus. There must be a strong erotic element, and it should celebrate the joy of sex."

LIGHTHOUSE, (II), Box 1377, Auburn WA 98071-1377. Editor: Tim Clinton. Magazine: 5½×8½; 56 pages. "Timeless stories and poems for family reading—G rated." Bimonthly. Estab. 1986. Circ. 300.
Needs: Adventure, contemporary, historical, humor/satire, juvenile (5-9 years), mainstream, prose poem, regional, romance (contemporary, historical and young adult), senior citizen/retirement, sports, suspense/mystery, western, young adult/teen (10-18 years). Receives 300 mss/month. Accepts 15 mss/issue; 90 mss/year. Publishes ms within 2 years of acceptance. Recently published work by Will Acker-

Market categories: (I) Beginning; (II) General; (III) Prestige; (IV) Specialized.

man, Nancy R. Herndon, Laura Battyanyi-Petose; published new writers within the last year. Length: 5,000 words maximum. Publishes short shorts.
How to Contact: Send complete mss, include Social Security number. No queries, please. Reports in 2 months on mss. SASE. Photocopied submissions OK. Accepts computer printout submissions. Sample copy for $3 (includes guidelines). Fiction guidelines for #10 SAE and 1 first class stamp.
Payment: Pays up to $50 for stories; up to $5 for poetry.
Terms: Author copies discounted at $1.50 each. Payment on publication for first rights and first North American serial rights.
Advice: "If there is a message in the story, we prefer it to be subtly hidden in the action. We feel there is a market for quality fiction stories that are entertaining and have standards of decency as well."

‡THE LIMBERLOST REVIEW, (II), HC 33, Box 1113, Boise ID 83706-9702. (208)344-2120. Editor: Richard Ardinger. A magazine of poetry, fiction, interviews, memoirs. Publishes several issues a year. Estab. 1976. Circ. varies 500-1,500.
Needs: Contemporary and experimental. Issues of the magazine often devoted to chapbooks. Receives 10-15 unsolicited mss/month. Accepts 1-2 mss/issue. Occasionally comments on rejected ms. Also publishes literary essays, poetry. Special interest in writers from the Northwest.
How to Contact: Send complete ms with cover letter and short bio. Reports in 2 months. SASE. Photocopied submissions OK. Accepts computer printout submissions. Sample copy for $10 with SASE.
Payment: Contributor's copies; charge for extras: author's discount 20%.
Terms: Pays on publication for first rights. Sends galleys to author to check.
Advice: "Most recent issues have been devoted to single authors in the form of books and chapbooks. Issue No. 21, for example, appeared as a collection of short stories by John Rember, entitled *Coyote in the Mountains.*"

LIMESTONE: A LITERARY JOURNAL, (II), University of Kentucky, Dept. of English, 1215 Patterson Office Tower, Lexington KY 40506-0027. Editor: Matthew J. Bond. Magazine: 6×9; 50-75 pages; standard text paper and cover; illustrations; photos. "We publish a variety of styles and attitudes, and we're looking to expand our offering." Annually. Estab. 1981. Circ. 1,000.
Needs: Experimental, humor/satire, literary, mainstream, prose poem. "Avoids stories and poetry that 'say something.'" Receives 200 mss/year. Accepts 15 mss/issue. Does not read mss May-Sept. Publishes ms an average of 6 months after acceptance. Published work by Guy Davenport, Wendell Berry, James Baker Hall; publishes new writers every year. Length: 3,000-5,000 words preferred; 5,000 words maximum. Publishes short shorts. Sometimes critiques rejected mss.
How to Contact: Send complete ms with cover letter, which should include "publishing record and brief bio." Reports in 1 month on queries; 7 months or longer on mss. SASE. Simultaneous and photocopied submissions OK. Accepts computer printout submissions. Sample copy $3.
Payment: Pays 2 contributor's copies.
Terms: Rights revert to author.
Advice: "We encourage all writers to send their most exacting, thought-filled writing. Send us writing where every word tells."

LININGTON LINEUP, (IV), Elizabeth Linington Society, 1223 Glen Terrace, Glassboro NJ 08028-1315. Editor: Rinehart S. Potts. Newsletter: 8½×11; 16 pages; bond paper and cover stock; illustrations and photographs. "For those interested in the publications of Elizabeth Linington (a/k/a Lesley Egan, Egan O'Neill, Anne Blaisdell, Dell Shannon) — historical fiction and detective mysteries — therefore material must relate in some way thereto." Bimonthly. Plans special fiction issue. Estab. 1984. Circ. 400.
Needs: *Charges reading fee of $1. Requires magazine subscription of $12 before reading.* Historical (general), literary, suspense/mystery. Upcoming theme: "Motion pictures made from Linington books." Receives 3-4 fiction mss/month. Accepts 1 ms/issue; 6 mss/year. Publishes ms 3 months after acceptance. Publishes short shorts. Also publishes literary essays, literary criticism, poetry. Sometimes comments on rejected mss.
How to Contact: Query first. Reports in 1 month. SASE. Photocopied and reprint submissions OK. Accepts computer printout submissions. Sample copy for $3. Reviews novels and short story collections.

Payment: Pays subscription to magazine.
Terms: Acquires first rights.
Advice: "Become familiar with Miss Linington's books and continuing characters. We have been receiving material which completely disregards the information cited above."

‡**LITE MAGAZINE, The Journal of Satire and Creativity, (I, II),** #203, 4707 Benson Ave., Baltimore MD 21227-1412. (301)247-8804. Editor: David W. Kriebel. Magazine: 8½×11; 52 pages; 60 lb. bond; glossy cover; 12-24 illustrations; some photographs. "Satire, poetry, short fiction, occasional nonfiction pieces. Our audience is intelligent, literate, and imaginative. They have the ability to step back and look at the world from a different perspective." Bimonthly. Estab. 1989. Circ. 10,000.
Needs: Experimental, fantasy, historical (general), horror, humor/satire, literary, psychic/supernatural/occult, science fiction, suspense/mystery. "No erotica, gay, lesbian. Nothing demeaning to any ethnic or religious group. No stories with an obvious or trite 'message.' No violence for its own sake." Receives 10-20 unsolicited mss/month. Accepts 4-8 mss/issue; 16-32 ms/year. Publishes mss 1-3 months after acceptance. Recently published work by Thomas Frank, Stacy Tuthill. Length: 2,500 words preferred; 6,000 words maximum. Publishes short shorts. Also publishes poetry. Sometimes comments on or critiques rejected mss.
How to Contact: Request guidelines, then send ms and cover letter. Include "information on the writer, focusing on what led him to write or create visual art. We want to know the person, both for our contributors guide 'Names in Lite' and to help build a network of creative people." Reports in 1 month. SASE. Simultaneous and photocopied submissions OK. Sample copy for $3.25, 9×12 SAE and 3 first class stamps. Fiction guidelines for #10 SAE and 1 first class stamp.
Payment: Pays contributor's copies; charges for extras.
Terms: Acquires one-time rights.
Advice: "We first look for quality writing, then we look at content and theme. It's not hard to tell a dedicated writer from someone who only writes for money or recognition. Fiction that resonates in the heart makes us take notice. It's a joy to read such a story."

THE LITERARY REVIEW, An International Journal of Contemporary Writing, Fairleigh Dickinson University, 285 Madison Ave., Madison NJ 07940. (201)593-8564. Editor-in-Chief: Walter Cummins. Magazine: 6×9; 128-152 pages; illustrations; photos. "Literary magazine specializing in fiction, poetry, and essays with an international focus." Quarterly. Estab. 1957. Circ. 2,000.
Needs: Works of high literary quality only. Upcoming theme: "New Myths - 500 Years After Columbus" (Fall 1992). Receives 30-40 unsolicited fiction mss/month. Approximately 1-2% of fiction is agented. Published Anne Brashler, Thomas E. Kennedy, Henry H. Roth; published new writers within the last year. Accepts 10-12 mss/year. Also publishes literary essays, literary criticism, poetry. Occasionally critiques rejected mss. Sometimes recommends other markets.
How to Contact: Send complete ms with SASE. "Cover letter should include publication credits." Photocopied submissions OK. Accepts computer printout submissions. Reports in 3 months on mss. Publishes ms an average of 1-1½ years after acceptance. Sample copy for $5; guidelines for SASE. Reviews novels and short story collections.
Payment: Pays 2 contributor's copies; 25% discount for extras.
Terms: Acquires first rights.
Advice: "Too much of what we are seeing today is openly derivative in subject, plot and prose style. We pride ourselves on spotting new writers with fresh insight and approach."

THE LITTLE MAGAZINE, (II), State University of New York at Albany, English Department, Albany NY 12222. Editor: Jan Ramjerdi. Magazine: 5½×8½; 300 pages; 70 lb. Nikusa paper; 10 pt. high gloss cover; cover illustrations. "Fiction and poetry for a literary audience." Annually. Estab. 1965.
Needs: Ethnic, experimental, feminist, gay, humor/satire, lesbian, literary, prose poem. No romance. Receives "roughly" 1,400 mss/issue over a 3-month reading period. Accepts 10 mss/issue. Reads only from September 15 to December 15. Publishes ms 6 months after acceptance. Published work by Edward Kleinschmidt, Simon Perchik, Vicki Lindner, Sussy Chako. Length: 4,500 words preferred; 6,000 words maximum. Publishes short shorts. Critiques or comments on rejected mss.
How to Contact: Send complete ms with SASE, but only send between September 15 and December 15. Reports in 1 month on queries; in 2 months on mss. Simultaneous, photocopied, reprint and computer printout submissions OK. Sample copy for $6.
Payment: Pays 2 contributor's copies.
Terms: Acquires first North American serial rights.
Advice: "We like a wide variety of work from traditional to experimental."

LLAMAS MAGAZINE, The International Camelid Journal, (IV), Clay Press Inc., Box 100, Herald CA 95638. (916)448-1668. Editor: Cheryl Dal Porto. Magazine: 8½×11; 128+ pages; glossy paper; 80 lb. glossy cover stock; illustrations and pictures. For llama owners and lovers. 8 issues/year. Estab. 1979. Circ. 5,500.
Needs: Adventure, historical, humor/satire. Receives 15-25 unsolicited fiction mss/month. Accepts 1-6 mss/issue; 12-24 mss/year. Publishes ms usually 3-4 months after acceptance. 15% of fiction is agented. Length: 2,000-3,000 words average. Publishes short shorts 300-1,000 words in length. Sometimes critiques rejected mss.
How to Contact: Send query to: Susan Ley, *Llamas* Asst. Editor, Box 1038, Dublin OH 43017. Reports in 1 month. Reprint submissions OK. Accepts computer printout submissions. Accepts electronic submissions via Apple 2 disk. Fiction guidelines free.
Payment: Pays $25-500, subscription to magazine and contributor's copies.
Terms: Pays on publication for first rights, first North American serial rights and one-time rights. Sends pre-publication galleys to author if requested.

LONG SHOT, Box 6231, Hoboken NJ 07030. Editors: Jack Wiler, Jessica Chosid, Tom Pulhamus, Danny Shot. Magazine: 5½×8½; 128 pages; 60 lb. paper; 10 pt. C1S cover; illustrations; photos. Estab. 1982. Circ. 1,500.
Needs: Adventure, confession, contemporary, erotica, ethnic, experimental, fantasy, feminist, gay, horror, humor/satire, lesbian, political, prose poem, psychic/supernatural/occult, science fiction, suspense/mystery, western. Receives 100 unsolicited mss/month. Accepts 4-5 mss/issue. Does not read mss in August. Publishes ms within 6 months after acceptance. Published work by Allen Ginsberg, Charles Bukowski, Robert Press, June Jordan; published new writers within the last year. Publishes short shorts. Also publishes poetry. Sometimes recommends other markets.
How to Contact: Send complete ms. Reports in 4-6 weeks. SASE. Simultaneous and photocopied submissions OK. Sample copy for $5 plus $1 postage.
Payment: Pays in contributor's copies.
Terms: Acquires one-time rights.

THE LONG STORY, (II), 11 Kingston St., North Andover MA 01845. *May be change of address in coming year. Please watch writing periodicals for notice.* (508)686-7638. Editor: R.P. Burnham. Magazine: 5½×8½; 150-200 pages; 60 lb. paper; 65 lb. cover stock; illustrations (b&w graphics). For serious, educated, literary people. No science fiction, adventure, romance, etc. "We publish high literary quality of any kind, but especially look for committed fiction; working class settings, left-wing themes, etc." Annually. Estab. 1983. Circ. 500.
Needs: Contemporary, ethnic, feminist and literary. Receives 30-40 unsolicited mss/month. Buys 6-7 mss/issue. Length: 8,000 words minimum; 20,000 words maximum. ("To accept 20,000 word story it would have to be right down our alley—about poor, oppressed people, i.e., committed fiction.") Sometimes recommends other markets.
How to Contact: Send complete ms with a brief cover letter. Reports in 2+ months. Publishes ms an average of 3 months to 1 year after acceptance. SASE. Photocopied submissions OK. Accepts computer printout submissions. Sample copy for $5.
Payment: Pays 2 contributor's copies; $4 charge for extras.
Terms: Acquires first rights.
Advice: "Read us first and make sure submitted material is the kind we're interested in. Send clear, legible manuscripts. We're not interested in commercial success; rather we want to provide a place for long stories, the most difficult literary form to publish in our country."

LOST, A Magazine of Horror and Dark Humor, (II), Lupus Publishing, 67 Seyler St., New Hamburg, Ontario N0B 2G0 Canada. (519)662-2725. Editor: Adam Thornton. Magazine: 5¾×8½; 40 pages; illustrations and photographs. "Horrific or black comedy in both stories and artwork. Graphic or quiet poems accepted as well." Estab. 1990.
Needs: Experimental, horror, prose poem, psychic/supernatural/occult. "Must be morbid or horrific." No "fantasy or science." Receives 20-25 unsolicited mss/month. Accepts 10 mss/issue. Publishes ms 1 or 2 months after acceptance. Length: 1,000 words average; 500 words minimum; 3,000 words maximum. Publishes short shorts. Length: 400 words. Always comments on rejected mss and recommends other markets.
How to Contact: Send complete manuscript with cover letter that includes some biographical info. Reports in 1 week. Photocopied submissions OK. Accepts computer printout submissions. Accepts electronic submissions. Fiction guidelines for SASE.

"We look for stories about ordinary people that while set in a specific location and dealing with a specific theme still connect to universal human experience," says R.P. Burnham, editor of The Long Story. For the cover, "I chose Rembrandt's drawing, 'Sleeping Girl,' first of all because it was a compelling image communicating in a few simple lines enormous trust, vulnerability, love and depth of humanity, and secondly because the image in artistic terms parallels our literary ideal." This copy of the drawing, as well as the rest of Rembrandt's work in the issue, is computer-generated.

Payment: Pays in contributor's copies. Publication is not copyrighted.
Advice: "Read popular horror stories, then send us something unlike the stuff you read. We are looking for fiction along the lines of Steve Rasnic Tem, Charles L. Grant, Douglas E. Winter, Richard Christian Matheson."

LOST AND FOUND TIMES, (II), Luna Bisonte Prods, 137 Leland Ave., Columbus OH 43214. (614)846-4126. Editor: John M. Bennett. Magazine: 5½×8½; 40 pages; good quality paper; good cover stock; illustrations; photos. Theme: experimental, avant-garde and folk literature, art. Published irregularly. Estab. 1975. Circ. 300.
Needs: Literary, contemporary, experimental, prose poem. Prefers short pieces. Also publishes poetry. Accepts approximately 2 mss/issue. Published work by Spryszak, Steve McComas, Willie Smith, Rupert Wondolowski; published new writers within the last year. Sometimes recommends other markets.
How to Contact: Query with clips of published work. SASE. Accepts computer printout submissions. Reports in 1 week on queries, 2 weeks on mss. Sample copy for $4.
Payment: Pays 1 contributor's copy.
Terms: Rights revert to authors.

LOST CREEK LETTERS, (I, II), Lost Creek Publications, RR2, Box 373A, Rushville MO 64484. (816)688-7834. Editor: Pamela Montgomery. Magazine: 5½×8½; 40-44 pages; copy bond paper; line cover art illustrations. "The only theme we have is *quality*. Completely open, with some taboos on genre for a college and post-college audience." Quarterly. Estab. 1990. Circ. 200.
Needs: Contemporary, ethnic, experimental, fantasy, feminist, humor/satire, literary, mainstream, science fiction, surrealism. No romance, western, religious, juvenile. Publishes cartoons.Plans special fiction issue. Receives 100+ unsolicited mss/month. Buys 3-5 mss/issue; 12-20 mss/year. Publishes ms 1-6 months after acceptance. Published work by John Weston and J.L. Lauinger. Length: 3,000 words average; 200 words minimum; 3,000 words maximum. Publishes short shorts. Also may publish literary essays; publishes poetry. Sometimes critiques rejected ms and recommends other markets.
How to Contact: Send complete manuscript with no cover letter. "Please *never* query." SASE. Simultaneous and photocopied submissions OK. Accepts computer printout submissions. Accepts electronic submissions via disk (must be IBM 5¼). Sample copy for $4.75. Fiction guidelines for #10 SAE and 1 first class stamp.

Payment: Pays $2-5 or contributor's copies.
Terms: Pays on publication for one-time rights. "We are read for *Best American Short Stories*. I nominate stories for the Pushcart Prize."
Advice: "A ms stands out if it is *rich* in detail and its characters are fully developed. A fine story is meaningful on more than an obvious superficial level. Polish is absolutely essential and can be achieved only by dedicated revising. Do *not* write a cover letter. Stories are like jokes; if they're good, they need no explanation. Send the ms only, with your name and address on the first page, your name on each subsequent page. A ms with no SASE goes directly into the trash unread."

‡LOST WORLDS, The Science Fiction and Fantasy Forum, (I, IV), HBD Publishing, P.O. Box 605, Concord NC 28025. (704)933-7998. Editor: Holley B. Drye. Newsletter: 8½ × 11; 24 pages; 24 lb. bond paper; b&w illustrations. "General interest science fiction and fantasy, as well as some specialized genre writing. For a broad-spectrum age groups, anyone interested in newcomers." Monthly. Estab. 1988. Circ. 150.
Needs: Experimental, fantasy, horror, psychic/supernatural/occult, science fiction, serialized novel. Publishes annual special fiction issue. Receives 7-15 unsolicited mss/month. Accepts 7-10 mss/issue; 100 and up mss/year. Publishes ms 3 months after acceptance. Length: 3,000 words preferred; 2,000 words minimum; 5,500 words maximum. Publishes short shorts. Sometimes critiques rejected mss and recommends other markets. "Although we do not publish every type of genre fiction, I will, if asked, critique anyone who wishes to send me their work."
How to Contact: Query first. "Cover letters should include where and when to contact the author, a pen name if one is preferred as well as their real name, and whether or not they wish their real names to be kept confidential." Reports in 2 weeks on queries; 1 month on mss. SASE (only if they wish return of their manuscript.) Simultaneous, photocopied and reprint submissions OK. Accepts computer printout submissions. Accepts electronic submissions via disk or modem. Sample copy for $1. Fiction guidelines free.
Payment: Pays contributor's copies.
Terms: Acquires one-time rights.
Advice: "I look for originality of story, good characterization and dialogue, well-written descriptive passages, and over-all story quality. The presentation of the work also makes a big impression, whether it be good or bad. Neat, typed manuscripts will always have a better chance than hand-written or badly typed ones. All manuscripts are read by either three or four different people, with an eye towards development of plot and comparison to other material within the writer's field of experience. Plagiarism is not tolerated, and we do look for it while reading a manuscript under consideration. Never be afraid to send us anything, we really are kind people."

LOUISIANA LITERATURE, A Review of Literature and Humanities, (II), Southeastern Louisiana University, Box 792, Hammond LA 70402. (504)549-5022. Editor: Tim Gautreaux. Magazine: 6¾ × 9¾; 100 pages; 70 lb. paper; card cover; illustrations; photos. "We publish literary quality fiction and essays by anyone. Essays should be about Louisiana material, but creative work can be set anywhere." Semiannually. Estab. 1984. Circ. 400 paid; 700 printed.
Needs: Literary, mainstream, regional. No sloppy ungrammatical manuscripts. Receives 60 unsolicited mss/month. Accepts 3 mss/issue; 6 mss/year. Does not read mss June-July. Publishes ms 6 months maximum after acceptance. Published work by Kelly Cherry and Louis Gallo; published new writers within the last year. Length: 3,500 words preferred; 1,000 words minimum; 6,000 words maximum. Also publishes literary essay (Louisiana themes), literary criticism, poetry. Sometimes comments on rejected mss.
How to Contact: Send complete ms. Reports in 1-2 months on mss. SASE. Photocopied submissions OK. Accepts computer printout submissions. Sample copy for $4. Reviews novels and short story collections by Louisiana authors only.
Payment: Pays up to $25 and contributor's copies.
Terms: Pays on publication for one-time rights.
Advice: "Cut out everything that is not a functioning part of the story. Make sure everything is spelled correctly. Use relevant specific detail in every scene."

Read the Business of Fiction section to learn the correct way to prepare and submit a manuscript.

THE LOUISVILLE REVIEW, (II), Department of English, University of Louisville, Louisville KY 40292. (502)588-6801. Editor: Sena Naslund. General Editor: Sam Bowling. Magazine: 6 × 8¼; 100 pages; Warren's Old Style paper; cover photographs. Semiannually. Estab. 1976. Circ. 750.
Needs: Contemporary, experimental, literary, prose poem. Receives 30-40 unsolicited mss/month. Accepts 6-10 mss/issue; 12-20 mss/year. Publishes ms 2-3 months after acceptance. Published work by Maura Stanton, Patricia Goedicke, Michael Cadnum. Length: 50 pages maximum. Publishes short shorts.
How to Contact: Send complete ms with cover letter. Reports on queries in 2-3 weeks; 2-3 months on mss. SASE. Photocopied submissions OK. Accepts computer printout submissions. Sample copy for $3. Fiction guidelines for #10 SAE and 1 first class stamp.
Payment: Pays in contributor's copies.
Terms: Acquires first North American serial rights.
Advice: Looks for "original concepts, fresh ideas, good storyline, engaging characters, a story that works."

‡LYNX, Journal of Renga, (II, IV), Spirit Lake Press, P.O. Box 169, Toutle WA 98649. (206)274-6661 or 274-6352. Editor: Terri Lee Grell. Magazine: 24-36 pages; newsprint paper; b&w illustrations and photographs. "Poetry commentary, stories and renga. Renga is linked verse; two or more poets cooperate to make a renga. The form dates back to 12th century Japan. For an adventurous audience." Quarterly. Estab. 1989. Circ. 500.
Needs: Experimental, literary, prose poem, translations. "No slick fiction. If it squeaks, send it to NYC." Receives 3-4 unsolicited mss/month. Accepts 1 ms/issue; 4 mss/year. Publishes ms within 4 months after acceptance. Recently published work by Hiroaki Sato, Gerald Burns, Miyazawa Kenji. Length: 2,000 words maximum. Publishes short shorts. Length: 250-500 words. Also accepts poetry. Sometimes critiques rejected mss and recommends other markets.
How to Contact: Send complete ms with cover letter. Reports in 1-2 months. SASE. Photocopied submissions OK. Sample copy for $2.
Payment: Pays contributor's copies and some payment by arrangement.
Terms: Pays on publication. Acquires first North American serial rights. Not copyrighted.
Advice: "If it can't easily slip into one genre or another, we love it. If a manuscript is perfect to a fault, we hate it. We despise factory fiction. We love fiction writers who finally give up on factory fiction, let go of the reins and tell us something dry and outrageous, fast and holy, truly. Make my day."

THE MACGUFFIN, (II), Schoolcraft College, Department of English, 18600 Haggerty Rd., Livonia MI 48152. (313)591-6400, ext. 449. Editor: Arthur J. Lindenberg. Fiction Editor: Elizabeth Hebron. Magazine: 5½ × 8½; 128 pages; 60 lb. paper; 110 lb. cover; b&w illustrations and photos. "*The MacGuffin* is a literary magazine which publishes a range of material including poetry, nonfiction and fiction. Material ranges from traditional to experimental. We hope our periodical attracts a variety of people with many different interests." Published 3 times/year. Quality fiction a special need. Estab. 1984. Circ. 500.
Needs: Adventure, contemporary, ethnic, experimental, fantasy, historical (general), humor/satire, literary, mainstream, prose poem, psychic/supernatural/occult, science fiction, translations. No religious, inspirational, confession, romance, horror, pornography. Receives 25-40 unsolicited mss/month. Accepts 5-10 mss/issue; 10-30 mss/year. Does not read mss between July 1 and August 15. Publishes 6 months to 2 years after acceptance. Agented fiction: 10-15%. Published work by Richard Kostelantz, Gayle Boss, Ann Knox; published new writers within the last year. Length: 2,000-2,500 words average; 400 words minimum; 4,000 words maximum. Publishes short shorts. Length: 400 words. Also publishes literary essays (June 1992 issue will be on "The Literary Essay"). Occasionally critiques rejected mss and recommends other markets.
How to Contact: Send complete ms with cover letter, which should include: "1. *Brief* biographical information; 2. Note that this *is not* a simultaneous submission." Reports in 6-8 weeks. SASE. Photocopied and reprint submissions OK. Accepts computer printout submissions. Sample copy for $3. Fiction guidelines free.
Payment: Pays 2 contributor's copies.
Terms: Acquires one-time rights.
Advice: "Be persistent. If a story is rejected, try to send it somewhere else. When we reject a story, we may accept the next one you send us. When we make suggestions for a rewrite, we may accept the revision. There seems to be a great number of good authors of fiction, but there are far too few places

Close-up

Robert Shapard
Founder and Editor
Manoa

When founders Robert Shapard and Frank Stewart decided to launch *Manoa*, they took the hard question head-on: Why did America need another literary journal? What new could a Hawaii-based publication contribute to the existing field?

"I think there are about 5,000 literary journals," says *Manoa* Editor Shapard. "We wondered what we could do that would be useful. And that's when we realized we had a network at hand of people who are familiar with what's going on in Asia and the Pacific. We also realized that most Americans know very little about what's going on in Korea, Japan and the South Pacific. They know some of the ancient literatures, but have very little access to what's happening now. There's a tremendous amount going on, not just politically and economically, but in both established literatures and emerging new ones."

Shapard and Stewart were awarded three years' worth of start-up funds from the University of Hawaii to begin publication of *Manoa* (which means in Hawaiian "vast and deep" and is also the name of the valley on Oahu in which the University of Hawaii is situated). In autumn of 1989, *Manoa: A Pacific Journal of International Writing* was launched, published as a double volume by the University of Hawaii Press. A hefty, 200-page, perfect-bound journal, *Manoa* is published semiannually and features poetry, black-and-white photography, book reviews and feature articles, in addition to fiction. Its fiction sections include short stories from American authors in addition to translated contributions from other writers. *Manoa*'s American fiction has included short stories by authors such as Ann Beattie and Joyce Carol Oates, and it is working to make the names of its Asian and Pacific contributors as familiar to American readers.

"The purpose of *Manoa* is to reorient people toward the Pacific, because we think most people are Eurocentric," says Shapard. "We see a lot of translations these days from eastern Europe and Latin America in literary journals, but there is the whole other half of the world from which almost nothing has been appearing. Our whole American tradition comes out of Europe, the old models, and there's been that interaction through the years across the Atlantic, but I think that is changing. The country is changing toward more multicultural writing and models, and Hawaii has interestingly enough always been multicultural. In a way, Hawaii is where the rest of the country is going. We think of *Manoa* as a bridge between East and West."

Eight corresponding editors gather fiction from Korea, Japan, the Philippines, China, South Asia, New Zealand, the South Pacific and Pacific Latin America. But the fact that *Manoa* is called a Pacific journal has created some confusion among contributors of American fiction, says Shapard. "What we don't necessarily want from American writers are stories set in the Pacific or Pacific exotica. It's funny, but magazines in Alaska probably get a lot of Eskimo stories from people who live in Florida. Japan, for instance, has the third-largest English-language readership in the world. And we want to present to them

© Pat Matsueda

Frank Stewart and Robert Shapard

the best American writing we can, and not necessarily stories about native girls on exotic islands."

What *Manoa* looks for from American writers is no different from what *The Iowa Review* and *Prairie Schooner* look for. "We're open to all kinds of fiction, and I guess we sort of tend toward traditional or mainstream but we're open to experimental work, too. We look for stories that are well-crafted, but more than that we look for stories that have energy and something to say. We look for stories that matter, that aren't just an amusement."

The journal has had no shortage of submissions from high-caliber authors—a large percentage of the fiction it has featured has come from writers whose work appears regularly in other national literaries, and who have novel and short story collections to their credit. Of the 1,000 manuscripts *Manoa* receives each year, some 15 are selected. But Shapard urges new writers not to be daunted by this.

"We like to discover and publish new writers, if it's a story we really like," he says. "In fact, we enlisted the help of a fiction writer here to do some guest editing on our last fiction section—the American side—and we'd only heard of one writer. So in principle, our idea is it's just the story that matters, not who it's from or how it got here."

Shapard adds that agents, while they are "helpful and convenient," are not essential. He does offer advice to writers who choose not to market their work through an agent. Many new writers seem to be confused about what information to include in their cover letters if they can't list the names of publications in which their work has been published, he says. Shapard encourages them to indicate clearly that if the story is accepted, it will be the writer's first publication. It's a selling point, he says, in that editors like to discover new writers. He also suggests that writers not summarize or explain their story in the cover letter. His final advice: "Read literary magazines, especially those to which you want to submit."

—Anne Bowling

for publication. However, I think this is changing. Make your characters come to life. Even the most ordinary people become fascinating if they live for your readers."

THE MADISON REVIEW, (II), Department of English, Helen C. White Hall, 600 N. Park St., University of Wisconsin, Madison WI 53706. Fiction Editors: Kathryn Arrington, Lesley Rosen. Magazine: 6×9; 180 pages. "Magazine of fiction and poetry with special emphasis on literary stories and some emphasis on midwestern writers." Published semiannually. Estab. 1978. Circ. 500.
Needs: Experimental and literary stories, prose poems and excerpts from novels. Receives 50 unsolicited fiction mss/month. Accepts 7-12 mss/issue. Published work by Richard Cohen, Fred Chappell and Janet Shaw. Published new writers within the last year. Length: no preference. Also publishes poetry.
How to Contact: Send complete ms with cover letter and SASE. "The letters should give one or two sentences of relevant information about the writer—just enough to provide a context for the work." Reports in 2 months on mss. Publishes ms an average of 4 months after acceptance. "We often do not report on mss during the summer." Sample copy $4.
Payment: Pays 2 contributor's copies; $2.50 charge for extras.
Terms: Acquires first North American serial rights.
Advice: "We are now willing to accept chapters of novels in progress and short short fiction. Write with surgical precision—then revise. Often the label 'experimental' is used to avoid reworking a piece. If anything, the more adventurous a piece of fiction is, the more it needs to undergo revision."

THE MAGE, A Journal of Fantasy and Science Fiction, (II, IV), Colgate University Student Association, Hamilton NY 13346. Contact: Editor. Magazine: 8½×11; about 64 pages; quality stock and cover; b&w illustrations. "Fiction, essays, poetry, artwork and commentary within the genre of science fiction and fantasy. Emphasis is on a balance of poetry, fiction and nonfiction. We do serialize longer works of exceptional quality." Semiannually. Estab. 1984. Circ. 900.
Needs: Experimental, fantasy, horror, science fiction. No "sword-and-sorcery adventure or stories based on Dungeons and Dragons and its ilk; no erotica." Receives 15-25 unsolicited fiction mss/month. Accepts 6-10 mss/issue; 12-20 mss/year. Does not read mss June through August. Generally publishes ms within 3 months of acceptance. Published work by Patricia Anthony, Eric Davin and David Lunde; published new writers within the last year. Length: 3,500-4,500 words average; 1,000 words minimum. Also publishes poetry. Usually critiques rejected mss.
How to Contact: Query first or send complete ms and cover letter with list of previous works published. Reports in 2 weeks on queries; 3-5 weeks on mss (report time is longer if submitted just before or during the summer). SASE for ms. Simultaneous and photocopied submissions OK. Accepts computer printouts. Sample copy $3.
Payment: Pays in contributor's copies.
Terms: Acquires first North American serial rights or one-time rights. Sometimes sends galleys to author.
Advice: "We are interested in writers who have practiced enough (even if nothing has been published) to develop a refined writing style. We are interested in presenting good writing first, but we do publish capsule reviews of new fiction. Submitting several of these to us will help a new writer develop some recognition of *The Mage*'s standards, which might help him/her when submitting a first manuscript to us."

MAGIC CHANGES (II), Celestial Otter Press, P.O. Box 658, Warrenville IL 60555. (708)416-3111. Editor: John Sennett. Magazine: 8½×11; 110 pages; 60 lb. paper; construction paper cover; illustrations; photos. "Theme: transformation by art. Material: poetry, songs, fiction, stories, reviews, art, essays, etc. For the entertainment and enlightenment of all ages." Annually. Estab. 1979. Circ. 500.
Needs: Literary, prose poem, science fiction, sports fiction, fantasy and erotica. "Fiction should have a magical slant." Accepts 8-12 mss/year. Receives approximately 15 unsolicited fiction mss each month. Published work by J. Weintraub, David Goodrum, Anne F. Robertson; published new writers within the last year. Length: 3,000 words maximum. Also publishes literary essays, literary criticism, poetry.
How to Contact: Send complete ms with SASE. Accepts computer printout submissions. Accepts disk submissions compatible with IBM or Macintosh. Prefers hard copy with disk submissions. Reports in 1 month. Publishes ms an average of 5 months after acceptance. Sample copy $5. Make check payable to John Sennett. Reviews novels and short story collections.
Payment: Pays 1-2 contributor's copies; $5 charge for extras.
Terms: Acquires first North American serial rights.
Advice: "Write about something fantastic in a natural way, or something natural in a fantastic way. We need good stories—like epic Greek poems translated into prose."

‡MAGIC REALISM, (II, IV), Pyx Press, P.O. Box 620, Orem UT 84059-0620. Editor: C. Darren Butler and Julie Thomas. Magazine: 5½ × 8½; 60 pages; 20 lb. paper; card stock or bond cover; b&w illustrations. "Magic realism, exaggerated realism, some genre fantasy/dark fantasy, literary fantasy, occasionally glib fantasy of the sort found in the folk and fairy tales; myths for a general, literate audience." Triannually. Estab. 1990. Circ. 200.

Needs: Experimental, fantasy, literary, magic realism. "No sorcery/wizardry, sleight-of-hand magicians, occult, or the Edward Eager *Half-Magic* sort of story that begins "The magic started when . . ."" Receives 50-70 unsolicited mss/month. Accepts 5-12 mss/issue; 20-30 mss/year. Publishes ms 4-12 months, sometimes longer after acceptance. Recently published work by Bruce Taylor, Steve Rasnic Tem, Leland Neville. Length: 3,500 words preferred; 100 words minimum; 6,000 words maximum. Publishes short shorts. Length: 500-1,500 words. Sometimes critiques rejected mss and recommends other markets.

How to Contact: Send complete ms with cover letter. Include bio, list of credits. Reports in 1 month on queries; 2-3 months, sometimes longer on mss. SASE. Photocopied and reprint submissions (if noted) OK. Accepts computer printout submissions. Sample copy for $4.95 (checks to C. Darren Butler). Fiction guidelines for SAE and 1 first class stamp.

Payment: Pays contributor's copies. Charges for extras.

Terms: Acquires first North American serial rights, one-time rights and non exclusive reprint rights in case we want to use the work in an anthology.

Advice: "I am accepting a broad range of material; I am not limited to imitation of the Latin American masters. I like finely controlled prose, feats of association; works where the fabric of reality is affected. If in doubt, send it."

THE MALAHAT REVIEW, (II), University of Victoria, Box 3045, Victoria, British Columbia V8W 3P4 Canada. (604)721-8524. Editor: Constance Rooke. Magazine: 6 × 9; 132 pages; photographs occasionally. Publishes fiction, poetry and reviews. Quarterly. Estab. 1967. Circ. 1,800.

Needs: Receives 100 unsolicited mss/month. Buys approximately 6 mss/issue; 25 mss/year. Publishes short shorts. Also publishes poetry. Occasionally critiques rejected mss.

How to Contact: Send complete ms with cover letter. SASE (Canadian postage or IRCs). Photocopied submissions OK. Accepts computer printout submissions. Sample copy for $6. Fiction guidelines free. Reviews novels and short story collections.

Payment: Pays $40 per 1,000 words; and contributor's copies.

Terms: Buys first rights.

Advice: "If it's good, we publish it. *The Malahat Review* is a "generalist" literary magazine, which is to say that it is open to all schools of writing and does not espouse any particular ideology or aesthetic. We believe that new writers should have the opportunity of appearing with celebrated writers, and we find that a mix of unknown and famous names results very naturally from our choice of the best work we receive."

MANOA, A Pacific Journal of International Writing, (III), English Dept., University of Hawaii Press, Honolulu HI 96822. (808)948-8833. Editor: Robert Shapard. Fiction Editors: Roger Whitlock and Jeff Carroll. Magazine: 7 × 10; 200 pages. "An American literary magazine, emphasis on top US fiction and poetry, but each issue has a major guest-edited translated feature of recent writings from an Asian/Pacific country." Semiannually. Estab. 1989.

Needs: Excerpted novel, contemporary, literary, mainstream and translation (from nations in or bordering on the Pacific). "Part of our purpose is to present top US fiction from throughout the US, not only to US readers, but to readers in Asian and Pacific countries. Thus we are not limited to stories related to or set in the Pacific — in fact, we do not want exotic or adventure stories set in the Pacific, but good US literary fiction of any locale." Accepts 10-12 mss/issue; 20-24/year. Publishes ms 6 months-1 year after acceptance. Agented fiction 50%. Published work by Anne Beattie, Ron Carlson and Francois Camoin. Publishes short shorts. Also publishes literary essays, literary criticism, poetry.

How to Contact: Send complete ms with cover letter or through agent. Reports in 1-6 weeks. SASE. Simultaneous and photocopied submissions OK. Sample copy $7. Reviews novels and short story collections. Send books to Reviews Editor.

Payment: "Highly competitive rates paid so far." Pays contributor copies.

Terms: Pays for first North American serial, plus one-time reprint rights. Sends galleys to author.

Advice: "Hawaii has come of age literarily and wants to contribute to the best of US mainstream. It's readership is (and is intended to be) mostly national, not local. It also wants to represent top US writing to a new international market, in Asia and the Pacific. Altogether we hope our view is a fresh one; that is, not facing East toward Europe but west toward 'the other half of the world.' We mostly run short stories."

MARK, A Journal of Scholarship, Opinion, and Literature, (II), University of Toledo, 2801 W. Bancroft SU2514, Toledo OH 43606. (419)537-4407. Editor: Brenda Wyatt. Magazine: 6×9; 72 pages; acid-free paper; some illustrations; photographs. "General theme is exploration of humanity and man's effort to understand the world around him." Annually. Estab. 1967. Circ. 3,500.
Needs: Contemporary, ethnic, humor/satire, literary, regional and science fiction. "We do not have the staff to do rewrites or heavy copyediting—send clean, legible mss only." No "typical MFA first-person narrative—we like stories, not reportage." Receives 20-25 unsolicited fiction mss/month. Accepts 7-10 mss/year. Does not read June to September. Publishes ms 6 months after acceptance. Publishes short shorts.
How to Contact: Send complete ms with cover letter, name, address and phone. Reports in January each year. Photocopied submissions OK. Accepts computer printouts. Sample copy $3 plus 7x10 SAE with 72¢ postage.
Payment: Pays 2 contributor's copies.
Terms: Acquires one-time rights.
Advice: "Beginning fiction writers should write in a style that is natural, not taught to them by others. More importantly, they should write about subjects they are familiar with. Be prepared for rejection, but good writing will always find a home."

THE MARYLAND REVIEW, Department of English and Modern Languages, University of Maryland Eastern Shore, Princess Anne MD 21853. (301)651-2200, ext. 262. Editor: Chester M Hedgepeth. Magazine: 6×9; 100-150 pages; quality paper stock; heavy cover; illustrations; "possibly" photos. "We have a special interest in black literature, but we welcome all sorts of submissions. Our audience is literary, educated, well-read." Annually. Estab. 1986. Circ. 500.
Needs: Contemporary, humor/satire, literary, mainstream, black. No genre stories; no religious, political or juvenile material. Accepts approx. 12-15 mss/issue. Publishes ms "within 1 year" after acceptance. Published work by John K. Crane, David Jauss; published new writers within the last year. Publishes short shorts. "Length is open, but we do like to include some pieces 1,500 words and under." Also publishes poetry.
How to Contact: Send complete ms with cover letter, which should include a brief autobiography. Reports "as soon as possible." SASE, *but does not return mss*. Photocopied submissions acceptable. No simultaneous submissions. "No fax copies, please." Accepts computer printout submissions. Sample copy for $6.
Payment: Pays in contributor's copies.
Terms: Acquires all rights.
Advice: "Think primarily about your *characters* in fiction, about their beliefs and how they may change. Create characters and situations that are utterly new. We will give your material a careful and considerate reading. Any fiction that is flawed by grammatical errors, misspellings, etc. will not have a chance. We're seeing a lot of fine fiction these days, and we approach each story with fresh and eager eyes. Ezra Pound's battle-cry about poetry refers to fiction as well: 'Make it New!' "

THE MASSACHUSETTS REVIEW, (II), Memorial Hall, University of Massachusetts, Amherst MA 01002. (413)545-2689. Editors: Mary Heath, Jules Chametzky, Paul Jenkins. Magazine: 6×9; 172 pages; 52 lb. paper; 65 lb. vellum cover; illustrations and photos. Quarterly.
Needs: Short stories. Does not read mss June 1-October 1. Published new writers within the last year. Approximately 5% of fiction is agented. Critiques rejected mss when time permits.
How to Contact: Send complete ms. No ms returned without SASE. Reports in 2 months. Publishes ms an average of 9-12 months after acceptance. Sample copy $5.50. Guidelines available for SASE.
Payment: Pays $50 maximum.
Terms: Pays on publication for first North American serial rights.
Advice: "Shorter rather than longer stories preferred (up to 28 pages). There are too many stories about 'relationships,' domestic breakups, etc."

MATI, Ommation Press, 5548 N. Sawyer, Chicago IL 60625. Editor: Effie Mihopoulos. "Primarily a poetry magazine, but we do occasional special fiction and science fiction issues." Quarterly. Estab. 1975. Circ. 1,000.

Needs: Literary, contemporary, science fiction, feminist, translations. No mystery, gothic, western, religious. Receives approximately 20 unsolicited fiction ms each month. Length: 1-2 pages. Also publishes poetry. Occasionally sends ms on to editors of other publications. Sometimes recommends other markets.
How to Contact: Send complete ms with SASE. Reports in 1 week-2 months. Sample copy $1.50 with 9×12 SASE (preferred) plus 90¢ postage.
Payment: Pays 1 contributor's copy; special contributor's rates available for extras.
Terms: Acquires first North American serial rights. "Rights revert to authors but *Mati* retains reprint rights."
Advice: "We want to see good quality writing and a neat ms with sufficient return postage; same size return as outside envelope and intelligent cover letter. Editor to be addressed as 'Dear Sir/Ms' instead of 'Dear Sir' when it's a woman editor."

MERLYN'S PEN, The National Magazine of Student Writing, Grades 7-10, (IV), Box 1058, East Greenwich RI 02818. (401)885-5175. Editor: R. Jim Stahl. Magazine 8⅛×10⅞; 36 pages; 50 lb. paper; 70 lb. gloss cover stock; illustrations; photos. Student writing only—grades 7 through 10, for libraries, homes and English classrooms. Bimonthly (September-April). Estab. 1985. Circ. 22,000.
Needs: Adventure, experimental, fantasy, historical (general), horror, humor/satire, literary, mainstream, regional, romance, science fiction, suspense/mystery, western, young adult/teen, editorial reviews, puzzles, word games, poetry. Must be written by students in grades 7-10. Receives 300 unsolicited fiction mss/month. Accepts 25 mss/issue; 100 mss/year. Publishes ms 3 months to 1 year after acceptance. Length: 1,500 words average; 25 words minimum; 4,000 words maximum. Publishes short shorts. Responds to rejected mss.
How to Contact: Send complete ms and cover letter with name, grade, age, home and school address, home and school telephone number, supervising teacher's name and principal's name. Reports in 10-12 weeks. SASE for ms. Accepts computer printouts. Sample copy for $3.
Payment: Pays 3 contributor's copies, charge for extras. Each author published receives a free copy of *The Elements of Style*.
Terms: Published works become the property of Merlyn's Pen, Inc.
Advice: "Write what you *know*; write where you are."

‡METROPOLITAIN, (II), City of Light Publications, 6307 N. 31st St., Arlington VA 22207. (703)536-4109. Editor: J.L. Bergsohn. Magazine: 5½×8½; 30-40 pages; 24 lb. Hammermill paper; illustrated cover; b&w illustrations. "*Metropolitain* is primarily geared toward showcasing the talents of Washington area writers for a multicultural audience." Quarterly. Estab. 1991. Circ. 250.
Needs: Contemporary, erotica, ethnic, experimental, feminist, gay, humor/satire, lesbian, literary, mainstream, prose poem, regional, translations. Receives 75 unsolicited mss/month. Accepts 2-3 mss/issue; 8-12 mss/year. Publishes ms up to 1 year after acceptance. Length: 5,000 words maximum. Publishes short shorts. Also publishes literary criticism, essays, poetry. Sometimes comments on or critiques rejected mss.
How to Contact: Send complete ms with cover letter. Include brief bio with list of publication credits. Reports in 2 weeks on queries; 4-6 weeks on mss. SASE. Simultaneous, photocopied and reprint submissions OK. Accepts computer printout submissions. Accepts electronic submissions via disk or modem. Sample copy for $3.
Payment: Pays contributor's copies; charges for extras.
Terms: Acquires one-time rights. "Sometimes" sends galleys to author.
Advice: "We look for clean, polished prose and dialogue that rings true. A firm command of both the English language and the craft of fiction writing is imperative. *You* are your own best editor. Every time you re-approach your ms you look at it with an increasingly experienced, discriminating eye. Always give your stories at least six months of maturation before sending them out."

MICHIGAN QUARTERLY REVIEW, University of Michigan, 3032 Rackham, Ann Arbor MI 48109-1070. (313)764-9265. Editor: Laurence Goldstein. "An interdisciplinary journal which publishes mainly essays and reviews, with some high-quality fiction and poetry, for an intellectual, widely read audience." Quarterly. Estab. 1962. Circ. 1,800.
Needs: Literary. No "genre" fiction written for a "market." Receives 200 unsolicited fiction mss/month. Buys 2 mss/issue; 8 mss/year. Published work by Charles Baxter, Bell Gale Chevigny and Jay Neugeboded; published new writers within the last year. Length: 1,500 words minimum; 7,000 words maximum; 5,000 words average. Also publishes poetry, literary essays.

How to Contact: Send complete ms with cover letter. "I like to know if a writer is at the beginning, or further along, in his or her career. Don't offer plot summaries of the enclosed story, though a background comment is welcome." SASE. Photocopied submissions OK. Accepts computer printout submissions (margins *not* justified). Sample copy for $2 and 2 first class stamps.
Payment: Pays $8-10/printed page.
Terms: Pays on publication for first rights. Awards the Lawrence Foundation Prize of $500 for best story in *MQR* previous year.
Advice: "Read back issues to get a sense of tone; level of writing. *MQR* is very selective; only send the very finest, best-plotted, most-revised fiction."

MID-AMERICAN REVIEW, (II), Department of English, Bowling Green State University, Bowling Green OH 43403. (419)372-2725. Fiction Editor: Ellen Behrens. Magazine: 5½ × 8½; 200 pages; 60 lb. bond paper; coated cover stock. "We publish serious fiction and poetry, as well as critical studies in modern literature, translations and book reviews." Biannually. Estab. 1981.
Needs: Experimental, traditional, literary, prose poem, excerpted novel and translations. Receives about 50 unsolicited fiction mss/month. Buys 5-6 mss/issue. Does not read June-August. Approximately 5% of fiction is agented. Recently published work by Steven Schwartz, Eve Shelnut, Philip Graham, Dan O'Brien; published new writers within the last year. Also publishes literary essays, literary criticism, poetry. Occasionally critiques rejected mss. Sometimes recommends other markets.
How to Contact: Send complete ms with SASE. Reports in about 3 months. Publishes ms an average of 3-6 months after acceptance. Sample copy for $4. Reviews novels and short story collections. Send books to reviews editor.
Payment: Pays $7/page up to $50; 2 contributor's copies; $2 charge for extras.
Terms: Pays on publication for one-time rights.
Advice: "We just want *quality* work of whatever vision and/or style. We are now looking for more translated fiction."

THE MIDCOASTER, (II), 2750 N. 45th St., Milwaukee WI 53210. Editor: Peter Blewett. Magazine: 8½ × 11; 48 pages. Literary magazine for a general audience. Annually. Estab. 1988. Circ. 300.
Needs: Contemporary, ethnic, experimental, humor/satire, literary, prose poem, regional, translations. Receives 6-10 unsolicited mss/month. Accepts 4-8 mss/issue. Publishes ms up to one year after acceptance. Published work by Dona Hickey, Jana Harris, José Dalísay. Length: 1,000 words average. Publishes short shorts. Also publishes literary essays, poetry. Sometimes critiques rejected mss.
How to Contact: Query first, or send complete manuscript (with cover letter). Reports in 2 weeks on queries; 8-10 weeks on mss. SASE. Simultaneous and photocopied submissions OK. Accepts computer printout submissions. Sample copy for $4.50. Free fiction guidelines. Reviews novels and short story collections.
Payment: Pays contributor's copies.
Terms: Acquires first rights. Sends galleys to author.

MIDDLE EASTERN DANCER, The International Monthly Magazine of Middle Eastern Dance & Culture, (II), Box 181572, Casselberry FL 32718-1572. (407)831-3402. Editor: Karen Kuzsel. Fiction Editor: Jeanette Spencer. Magazine: 8½ × 11; 36 pages; 60 lb. stock; enamel cover; illustrations; photos. "Our theme is Middle Eastern dance and culture. We run seminar listings, professional directory, astrology geared to dancers, history, interviews, poetry, recipes, reviews of movies, clubs, shows, records, video, costuming, personal beauty care, exercise and dance choreography." Monthly. Estab. 1979. Circ. 2,500.
Needs: No fiction that does not relate to Middle-Eastern dance or culture. Receives 5 unsolicited ms/month. Publishes ms within 4 months after acceptance. Published work by Alan Fisher, Jeanette Larson and Sid Hoskins; published new writers within the last year. *Charges $10 if comments are desired.* Occasionally critiques rejected mss. Recommends other markets.
How to Contact: Send complete ms with cover letter, which should include "background in Middle Eastern dance or culture, why they came to write this story and how they know of the magazine." Reports in 1 month on queries. SASE. Photocopied and reprint submissions OK "if not to other Middle Eastern dance and culture publication." Accepts computer printout submissions. Sample copy $1 or send 9x12 SAE and 75¢ postage.
Payment: Pays $10-25 and 2 contributor's copies.
Terms: Pays on acceptance for one-time rights.
Advice: "Stick strictly to Middle Eastern dance/culture."

‡**MIDLAND REVIEW, An Annual Journal of Contemporary Lit, Lit. Crit. & Art, (II)**, Oklahoma State University, English Dept., Morrill Hall, Stillwater OK 74078. (405)744-9474. Magazine: 6½ × 9½; 100 pages; 80 lb. paper; perfect bond cover stock; illustrations; photos. "A mixed bag of quality work." For "anyone who likes to read and for those that want news that folks in Oklahoma are alive. Publishes 30-40% OSU student material." Annually. Estab. 1985. Circ. 500.

Needs: Ethnic, experimental, feminist, historical (general), horror, literary, prose poem, psychic/ supernatural/occult, regional, science fiction, translations. Receives 15 unsolicited fiction mss/month. Accepts 4 mss/issue. Publishes ms 2-6 months after acceptance. Published work by Jene Friedemann, Steffie Corcoran, Bruce Michael Gans; published new writers within the last year. Length: 4-10 pages double-spaced, typed. Publishes short shorts of 2-4 pages. Also publishes literary essays, literary criticism, poetry.

How to Contact: Send complete manuscript with cover letter. Reports in 6-8 weeks on queries. SASE for ms. Simultaneous and photocopied submissions OK. Accepts computer printouts. Sample copy for $5, 90¢ postage and 9 × 12 SAE. Fiction guidelines for #10 SAE and 1 first class stamp.

Payment: Pays 1 contributor's copy.

Terms: Copyright reverts to author.

Advice: "We want to encourage good student stories by giving them an audience with more established writers."

‡**MIDNIGHT ZOO, (II)**, Experiences Unlimited. P.O. Box 8040, Walnut Creek CA 94596. (415)942-5116. Editor: Jon L. Herron. Fiction Editor: Robert L. Fleck. Magazine: 8½ × 11; 120+ pages; 20 lb. bond paper; 100 lb. glossy cover; b&w illustrations and photographs. "Horror, science fiction and fantasy stories and poems plus science fact, interviews, reviews, writer's information, profiles, strange happenings for all ages interested in this genre." Bimonthly. Estab. 1990. Circ. 3,000+.

Needs: Fantasy, horror, prose poem, psychic/supernatural/occult, science fiction. Publishes annual special fiction issue. In addition to our bimonthly magazine, each year we publish, in December, a 500-600 page anthology of horror, science fiction, fantasy and science fact. We will accept stories up to 15,000 words in the anthology. Receives 120 unsolicited mss/month. Buys 20 mss/issue for bimonthly, 50 mss/issue for anthology; 190+ mss/year. Publishes ms within 2 issues after acceptance. Recently pubished work by Ardath Mayhar, Poul Anderson, Kevin J. Anderson. Length: 3,000 words preferred; 500 words minimum; 10,000 words maximum (except for anthology—15,000). Publishes short shorts. Sometimes critiques rejected mss and recommends other markets.

How to Contact: Send complete ms with cover letter. Include Social Security number, telephone number and a short bio. Reports in 1 month on queries; 2 weeks-3 months on mss. SASE. Simultaneous, photocopied and reprint (very few) submissions OK. Accepts computer printout submissions. Accepts electronic submissions via disk or modem (MicroSoft Word 5, Word Perfect or ASCII). Sample copy for $6. Fiction guidelines for SAE and 1 first class stamp.

Payment: Pays ½-1¢/word, subscription to magazine, contributor's copies, reduced charge for extras.

Terms: Pays on publication for first North American serial rights. Sometimes sends galleys to author.

Advice: "First a ms must be well written and have an original idea or an original twist on an established idea. Good spelling and grammar are important. However, we work with writers who we feel show potential and in many cases have gone through 5 or 6 re-writes in order to get the best possible story from the writer. We remain dedicated to assisting new and under-published writers attain publication through our magazine and have even assisted writers in getting published in other magazines." Sponsors contest: $5 entry fee for stories. Prizes each year—$100 best fiction, 2nd and 3rd prizes and honorable mentions.

MINAS TIRITH EVENING-STAR, (IV), W.W. Publications, Box 373, Highland MI 48357-0373. (813)585-0985. Editor: Philip Helms. Magazine: 8½ × 11; 40+ pages; typewriter paper; black ink illustrations; photos. Magazine of J.R.R. Tolkien and fantasy—fiction, poetry, reviews, etc. for general audience. Quarterly. Published special fiction issue; plans another. Estab. 1967. Circ. 500.

Needs: "Fantasy and Tolkien." Upcoming theme: "J.R.R. Tolkien's 100th Birthday!" Receives 5 unsolicited mss/month. Accepts 1 ms/issue; 5 mss/year. Published new writers within the last year. Length: 1,000-1,200 words preferred; 5,000 words maximum. Also publishes short shorts. Also publishes literary essays, literary criticism, poetry. Occasionally critiques rejected ms.

How to Contact: Send complete ms and bio. Reports in 1 week on queries; 2 weeks on mss. SASE. Photocopied and previously published submissions OK. Accepts computer printout submissions. Sample copy for $1. Reviews novels and short story collections.

Terms: Acquires first rights.
Advice: Goal is "to expand knowledge and enjoyment of J.R.R. Tolkien's and his son Christopher Tolkien's works and their worlds."

MIND IN MOTION, A Magazine of Poetry and Short Prose, (II), Box 1118, Apple Valley CA 92307. (619)248-6512. Editor: Céleste Goyer. Magazine: 5½ × 8½; 54 pages; 20 lb. paper; 50 lb. cover. "We prefer to publish works of substantial brilliance that engage and encourage the readers' mind." Quarterly. Estab. 1985. Circ. 350.
Needs: Experimental, fantasy, humor/satire, literary, prose poem, science fiction. No "mainstream, romance, nostalgia, un-poetic prose; anything with a slow pace or that won't stand up to re-reading." Receives 50 unsolicited mss/month. Buys 5 mss/issue; 40 mss/year. Publishes ms 2 weeks to 3 months after acceptance. Published work by Robert E. Brimhall, Warren C. Miller, Michael K. White. Length: 2,000 words preferred; 250 words minimum; 3,500 words maximum. Also publishes poetry. Sometimes critiques rejected mss and occasionally recommends other markets.
How to Contact: Send complete ms. "Cover letter or bio not necessary." SASE. Simultaneous (if notified) and photocopied submissions OK. Accepts computer printout submissions. Sample copy for $3.50. Fiction guidelines for #10 SAE and 1 first class stamp.
Payment: One contributor's copy when financially possible; charge for extras.
Terms: Acquires first North American serial rights.
Advice: "We look for fiction with no wasted words that demands re-reading, and startles us continually with the knowledge that such genius exists. Send works of cosmic pressure written poetically."

‡MIND MATTERS REVIEW, (I,II), Box 234, 2040 Polk St., San Francisco CA 94109. (415)775-4545. Editor: Carrie Drake. Magazine: 8 1/2 × 11; 30-64 pages; illustrations and photos. "*MMR* is basically a philosophical publication. We have published two short stories that were written in the form of parables." Audience is "conservative intellectually, but liberal fiscally." Quarterly. Estab. 1988. Circ. 1,000.
Needs: Historical (general), literary, prose poem. No "utopian" fiction. Buys 1 ms/issue; 4 mss/year. Publishes ms 6-12 months after acceptance. Recently published Manuel Dominguez and Charles Corry. Length: 800 words preferred; 400 words minimum; 1,000 words maximum.
How to Contact: Query first. Reports in 3 weeks. SASE. Simultaneous, photocopied and reprint submissions OK. Sample copy for $3.50. Fiction guidelines for SASE.
Payment: Pays contributor's copies.
Terms: Acquires one-time rights. Sends galleys to author.
Advice: "A beginning fiction writer for *MMR* should first be familiar with the overall frame of reference of *MMR* and its range of flexibility and limitations. We seek writers who are able to tap moral principles as a source of imagination and inspiration. The moral principle can be atheistic or Christian or Buddhist—whatever—as long as there is a logical structure. Characters and plots do not have to be complex or have stong emotional appeal as long as they draw attention to life experiences that give the reader something to think about."

‡MINDSCAPES, A Literary Magazine of Short Fiction, (II), Juno Press, 2252 Beverly Glen Place, Los Angeles CA 90077. (213)474-0959. Editor: Beverly Bernstein. Magazine: 8½ × 11; 60 pages; 60 lb. paper; illustrations. *Mindscapes* prints "literary and mainstream short story fiction for an educated adult audience." Semiannually. Estab. 1991. Circ. 250.
Needs: Adventure, contemporary, experimental, humor/satire, literary, mainstream. No pornography, no fragments. Publishes annual special fiction issue. Receives 30 unsolicited mss/month. Buys 12 mss/issue; 20-24 mss/year. Publishes ms within 6 months after acceptance. Recently published work by Rachelle Benveniste, Sandra Tsing Loh, Ann Marple, Beverly Olevin. Length: 1500 words preferred; 500 words minimum; 4,000 words maximum. Publishes short shorts. Sometimes critiques rejected mss and recommends other markets.
How to Contact: Send complete ms with cover letter. Include previous publications and one-sentence summary of the story. Reports in 1 month. SASE. Simultaneous submissions OK. Accepts computer printout submissions. Sample copy $7.50.
Payment: Pays free subscription to magazine.
Terms: Acquires one-time rights.
Advice: "Send us clean, correct manuscripts. We are interested in dynamic, unique stories. If you can hold an audience reading it aloud, it stands a good chance for being right for us. Strong characterrs, dramatic plots and tales that touch the heart are what we're looking for. Dense material with obscure symbolism and no point should go to somebody else."

MINNESOTA INK, (II), 27 Empire Dr., St. Paul MN 55103. (612)255-1306. Managing Editor: Valerie Hockert. Variable number of pages; 40 lb. paper; illustrations and photographs. "A bimonthly publication designed to provide guidance and advice as well as inspiration for writers and other people interested in writing (e.g., the college student, the business person)." Monthly. Estab. 1987.
Needs: Adventure, contemporary, experimental, fantasy, humor/satire, mainstream, regional, romance (contemporary, historical), science fiction, senior citizen/retirement, suspense/mystery, western, young adult/teen (12-18 years). Receives about 100 unsolicited mss/month. Publishes mss "usually a couple months" after acceptance. Length: 500 words minimum; 1,500 words maximum. Also publishes poetry. Sometimes critiques rejected mss.
How to Contact: Send complete ms with cover letter and biographical sketch. Reports in 1-2 months. SASE. Photocopied submissions OK. Sample copy for $4. Fiction guidelines for SASE.
Payment: Pays in contributor's copies or subscription.
Terms: Acquires first rights. Sponsors contests and awards for fiction writers. "Contest announcements are published in publication."

THE MINNESOTA REVIEW, A Journal of Committed Writing, (II), English Dept., SUNY-Stony Brook, Stony Brook NY 11794. (516)632-7400. Editors: Helen Cooper, William J. Harris, Michael Sprinker, Susan Squier. Fiction Editor: Fred Pfeil. Magazine: 5¼×8; approximately 160 pages; some illustrations; occasional photos. "We emphasize political writing, favoring especially socialist and feminist work." Semiannually. Estab. 1960. Circ. 1,000.
Needs: Experimental, fantasy, feminist, gay, historical (general), lesbian, literary, science fiction. Receives 20 mss/month. Accepts 3-4 mss/issue; 6-8 mss/year. Publishes ms within 6 months to 1 year after acceptance. Published work by Enid Dame, Ellen Gruber Garvey, John Berger. Length: 5,000-6,000 words preferred. Publishes short shorts. Also publishes literary essays, literary criticism, poetry. Sometimes critiques rejected mss and recommends other markets.
How to Contact: Send complete ms with optional cover letter. Reports in 2-3 weeks on queries; 2-3 months on mss. SASE. Accepts computer printout submissions. Sample copy for $4. Fiction guidelines are free. Reviews novels and short story collections. Send books to book review editor.
Payment: Pays in contributor's copies. Charge for extra copies.
Terms: Acquires first rights.
Advice: "Write good stories with explicit political themes. Read back issues of *MR* for a sense of our collective taste."

MIORITA, A JOURNAL OF ROMANIAN STUDIES, (IV), The Dept. FLLL, Dewey 482, University of Rochester, Rochester NY 14627. (716)275-4258 or (716)275-4251. Co-Editors: Charles Carlton and Norman Simms. Magazine: 5½×8½; Xerox paper; occasional illustrations. Magazine of "essays, reviews, notes and translations on all aspects of Romanian history, culture, language and so on," for academic audience. Annually. Estab. 1973. Circ. 200.
Needs: Ethnic, historical, literary, regional and translations. "All categories contingent upon relationship to Romania." Receives "handful of mss per year." Accepts "no more than one per issue." Length: 2,000 words maximum. Occasionally critiques rejected mss.
How to Contact: Send complete ms. SASE preferred. Previously published work OK (depending on quality). Accepts computer printout submissions.
Payment: "We do not pay."

THE MISS LUCY WESTENRA SOCIETY OF THE UNDEAD, 125 Taylor Street, Jackson TN 38301. (901)427-7714. Editor: Lewis Sanders. Newsletter: "Vampires/Dracula, modern/classic, very, very short fiction." Estab. 1989.
Needs: Vampires. "Very, very short fiction on vampires, Gothic, modern, erotic, but no porno or sleaze. Must be sent camera ready with a proper SASE." Length: 500 words average. Publishes short shorts of 500 words or less.
How to Contact: Send complete ms with cover letter. Reports on queries "as soon as possible." SASE. Simultaneous and reprint submissions OK. Sample copy $5, #10 SAE and 2 first class stamps. Fiction guidelines for #10 SAE and 2 first class stamps.
Payment: Pays 1 contributor's copy.
Terms: Acquires one-time rights. Publication not copyrighted.

MISSISSIPPI REVIEW, (I, II), University of Southern Mississippi, Southern Station, Box 5144, Hattiesburg MS 39406. (601)266-4321. Editor: Frederick Barthelme. "Literary publication for those interested in contemporary literature—writers, editors who read to be in touch with current modes." Semiannually. Estab. 1972. Circ. 1,500.
Needs: Literary, contemporary, fantasy, humor, translations, experimental, avant-garde and "art" fiction. No juvenile. Buys varied amount of mss/issue. Does not read mss in summer. Length: 100 pages maximum.
How to Contact: Send complete ms with SASE including a short cover letter. Accepts computer printout submissions. Sample copy for $5.50.
Payment: Pays in author's copies.
Terms: Acquires first North American serial rights.

MISSISSIPPI VALLEY REVIEW, (III), Western Illinois University, Dept. of English, Simpkins Hall, Macomb IL 61455. Editors: John Mann and Tama Baldwin. Magazine: 64 pages; original art on cover. "A small magazine, *MVR* has won 16 Illinois Arts Council awards in poetry and fiction. We publish stories, poems and reviews." Biannually. Estab. 1971. Circ. 800.
Needs: Literary, contemporary. Upcoming theme: "The Writer as Witness" (Spring, 1992). Does not read mss in summer. Published work by Ray Bradbury, Gwendolyn Brooks, Louise Erdrich, Al Hirschfeld. Also publishes poetry.
How to Contact: Send complete ms with SASE. Reports in 3 months. Sample copy for $5.
Payment: Pays 2 contributor's copies.
Terms: Individual author retains rights.
Advice: "Persistence."

THE MISSOURI REVIEW, (II), 1507 Hillcrest Hall, University of Missouri, Columbia MO 65211. (314)882-4474. Editor: Greg Michalson. Magazine: 6×9; 256 pages. Theme: fiction, poetry, essays, reviews, interviews, cartoons. "All with a distinctly contemporary orientation. For writers, and the general reader with broad literary interests. We present non-established as well as established writers of excellence. The *Review* frequently runs feature sections or special issues dedicated to particular topics frequently related to fiction." Published 3 times/academic year. Estab. 1977. Circ. 2,750.
Needs: Literary, contemporary; open to all categories except juvenile, young adult. Receives approximately 300 unsolicited fiction mss each month. Buys 6-8 mss/issue; 18-25 mss/year. Published new writers within the last year. No preferred length. Also publishes literary essays, poetry. Critiques rejected mss "when there is time."
How to Contact: Send complete ms with SASE. Reports in 10 weeks. Sample copy for $5.
Payment: Pays $20/page minimum.
Terms: Pays on signed contract for all rights.
Advice: Awards William Peden Prize in fiction; $1,000 to best story published in *Missouri Review* in a given year. Also sponsors Editors' Prize Contest with a prize of $750.

‡MOBIUS, The Journal of Social Change, (II), 1149 E. Mifflin, Madison WI 53703. (608)255-4224. Editor: Fred Schepartz. Magazine: 8½×11; 16-32 pages; 60 lb. paper; 60 lb. cover. "Looking for fiction which uses social change as either a primary secondary theme. This is broader than most people think. Need social relevance in one way or another. For an artistically and politically aware and curious audience." Quarterly. Estab. 1989. Circ. 150.
Needs: Contemporary, ethnic, experimental, fantasy, feminist, gay, historical (general) horror, humor/satire, lesbian, literary, mainstream, prose poem, science fiction. "No porn, no racist, sexist or any other kind of ist. No Christian or spiritually proselytizing fiction." Receives 1 unsolicited ms/month. Accepts 2-3 mss/issue. Publishes ms 3-9 months after acceptance. Recently published work by Larry Edgerton, Andrea Masher, Dennis Trudell. Length: 3,500 words preferred; 500 words minimum; 5,000 words maximum. Publishes short shorts. Length: 300 words. Sometimes critiques rejected mss.
How to Contact: Send complete ms with cover letter. Reports in 1-2 months. SASE. Simultaneous, photocopied and reprint submissions OK. Accepts computer printout submissions. Sample copy for $1.25, 9×12 SAE and 3 first class stamps. Fiction guidelines for 9×12 SAE and 4-5 first class stamps.
Payment: Pays contributor's copies.
Terms: Acquires one-time rights.
Advice: Looks for "first and foremost, good writing. Prose must be crisp, polished, story must pique my interest and make me care due to a certain intellectual, emotional aspect. Second, *Mobius* is about social change. We want stories that make some statement about the society we live in, either on a

Close-up

Speer Morgan
Editor
The Missouri Review

"We really take pleasure in [publishing] first stories," says Speer Morgan, editor of *The Missouri Review*. "That is the domain of a good literary magazine. That's what we regard as our territory." He feels discovering new voices is an important part of his job.

Literary magazines offer great opportunities for beginning writers, he says, though he admits the competition, even at low-paying markets, is fierce. "You've got a lot of people banging on the door and the room is small. It's a matter of numbers. There's just a limited number of really decent places to publish."

The Missouri Review, the literary magazine of the University of Missouri, is published three times a year and receives more than 100 stories each week during the school year and between 50 and 60 stories each week during the summer.

Morgan and his staff are always looking for stories that their readers will not forget. "We're concerned to have stories that are memorable," he says, adding that style and technique are secondary to a powerful narrative. "Our taste tends to go to a good story. We like stories that are lively." He bristles at the stereotype of university-supported literary magazines as dry, pompous and boring. "We don't believe a literary magazine is something you just put on the coffee table. We believe the subscribers should read it, should want to read it."

To this end, he and his staff are careful to avoid publishing what he calls "the compromise story," meaning the one that the fewest editors dislike. Instead, he will publish a story that he doesn't especially like if one of his editors is staunchly in favor of it. "When you have a strong response to a story, it implies that something is going on there. You want stories that people are going to talk about, pro and con."

Specifically, Morgan likes stories that feature a "real, authentic voice," and he is constantly seeking the unusual. Like many editors, he sees a great many stories involving the same subject matter: Domestic discord. "People write those stories because it's important. One simply sees too many of them." He also sees too much straight realism, and is on the lookout for "writing that's not stuck in the real world." He is sorry to see so few writers working with magical fiction. "We like it when we see something really unusual," he says. "We've published all kinds of strange things and enjoyed doing it."

Pet peeves, of which Morgan admits he has a few, include stories printed in dot-matrix. As for cover letters, he has no strong opinion. "They're irrelevant," he says. "A list of credits may help get a good reading, but since we're not looking for credentials, it's also fairly irrelevant to us."

His advice to writers is "Don't follow trends. Be true to yourself and try to find your own voice."

—Jack Heffron

macro or micro level. Not that your story needs to preach from a soapbox (actually, we prefer that it doesn't) but your story needs to have *something* to say."

THE MONOCACY VALLEY REVIEW, (II), Mt. St. Mary's College, Emmitsburg MD 21727. (301)447-6122. Editor: William Heath. Fiction Editor: Roser Camiacals-Heath. Magazine: 8½×11; 72 pages; high-quality paper; illustrations and photographs. For readers in the "Mid-Atlantic region; all persons interested in literature." Annually. Estab. 1986. Circ. 500.
Needs: Adventure, contemporary, experimental, historical, humor/satire, literary, mainstream, prose poem reviews. "We would not exclude any categories of fiction, save pornographic or obscene. Our preference is for realistic fiction that dramatizes things that matter." Receives 20-25 unsolicited mss/ month. Buys 3-5 mss/issue. Does not read mss March, October. Publishes ms 6 weeks after acceptance. Published work by Ann Knox; Maxine Combs; Doris Selinsky. Length: 3,000-4,000 words preferred; no minimum; 10,000 words maximum. Also publishes poetry. Sometimes critiques rejected mss.
How to Contact: Query first or ask for submission guidelines. Send 50-word bio. Reports in 4 weeks on queries; 1-4 months on mss. SASE. Simultaneous and photocopied submissions OK. Accepts computer printout submissions. Sample copy for $5. Fiction guidelines for #10 SAE and 1 first class stamp. Reviews novels and short story collections.
Payment: Pays $10-25 and contributor's copies.
Terms: Pays on publication.
Advice: "Be patient in receiving a response. Manuscript readings take place about eight weeks before the publication date (April 15). Submit in Fall and early Winter. I would not advise submitting in November and December. Deadline for submissions: January 15th."

‡THE MONTHLY INDEPENDENT TRIBUNE TIMES JOURNAL POST GAZETTE NEWS CHRONICLE BULLETIN, The Magazine to Which No Superlatives Apply, (II), 1630 Allston Way, Berkeley CA 94703. Editor: T.S. Child. Fiction Editor: Denver Tucson. Magazine: 5½×8; 8 pages; 60 lb. paper; 60 lb. cover; illustrations and photographs. "Our theme is the theme of utter themelessness. We publish anything. In the past, we have published short stories, short short stories, the world's shortest story, plays, game show transcriptions, pictures made of words, teeny-weeny novelinis." Published irregularly. Estab. 1983. Circ. 500.
Needs: Adventure, experimental, humor/satire, preschool (1-4 years), psychic/supernatural/occult, suspense/mystery. "If it's serious, literary, perfect, well-done or elegant, we don't want it. If it's wacky, bizarre, unclassifiable, funny, cryptic or original, we might." Nothing "pretentious; serious; important; meaningful; honest." Receives 10 unsolicited mss/month. Accepts 1-2 mss/issue. Accept manuscripts published in next issue. Length: 400 words preferred. 1,200 words maximum. Publishes short shorts. Length: 400 words. Sometimes critiques rejected mss.
How to Contact: Send complete ms with cover letter. Reports in 2 months. SASE. Photocopied submissions OK. Accepts computer printout submissions. Sample copy $.50, any size SAE and 1 first class stamp.
Payment: Pays free subscription (2 issues); 3 contributor's copies.
Terms: Not copyrighted.
Advice: "First of all, work must be *short*—1,200 words maximum, but the shorter the better. It must make me either laugh or scratch my head, or both. Things that are slightly humorous, or written with any kind of audience in mind are returned. We want writing that is spontaneous, unconscious, boundary-free. If you can think of another magazine that might publish your story, send it to them, not us. Send us your worst, weirdest stories, the ones you're too embarrassed to send anywhere else."

‡THE MOODY STREET REVIEW, (II), Edge Press, Apt. 2, 205 E. 78th St., New York NY 10021. Editor: David Gibson. Magazine: 8½×11; 65-75 lb. cover; illustrations and photographs. "Beat sensitivity, not style—fiction, poetry, nonfiction. For literary, artistic, down to earth bare bones types." Annually. Estab. 1988. Circ. 300.
Needs: Condensed/excerpted novel, contemporary, ethnic, humor/satire, literary, mainstream, regional, translations (from French). Receives 50-75 unsolicited mss/month. Publishes 2 mss/issue. Does not read mss August-April. Recently published work by Rod Kessler, Catherine Gammon. Length: 10,000 words preferred; 5,000 words minimum; 20,000 words maximum. Sometimes critiques rejected mss and recommends other markets.

How to Contact: Reports in 1-3 months on mss. SASE. Sample copy $5 (payable to David Gibson). Fiction guidelines for $1, 5½×8½ SAE and $1-1.50 postage.
Payment: *Charges $1 reading fee.* Pays 2 contributor's copies.
Terms: Not copyrighted.
Advice: "Of course, use of vivid imagery and sentence rhythm are important. But most of all, a proportionate sense of distance between the narrator—whether, it be an omniscient or limited one—and the subjects of a given story is the hardest to achieve. Stories should have all of these aspects as well as emotionally involving the reader in the very first few sentences. This does not, of course, mean it should imitate the pseudo-pathos and melodrama of television programs. As long as a character's feelings stand out, as a real person's would—that is what will draw a reader into the story. Know what a beat sensitivity is. Read Blake, Whitman, the symbolist poets, Thomas Wolfe, the surrealist poets; and so on. Don't imitate, emulate, and know the difference between these two words."

‡**MOON, (II),** Qamar Illustrated, #1R, 211 W. 21st St., New York NY 10011. (212)727-3441. Co-Editors: Kevin Gray, Nelson Kim, Cameron McWhirter and Margaret Mittelbach. Magazine: 8 1/2×11; 40 pages; card cover; illustrations and photographs. "*Moon* prints quality writing, all styles—fiction, poetry, nonfiction—for a cryptic, squamous audience." Published 3 times/year. Estab. 1991. Circ. 300.
Needs: Contemporary, ethnic, experimental, feminist, gay, horror, humor/satire, lesbian, literary, prose poem, psychic/supernatural/occult, translations. Special interest in "conspiracy" and "paranoid" fiction. No "relationship stories. Standard boyfriend/girlfriend trauma." Receives 5 unsolicited mss/month. Buys 5-8 mss/issue; 15-24 mss/year. Publishes ms 2-3 months after acceptance. Recently published work by Peter Meinke, Percy Magnus and Sono Motoyama. Length: 300 words minimum; 3,000 words maximum. Publishes short shorts. Sometimes critiques rejected mss.
How to Contact: Send complete ms with cover letter. Reports in 6 weeks. SASE. Simultaneous, photocopied and reprint submissions OK. Accpets computer printout submissions. Sample copy for $3.50.
Payment: Pays contributor's copies.
Terms: Acquires one-time rights. Sends galleys to author.
Advice: "We're trying to encourage good, new American writing that helps define the times we live (or don't live) in and the times to come."

‡**MOSAIC, A Torch Magazine of the Arts, (II, IV),** 318 Ave. F, Brooklyn NY 11218. Editor: Y. David Shulman. Magazine: illustrations. "Forum for writers and artists involved with Torah stories, translations, poetry, interviews, artwork. For those interested in literature and the arts and the Judaic tradition." Published irregularly. Estab. 1990. Circ. 500.
Needs: Excerpted novel, contemporary, ethnic, experimental, fantasy, historical (general) humor/satire, literary, mainstream, prose poem, religious/inspirational, science fiction, translations, young adult. Accepts 1-2 mss/issue. Length: 3,000 words preferred; 1,000 words minimum; 6,000 words maximum. Publishes short shorts. Sometimes critiques rejected mss.
How to Contact: Query with clips of published work or send complete ms with cover letter. Reports in 2 weeks. SASE. Simultaneous, photocopied and reprint submissions OK. Accepts computer printout submissions. Accepts electronic submissions via disk or modem. Sample copy for $2.
Payment: Pays contributor's copies.
Terms: Sends galleys to author.
Advice: "Provides a forum for Torah-involved writers and artists."

THE MOUNTAIN LAUREL, Monthly Journal of Mountain Life, Foundation Inc., P.O. Box 562, Wytheville VA 24382. (703)228-7282. Editor: Susan M. Thigpen. Tabloid: 28 pages; newsprint, illustrations and photographs. "Everyday details about life in the Blue Ridge Mountains of yesterday, for people of all ages interested in folk history." Monthly. Estab. 1983. Circ. 20,000.
Needs: Historical, humor, regional. "Stories must fit our format—we accept seasonal stories. There is always a shortage of good Christmas stories. A copy of our publication will be your best guidelines as to what we want. We will not even consider stories containing bad language, sex, gore, horror." Receives approximately 40 unsolicited fiction mss/month. Accepts up to 5 mss/issue; 60 mss/year. Publishes ms 2 to 6 months after acceptance. Length: 500-600 words average; no minimum; 1,000 words maximum. Publishes short shorts. Length 300 words. Sometimes critiques rejected mss. Recommends other markets.

How to Contact: Send complete ms with cover letter, which should include "an introduction to the writer as though he/she were meeting us in person." Reports in 1 month. SASE. Simultaneous and photocopied submissions OK. Accepts computer printout submissions. Sample copy for 9×12 SAE and 5 first class stamps. Fiction guidelines for #10 SAE and 1 first class stamp.

Payment: Pays in contributor's copies.

Terms: Acquires one-time rights.

Advice: "Tell a good story. Everything else is secondary. A tightly written story is much better than one that rambles. Short stories have no room to take off on tangents. *The Mountain Laurel* has published the work of many first-time writers as well as works by James Still and John Parris. First publication ever awarded the Blue Ridge Heritage Award."

MOVING OUT, Feminist Literary & Arts Journal, (IV), Box 21249, Detroit MI 48221. Contact: Margaret Kaminski, co-editor. Magazine: 8½×11; 75 pages; medium paper; heavy cover; illustrations; photos. Magazine of "material which captures the experience of women, for feminists and other humane human beings." Annually. Estab. 1970. Circ. 1,000.

Needs: Feminist, lesbian and senior citizen/retirement. No androcentric creations. Accepts about 10-20 mss/issue. Published poetry by Jan Worth and Denise Bergman. Occasionally critiques rejected mss.

How to Contact: Send complete ms with SASE. Accepts computer printout submissions. Reports in 6-12 months. Sample copy for $9 (old issue $3.50); guidelines for SASE.

Payment: Pays 1 contributor's copy.

Terms: Acquires first rights.

Advice: "We like to see work that explores women's aesthetics, as well as that which represents varied experiences of the poor, the handicapped, the minorities, the lonely. Be fearless. Do not add to the mountains of sappy poetry and prose out there. Show us the reality of what you know, not what you think might sound 'poetic'."

MYSTERY NOTEBOOK (Ashenden), (II, IV), Box 1341, F.D.R. Station, New York NY 10150. Editor: Stephen Wright. Journal and Newsletter: 8½×11; 10-16 pages and occasional double issues; photocopied; self cover; illustrations and photos sometimes. "Mystery books, news, information; reviews and essays. Ashendon section is devoted to Somerset Maugham and his works." For mystery readers and writers and for Maugham readers and scholars. Quarterly. Estab. 1984. Circ. (approx.) 1,000.

Needs: Excerpted novel (suspense/mystery). Receives few unsolicited mss. Length: brief. Short shorts considered. Also publishes articles and essays (brief) on Maugham and his works. Occasionally comments on rejected ms.

How to Contact: Query. Reports in 3 weeks on queries; 1 month on mss. SASE for ms. Photocopied and previously published submissions OK (if query first). Sample copies or back issues $7.50 double issues $15.

Payment: None. "If author is a regular contributor, he or she will receive complimentary subscription. Usually contributor receives copies of the issue in which contribution appears."

Advice: "Mystery magazines use all kinds of stories in various settings. This is also true of mystery books except that no matter what kind of detective is the protagonist (private eye, amateur, police and all the rest) the novel must be the best of its kind—even for consideration. Mystery fiction books have increased in demand—*but* the competition is more keen than ever. So only those with real talent *and* a superb knowledge of mystery-writing craft have any chance for publication. It also helps if you know and understand the current market."

MYSTERY TIME, An Anthology of Short Stories, (I), Box 1870, Hayden ID 83835. (208)772-6184. Editor: Linda Hutton. Booklet: 5½×8½; 44 pages; bond paper; illustrations. "Annual collection of short stories with a suspense or mystery theme for mystery buffs." Estab. 1983.

Needs: Suspense/mystery only. Receives 10-15 unsolicited fiction mss/month. Accepts 10-12 mss/year. Published work by Elizabeth Lucknell, Loretta Sallman Jackson, Vickie Britton. Published new writers within the last year. Length: 1,500 words maximum. Occasionally critiques rejected mss and recommends other markets.

How to Contact: Send complete ms with SASE. "No cover letters." Simultaneous, photocopied and previously published submissions OK. Accepts computer printout submissions. Reports in 1 month on mss. Publishes ms an average of 6-8 months after acceptance. Sample copy for $3.50. Fiction guidelines for #10 SAE and 1 first class stamp.

Realizing the market for murder mysteries was small, Linda Hutton, admittedly a lover of the genre, decided to create one more place for mystery writers to submit their work. Thus, Mystery Time, an annual anthology of short stories with a suspense/mystery theme, was born. The latest issue, pictured here, uses clip art as illustration. The man seated in the chair appears to be "kind of like a villain in a melodrama," Hutton says. She hopes this "reader" will encourage the reading of more suspense/mystery fiction. As editor, Hutton also stresses that a strong plot is the key to inclusion in her publication.

Payment: Pays ¼¢/word minimum; 1¢/word maximum; 1 contributor's copy; $2.50 charge for extras
Terms: Acquires one-time rights. Buys reprints. Sponsors annual short story contest.
Advice: "Study a sample copy and the guidelines. Too many amateurs mark themselves as amateurs by submitting blind."

THE MYTHIC CIRCLE, (I), The Mythopoeic Society, Box 6707, Altadena CA 91001. Co-Editors: Tina Cooper and Christine Lowentrout. Magazine: 8½ × 11; 50 pages; high quality photocopy paper; illustrations. "A tri-quarterly fantasy-fiction magazine. We function as a 'writer's forum,' depending heavily on letters of comment from readers. We have a very occasional section called 'Mythopoeic Youth' in which we publish stories written by writers still in high school/junior high school, but we are not primarily oriented to young writers. We have several 'theme' issues (poetry, American fantasy) and plan more of these in the future." Triquarterly. Estab. 1987. Circ. 150.
Needs: Short fantasy. "No erotica, no graphic horror, no 'hard' science fiction." Receives 25 + unsolicited ms/month. Accepts 19-20 mss/issue. Publishes ms 2-8 months after acceptance. Published work by Charles de Lint, Gwyneth Hood, Angelee Sailer Anderson; published new writers within the last year. Length: 3,000 words average. Publishes short shorts. Length: 8,000 words maximum. Always critiques rejected mss; may recommend other markets."
How to Contact: Send complete ms with cover letter. "We give each ms a personal response. We get many letters that try to impress us with other places they've appeared in print—that doesn't matter much to us." Reports in 6-12 weeks. SASE. Photocopied submissions OK; no simultaneous submissions. Accepts computer printout submissions and IBM or MAC floppies. Sample copy for $5.50; fiction guidelines for #10 SASE.
Payment: Pays in contributor's copies; charges for extras.
Terms: Acquires one-time rights.
Advice: "There are very few places a fantasy writer can send to these days. *Mythic Circle* was started up because of this; also, the writers were not getting any kind of feedback when (after nine or ten months) their mss were rejected. We give the writers personalized attention—critiques, suggestions—and we rely on our readers to send us letters of comment on the stories we publish, so that the writers can see a response. Don't be discouraged by rejections, especially if personal comments/suggestions are offered."

‡NAHANT BAY, (II), What Cheer Press, 45 Puritan Rd., Swampscott MA 01907. (617)595-3722. Editors: Kim A. Pederson and Kalo Clarke. Magazine: 5¼ × 8½; 60-65 pages; 20 lb. bond paper; illustrations and photographs. "Short stories, essays and poetry for those interested in quality fiction." Annually. Estab. 1990.

Needs: Adventure, condensed/excerpted novel, contemporary, erotica, ethnic, experimental, fantasy, feminist, gay, historical, horror, humor/satire, lesbian, literary, mainstream, prose poem, psychic/supernatural/occult, regional, science fiction, suspense/mystery, translations. No romance, juvenile, teen, religious, confession. Receives 5-10 unsolicited mss/month. Accepts 2-3 mss/issue. Recently published work by Sue William Silverman, Michael Kramer, Patricia Flinn. Length: 1,250 words minimum; 2,500 words maximum. Publishes short shorts. Sometimes critiques rejected mss and recommends other markets.

How to Contact: Send complete ms with cover letter. Include brief biographical information. Reports in 2 months on mss. SASE. Simultaneous, photocopied submissions OK. Accepts computer printout submissions. Accepts electronic submissions via disk or modem. Sample copy for $4, SAE and 5 first class stamps. Fiction guidelines for #10 SAE and 1 first class stamp.

Payment: Pays contributor's copies. Charge for extras.

Terms: Acquires first North American serial rights.

Advice: Looks for striking use of language; compelling characters and story; sense of humor; sense of irony.

‡**NASSAU REVIEW, (I, II),** Nassau Community College, State University of New York, Stewart Ave., Garden City NY 11596. (516)222-7186. Editor: Paul A. Doyle. Fiction Editor: Virginia A. Moran. Magazine: 5½ × 8½; 80-120 pages; heavy stock paper; b&w illustrations and photographs. For "college teachers, libraries, educated college-level readers." Annually. Estab. 1964.

Needs: Contemporary, fantasy, historical (general), literary, mainstream, serialized novel. Receives 2 unsolicited mss/month. Accepts 5 mss/issue. Does not read mss January-August. Publishes ms 6 months after acceptance. Recently published work by Dick Wimmer, Louis Phillips, Norbert Petsch. Length: 800-1,500 words preferred; 1,000 words minimum; 1,500 words maximum. Publishes short shorts.

How to Contact: Send complete ms with cover letter. Include basic publication data. Reports in 1 month on queries; 6 months on mss. SASE. Simultaneous submissions OK. Accepts computer printout submissions. Sample copy for 9 × 12 SAE.

Payment: No payment.

Terms: Acquires first rights or one-time rights.

Advice: Looks for "imaginative, concrete writing on interesting characters and scenes." Send story ms before Oct. 31. $150 prize to best story published each year.

NCASA JOURNAL, A Publication of the National Coalition Against Sexual Assault, (II), Suite 500, 123 S. 7th St., Springfield IL 62701, (217)753-4117. Editor: Becky Bradway. Newsletter: 8½ × 11; 12-16 pages; illustrations and photographs. "*NCASA Journal* is a forum for commentary, information and creative work concerning sexual assault and the anti-sexual assault movement." Quarterly. Estab. 1985. Circ. 850.

Needs: Condensed/excerpted novel, contemporary, ethnic, experimental, feminist, gay, humor/satire, literary, prose poem, regional, serialized novel, translations. Fiction and poetry are included in a special section, "Voices of Survivors." Work should be written by survivors of rape or incest. "All fiction must be grounded in a feminist perspective. We will not accept work that is racist, classist, or heterosexist." Accepts 1-2 mss/issue; 4-6 mss/year. Publishes ms up to 1 year after acceptance. Length: 3,000 words average; 500 words minimum; 5,000 words maximum. Publishes short shorts. Sometimes critiques rejected mss and recommends other markets.

How to Contact: Send complete manuscript with cover letter. Include publication and professional background, if any. Reports in 6 weeks on mss. SASE. Simultaneous and reprint submissions OK. Accepts computer printout submissions. Sample copy $4. Fiction guidelines for SASE and 1 first class stamp.

Market conditions are constantly changing! If you're still using this book and it is 1993 or later, buy the newest edition of Novel & Short Story Writer's Market at your favorite bookstore or order directly from Writer's Digest Books.

Payment: Pays 3 contributor's copies.
Terms: Acquires first rights.
Advice: "*NCASA Journal* is looking for well-written, thoughtful fiction and poetry from survivors of rape and incest. Fiction may be based upon personal experience, but should utilize the mechanics of the story form: plot, characterization, dialogue, etc. Think through your story. Spend time with it. Revise it, many times. A strong scene showing an experience is almost always more powerful than a personal monologue."

NEBO, A Literary Journal, (I), Arkansas Tech University, Dept. of English, Russellville AR 72801. (501)968-0256. Contact: Editor. Literary, fiction and poetry magazine: 5×8; 50-60 pages. For a general, academic audience. Annually. Estab. 1983. Circ. 500.
Needs: Literary, mainstream, reviews. Upcoming theme: "Fantastic Literature," ghost stories, supernatural and science fiction, metaphysical experimental fiction (Nov. 15, 1992). Receives 20-30 unsolicited fiction mss/month. Accepts 2 mss/issue; 6-10 mss/year. Does not read mss May 1-Sept. 1. Published new writers within the last year. Length: 3,000 words maximum. Also publishes literary essays, literary criticism, poetry. Occasionally critiques rejected mss.
How to Contact: Send complete ms with SASE and cover letter with bio. Accepts computer printout submissions. Reports in 3 months on mss. Publishes ms an average of 6 months after acceptance. Sample copy $5. "Submission deadlines for all work are Nov. 15 and Jan. 15 of each year." Reviews novels and short story collections.
Payment: Pays 1 contributor's copy.
Terms: Acquires one-time rights.
Advice: "A writer should carefully edit his short story before submitting it. Write from the heart and put everything on the line. Don't write from a phony or fake perspective. Frankly, many of the manuscripts we receive should be publishable with a little polishing. Manuscripts should *never* be submitted with misspelled words or on 'onion skin' or colored paper."

THE NEBRASKA REVIEW, (II), University of Nebraska at Omaha, ASH 212, Omaha NE 68182-0324. (402)554-2771. Fiction Editor: James Reed. Magazine: 5½×8½; 72 pages; 60 lb. text paper; chrome coat cover stock. "*TNR* attempts to publish the finest available contemporary fiction and poetry for college and literary audiences." Publishes 2 issues/year. Estab. 1973. Circ. 500.
Needs: Contemporary, humor/satire, literary and mainstream. Receives 40 unsolicited fiction mss/month. Accepts 4-5 mss/issue, 8-10 mss/year. Does not read April 1-September 1. Published work by Elizabeth Evans, Stephen Dixon and Peter Leach; published new writers within the last year. Length: 5,000-6,000 words average. Also publishes poetry.
How to Contact: Send complete ms with SASE. Photocopied submissions OK. Reports in 1-2 months. Publishes ms an average of 6-9 months after acceptance. Sample copy $2.50.
Payment: 2 free contributor's copies plus 1 year subscription; $2 charge for extras.
Terms: Acquires first North American serial rights.
Advice: "Write 'honest' stories in which the lives of your characters are the primary reason for writing and techniques of craft serve to illuminate, not overshadow, the textures of those lives. Sponsors a $300 award/year—write for rules."

NEGATIVE CAPABILITY (II), A Literary Quarterly, 62 Ridgelawn Dr. E., Mobile AL 36608. (205)661-9114. Editor-in-Chief: Sue Walker. Managing Editor: Richard G. Beyer. Magazine: 5½×8½; 160 pages; 70 lb. offset paper; 4 color/varnish cover stock; illustrations; photos. Magazine of short fiction, prose poems, poetry, criticism, commentaries, journals and translations for those interested in contemporary trends, innovations in literature. Triquarterly. Estab. 1981. Circ. 1,000.
Needs: Adventure, contemporary, ethnic, experimental, fantasy, feminist, gothic/historical romance, historical (general), literary, prose poem, psychic/supernatural/occult, regional, romance (contemporary), science fiction, senior citizen/retirement, suspense/mystery, translations. Accepts 2-3 mss/issue, 6-10 mss/year. Does not read July-Sept. Publishes short shorts. Published work by A.W. Landwehr, Gerald Flaherty and Richard Moore; published new writers within the last year. Length: 1,000 words minimum. Also publishes literary essays, literary criticism. Sometimes recommends other markets.
How to Contact: Query or send complete ms. SASE. Reports in 2 weeks on queries; 6 weeks on mss. Publishes ms an average of 6 months after acceptance. Sample copy $5. Reviews novels and short story collections.

Payment: Pays 2 contributor's copies.
Terms: Acquires first rights, first North American serial rights or one-time rights. Sends galleys to author.
Advice: "We consider all manuscripts and often work with new authors to encourage and support. We believe fiction answers a certain need that is not filled by poetry or nonfiction." Annual fiction competition. Deadline Dec. 1.

‡NEOPHYTE, (I, IV), Jemar Publishing, 11220 Hooper Rd., Baton Rouge LA 70818-3803. (504)261-4251. Editor: Jeffery W. Behrnes. Magazine: digest-sized; 40 pages; bond paper; illustrations. "Science fiction/science fiction short stories." Bimonthly. Estab. 1991. Circ. 100.
Needs: Science fiction and articles on writing science fiction. Plans special fiction issue in the future. Receives 20-40 unsolicited mss/month. Accepts 2-4 mss/issue; 12-20 mss/year. Publishes ms 2-3 months after acceptance. Recently published work by J. Walker Bell, Steve Antczak. Length: 3,000 words preferred; 2,000 words minimum; 10,000 words maximum. Sometimes critiques rejected mss and recommends other markets.
How to Contact: Send complete ms with cover letter. Include "short description of story and brief background on author (introduce yourself)." Reports in 2-4 weeks. SASE. Photocopied and reprint submissions OK. Accepts computer printout submissions. Accepts electronic submissions via disk (IBM, ASCII or WordPerfect). Sample copy for $2. Fiction guidelines for #10 SAE and 1 first class stamp.
Payment: Pays in contributor's copies. Charge for extras.
Terms: Acquires one-time rights.
Advice: "The criteria used are that the story *is* a story in the science fiction genre and that it contains all components that make it a story. Read lots of science fiction, both the classics and the experimental. We work with new or previously unpublished authors."

THE NEW CRUCIBLE, A Magazine About Man and His Environment, (I), RRI, Box 76, Stark KS 66775-9802. Editor: Garry De Young. Magazine: 8½ × 11; variable number of pages; 20 lb. paper; soft cover; illustrations and photographs. Publishes "environmental material – includes the total human environment." Monthly. Plans special fiction issue. Estab. 1964.
Needs: Atheist. "Keep material concise, use clear line drawings. Environmentalists must be Materialists because the environment deals with matter. Thus also evolutionists. Keep this in mind. Manuscripts not returned. Will not accept religious or other racist or sexist material." Length: concise preferred. Publishes short shorts. Also publishes literary criticism, poetry. Sometimes critiques rejected mss. Publishes original cartoons.
How to Contact: Send complete ms with cover letter. Cover letter should include "biographical sketch of author." SASE. Simultaneous, photocopied and reprint submissions OK. Accepts computer printout submissions. Sample copy for $2, 9 × 12 SAE and 4 first class stamps.
Payment: Pays in contributor's copies.
Terms: *Charges $1/page reading fee.* "Will discuss rights with author."
Advice: "Be gutsy! Don't be afraid to attack superstitionists. Attack those good people who remain so silent – people such as newspaper editors, so-called scientists who embrace superstition such as the Jesus myth or the Virgin Mary nonsense. We publish the works of Elbert Hubbard and also the Haldeman-Julius Little Blue Books which were the forerunners of the present paperbacks. Many are considered taboo by local libraries. We also solicit material critical of Zionist expansionism."

NEW DELTA REVIEW, (II), English Dept./Louisiana State University, Baton Rouge LA 70803. (504)388-5922. Editor: Janet Wondra. Fiction Editor: David Racine. Magazine: 6 × 9; 75-125 pages; high quality paper; glossy card cover; illustrations; photographs. "No theme or style biases. Poetry, fiction primarily; also creative essays, literary interviews and reviews." Semi-annually. Estab. 1984.
Needs: Contemporary, experimental, humor/satire, literary, mainstream, prose poem, translations. Receives 120 unsolicited mss/ month. Accepts 4-8 mss/issue. Recently published work by Susan Sonde, John McNally, Jacques Servin, Beth Meekins; (awarded Pushcart Prize, 1990-1991, for Thomas E. Kennedy's "Murphy's Angel"); published new writers within the last year. Length: 2,500 words average; 250 words minimum. Publishes short shorts. Also publishes poetry. Sometimes critiques rejected mss.
How to Contact: Send complete ms with cover letter. Cover letter should include "credits, if any; no synopses, please." Reports on mss in 6-8 weeks. SASE. Mss deadlines September 30 for fall; March 1 for spring. Prefers photocopied submissions. Sample copy $4. Reviews novels and short story collections.

Payment: Pays in contributor's copies. Charge for extras.
Terms: Acquires first North American serial rights. Sponsors award for fiction writers in each issue. Eyster Prize-$50 plus notice in magazine. Mss selected for publication are automatically considered.
Advice: "The question we are asked most is still what *kind* of fiction we like. We answer: The good kind. Be brave. Explore your voice. Make sparks fly off your typewriter. Send your best work, even if others have rejected it. And don't forget the SASE if you want a response."

NEW FRONTIER, (IV), 46 North Front, Philadelphia PA 19106. (215)627-5683. Editor: Sw. Virato. Magazine: 8 × 10; 48-60 pages; pulp paper stock; illustrations and photos. "We seek new age writers who have imagination yet authenticity." Monthly. Estab. 1981. Circ. 60,000.
Needs: New age. "A new style of writing is needed with a transformation theme." Receives 10-20 unsolicited mss/month. Accepts 1-2 mss/issue. Publishes ms 3 months after acceptance. Agented fiction "less than 5%." Published work by John White, Laura Anderson; published work by new writers within the last year. Length: 1,000 words average; 750 words minimum; 2,000 words maximum. Publishes short shorts. Length: 150-500 words. Occasionally critiques rejected mss and recommends other markets.
How to Contact: Send complete ms with cover letter, which should include author's bio and credits. Reports in 2 months on mss. SASE for ms. Simultaneous, photocopied and reprint submissions OK. Accepts computer printout submissions. Sample copy for $2. Fiction guidelines for #10 SAE and 1 first class stamp.
Terms: Acquires first North American serial rights and one-time rights.
Advice: "The new age market is ready for a special kind of fiction and we are here to serve it. Don't try to get an A on your term paper. Be sincere, aware and experimental. Old ideas that are senile don't work for us. Be fully alive and aware—tune in to our new age audience/readership."

‡NEW KENT QUARTERLY, (II), S.P.P.C., Kent State University, Box 26, Student Activities, Kent OH 44242. Editor: Kimberly A. Littlepage. Magazine: 8½ × 11; 50 pages; b&w illustrations and photographs. "The *NKQ* is a poetry, short story, photography and art annual." Annually. Estab. 1975. Circ. up to 2,000.
Needs: Open. Receives 3-4 unsolicited mss/month. Does not read mss in summer months. Publishes short shorts. Sometimes comments on rejected mss and recommends other markets.
How to Contact: Send complete ms with cover letter. SASE. Simultaneous, photocopied and reprint submissions OK. Accepts computer printout submissions. Free sample copy. Fiction guidelines for #10 SAE.
Payment: Pays in contributor's copies.
Terms: Acquires one-time rights. Rights revert to author after 60 days.

NEW LAUREL REVIEW, (II), 828 Lesseps St., New Orleans LA 70117. Editor: Lee Meitzen Grue. Magazine: 6 × 9; 120 pages; 60 lb. book paper; Sun Felt cover; illustrations; photo essays. Journal of poetry, fiction, critical articles and reviews. "We have published such internationally known writers as James Nolan, Tomris Uyar and Yevgeny Yevtushenko." Readership: "Literate, adult audiences as well as anyone interested in writing with significance, human interest, vitality, subtlety, etc." Annually. Estab. 1970. Circ. 500.
Needs: Literary, contemporary, fantasy and translations. No "dogmatic, excessively inspirational or political" material. Accepts 1-2 fiction mss/issue. Receives approximately 50 unsolicited fiction mss each month. Length: about 10 printed pages. Also publishes literary essays, literary criticism, poetry. Critiques rejected mss when there is time.
How to Contact: Send complete ms with SASE. Reports in 3 months. Sample copy $6. Reviews novels and short story collections.
Payment: Pays 1 contributor's copy.
Terms: Acquires first rights.
Advice: "We are interested in international issues pointing to libraries around the world. Write fresh, alive 'moving' work. Not interested in egocentric work without any importance to others. Be sure to watch simple details such as putting one's name and address on ms and clipping all pages together. Caution: Don't use overfancy or trite language."

NEW LETTERS MAGAZINE, (I, II), University of Missouri-Kansas City, 5100 Rockhill Rd., Kansas City MO 64110. (816)235-1168. FAX: (816)235-5191. Editor: James McKinley. Magazine: 14 lb. cream paper; illustrations. Quarterly. Estab. 1971 (continuation of *University Review*, founded 1935). Circ. 2,500.

Needs: Contemporary, ethnic, experimental, humor/satire, literary, mainstream, translations. No "bad fiction in any genre." Published work by Richard Rhodes, Jascha Kessler, Josephine Jacobsen; published work by new writers within the last year. Agented fiction: 10%. Also publishes short shorts. Occasionally critiques rejected mss.
How to Contact: Send complete ms with cover letter. Does not read mss May 15-October 15. Reports in 3 weeks on queries; 6-8 weeks on mss. SASE for ms. Photocopied submissions OK. No multiple submissions. Accepts computer printouts. Sample copy: $8.50 for issues older than 5 years; $5.50 for 5 years or less.
Payment: Honorarium—depends on grant/award money; 2 contributor's copies. Sends galleys to author.
Advice: "Seek publication of representative chapters in high-quality magazines as a way to the book contract. Try literary magazines first."

NEW METHODS, The Journal of Animal Health Technology, (IV), Box 22605, San Francisco CA 94122-0605. (415)664-3469. Editor: Ronald S. Lippert, AHT. Newsletter ("could become magazine again"): 8½×11; 4-6 pages; 20 lb. paper; illustrations; "rarely" photos. Network service in the animal field educating services for mostly professionals in the animal field; e.g. animal health technicians. Monthly. Estab. 1976. Circ. 5,608.
Needs: Animals: adventure, condensed novel, contemporary, experimental, historical, mainstream, regional. No stories unrelated to animals. Receives 12 unsolicited fiction mss/month. Buys one ms/issue; 12 mss/year. Length: Open. "Rarely" publishes short shorts. Occasionally critiques rejected mss. Recommends other markets.
How to Contact: Query first with theme, length, expected time of completion, photos/illustrations, if any, biographical sketch of author, all necessary credits or send complete ms. Report time varies. SASE for query and ms. Simultaneous and photocopied submissions OK. Accepts computer printouts. Sample copy $2 for *NSSWM* readers. Fiction guidelines for #10 SAE and 1 first class stamp.
Payment: Varies.
Terms: Pays on publication for one-time rights.
Advice: Sponsors contests: theme changes but is generally the biggest topics of the year in the animal field. "Emotion, personal experience—make the person feel it. We are growing."

NEW MEXICO HUMANITIES REVIEW, (II), Humanities Dept., New Mexico Tech, Box A, Socorro NM 87801. (505)835-5445. Editors: John Rothfork and Jerry Bradley. Magazine: 5½×9½; 150 pages; 60 lb. Lakewood paper; 482 ppi cover stock; illustrations; photos. Review of poetry, essays and prose of Southwest. Readership: academic but not specialized. Published 2 times/year. Estab. 1978. Circ. 650.
Needs: Literary and regional. "No formula." Accepts 40-50 mss/year. Receives approximately 50 unsolicited fiction mss/month. Length: 6,000 words maximum. Publishes short shorts. Critiques rejected mss "when there is time." Sometimes recommends other markets.
How to Contact: Send complete ms with SASE. Accepts computer printout submissions. Reports in 2 months. Publishes ms an average of 6 months after acceptance. Sample copy $5.
Payment: 1 year subscription.
Terms: Sends galleys to author.
Advice: Mss are rejected because they are "unimaginative, predictable and technically flawed. Don't be afraid to take literary chances—be daring, experiment."

NEW ORLEANS REVIEW, (II), Box 195, Loyola University, New Orleans LA 70118. (504)865-2294. Editor: John Mosier. Magazine: 8½×11; 100 pages; 60 lb. Scott offset paper; 12+ King James C1S cover stock; photos. "Publishes poetry, fiction, translations, photographs, nonfiction on literature and film. Readership: those interested in current culture, literature." Quarterly. Estab. 1968. Circ. 1,000.
Needs: Literary, contemporary, translations. Buys 9-12 mss/year. Length: under 40 pages.
How to Contact: Send complete ms with SASE. Does not accept simultaneous submissions. Accepts computer printout submissions. Accepts disk submissions; inquire about system compatibility. Prefers hard copy with disk submission. Reports in 3 months. Sample copy $9.
Payment: "Inquire."
Terms: Pays on publication for first North American serial rights. Sends galleys to author.

‡NEW PATHWAYS, Into Science Fiction and Fantasy, (II), P.O. Box 475174, Garland TX 75047-5174. Editor: Michael G. Adkisson. Magazine: 8×10¾; 60-70 pages; uncoated stock; enamel 2-color cover; 13-20 illustrations per issue. "We like literary quality SF and fantasy. We want a nice blend of traditional and avant-garde work for sophisticated readers of SF with a sense of humor and adventure. We also run film reviews with photos." Quarterly. Estab. 1986. Circ. 1,200.

Needs: Experimental, fantasy, literary, mainstream "if it's off the wall," science fiction, translations. No "lousy fiction, Dick and Jane fiction." No more than one submission at a time. Receives 30-50 unsolicited mss/month. Buys 4-5 mss/issue; approximately 20 mss/year. Publishes ms generally within the next 4 issues. Length: 2,000-5,000 words average; 5,000 words maximum. Occasionally critiques rejected mss or recommends other markets.

How to Contact: Send complete ms with cover letter. "The cover letter is very important! I like to have publishing history, biographical note, a note on the story if appropriate, comments on own work or on the magazine." Reports in 2 weeks on queries; 4-6 weeks on mss. SASE. Photocopied submissions OK. Accepts computer printout submissions. Query for electronic submission info. Sample copy for $4, SAE and $1 postage. Fiction guidelines for #10 SAE and 1 first class stamp.

Payment: Pays $20 and contributor's copies.

Terms: Pays on publication for one-time rights.

Advice: "I like experimental writing. I like traditional SF and avant-garde work. I like thick, rich writing and well rounded characters. We are the conscience of science fiction with a big grin. We publish intelligent, thought-provocative stories and provide an assortment of humor, art, photos, comix, and reviews."

THE NEW PRESS, (II), 53-35 Hollis Ct. Blvd., Flushing NY 11365. (718)217-1464. Publisher: Bob Abramson. Magazine: 8½×11; 32 pages; medium bond paper and glossy cover stock; illustrations and photographs. "Poems, short stories, commentary, personal journalism. Original and entertaining." Quarterly. Estab. 1984.

Needs: Adventure, confession, ethnic, experimental, fantasy, humor/satire, literary, mainstream, prose poem, serialized/excerpted novel, spiritual, sports, translations. No gratuitous violence. Receives 10 unsolicited mss/month. Accepts 2 mss/issue; 8 mss/year. Publishes ms 12 months after acceptance. Published new writers within the last year. Length: 3,000 words maximum; 100 words minimum. Also publishes literary essays, literary criticism, poetry. Sometimes critiques rejected mss and recommends other markets.

How to Contact: Send complete ms with cover letter. Reports in 2 months. SASE. Simultaneous, photocopied and reprint submissions OK. Accepts computer printout submissions. Sample copy $3; fiction guidelines free. $12 for one-year (4 issues) subscription.

Payment: Pays in contributor's copies and awards $50 for most significant prose in each issue.

Terms: Buys one-time rights.

THE NEW QUARTERLY, New Directions in Canadian Writing, (II, IV), ELPP, University of Waterloo, Waterloo, Ontario N2L 3G1 Canada. (519)885-1212, ext. 2837. Managing Editor: Mary Merikle. Fiction Editors: Peter Hinchcliffe, Kim Jernigan. Magazine: 6×9; 80-120 pages; perfect bound cover, b&w cover photograph; photos with special issues. "We publish poetry, short fiction, excerpts from novels, interviews. We are particularly interested in writing which stretches the bounds of realism. Our audience includes those interested in Canadian literature." Quarterly.

Needs: "I suppose we could be described as a 'literary' magazine. We look for writing which is fresh, innovative, well crafted. We promote beginning writers alongside more established ones. Ours is a humanist magazine—no gratuitous violence, though we are not afraid of material which is irreverent or unconventional. Our interest is more in the quality than the content of the fiction we see." Published recent special issues on magic, realism in Canadian writing, family fiction and Canadian Mennonite writing. Receives approx. 50 unsolicited mss/month. Buys 5-6 mss/issue; 20-24 mss/year. Publishes ms usually within 6 months after acceptance. Recently published work by Diane Schoemperlen, Patrick Roscoe and Steven Heighton; published new writers within the last year. Length: up to 20 pages. Publishes short shorts. Also publishes poetry. Sometimes recommends other markets.

How to Contact: Send complete ms with cover letter, which should include a short biographical note. Reports in 1-2 weeks on queries; approx. 3 months on mss. SASE for ms. Photocopied submissions OK. Accepts computer printout submissions. Sample copy for $4.

The double dagger before a listing indicates that the listing is new in this edition. New markets are often the most receptive to freelance contributions.

Payment: Pays $100 and contributor's copies.
Terms: Pays on publication for first North American serial rights.
Advice: "Send only one well polished manuscript at a time. Persevere. Find your own voice. The primary purpose of little literary magazines like ours is to introduce new writers to the reading public. However, because we want them to appear at their best, we apply the same standards when judging novice work as when judging that of more established writers."

the new renaissance, (II), 9 Heath Rd., Arlington MA 02174. Fiction Editors: Louise T. Reynolds, Harry Jackel and Patricia Michaud. Magazine: 6×9; 144-208 pages; 70 lb. paper; laminated cover stock; artwork; photos. "An international magazine of ideas and opinions, emphasizing literature and the arts, *tnr* takes a classicist position in literature and the arts. Publishes a variety of very diverse, quality fiction, always well crafted, sometimes experimental. *tnr* is unique among literary magazines for its marriage of the literary and visual arts with political/sociological articles and essays. We publish the beginning as well as the emerging and established writer." Biannually. Estab. 1968. Circ. 1,500.
Needs: Literary, humor, prose poem, translations, off-beat, quality fiction, and, occasionally, experimental fiction. "We don't want to see heavily plotted stories with one-dimensional characters or heavily academic or 'poetic' writing, or fiction that is self-indulgent." Buys 5-6 mss/issue, 8-13 mss/year. Receives approximately 60-90 unsolicited fiction mss each month. Reads only from Jan. 2 thru June 30 of any year. Agented fiction approx. 8-12%. Recently published work by Mary Ellen Beveridge, Valerie Hobbs. Published new writers within the last year. Length of fiction: 3-36 pages. Also publishes literary essays, literary criticism, poetry. Comments on rejected mss "when there is time and when we want to encourage the writer or believe we can be helpful."
How to Contact: Send complete ms with SASE (IRCs) of sufficient size for return. "Inform us if multiple submission." Reluctantly accepts computer printout submissions. Reports in 4-6 months. Publishes ms an average of 18-24 months after acceptance. Sample copy $5.80 for 2 back issues, or $7.40 for recent issue. Current issue is $9. Reviews novels and short story collections.
Payment: Pays $40-80 after publication; 1 contributor's copy. Query for additional copies.
Terms: Acquires all rights in case of a later *tnr* book collection; otherwise, rights return to the writer.
Advice: "We represent one of the best markets for writers, because we publish a greater variety (of styles, statements, tones) than most magazines, small or large. Study *tnr* and then send your best work; we will read 2 manuscripts if they are 4 pages or less; for mss 6 pages or more, send only one ms. Manuscripts are rejected because writers do not study their markets and send out indiscriminately. Fully one-quarter of our rejected manuscripts fall into this category; others are from tyro writers who haven't yet mastered their craft, or writers who are not honest, or who haven't fully thought their story through, or from writers who are careless about language. Also, many writers feel compelled to 'explain' their stories to the reader instead of letting the story speak for itself."

NEW VIRGINIA REVIEW, An Anthology of Literary Work by and Important to Virginians, (II), 1306 East Cary St., 2A, Richmond VA 23219. (804)782-1043. Editor: Mary Flynn. Magazine: 6½×10; 180 pages; high quality paper; coated, color cover stock. "Approximately one half of the contributors have Virginia connections; the other authors are serious writers of contemporary fiction. Published January, May and October. Estab. 1978. Circ. 2,000.
Needs: Contemporary, experimental, literary, mainstream, serialized/excerpted novel. No blue, sci-fi, romance, children's. Receives 50-100 unsolicited fiction mss/month. Accepts an average of 15 mss/issue. Does not read from April 1 to September 1. Publishes ms an average of 6-9 months after acceptance. Length: 5,000-6,500 words average; no minimum; 8,000 words maximum. Also publishes poetry. Sometimes critiques rejected mss.
How to Contact: Send complete ms with cover letter, name, address, telephone number, brief biographical comment. Reports in 6 weeks on queries; up to 6 months on mss. "Will answer questions on status of ms." SASE. Photocopied submissions OK. Accepts computer printout submissions. Sample copy $13.50 and 9x12 SAE with 5 first-class stamps.
Payment: Pays $10/printed page; contributor's copies; charge for extras, ½ cover price.
Terms: Pays on publication for first North American serial rights. Sponsors contests and awards for Virginia writers only.
Advice: "Since we publish a wide range of styles of writing depending on the tastes of our guest editors, all we can say is—try to write good strong fiction, stick to it, and try again with another editor."

NEXT PHASE, (I, II), Phantom Press, 47 Fairfield St., New Haven CT 06515. (203)397-8776. Editor: Michael White. Fiction Editor: Kim Means. 8½×11; 12 pages. "Science fiction fantasy with humane twist for experimental comic/graphic novel/sci fi fantasy fans." Quarterly. Estab. 1989. Circ. 1,000.

Needs: Experimental, fantasy, horror, science fiction. Publishes annual special fiction issue. Receives 4-10 unsolicited mss/month. Accepts 2 mss/issue; 8 mss/year. Publishes short shorts. Also publishes poetry. Sometimes critiques rejected mss and recommends other markets.
How to Contact: Send complete manuscript with cover letter. SASE. Simultaneous, photocopied and reprint submissions OK. Accepts computer printout submissions. Sample copy for $1 per issue includes postage.
Payment: Pays contributor's copies.
Terms: Acquires one-time rights.

NEXUS, (II), Wright State University, 006 University Center, Dayton OH 45435. (513)873-2031. Editor: Ted Cains. Magazine: 8½×11; 90-140 pages; good coated paper; heavy perfect-bound cover; b&w illustrations and photography. "International arts and literature for those interested." 3 times per year. Circ. 2,000.
Needs: Contemporary, experimental, literary, regional, translations. No sci-fi, western, romance. Receives 25-30 unsolicited mss/month. Accepts 2-3 mss/issue; 6-10 mss/year. Does not read mss June-Sept. Publishes ms 2-6 months after acceptance. Recently reprinted Alain Robbe Grillet and Stuart Dybek (audial reading). Length: 4,000 words average; 500 words minimum; 7,500 words maximum. Publishes short shorts of any length. Also publishes literary essays, literary criticism, poetry. Sometimes critiques rejected mss and recommends other markets.
How to Contact: Send complete manuscript with cover letter including "any previous publishers of your work. *Do not* explain anything about the story." Reports in 2 weeks on queries; 1-2 months on mss. SASE. Simultaneous, photocopied and reprint submissions OK. Sample copy for $5. Fiction guidelines for #10 SAE and 1 first class stamp. Reviews novels and short story collections.
Payment: Pays contributor's copies.
Terms: Acquires first North American serial rights.
Advice: "Simplicity and a perfection of style (description, simile, dialogue) always make a lasting impression. Good, careful translations receive favored readings."

NIGHT OWL'S NEWSLETTER, (II, IV), Julian Associates, 6831 Spencer Hwy., #203, Pasadena TX 77505. (713)930-1481. Editor: Debbie Jordan. Newsletter: 8½×11; 16 pages; 20 lb. copy paper; cartoons. A newsletter for "night owls—people who can't sleep through much of the hours between midnight and 6 a.m. and usually want to sleep late in the morning." Quarterly. Estab. 1990.
Needs: Excerpted novel, experimental, fantasy, humor/satire, literary. "All variations must relate to the subject of night owls. No erotica." Accepts 1-2 mss/issue; 4-10 mss/year. Publishes ms 3-9 months after acceptance. Recently published work by Michael Thibodeaux. Length: 500-700 words preferred; 250 words minimum; 1,000 words maximum. Publishes short shorts. Critiques or comments on rejected mss. Recommends other markets.
How to Contact: Send complete ms with cover letter. Include short bio and credits. Reports in 1 month. SASE. Simultaneous, photocopied, reprint and computer printout submissions OK. Accepts electronic submissions. Sample copy for $3.50. Fiction guidelines for #10 SAE and 1 first-class stamp.
Payment: Pays $1 minimum plus 1 contributor's copy; charges for extras.
Terms: Buys one-time rights.
Advice: "We are most interested in a humorous and intelligent approach to the problem of people not being able to get to sleep or stay asleep at night and/or unable to wake up in the morning. This means the writer must understand the problem and have information to help others (besides suggesting drugs, alcohol or sex) or offer humorous support."

NIGHTSUN, Department of English, Frostburg State University, Frostburg MD 21532. Co-Editors: Doug DeMars and Barbara Wilson. Magazine: 5½×8½; 64 pages; recycled paper. "Although *Nightsun* is now primarily a journal of poetry and interviews, we are still looking for excellent short-short fiction (5-6 pgs. maximum)." Annually. Estab. 1981. Circ. 300-500.
How to Contact: Send inquiry with SASE. Reports within 3 months. Sample copy $6.50.
Payment: Pays 2 contributor's copies.
Terms: Acquires one-time rights (rights revert to author after publication).

NIMROD, International Literary Journal, (II), Arts & Humanities Council of Tulsa, 2210 S. Main, Tulsa OK 74114. Editor-in-Chief: Francine Ringold. Magazine: 6×9; 160 pages; 60 lb. white paper; illustrations; photos. "We publish one thematic issue and one awards issue each year. A recent theme was "Clap Hands and Sing: Writers of Age," a compilation of poetry, prose and fiction by authors, such as Kumin, Clampitt, Stafford and Kunitz who are over age 65. We seek vigorous, imaginative, quality writing." Published semiannually. Estab. 1956. Circ. 3,000+.

Needs: "We accept contemporary poetry and/or prose. May submit adventure, ethnic, experimental, prose poem, science fiction or translations." Upcoming themes: International theme, concentrating on Eastern Europe (April 1992); "Australian Issue" (Spring, 1993). Receives 120 unsolicited fiction mss/month. Published work by Josephine Jacobson, Gish Jen; published new writers within the last year. Length: 7,500 words maximum. Also publishes poetry.

How to Contact: Reports in 3 weeks-3 months. Sample copy: "to see what *Nimrod* is all about, send $5.90. Be sure to request an awards issue."

Payment: Pays 3 contributor's copies.

Terms: Acquires one-time rights.

Advice: "Read the magazine. Write well. Be courageous. No superfluous words. No clichés. Keep it tight but let your imagination flow. Read the magazine. Strongly encourage writers to send #10 SASE for brochure. Annual literary contest with prizes of $1,000 and $500. Send #10 (business-size) SASE for full contest details."

NO IDEA MAGAZINE, (I), P.O. Box 14636, Gainesville FL 32604-4636. Editor: Var Thëlin. Magazine: 8½×11; 64 pages, 16 four-color pages; 37 lb. newsprint; illustrations and photographs. Each issue comes with a hard-vinyl 7-inch record. "Mostly underground/punk/hardcore music and interviews, but we like delving into other art forms as well. We publish what we feel is good—be it silly or moving." Sporadically. Estab. 1985.

Needs: Adventure, contemporary, experimental, fantasy, horror, humor/satire, science fiction, suspense/mystery. "Humor of a strange, odd manner is nice. We're very open." Receives 5-10 mss/month. Publishes ms up to 6 months after acceptance. Publishes mostly short shorts. Length: 1-6 pages typed.

How to Contact: Send complete manuscript with cover letter. Photocopied submissions OK. Accepts computer printout submissions. Sample copy $3. Checks to Var Thëlin. Reviews novels and short story collections.

Payment: Pays in contributor's copies.

Terms: Acquires one-time rights.

Advice: "A query with $3 will get you a sample of our latest issue and answers to any questions asked. Just because we haven't included a writer's style of work before doesn't mean we won't print their work. Perhaps we've never been exposed to their style before."

‡NO NEWZ, Fine Funky Fiction, Poetry and Art, (I), 32 Harrison Ave., Highland Park NJ 08904. Editor: Eva Hopkins. Fiction Editor: Theresa Lindquist. Newsletter: 8½×11; 50 pages; card stock cover; b&w illustrations. "The idea behind *No Newz* is to give writers who don't have much exposure a springboard into the public view. For other writers, artists and publishers, mostly." Estab. 1988. Circ. 2,000.

Needs: Adventure, erotica, ethnic, experimental, fantasy, feminist, gay, historical (general), horror, humor/satire, lesbian, literary, mainstream, prose poem, psychic/supernatural/occult, regional, science fiction, suspense/mystery, young adult/teen. Plans special fiction issue. Receives 10 unsolicited mss/month. Accepts 2 mss/issue; 8 mss/year. Does not read mss in the summer. Publishes ms 4 months after acceptance. Recently published work by Erol Sari, Eliot Katz, Richard Woobridge III. Length: 1,500 words preferred; 100 words minimum; 5,000 words maximum. Publishes short shorts. Sometimes critiques rejected mss and recommends other markets.

How to Contact: Query first. Reports in 3 weeks on queries; 1 month on mss. SASE. Simultaneous, photocopied submissions OK. Accepts computer printout submissions. Sample copy for 9×12 SAE and 5 first class stamps. Fiction guidelines free.

Payment: Pays subscription to magazine.

Terms: Acquires first North American serial rights.

Advice: "*No Newz* prefers fiction written by people who love language: who are not afraid to use an unusual eclectic word, for fear of being misunderstood. HOWEVER (to totally contradict ourselves) one should not be *afraid* of simplicity, either, or lose meaning in foppish phrases. A ms with lyrical language and compelling plotline catches our eye! *Please* don't lose your plotline in a lot of plaintive *guck!* Be intricate without being dry. Otherwise, it's hard to follow. And have FUN! Don't worry too much about what *No Newz* thinks, or is looking for. Just *enjoy* your writing!"

THE NOCTURNAL LYRIC, (I), Box 2602, Pasadena CA 91102-2602. (818)585-9337. Editor: Susan Moon. Digest: 5½×8½; 22 pages; illustrations. "We are a non-profit literary journal, dedicated to printing fiction by new writers for the sole purpose of getting read by people who otherwise might have never seen their work." Bimonthly. Estab. 1987. Circ. 150.
Needs: Experimental, fantasy, horror, humor/satire, psychic/supernatural/occult, science fiction, poetry. "We will give priority to unusual, creative pieces." Upcoming themes: "We're considering doing an all-vampire issue in late 1992, perhaps for Halloween." Receives approx. 50 unsolicited mss/month. Publishes ms 4-8 months after acceptance. Publishes short shorts. Length: 2,000 words maximum. Also publishes poetry.
How to Contact: Send complete ms with cover letter. Cover letter should include "something about the author, what areas of fiction he/she is interested in." Reports in 1 week on queries; 2-3 months on mss. SASE. Simultaneous, photocopied and reprint submissions OK. Accepts computer printout submissions. Sample copy $1.25 (checks made out to Susan Moon, editor). Fiction guidelines for #10 SAE and 1 first class stamp.
Payment: No payment. Pays neither in cash nor contributor's copies.
Terms: Publication not copyrighted.
Advice: "Please stop wasting your postage sending us things that are in no way bizarre. We're getting more into strange, surrealistic horror and fantasy, or silly, satirical horror. If you're avant-garde, we want you!"

NOMOS, Studies in Spontaneous Order, (II, IV), Nomos Press, Inc., 257 Chesterfield, Glen Ellyn IL 60137. (708)858-7184. Editor: Carol B. Low. 8½×11; 32 pages; original illustrations. "Essays, poems, fiction, letters relating to Libertarian concepts and culture for a Libertarian audience." Quarterly. Estab. 1982. Circ. 450 paid; 1,000 total.
Needs: Historical (general), humor/satire, science fiction, suspense/mystery. "We are a strictly hardcore Libertarian magazine and only consider relevant fiction. Reviews of novels also accepted." Receives 1 unsolicited ms/month. Accepts 1 ms/issue; 4 mss/year. Publishes ms 4-8 months after acceptance. Length: 500-2,000 words average; 2,000 words maximum. Publishes short shorts. Occasionally critiques rejected mss.
How to Contact: Send complete manuscript with cover letter. Reports in 5-6 months on mss. SASE. Photocopied submissions OK. Accepts computer printout submissions. Accepts electronic submissions. Sample copy $4.50. Fiction guidelines for #10 SAE. Reviews novels.
Payment: Pays choice of free subscription to magazine or contributor's copies.
Terms: Acquires one-time rights. Sends galleys or letter detailing edits or desired corrections to author.

THE NORTH AMERICAN REVIEW, University of Northern Iowa, Cedar Falls IA 50614. Editor: Robley Wilson. Publishes quality fiction. Quarterly. Estab. 1815. Circ. 4,500.
Needs: "We print quality fiction of any length and/or subject matter. Excellence is the only criterion." Reads fiction *only* from Jan. 1 to March 31. Published new writers (about 25%) within the last year. No preferred length.
How to Contact: Send complete ms with SASE. Reports in 2-3 months. Sample copy $3.50.
Payment: Pays approximately $10/printed page. 2 free author's copies. $3.50 charge for extras.
Terms: Pays on acceptance for first North American serial rights.
Advice: "We stress literary excellence and read 3,000 manuscripts a year to find an average of 35 stories that we publish. Please *read* the magazine first."

NORTH ATLANTIC REVIEW, (II), North Eagle Corp. of NY, 15 Arbutus Ln., Stony Brook NY 11790. (516)751-7886. Editor: John Gill. Magazine: 7×9; 200 pages; glossy cover. "Sixties and general interest." Estab. 1989. Circ. 500.
Needs: "General fiction and fiction about the sixties—1960-1975—JFK, Vietnam, RFK, King, Kent State, etc." Has published special fiction issue. Accepts 12 mss/issue; 25 mss/year. Publishes ms 6-10 months after acceptance. Length: 3,000-7,000 words average. Publishes short shorts. Sometimes critiques rejected mss and recommends other markets.
How to Contact: Send complete manuscript with cover letter. Reports in 4-6 months on queries. SASE. Simultaneous and photocopied submissions OK. Accepts computer printout submissions. Sample copy for $10.

NORTH DAKOTA QUARTERLY, (II), University of North Dakota, Box 8237, University Station, Grand Forks ND 58202. (701)777-3321. Editor: Robert W. Lewis. Fiction Editor: William Borden. Magazine: 6×9; 200 pages; bond paper; illustrations; photos. Magazine publishing "essays in humanities; some short stories; some poetry." University audience. Quarterly. Estab. 1910. Circ. 800.

Needs: Contemporary, ethnic, experimental, feminist, historical (general), humor/satire and literary. Upcoming theme: "Contemporary Yugoslav literature in English translation" (Fall 1992). Plans an annual anthology or special edition. Receives 15-20 unsolicited mss/month. Accepts 4 mss/issue; 16 mss/year. Recently published work by Jerry Bumpus, Dusty Sklar, Daniel Curley; published new writers within the last year. Length: 3,000-4,000 words average. Also publishes literary essays, literary criticism, poetry. Sometimes critiques rejected mss.

How to Contact: Send complete ms with cover letter. "But they need not be much more than hello; please read this story; I've published (if so, best examples) . . ." SASE. Reports in 3 months. Publishes ms an average of 6-8 months after acceptance. Sample copy $5. Reviews novels and short story collections.

Payment: Pays 5 contributor's copies; 20% discount for extras; year's subscription.

Terms: Acquires one-time rights.

Advice: "We may publish a higher average number of stories in the future—4 rather than 2. Read widely. Write, write; revise, revise."

‡NORTH EAST ARTS MAGAZINE, (II), Boston Arts Organization, Inc., J.F.K. Station, P.O. Box 6061, Boston MA 02114. Editor: Mr. Leigh Donaldson. Magazine: 6½×9½; 32-40 pages; matte finish paper; card stock cover; illustrations and photographs. Bimonthly. Estab. 1990. Circ. 750.

Needs: Ethnic, gay, historical (general), literary, prose poem. No obscenity, racism, sexism, etc. Receives 50 unsolicited mss/month. Accepts 1-2 mss/issue; 5-7 mss/year. Publishes ms 2-4 months after acceptance. Agented fiction 20%. Length: 750 words preferred. Publishes short shorts. Sometimes critiques rejected mss.

How to Contact: Send complete ms with cover letter. Include short bio. Reports in 3 weeks on queries; 2-4 months on mss. SASE. Simultaneous and photocopied submissions OK. Sample copy for $3.50, SAE and 75¢ postage. Fiction guidelines free.

Payment: Pays 2 contributor's copies.

Terms: Acquires first North American serial rights. Sometimes sends galleys to author.

Advice: Looks for "creative/innovative use of language and style. Unusual themes and topics."

‡NORTHERN ARIZONA MANDALA, (II), S. Bruno Affiliates, P.O. Box 3387, Prescott AZ 86302. (602)776-8947. Editor: Stephen Bruno. Magazine: 11×14; 44 pages; high-quality recycled newsprint paper. "Literary magazine encouraging all people to display interest in artistic expression. Literature, photography, art, wide variety of subject matter presented in positive form. For general audience." Monthly. Estab. 1991. Circ. 5,000.

Needs: Adventure, condensed/excerpted novel, contemporary, experimental, fantasy, historical (general), horror, humor/satire, literary, mainstream, prose poem, romance (historical), science fiction, senior citizen/retirement, serialized novel, suspense/mystery, translations, western. "No subject matter that has negative or violent plots, themes or results or subject matter that would be interpreted as racist or derogatory to any specific group of people." Receives 15-20 unsolicited mss/month. Buys 2-4 mss/issue. Recently published work by Carla Lambert, Christina Hecht-Schroeder. Length: 2,500 words preferred; 1,000 words minimum; 5,000 words maximum. Sometimes critiques rejected mss and recommends other markets.

How to Contact: Query first or query with clips of published work "If manuscripts are sent must conform to *The Chicago Manual of Style*." Reports in 4-10 weeks. SASE. Accepts electronic submissions via disk or modem. Sample copy for $2, 9×12 SAE and $1 postage.

Payment: Pays $.01/word and contributor's copies.

Terms: Pays on publication for first North American serial rights.

Advice: Looks for "works appropriate for an educated public of diverse backgrounds and training. Writing style should be lively, informal and straight-forward with subject matter functional and down-to-earth. We encourage beginning writers to readily submit works. Enclose proper SASE and ask for information, opinions. The main focus of our publication is to help people express artistic talent in a friendly environment."

THE NORTHWEST GAY & LESBIAN READER, Art, Opinion and Literature, (I, IV), Beyond the Closet Bookstore, 1501 Belmont Ave., Seattle WA 98122. (206)322-4609. Editor: Ron Whiteaker. Tabloid: 11×17; 16 pages; newsprint paper, illustrations, photographs. "A wide range of formats reflecting the gay/lesbian/bisexual experience." Bimonthly. Estab. 1989. Circ. 4,000.

Needs: Gay, lesbian, bisexual. "Light erotica OK. No hard-core erotica, or 'abusive attitude' fiction." Receives 2 unsolicited mss/month. Accepts 1 ms/issue. Publishes ms 2 months after acceptance. Published work by William Freeberg, Aubrey Hart Sparks, Jill Sunde. Length: 2,000 words preferred; 1,000 words minimum; 3,000 words maximum. Publishes short shorts.

How to Contact: Send complete ms with cover letter. Include "a bit about the story and its author." Reports in 2 weeks on queries; 2 months on mss. SASE. Photocopied submissions OK. Accepts electronic submissions—IBM compatible disk in generic (ASCII) word processing format. Sample copy for 75¢, 9×12 SAE and 3 first class stamps. Fiction guidelines for #10 SAE and 1 first class stamp.

Payment: Pays in contributor's copies and free subscription.

Terms: Acquires one-time rights.

Advice: "A story that is clever and well-written and contains original ideas is considered first, rather than the hackneyed, over-done story lines containing redundant dogma and irritating buzzwords. Reflect the gay/lesbian/bisexual experience."

NORTHWEST REVIEW, (II), 369 PLC, University of Oregon, Eugene OR 97403. (503)346-3957. Editor: John Witte. Fiction Editor: Cecelia Hagen. Magazine: 6×9; 140-160 pages; coated paper; high quality cover stock; illustrations; photos. "A general literary review featuring poems, stories, essays and reviews, circulated nationally and internationally. For a literate audience in avant-garde as well as traditional literary forms; interested in the important younger writers who have not yet achieved their readership." Published 3 times/year. Estab. 1957. Circ. 1,200.

Needs: Literary, contemporary, feminist, translations and experimental. Accepts 4-5 mss/issue, 12-15 mss/year. Receives approximately 100 unsolicited fiction mss each month. Published work by Susan Stark, Madison Smartt Bell, Maria Flook, Charles Marvin; published new writers within the last year. Length: "Mss longer than 40 pages are at a disadvantage." Also publishes literary essays, literary criticism, poetry. Critiques rejected mss when there is time. Sometimes recommends other markets.

How to Contact: Send complete ms with SASE. "No simultaneous submissions are considered." Accepts computer printout submissions. Reports in 3-4 months. Sample copy $3.50. Reviews novels and short story collections. Send books to Cecelia Hagen.

Payment: Pays 3 contributor's copies; 40% discount on extras.

Terms: Acquires first rights.

Advice: "Persist. Copy should be clean, double-spaced, with generous margins. Careful proofing for spelling and grammar errors will reduce slowing of editorial process." Mss are rejected because of "unconvincing characters, overblown language, melodramatic plot, poor execution."

NOTEBOOK/CUADERNO: A LITERARY JOURNAL, (II, IV), Esoterica Press, P.O. Box 15607, Rio Rancho NM 87174. Editor: Ms. Yoly Zentella. Magazine: 5½×8½; 100 pages; bond paper; 90 lb. cover stock; illustrations. "Accepting fiction and nonfiction. *Notebook*'s emphasis is on history, culture, art and literary critique and travel pieces. For ages 25-50, writers, artists, educators, some academia." Semiannually. Publishes special ethnic issues, e.g. Native American, Pacific, Asian. Estab. 1985. Circ. 100, "including many libraries."

Needs: Ethnic, (focusing especially on Chicano and Latino American pieces in English and Spanish), historical (Latino American, European and Muslim), humor/satire, literary, regional. "One yearly issue featured exclusively Chicano and Latino American writers, and we need black-American writers." Absolutely no explicit sex or obscenities accepted, but tasteful eroticism considered. Receives approximately 40-50 unsolicited fiction mss/month. Published work by Jan Beastrom, R. Ivanov Reyez, Tom Lane; published new writers within the last year. Length: 2,000 words average; 2,500 words maximum. Also "at times" publishes poetry. Sometimes critiques rejected mss.

How to Contact: Send complete ms with cover letter and short biography. Reports in 4-6 weeks on queries; 1-2 months on mss. Always SASE for ms and correspondence. Accepts computer printouts. Sample copy $6 plus $1 p/h. Expects contributor to subcribe, or buy subscription for a Library of their choice. Make checks payable to Esoterica Press. Fiction guidelines for #10 SAE and 1 first class stamp. Reviews novels and short story collections.

Payment: Pays 1 contributor's copy, charges for extras.

Terms: Acquires first North American serial rights. "Rights revert to author upon publication."

Advice: "We are now planning more fiction in our issues and less poetry. We are also considering novellas for publication, appearing exclusively in one issue."

NOTES FROM THE SOUTHWEST (II, IV), (formerly *Northland Quarterly*), 1522 E. Southern Ave. Box 2161, Tempe AZ 85282. Editor: Jody Namio Wallace. Magazine: 5×8; approx. 100-125 pages; 60 lb. offset paper; 10 pt. cover stock; b&w illustrations; line drawings; cover photos. "Contemporary writing for discriminating reader. Short fiction, poetry, commentary and reviews. International publication, with emphasis on writers in upper-tier states and Canada. *Quarterly* features politically oriented writings, as well as regional writers and contemporary fiction from throughout US." Quarterly. Estab. 1987 (under new name 1991).
Needs: Condensed/excerpted novel, contemporary, feminist, literary, mainstream, regional, romance, serialized novel, progressive issues, political fiction. No religious, young romance. Receives 20-40 mss/month. Accepts 3-5 mss/issue. Publishes ms within 3-6 months of acceptance. Published work by Robert Flaum, Marcella Taylor, Robert Funge. Length: 1,500 words minimum; 4,000 words maximum. Publishes short shorts. Length: 300 words minimum. Sometimes critiques rejected mss and recommends other markets.
How to Contact: Query first, query with clips of published work or send complete ms with cover letter, which should include "general description of work, genre. Other places submitted, if any." Reports on queries in 2-3 months. SASE. Simultaneous, photocopied and some reprint submissions OK. Accepts computer printout submissions. Accepts electronic submissions via disk. Sample copy for $4, 5×8 SAE and 4 first class stamps. Fiction guidelines for #10 SAE and 1 first class stamp.
Payment: Pays in contributor's copies.
Terms: Sends galleys to author if requested. Sponsors awards for fiction and poetry writers. "Write for information."
Advice: Looks for "contemporary, adult fiction of high quality. We adopt an unprejudiced, open attitude for all manuscripts submitted, and have published world-class writers as well as beginners."

NOW & THEN, (IV), Center for Appalachian Studies and Services, East Tennessee State University, Box 19180A, Johnson City TN 37614-0002. (615)929-5348. Editor: Pat Arnow. Magazine: 8½×11; 36-52 pages; coated paper and cover stock; illustrations; photographs. Publication focuses on Appalachian culture, present and past. Readers are mostly people in the region involved with Appalachian issues, literature, education." 3 issues/year. Estab. 1984. Circ. 880.
Needs: Ethnic, literary, regional, serialized/excerpted novel, prose poem, spiritual and sports. "Absolutely has to relate to Appalachian theme. Can be about adjustment to new environment, themes of leaving and returning, for instance. Nothing unrelated to region." Upcoming themes: "Scottish—Appalachian Connection" (Summer '92, deadline March '92); "Sports and Recreation in Appalachia" (Fall '92, deadline July '92); "Education in Appalachia" (Spring '93, deadline Nov. '92); "Civil War in Appalachia" (Summer '93, deadline March '93). Accepts 2-3 mss/issue. Publishes ms 3-4 months after acceptance. Published work by Gurney Norman, Lance Olsen, George Ella Lyon; published new writers within the last year. Length: 3,000 words maximum. Publishes short shorts. Also publishes literary essays, poetry.
How to Contact: Send complete ms with cover letter. Reports in 3 months. Include "information we can use for contributor's note." SASE. Simultaneous and photocopied submissions OK. Accepts computer printout submissions. Sample copy $3.50. Reviews novels and short story collections.
Payment: Pays up to $50 per story, contributor's copies, one year subscription.
Terms: Buys first-time rights.
Advice: "We're emphasizing Appalachian culture, which is not often appreciated because analysts are so busy looking at the trouble of the region. We're doing theme issues. Beware of stereotypes. In a regional publication like this one we get lots of them, both good guys and bad guys: salt of the earth to poor white trash. Sometimes we get letters that offer to let us polish up the story. We prefer the author does that him/herself." Send for list of upcoming themes.

NRG, (II), Skydog Press, 6735 SE 78th, Portland OR 97206. Editor: Dan Raphael. Magazine/tabloid: 11×17; 20 pages; electrobrite paper; illustrations; photos. For the "creative and curious." Theme is "open-ended, energized, non-linear emphasis on language and sounds"; material is "spacial, abstract, experimental." Semiannually. Estab. 1976. Circ. 1,000.

Market categories: (I) Beginning; (II) General; (III) Prestige; (IV) Specialized.

Needs: Contemporary, experimental, literary and prose poem. Receives 8 unsolicited mss/month. Accepts 6 mss/issue; 11 mss/year. Published work by S.P. Stressman, Willie Smith, Don Webb. Length: 1,000 words average; 3,000 words maximum. Occasionally critiques rejected mss.
How to Contact: Send complete ms with SASE and cover letter stating where you learned of magazine; list of 3-5 previous publications. Reports in 1 month on mss. Simultaneous and photocopied submissions OK. Accepts computer printout submissions. Publishes ms an average of 1 year after acceptance. Sample copy $1.50. "Best guideline is sample copy."
Payment: Pays in free contributor's copies only, ½ cover price charge for extras.
Terms: Acquires one-time rights.
Advice: "I'm trying to get more fiction, but am strict in my editorial bias. I don't want it to add up or be purely representational. Energy must abound in the language, or the spaces conjured. Forget what you were taught. Let the story tell you."

NUCLEAR FICTION, (II,V), P.O. Box 49019, Austin TX 78765. (512)478-7262. Editor: Brian Martin. Magazine. "A bimonthly magazine of sci-fi, fantasy and horror. Includes film and book reviews, art, poetry." Estab. 1988.
Needs: Horror, fantasy and science fiction. Length: Open. Also publishes literary criticism, poetry.
How to Contact: Send complete ms; cover letter optional. Reports in 4-6 weeks on average. Sample copy for $3. Reviews novels and short story collections. Send books to Brian Martin, Editor, 2518 Leon St. #107, Austin TX 78705.
Payment: Pays ½¢/word for fiction. (Minimum payment $7.50.)
Terms: Pays on acceptance; for first North American serial rights.
Advice: "Be mindful of the fundamentals of story telling. Otherwise, no strict requirements here; good work is to be found in all types of imaginative fiction."

LA NUEZ, (II, IV), P.O. Box 1655, New York NY 10276. (212)260-3130. Editor: Rafael Bordao. Magazine: 8½×11; 32 pages; 60 lb. offset paper; glossy cover; illustrations and photographs. "*Spanish language* literary magazine (poetry, short fiction, criticism, reviews) for anyone who reads Spanish and loves poetry and literature. Many of our readers are professors, writers, critics and artists. Quarterly. Estab. 1988. Circ. 1,000.
Needs: Spanish only. Literary. "Nothing more than 6 pages. No political or religious themes." Publishes "very few" mss/issue, "because of space limitations." Publishes ms 3-6 months after acceptance. Length: 6 pages or less. Publishes short shorts. Also publishes literary essays, literary criticism, poetry.
How to Contact: Send complete ms with cover letter and short bio, SASE. Reports in 6-8 weeks. Sample copy for $3.50. Fiction guidelines for #10 SAE and 1 first class stamp. Reviews novels and short story collections.
Payment: Pays 2 contributor's copies.
Advice: Publication's philosophy is "to publish the high quality poetry and literature in Spanish of writers from the rich diversity of cultures, communities and countries in the Spanish-speaking world."

THE OAK, (I), (formerly *Writers Newsletter*), 1530 7th St., Rock Island IL 61201. (309)788-3980. Editor: Betty Mowery. 8½×11; 8-14 pages. "Anything of help to writers." Bimonthly. Estab. 1991. Circ. 385.
Needs: Adventure, contemporary, experimental, historical (general), humor/satire, mainstream, prose poem, regional, religious/inspiration, romance, spiritual, suspense/mystery. No erotica. Receives about 12 mss/month. Buys or accepts up to 6 mss/issue. Publishes ms within 3 months of acceptance. Published new writers within the last year. Length: 500 words maximum. Publishes short shorts. Length: 200 words.
How to Contact: Send complete ms. Reports in 1 week. SASE. Simultaneous, photocopied and reprint submissions OK. Accepts computer printout submissions. Sample copy $1. Subscription $10 for 6 issues.
Payment: Pays in contributor's copies.
Terms: Acquires first rights.
Advice: "Just send a manuscript, but first read a copy of our publication to get an idea of what type of material we take. Please send SASE. If not, manuscripts *will not* be returned. Be sure name and address is on the manuscript."

THE OHIO REVIEW, (II), 209C Ellis Hall, Ohio University, Athens OH 45701-2979. (614)593-1900. Editor: Wayne Dodd. Assistant Editor: Robert Kinsley. Magazine: 6×9; 144 pages; illustrations on cover. "We attempt to publish the best poetry and fiction written today. For a mainly literary audience." Triannually. Estab. 1971. Circ. 2,000.

Needs: Contemporary, experimental, literary. "We lean toward contemporary on all subjects." Receives 150-200 unsolicited fiction mss/month. Accepts 3 mss/issue. Does not read mss June 1-August 31. Publishes ms 6 months after acceptance. Agented fiction: 1%. Also publishes poetry. Sometimes critiques rejected mss and/or recommends other markets.
How to Contact: Query first or send complete ms with cover letter. Reports in 6 weeks. SASE. Photocopied submissions OK. Accepts computer printouts. Sample copy $4.25. Fiction guidelines for #10 SASE.
Payment: Pays $5/page, free subscription to magazine, 2 contributor's copies.
Terms: Pays on publication for first North American serial rights. Sends galleys to author.
Advice: "We feel the short story is an important part of the contemporary writing field and value it highly. Read a copy of our publication to see if your fiction is of the same quality. So often people send us work that simply doesn't fit our needs."

OLD HICKORY REVIEW, (II), Jackson Writers Group, Box 1178, Jackson TN 38302. (901)424-3277 or (901)664-5959. Editor: Edna Lackie. Fiction Editors: Dorothy Stanfill and Donald Phillips. Magazine: 8½×11; approx. 90 pages. "Usually two short stories and 75-80 poems—nothing obscene or in poor taste. For a family audience." Semiannually. Plans special fiction issue. Estab. 1969. Circ. 300.
Needs: Contemporary, experimental, fantasy, literary, mainstream. Receives 4-5 unsolicited fiction mss/month. Accepts 2 mss/issue; 4 mss/year. Publishes ms no more than 3-4 months after acceptance. Length: 2,500-3,000 words. Publishes short shorts. Also publishes poetry. Sometimes critiques rejected mss and recommends other markets.
How to Contact: Send complete ms with cover letter, which should include "credits." Reports on queries in 2-3 weeks; on mss in 1-2 months. SASE. Photocopied submissions OK. Accepts computer printouts. Sample copy available. Fiction guidelines for SAE.
Payment: Pays in contributor's copies; charge for extras. Sponsors contests for fiction writers, "advertised in literary magazine and with flyers."
Advice: "We are tired of war, nursing homes, abused children, etc. We are looking for things which are more entertaining. No pornographic fiction, no vile language. Our publication goes into schools, libraries, etc."

THE OLD RED KIMONO, (II), Box 1864, Rome GA 30162. (404)295-6312. Editors: Ken Anderson and Jonathan Hershey. Magazine: 8×11; 65-70 pages; white offset paper; 10 pt. board cover stock. Annually. Estab. 1972. Circ. 1,200.
Needs: Literary. "We will consider good fiction regardless of category." Receives 20-30 mss/month. Buys 6-8 mss/issue. Does not read mss March 15-September 1. "Issue out in May every year." Recently published work by Thomas Feeny, David Huddle, Peter Huggins. Length: 2,000-3,000 words preferred; 5,000 words maximum. Publishes short shorts. "We prefer short fiction." Also publishes poetry.
How to Contact: Send complete ms with cover letter. Reports in 2 weeks on queries; 2-3 months on mss. SASE. Photocopied submissions OK. Accepts computer printout submissions. Fiction guidelines for #10 SAE and 1 first class stamp.
Payment: Pays in contributor's copies.
Terms: Acquires first rights.

ONCE UPON A WORLD, (II), Route 1, Box 110A, Nineveh IN 46164. Editor: Emily Alward. Magazine: 8½×11; 80-100 pages; standard white paper; colored card stock cover; pen & ink illustrations. "A science fiction and fantasy magazine with emphasis on alternate-world cultures and stories of idea, character and interaction. Also publishes book reviews and a few poems for an adult audience, primarily readers of science fiction and fantasy." Annually. Estab. 1988. Circ. 100.
Needs: Fantasy, science fiction. "No realistic" stories in contemporary settings; horror; stories using Star Trek or other media characters; stories with completely negative endings." Receives 20 unsolicited mss/month. Accepts 8-12 mss/issue; per year "varies, depending on backlog." Publishes ms from 2 months to 1½ years after acceptance. Published work by Janet Reedman and Mark Andrew Garland. Length: 3,000 words average; 400 words minimum; 10,000 words maximum. Publishes short shorts. Also publishes poetry. Sometimes critiques rejected mss and recommends other markets.
How to Contact: Send complete manuscript. Reports in 2-4 weeks on queries; 2-16 weeks on mss. SASE. Photocopied submissions OK. Accepts computer printout submissions. Sample copy $8.50; checks to Emily Alward. Fiction guidelines for #10 SAE and 1 first class stamp. Reviews novels and short story collections.

Payment: Pays contributor's copies.
Terms: Acquires first rights. "Stories copyrighted in author's name; copyrights not registered."
Advice: "Besides a grasp of basic fiction technique, you'll need some familiarity with the science fiction and fantasy genres. We suggest reading some of the following authors whose work is similar to what we're looking for: Isaac Asimov, Poul Anderson, Norman Spinrad, David Brin, Anne McCaffrey, Marion Zimmer Bradley, Mercedes Lackey, Katharine Kimbriel."

"Once Upon a World features stories that are set on other worlds of their authors' invention," says Editor Emily Alward. "We try to publish stories that stimulate thought, imagination and emotion, as good fiction has always done." This cover was chosen because it "very closely matches the mood of two of the longer stories in this issue, each of which includes a young woman undergoing a transformation," Alward explains. "The various elements of the picture also convey the mix of science fiction and fantasy that we aim for. Overall, I found it striking and unforgettable." The illustrators are Marge Simon and Cathy Buburuz.

Copyright 1990   simon & buburuz

ONIONHEAD, (II), Literary Quarterly, Arts on the Park, Inc., 115 N. Kentucky Ave., Lakeland FL 33801. (813)680-2787. Editors: Charles Kersey, Dennis Nesheim, Dudley Uphoff. Editorial Assistant: Anna Wiseman. Magazine: Digest-sized; 40 pages; 20 lb. bond; glossy card cover. "Provocative political, social and cultural observations and hypotheses for a literary audience—an open-minded audience." Estab. 1989. Circ. 250.
Needs: Contemporary, ethnic, experimental, feminist, gay, humor/satire, lesbian, literary, prose poem, regional. "Must have a universal point (International)." Publishes short fiction in each issue. Receives 100-150 unsolicited titles/month. Acquires approximately 28 mss/issue; 100 titles (these numbers include: poetry, short prose and essays)/year. Publishes ms within 18 months of acceptance. Recently published work by Lyn Lifshin, A.D. Winans, Jessica Freeman, Laurel Speer. Length: 3,000 words average; 4,000 words maximum. Publishes short shorts. Also publishes poetry.
How to Contact: Send complete manuscript with cover letter that includes brief bio and SASE. Reports in 2 weeks on queries; 2 months on mss. Photocopied submissions OK. Accepts computer printout submissions. Sample copy $3 postpaid. Fiction guidelines for #10 SAE and 1 first class stamp.
Payment: Pays in contributor's copy. Charge for extras.
Terms: Acquires first North American serial rights.
Advice: "Review a sample copy of *Onionhead* and remember *literary quality* is the prime criterion. Avoid heavy-handed approaches to social commentary—be subtle, not didactic."

OTHER VOICES, (II), The University of Illinois at Chicago, Dept of English (M/C 162), Box 4348, Chicago IL 60680. (312)413-2209. Editors: Sharon Fiffer and Lois Hauselman. Magazine: 5⅞ × 9; 168-205 pages; 60 lb. paper; coated cover stock; occasional photos. "Original, fresh, diverse stories and novel excerpts" for literate adults. Semiannually. Estab. 1985. Circ. 1,500.
Needs: Contemporary, experimental, humor/satire, literary, excerpted novel. No taboos, except ineptitude and murkiness. No fantasy, horror, juvenile, psychic/occult. Receives 45 unsolicited fiction mss/month. Accepts 20-23 mss/issue. Publishes ms approx. 3-6 months after acceptance. Agented fiction 40%. Published work by Barbara Lefcowitz, Susan B. Weston; published new writers within the last year. Length: 4,000 words average; 5,000 words maximum. Also publishes short shorts "if paired

together" of 1,000 words. Only occasionally critiques rejected mss or recommends other markets.
How to Contact: Send mss with SASE or submit through agent. Cover letters "should be brief and list previous publications. Also, list title of submission. Most beginners' letters try to 'explain' the story—a big mistake." Reports in 10-12 weeks on mss. SASE. Photocopied submissions OK. Accepts computer printouts. Sample copy $5.90 (includes postage). Fiction guidelines for #10 SAE and 1 first class stamp. Occasionally reviews novels and short story collections; query first.
Payment: Pays in contributor's copies and modest cash gratuity.
Terms: Acquires one-time rights.
Advice: "There are so *few* markets for *quality* fiction! We—by publishing 40-45 stories a year—provide new and established writers a forum for their work. Send us your best voice, your best work, your best best."

OTHER WORLDS, Science Fiction-Science Fantasy, (II), Gryphon Publications, Box 209, Brooklyn NY 11228. Editor: Gary Lovisi. Magazine: 5 × 8; 40-60 pages; offset paper; card/color cover; illustrations and photographs. "Adventure—or action-oriented SF—stories that are fun to read." Annually. Estab. 1988. Circ. 300.
Needs: Science fiction. No high fantasy, sword and sorcery. Receives 12 unsolicited mss/month. Buys 2-4 mss/issue. Publishes ms 1-2 years (usually) after acceptance. Length: 3,000 words maximum. Publishes short shorts. Length: 500-1,000 words. Sometimes critiques rejected mss and recommends other markets.
How to Contact: Send complete ms with cover letter. Reports in 2 weeks on queries; 1 month on mss. SASE. Photocopied submissions OK. Accepts computer printout submissions. Sample copy $4. Free fiction guidelines. May review novels and short story collections. Query first.
Payment: Pays in contributor's copies.
Terms: Acquires first North American serial rights. Copyright reverts to author.

‡**OUR WRITE MIND, (II),** Julian Associates, #203, 6831 Spencer Hwy., Pasadena TX 77505. (404)889-2597. Editor: Robin Parker. Magazine: 8½ × 11; 60 pages; 20 lb. paper; 60 lb. paper cover. "*OWM* contains fiction, nonfiction and poetry on writing and writers—the art and business of writing." Annually. Estab. 1991. Circ. 150.
Needs: Writing and writers. Receives 2-3 unsolicited mss/month. Buys up to 6 mss/issue. Publishes ms 1-2 years after acceptance. Recently published work by Deborah Harris, Steve Bowen, Joseph Guinn. Length: 750 words preferred; 250 words minimum; 1,000 words maximum. Publishes short shorts. Length: 250-500 words. Also publishes poetry (on writers or writing).
How to Contact: Send complete ms with cover letter. Include a "short bio—not lifetime resumé." Reports in 2-4 weeks on queries; 2-6 weeks on mss. SASE. Simultaneous, photocopied, reprint submissions OK. Accepts computer printout submissions. Sample copy for $9.50. Fiction guidelines for #10 SAE and 1 first class stamp.
Payment: Pays $1 minimum and 1 contributor's copy and "at least $1"; discount for extras to our writers.
Terms: Buys one-time rights.
Advice: "Entertain us while you're educating us. We like to smile and laugh while we think and learn. While we don't judge first by technical qualities of a ms, a badly written or sloppy ms does distract from the quality of the story—they give away an amateur."

OUROBOROS, (II), 3912 24th St., Rock Island IL 61201-6223. Editor and Publisher: Erskine Carter. Magazine: 6 × 9; 76 pages; 60 lb offset paper; 80 lb cover; b&w illustrations. "We publish fiction (short stories), poetry and art for thoughtful readers." Published irregularly. Estab. 1985. Circ. 400.
Needs: Adventure, contemporary, experimental, fantasy, historical (general), horror, humor/satire, literary, mainstream, psychic/supernatural/occult, science fiction, suspense/mystery. "We are mainly interested in stories about people, in situations of conflict or struggle. We want to see *real* characters at odds with others, themselves, their universe. No racist/right-wing/anti-minority material." Receives 40-50 unsolicited mss/month. Accepts 8-10 mss/issue; 32-40 mss/year. Publishes ms 3 months to 1 year after acceptance. Published work by W. Rose, C. Stevenson, D. Starkey; published new writers within the last year. Length: 2,500 words average; 3,500 words maximum. Publishes short shorts. Length: 500 words. Also publishes poetry. Sometimes critiques rejected mss and recommends other markets.
How to Contact: Request guidelines and a sample copy. Reports in 2 weeks. SASE. Photocopied and reprint submissions OK. Accepts computer printout submissions. Sample copy of current issue $4.50. Back issues available.

Payment: Pays in contributor's copies.

Terms: Rights revert to author. Sends galleys to author.

Advice: "The beginning writer *can* break in here and learn valuable lessons about writing and publishing. Obtain a sample copy, write something you think will grab us, then submit. Get to know the markets. Don't waste time, energy and postage without researching."

OUTERBRIDGE, (II), English A-323, The College of Staten Island (CUNY), 715 Ocean Terr., Staten Island NY 10301. (212)390-7654. Editor: Charlotte Alexander. Magazine: 5½ × 8½; approx. 110 pages; 60 lb. white offset paper; 65 lb. cover stock. "We are a national literary magazine publishing mostly fiction and poetry. To date, we have had three special focus issues (the 'urban' and the 'rural' experience, 'Southern'). For anyone with enough interest in literature to look for writing of quality and writers on the contemporary scene who deserve attention. There probably is a growing circuit of writers, some academics, reading us by recommendations." Annually. Estab. 1975. Circ. 500-700.

Needs: Literary. "No *Reader's Digest* style; that is, very popularly oriented. We like to do interdisciplinary features, e.g., literature and music, literature and science and literature and the natural world." Upcoming themes: "Animal World;" "Farms and Farming;" "Send-ups of PC," (politically correct language). Accepts 8-10 mss/year. Does not read in July or August. Published work by William Davey, Ron Berube, Patricia Ver Ellen; published new writers within the last year. Length: 10-25 pages. Also publishes poetry. Sometimes recommends other markets.

How to Contact: Query. Send complete ms with cover letter. "Don't talk too much, 'explain' the work, or act apologetic or arrogant. If published, tell where, with a brief bio." SASE. Reports in 2 weeks on queries, 2 months on mss. Sample copy $5 for annual issue.

Payment: Pays 2 contributor's copies. Charges ½ price of current issue for extras to its authors.

Terms: Acquires one-time rights. Requests credits for further publication of material used by *OB*.

Advice: "Read our publication first. Don't send out blindly; get some idea of what the magazine might want. A *short* personal note with biography is appreciated. Competition is keen. Read an eclectic mix of classic and contemporary. Beware of untransformed autobiography, but *everything* in one's experience contributes."

‡OXALIS, A Literary Magazine, (II), Stone Ridge Poetry Society, P.O. Box 3993, Kingston NY 12401. (914)687-7942. Editor: Shirley Powell. Fiction Editor: Mildred Barker. Magazine: 8½ × 11; 48-60 pages; 60 lb. recycled paper; 65 lb. recycled cover. "A selection of the best in poetry and fiction presented in an attractive package. For people interested in good writing." Quarterly. Estab. 1988. Circ. 350.

Needs: Adventure, contemporary, erotica, ethnic, experimental, fantasy, feminist, gay, historical, horror, humor/satire, lesbian, literary, mainstream, prose poem, regional, romance (contemporary, historical), science fiction, senior citizen/retirement, sports, suspense/mystery, western, contemporary issues: environment, human rights. "Nothing sentimental or preachy." No children's literature. Receives 10 unsolicited mss/month. Accepts 2-7 mss/issue; 12 mss/year (Magazine is about half poetry, half fiction.) Publishes ms 6-15 months after acceptance. Recently published work by Gertrude Reiss, Holly Beye, Stephen Phillip Policoff. Length: 4,000 words maximum. Publishes short shorts. Also publishes poetry.

How to Contact: Include "2 or 3 sentence bio suitable for Contributors' Page." Reports in 2 weeks on queries; 1 month on mss. SASE. Simultaneous submissions OK. Accepts computer printout submissions. Sample copy for $4. Fiction guidelines for #10 SAE and 1 first class stamp.

Payment: Pays 2 contributor's copies.

Terms: Acquires first rights or one-time rights.

Advice: Looks for "Something different from anything I've read before. Something that changes my mind or shakes me up. Fiction I can't forget. Read *Oxalis* and acquaint yourself with contemporary writing. Then write something better."

OXFORD MAGAZINE, (II), Bachelor Hall, Miami University, Oxford OH 45056. (513)529-5256. Fiction Editor: Kathryn C. Lacey. Magazine: 6 × 9; 85-100 pages; illustrations. Biannually. Estab. 1985. Circ. 500-1,000.

Needs: Ethnic, experimental, feminist, gay, humor/satire, lesbian, literary, translations. Receives 50-60 unsolicited mss/month. Does not read mss May through August. Published new writers within the last year. Length: 2,000-3,000 words average; 4,000 words maximum. Publishes short shorts. Also publishes literary essays, literary criticism, poetry.

How to Contact: Send complete ms with cover letter, which should include a short bio or interesting information. Reports in 3-4 months on mss. SASE. Photocopied submissions OK. Accepts computer printout submissions. Sample copy for $4, 10×12 SAE and 4 first class stamps. Reviews novels and short story collections. Send books to Collin Brooke, managing editor.
Payment: Pays a small honorarium and 1 year subscription.
Terms: Acquires one-time rights.
Advice: "We look for writing that makes sense: fiction that makes you put down your spoon and reread the page until your soup goes cold."

OYEZ REVIEW, (I, II), 430 S. Michigan Ave., Chicago IL 60605. (312)341-2017. Editor: Sarah Kusar. Magazine: 5½×8½; 91 pages; b&w camera ready illustrations and photos. Looking for "what is fresh and good" for Chicago audience. Annually. Estab. 1967. Circ. 500.
Needs: Contemporary, experimental, feminist, literary and regional. Accepts 2-5 mss/issue. Length: "about 10 pages, double-spaced." Also publishes poetry.
How to Contact: Send complete ms with SASE. Reports in 3 months on ms. Photocopied submissions OK. Sample copy $4.
Payment: Pays 5 contributor's copies.
Terms: Acquires one-time rights.
Advice: *"Oyez* encourages imaginative fiction, good dialogue, good characterization. Because our magazine is small and we have more poetry than fiction, we need/want *good,* but short fiction. We are interested in seeing what all writers can do—not just previously published writers. Since our staff changes from year to year, so does the philosophy of the publication—this year we are trying to delve into the collective American unconscious!"

P.I. MAGAZINE, Fact and Fiction about the World of Private Investigators, (II), 755 Bronx, Toledo OH 43609. (419)382-0967. Editor: Bob Mackowiak. Magazine: 8½×11; about 50 pages; coated white paper and cover; illustrations and photographs. "All about private eyes: personality profiles and stories about professional investigators; original fiction; books, movie, video, games, etc. Audience includes private eye and mystery fans." Quarterly. Estab. 1988. Circ. 750
Needs: Adventure, humor/satire, suspense/mystery. "Principal character must be a private detective—not a police detective, spy or school teacher who solves murders on the side. No explicit sex." Buys 4-6 mss/issue. Publishes ms 2-3 months after acceptance. Published work by Curtis Fischer; column by Bill Palmer. Length: 2,500 words preferred; 500 words minimum; 5,000 words maximum. Publishes short shorts. Sometimes critiques rejected ms and recommends other markets if possible.
How to Contact: Send complete ms with cover letter. Reports in 4 months. SASE. Simultaneous and photocopied submissions OK. Accepts computer printout submissions. Single copy for $4.75."
Payment: Pays $15 minimum; $25 for fiction; contributor's copies; charge for extras.
Terms: Pays on publication for one-time rights.
Advice: "Private eye stories do not need to be murder mysteries, and they do not need to start with a client walking into the detective's run-down office. How about a successful private investigator making good money—most of the real P.I.s run profitable businesses."

THE P.U.N. (PLAY ON WORDS), (II), The Silly Club and Michael Rayner, Box 536-583, Orlando FL 32853. (407)898-0463. Editor: Danno Sullivan. Newsletter: 8 pages; cartoons. "All polite humor. Polite, meaning no foul language, sex, etc. As a joke, something like 'Child Abuse with Dr. Seuss' is OK. We have an intelligent readership. They don't mind puzzling a bit to get the joke, but they also enjoy plain silliness." Published bimonthly. Estab. 1982. Circ. 400.
Needs: Humor/satire. Receives 20 unsolicited fiction mss/month. Accepts 1-3 mss/issue; 10-20 mss/year. Publishes ms "usually next issue" after acceptance. Length: short shorts, 1 page or less. Sometimes critiques rejected mss.
How to Contact: Send complete ms with cover letter. Reports in 2-3 weeks. SASE. Simultaneous, photocopied and reprint submissions OK. Accepts computer printouts. Sample copy for #10 SASE and $1.
Payment: Pays $1 minimum, $15 maximum; contributor's copies.
Terms: Pays on acceptance for one-time rights.
Advice: "Keep it short. Keep it obviously (even if it's subtle) funny. Above all, don't write like Erma Bombeck. We get a lot of 'cute' material—*Readers Digest*-style, which is not for us. We like short *articles,* as opposed to stories. Fiction presented as fact."

PABLO LENNIS, (I, IV), The Magazine of Science Fiction, Fantasy and Fact, Halcyon Press, Fandom House, 30 North 19th St., Lafayette IN 47904. Editor: John Thiel. Magazine: 8½×11; 22 pages; standard stock; illustrations and "occasional" photos. "Science fiction, fantasy, science, research and mystic for scientists and science fiction and fantasy appreciators." Published 4-5 times/year.
Needs: Fantasy, psychic/supernatural/occult, science fiction, spiritual. Receives 25 unsolicited mss/ year. Accepts 3 mss/issue; 15 mss/year. Publishes ms 6 months after acceptance. Published work by Eugene Flinn, Archie Taylor, Martha Collins; published new writers within the last year. Length: 1,500 words average; 3,000 words maximum. Also publishes literary criticism, poetry. Occasionally critiques rejected mss and recommends other markets.
How to Contact: "Method of submission is author's choice but he might prefer to query. No self-statement is necessary." Reports in 2 weeks. Does not accept computer printouts.
Payment: Pays in contributor's copies.
Terms: Publication not copyrighted.
Advice: "*Novel and Short Story Writer's Market* has brought in many new manuscripts, so my rate of publication has slowed down, but I don't reject frequently and then with good reasons. If you want to write a really good story, stick to materially perceived reality in setting scenes and saying something the reader would like to hear. Always have an understandable framework from which to depart imaginatively. I like an optimistic approach and one which is elevating to readers, and do have editorial taboos against unpleasant and abusive language."

PAINTED BRIDE QUARTERLY, (II), Painted Bride Art Center, 230 Vine St., Philadelphia PA 19106. (215)925-9914. Editor: Teresa Leo. Literary magazine: 6×9; 96-100 pages; illustrations; photos. Quarterly. Estab. 1975. Circ. 1,000.
Needs: Contemporary, ethnic, experimental, feminist, gay, lesbian, literary, prose poem and translations. Receives 10 unsolicited mss/week. Accepts 2 mss/issue; 8 mss/year. Published new writers within the last year. Length: 3,000 words average; 5,000 words maximum. Publishes short shorts. Also publishes literary essays, literary criticism, poetry. Occasionally critiques rejected mss.
How to Contact: Send complete ms. Reports in 3 weeks-3 months. SASE. Accepts computer printout submissions. Sample copy $5. Reviews novels and short story collections. Send books to Lou McKee.
Payment: Pays 1 contributor's copy, 1 year free subscription, 50% off additional copies.
Terms: Acquires first North American serial rights.
Advice: "We want quality in whatever—we hold experimental work to as strict standards as anything else. Many of our readers write fiction; most of them enjoy a good reading. We hope to be an outlet for quality. A good story gives, first, enjoyment to the reader. We've seen a good many of them lately, and we've published the best of them."

‡PAINTED HILLS REVIEW, (II), P.O. Box 494, Davis CA 95617. (916)756-5987. Editors: Michael Ishii, Kara Kosmatka. Magazine: 5½×8½; 48 pages. "Our only criterion for the work we publish is solid, well-written work. We publish poems, fiction (short stories and novel excerpts), plus b&w art for those interested in the literary arts, in the *craft* of writing." Quarterly. Estab. 1990. Circ. 300.
Needs: Excerpted novel, confession, contemporary, ethnic, experimental, historical (general), humor/ satire, literary, prose poem, regional, religious/inspirational, translations, western, young adult/teen. No "gay/lesbian, pornography, occult/New Age, horror/shock fiction." Plans special fiction issue. Receives 10-30 unsolicited mss/month. Accepts 1-3 mss/issue; 8-10 mss/year. Publishes ms 2 months to 1 year after acceptance. Recently published work by Omar Castañeda, Mark Wisniewski, James Sallis, Lia Smith. Length: 2,500 words preferred; 4,000 words maximum. Publishes short shorts. Sometimes critiques rejected mss.
How to Contact: Send complete ms with cover letter. Include a short bio of author (a paragraph). Reports in 1 week on queries; 4-6 weeks on mss. SASE. Photocopied submissions OK. Accepts computer printout submissions. Sample copy for $3. Fiction guidelines for #10 SAE and 1 first class stamp.
Payment: Pays 2 or more contributor's copies.
Terms: Acquires one-time rights. All rights revert to author upon publication.
Advice: Ask: "Does it look as if it was written in one sitting and never looked at again? Or has it been worked on? Does the narration flow smoothly? Is the language awkward? Is there an interesting-enough conflict and resolution in the story? Basically, is it well-written?" Sponsors annual fiction contest; send SASE for details.

Read the Business of Fiction section to learn the correct way to prepare and submit a manuscript.

‡**PALACE CORBIE, (II),** Merrimack Books, P.O. Box 158, Lynn IN 47355. (317)935-0232. Editor: Wayne Edwards. Magazine: 8½×11; 48-96 pages; card stock cover; b&w illustrations. "Perseverance in the face of adversity, doom and despair for a horror/dark fantasy audience." Semiannually. Estab. 1992.
Needs: Adventure, contemporary, erotica, ethnic, experimental, fantasy, feminist, gay, historical (general), horror, lesbian, literary, psychic/supernatural/occult, religious/inspirational, science fiction, translations. Publishes annual special fiction issue. Receives about 100 unsolicited mss/month. Accepts about 8 mss/issue; 16-20 mss/year. Publishes ms 6 months after acceptance. Length: No preference. Publishes short shorts. Sometimes critiques rejected mss and recommends other markets.
How to Contact: Send complete ms, cover letter (optional). Reports in 2 weeks on queries; 3 weeks on mss. SASE. Photocopied and reprint submissions OK. Accepts computer printout submissions. Accepts electronic submissions via disk (MACWORD only). Fiction guidelines for #10 SAE and 1 first class stamp.
Payment: Pays contributor's copies. Charges for extras.
Terms: Acquires one-time rights. Sends galleys to author.
Advice: "Quality of writing only. What aggravates me the most, however, is a story with *no* plot. I see a lot of those."

‡**PANDORA, (I),** 2844 Grayson, Ferndale MI 48220. Editor: Meg Mac Donald. Anthology: 5½×8½; 72 pages; offset paper; perfect-bound, 2-color laminated cover; b&w illustrations. Magazine for science fiction and fantasy readers. Published 2 times/year. Estab. 1978. Circ. 500.
Needs: Fantasy, science fiction. "Nothing X-rated; no horror; no gratuitous violence or sex. Unless the author created the universe, she/he should not send us stories in that universe." Receives 200 unsolicited fiction mss/month. Buys 6-10 mss/issue, 20 mss/year. Publishes ms 6 months-1 year after acceptance on average, sometimes as long as 2 years. Published many new writers within the last year. Length: 5,000 words average; 10,000 words maximum (occasional stories may be longer). Always critiques rejected mss. Also publishes poetry. Sometimes recommends other markets.
How to Contact: Send complete ms with cover letter, which should include relevant publication history. Reports in 2 weeks on queries; 2-3 months on mss. Photocopied and previously published submissions OK. Accepts computer printout submissions. Sample copy $5 (US); $7 (Canada/Mexico); $10 overseas. Fiction guidelines for SASE.
Payment: Pays 1-2¢/word and 1 contributor's copy.
Terms: Pays on publication for first North American serial rights, second rights or one-time rights on previously published mss.
Advice: "Steering away from horror of all kinds and fantasy set in mundane or contemporary society. Know your market! Read and study fiction everywhere, but know a given market well before trying to crack it. We receive a large number of inappropriate material. Read *Pandora* to get to know our needs and preferences. Above all write what your heart leads you to write, what moves you, excites you, frightens you. Use your gift for words as wisely as you can—don't write to hurt—write to enlighten! Good luck!"

THE PANHANDLER, A Magazine of Poetry and Fiction, (II), The University of West Florida, English Dept., Pensacola FL 32514. (904)474-2923. Editors: Michael Yots and Stanton Millet. Magazine: 6×9; 64 pages; 40 lb paper; 70 lb cover stock. Semiannually. Estab. 1976. Circ. 500.
Needs: Contemporary, ethnic, experimental, humor/satire, literary and mainstream. No Sci Fi, horror, erotica. Plans to publish special fiction or anthology issue in the future. Receives 10 unsolicited mss/month. Accepts 2-4 mss/issue; 8-10 mss/year. Publishes ms 3-8 months after acceptance. Length: 1,500-3,000 words; 2,500 average. Sometimes critiques rejected mss and recommends other markets.
How to Contact: Send complete ms with cover letter. Including writing experience, publications. Reports in 1-4 months. SASE. Simultaneous submissions OK. Sample copy $2. Fiction guidelines for #10 SAE and 1 first class stamp.
Payment: Pays in contributor's copies.
Terms: Acquires first rights.
Advice: "We look for engaging narrative voice. Characters whose concerns are of interest to readers. Real, everyday problems, dilemmas. Clear, efficient narrative style. Manuscript must lead the reader through the story and make him feel on completion that it was worth the trip."

THE PAPER BAG, (I, II), Box 268805, Chicago IL 60626-8805. (312)285-7972. Editor: Michael H. Brownstein. Magazine: 5½×8½; 25-40 pages; cardboard cover stock; illustrations. Quarterly. Estab. 1988. Circ. 300.

Needs: Adventure, contemporary, erotica, ethnic, experimental, fantasy, feminist, horror, literary, mainstream, prose poem, suspense/mystery and western. Plans to publish special fiction or anthology issue in the future. Receives 10 unsolicited mss/month. Accepts 2-4 mss/issue; 36-60 mss/year. Publishes mss 3 months to 1 year after acceptance. Under 500 words preferred; 500 words maximum. "Has to be under 500 words." Sometimes critiques rejected mss and recommends other markets.
How to Contact: Send complete ms with cover letter. "Include brief bio for our contributor's page." Reports in 1 week on queries; 1 week to 3 months on mss. SASE. Photocopied submissions OK. Sample copy $2.50. Fiction guidelines for SAE and 1 first class stamp.
Payment: Pays in contributor's copies.
Terms: Acquires first rights. Sometimes sends pre-publication galleys to the author.

PAPER RADIO, (I,II), Suite 797, N 4th, Coeur d'Alene ID 83814. Editor: N.S. Kvern. Magazine: 8½×11; 48-64 pages; photocopied and/or offset paper and cover; illustrations; b&w photographs. "We're open to anything, but it has to be short—usually less than 2,500 words." Readers are "mostly people who are interested in avant garde, mail art, photocopied art, political, bizarre, surrealism, cyberpunk, literary/experimental writing and computers." Published 2-3 times/year. Estab. 1986. Circ. 2,000.
Needs: Erotica, experimental, fantasy, literary, prose poem, science fiction. Receives 25 unsolicited fiction mss/month. Accepts 4-5 mss/issue; 12-15 mss/year. Publishes ms an average of 2-3 months after acceptance. Length: 2,000 words average; 3,500 words maximum. Publishes short shorts. Sometimes critiques rejected mss.
How to Contact: Send complete ms with cover letter. "some autobiographical information is helpful—one or two paragraphs—and I like to know where they hear about our magazine." Reports in 2 months. SASE. Simultaneous or photocopied submissions OK. Accepts computer printout submissions. Sample copy $4.
Payment: Pays contributor's copies.
Terms: Acquires first rights, "artist can publish material elsewhere simultaneously."
Advice: "We are devoted to the cause of experimentation and literature and we like a wide variety of fiction. Best to see a sample copy. Our publication is orderly in its chaos, wild and untameable in its order."

PARAGRAPH, A Magazine of Paragraphs, (II), Box 326, Tuscaloosa AL 35401. (205)759-2994. Co-Editors: Walker Rumble and Karen Donovan. Magazine: 4¼×5½; 38 pages. "No particular theme—we publish collections of paragraphs for a general audience." Published 3 times/year. Estab. 1985. Circ. 700.
Needs: "Any topic is welcome, including experimental writing. Our only requirement is that paragraphs must be 200 words or less." Receives 30-40 unsolicited mss/month. Accepts 30-33 mss/issue; 90 mss/year. Publishes ms 2-3 months after acceptance. Published work by Lisa Shea, Laurel Speer, Conger Beasley Jr., Jennifer Lodde, Gary Fincke. Length: 200 words. Also publishes literary essays, but 200 words maximum, of course. Sometimes critiques rejected mss.
How to Contact: Send complete manuscript with cover letter. Reports in 1 week on queries; 2 months on mss. SASE. Simultaneous and photocopied submissions OK. Accepts computer printout submissions. Sample copy $3. Fiction guidelines for SAE and 1 first class stamp.
Payment: Pays contributor's copies and charges for extras.
Terms: Acquires first rights. Sends galleys to author.

THE PARIS REVIEW (II), 45-39 171 St. Pl., Flushing NY 11358 (business office only, send mss to address below). Editor: George A. Plimpton. Managing Editor: James Linville. Magazine: 5¼×8½; about 240 pages; 50 lb. paper; 10 pt. CIS cover stock; illustrations and photographs. "Fiction and poetry of superlative quality, whatever the genre, style or mode. Our contributors include prominent, as well as little-known and previously unpublished writers. 'The Art of Fiction' interview series includes important contemporary writers discussing their own work and the craft of writing." Quarterly.
Needs: Committed work of boldness and originality, combining excellence of form and voice. Receives about 1,000 unsolicited fiction mss each month. Published work by Raymond Carver, Elizabeth Tallent, Rick Bass, John Koethe, Sharon Olds, Derek Walcott, Carolyn Kizer, Tess Gallagher, Peter Handke, Denis Johnson, Bobbie Ann Mason, Harold Brodkey, Joseph Brodsky, John Updike, Andre Dubus, Galway Kinnell, E.L. Doctorow and Philip Levine. Published new writers within the last year. No preferred length. Also publishes literary essays, poetry.

How to Contact: *Send complete ms with SASE to Fiction Editor, 541 E. 72nd St., New York NY 10021.* Reports in 6-8 weeks on mss. Sample copy $7. Reviews novels and short story collections. Send books to Elizabeth Gaffney.
Payment: Pays $100-500; 2 contributor's copies. Regular charge for extras.
Terms: Pays on publication for first North American serial rights. Sends galleys to author.
Advice: *"The Paris Review* has the widest circulation of any literary journal. We are devoted to helping talented, original writers find larger audiences."

PARTING GIFTS, (II), 3006 Stonecutter Terrace, Greensboro NC 27405. Editor: Robert Bixby. Magazine: 5×8; 40 pages. "High quality insightful fiction, very brief and on any theme." Semiannual. Estab. 1988.
Needs: "Brevity is the second most important criterion behind literary quality." Publishes ms within one year of acceptance. Length: 250 words minimum; 1,000 words maximum. Also publishes literary criticism, poetry. Sometimes critiques rejected mss.
How to Contact: Send complete ms with cover letter. Reports in 1 day on queries; 1-7 days on mss. SASE. Accepts computer printout submissions. Reviews novels and short story collections.
Payment: Pays in contributor's copies.
Terms: Acquires one-time rights.
Advice: "Read the works of Amy Hempel, Jim Harrison, C.K. Williams and Janet Kauffman, all excellent writers who epitomize the writing *Parting Gifts* strives to promote."

PARTISAN REVIEW, (II), 236 Bay State Rd., Boston MA 02215. (617)353-4260. Editor: William Phillips. Executive Editor: Edith Kurzweil. Magazine: 6×9; 160 pages; 40 lb. paper; 60 lb. cover stock. "Theme is of world literature and contemporary culture: fiction, essays and poetry with emphasis on the arts and political and social commentary, for the general intellectual public; schoiars." Quarterly. Estab. 1934. Circ. 8,000.
Needs: Contemporary, experimental, literary, prose poem, regional and translations. Receives 100 unsolicited fiction mss/month. Buys 2 mss/issue; 8 mss/year. Published work by José Donosó, Isaac Bashevis Singer, Doris Lessing; published new writers within the last year. Length: open. Publishes short shorts.
How to Contact: Send complete ms with SASE and cover letter listing past credits. Photocopied submissions OK. Accepts computer printout submissions. Reports in 4 months on mss. Sample copy for $5 and $1 postage.
Payment: Pays $25-200; 1 free contributor's copy.
Terms: Pays on publication for first rights.
Advice: "Please, research the type of fiction we publish. Often we receive manuscripts which are entirely inappropriate for our journal. Sample copies are available and this is a good way to determine audience."

PASSAGER, A Journal of Remembrance and Discovery, (II, IV), University of Baltimore, 1420 N. Charles, Baltimore MD 21201-5779. Editor: Kendra Kopelke. Fiction Editor: Sally Darnowsky. Magazine: 8¼ square; 32-36 pages; 70 lb. paper; 80 lb. cover; photographs. "We publish stories and novel excerpts to 3,000 words, poems to 50 lines. Query for interviews." Quarterly. Estab. 1990. Circ. 750.
Needs: "Publishes personal voices that speak about the strangeness and wonder of the passage of time. Special interest in older writers, but publishes all ages." Receives 300 unsolicited mss/month. Accepts 3-4 prose mss/issue; 12-15/year. Publishes ms up to 1 year after acceptance. Recently published work by Elisavietta Ritchie, Lawrence Durrell, Edmund Keeley, Ronnie Gilbert. Length: 250 words minimum; 3,000 words maximum. Publishes short shorts. Also publishes literary essays, poetry. Length: 250 words. Often critiques rejected mss.
How to Contact: Send complete ms with cover letter. Reports in 3 months on mss. SASE. Photocopied submissions OK. Accepts computer printout submissions. Sample copy for $3.50. Fiction guidelines for #10 SAE and 1 first class stamp.
Payment: Pays free subscription to magazine and contributor's copies.
Terms: Acquires first North American serial rights. Sometimes sends galleys to author.
Advice: *"Get a copy* so you can see the quality of the work we use. We often reject beautifully written work that is bland in favor of rougher work that has the spark we're looking for. In those cases, we try to work with the author to bring the work to a publishable condition—if possible."

PASSAGES NORTH, (II), Kalamazoo College, 1200 Academy St., Kalamazoo MI 49007. Editors: Ben Mitchell. Fiction Editor: Mary La Chapelle. Tabloid: 11¼ × 14; 32 pages; white uncoated paper; original art and photography. Readership: general and literary. Semiannual. Estab. 1979. Circ. 2,500.
Needs: Short fiction. "Excellence is our only criteria. Subjects and genre are open." Accepts 5-10 mss/year. Published works by Susan Straight, Gary Gildner; published new writers within the last year. Length: 500-10,000 words. Critiques returned mss when there is time.
How to Contact: Send complete mss with SASE and brief letter of previous publication, awards. Reports in 3 weeks to 2 months. Publishes an average of 3-6 months after acceptance. Sample copy $3.
Payment: Pays 3 contributor's copies. Frequent honoraria.
Terms: Rights revert to author on publication. No reprints.
Advice: *"Passages North* seeks excellent writing in a variety of genres including short fiction, memoirs, natural history and criticism."

PEARL, A Literary Magazine, (II, IV), 3030 E. Second St., Long Beach CA 90803. (213)434-4523. Editors: Joan Jobe Smith, Marilyn Johnson and Barbara Hauk. Magazine: 5½ × 8½; 64 pages; 60 lb. bond paper; 80 lb. gloss cover; b&w drawings and graphics. "We are primarily a poetry magazine, but we do publish some *very short* fiction and nonfiction. We are interested in lively, readable prose that speaks to *real* people in direct, living language; for a general literary audience." Semiannually. Estab. 1974 ("folded" after 3 issues but began publishing again in 1987). Circ. 500.
Needs: Contemporary, humor/satire, literary, mainstream, prose poem. "We will only consider short-short stories up to 1,200 words. For longer stories, we suggest entering our annual short story contest. Although we have no taboos stylistically or subject-wise, obscure, predictable, sentimental, or cliché-ridden stories are a turn-off." Plans special fiction issue. Receives 4-5 unsolicited mss/month. Accepts 1-2 mss/issue; 2-4 mss/year. Publishes ms 6 months to 1 year after acceptance. Recently published work by MacDonald Harris, Josephine Marshall, Donna Hibert. Length: 1,000 words average; 500 words minimum; 1,200 words maximum. Also publishes poetry.
How to Contact: Send complete manuscript with cover letter including publishing credits and brief biographical information. Reports in 6-8 weeks on mss. SASE. Photocopied submissions OK. Accepts computer printout submissions. Sample copy $5 (postpaid). Fiction guidelines for #10 SAE and 1 first class stamp.
Payment: Pays 2 contributor's copies.
Terms: Acquires first North American serial rights. Sends galleys to author. *"Pearl* holds an annual short story contest. Submission period: December 1-March 1. Award: $50, publication in *Pearl*, 10 copies. $5 entry fee. Maximum length: 4,000 words. Send SASE for complete guidelines."
Advice: "We look for vivid, *dramatized* situations and characters, stories written in an original 'voice,' that make sense and follow a clear narrative line. What makes a manuscript stand out is more elusive, though—more to do with feeling and imagination than anything else . . ."

THE PEGASUS REVIEW, (I, IV), Box 134, Flanders NJ 07836. (201)927-0749. Editor: Art Bounds. Magazine: 5½ × 8½; 6-8 pages; illustrations. "Our magazine is a bimonthly, done entirely in calligraphy, illustrated. Each issue is based on a specific theme for those who appreciate quality in both writing and presentation. Plans new features, more pages in 1992." Estab. 1980. Circ. 200.
Needs: Humor/satire, literary, prose poem and religious/inspirational. Upcoming themes: "Courage" (January/February); "Dreams" (March/April); "Friends" (May/June); "America" (July/August); "Autumn" (September/October); "Christmas" (November/December). "Themes may be approached by humor, satire, inspirational, autobiographical, prose. Try to avoid the obvious." Receives 50 unsolicited mss/month. Accepts 60 mss/year. Recently published work by John Tannehill, Don Shea, Marie Ferneau; published new writers within the last year. Publishes short shorts 3 pages; 500 words. Themes are subject to change, so query if in doubt. Critiques rejected mss.
How to Contact: Send complete ms. SASE "a must." Cover letter with author's background and full name—no initials. Photocopied submissions OK. Accepts computer printout submissions. Simultaneous submissions acceptable, if so advised. Sample copy $2. Fiction guidelines for SAE.
Payment: Pays 2 contributor's copies. Occasional book awards.
Terms: Acquires one-time rights.
Advice: "Read and write, they both go hand in hand. Our needs call for brevity due to our calligraphy format. Fiction should be no longer than 3 pages. Study your markets, learn their slant and then submit. Above all, persevere."

PEMBROKE MAGAZINE, (I, II), Box 60, Pembroke State University, Pembroke NC 28372. (919)521-4214, ext. 433. Editor: Shelby Stephenson. Fiction Editor: Stephen Smith. Magazine: 9 × 10; 225 pages; illustrations; photos. Magazine of poems and stories plus literary essays. Annually. Estab. 1969. Circ. 500.
Needs: Open. Receives 40 unsolicited mss/month. Publishes short shorts. Published work by Fred Chappell, Robert Morgan; published new writers within the last year. Length: open. Occasionally critiques rejected mss and recommends other markets.
How to Contact: Send complete ms. Reports immediately to 3 months. SASE. Accepts computer printout submissions. Sample copy $3 and 9 × 10 SAE.
Payment: Pays 1 contributor's copy.
Advice: "Write with an end for *writing*, not publication."

PENNSYLVANIA ENGLISH, (II), English Department, Penn State University—Erie, Humanities Division, Erie PA 16563. Editor: Dean Baldwin. Fiction Editor: Chris Dubbs. Magazine: 7 × 8½; 100 pages; 20 lb. bond paper; 65 lb. matte cover. For "teachers of English in Pennsylvania at the high school and college level." Semiannually. Estab. 1985. Circ. 300.
Needs: Literary, contemporary mainstream. Does not read mss from May to August. Publishes ms an average of 6 months after acceptance. Length: 5,000 words maximum. Publishes short shorts. Also publishes literary essays, literary criticism, poetry. Sometimes critiques rejected mss.
How to Contact: Send complete ms with cover letter. Reports in 2 months. SASE. Simultaneous, computer printout and photocopied submissions OK.
Payment: Pays in contributor's copies.
Terms: Acquires first North American serial rights.

PEOPLENET, "Where People Meet People," (IV), Box 897, Levittown NY 11756. (516)579-4043. Editor: Robert Mauro. Newsletter: 8½ × 11; 12 pages; 20 lb. paper; 20 lb. cover stock. "Romance stories featuring disabled characters." Quarterly. Estab. 1987. Circ. 200.
Needs: Romance, contemporary and disabled. Main character must be disabled. Accepts 1-2 mss/issue; 4-8 mss/year. Publishes ms up to 2 years after acceptance. Length: 500-1,000 words; 800-1,000 average. Publishes short shorts. Also publishes literary criticism, poetry.
How to Contact: Send complete ms and SASE. Reports in 1 week "*only* if SASE there." Accepts computer printout submissions. Fiction guidelines for #10 SAE and 1 first class stamp.
Payment: Pays 1¢/word on acceptance.
Terms: Acquires first rights.
Advice: "We are looking for stories of under 1,000 words on romance with a disabled man or woman as the main character. No sob stories or 'super crip' stories. Just realistic romance. No porn. Love, respect, trust, understanding and acceptance are what I want."

PERCEPTIONS, (I), 1530 Phillips, Missoula MT 59802. (406)543-5875. Editor: Temi Rose. Magazine: 4 × 5; 20 pages. Publishes "primarily women's perceptions," for readers of "all ages, both sexes." Published 3 times/year. Plans special fiction issue. Estab. 1982. Circ. 100.
Needs: Adventure, condensed/excerpted novel, confession contemporary, experimental, fantasy, feminist, prose poem, psychic/supernatural/occult, religious/inspirational, science fiction, suspense/mystery. Accepts 1 ms/issue. Length: four pages tops. Publishes short shorts. Collected by University of Wisconsin, Madison Serials Library; produces poetry videos with permission of writers. Critiques rejected mss "only if requested."
How to Contact: Query first. Reports in 2-3 weeks on queries; in 1 month on mss. SASE. Simultaneous, photocopied and reprint submissions OK. Accepts computer printout submissions. Accepts electronic submissions via disk or modem. Sample copy $4. Fiction guidelines for SAE and 1 first class stamp.
Payment: Pays in contributor's copies.

‡PEREGRINE, The Journal of Amherst Writers and Artists, (II), Amherst Writers and Artists Press, Box 1076, Amherst MA 01004. (413)253-3307. Magazine: 5 × 7; 90 pages; sturdy matte white paper; heavier cover stock; perfect-bound; illustrations occasionally. "Poetry and prose—short stories, short short stories, and occasionally prose fantasies or reflections that are fiction yet are not stories." Annually.
Needs: "No specific 'category' requirements; we publish what we love." Accepts 2-4 mss/issue. Publishes ms an average of 6 months after acceptance. Recently published work by Anna Kirwan Vogel, Margaret Robison, Barbara VanNoord; published new writers within the last year. Length: 1,000-

2,500 words preferred. Publishes short shorts. "Short pieces have a better chance of publication."
How to Contact: Send complete ms with cover letter, which should include brief biographical note. Reports in 3-6 months. SASE. Simultaneous and photocopied submissions OK. Accepts computer printout submissions. Sample copy $3 plus $2 postage.
Payment: Pays contributor's copies.
Terms: All rights return to writer upon publication.

PHOEBE, A Journal of Literary Arts, (II), George Mason University, 4400 University Dr., Fairfax VA 22030. (703)993-2915. Editor: Rex Batson. Fiction Editors: John Latonna, Cathie Cruise. Magazine: 6×9; 116 pages; 80 lb. quality paper; 0-5 illustrations per issue; 0-10 photographs per issue. "We publish fiction, poetry, photographs, illustrations and some reviews." Published 2 times/year. Estab. 1972. Circ. 2,500.
Needs: "Looking for a broad range of poetry, fiction and essays. Encourage writers and poets to experiment, to stretch the boundaries of genre." No romance, western, juvenile, erotica. Receives 20 mss/month. Accepts 5-7 mss/issue; 20-28 mss/year. Does not read mss in summer. Deadlines for mss are: September 25th for Fall issue; February 10th for Spring issue. Publishes ms 3-6 months after acceptance. Length: "no more than 35 pages. Also publishes literary essays, literary criticism, poetry.
How to Contact: Send complete ms with cover letter. Include "name, address, phone. Brief bio." SASE. Photocopied submissions OK. Sample copy $3.25.
Payment: Pays 4 contributor's copies.
Terms: Acquires one-time rights. All rights revert to author.
Advice: "We are interested in a variety of fiction, poetry and nonfiction. We suggest potential contributors study previous issues."

PIG IRON, (II), Box 237, Youngstown OH 44501. (216)783-1269. Editor: Jim Villani. Magazine. 8½×11; 128 pages; 60 lb. offset paper; 85 pt. coated cover stock; b&w illustrations; b&w 120 line photographs. "Contemporary literature by new and experimental writers." Annually. Estab. 1975. Circ. 1,000.
Needs: Literary and thematic. No mainstream. Upcoming theme: "The American Dream" (deadline: September 1992). Buys 10-20 mss/issue. Receives approximately 75-100 unsolicited fiction mss each month. Recently published work by Laural Speer, Eve Shelnutt, Reg Saner, Rhona McAdam. Length: 8,000 words maximum. Also publishes literary essays, poetry.
How to Contact: Send complete ms with SASE. No simultaneous submissions. Accepts computer printout submissions. Reports in 3 months. Sample copy $3.
Payment: Pays $5/printed page; 2 contributor's copies; $5 charge for extras.
Terms: Pays on publication for first North American serial rights.
Advice: "Looking for works that do not ignore psychological development in character and plot/action." Mss are rejected because of "lack of new ideas and approaches. Writers need to work out interesting plot/action and setting/set. Read a lot; read for stylistic innovation. Send SASE for current theme list."

THE PIKESTAFF FORUM, (II), Box 127, Normal IL 61761. (309)452-4831. Editors: Robert D. Sutherland, James Scrimgeour, James McGowan and Curtis White. Tabloid: 11½×17½; 40 pages; newsprint paper; illustrations; photos. "*The Pikestaff Forum* is a general literary magazine publishing poetry, prose fiction, drama." Readership: "General literary with a wide circulation in the small press world. Readers are educated (but not academic) and have a taste for excellent serious fiction." Published irregularly—"whenever we have sufficient quality material to warrant an issue." Estab. 1977. Circ. 1,000.
Needs: Literary and contemporary with a continuing need for good short stories or novel excerpts. "We welcome traditional and experimental works from established and non-established writers. We look for writing that is clear, concise and to the point; contains vivid imagery and sufficient concrete detail; is grounded in lived human experience; contains memorable characters and situations. No confessional self-pity or puffery; self-indulgent first or second drafts; sterile intellectual word games or five-finger exercises or slick formula writing, genre-pieces that do not go beyond their form (westerns, mysteries, gothic, horror, science fiction, swords-and-sorcery fantasy), commercially oriented mass-market stuff, violence for its own sake, racist or sexist material or pornography (sexploitation)." Accepts 1-4 mss/issue. Receives approximately 15-20 unsolicited fiction mss each month. Published work by Constance Pierce, Linnea Johnson; published new writers within the last year. Length: from 1 paragraph to 4,000 or 5,000 words. Also publishes poetry. Critiques rejected mss when there is time.

How to Contact: Query. Send complete ms. SASE. Accepts computer printout submissions. Reports in 3 weeks on queries, 3 months on mss. Publishes ms up to 1 year after acceptance. Sample copy $2.
Payment: Pays 3 contributor's copies. Cover price less 50% discount for extras.
Terms: Acquires first rights. Copyright remains with author.
Advice: "We are highly selective, publishing only 3% of the stories that are submitted for consideration. Read other authors with an appreciative and critical eye; don't send out work prematurely; develop keen powers of observation and a good visual memory; get to know your characters thoroughly; don't let others (editors, friends, etc.) define or 'determine' your sense of self-worth; be willing to learn; outgrow self-indulgence. Develop discipline. Show, don't tell; and leave some work for the reader to do. Write for the fun of it (that way there's a sure return for the investment of time and effort). Always write to achieve the best quality you can; be honest with yourself, your potential readers, and your story. Learn to become your own best editor: know when you've done well, and when you haven't done as well as you can. Remember: there's a lot of competition for the available publication slots, and editorial bias is always a factor in what gets accepted for publication. Develop a sense of humor about the enterprise."

PIKEVILLE REVIEW, (II), Pikeville College, Pikeville KY 41501. (606)432-9341. Editor: James Alan Riley. Magazine: 5 × 8; 80-100 pages; 60 lb. paper. "Fiction, poetry, interviews, essays and book reviews for literate audience." Annually. Estab. 1988. Circ. 500.
Needs: Contemporary, experimental, literary, prose poem, translations. Receives 20 unsolicited mss/month. Accepts 1 mss/issue. Published work by Malcolm Glass and Jim Wayne Miller. Publishes short shorts. Also publishes literary essays. Sometimes critiques rejected mss and recommends other markets.
How to Contact: Send complete manuscript with cover letter. Reports in 6 weeks to 5 months on mss. SASE. Photocopied submission OK. Accepts computer printout submissions. Sample copy $3. Fiction guidelines for SAE.
Payment: Pays contributor's copies.
Terms: Acquires one-time rights. "$50 to the best story selected for each issue and $50 to the best creative essay."

THE PINEHURST JOURNAL, Pinehurst Press, P.O. Box 360747, Milpitas CA 95036. (408)945-0986. Editor: Michael K. McNamara. Magazine: 8½ × 11; 40 pages; recycled 24 lb. paper; 60 lb. cover; uses illustrations. "Fiction, nonfiction and poetry for an educated audience appreciative of polished, thought-provoking work." Quarterly. Estab. 1990. Circ. 250.
Needs: Contemporary, erotica, experimental, feminist, gay, historical (general), horror, humor/satire, lesbian, literary, mainstream, prose poem, suspense/mystery. "No hard sci-fi, fantasy, occult, swords and sorcery, slasher or porn, travel or religious. No formula western or romance." Receives 80 mss/month. Accepts 17 mss/issue; 65-70 mss/year. Publishes ms 1-4 months after acceptance. Length: 2,000 words average; 750 words minimum; 4,000 words maximum. Publishes short shorts. Length: 200-400 words. Publishes literary essays, some literary criticism, some poetry. Critiques mss and recommends other markets.
How to Contact: Send complete manuscript with cover letter and short bio which includes publishing successes, if any. Indicate whether piece is a simultaneous submittal. Reports in 1 month or less on queries; 2 months or less on mss. SASE. Simultaneous and photocopied submissions OK. Accepts computer printout submissions. Sample copy for $4.75. Guidelines for #10 SAE and 1 first class stamp.
Payment: Pays $5 and 1 contributor's copy. Charge for extras.
Terms: Buys one-time rights.
Advice: "Try to make each word pull its own weight and polish, polish, polish then punctuate, punctuate, punctuate."

THE PIPE SMOKER'S EPHEMERIS, (I, II, IV), The Universal Coterie of Pipe Smokers, 20-37 120 St., College Point NY 11356. Editor: Tom Dunn. Magazine: 8½ × 11; 54-66 pages; offset paper and cover; illustrations; photos. Pipe smoking and tobacco theme for general and professional audience. Irregular quarterly. Estab. 1964.

The double dagger before a listing indicates that the listing is new in this edition. New markets are often the most receptive to freelance contributions.

Needs: Historical (general), humor/satire, literary, pipe smoking related. Publishes ms up to 1 year after acceptance. Length: 2,500 words average; 5,000 words maximum. Also publishes short shorts. Occasionally critiques rejected mss.
How to Contact: Send complete ms with cover letter. Reports in 2 weeks on mss. Simultaneous, photocopied submissions and reprints OK. Accepts computer printouts. Sample copy for 8½×11 SAE and 6 first class stamps.
Terms: Acquires one-time rights.

‡**PLOTS MAGAZINE, (I, II)**, P.O. Box 371, Kewanee IL 61443. (309)852-0332. Editor: Margi L. Washburn. Magazine: 8½×11; 60 pages; semi-gloss cover; illustrations. "*PLOTS* = (1) *Scary* fiction/poetry. (2) Good *plot* fiction, poetry, artwork, cartoons. For fans of *Thriller, Twilight Zone, Alfred Hitchcock*; chiller-type stories you would be afraid to read alone." Quarterly. Estab. 1990. Circ. 500.
Needs: Horror, psychic/supernatural/occult, suspense. "No excessive gore, violence or sexual situations." Plans special fiction issue. Receives 25 unsolicited mss/month. Buys 7-10 mss/issue; 25-40 mss/year. Publishes ms 6 months after acceptance. Recently published work by Jane Frazier, Sidney Seward, Terri Willits. Length: 2,500 words preferred; 100 words minimum; 10,000 words maximum. Publishes short shorts. Length: 250 words. Sometimes critiques rejected mss and recommends other markets.
How to Contact: Send complete ms with cover letter. Include "any pertinent questions to *PLOTS* and I'm always interested in the writer's background." Reports in 2 weeks on queries; 1 month on mss. SASE. Simultaneous, photocopied and reprint submissions OK. Accepts computer printout submissions. Sample copy for $4.50. Fiction guidelines for #10 SAE and 1 first class stamp.
Payment: Pays ½¢/word and 1 contributor's copy.
Terms: Pays on acceptance. Offers 50% kill fee. Buys first North American serial rights or one-time rights.
Advice: "I confess: I like to see the writing rules followed. It's good to see clean, crisp copy with few typos, dark lettering, double-spacing and *margins*. Also, I find the work sent in this way tends to belong to someone with a good tale to share. A chatty cover letter is welcome over none at all. If the story makes me shiver, rips at my heart, numbs my brain or makes my jaw drop, I'll buy it!"

PLOUGHSHARES, (II), Emerson College, 100 Beacon St., Boston MA 02116. (617)578-8753. Executive Director: DeWitt Henry. "Our theme is new writing (poetry, fiction, personal essays) that addresses contemporary adult readers who look to fiction and poetry for help in making sense of themselves and of each other." Triquarterly. Estab. 1971. Circ. 3,800.
Needs: Literary, prose poem. "No genre (science fiction, detective, gothic, adventure, etc.), popular formula or commercial fiction whose purpose is to entertain rather than to illuminate." Buys 20+ mss/year. Receives approximately 400-600 unsolicited fiction mss each month. Published work by Rick Bass, Joy Williams, Andre Dubus; published new writers within the last year. Length: 300-6,000 words.
How to Contact: "Query for guidelines and examine a sample issue. Reading periods and needs vary." Cover letter should include "previous pubs." SASE. Reports in 5 months on mss. Sample copy $7.95. (Please specify fiction issue sample.) Fiction guidelines for SASE.
Payment: Pays $10/page to $50 maximum, plus copies. Offers 50% kill fee for assigned ms not published.
Terms: Pays on publication for first North American serial rights.
Advice: "Be familiar with our fiction issues, fiction by our writers and by our various editors (e.g., Rosellen Brown, Tim O'Brien, Jay Neugeboren, Jayne Anne Phillips, James Alan McPherson) and more generally acquaint yourself with the best short fiction currently appearing in the literary quarterlies, and the annual prize anthologies (*Pushcart Prize, O. Henry Awards, Best American Short Stories*). Also realistically consider whether the work you are submitting is as good as or better than—in your own opinion—the work appearing in the magazine you're sending to. What is the level of competition? And what is its volume? (In our case, we accept about 1 ms in 200.) Never send 'blindly' to a magazine, or without carefully weighing your prospect there against those elsewhere. Always keep a copy of work you submit."

THE PLOWMAN, (II), Box 414, Whitby Ontario L1N 5S4 Canada. Editor: Tony Scavetta. Tabloid: 112 pages; illustrations and photos. "We are the largest chapbook publisher in the world, over 400 books to our name." Monthly. Estab. 1988. Circ. 10,000.
Needs: Adventure, confession, contemporary, ethnic, historical (general), juvenile (5-9 years), literary, mainstream, preschool (1-4 years), prose poem, regional, religious/inspirational, romance, senior citizen/retirement, translations, western and young adult/teen (10-18). Plans to publish special fiction

issue or an anthology in the future. Publishes ms 3 months after acceptance. Length: 1 typewritten page. Sometimes critiques rejected mss and recommends other markets.

How to Contact: Send complete ms with cover letter. Reports in 1 week. Enclose IRCs. Simultaneous, photocopied and reprint submissions OK. Accepts computer printout submissions. Sample copy and fiction guidelines for SAE.

Payment: Pays in contributor's copies; charges for extras.

Terms: Acquires one-time rights. Sends galleys to author.

POETIC SPACE, Poetry & Fiction, (I, II), P.O. Box 11157, Eugene OR 97440. Editor: Don Hildenbrand. Fiction Editor: Thomas Strand. Magazine: 8×11; 16 pages; light paper; medium cover; b&w art. "Social, political, avant-garde, erotic, environmental material for a literary audience." Biannual (Sept. and March). Estab. 1983. Circ. 600.

Needs: Contemporary, erotica, ethnic, experimental, fantasy, feminist, gay, humor/satire, lesbian, literary, prose poem, regional, serialized novel, translations. No sentimental, romance, mainstream. Plans special anthology issue Spring '92. Receives 10-12 unsolicited mss/month. Accepts 2 mss/issue; 4-6 mss/year. Publishes ms 3-4 months after acceptance. Recently published work by Nathan Versace and Louise A. Blum. Length: 1,500-2,000 words average. Publishes short shorts. Also publishes literary essays, literary criticism, poetry. Sometimes critiques rejected mss and recommends other markets.

How to Contact: Send complete manuscript with cover letter that includes basic info/credits. Reports in 1-2 weeks on queries; 1-2 months on mss. SASE. Photocopied submissions OK. Accepts computer printout submissions. Sample copy for $2, 4×9 SAE and 45¢ postage. Fiction guidelines for #10 SAE and 1 first class stamp. Reviews novels and short story collections. Send books to Don Hildenbrand.

Payment: Pays contributor's copies.

Terms: Acquires one-time rights or "reserves anthology rights."

POETRY FORUM SHORT STORIES, (I, II), Poetry Forum, 5713 Larchmont Dr., Erie PA 16509. (814)866-2543. FAX: (814)866-2543 (fax hours 8-10 a.m., 5-8 p.m.). Editor: Gunver Skogsholm. Newspaper: 7×8½; 34 pages; card cover; illustrations. "Human interest themes (no sexually explicit or racially biased or blasphemous material) for the general public—from the grassroot to the intellectual." Quarterly. Estab. 1989. Circ. 400.

Needs: Confession, contemporary, ethnic, experimental, fantasy, feminist, historical, literary, mainstream, prose poem, religious/inspirational, romance, science fiction, senior citizen/retirement, suspense/mystery, young adult/teen. "No blasphemous, sexually explicit material." Publishes annual special fiction issue. Receives 50 unsolicited mss/month. Accepts 12 mss/issue; 40 mss/year. Publishes ms 6 months after acceptance. Agented fiction less than 1%. Recently published work by Bernard Hewitt, Don Peyer, Jess Wilbanks. Length: 2,000 words average; 500 words minimum; 5,000 words maximum. Also publishes literary essays, literary criticism, poetry.

How to Contact: Send complete manuscript with cover letter. Reports in 6 weeks to 2 months on mss. SASE. Simultaneous, photocopied and reprint submissions OK. Accepts computer printout submissions. "Accepts electronic submissions via disk gladly." Sample copy $3. Fiction guidelines for SAE and 1 first class stamp. Reviews novels and short story collections.

Terms: Acquires one-time rights.

Advice: Also sponsors contest.

POETRY HALIFAX DARTMOUTH, (I, II), BS Poetry Society, Box 7074 North, Halifax, Nova Scotia B3K 5J4 Canada. Editor: Mark Hamilton. Magazine: 7×8½; 24 pages; bond paper; card stock cover. Bimonthly. Estab. 1986. Circ. 300.

Needs: Experimental, humor/satire, literary and prose poem. Receives 1 or 2 unsolicited mss/month; accepts 3-4 mss/year. Publishes ms 3-6 months after acceptance. Publishes short shorts. Also publishes literary essays, literary criticism, poetry. Sometimes critiques rejected mss.

How to Contact: Send complete ms with cover letter and short bio. Reports in 3 months on queries. SASE. Photocopied submissions OK. Accepts computer printout submissions. Sample copy $2. Fiction guidelines for #10 SAE and 1 first class stamp (IRC). Reviews novels and short story collections.

Payment: Pays $5 (Canadian) and 2 contributor's copies.

Terms: Pays on publication for first North American serial rights.

POETRY MAGIC PUBLICATIONS, (I), 1630 Lake Dr., Haslett, MI 48840. (517)339-8754. Editor: Lisa Roose-Church. Magazine: 8½×11; b&w illustrations. "Publishes poetry and articles relating to writing. Have used other themes. We will consider just about anything of high quality." Quarterly. Estab. 1988.

Needs: Contemporary, humor, prose poem. No pornography, science fiction, horror, fantasy. "We publish anthologies that writers can submit work for. Our next title is "Over the Rainbow, Volume II" and is scheduled for October 1992." Receives over 100 mss/month. Accepts 2 mss/issue. Publishes ms within 6 months of acceptance. Published work by Scott Sonders. Length: 50-500 words preferred; 50 words minimum; 1,000 words sometimes. Also publishes poetry. Sometimes critiques rejected mss and recommends other markets.

How to Contact: Query first, query with clips of published work or send complete ms with cover letter. Reports in 2-4 weeks. SASE. Simultaneous (if stated), photocopied and reprint submissions OK. Accepts computer printout submissions. Sample copy for $4.50. Fiction guidelines for #10 SAE and 1 first class stamp.

Payment: Pays in contributor's copies (minimum) to $100 (maximum).

Terms: Acquires first rights or one-time rights.

Advice: "Correct usage of grammar, punctuation, etc. is important. We prefer fiction that is quality reading, which entices the reader for more from that author. Because we get less fiction than poetry, we are selective because our readers want to be enticed, enthralled and overwhelmed with a story. If it doesn't do this for the editor she will not accept it. Experiment and create your own style."

POETRY MOTEL, (II), Suburban Wilderness Press, 1619 Jefferson, Duluth MN 55812. Editor: Pat McKinnon. Fiction Editor: Bud Bracken. Magazine: 7 × 8½; 50-80 pages; 20 lb. paper; various cover; various amount of illustrations and photographs. "We're wide open though we lean toward wry satire and hilarity." 1-2 times annually. Estab. 1984. Circ. 500.

Needs: Condensed/excerpted novel, contemporary, erotica, ethnic, fantasy, feminist, gay, humor/satire, lesbian, literary, prose poem, science fiction. "Nothing along the popular/genre lines." Receives 2-5 unsolicited mss/month. Accepts 2-5 mss/issue; 2-10 mss/year. Publishes ms 1 month to 2 years after acceptance. Recently published work by Willie Smith, Gregory Burnham, Hugh Knox. Length: 300 words average; 25 words minimum; 1,500 words maximum. Publishes short shorts. Length: 300-500 words. Also publishes literary essays, literary criticism, poetry. Sometimes critiques rejected mss.

How to Contact: Send complete manuscript with cover letter. Reports in 1 week on queries; 1 week to 1 month on mss. SASE. Simultaneous, photocopied and reprint submissions OK. Accepts computer printout submissions. Sample copy $5. Fiction guidelines for #10 SAE and 1 first class stamp. Reviews novels and short story collections.

Payment: Pays contributor's copies. Charge for extras.

Terms: Acquires one-time rights.

Advice: "Read what we print first since it is beyond description and never what you might imagine."

THE POINTED CIRCLE, (II), Portland Community College-Cascade, 705 N. Killingsworth St., Portland OR 97217. (503)244-6111 ext. 5405. Editors: Student Editorial Staff. Magazine: 7 × 8½; approx. 80 pages; b&w illustrations and photographs. "Anything of interest to educationally/culturally mixed audience." Annually. Estab. 1980.

Needs: Contemporary, ethnic, literary, prose poem, regional. "We will read whatever is sent, but encourage writers to remember we are a quality literary/arts magazine intended to promote the arts in the community." Accepts 3-7 mss/year. We accept submissions only December 1-March 1, for October 1 issue. Length: 3,500 words average; 500 words minimum; 5,000 words maximum. Publishes short shorts. Length: 100 words. Rarely critiques rejected mss and sometimes recommends other markets.

How to Contact: Send complete manuscript with cover letter and brief bio. SASE. Simultaneous and photocopied submissions OK. Accepts good quality computer printouts. Sample copy for $3.50. Fiction guidelines for #10 SAE and 1 first class stamp.

Payment: Pays in contributor's copies.

Terms: Acquires one-time rights.

Advice: "Looks for quality—topicality—nothing trite. The author cares about language and acts responsibly toward the reader, honors the reader's investment of time and piques the reader's interest."

THE PORTABLE WALL, (II), Basement Press, 215 Burlington, Billings MT 59101. (406)256-3588. Editor: Daniel Struckman. Fiction Editor: Gray Harris. Magazine: 6 × 9¼; 40 pages; cotton rag paper; best quality cover; line engravings; illustrations. "We consider all kinds of material. Bias toward humor." Published 2 times/year. Estab. 1977. Circ. 400.

Needs: Adventure, contemporary, ethnic, experimental, feminist, historical, humor/satire, literary, mainstream, prose poem, regional, science fiction, senior citizen, sports, translations. "We favor short pieces and poetry." Upcoming themes: "Justice and Journalism (Spring 1992)"; "Feminism and Sexuality on the Montana Frontier" (Fall 1992). Receives 5-10 unsolicited mss/month. Accepts 3-4 mss/issue; 6-8 mss/year. Publishes ms 6 months to a year after acceptance. Published works by Gray Harris, Wilbur Wood. Length: 2,000 words preferred. Publishes short shorts. Also publishes literary essays, literary criticism, poetry. Sometimes critiques rejected mss.

How to Contact: Send complete ms with cover letter. Reports in 2 weeks on mss. SASE. Accepts computer printout submissions. Sample copy $6.50.

Payment: Pays subscription to magazine.

Terms: Acquires one-time rights.

Advice: "We like language that evokes believable pictures in our minds and that tells news."

‡BERN PORTER INTERNATIONAL, Bern Porter Books, 22 Salmond St., Belfast ME 04915. (207)338-6798. Editor: Bern Porter. Magazine: 8½ × 11; 98-132 pages; illustrations and photographs. "High literary quality with international flavor." Bimonthly. Estab. 1991.

Needs: Experimental, literary, prose poem, translations, international. Publishes special fiction issue. Receives 30-50 unsolicited mss/month. Buys 10-15 mss/issue. Publishes ms immediately after acceptance. Length: Open. Publishes short shorts. Comments on or critiques rejected mss and recommends other markets.

How to Contact: Query first. Reports in 1 week. SASE. Simultaneous, photocopied and reprint submissions OK. Accepts computer printout submissions. Accepts electronic submissions via disk or modem. Sample copy and fiction guidelines free.

Payment: Pays 6¢/word.

Terms: Pays on publication. Buys world rights. Sends galleys to author.

PORTLAND REVIEW, (I, II), Portland State University, Box 751, Portland OR 97207. (503)725-4533. Editor: Jan Sellon. "The *Review* is looking for fiction, poetry and essays that linger in the mind's eye with frightful clarity after the magazine has been put aside and the business of life resumed." Published 2 times/year. Estab. 1955. Circ. 1,500.

Needs: "More good fiction and essays and less bad poetry." Length: 3,000 words maximum.

How to Contact: Submit complete ms with personal biographical note, SASE. Photocopied submissions OK. Reports in 6 weeks. Sample copy for $5.

Payment: Pays 1 contributor's copy.

Terms: Acquires one-time rights.

Advice: "We want to increase the ratio of fiction to poetry. Stick with a few magazines and let them really get to know your work."

POSKISNOLT PRESS, Yesterday's Press, (I, II, IV), Yesterday's Press, 224 82nd St., Brooklyn NY 11209. (718)680-3899. Editor: Patricia D. Coscia. Fiction Editor: Richard B. Murray. Magazine: 7 × 8½; 20 pages; regular typing paper. Estab. 1989. Circ. 100.

Needs: Contemporary, erotica, ethnic, experimental, fantasy, feminist, gay, humor/satire, lesbian, literary, mainstream, prose poem, psychic/supernatural/occult, romance, young adult, senior citizen/retirement, western, young adult/teen (10-18 years). "X-rated material is not accepted!" Plans to publish a special fiction issue or anthology in the future. Receives 50 unsolicited mss/month. Accepts 30 mss/issue; 100+ mss/year. Publishes ms 6 months after acceptance. Length: 200 words average; 100 words minimum; 500 words maximum. Publishes short shorts. Length: 100-500 words. Sometimes critiques rejected mss and recommends other markets.

How to Contact: Query first with clips of published work or send complete manuscript with cover letter. Reports in 1 week on queries; 6 months on mss. SASE. Accepts simultaneous, photocopied and computer printout submissions. Sample copy for $4 with #10 SASE and $2 postage. Fiction guidelines for #10 SASE and $2 postage.

Payment: Pays with subscription to magazine or contributor's copies; charges for extras.

Terms: Acquires all rights, first rights or one-time rights.

THE POST, (II), Publishers Syndication International, Suite 856, 1377 K St., Washington DC 20005. Editor: A.P. Samuels. Newspaper: 8½ × 11; 32 pages. Monthly. Estab. 1988.

Needs: Adventure, romance and suspense/mystery. "No explicit sex, gore, extreme violence or bad language." Receives 75 unsolicited mss/month. Buys 1 ms/issue; 12 mss/year. Time between acceptance and publication varies. Agented fiction 10%. Length: 10,000 words average.

How to Contact: Send complete manuscript with cover letter. Reports on mss in 5 weeks. Accepts computer printout submissions. Fiction guidelines for #10 SAE and 1 first class stamp.
Payment: Pays ½¢ to 4¢/word.
Terms: Pays on acceptance for all rights.

POTATO EYES, Appalachian Voices, (II), Nightshade, Box 76, Troy ME 04987. (207)948-3427. Editors: Carolyn Page and Roy Zarucchi. Magazine: 6×9; 108 pages; 60 lb text paper; 80 lb Curtis flannel cover. "We tend to showcase Appalachian talent from Alabama to Quebec, and in doing so, we hope to dispel hackneyed stereotypes and political borders. Our subscribers have included: boat builder, teacher, dairy farmer, college prof, doctor, lawyer, world traveler, lumberman . . . and that was just in last week's batch." Estab. 1988. Circ. 800.
Needs: Contemporary, humor/satire, literary, mainstream, regional, and rural themes. Plans a *1992 All New Potato Eyes Reader.* "Short stories will be accepted for *either Potato Eyes* magazine *or* the reader. Same rules apply to both." Receives 30 unsolicited mss/month. Accepts 5-6 mss/issue; 10-12 mss/year. Publishes ms 6 months-1 year after acceptance. Recently published work by Simone Poirier-Bures, Alyce Ingram, Paul Milenski and Alice Sink. Length: 3,000 words maximum; 2,000 average. Publishes short shorts. Length: 450 words. Also publishes poetry. Sometimes critiques rejected mss and recommends other markets.
How to Contact: Send complete ms with cover letter. Reports in 2 weeks-2 months on mss. SASE. Accepts computer printout submissions. Sample copy $5, including postage. Fiction guidelines with #10 SAE.
Payment: Pays in contributor's copies.
Terms: Acquires first North American serial rights.
Advice: "We care about the larger issues, including pollution, ecology, bio-regionalism, uncontrolled progress and "condominia," as well as the rights of the individual, particularly the elderly. We care about television, the great sewer pipe of America, and what it is doing to America's youth. We are exploring these issues with writers who have originality, a reordered perspective, and submit to us generous sprinklings of humor and satire. Although we do occasionally comment on valid fiction, we have walked away unscathed from the world of academia and refuse to correct manuscripts. We respect our contributors and treat them as professionals, however, and write personal responses to every submission if given an SASE. We expect the same treatment—clean copy without multi folds or corrections. We like brief non-Narcissistic cover letters containing the straight scoop. We suggest that beginning fiction writers spend the money they have set aside for creative writing courses or conferences and spend it instead on subscriptions to good little literary magazines."

‡**POTENT APHRODISIAC, (I, II),** Suite 169, 4845 South Rainbow Blvd., Las Vegas NV 89103. Magazine: 8½×11; 69 pages; illustrations. "Strange, fantastic erotic/love/romance stories, art, poetry for adult men and women." Semiannually. Estab. 1991. Circ. 125.
Needs: Erotic: adventure, confession, erotica, fantasy, horror, humor/satire, lesbian, literary, psychic/supernatural/occult, romance (contemporary, historical), science fiction, suspense/mystery, western. "Everything *has* to be erotic in addition to these categories. No gross out, real gory horror stories. No stuff like rape, incest, male homosexuality, S&M torture." Publishes special fiction issue. Receives 20 unsolicited mss/month. Accepts 8 mss/issue; 16 mss/year. Publishes ms 4-12 months after acceptance. Recently published work by Bobby G. Warner, Erik Buck. Length: 3,000 words preferred, 500 words minimum, 6,000 words maximum. Sometimes critiques rejected mss.
How to Contact: Send complete ms with cover letter. Reports in 1-3 weeks on queries; 3-8 weeks on mss. SASE. Photocopied submissions OK. Accepts computer printout submissions. Sample copy for $5.50. Fiction guidelines for #10 SAE and 1 first class stamp.
Payment: Pays in contributor's copies.
Terms: Acquires one-time rights. Not copyrighted.
Advice: "I select what I like: A good, entertaining story with good characters. I like clear beginnings, middles and endings. I'm also in the market for nonfiction articles on sexual subjects and *Penthouse*-type letters of sexual experiences."

‡**POTPOURRI, (II),** P.O. Box 8278, Prairie Village KS 66208. (913)642-1503. Editor: Polly W. Swafford. Fiction Editor: Candy Schock. Newspaper: 12×14; 20 pages. "Literary journal: short stories verse, essays, travel, prose-poetry for a general adult audience." Monthly. Estab. 1989.
Needs: Adventure, contemporary, ethnic, experimental, fantasy, historical (general), humor/satire, literary, mainstream, prose poem, romance (contemporary, historical), science fiction, suspense/mystery, western. "*Potpourri* accepts a broad genre; hence its name. Guidelines specify no religious, confes-

sional, racial, political, erotic, abusive or sexual preference materials unless fictional and necessary to plot." Plans special fiction issue. Receives 75 unsolicited mss/month. Accepts 8-10 mss/issue; 100-120 mss/year. Publishes ms 3-6 months after acceptance. Agented fiction 1%. Recently published work by William Wu, David Ohle, Susan M. Schmeltz. Length: 2,500 words maximum. Also publishes poetry. Sometimes critiques on rejected mss and recommends other markets.

How to Contact: Send complete ms with cover letter. Include "complete name, address, phone number, brief summary statement about submission, short bio on author." Reports in 3-6 weeks on queries; 2-4 months on mss. SASE. Simultaneous, photocopied submissions OK. Accepts computer printout submissions. Sample copy for 9 × 12 SAE and 3 first class stamps. Fiction guidelines for #10 SAE and 1 first class stamp.

Payment: Pays contributor's copies.

Terms: Acquires first rights.

Advice: Looks for "first: Reader appeal. Does the manuscript spark immediate interest and the introduction create the effect that will dominate? Second: Action in dialogue or narration that tells the story. Third: Escalation of conflicts and resolution. Conclusion needs to leave something with the reader to be long remembered. We look for the unusual twist. Ask yourself: Is the story idea different? Does the story hold the reader's interest from the very beginning to the end? Try reading your story aloud to yourself and to others. Does your mind wander/ Watch the body language of your listeners for positive or negative reactions."

THE POTTERSFIELD PORTFOLIO, (II,IV), Wild East Publishing Co-operative Ltd., P.O. Box 1135, Stn. A, Fredericton, New Brunswick E3B 5C2 Canada. Editors: Shari Andrews, Joe Blades, Jo-Anne Elder, Raymond Fraser, Carlos Gomes, Margaret McLeod. Magazine 6 × 9; 96 pages; book paper; perfect bound; coated cover stock; artwork. "Quality fiction in English, French and Spanish from a diversity of visions and voices." Semiannually. Estab. 1979.

Needs: Receives 15-30 fiction mss/month. Buys 5-6 fiction mss/issue. Published work by Robert Gibbs, Sylvia Morize, Martine Jacquot; published new writers within the last year. Publishes short shorts. Sometimes comments on rejected mss.

How to Contact: Send complete ms with cover letter and enough information for short bio in journal. Reports in 2 months. SASE. Accepts computer printout submissions. Sample copy $6 (US).

Payment: Pays $10/printed page and contributor's copies.

Terms: Pays on publication for first Canadian serial rights.

PRAIRIE FIRE, (II), Prairie Fire Press Inc., Room 423, 100 Arthur St., Winnipeg, Manitoba R3B 1H3 Canada. (204)943-9066. Managing Editor: Andris Taskans. Fiction Editor: Ellen Smythe. Magazine: 6 × 9; 128 pages; offset bond paper; sturdy cover stock; illustrations; photos. "Essays, critical reviews, short fiction and poetry. For writers and readers interested in Canadian literature." Published 4 times/year. Estab. 1978. Circ. 1,200.

Needs: Literary, contemporary, experimental, prose poem, reviews. "We will consider work on any topic of artistic merit, including short chapters from novels-in-progress. We wish to avoid gothic, confession, religious, romance and pornography." Buys 3-6 mss/issue, 12-24 mss/year. Does not read mss in summer. Recently published work by David Arnason, Sandra Birdsell, Ven Begamudne, Cecelia Frey; published new writers within the last year. Receives 24-30 unsolicited fiction mss each month. Publishes short shorts. Length: 8,000 maximum; no minimum; 3,000 words average. Also publishes literary essays, literary criticism, poetry. Critiques rejected mss "if requested and when there is time." Sometimes recommends other markets.

How to Contact: Send complete ms with IRC w/envelope and short bio. Reports in 2-3 months. Sample copy for $7 (Canadian). Reviews novels and short story collections. Send books to Scott Ellis.

Payment: Pays $60 for the first page, $30 for each additional page. 1 free author's copy. 60% of cover price for extras.

Terms: Pays on publication for first North American serial rights. Rights revert to author on publication.

Advice: "We are publishing more fiction, and we are commissioning illustrations. Read our publication before submitting. We prefer Canadian material. Most mss are not ready for publication. Be neat, double space, and put your name and address on everything! Be the best writer you can be."

THE PRAIRIE JOURNAL OF CANADIAN LITERATURE, (I, II, IV), Prairie Journal Press, Box 997, Station G, Calgary, Alberta T3A 3G2 Canada. Editor: A.E. Burke. Journal: 7 × 8½; 50-60 pages; white bond paper; Cadillac cover stock; cover illustrations. Journal of creative writing and scholarly essays, reviews for literary audience. Semiannually. Published special fiction issue last year. Estab. 1983.

Needs: Contemporary, literary, prose poem, regional, excerpted novel, novella, typed single space. Canadian authors given preference. No romance, erotica, pulp. Publishes genre series open to submissions: *Prairie Journal Poetry II* and *Prairie Journal Fiction III*. Receives 20-40 unsolicited mss each month. Accepts 10-15 mss/issue; 20-30 mss/year. Suggests sample issue before submitting ms. Recently published work by Nancy Ellen Russell, Carla Mobley, Patrick Quinn; published new writers within the last year. Length: 2,500 words average; 100 words minimum; 3,000 words maximum. Also publishes literary essays, literary criticism, poetry. Sometimes critiques rejected mss and recommends other markets.

How to Contact: Send complete ms. Reports in 1 month. SASE or SAE and IRC. Photocopied submissions OK. Accepts computer printout submissions. Sample copy $3 (Canadian) and SAE with $1.10 for postage or IRC. Include cover letter of past credits, if any. Reply to queries for SAE with 48¢ for postage or IRC. No American stamps. Reviews novels and short story collections.

Payment: Pays contributor's copies and modest honoraria.

Terms: Acquires first North American serial rights. In Canada author retains copyright.

Advice: Interested in "innovational work of quality. Beginning writers welcome. There is no point in simply republishing known authors or conventional, predictable plots. Of the genres we receive fiction is most often of the highest calibre. It is a very competitive field. Be proud of what you send. You're worth it."

PRAIRIE SCHOONER, (II), University of Nebraska, English Department, 201 Andrews Hall, Lincoln NE 68588-0334. (402)472-3191. Editor: Hilda Raz. Magazine: 6×9; 144 pages; good stock paper; heavy cover stock. "A general literary quarterly of stories, poems, essays and reviews for a general, educated audience that reads for pleasure." Quarterly. Estab. 1927. Circ. 2,500.

Needs: Good fiction. Accepts 4-5 mss/issue. Receives approximately 150 unsolicited fiction mss each month. Recently published work by Nancy Willard, Leo Litwak, David Michael Kaplan, Debra Spark; published new writers within the last year. Length: varies. Also publishes poetry.

How to Contact: Send complete ms with SASE and cover letter listing previous publications—where, when. Reports in 3 months. Sample copy $2. Reviews novels and short story collections.

Payment: Pays 3 free author's copies and prize money awarded.

Terms: Acquires all rights. Will reassign rights upon request after publication.

Advice: "*Prairie Schooner* is eager to see fiction from beginning and established writers. Be tenacious. Accept rejection as a temporary setback and send out rejected stories to other magazines." Annual prize of $500 for best fiction, $500 for best new writer (poetry or fiction), $500 for best poetry; additional prizes, $250-1,000.

‡PRIMAL VOICES, (I), Lambert/McIntosh Enterprises, P.O. Box 3179, Poughkeepsie NY 12603. (914)626-5130. Fiction Editors: Carol Lambert, Susan McIntosh, Lee Schryver. Magazine: 8½×11; 52 pages; 20 lb. paper; glossy cover; illustrations and photographs. "Endangered species, homeless, seniors, handicapped, retarded, incarcerated (the voiceless) for humanitarians." Quarterly. Estab. 1990. Circ. 100.

Needs: Condensed/excerpted novel, ethnic, experimental, fantasy, feminist, gay, historical (general), horror, humor/satire, literary, prose poem, regional, senior citizen/retirement, sports (exceptional), translations. No "hunting, human or animal abuse, violence or sexist writing." Plans special fiction issue. Receives 20 unsolicited mss/month. Accepts no more than 2 mss/issue; 8 mss/year. Does not read mss in August. Publishes ms 2 months after acceptance. Recently published work by Patty Somlo. Length: 1,200 words preferred; 500 words minimum; 1,500 words maximum. Sometimes critiques rejected mss and recommends other markets.

How to Contact: Send complete ms with cover letter. Include "a short bio for our Contributor's Notes." Reports in 6-8 weeks. SASE. Simultaneous, photocopied and reprint submissions OK. Accepts computer printout submissions. Sample copy for $5, SAE and 4 first class stamps. Fiction guidelines for #10 SAE and 1 first class stamp.

Payment: Pays contributor's copies.

Terms: Acquires one-time rights.

Advice: Looks for "characters and story that are both real and believable. The story is well written and proofread by the author with attention paid to grammar and spelling in the text. Think about your own concerns and about the things in our society that need to be addressed and/or changed."

PRIMAVERA, (II, IV), Box 37-7547, 700 E 61st St., Chicago IL 60637. (312)324-5920. Editorial Board. Magazine: 5½×8½; 100 pages; 60 lb. paper; glossy cover; illustrations; photos. Literature and graphics reflecting the experiences of women: poetry, short stories, photos, drawings. Readership: "an audience interested in women's ideas and experiences." Annually. Estab. 1975. Circ. 1,000.

Needs: Literary, contemporary, science fiction, fantasy, feminist, gay/lesbian and humor. "We dislike slick stories packaged for more traditional women's magazines. We publish only work reflecting the experiences of women, but also publish mss by men." Accepts 6-10 mss/issue. Receives approximately 40 unsolicited fiction mss each month. Recently published work by Kathryn Christman, Dawn Newton, C.D. Collins; published new writers within the last year. Length: 25 pages maximum. Also publishes poetry. Critiques rejected mss when there is time. Often gives suggestions for revisions and invites resubmission of revised ms. Occasionally recommends other markets

How to Contact: Send complete ms with SASE. Cover letter not necessary. Accepts computer printout submissions, "if assured it is not a multiple submission." Reports in 1 week–5 months on mss. Publishes ms up to 1 year after acceptance. Sample copy $5; $6 for recent issues. Guidelines for #14 SASE.

Payment: Pays 2 contributor's copies.

Terms: Acquires first rights.

PRISM INTERNATIONAL, (II), E462-1866 Main Mall, University of British Columbia, Vancouver, British Columbia V6T 1Z1 Canada. (604)228-2514. Executive Editor: Patricia Gabin. Editor: Roger Cove. Magazine: 6×9; 72-80 pages; Zephyr book paper; Cornwall, coated one side cover; photos on cover. "A journal of contemporary writing – fiction, poetry, drama, creative non-fiction and translation. *Prism's* audience is world-wide, as are our contributors." Readership: "Public and university libraries, individual subscriptions, bookstores – an audience concerned with the contemporary in literature." Published 4 times/year. Estab. 1959. Circ. 1,200.

Needs: Literary, contemporary, prose poem or translations. "Most any category as long as it is *fresh*. No overtly religious, overtly theme-heavy material or anything more message- or category-oriented than self-contained." Buys approximately 70 mss/year. Receives 50-100 unsolicited fiction mss each month. Published new writers within the last year. Length: 5,000 words maximum "though flexible for outstanding work." Publishes short shorts. Also publishes poetry. Critiques rejected mss when there is time. Occasionally recommends other markets.

How to Contact: Send complete ms with SASE or SAE, IRC and cover letter with bio, information and publications list. "Keep it simple. US contributors take note: US stamps are not valid in Canada and your ms will not likely be returned if it contains US stamps. Send International Reply Coupons instead." Accepts computer printout submissions. Reports in 3 months. Sample copy $4 (Canadian).

Payment: Pays $20 (Canadian)/printed page, 1 free year's subscription.

Terms: Pays on publication for first North American serial rights.

Advice: "Too many derivative, self-indulgent pieces; sloppy construction and imprecise word usage. There's not enough attention to voice and not enough invention. We are committed to publishing outstanding literary work in all genres." Sponsors annual short fiction contest. Contest issue comes out in April. Grand prize is $2,000 (Canadian). Send SASE (IRC) for details.

PRISONERS OF THE NIGHT, An Adult Anthology of Erotica, Fright, Allure and . . . Vampirism, (II), MKASHEF Enterprises, Box 368, Poway CA 92074-0368. Editor: Alayne Gelfand. Magazine: 8½×11; 50-80 pages; 20 lb. paper; slick cover; perfect bound; illustrations. "An adult, erotic vampire anthology of original character stories and poetry. Heterosexual and homosexual situations included." Annually. Estab. 1987. Circ. approx. 5,000.

Needs: Adventure, contemporary, erotica, experimental, fantasy, feminist, gay, lesbian, literary, prose poem, psychic/supernatural/occult, science fiction, suspense/mystery. "All stories must be vampire stories, with unique characters, unusual situations." No fiction that deals with anyone else's creations, i.e., no "Dracula" stories. Receives 30-50 unsolicited fiction mss/month. Accepts 5-12 mss/issue. Publishes ms 1-11 months after acceptance. Recently published work by Pauline Kerwath, Kay Reynolds, Charlee Jacob, Wendy Rathbone; published new writers within the last year. Length: under 10,000 words. Publishes short shorts. Sometimes critiques rejected mss. Recommends other markets.

How to Contact: Send complete ms with short cover letter. "A brief introduction of author to the editor; name, address, *some* past credits if available." Reports in 1 week on queries; 2-4 months on mss. Reads *only* September-March. SASE. Photocopied submissions OK. Accepts electronic submissions via IBM Word Perfect (4.2 or 5.1), disk. Sample copy #1-4, $15; #5, $12. Fiction guidelines for #10 SAE and 1 first class stamp.

Payment: Pays 1¢/word for fiction.
Terms: Pays on publication for first North American serial rights.
Advice: "The unique *type* of vampire will catch my eye quickest. Don't be trite, don't do the expected with your plot. Erotic, sensual elements are preferred to the cerebral. No graphic blood and guts. Detailed characterization is required. No pornography; I do not want cheap or tawdry sex for shock value; no "singles bar" or prostitution themes. Graphic erotica *is* acceptable. Be original, stretch your imagination."

‡PROBE POST, Canada's Environmental Magazine, (IV), Pollution Probe Foundation, 12 Madison Ave., Toronto, Ontario M5R 2S1 Canada. (416)926-1647. Editor: Richard Beharriell. Magazine: photographs. "Environmental magazine in a news format." Quarterly.
Needs: Environment. "Sometimes we print poems and less often short stories—but would be interested in publishing more."
Payment: Pays contributor's copies.
Terms: Acquires one-time rights.

PROCESSED WORLD, (II), #1829, 41 Sutter St., San Francisco CA 94104. (415)626-2160. Editor: Chris Carlsson. Magazine: 8½×11; 64 pages; 20 lb. bond paper; glossy cover stock; illustrations; photos. "Magazine about work, office work, computers and hi-tech (satire)." Biannually. May publish special fiction issue. Estab. 1981. Circ. 5,000.
Needs: Comics, confession, "tales of toil," contemporary, fantasy, humor/satire, literary, science fiction. Accepts 1-2 mss/issue; 3-6 mss/year. Recently published work by James Pollack. Published new writers within the last year. Length: 1,250 words average; 100 words minimum; 1,500 words maximum. Occasionally critiques rejected ms.
How to Contact: Send complete ms. Reports in 4 months. SASE. Simultaneous and photocopied submissions OK. Accepts computer printout submissions. Sample copy $5.
Payment: Pays subscription to magazine.
Terms: Acquires one-time rights.
Advice: "Make it real. Make it critical of the status quo. Read the magazine before you send us a story."

PROPHETIC VOICES, An International Literary Journal, (II), Heritage Trails Press, 94 Santa Maria Dr., Novato CA 94947. (415)897-5679. Editor: Goldie L. Morales. Fiction Editors: Ruth Wildes Schuler and Jeanne Leigh Schuler. Magazine: 6¾×8¼; 100-144 pages; bond paper; textured cover; illustrations and photographs. "Material with a social awareness/ecology slant for an adult audience. Interested in material from other countries." Semiannually.
Needs: Historical (general) and prose poem. "We want gripping material that is also educational." No religious, sexual, juvenile, sports, young adult. Receives 10 unsolicited mss/month. Accepts 1 or 2 mss/issue; 3 or 4 mss/year. Publishes ms 1-3 years after acceptance. Recently published work by P. Raja, Denver Stull and Kirpal Gordon. Publishes short shorts. Recommends other markets.
How to Contact: Send complete manuscript. Reports in 5 weeks on queries; 3 months on mss. SASE. Simultaneous, photocopied and reprint submissions OK. Sample copy $6.
Payment: Pays contributor's copy.
Terms: Acquires one-time rights.
Advice: "A story should be different, educational—one that a reader is not likely to forget. Material must have universal and timeless appeal. We are not interested in trendy stories or those appealing only to a limited region or geographical locale."

PROVINCETOWN ARTS, (II), Provincetown Arts, Inc., 650 Commercial St., P.O. Box 35, Provincetown MA 02657. (508)487-3167. Editor: Christopher Busa. Magazine: 9×12; 184 pages; 60 lb. uncoated paper; 12 pcs. cover; illustrations and photographs. "*PA* focuses broadly on the artists, writers and theater of America's oldest continuous art colony." Annually. Estab. 1985. Circ. 8,000.
Needs: Plans special fiction issue. Receives 150 unsolicited mss/year. Buys 3 mss/issue. Publishes ms 3 months after acceptance. Recently published work by Carole Maso and Hilary Masters. Length: 3,000 words average; 1,500 words minimum; 5,000 words maximum. Publishes short shorts. Length: 1,500-5,000 words. Also publishes literary essays, literary criticism, poetry. Sometimes critiques rejected mss and recommends other markets.
How to Contact: Send complete manuscript with cover letter including previous publications. Reports in 2 weeks on queries; 3 months on mss. SASE. Photocopied submissions OK. Sample copy $7.50. Reviews novels and short story collections.

Payment: Pays $75-300.
Terms: Pays on publication for first rights. Sends galleys to author.

PSI, (II), Suite 856, 1377 K Street NW, Washington DC 20005. Editor: A.P. Samuels. Magazine: 8½×11; 32 pages; bond paper; self cover. "Mystery and romance." Bimonthly. Estab. 1987.
Needs: Romance (contemporary, historical, young adult), suspense/mystery. Receives 35 unsolicited mss/month. Buys 1-2 mss/issue. Published work by Sharon K. Garner, Michael Riedel; published new writers within the last year. Length: 10,000 words average. Publishes short shorts. Critiques rejected mss "only on a rare occasion."
How to Contact: Send complete ms with cover letter. Reports in 2 weeks on queries; 4 weeks on mss. SASE. Accepts computer printout submissions. Accepts electronic submissions via disk.
Payment: Pays 1-4¢/word plus royalty.
Terms: Pays on acceptance for first North American serial rights.
Advice: "Manuscripts must be for a general audience. Just good plain story telling (make it compelling). No explicit sex or ghoulish violence."

‡PSYCHOTRAIN, (II), Hyacinth House Publications, 290 Wiles St., Morgantown WV 26505. Editor: Shannon Frach. Magazine; 8½×11; 25-35 pages; 20 lb. paper; cardstock; illustrations. "*PsychoTrain* is a new journal of poetry, fiction, and art that welcomes intense, earthy, decadent, and often risqué work from a wide array of authors, including both beginners and more established. I publish for a generally left-of-center audience that appreciates humor noir, radical writing, and tough, edgy fiction." Estab. 1991. Circ. 100.
Needs: Condensed/excerpted novel, erotica, ethnic, experimental, feminist, gay, horror, humor/satire, lesbian, literary, prose poem, psychic/supernatural/occult, translations, "Pagan, Dada/surrealism, counterculture, subcultural writing of any and all persuasions." "No candy-coated, dandyfied fiction here. Just pure, old-fashioned decadence. Nothing didactic. No hand-wringing sentimentalism. No whining unless it's really damned funny." Plans special ficition issue. Receives 8-15 unsolicited mss/ month. Buys 2-4 mss/issue. Publishes ms 2-6 months after acceptance. Recently published work by Gomez Robespierre, Randal Seyler, Ray Kardiner, Paige Avalene. Length: 50 words minimum; 5,000 words maximum. Publishes short shorts. Sometimes critiques rejected mss and recommends other markets.
How to Contact: Send complete ms with cover letter. "A cover letter is not necessary. If you send one, don't give me a mere list of credits. Don't try to impress me via the cover letter—nothing spells 'amateur' faster." Reports in 3 weeks on queries; 2-5 months on mss. SASE. Simultaneous, photocopied and reprint submissions OK. Accepts computer printout submissions. Sample copy for $3. Fiction guidelines for #10 SAE and 1 first class stamp.
Payment: Pays in contributor's copies; charges for extras.
Terms: Acquires one-time rights.
Advice: "A manuscript often stands out if it makes me laugh so hard I blow whatever I'm drinking out of my nose. If it makes me laugh so hard I wet my pants, the author wins a free subscription for a year. Horror submissions should make me want to relocate to another continent immediately. The sex scenes should be outrageous and inventive. The kind of writing I'm interested in should paint the most vivid, wildly graphic pictures imaginable to the human mind with the sheer nerve and elegance of someone who understands the raw precision and stunning power of words. *PsychoTrain* is currently handling material that is too depraved even for *Brownbag Press*, which is saying something. Anything goes. Mail me the most twisted, bizarre, abrasive material you've got—I'm looking for two-fisted, maximum-energy writing. Despite what Dr. Zip told you in your freshman creative writing seminar, the use of shock value in fiction is fine here. Your material must meet the dual challenge of possessing both brain-shattering weirdness and high-quality writing."

THE PUB, (I, II), Ansuda Publications, Box 158J, Harris IA 51345. Editor/Publisher: Daniel R. Betz. Magazine: 5½×8½; 72 pages; mimeo paper; heavy stock paper; illustrations on cover. "We prefer stories to have some sort of social impact within them, no matter how slight, so our fiction is different from what's published in most magazines. We aren't afraid to be different or publish something that might be objectionable to current thought. *Pub* is directed toward those people, from all walks of life, who are themselves 'different' and unique, who are interested in new ideas and forms of reasoning. Our readers enjoy *Pub* and believe in what we are doing." Published 2 times/year. Estab. 1979. Circ. 350.

Needs: Literary, psychic/supernatural/occult, fantasy, horror, mystery, adventure, serialized and condensed novels. "We are looking for honest, straightforward stories. No love stories or stories that ramble on for pages about nothing in particular." Buys reprints. Accepts 4-6 mss/issue. Receives approximately 35-40 unsolicited fiction mss each month. Published new writers within the last year. Length: 8,000 words maximum. Also publishes poetry. Sometimes recommends other markets.

How to Contact: Send complete ms with SASE. Accepts computer printout submissions. Reports in 1 month. Publishes ms an average of 6 months after acceptance. Sample copy $3. Guidelines for #10 SASE.

Payment: Pays 2 contributor's copies. Cover price less special bulk discount for extras.

Terms: Acquires first North American serial rights and second serial rights on reprints.

Advice: "Read the magazine—that is *very* important. If you send a story close to what we're looking for, we'll try to help guide you to exactly what we want. We appreciate neat copy, and if photocopies are sent, we like to be able to read all of the story. Fiction seems to work for us—we are a literary magazine and have better luck with fiction than articles or poems."

PUCKERBRUSH REVIEW, (I, II), Puckerbrush Press, 76 Main St., Okono ME 04473. (207)866-4868/581-3832. Editor: Constance Hunting. Magazine: 9×12; 80-100 pages; illustrations. "We publish mostly new Maine writers; interviews, fiction, reviews, poetry for a literary audience." Semiannually. Estab. 1979. Circ. approx. 500.

Needs: Experimental, gay (occasionally), literary, belles-lettres. "Nothing cliché." Upcoming themes: "Issue XII will have focus on war, but not exclusively" (Winter 1992). Receives 30 unsolicited mss/month. Accepts 6 mss/issue; 12 mss/year. Publishes ms 1 year after acceptance. Recently published work by Dwight Cathcart, Tema Nason. Sometimes publishes short shorts. Also publishes literary essays, literary criticism, poetry. Sometimes critiques rejected mss and recommends other markets.

How to Contact: Send complete manuscript with cover letter. Reports in 2 months. SASE. Simultaneous submissions OK. Sample copy $2. Fiction guidelines for SASE. Sometimes reviews novels and short story collections.

Payment: Pays in contributor's copies.

Advice: "Just write the story as it would like you to do."

PUERTO DEL SOL, (I), New Mexico State University, Box 3E, Las Cruces NM 88003. (505)646-3931. Editor-in-Chief: Kevin McIlvoy. Magazine: 6×9; 200 pages; 60 lb. paper; 70 lb. cover stock; photos sometimes. "We publish quality material from anyone. Poetry, fiction, art, photos, interviews, reviews, parts-of-novels, long poems." Semiannually. Estab. 1961. Circ. 1,000.

Needs: Contemporary, ethnic, experimental, literary, mainstream, prose poem, excerpted novel and translations. Receives varied number of unsolicited fiction mss/month. Accepts 8-10 mss/issue; 12-15 mss/year. Does not read mss May-August. Published work by Ken Kuhlken, Susan Thornton; published new writers within the last year. Also publishes poetry. Occasionally critiques rejected mss.

How to Contact: Send complete ms with SASE. Simultaneous and photocopied submissions OK. Accepts computer printout submissions. Reports in 2 months. Sample copy $4.

Payment: Pays 3 contributor's copies.

Terms: Acquires one-time rights (rights revert to author).

Advice: "We are open to all forms of fiction, from the conventional to the wildly experimental, as long as they have integrity and are well written. Too often we receive very impressively 'polished' mss that will dazzle readers with their sheen but offer no character/reader experience of lasting value."

PULPHOUSE, A Fiction Magazine, (II), Box 1227, Eugene OR 97440. Editor: Dean Wesley Smith. Magazine: 8½×11; 48 pages; saddle stitched; web printed. Estab. 1988. Has 10,000 copies in print.

Needs: Fantasy, horror, science fiction, speculative fiction. Published work by Harlan Ellison, Kate Wilhelm, Michael Bishop, Charles de Line, George Alec Effinger; published new writers within the last year. Length: 7,500 words maximum.

How to Contact: Send complete ms with cover letter "that gives publication history, work history, or any other information relevant to the magazine. Don't tell us about the story. The story will tell us about the story." SASE. Sample copy for $2.50. Fiction guidelines for #10 SAE and 1 first class stamp.

Payment: Pays 3-6¢/word.

Terms: Pays on acceptance for first serial rights.

Advice: "*Pulphouse* needs fiction that takes risks, that presents viewpoints not commonly held in the field. Although such fiction can include experimental writing, it is usually best served by clean, clear prose. We are looking for strong characterization, fast-moving plot, and intriguing settings."

PULSAR, Science Fiction and Fantasy, (II), Tony Ubelhor, P.O. Box 886, Evansville IN 47706. (812)479-7022. Editor: Tony Ubelhor. Magazine: 8×11; 60 pages; 20 lb. paper; glossy cover; b&w illustrations and photographs. "Science fiction and fantasy stories, articles, interviews for an adult audience." Semiannually. Estab. 1986. Circ. 400.
Needs: Fantasy, science fiction. "Always looking for articles and retrospectives on the science fiction field, as well as interviews with writers and notable fans." No horror. Publishes annual special fiction issue. Receives 10 unsolicited mss/month. Accepts 5-10 mss/issue; 10-20 mss/year. Publishes ms 1-6 months after acceptance. Recently published work by Mike Resnick, Arlan Andrews, C.S. Williams. Length: 6,000 words average; 1,500 words minimum; 12,000 words maximum. Publishes short shorts. Length: about 6,000-10,000 words. Also publishes literary essays, literary criticism, poetry. Sometimes critiques rejected mss.
How to Contact: Send complete manuscript with cover letter. Reports in 4-6 weeks on queries; 1-3 months on mss. SASE. Photocopied and reprint submissions OK. Accepts computer printout submissions. Sample copy $4. Fiction guidelines for SAE and 1 first class stamp. Reviews novels and short story collections (science fiction/fantasy works only).
Payment: Pays in contributor's copies. Charge for extras.
Terms: Acquires first North American serial rights.
Advice: "We encourage beginning writers. A rejection from us is always an invitation to submit again."

QUARRY, (II), Quarry Press, Box 1061, Kingston, Ontario K7L 4Y5 Canada. (613)548-8429. Editor: Steven Heighton. Magazine: 5½×8½; 120 pages; #1 book 120 paper; 160 lb. Curtis Tweed cover stock; illustrations; photos. "Quarterly anthology of new Canadian poetry, prose. Also includes graphics, photographs and book reviews. We seek readers interested in vigorous, disciplined, new Canadian writing." Published special fiction issue; plans another. Estab. 1952. Circ. 1,100.
Needs: Experimental, fantasy, literary, science fiction, serialized/excerpted novel and translations. "We do not want highly derivative or clichéd style." Receives 80-100 unsolicited fiction mss/month. Buys 4-5 mss/issue; 20 mss/year. Does not read in July. Less than 5% of fiction is agented. Published work by Diane Schoemperlen, David Helwig, Joan Fern Shaw; published new writers within the last year. Length: 3,000 words average. Publishes short shorts. Usually critiques rejected mss and recommends other markets.
How to Contact: Send complete ms with SAE, IRC and brief bio. Photocopied submissions OK. Accepts computer printout submissions. Publishes ms an average of 3-6 months after acceptance. Sample copy $5 with 4×7 SAE and 35¢ Canadian postage or IRC.
Payment: Pays $10/page; 1 year subscription to magazine and 1 contributor's copy.
Terms: Pays on publication for first North American serial rights.
Advice: "Read previous *Quarry* to see standard we seek. Read Canadian fiction to see Canadian trends. We seek aggressive experimentation which is coupled with competence (form, style) and stimulating subject matter. We also like traditional forms. Our annual prose issue (spring) is always a sellout. Many of our selections have been anthologized. Don't send US stamps or SASE (if outside Canada). Use IRC. Submit with brief bio."

QUARTERLY WEST, (II), University of Utah, 317 Olpin Union, Salt Lake City UT 84112. (801)581-3938. Editors: Tom Hazuka, Bernard Wood. Magazine: 6×9; 150+ pages; 60 lb. paper; 5-color cover stock; illustrations and photographs rarely. "We try to publish a variety of fiction by writers from all over the country. Our publication is aimed primarily at an educated audience which is interested in contemporary literature and criticism." Semiannually. "We sponsor biennial novella competition." Estab. 1976. Circ. 1,000.
Needs: Literary, contemporary, translations. Buys 6-8 mss/issue, 12-16 mss/year. Receives approximately 200 unsolicited fiction mss each month. Published work by Andre Dubus and Chuck Rosenthal; published new writers within the last year. No preferred length. Critiques rejected mss when there is time. Sometimes recommends other markets.
How to Contact: Send complete ms. Cover letters welcome. SASE. Accepts computer printout submissions. Reports in 2 months; "sooner, if possible." Sample copy for $4.50.
Payment: Pays $25-50, possibly more; 2 contributor's copies.
Terms: Pays on publication for first North American serial rights.
Advice: "Write a clear and unified story which does not rely on tricks or gimmicks for its effects." Mss are rejected because of "poor style, formula writing, clichés, weak characterization. Don't send more than one story per submission, but submit as often as you like."

QUEEN OF ALL HEARTS, (II), Queen Magazine, Montfort Missionaries, 26 S. Saxon Ave., Bay Shore NY 11706. (516)665-0726. Managing Editor: Roger M. Charest, S.M.M. Magazine: 7¾ × 10¾; 48 pages; self cover stock; illustrations; photos. Magazine of "stories, articles and features on the Mother of God by explaining the Scriptural basis and traditional teaching of the Catholic Church concerning the Mother of Jesus, her influence in fields of history, literature, art, music, poetry, etc." Bimonthly. Estab. 1950. Circ. 5,000.
Needs: Religious/inspirational. "No mss not about Our Lady, the Mother of God, the Mother of Jesus." Length: 1,500-2,000 words. Sometimes recommends other markets.
How to Contact: Send complete ms with SASE. Photocopied submissions OK. Reports in 1 month on mss. Publishes ms 6 months to one year after acceptance. Sample copy $1.75 with 9 × 12 SAE.
Payment: Varies. Pays 6 contributor's copies.
Advice: "We are publishing stories with a Marian theme."

QUEEN'S QUARTERLY, A Canadian Review, (II, IV), Queen's University, Kingston, Ontario K7L 3N6 Canada. (613)545-2667. Editor: Boris Castel. Magazine: 6 × 9; 800 pages/year; illustrations. "A general interest intellectual review, featuring articles on science, politics, humanities, arts and letters. Book reviews, poetry and fiction." Published quarterly. Estab. 1893. Circ. 3,000.
Needs: Adventure, contemporary, experimental, fantasy, historical (general), humor/satire, literary, mainstream, science fiction and women's. "*Special emphasis on work by Canadian writers.*" Buys 2 mss/issue; 8 mss/year. Published work by Janette Turner Hospital; published new writers within the last year. Length: 5,000 words maximum. Also publishes literary essays, literary criticism, poetry.
How to Contact: "Send complete ms and a copy on disk in Wordperfect – only one at a time – with SASE." Photocopied submissions OK if not part of multiple submission. Accepts computer printout submissions. Reports within 3 months. Sample copy $6.50. Reviews novels and short story collections.
Payment: Pays $100-300 for fiction, 2 contributor's copies and 1-year subscription; $5 charge for extras.
Terms: Pays on publication for first North American serial rights. Sends galleys to author.

RADIO VOID, (II), Radio Zero, P.O. Box 5983, Providence RI 02903. Publisher: Brian T. Gallagher. Fiction Editor: Christopher Pierson. Magazine: 8½ × 11; 72 pages; newsprint paper; illustrations and photographs (varies). "Conflicting, themeless variety...an eclectic blend in which, when sifted, can be found a common literary thread." Biannual. Estab. 1986. Circ. 1,000.
Needs: Open to all types of fiction. Receives approx. 20 unsolicited fiction mss/month. Accepts 10-12 mss/issue; 80-100 mss/year. Publishes ms 3-4 months after acceptance. Recently published work by James Keller, Jonathan Thomas. Length: Open. Publishes short shorts. Also publishes literary essays, literary criticism, poetry. Critiques or comments on rejected mss.
How to Contact: Send complete ms with cover letter. Include name, address, biographical paragraph. Reports in 1 month on queries; in 2 months on mss. SASE. Photocopied submissions OK. Sample copy for $2. Fiction guidelines for #14 SAE and 1 first class stamp. Reviews novels and short story collections. Send books to Zoë Pierson.
Payment: Pays in contributor's copies and free business card-size ad.
Terms: "We do not purchase rights--author offers us a loan."

RAG MAG (II), Box 12, Goodhue MN 55027. (612)923-4590. Publisher/Editor: Beverly Voldseth. Magazine: 5½ × 8½; 60 pages; varied paper quality; illustrations; photos. "We are eager to print poetry, prose and art work. We are open to all styles." Semiannually. Estab. 1982. Circ. 200.
Needs: Adventure, comics, contemporary, erotica, ethnic, experimental, fantasy, feminist, literary, mainstream, prose poem, regional. "Anything well written is a possibility. No extremely violent or pornographic writing." Receives 20 unsolicited mss each month. Accepts 1-2 mss/issue. Published work by Sigi Leonhard, Lynne Burgess and Pat McKinnon; published new writers within the last year. Length: 1,000 words average; 2,200 words maximum. Occasionally critiques rejected mss. Sometimes recommends other markets.
How to Contact: Send complete ms. Reports in 2 months. SASE. Simultaneous, photocopied and previously published submissions OK. Accepts computer printout submissions. Single copy $4.50.
Payment: Pays 1 contributor's copy; $4.50 charge for extras.
Terms: Acquires one-time rights.
Advice: "Submit clean copy on regular typing paper (no tissue-thin stuff). We want fresh images, sparse language, words that will lift us out of our chairs. I like the short story form. I think it's powerful and has a definite place in the literary magazine."

RAINBOW CITY EXPRESS, (I,II,IV), Box 8447, Berkeley CA 94707-8447. Editor: Helen B. Harvey. Magazine: 8½×11; 60-80 pages; 20 lb. bond paper; illustrations. "We are only interested in topics pertaining to spiritual awakening and evolution of consciousness. For highly educated, well-read, psychologically sophisticated, spiritually evolving and ecologically conscious free-thinkers." Feminist orientation. Quarterly. Estab. 1988. Circ. 1,000.

Needs: Feminist, literary, prose poem, religious/inspirational and spirituality. "We only accept *short fiction* and absolutely no novels or long fiction. No immature, romantic, violent, sexist material." Receives 60-90 unsolicited mss/month. Buys 4-10 mss/issue; 20-40 mss/year. Publishes ms 3-6 months after acceptance. Will publish in the coming year work by David Warner, Helen B. Harvey and Daniel Panger. Length: 200-1,000 words; 500-800 average. Almost always critiques rejected mss and sometimes recommends other markets.

How to Contact: "Order a sample copy and *read it first!* Then send a complete manuscript with SASE." Reports on queries in 2-4 weeks; 3-6 months on mss. All submissions *must* contain SASE! Sample copy $6 postpaid. Writer's guidelines for #10 SASE and 2 first class stamps.

Payment: "Payment is arranged on individual basis. Some cash 'honorariums' and every contributor always receives a copy of issue containing her or his work." Pays $5-50.

Terms: Pays on publication. Buys one-time rights.

Advice: Looks for "intelligent, lively, well-written material, with a substantial and plausible plot and characters. Topics must be related to our Spirituality/Consciousness slant. *Read* 1-2 copies of *RCE* first! *Rainbow City Express* is very unique and it is impossible to write for our publication without first becoming familiar with it. Please study a recent issue before submitting. We prefer *true* (nonfiction) stories related to spiritual awakening."

RE ARTS & LETTERS [REAL], (II), "A Liberal Arts Forum," Stephen F. Austin State University, P.O. Box 13007, Nacogdoches TX 75962. (409)568-2101. Editor: Lee Schultz. Academic Journal: 6×10; perfect-bound; 120-150 pages; "top" stock. "65-75% of pages composed of fiction (2-4 stories per issue), poetry (20-60 per issue), an occasional play, book reviews (assigned after query), and interviews. Other 25-35% comprised of articles in scholarly format. Work is reviewed based on the intrinsic merit of the scholarship and creative work and its appeal to a sophisticated international readership (U.S., Canada, Great Britain, Ireland, Brazil, Puerto Rico, Italy)." Semiannual. Estab. 1968. Circ. 400+.

Needs: Adventure, contemporary, genre, feminist, science fiction, historical, experimental, regional. No beginners. Receives 35-70 unsolicited mss per month. Accepts 2-5 fiction mss/issue. Publishes 1-6 months after acceptance; one year for special issues. Published work by Joe R. Lansdale, Lewis Shiner, Walter McDonald, Peter Mattheisson. Length 1,000-7,000 words. Occasionally critiques rejected mss and conditionally accepts on basis of critiques and changes. Recommends other markets.

How to Contact: Send complete ms with cover letter. No simultaneous submissions. Reports in 2 weeks on queries; 3-4 weeks on mss. SASE. Accepts "letter quality" computer submissions. Sample copy and writer's guidelines $5. Guidelines for SASE.

Payment: Pays 1 contributor's copy; charges for extras.

Terms: Rights revert to author.

Advice: "Please study an issue. Have your work checked by a well-published writer—who is not a good friend."

RECONSTRUCTIONIST, (II), Federation of Reconstructionist Congregations & Havurot, Church Rd. and Greenwood Ave., Wyncote PA 19095. (215)887-1988. Editor: Joy Levitt. Magazine: 8½×11; 32 pages; illustrations; photos. "Review of Jewish culture—essays, fiction, poetry of Jewish interest for American Jews." Published 6 times/year. Estab. 1935. Circ. 9,000.

Needs: Ethnic. Receives 10 unsolicited mss/month; buys 15 mss/year. Publishes ms 1-2 years after acceptance. Published work by Myron Taube, Lev Raphael; published new writers within the last year. Length: 2,500 words average; 3,000 words maximum. Publishes short shorts. Recommends other markets.

How to Contact: *Send mss only to Joy Levitt, Box 1336, Roslyn Heights NY 11577.* All other material should be sent to the Pennsylvania address. Send complete ms with cover letter. Reports in 6-8 weeks. SASE for mss. Photocopied submissions OK. Accepts computer printouts. Sample copy free.

Payment: Pays $25-36 and contributor's copies.

Terms: Pays on publication for first rights.

RED CEDAR REVIEW, (II), Dept. of English, Morrill Hall, Michigan State University, East Lansing MI 48825. (517)355-7570. Contact: Fiction Editor. Magazine: 5½×8½; 60-80 pages; quality b&w illustrations and b&w photos. Theme: "literary—poetry, fiction, book reviews, one-act plays, interviews, graphics." Biannually. Estab. 1963. Circ. 400+.

Needs: Literary, feminist, regional and humorous. Accepts 3-4 mss/issue, 6-10 mss/year. Published new writers within the last year. Length: 500-7,000 words. Also publishes poetry.

How to Contact: Send complete ms with SASE. Reports in 2-3 months on mss. Publishes ms up to 4 months after acceptance. Reviews novels and short story collections. Sample copy $2.

Payment: Pays 2 contributor's copies. $2.50 charge for extras.

Terms: Acquires first rights.

Advice: "Read the magazine and good literary fiction. There are many good writers out there who need a place to publish, and we try to provide them with that chance for publication. We prefer short stories that are experimental and take risks. Make your style unique—don't get lost in the mainstream work of the genre."

THE REDNECK REVIEW OF LITERATURE, (II, IV), 2919 N. Donner Ave., Milwaukee WI 53211. (414)332-6881. Editor: Penelope Reedy. Magazine: 8½×11; 80 pages; offset paper; cover varies from semi-glossy to felt illustrations; photos. "I consider *Redneck* to be one of the few—perhaps the only—magazines in the West seeking to bridge the gap between literate divisions. My aim is to provide literature from and to the diverse people in the western region. *Redneck* is not a political publication and takes no sides on such issues. Readership is extremely eclectic including ranchers, farmers, university professors, writers, poets, activists, civil engineers, BLM conservation officers, farm wives, attorneys, judges, truck drivers." Semiannually. Estab. 1975. Circ. 500.

Needs: "Publishes poetry, fiction, plays, essays, book reviews and folk pieces." Upcoming themes: Texas "What's Real in the Heart of Texas" (Spring 1992); Icons/Iconoclasts "Have Words Will Travel" (Fall 1992). Receives 10 "or so" unsolicited mss/month. Receives 4-5 mss/issue. Recently published work by Rafael Zepeda, Clay Reynolds and Gerald Haslam; published new writers within the last year. Length: 1,500 words minimum; 2,500 words maximum. Also publishes literary essays, literary criticism, poetry.

How to Contact: Send complete ms. SASE. No simultaneous submissions. Reprint submissions from established writers OK. Sample copy for $6 with $1 postage.

Payment: Pays in contributor's copies.

Terms: Rights returned to author on publication.

Advice: "Use strong sense of place. Give characters action, voices. Tell the truth rather than sentimentalize. *Redneck* deals strictly with a contemporary viewpoint/perspective, though the past can be evoked to show the reader how we got here. Nothing too academic or sentimental reminiscences. I am not interested in old-time wild west gunfighter stories."

REFLECT, (II, IV), 3306 Argonne Ave., Norfolk VA 23509. (804)857-1097. Editor: W.S. Kennedy. Magazine: 5½×8½; 48 pages; pen & ink illustrations. "Spiral Mode fiction and poetry for writers and poets—professional and amateur." Quarterly. Estab. 1979.

Needs: Spiral fiction. "The four rules to the Spiral Mode fiction form are : (1) The story a situation or condition. (2) The outlining of the situation in the opening paragraphs. The story being told at once, the author is not overly-involved with dialogue and plot development, may concentrate on *sound*, *style*, *color*—the superior elements in art. (3) The use of a concise style with euphonic wording. Good poets may have the advantage here. (4) The involvement of Spiral Fiction themes—as opposed to Spiral Poetry themes—with love, and presented with the mystical overtones of the Mode." No "smut, bad taste, anarchist . . ." Accepts 2-6 mss/issue; 8-24 mss/year. Publishes ms 3 months after acceptance. Recently published work by Ruth Wildes Schuler, B.Z. Niditch, Patricia Anne Treat. Length: 1,500 words average; 2,500 words maximum. Publishes short shorts. Sometimes critiques rejected mss and recommends other markets.

How to Contact: Send complete manuscript with cover letter. Reports in 2 months on mss. SASE. Accepts computer printout submissions. Sample copy $2. Free fiction guidelines.

Payment: Pays contributor's copies.

Terms: Acquires one-time rights. Publication not copyrighted.

Advice: "Subject matter usually is not relevant to the successful writing of Spiral Fiction, as long as there is some element or type of *love* in the story, and provided that there are mystical references. (Though a dream-like style may qualify as 'mystical.')"

REFLECTIONS, (II, IV), Journalism Class, Box 368, Duncan Falls OH 43734. (614)674-5209. Editor: Dean Harper. Magazine: 8½x11; 32 pages; "very good" paper; "excellent" cover stock; illustrations; photos. Publishes "good wholesome stories primarily for 10-18 year olds." Estab. 1980. Circ. 1,000.
Needs: Adventure, juvenile, religious/inspirational, science fiction, senior citizen/retirement, prose poem, spiritual, sports, suspense/mystery, western, young adult/teen (10-18 years). Receives 10-20 mss/month. Accepts 1-5 mss/issue; 2-10 mss/year. Publishes ms within 1-5 months of acceptance. Published work by Celia and Melissa Pinson, Michelle Hurst, Natasha Snitkovsky; pulblished new writers within the last year. Length: 500 words minimum; 5,000 words maximum. Publishes short shorts. Sometimes critiques rejected mss and recommends other markets.
How to Contact: Send complete mss with cover letter. Reports in 2 weeks. SASE. Simultaneous, photocopied and reprint submissions OK. Accepts computer printout submissions, including dot-matrix. Sample copy for $2, #10 SAE and 1 first class stamp. Fiction guidelines for #10 SAE and 1 first class stamp.
Payment: Pays in contributor's copies.
Terms: Acquires one-time rights. Publication copyrighted.
Advice: "We always welcome good writing. Please avoid overuse of 'got.' Keep sending your writing. Read it first to others for opinions. Ask for suggestions from editors."

RENEGADE, (II), Box 314, Bloomfield MI 48303. (313)972-5580. Editor: Michael E. Nowicki. Magazine: 5½×8½; 32 pages; 4-5 illustrations. "We are open to all forms except erotica and we publish whatever we find good." Estab. 1988. Circ. 100.
Needs: Adventure, condensed/excerpted novel, contemporary, experimental, fantasy, feminist, historical (general), horror, humor/satire, literary, mainstream, prose poem, psychic/supernatural/occult, religious/inspirational, romance, science fiction, suspense/mystery, translations and western. Receives 40-50 unsolicited mss/month. Accepts 2 mss/issue; 4 mss/year. Publishes ms 6 months after acceptance. Published work by Sam Astrachan. Length: 400-4,000 words; 3,000 average. Publishes short shorts. Length: 400 words. Also publishes literary essays, literary criticism, poetry. Sometimes critiques rejected mss and recommends other markets.
How to Contact: Send complete ms with cover letter. Reports in 2 weeks to 1 month on queries; 3 weeks to 2 months on mss. SASE. Sample copy $2. Fiction guidelines for #10 SAE and 1 first class stamp. Reviews novels and short story collections.
Payment: Pays in contributor's copies.
Terms: All rights revert to author. Publication not copyrighted.
Advice: "We look for characters which appear to be real and deal with life in a real way, as well as the use of plot to forefront the clash of personalities and the theme of the work. Take advice cautiously and apply what works. Then submit it. We are always happy to critique work we read."

RENOVATED LIGHTHOUSE PUBLICATIONS, (II), P.O. Box 100, Riparius NY 12862. Editor: R. Allen Dodson. Chapbooks and magazines; 5½×8½; 32 pages; card cover; illustrations and photographs. "Mostly poetry-related, but will consider all literary and artistic mediums and subjects for freelancers and general audiences with literary interest." Estab. 1986. Circ. 200.
Needs: Adventure, experimental, fantasy, historical (general), literary, mainstream, prose poem, regional, science fiction, New Age. Receives 100 unsolicited mss/month. Buys 10 mss/year. Publishes ms 1 year average after acceptance. Also publishes literary essays, literary criticism, poetry. Sometimes critiques rejected mss and sometimes recommends other markets.
How to Contact: Query with cover letter and credits; *we're overstocked for 1992.* "Personal information and comments about the story—I like to get to know my writers." Reports in 1 month. SASE. Photocopied submissions OK. Accepts computer printout submissions. Sample copy $2.90. Fiction guidelines available. Reviews novels and short story collections.
Payment: Pays 20% royalties for 1 year for chaps or pays $1 plus copy for appearance in magazine.
Terms: Sends galleys to author.

RESPONSE, A Contemporary Jewish Review, (II, IV), 27 W. 20th St., 9th Floor, New York NY 10011. (212)675-1168. Editor: Paul Lerner. Magazine: 6×9; 96 pages; 70 lb. paper; 10 pt. C1S cover; illustrations; photos. "Fiction, poetry and essays with a Jewish theme, for Jewish students and young adults." Quarterly. Estab. 1967. Circ. 1,500.
Needs: Contemporary, ethnic, experimental, feminist, historical (general), humor/satire, literary, prose poem, regional, religious, spirituals, translations. "Stories in which the Holocaust plays a major role must be exceptional in quality. The shrill and the morbid will not be accepted." Receives 5-10 unsolicited mss/month. Accepts 5-10 mss/issue; 10-15 mss/year. Publishes ms 2-4 months after accep-

tance. Length: 15-20 pages (double spaced). Publishes short shorts. Sometimes recommends other markets.

How to Contact: Send complete ms with cover letter; include brief biography of author. "Do not summarize story in cover letter." Reports in 2 months on mss. SASE. Photocopied submissions are OK. Accepts computer printout submissions. Sample copy $6; free guidelines.

Payment: Pays in contributor's copies.

Terms: Acquires all rights.

Advice: "In the best pieces, every word will show the author's conscious attention to the craft. Subtle ambiguities, quiet ironies and other such carefully handled tropes are not lost on *Response*'s readers. Pieces that also show passion that is not marred by either shrillness or pathos are respected and often welcomed. Writers who write from the gut or the muse are few in number. *Response* personally prefers the writer who thinks about what he or she is doing, rather than the writer who intuits his or her stories."

REVIEW LA BOOCHE, (II), 110 S. 9th, Columbia MO 65201. (314)874-8772. Editors: Michel Jabbour and Gerald Dethrow. 6×9; 100 pages; 60 lb. paper; 80 lb. Irish linen cover. "No theme. Tightly constructed stories with strong use of poetics for everyone." Annually. Estab. 1976. Circ. 500.

Needs: Adventure, contemporary, experimental, historical (general), literary, mainstream. "Needs short stories under 5,000 words." Published work by Nancy Lord, Nolan Briterfield and Dennis Danvers. Length: 5,000 words. Publishes short shorts. Also publishes literary essays, literary criticism, poetry.

How to Contact: Send complete manuscript with cover letter. Reports in 2 weeks-1 month. SASE. Accepts photocopied and computer printout submissions.

Payment: Pays contributor's copies.

Terms: Acquires first rights.

Advice: "Charge the language with active verbs and use adjectives sparingly unless they contribute to expanding the boundaries of the nouns they border."

‡REVIEW, LATIN AMERICAN LITERATURE AND ARTS, 680 Park Ave., New York NY 10021. (212)249-8950. Editor: Alfred Mac Adam. "Magazine of Latin American fiction, poetry and essays in translation for academic, corporate and general audience." Biannually.

Needs: Literary. No political or sociological mss. Upcoming themes: "Latin American film/video" (Spring 1992); "Changing Spaces": travel issue (Fall 1992). Receives 5 unsolicited mss/month. Buys 8 mss/issue; 16 mss/year. Length: 1,500-2,000 words average. Occasionally critiques rejected mss.

How to Contact: Query first or send complete ms. Reports in several months. Previously published submissions OK if original was published in Spanish. Sample copy free. Reviews novels and short story collections. Send books to Daniel Shapiro, Managing Editor.

Payment: Pays $50-200, and 2-3 contributor's copies.

Terms: Pays on publication.

Advice: "We are always looking for good translators."

‡RHINO, (II), 8403 W. Normal Ave., Niles IL 60648. Fiction Editor: Kay Meier. Magazine: 5½×8; 80 pages, "best" quality paper; 65 lb. Tuscani cover stock; cover illustrations only. "Exists for writers of short prose and poetry—for new writers whose eyes and ears for language are becoming practiced, and whose approaches to it are individualistic. Aimed toward the poetically inclined." Annually. Estab. 1976. Circ. 500.

Needs: "Short prose (sometimes up to 10 pages). We aim for artistic writing; we also accept the well-written piece of wide or general appeal." Receives approximately 4 unsolicited fiction mss each month. "We 'read' mss between March 1-May 31." Published work by Gary Fincke and Lois Hauselmann; published new writers within the last year. Also publishes poetry. Critiques rejected mss "when there is time." Sometimes recommends other markets.

How to Contact: *Charges $3 reading fee.* Send complete ms with cover letter with credits and SASE. Accepts computer printout submissions. Reports in 6 weeks on mss. Recommends other markets. Sample copy $5 plus $1.05 postage.

 The double dagger before a listing indicates that the listing is new in this edition. New markets are often the most receptive to freelance contributions.

Payment: Pays 1 contributor's copy.
Terms: Acquires one-time rights.
Advice: "We recommend you know how to construct a variety of idiomatic English sentences; take as fresh an approach as possible toward the chosen subject; and take time to polish the ms for its keenest effect. Don't be afraid to experiment with form." Mss are rejected because they are "either too grim or too sentimental. We like strong writing—human warmth, humor, originality, beauty! Our publication appears the first week in October of each year."

RIVER CITY, Memphis State Review, Dept. of English, Memphis State University, Memphis TN 38152. (901)678-8888. Editor: Sharon Bryan. Magazine: 6×9; 100 pages. National review of poetry, fiction and nonfiction. Semiannually. Estab. 1980. Circ. 1,200.
Needs: Novel excerpts, short stories. Published work by Fred Busch; published new writers within the last year.
How to Contact: Send complete ms with SASE. Sample copy $4.
Payment: Annual $100 prize for best poem or best short story and 2 contributor's copies. "We pay if grant monies are available."
Terms: Acquires first North American serial rights.
Advice: "We're soliciting work from writers with a national reputation, and are occasionally able to pay, depending on grants received. I would prefer no cover letter. *River City* Writing Awards in Fiction: $2,000 1st prize, $500 2nd page, $300 3rd prize. See magazine for details."

RIVER STYX, (II), Big River Association, 14 S. Euclid, St. Louis MO 63108. (314)361-0043. Editor: Lee Fournier. Magazine: 6×8; 90 pages; visual art (b&w). "No theme restrictions, high quality, intelligent work." Triannual. Estab. 1975.
Needs: Excerpted novel chapter, contemporary, ethnic, experimental, feminist, gay, satire, lesbian, literary, mainstream, prose poem, translations. "Avoid 'and then I woke up' stories." Receives 15 unsolicited mss/month. Buys 1-3 mss/issue; 3-8 mss/year. Reads only in September and October. Published work by Bonita Friedman, Leslie Becker, Fred Viebahn. Length: no more than 20-30 manuscript pages. Publishes short shorts. Also publishes poetry. Sometimes critiques rejected mss and recommends other markets.
How to Contact: Send complete manuscript with name and address on every page. Reports in 2 months on mss. Photocopied and reprint submissions OK. Accepts computer printout submissions. Sample copy $7. Fiction guidelines for #10 SAE and 1 first class stamp.
Payment: Pays $8/page maximum, free subscription to magazine and contributor's copies.
Terms: Pays on publication for first North American serial rights.
Advice: Looks for "writer's attention to the language and the sentence; responsible, controlled narrative."

RIVERSIDE QUARTERLY, (II,IV), 807 Walters #107, Lake Charles LA 70605. (318)477-7943. Editor: Leland Sapiro. Fiction Editor: Redd Boggs. Magazine: 5½×8½; 64 pages; illustrations. Quarterly. Estab. 1964. Circ. 1,100.
Needs: Fantasy and science fiction. Accepts 1 ms/issue; 4 mss/year. Publishes ms 6 months after acceptance. Length: 3,500 words maximum; 3,000 words average. Publishes short shorts. Also publishes literary essays, literary criticism, poetry. Critiques rejected mss.
How to Contact: *Send directly to fiction editor, Redd Boggs, Box 1111, Berkeley, CA 94701.* Send complete ms with cover letter. Reports in 2 weeks. SASE. Simultaneous submissions OK. Accepts electronic submissions. Sample copy $2. Reviews novels and short story collections.
Payment: Pays in contributor's copies.
Terms: Acquires one-time rights. Sends galleys to author.
Advice: "Would-be contributors are urged to first inspect a copy or two of the magazine (available at any major college or public library) to see the *kind* of story we print."

RIVERWIND, (II,IV), General Studies/Hocking College, Nelsonville OH 45764. (614)753-3591 (ext. 2375). Editors: Audrey Naffziger, C.A. Dubielak. Magazine: 6×9; 60 lb. paper; cover illustrations. "College press, small literary magazine." Annually. Estab. 1975.
Needs: Adventure, contemporary, erotica, ethnic, feminist, historical (general), horror, humor/satire, literary, mainstream, prose poem, spiritual, sports, regional, translations, western. No juvenile/teen fiction. Receives 30 mss/month. Does not read during the summer. Published work by Roy Bentley, Kate Hancock; published new writers within the last year. Sometimes critiques rejected mss.

How to Contact: Send complete ms with cover letter. Reports on mss in 1-4 months. SASE. Photocopied submissions OK.
Payment: Pays in contributor's copies.
Advice: "Your work must be strong, entertaining. It helps if you are an Ohio/West Virginia writer. We hope to print more fiction. We now publish mainly regional writers (Ohio, West Virginia, Kentucky)."

ROANOKE REVIEW, (II), Roanoke College, English Department, Salem VA 24153. (703)375-2500. Editor: Robert R. Walter. Magazine: 6×9; 40-60 pages. Semiannually. Estab. 1967. Circ. 300.
Needs: Receives 30-40 unsolicited mss/month. Accepts 2-3 mss/issue; 4-6 mss/year. Publishes ms 6 months after acceptance. Length: 2,500 words minimum; 7,500 words maximum. Publishes short shorts. Occasionally critiques rejected mss.
How to Contact: Send complete ms with cover letter. Reports in 1-2 weeks on queries; 8-10 weeks on mss. SASE for query. Photocopied submissions OK. Accepts computer printout submissions. Sample copy $2.
Payment: Pays in contributor's copies.

THE ROCKFORD REVIEW, (II), The Rockford Writers Guild, Box 858, Rockford IL 61105. Fiction Editor: David Ross. Magazine: 5⅜×8½; 96 pages; b&w illustrations; b&w photos. "We look for poetry with control of poetic line and devices with a fresh approach to old themes or new insights into the human condition whether in prose or poetry." Annually. Estab. 1971. Circ. 500.
Needs: Ethnic, experimental, fantasy, feminist, historical (general), humor/satire, literary and regional. Published work by Eugene C. Flinn, John Pesta, George Keithly, Stacy Tuthill, Peter Blunett and Robert Klein Engler. Length: Up to 2,500 words. Also publishes poetry.
How to Contact: Send complete ms. "Include a short biographical note—no more than four sentences." Reports in 4-6 weeks on mss. SASE. Accepts simultaneous and photocopied submissions, reprints (as long as acknowledgement included) and computer printouts. Sample copy $6. Fiction guidelines for SASE.
Payment: Pays contributor's copies. "Two editor's choice cash prizes per issue."
Terms: Acquires first North American serial rights.
Advice: "Any subject or theme goes as long as it enhances our understanding of our humanity."

ROHWEDDER, International Journal of Literature & Art, (II, IV), Rough Weather Press, Box 29490, Los Angeles CA 90029. Editor: Hans-Jurgen Schacht. Fiction Editors: Robert Dassanowsky-Harris and Nancy Antell. Magazine: 8½×11; 50+ pages; 20 lb. paper; 90 lb. cover; illustrations; photos. "Multilingual/cultural poetry and short stories. Graphic art and photography." Published semi-annually. Estab. 1986.
Needs: Contemporary, ethnic, experimental, feminist, literary, regional, translations (with rights). No fillers. Upcoming themes: Contemporary Media (Fall 1992). Receives 20-50 unsolicited mss/month. Accepts 1-3 mss/issue; 6 mss/year. Publishes ms 1-3 months after acceptance. Length: 1,500-2,500 words average; 200 words minimum; 2,500 words maximum. Publishes short shorts. Also publishes literary essays, poetry. Sometimes critiques rejected mss and recommends other markets.
How to Contact: Include bio with submission. Reports in 2 weeks on queries; 3 months on mss. SASE. Photocopied submissions OK. Accepts computer printout submissions. Sample copy $5.
Payment: Pays in contributor's copies, charges for extras.
Terms: Acquires one-time right.
Advice: "Go out as far as you have to but remember the basics: clear, concise style and form."

‡RUBY'S PEARLS, (I, II), A.C. Aarbus Publishing Inc., Rt. 1, Box 444, Callahan FL 32011. Editor: Del Freeman. Fiction Editor: Patsy Sauls. Magazine: Electronic; page number varies. "All fiction, no porn, no poetry, general interest." Monthly. Estab. 1991. "Uploaded electronically to BBSs nationwide."
Needs: Condensed/excerpted novel, contemporary, experimental, humor/satire, mainstream, suspense/mystery. "Stories can be submitted on either size disk, ASCII, IBM format only. Will return if mailer (pre-paid) is enclosed." No porn, erotica. Buys 1-2 mss/issue; 24-30 mss/year. Publishes ms 1-2 months after acceptance. Recently published work by Patsy Sauls, Betty Duckworth, Mary Ellen Wofford. Publishes short shorts. Length: 250 up (unless it's really killer). Sometimes comments on rejected ms.
How to Contact: Contact by mail, by disk, complete story. Reports in 1-2 months. "Prepaid disk mailer is required." Simultaneous submissions OK. Accepts electronic submissions via disk or modem. For sample copy: "Write me and I'll respond with name and number of nearest BBS where it can be found."

Payment: No payment.
Terms: Only the privilege to reproduce electronically once. All rights remain with author.
Advice: "We're looking for something different—unusual, i.e., November story by Mary Ellen Wofford, "Clarice & The Big Red One" is modern day encounter between semi-truck and amorous dragon. We loved it!"

‡SALAD, A Reader, (I, II), Moonface Press, Box 64980-306, Dallas TX 75206. (214)696-8990. Editor: Elaine Liner. Magazine; 5×6½; 74 pages; 20 lb. bond; handmade paper. Strathmore Beau Brilliant cover. "New fiction and poetry. Not too serious. Not ultra-lit. Open to oddities such as lists, eulogies, letters, short-short plays or scenes from plays. For people who are as sick as we are of water-image poems and short stories about New York writers and models and what they eat and drink." Annually. Estab. 1990.
Needs: Contemporary, experimental, humor/satire, literary, regional. "No violent fiction, please. No stories expressing violence toward women, children or animals." Receives 25-40 unsolicited mss/month. Buys 6-10 mss/issue. Publishes ms up to 9 months after acceptance. Recently published work by Robert Liner, Sara Hickman, John Shore, John Eaton, Clay McNear. Length: 1,000 words preferred. Publishes short shorts. Sometimes critiques rejected mss ("if I think I want to see more work by that author").
How to Contact: Send complete ms with cover letter. Include "a little bio info, mention previously published work, some background perhaps on why submitting this mss to *Salad*." Reports in 1 month. SASE. Simultaneous, photocopied submissions OK. Accepts computer printout submissions. Sample copy for $5.
Payment: Pays 2 contributor's copies. Charges for extras.
Terms: Acquires first North American serial rights or one-time rights.
Advice: "If the writer has a sense of humor, that's an immediate grabber. I like to be surprised, get a little shove, see a little experimentation in how the words are used. A new, fresh voice—not the humdrum type of super-serious literary, I'll-see-you-at-the-next-poetry-reading stuff—interests us. Neatness counts a lot. Read an issue first. Then, take your best story and edit out at least a third of it. We like tight, bright writing. Read your story aloud to yourself or to a friend and when it sounds great, send that version."

‡SALMON MAGAZINE, (I, II), P.O. Box 440313, Somerville MA 02144. Editor: Andrew Tang. Fiction Editor: Anna Watson. Magazine: 5½×8; 150-200 pages; glossy card stock cover; illustrations and photographs. For "a literary audience." Quarterly. Estab. 1991.
Needs: Excerpted novel, contemporary, erotica, ethnic, experimental, fantasy (as long as there's no unicorn), feminist, gay, horror, lesbian, literary, prose poem, regional, science fiction, senior citizen/retirement, suspense/mystery, translation, western. No "pornography, religious fiction, men's adventure, political propaganda." Receives 20-25 unsolicited mss/month. Accepts 11 mss/issue; 20-23 mss/year. Does not read mss July and August. Accepts manuscript published in next issue. Recently published work by Edwidge Danticat, Katherine Min, Val Gerstle. Length: 3,000 words preferred; 5,000 words maximum. Publishes short shorts. Sometimes critiques rejected ms and recommends other markets.
How to Contact: Send complete ms with or without cover letter. Reports in 1-2 weeks on queries; 1-2 months on mss. SASE. Simultaneous, photocopied and reprint submissions OK. Accepts computer printout submissions. Fiction guidelines for #10 SAE and 1 first class stamp.
Payment: Pays contributor's copies. Charges for extras.
Terms: Acquires one-time rights. Sends pre-publication galleys to the author "on occasion—we check before changing anything big."
Advice: "The most important quality is emotional honesty. If a manuscript lacks integrity, if it is manipulative, I become uninterested. I like writing that makes me see words and phrases in a new light; I'm interested in stories incorporating questions of gender, race . . . identity. I like to be surprised, shocked, moved . . . ."

SALOME: A JOURNAL FOR THE PERFORMING ARTS, (I, II, IV), Ommation Press, 5548 N. Sawyer, Chicago IL 60625. Editor: Effie Mihopoulos. "*Salome* seeks to cover the performing arts in a thoughtful and incisive way." Quarterly. Estab. 1976. Circ. 1,000.
Needs: Literary, contemporary, science fiction, fantasy, women's, feminist, gothic, romance, mystery, adventure, humor, serialized novels, prose poems, translations. "We seek good quality mss that relate to the performing arts or fiction with strong characters that somehow move the reader." Receives approximately 25 unsolicited fiction mss each month; accepts 40 mss/year. No preferred length. Some-

times sends mss on to editors of other publications and recommends other markets.
How to Contact: Send complete ms with SASE. Reports in 1 month. Sample copy $4, 9 × 12 SASE with 90¢ (book-rate) postage preferred.
Payment: Pays 1 contributor's copy. Contributor's rates for extras upon request.
Terms: Acquires first North American serial rights. "Rights revert to author, but we retain reprint rights."
Advice: "Write a well-written story or prose poem." Rejected mss are "usually badly written — improve style, grammar, etc. — too often writers send out mss before they're ready. See a sample copy. Specify fiction interest."

SALT LICK PRESS, (II), Salt Lick Foundation, 1909 Sunny Brook Dr., Austin TX 78723-3449. Editor: James Haining. Magazine: 8½ × 11; 64 pages; 60 lb. offset stock; 80 lb. text cover; illustrations and photos. Irregular. Estab. 1969.
Needs: Contemporary, erotica, ethnic, experimental, feminist, gay, lesbian, literary. Receives 25 unsolicited mss each month. Accepts 2 mss/issue. Length: open. Occasionally critiques rejected mss.
How to Contact: Send complete ms with cover letter. Reports in 2 weeks on queries; 4 weeks on mss. SASE. Simultaneous, photocopied and reprint submissions OK. Accepts computer printout submissions. Sample copy $5, 9 × 12 SAE and 3 first class stamps.
Payment: Pays in contributor's copies.
Terms: Acquires first North American serial rights. Sends galleys to author.

SAMISDAT, (II), 456 Monroe Turnpike, Monroe CT 06468. Editor: Merritt Clifton. Magazine: 5½ × 8½; 60-80 pages; offset bond paper; vellum bristol cover stock; illustrations; photos. Publication is "environmentalist, pro-animal rights, anti-war, anti-nuke, emphatically non-leftist — basically anarchist." Publishes essays, reviews, poetry and original artwork in approximately equal proportions. Audience consists of "people constructively and conscientiously engaged in changing the world." Subscribers include many secretaries, journalists, blue-collar workers and housewives "but very few bureaucrats." Annually. Estab. 1973. Circ. 400 +.
Needs: Adventure, contemporary, erotica, ethnic, experimental, fantasy, feminist, gay, historical (general), humor/satire, lesbian, literary, mainstream, prose poem, regional, science fiction, serialized/excerpted novel, sports, suspense/mystery, translations, western. "We're pretty damned eclectic if something is done well. Formula hackwork and basic ineptitude, though, won't ever hack it here. No whimsy; no self-indulgent whines about the difficulty of being a sensitive writer/artist." Receives approximately 10-100 unsolicited mss/month. Accepts 2-5 mss/issue. Publishes ms 2-5 months after acceptance. Recently published work by Miriam Sagan, Thomas Michael McDade, W.D. Ehrhart; published new writers within the last year. Length: 1,500-5,000 words. Publishes short shorts. Length: up to 1,000 words. Also publishes literary essays, poetry. Sometimes recommends other markets or critiques rejected mss.
How to Contact: Send complete ms with cover letter. "I like to know how old the author is, what he/she does for a living, and get a ballpark idea of writing experiences, but I do not want to see mere lists of credits. I also like to know why a writer is submitting here in particular." Reports in 1 week on queries and mss. SASE. Reprint submissions OK. "Does not read photocopies or multiple submissions of any kind." Accepts computer printout submissions. Sample copy $2.50.
Payment: Pays in contributor's copies.
Terms: Acquires one-time rights.
Advice: "I'm editor, publisher, printer, distributor, and therefore I do as I damned well please. Over the past 18 years I've found enough other people who agree with me that short stories are worthwhile that my magazine manages to support itself, more or less in the tradition of the old-time radical magazines that published the now-classical short story writers. Know the factual background to your material, e.g., if writing a historical piece, get the details right."

SAN GABRIEL VALLEY MAGAZINE, (IV), Miller Books, 2908 W. Valley Blvd., Alhambra CA 91803. (213)284-7607. Editor: Joseph Miller. Magazine: 5¼ × 7¼; 48 pages; 60 lb. book paper; vellum bristol cover stock; illustrations; photos. "Regional magazine for the Valley featuring local entertainment, dining, sports and events. We also carry articles about successful people from the area. For upper-

Market categories: (I) Beginning; (II) General; (III) Prestige; (IV) Specialized.

middle-class people who enjoy going out a lot." Bimonthly. Published special fiction issue last year; plans another. Estab. 1976. Circ. 3,000.

Needs: Contemporary, inspirational, psychic/supernatural/occult, western, adventure and humor. No articles on sex or ERA. Receives approximately 10 unsolicited fiction mss/month. Buys 2 mss/issue; 20 mss/year. Length: 500-2,500 words. Also publishes short shorts. Recommends other markets.

How to Contact: Send complete ms with SASE. Accepts computer printout submissions. Reports in 2 weeks on mss. Sample copy $1 with 9×12 SASE.

Payment: Pays 5¢/word; 2 contributor's copies.

Terms: Payment on acceptance for one-time rights.

SAN JOSE STUDIES, (II), San Jose State University, One Washington Square, San Jose CA 95152. Editor: Fauneil J. Rinn. Magazine: digest-sized; 112-144 pages; good paper and cover; occasional illustrations and photos. "A journal for the general, educated reader. Covers a wide variety of materials: fiction, poetry, interviews, interdisciplinary essays. Aimed toward the college-educated common reader with an interest in the broad scope of materials." Triannually. Estab. 1975. Circ. 500.

Needs: Social and political, literary, humor, ethnic and regional. Receives approximately 20 unsolicited fiction mss each month. Published work by Molly Giles, Richard Flanagan. Length: 2,500-5,000+ words. Also publishes literary essays, literary criticism, poetry. Critiques rejected mss when there is time. Sometimes recommends other markets.

How to Contact: Send complete ms with SASE. Accepts computer printout submissions. Prefers letter-quality. Reports in 2 months. Publishes ms an average of 6 months to 1 year after acceptance. Sample copy $4.

Payment: Pays 2 contributor's copies. Annual $100 award for best story, essay or poem.

Terms: Acquires first rights. Sends galleys to author.

Advice: "Name should appear *only* on cover sheet. We seldom print beginning writers of fiction or poetry."

SAND HILLS REVIEW (II), (formerly *St. Andrews Review*), 2200 Airport Rd., Pinehurst NC 28374. (919)692-6185. FAX: (919)692-2756. Editor: Stephen E. Smith. General literary magazine for literary and fine arts audience. Semiannually. Estab. 1970. Circ. 1,000.

Needs: Condensed novel, contemporary, experimental, fantasy, historical (general), humor/satire, literary, mainstream and prose poem. Receives 75 unsolicited mss/month. Accepts 2-6 mss/issue; 5-12 mss/year. Published work by Fred Chappell, Michael McFee, Edward Falco; published new writers within the last year.

How to Contact: Send complete ms. Reports in 2 months. SASE. Simultaneous and photocopied submissions OK. Accepts computer printout submissions. Sample copy $5 with legal-sized SAE and 3 first class stamps.

Payment: Pays 2 contributor's copies.

Terms: Rights to individual works revert to author after publication.

Advice: "Please write about what really concerns you and tell the truth, no matter how unseasonal or unsalable your kind of fiction appears to be. Please don't copy anyone else; and please attend workshops, formal and informal, in which you share your work with those who will offer constructive criticism."

SANSKRIT, Literary Arts Publication of UNC Charlotte, (II), University of North Carolina at Charlotte, Highway 49, Charlotte NC 28223. (704)547-2326. Editor: Christy Beatty. Fiction Editor: Lance Phillips. Magazine: 9×15, 60-90 pages. "We are a general lit/art mag open to all genres, if well written, for college students, alumni, writers and artists across the country." Annually. Estab. 1968.

Needs: Contemporary, erotica, ethnic, experimental, feminist, gay, humor/satire, lesbian, literary, mainstream, prose poem, regional, translations. No formula, western, romance. Upcoming theme: How literature reflects/affects/influences REAL LIFE. Receives 2-4 unsolicited mss/month. Accepts 3-6 mss/issue. Does not read mss in summer. Publishes in late March. Recently published work by Nann Budd, P.L. Thomas, Jerry Saviano. Length: 250 words minimum; 5,000 words maximum. Publishes short shorts. Also publishes poetry. Sometimes critiques rejected mss.

How to Contact: Send complete manuscript with cover letter. SASE. Simultaneous and photocopied submissions OK. Accepts computer printout submissions. Sample copy $6. Fiction guidelines for #10 SAE.

Payment: Pays contributor's copies.
Terms: Acquires one-time rights. Publication not copyrighted.
Advice: "A tight cohesive story, in an often shattered world, wins my heart. I like quirkiness just to the point of self indulgence. There is a fine line ... there are many fine lines ... walk as many as you can."

SANTA MONICA REVIEW, (III), Santa Monica College, 1900 Pico Blvd., Santa Monica CA 90405. (213)450-5150. Editor: James Krusoe. Magazine: 5½×8; 140 pages, rag paper. Semiannually. Estab. 1988. Circ. 1,000.
Needs: Contemporary, literary. Accepts 5 mss/issue; 10 mss/year. Publishes mss varying amount of time after publication. Published work by Ann Beattie, Arturo Vivante and Guy Davenport.
How to Contact: Send complete ms with cover letter. Reports in 3 months on mss. SASE. Simultaneous and photocopied submissions OK. Sample copy $6.
Payment: Free subscription to magazine, contributor's copies.
Terms: Acquires one-time rights.
Advice: "We are *not* actively soliciting beginning work. We want to combine high quality West Coast, especially Los Angeles, writing with that from the rest of the country."

SCRIVENER, (II), 853 Sherbrooke St. W., Montreal, Quebec H3A 2T6 Canada. Editors: Thea Boyanowsky, Sam Anson. Magazine: 5½×7½; 120 pages; matte paper; illustrations; b&w photos. "*Scrivener* is a creative journal publishing fiction, poetry, graphics, photography, reviews, interviews and scholarly articles. We publish the best of new and established writers. We examine how current trends in North American writing are rooted in a pervasive creative dynamic; our audience is mostly scholarly and in the writing field." Annually. Estab. 1980. Circ. 800.
Needs: Open, "good writing." Upcoming theme: "Best of Montreal." Receives 40 unsolicited mss/month. Accepts 20 mss/year. Does not read mss May 1-Sept 1. Publishes ms up to 6 months after acceptance. Published work by James Conway, Colin Wright, Louis Phillips; published new writers within the last year. Length: 25 pages maximum. Occasionally publishes short shorts. Also publishes literary essays, literary criticism, poetry. Often critiques rejected mss. Sometimes recommends other markets.
How to Contact: Query first. Order sample copy ($5); send complete ms with cover letter with "critical statements; where we can reach you; biographical data; education; previous publications." Reports in 4 months on queries and mss. SASE/IRC preferred but not required. Simultaneous, photocopied submissions and reprints OK. Accepts computer printouts. Sample copy $5 (US in USA; Canadian in Canada). Fiction guidelines for SAE/IRC. Reviews novels and short story collections. Send books to Nonfiction Editor.
Payment: Pays contributor's copies; charges for extras.
Advice: "Send us your best stuff. Don't be deterred by rejections. Sometimes a magazine just isn't looking for your *kind* of writing. Don't neglect the neatness of your presentation."

THE SEATTLE REVIEW, (II), Padelford Hall GN-30, University of Washington, Seattle WA 98195. (206)543-9865. Editor: Donna Gerstenberger. Fiction Editor: Charles Johnson. Magazine: 6×9. "Includes general fiction, poetry, craft essays on writing, and one interview per issue with a Northwest writer." Semiannually. Published special fiction issue. Estab. 1978. Circ. 1,000.
Needs: Contemporary, ethnic, experimental, fantasy, feminist, gay, historical, horror, humor/satire, lesbian, literary, mainstream, prose poem, psychic/supernatural/occult, regional, science fiction, excerpted novel, suspense/mystery, translations, western. "We also publish a series called Writers and their Craft, which deals with aspects of writing fiction (also poetry) — point of view, characterization, etc., rather than literary criticism, each issue." Does not want to see "anything in bad taste (porn, racist, etc.)." Receives about 50 unsolicited mss/month. Accepts about 3-6 mss/issue; about 4-10 mss/year. Reads mss all year but "slow to respond in summer." Agented fiction 25%. Published work by David Milofsky, Lawson Fusao Inada and Liz Rosenberg; published new writers within the last year. Length: 3,500 words average; 500 words minimum; 10,000 words maximum. Publishes short shorts. Sometimes critiques rejected mss. Occasionally recommends other markets.
How to Contact: Send complete ms. "If included, cover letter should list recent publications or mss we'd seen and liked, but been unable to publish." Reports in 3 months. SASE. Accepts computer printout submissions. Sample copy "half-price if older than one year." Current issue $4.50; some special issues $5.50–6.50.

Payment: Pays 0-$100, free subscription to magazine, 2 contributor's copies; charge for extras.
Terms: Pays on publication for first North American serial rights. Copyright reverts to writer on publication; "please request release of rights and cite *SR* in reprint publications." Sends galleys to author.
Advice: "Beginners do well in our magazine if they send clean, well-written manuscripts. We've published a lot of 'first stories' from all over the country and take pleasure in discovery."

‡**THE SECRET ALAMEDA, An Unusual Quarterly Magazine, (II),** P.O. Box 527, Alameda CA 94501. (510)521-5597. Editor: Richard Whittaker. Magazine: 8½×11; 44-60 pages; 70 lb. text coated paper; illustrations and photographs. "We publish humor, art and quality fiction. Also open to articles and interviews." Audience is "hard to define. We think educated audience. Would like Garrison Keillor, Woody Allen, Ernie Kovacs, Mark Twain." Quarterly. Estab. 1991. Circ. 750-1,000.
Needs: Humor/satire, literary. "Not interested in erotica, politics, polemics (except if we like it)." Accepts 3-4 mss/issue. Publishes ms 2 weeks to 6 months after acceptance. Recently published work by Wm. Dudley, Rue Harrison, Maxwelle Maxfield, Jr. Length: 500-3,000 words. Sometime critiques rejected mss.
How to Contact: Send complete ms with cover letter. Reports in 2 weeks. SASE. Simultaneous, photocopied and reprint submissions OK. Accepts computer printout submissions. Sample copy for $4.
Payment: Pays possible free subscription and up to 10 contributor's copies.
Terms: Acquires one-time rights.
Advice: Work "should have some refinement and not be essentially nihilistic—I appreciate subtle humor in humor writing and fiction which doesn't leave me depressed—but simpleminded optimism is hard to swallow too."

" 'The Fishing Issue,' as we dealt with it, included 'fishing' on many levels and from a number of different angles/anglers," says Richard Whittaker, The Secret Alameda's editor and publisher. For the cover, "I choose these photos because I thought they illustrated our theme," he explains. "I also felt that these photos in combination aptly characterized the nature of the magazine as it strives to be: humorous, thoughtful and artistic." The photos are taken from Craig Vista Svare's "Fishin' Series." Other photos and excerpts from the series are included in the issue. Svare is a doctoral candidate at the Graduate Theological Union in Berkeley, California.

SEEMS, (II), Lakeland College, Sheboygan WI 53081. (414)565-3871. Editor: Karl Elder. Magazine: 7×8½; 40 pages. "We publish fiction and poetry for an audience which tends to be highly literate. People read the publication, I suspect, for the sake of reading it." Published irregularly. Estab. 1971. Circ. 300.
Needs: Literary. Accepts 4 mss/issue. Receives approximately 12 unsolicited fiction mss each month. Published work by John Birchler; published new writers within the last year. Length: 5,000 words maximum. Publishes short shorts. Also publishes poetry. Critiques rejected mss when there is time.

How to Contact: Send complete ms with SASE. Accepts computer printout submissions. Reports in 2 months on mss. Publishes ms an average of 1-2 years after acceptance. Sample copy $3.
Payment: Pays 1 contributor's copy; $3 charge for extras.
Terms: Rights revert to author.
Advice: "Send clear, clean copies. Read the magazine in order to help determine the taste of the editor." Mss are rejected because of "lack of economical expression, or saying with many words what could be said in only a few. Good fiction contains all of the essential elements of poetry; study poetry and apply those elements to fiction. Our interest is shifting to story poems, the grey area between genres."

SENSATIONS, (I,II), 2 Radio Ave., A5, Secaucus NJ 07094. Founder: David Messineo. Magazine: 8½×11; 50-70 pages; 20 lb. inside paper, 67 lb. cover paper; vellum cover; black ink line illustrations. "We publish short stories and poetry, no specific theme, for a liberal, worldly audience who reads for pleasure." We also do the Rediscovering America in Poetry research series. Publishes 2 times/year. Estab. 1987. Circ. 250.
Needs: Adventure, contemporary, fantasy, gay, historical, horror, humor/satire, lesbian, literary, mainstream, prose poem, regional, romance (historical), science fiction, suspense/mystery, western. "We're not into gratuitous profanity, pornography, or violence. Sometimes these are needed to properly tell the tale. We'll read anything unusual, providing it is submitted in accordance with our submission policies. No abstract works only the writer can understand." Accepts 4 mss/issue. Publishes ms 2 months after acceptance. Published work by Patricia Flinn, Karl Luntta and Ed Condon."
How to Contact: "Send name, address, a paragraph of background information about yourself, a paragraph about what inspired the story. We'll send submission guidelines when we are ready to judge material." Reports in 1-2 weeks on queries; 4-6 weeks on mss. SASE for brochure. Simultaneous and photocopied submissions OK. Accepts computer printout submissions. Accepts electronic submissions (Macintosh only). *Must first purchase* sample copy $8. Check payable to "David Messineo." *"Do not submit material before reading submission guidelines."* Next deadline: July 4, 1992.
Payment: No payment.
Terms: Acquires one-time rights.
Advice: "Each story must have a strong beginning that grabs the reader's attention in the first two sentences. Characters have to be realistic and well-described. Readers must like, hate, or have some emotional response to your characters. Setting, plot, construction, attention to detail—all are important. We work with writers to help them improve in these areas, but the better the stories are written before they come to us, the greater the chance for publication. Purchase sample copy first and read the stories, then determine which of your stories is most appropriate to submit. Our fourth issue includes part one of a five-part research project detailing poetry written in and about America in the 1500s and 1600s, which may also be of interest to you." Send SASE for information on our Fiction Contest (Top Prize $250) between October and December, 1992.

‡SEQUOIA, Stanford Literary Magazine, Storke Publications Bldg., Stanford CA 94305. Fiction Editor: Mark Clevenger. "Literary journal ranges from traditional to avant-garde for college students to retired people." Semiannually. Estab. 1887. Circ. 500.
Needs: "Literary excellence is the primary criterion. We'll consider anything but prefer literary, ethnic, avant-garde, experimental." Receives 50 mss/month. Accepts 2-3 mss/issue; 24-30 mss/year. Publishes ms 2 weeks to 2 months after acceptance. Length: 8,000 words or 20 pages maximum.
How to Contact: Send complete ms with SASE. Tries to report in 3 months "during academic year." Sample copy $6.
Payment: Pays 1-2 contributor's copies. Contributor's rates on request.
Terms: Author retains rights.

THE SEWANEE REVIEW, (III), University of the South, Sewanee TN 37375. (615)598-1245. Editor: George Core. Magazine: 6×9; 192 pages. "A literary quarterly, publishing original fiction, poetry, essays on literary and related subjects, book reviews and book notices for well-educated readers who appreciate good American and English literature." Quarterly. Estab. 1892. Circ. 3,000.
Needs: Literary, contemporary. No translations, juvenile, gay/lesbian, erotica. Buys 10-15 mss/year. Receives approximately 100 unsolicited fiction mss each month. Does not read mss June 1-August 31. Published new writers within the last year. Length: 6,000-7,500 words. Critiques rejected mss "when there is time." Sometimes recommends other markets.

How to Contact: Send complete ms with SASE and cover letter stating previous publications, if any. Accepts computer printout submissions. Reports in 1 month on mss. Sample copy $6 plus 50¢ postage.
Payment: Pays $10-12/printed page; 2 contributor's copies; $3.50 charge for extras. Writer's guidelines for SASE.
Terms: Pays on publication for first North American serial rights and second serial rights by agreement.
Advice: "Send only one story at a time, with a serious and sensible cover letter. We think fiction is of greater general interest than any other literary mode."

SHATTERED WIG REVIEW, (I, II), Shattered Wig Productions, 523 E. 38th St., Baltimore MD 21218-1930. (301)243-6888. Editor: Collective. Magazine: 70 pages; "average" paper; cardstock cover; illustrations and photos. "Open forum for the discussion of the absurdo-miserablist aspects of everyday life. Fiction, poetry, graphics, essays, photos." Semiannually. Estab. 1988. Circ. 300.
Needs: Confession, contemporary, erotica, ethnic, experimental, feminist, gay, humor/satire, juvenile (5-9 years), lesbian, literary, preschool (1-4 years), prose poem, psychic/supernatural/occult, regional, senior citizen/retirement, serialized/excerpted novel, translations, young adult/teen (10-18), meat, music, film, art, pickles, revolutionary practice." Does not want "anything by Ann Beattie or John Irving." Receives 15-20 unsolicited mss/month. Publishes ms 2-4 months after acceptance. Published work by Al Ackerman, Jake Berry, Bella Donna; published new writers within the last year. Publishes short shorts. Also publishes literary criticism, poetry. Sometimes critiques rejected mss and recommends other markets.
How to Contact: Send complete ms with cover letter or "visit us in Baltimore." Reports in 1 month. SASE for ms. Simultaneous, photocopied and reprint submissions OK. Accepts computer printout submissions. Sample copy for $3 and SAE.
Payment: Pays in contributor's copies.
Terms: Acquires one-time rights.
Advice: "The arts have been reduced to imploding pus with the only material rewards reserved for vapid stylists and collegiate pod suckers. The only writing that counts has no barriers between imagination and reality, thought and action. We publish any writing that addresses vital issues. Send us at least 3 pieces so we have a choice."

SHAWNEE SILHOUETTE, (II), Shawnee State University, 940 Second St., Portsmouth OH 45662. (614)354-3205. Fiction Editor: Tamela Carmichael. Magazine: 5×7; 40 pages; illustrations and photos. Quarterly.
Needs: Adventure, contemporary, historical, humor/satire, literary, mainstream, regional, romance, science fiction, suspense/mystery. Receives 3 unsolicted mss/month. Accepts 3 mss/issue. Does not read mss in summer. Publishes ms an average of 3-6 months after acceptance. Published new writers within the last year. Length: 800 words average; 400 words minimum; 1,000 words maximum. Publishes short shorts. Occasionally critiques rejected mss.
How to Contact: Send complete ms with cover letter. Reports in 3 weeks on queries. SASE. Photocopied submissions OK. Accepts computer printout submissions. Sample copy $2, 5×7 SAE and postage.
Payment: Pays in contributor's copies.
Terms: Acquires one-time rights.

‡SHOCKBOX, The Literary/Art Magazine with Teeth, (II), P.O. Box 7226, Nashua NH 03062. (603)888-8549. Editor: C.F. Roberts. Magazine: digest-sized; 44 pages. "We publish raw, jarring experimental literary fiction that should in one way or another illuminate the human condition. For generally alternative art/lit., underground audience." Quarterly. Estab. 1991.
Needs: Contemporary, experimental, humor/satire, literary. "No slick, watered-down prose. No contrived TV-Movie-of-the-Week fodder." Plans future special fiction issue. Receives 5 unsolicited mss/month. Accepts 3 mss/issue; 20 mss/year. Time varies between acceptance and publication. Recently published work by Paul Vassar, Ronald Edward Kittell. Length: 1,000 words preferred. Publishes short shorts. Sometimes comments on rejected mss and recommends other markets.
How to Contact: Query first. Include name, address, short bio. Reports in 1 week on queries. SASE. Simultaneous, photocopied and reprint submissions OK. Sample copy for $2.50. Fiction guidelines for #10 SAE.

Payment: Pays in contributor's copies.
Terms: Acquires first rights or one-time rights. Sends galleys to author.
Advice: "I look for incendiary work. I want someone to illuminate life for me in a startling new way and to stretch the boundaries of theme, style and content. I will gladly forsake a part of refinement to discover feeling and vitality in its place. Show me pain, show me experience, show me trauma as enlightenment. Show me your deepest fantasy or your worst nightmare. Show me alarm. Show me chaos. Show me attitude. Just let me say that a writer, shouldn't fall over him/herself so as to sacrifice intuitive fire for rote, tired academic discipline. It helps to know what you're doing, yes, but don't let it CONTROL you. A brave and meaningful writer, in my opinion, works without a net."

SHOOTING STAR REVIEW, (II, IV), 7123 Race St., Pittsburgh PA 15208. (412)731-7039. Editor: Sandra Gould Ford. Magazine: 8½ × 11; 32 pages; 60 lb. white paper; 80 lb. enamel glossy cover; generously-illustrated; photos. "Dedicated to the Black African-American experience." Quarterly. Estab. 1987. Circ. 1,500.
Needs: Contemporary, experimental, literary, regional, young adult, translations. Each issue has a different theme: "Behind Bars" (deadline March 1); "Marching to a Different Beat" (deadline June 1); "A Salute to African-American Male Writers" (deadline September 1); "Mothers and Daughters" (deadline November 15). Writers should send a SASE for guidelines. No juvenile, preschool. Receives 30-40 unsolicited mss/month. Publishes 5-8 mss/issue. Publishes ms 4-12 months after acceptance. Length: 1,800 words preferred; 3,500 words maximum. Publishes short shorts. Length: 1,000 words or less. Sometimes critiques rejected mss and recommends other markets.
How to Contact: Send complete ms with cover letter. "We like to promote the writer as well as their work and would appreciate understanding who the writer is and why they write." Reports within 1 month on queries; 10-12 weeks on mss. SASE. Simultaneous, photocopied and reprint submissions OK. Accepts computer printout submissions. Accepts electronic submissions via "IBM compatible, 5¼" double sided/double density disk, ASCII non-formated." Sample copy for $3. Fiction guidelines for #10 SAE and 1 first class stamp.
Payment: Pays $15-50 maximum and 2 contributor's copies; charge for extras.
Terms: Pays on publication for first North American serial rights. Sends galleys to author upon request, if time permits.
Advice: "*Shooting Star Review* was started specifically to provide a forum for short fiction that explores the Black experience. We are committed to this art form and will make space for work that satisfies our guidelines. Upcoming themes—"Home & Community"—exploring the worlds that make us; "Star Child"—fanciful studies of the zodiac; "The Heritage"—thoughts about what growing old can mean; "Juneteenth"—the celebration of emancipation.

‡**THE SHORT STORY DIGEST, (II),** Caldwell Publishing, Box 1183, Richardson TX 75083. Editor: Wayne Caldwell. Magazine: 5⅛ × 8½; 32-40 pages; 70 Warren Flo cover; illustrations and photographs. "We want to open a new market for short fiction." Quarterly. Estab. 1991. Circ. 1,000.
Needs: Adventure, contemporary, fantasy, horror, humor/satire, mainstream, psychic/supernatural/occult, science fiction, suspense/mystery, western. "Please no excessive blood and guts, porno." No sword and sorcery. Receives 50-100 unsolicited mss/month. Buys 8-12 mss/issue; 32-50 mss/year. Recently published work by Douglas Bryce, Maggie Cooper, H.W. Christopher. Length: 1,500-2,000 words preferred; 500 words minimum; 3,000 words maximum. Publishes short shorts (but not often).
How to Contact: Send complete ms with cover letter. Include Social Security number. Reports in 8-10 weeks on mss. SASE. Photocopied submissions OK. Accepts computer printout submissions. Accepts electronic submissions. Sample copy for $3. Fiction guidelines for #10 SAE and 1 first class stamp.
Payment: Pays 1¢/word (more if ms is exceptional).
Terms: Pays on publication for first North American serial rights and 1 reprint in case we publish a "Best Of."
Advice: "Have a friend read it. If he likes it, then the flow of the story is good. A new author can sometimes edit their own story to death, thinking it is not good enough to submit. Take a chance, the worst that can happen is a rejection notice in the mail. Don't get mad at rejection. Sometimes a ms is rejected because of lack of space or the idea does not fit what the editor is looking for at that time."

SHORT STUFF MAGAZINE FOR GROWN-UPS, (II), Bowman Publications, P.O. Box 7057, Loveland CO 80537. (303)669-9139. Editor: Donna Bowman. Magazine: 8½ × 11; 40 pages; bond paper; enamel cover; b&w illustrations and photographs. "Nonfiction is regional—Colorado and adjacent states. Fiction and humor must be tasteful, but can be any genre, any subject. We are designed to be a *Reader's Digest* of fiction. We are found in professional waiting rooms, etc." Monthly.

Needs: Adventure, contemporary, historical (general), humor/satire, mainstream, regional, romance (contemporary/historical), suspense/mystery, western. No erotica. Upcoming themes: Holidays—St. Patrick's Day, Easter, Mother's Day, Father's Day, July 4th, Halloween, Thanksgiving, Christmas, "Celebrate August" and "Valentine's Day." Plans special fiction issue. Receives 100 unsolicited mss/month. Buys 9-12 mss/issue; 76 mss/year. Publishes ms 3 months after acceptance. Recently published work by Dean Ballenger and Dorothy Roberts. Length: 1,000 words average; 1,500 words maximum. Also publishes some poetry.
How to Contact: Send complete manuscript with cover letter. Include SASE. Reports in 3 months. Photocopied and reprint submissions OK. Accepts computer printout submissions. Sample copies with SAE and 98¢ postage. Fiction guidelines for SAE. Reviews novels and short story collections.
Payment: Pays $10-50 and subscription to magazine.
Terms: Pays on publication for first North American serial rights.
Advice: "We seek a potpourri of subjects each issue. A new slant, a different approach, fresh viewpoints—all of these excite us. We don't like gore, salacious humor or perverted tales. Prefer third person. Be sure it is a story with a beginning, middle and end. It must have dialogue. Many beginners do not know an essay from a short story."

‡SIDE SHOW, Short Story Annual, (II), Somersault Press, P.O. Box 1428, El Cerrito CA 94530-1428. (510)215-2207. Editor: Shelley Anderson, Kathe Stoltz and Marjorie K. Jacobs. Book (paperback): 5½×8½; 300 pages; 50 lb. paper. "Quality short stories for a general, literary audience." Annually. Estab. 1991. Circ. 250.
Needs: Contemporary, ethnic, feminist, gay, humor/satire, lesbian, literary, mainstream. Nothing genre, religious, pornographic. Receives 50-60 unsolicited mss/month. Buys 25-30 mss/issue. Does not read mss in August. Publishes ms up to 1 year after acceptance. Recently published work by Ann Hood, Susan Ito, Paul Perry. Length: Open. Publishes short shorts. Sometimes critiques rejected mss and recommends other markets.
How to Contact: All submissions entered in contest. *$10 entry fee.* Send complete ms with cover letter and entry fee. Reports in 2-3 weeks on mss. SASE. Simultaneous, photocopied submissions OK. Accepts computer printout submissions. Sample copy for $10 and $3.50 postage and handling ($.83 sales tax Cal. residents).
Payment: Pays $5 per printed page.
Terms: Pays on publication for all rights. Sends galleys to author. All submissions entered in our contest for cash prizes $30 (1st); $25 (2nd); $20 (3rd).
Advice: Looks for "readability, vividness of characterization, coherence, inspiration, interesting subject matter, point of view, originality, plausibility."

SIDETREKKED, (I, IV), Science Fiction London, 304-25 Grand Ave., London, Ontario N6C 1L3 Canada. (519)660-8883. Editor: Timothy Blahout. Newspaper: 7×8½; 36-40 pages; bond paper, b&w drawings, halftone photographs. "Science fiction for science fiction readers, mostly adults." Quarterly. Estab. 1980. Circ. 200.
Needs: Fantasy, science fiction. "We will consider any story with a science fictional slant. Because sf tends to be all-embracing, that could include horror, humor/satire, romance, suspense, feminist, gay, ethnic, etc.—yes, even western—but the science fiction classification must be met, usually by setting the story in a plausible, futuristic universe." Receives 3-5 unsolicited fiction mss/month. Accepts 3-8 mss/issue. Time between acceptance and publication varies. Published work by Joe Beliveau, Dave Seburn. Length: 1,000-5,000 words preferred. "No hard-and-fast rules, but we can't accommodate novelettes or novellas." Publishes short shorts. Critiques or comments on rejected mss, if requested by the author. Recommends other markets on occasion.
How to Contact: Send complete ms with cover letter. Reports in 3 weeks on queries; in 1 month on mss. SASE. Photocopied and computer printout submissions OK. Sample copy for $2 (Canadian) and 9×10 SAE.
Payment: Pays in contributor's copies.
Terms: Acquires first North American serial rights.
Advice: "We are presently running a short fiction contest in celebration of our sponsoring club's 10th anniversary. If sponsorship can be arranged, we would consider making it an annual event. We are more forgiving than most fiction markets and we try to work with new writers. What makes us want to work with a writer is some suggestion that he or she understands what makes a good story. What makes a manuscript stand out? Tell a good story. The secondary things are fixable if the story is there, but if it is not, no amount of tinkering can fix it."

SIGN OF THE TIMES, A Chronicle of Decadence in the Atomic Age, (II), 3819 NE 15th, Portland OR 97212. (206)323-6764. Editor: Mark Souder. Tabloid: 8 × 10; 32 pages; book paper; 120 lb. cover stock; illustrations; photos. "Decadence in all forms for those seeking literary amusement." Semiannually. Published special fiction issue last year; plans another. Estab. 1980. Circ. 750.
Needs: Comics, erotica, experimental, gay, lesbian. No religious or western manuscripts. Receives 6 unsolicited mss/month. Buys 10 mss/issue; 20 mss/year. Published work by Gary Smith, Willie Smith, Ben Satterfield. Length: 3,000 words average; 500 words minimum, 5,000 words maximum. Publishes short shorts. Sometimes comments on rejected mss and recommends other markets.
How to Contact: Send complete ms with cover letter and bio. Reports in 6 weeks on mss. SASE. Photocopied submissions OK. Accepts computer printout submissions. Sample copy $3.50. Fiction guidelines for #10 SASE.
Payment: Pays up to $20, subscription to magazine, 2 contributor's copies; 1 time cover price charge for extras.
Terms: Pays on publication for first rights plus anthology in the future.

THE SIGNAL, (II), Network International, Box 67, Emmett ID 83617. Editors: Joan Silva and David Chorlton. Magazine: 8½ × 11; 68 pages; good paper; some art; photos. "Wide open. Not restricted to 'literature.' Poetry, essays, reviews, comment, interviews, speculative thought." Semiannually. Estab. 1987.
Needs: Literary, translations. No "religious dogma, journeys of self-discovery in a '57 Chevrolet, catalogues of family members." Receives few unsolicited mss/month. Accepts "perhaps 1" ms/issue. Publishes ms 6 months to 1 year after acceptance. Length: 3,000 words maximum. Publishes short shorts. Also publishes literary essays, literary criticism, poetry.
How to Contact: "Just send us the story. Cover letter optional." Reports in 10 weeks on mss. SASE. Photocopied submissions OK. Accepts computer printout submissions. Sample copy $4. Fiction guidelines for #10 SAE and 1 first class stamp. Reviews novels and short story collections.
Payment: Pays in contributor's copies.
Terms: Acquires first rights.
Advice: "We want to remain open to all writing. Although unable to publish very much fiction, we do look for ideas expressed in any form."

THE SILVER WEB, (II), (formerly *The Sterling Web*), Buzzcity Press, Box 38190, Tallahassee FL 32315. Editor: Ann Kennedy. Magazine: 8½ × 11; 64 pages; 20 lb. paper; glossy cover; b&w illustrations and photographs. "Speculative fiction for those that seek to be challenged – all ages." Semiannually. Estab. 1989.
Needs: Experimental, fantasy, horror, humor/satire, psychic/supernatural/occult, science fiction. "No slash n' gore, no predictable endings." Upcoming theme: the "Bug" issue (March 1992). Publishes annual special fiction issue. Receives 30-40 unsolicited mss/month. Accepts 8-12 mss/issue. Publishes ms 6-12 months after acceptance. Length: 2,500 words; 5,000 words maximum. Publishes short shorts. Also publishes poetry. Sometimes critiques on rejected ms and recommends other markets.
How to Contact: "Get guidelines, or better yet, a copy of our magazine, and then submit." Reports in 4-6 weeks on queries; 1 month on mss. SASE. Photocopied submissions OK. Accepts computer printout submissions. Accepts electronic submissions. Sample copy $4.75 plus $1 postage and handling. Fiction guidelines for #10 SAE and 1 first class stamp. Reviews novels and short story collections.
Payment: Pays ½¢/word plus 1 contributor's copy. Discount to writers for additional copies.
Terms: Acquires first North American serial rights.
Advice: "The kind of work I look for is a piece that will stay with me long after I've finished reading it. It must paint pictures in my mind that are not easily erased. Read a copy of our magazine, at least – get our Writer's Guidelines."

SILVERFISH REVIEW, (IV), Silverfish Press, Box 3541, Eugene OR 97403. (503)344-5060. Editor: Rodger Moody. High quality literary material for a general audience. Published irregularly. Estab. 1979. Circ. 750.
Needs: Literary. Accepts 1-2 mss/issue. Also publishes literary essays, poetry.
How to Contact: Send complete ms with SASE. Reports in 2-3 months on mss. Sample copy $3 and $1 for postage.
Payment: Pays 5 contributor's copies. $5/page when funding permits.
Terms: Rights revert to author.
Advice: "We publish primarily poetry; we will, however, publish good quality fiction."

SING HEAVENLY MUSE!, (II), Box 13320, Minneapolis MN 55414. Editor: Sue Ann Martinson. Magazine: 6×9; 125 pages; 55 lb. acid-free paper; 10 pt. glossy cover stock; illustrations; photos. Women's poetry, prose and artwork. Semiannually. Estab. 1977.
Needs: Literary, feminist, prose poem and ethnic/minority. Receives approximately 30 unsolicited fiction mss each month. "Accepts mss for consideration only in April and September." Published work by Helene Cappuccio, Erika Duncan, Martha Roth. Publishes short shorts. Also publishes literary essays, poetry. Sometimes recommends other markets.
How to Contact: Query for information on theme issues or variations in schedule. Include cover letter with "brief writing background and publications." Accepts computer printout submissions. Reports in 1-3 months on queries and mss. Publishes ms an average of 1 year after acceptance. Sample copy $3.50.
Payment: Pays 2 contributor's copies.
Terms: Pays on publication for first rights.
Advice: "Try to avoid preaching. Look for friends also interested in writing and form a mutual support-and-criticism group."

SINISTER WISDOM, (IV), Box 3252, Berkeley CA 94703. Editor: Elana Dykewomon. Magazine: 5½×8½; 128-144 pages; 55 lb. stock; 10 pt C1S cover; illustrations; photos. Lesbian-feminist journal, providing fiction, poetry, drama, essays, journals and artwork. Quarterly. 1991 issues included a "15th Anniversary Issue Retrospective" and "Lesbian and Class." Estab. 1976. Circ. 3,000.
Needs: Lesbian, adventure, contemporary, erotica, ethnic, experimental, fantasy, feminist, historical, humor/satire, literary, prose poem, psychic, regional, science fiction, sports, translations. No heterosexual or male-oriented fiction; nothing that stereotypes or degrades women. Upcoming theme: "Lesbians of Color" (deadline February 11, 1992); two more theme issues undecided, (inquire). Receives 50 unsolicited mss/month. Accepts 25 mss/issue; 75-100 mss/year. Publishes ms 1 month to 1 year after acceptance. Published work by Melanie Kaye/Kantrowitz, Adrienne Rich, Terri L. Jewell and Gloria Anzaldúa; published new writers within the last year. Length: 2,000 words average; 500 words minimum; 4,000 words maximum. Publishes short shorts. Also publishes literary essays, literary criticism, poetry. Occasionally critiques rejected mss. Sometimes recommends other markets.
How to Contact: Send 2 copies of complete ms with cover letter, which should include a brief author's bio to be published when the work is published. Reports in 2 months on queries; 6 months on mss. SASE. Photocopied submissions OK. Accepts computer printout submissions. Sample copy $6.25. Reviews novels and short story collections. Send books to "Attn: Book review."
Payment: Pays in contributor's copies.
Terms: Rights retained by author.
Advice: The philosophy behind *Sinister Wisdom* is "to reflect and encourage the lesbian movements for social change, especially change in the ways we use language."

‡SISYPHUS, Art & Entertainment Between the Lakes, (I), 8 Asticou Rd., Boston MA 02130-3517. (617)983-5291. Editor: Christopher Corbett-Fiacco. Magazine: 5×8; 28 pages; colored cover; illustrations. "A bimonthly desktop literary magazine that exists to provide another outlet for the vision of artists through the publication of poetry, prose and line drawn or sketch artwork. Our motto, 'SISYPHUS may be small, but not insignificant,' pretty much sums us up." Bimonthly. Estab. 1990.
Needs: Contemporary, ethnic, experimental, fantasy, feminist, gay, historical (general), humor/satire, lesbian, literary, mainstream, science fiction, suspense/mystery. "No overtly religious, rightist, leftist, pseudo-anything lacking honesty of purpose and voice." Plans special fiction issue. Receives 5 unsolicited mss/month. Accepts 1-2 mss/issue; 6-12 mss/year. Publishes ms within 3 issues after acceptance. Length: 1,500 words preferred; 200 words minimum; 2,000 words maximum. Also publishes poetry. Sometimes critiques rejected mss (only if asked to) and sometimes recommends other markets.
How to Contact: Send complete ms with cover letter. Reports in 2 weeks. SASE. Simultaneous, photocopied and reprint submissions OK. Accepts computer printout submissions. Sample copy for $1.75 (US); $2.50 (International); more for current issue. Fiction guidelines free.

Read the Business of Fiction section to learn the correct way to prepare and submit a manuscript.

Payment: Pays 1 contributor's copy.
Terms: Acquires one-time rights.
Advice: Looks for "well-edited work; clarity of thought, intent, voice; proper use of grammar, correct spelling; honesty from author; meaningful engagement—something that 'clicks.'" Sponsors themed prose/poetry contests bimonthly. Send SASE for info.

SKYLARK, (I), Purdue University, 2200 169th St., Hammond IN 46323. (219)989-2262. Editor: Pamela Hunter. Magazine: 8½×11; 100 pages; illustrations; photos. Fine arts magazine—short stories, poems and graphics for adults. Annually. Estab. 1971. Circ. 500-1,000.
Needs: Contemporary, ethnic, experimental, fantasy, feminist, humor/satire, literary, mainstream, prose poem, regional, science fiction, serialized/excerpted novel, spiritual, sports, suspense/mystery and western. Upcoming theme: "Rites of Passage" (submit January-May 1992). Receives 15 mss/month. Accepts 6-7 mss/issue. Recently published work by Daniel Meltzer, Margaret Davis, Hallie Parker; published new writers within the last year. Length: 4,500 words maximum. Also publishes literary essays, poetry.
How to Contact: Send complete ms. SASE for ms. Photocopied submissions OK. Accepts computer printout submissions. Sample copy $5; back issue $3.
Payment: Pays 1 contributor's copy.
Terms: Acquires first rights. Copyright reverts to author.
Advice: "The goal of *Skylark* is to encourage *creativity* and give beginning and published authors showcase for their work. Check for spelling errors or typos."

SLATE AND STYLE, Magazine of the National Federation of the Blind Writers Division, (IV), NFB Writer's Division, 2704 Beach Drive, Merrick NY 11566. Editor: Loraine E. Stayer. Fiction Editor: Loraine Stayer. Newsletter: 8×10; 32 print/Braille pages; cassette and large print. "Articles of interest to writers, and resources for blind writers." Quarterly. Estab. 1982. Circ. 200.
Needs: Adventure, contemporary, fantasy, humor/satire, blindness. No erotica. "Avoid theme of death and handicapped." Does not read June, July. Length: 2,000 words average; 1,000 words minimum; 6,000 words maximum. Publishes short shorts. Also publishes literary criticism, poetry. Critiques rejected mss only if requested. Sometimes recommends other markets.
How to Contact: Query first. Reports on queries in 2 weeks; 1 month on mss. Photocopied submissions OK. Sample copy $2.50 and cassette mailer if tape requested. Large print copies also available. "Sent Free Matter For The Blind. If not blind, send 2 stamps."
Payment: Pays in contributor's copies.
Terms: Acquires one-time rights. Publication not copyrighted. Sponsors contests for fiction writers.
Advice: "Keep a copy. Editors can lose your work. Consider each first draft as just that and review your work before you send it. SASE a must."

SLIPSTREAM, (II, IV), Box 2071, New Market Station, Niagara Falls NY 14301. (716)282-2616. Editor: Dan Sicoli. Fiction Editors: R. Borgatti, D. Sicoli and Livio Farallo. Magazine: 7×8½; 80-120 pages; high quality paper and cover; illustrations; photos. "We use poetry and short fiction with a contemporary urban feel." Estab. 1981. Circ. 300.
Needs: Contemporary, erotica, ethnic, experimental, fantasy, humor/satire, literary, mainstream, prose poem and science fiction. No religious, juvenile, young adult or romance. Receives over 75 unsolicited mss/month. Accepts 2-8 mss/issue; 6-12 mss/year. Publishes short shorts under 15 pages. Published work by Gregory Burnham, Nan D. Hayes and Kurt Nimmo. Rarely critiques rejected mss. Sometimes recommends other markets.
How to Contact: "We are currently backlogged with fiction. Query before submitting." Reports within 2 months. SASE. Accepts computer printout submissions. Sample copy $5. Fiction guidelines for #10 SASE.
Payment: Pays 2 contributor's copies.
Terms: Acquires one-time rights on publication.
Advice: "Writing should be honest, fresh; develop your own style. Check out a sample issue first. Don't write for the sake of writing, write from the gut as if it were a biological need. Write from experience and mean what you say, but say it in the fewest number of words."

THE SMALL POND MAGAZINE, (II), Box 664, Stratford CT 06497. (203)378-4066. Editor: Napoleon St. Cyr. Magazine: 5½×8½; 42 pages; 60 lb. offset paper; 65 lb. cover stock; illustrations (art). "Features contemporary poetry, the salt of the earth, peppered with short prose pieces of various kinds.

The college educated and erudite read it for good poetry, prose and pleasure." Triannually. Estab. 1964. Circ. 300.

Needs: "Rarely use science fiction or formula stories you'd find in *Cosmo, Redbook, Ladies Home Journal,* etc." Buys 10-12 mss/year. Longer response time in July and August. Receives approximately 50 unsolicited fiction mss each month. Length: 200-2,500 words. Critiques rejected mss when there is time. Sometimes recommends other markets.

How to Contact: Send complete ms with SASE and short vita. Accepts good copy computer printout submissions. Reports in 2 weeks-1 month. Publishes ms an average of 2 months to 1 year after acceptance. Sample copy $3; $2.50 for back issues.

Payment: Pays 2 contributor's copies; $2/copy charge for extras.

Terms: Acquires for all rights.

Advice: "Send for a sample copy first. All mss must be typed. Name and address and story title on front page, name of story on succeeding pages and paginated." Mss are rejected because of "tired plots and poor grammar; also over-long—2,500 words maximum. Don't send any writing conference ms unless it got an A or better."

SMILE, (IV), Box 3502, Madison WI 53704. (608)258-1305. Editor: Fred Wagwroth. Magazine: 8½×11; 28 pages; colored cover; illustrations; photos. Publishes material on "non-mainstream politics; political theory and practice." Semiannually. Plans special fiction issue. Estab. 1987. Circ. 1,500.

Needs: "Anarchist or communist topics that deal with the psychosocial liberation from the oppressive society." Receives 2 unsolicited fiction mss/month. Length: 200 words minimum; 800 words maximum. Sometimes critiques rejected mss.

How to Contact: Query with clips of published work or send complete mss with cover letter. Simultaneous, photocopied and reprint submissions OK. Accepts computer printout submissions. Accepts electronic submissions via disk or modem. Sample copy for SAE and 6 first class stamps.

Payment: Pays 2 contributor's copies.

Terms: "Everything printed is free to be copied by anyone." Publication is not copyrighted.

SNAKE NATION REVIEW, (II), Snake Nation Press, Inc. 2920 North Oak, Valdosta GA 31602. (912)242-1503. Editor: Roberta George. Fiction Editor: Janice Daugharty. Newspaper: 6×9; 110 pages; acid free 70 lb. paper; 90 lb. cover; illustrations and photographs. "We are interested in all types of stories for an educated, discerning, sophisticated audience." Semiannually. Estab. 1989. Circ. 700.

Needs: "Short stories of 5,000 words or less, poems (any length), art work that will be returned after use." Condensed/excerpted novel, contemporary, erotica, ethnic, experimental, fantasy, feminist, gay, horror, sumor/satire, lesbian, literary, mainstream, prose poem, psychic/supernatural/occult, regional, science fiction, senior citizen/retirement, suspense/mystery. "We want our writers to have a voice, a story to tell, not a flat rendition of a slice of life." Plans annual anthology. Receives 50 unsolicited mss/month. Buys 8-10 mss/issue; 20 mss/year. Publishes ms 3-6 months after acceptance. Agented fiction 1%. Recently published work by Judith Oitiz Cofer, Victor Miller. Length: 3,500 words average; 300 words minimum; 5,500 words maximum. Publishes short shorts. Length: 500 words. Also publishes literary essays, poetry. Sometimes critiques rejected mss and recommends other markets.

How to Contact: Send complete manuscript with cover letter. Reports on queries in 3 months. SASE. Photocopied submissions OK. Accepts computer printout submissions. Sample copy for $5, 8×10 SAE and 90¢ postage. Fiction guidelines for SAE and 1 first class stamp.

Payment: Pays $100 maximum and contributor's copies.

Terms: Buys first rights. Sends galleys to author.

Advice: "Looks for clean, legible copy and an interesting, unique voice that pulls the reader into the work." Spring contest: short stories (5,000 words); $300 first prize, $200 second prize, $100 third prize; entry fee $5 for stories $1 for poems.

SNAKE RIVER REFLECTIONS, (I), 1863 Bitterroot Dr., Twin Falls ID 83301. (208)734-0746 (evenings). Editor: Bill White. Newsletter: 5½×8½; 8 pages; illustrations. "General interest newsletter with social commentary." Published 10 times/year. Estab. 1990. Circ. approximately 300.

Needs: Literary, regional, suspense/mystery, humor/satire and western. No erotica, gay, lesbian, religious or occult fiction. Accepts 1 ms/issue; 10 mss/year. Publishes ms within 1-2 months of acceptance. Length: 500 words maximum. Also publishes literary essays, literary criticism, poetry. Sometimes critiques rejected mss and recommends other markets.

How to Contact: Include SASE. Photocopied submissions OK. Accepts computer printout submissions. Sample copy 55¢. Fiction guidelines for #10 SASE.
Payment: Pays 2 contributor's copies.
Terms: Acquires first rights.
Advice: "Be persistent. Study a sample of our publication. Make your story exciting."

THE SNEAK PREVIEW, (I), Box 639, Grants Pass OR 97526. (503)474-3044. Editor: Curtis Hayden. Fiction Editor: Claire Pennington. Tabloid; 9¾ × 14; 24-32 pages; newsprint paper and cover; illustrations; photos. "News and arts biweekly of local events, with one page reserved for writers and poets to submit stories and poems." Biweekly. Estab. 1986. Circ. 12,500.
Needs: Humor/satire (especially), prose poem, regional. "Nothing that would offend the scruples of a small town in southern Oregon." Receives 2 unsolicited mss/month. Buys 1 ms/issue; 26 mss/year. Publishes ms within 2 weeks-6 months of acceptance. Published work by Leo Curzen, Cher Manuel, Garfield Price. Also publishes poetry. Length: 250 words average; 200 words minimum; 300 words maximum.
How to Contact: Query first. Reports in 2 weeks. SASE (65¢ postage is a must). Simultaneous, photocopied and reprint submissions OK. Accepts computer printout submissions. Guidelines for SASE.
Payment: Pays in contributor's copies.
Terms: Publication not copyrighted.
Advice: "We need more people like Hunter Thompson. Everybody thinks the New-York-City-let's-get-serious-about-life-and-our-'art' is where it's at."

‡SONOMA MANDALA, (II), Dept. of English, Sonoma State University, 1801 E. Cotati Ave., Rohnert Park CA 94928. Faculty Advisor: Elizabeth Herron. Magazine: 7 × 8½; approx. 100 pages; bond paper; card cover stock; some illustrations; some photos. "We have no static thematic preference. We publish several short pieces (up to 2,500 words) of fiction in each issue." For campus community of a small liberal arts college and the surrounding rural/residential area. Annually. Estab. 1972. Circ. 500-1,000.
Needs: Contemporary, ethnic, experimental, feminist, gay, humor/satire, lesbian, literary, mainstream, prose poem, translations, western, regional. Receives 10-15 unsolicited fiction mss/month. Accepts 3-5 mss/issue. Does not read ms August 15 to November 15. Publishes 9-12 months after acceptance. Published new writers within the last year. Length: 1,000 words average; 2,500 words maximum. Publishes short shorts.
How to Contact: Send complete ms with cover letter. "Include info on simultaneous submissions, which we allow, if so indicated in cover letter. Always include address and telephone number, if needed." Reports in 1-5 months. SASE for ms. Photocopied submissions OK. Sample copy $6 postpaid.
Payment: Pays 2 contributor's copies.
Terms: Acquires one-time rights; rights revert to author upon publication.
Advice: "Read the literary magazines, and, if you believe in your work, keep submitting it to other publications. Especially interested in SSU and SF Bay area writers, but consider all quality submissions."

SONORA REVIEW, (II), University of Arizona, Department of English, Tucson AZ 85721. (602)621-8077. Editor: Tony Brown. Fiction Editor: Jane Martin. Magazine: 6 × 9; 150 pages; 16 lb. paper; 20 lb. cover stock; photos seldom. *Sonora Review* publishes short fiction and poetry of high literary quality. Semiannually. Estab. 1980. Circ. 650.
Needs: Literary. "We are open to a wide range of stories with accessibility and vitality being important in any case. We're not interested in genre fiction, formula work." Upcoming themes: "Bilingual fiction and poetry from Eastern Europe and South America," (Winter 1992); "Bilingual fiction, poetry, folklore from Native Americans" (prefer Southwest) (Summer 1993). Buys 4-6 mss/issue. Agented fiction 10%. Published work by Nancy Lord, Robyn Oughton, Ron Hansen. Length: open, though prefers work under 25 pages. Also publishes literary essays, literary criticism, poetry. Sometimes recommends other markets.
How to Contact: Send complete ms with SASE and cover letter with previous publications. Accepts computer printout submissions. Reports in 2 months on mss, longer for work received during summer (May-August). Publishes ms an average of 2-6 months after acceptance. Sample copy $5.

Payment: Pays 2 contributor's copies; $2 charge for extras. Annual cash prizes.
Terms: Acquires first North American serial rights. Fall issue features fiction contest winnter: 1st prize, $150; 2nd prize $50. Submit by October 1.
Advice: "We have increased the size of the magazine at 50% and are developing more special features connecting special themes and regions. Let the story sit for several months, then review it to see if you still like it. If you're unsure, keep working on it *before* sending it out. All mss are read carefully, and we try to make brief comments if time permits. Our hope is that an author will keep us interested in his or her treatment of a subject by using fresh details and writing with an authority that is absorbing." Mss are rejected because "1) we only have space for 6-8 manuscripts out of several hundred submissions annually, and 2) most of the manuscripts we receive have some merit but are not of publishable quality. It would be helpful to receive a cover letter with all manuscripts."

SOUNDINGS EAST, (II), English Dept., Salem State College, Salem MA 01970. (508)741-6270. Advisory Editor: Rod Kessler. Magazine: 5½ × 8½; 64 pages; illustrations; photos. "Mainly a college audience, but we also distribute to libraries throughout the country." Biannually. Estab. 1973. Circ. 2,000.
Needs: Literary, contemporary, prose poem. No juvenile. Publishes 4-5 stories/issue. Receives 30 unsolicited fiction mss each month. Does not read April-August. Published work by James Brady, Terry Farish and Christina Shea; published new writers within the last year. Length: 250-5,000 words. "We are open to short pieces as well as to long works."
How to Contact: Send complete ms with SASE between September and March. Accepts computer printout submissions. Reports in 2 months on mss. Sample copy $3.
Payment: Pays 2 contributor's copies.
Terms: All publication rights revert to authors.
Advice: "We're impressed by an excitement — coupled with craft — in the use of the language. It also helps to reach in and grab the reader by the heart."

SOUTH CAROLINA REVIEW, (II), Clemson University, Clemson SC 29634-1503. (803)656-3229. Editors: R.J. Calhoun, Frank Day and Carol Johnston. Managing Editor: Mark Winchell. Magazine: 6 × 9; 200 pages; 60 lb. cream white vellum paper; 65 lb. cream white vellum cover stock; illustrations and photos rarely. Semiannually. Estab. 1967. Circ. 700.
Needs: Literary, contemporary, humor and ethnic. Receives approximately 50-60 unsolicited fiction mss each month. Does not read mss June-August. Published work by Joyce Carol Oates, Rosanne Coggeshall, Stephen Dixon; published new writers within the last year. Rarely critiques rejected mss.
How to Contact: Send complete ms with SASE. Accepts computer printout submissions. Reports in 2 months on mss. Sample copy $5.
Payment: Pays in contributor's copies.
Advice: Mss are rejected because of "poorly structured stories, or stories without vividness or intensity. The most celebrated function of a little magazine is to take a chance on writers not yet able to get into the larger magazines — the little magazine can encourage promising writers at a time when encouragement is vitally needed. (We also publish 'name' writers, like Joyce Carol Oates, Stephen Dixon, George Garrett.) Read the masters extensively. Write and write more, with a *schedule*. Listen to editorial advice when offered. Don't get discouraged with rejections. Read what writers say about writing (e.g. *The Paris Review* Interviews with George Plimpton, gen. ed.; Welty's *One Writer's Beginnings,*etc). Take courses in writing and listen to, even if you do not follow, the advice."

SOUTH DAKOTA REVIEW, (II), University of South Dakota, Box 111, University Exchange, Vermillion SD 57069. (605)677-5966. Editor: John R. Milton. Magazine: 6 × 9; 150+ pages; book paper; glossy cover stock; illustrations sometimes; photos on cover. "Literary magazine for university and college audiences and their equivalent. Emphasis is often on the West and its writers, but will accept mss from anywhere. Issues are generally fiction and poetry with some literary essays." Quarterly. Estab. 1963. Circ. 500.
Needs: Literary, contemporary, ethnic, experimental, excerpted novel, regional and translations. "We like very well-written stories. Contemporary western American setting appeals, but not necessary. No formula stories, sports or adolescent 'I' narrator." Receives 30 unsolicited fiction mss/month. Accepts about 10-20 mss/year, more or less. Assistant editor accepts mss in June-July, sometimes August. Agented fiction 5%. Publishes short shorts of 5 pages double-spaced typescript. Published work by Ed Loomis, Max Evans, Dennis Lynds; published new writers the last year. Length: 1,300 words minimum; 6,000 words maximum. (Has made exceptions, up to novella length.) Sometimes recommends other markets.

Close-up

Bruce Upbin
Managing Editor
Sonora Review

"We don't tend toward mainstream fiction," says *Sonora Review* Managing Editor Bruce Upbin. "We try to experiment with things that are slightly askew—but not so askew as to be misunderstood."

Upbin is one of several University of Arizona graduate students on the staff of the literary magazine. Established in 1980, the *Sonora Review* is run completely by students who handle everything from manuscript selection to printing. Out of the 700 fiction submissions the students receive for each semiannual issue, they publish about four or five.

"We are looking for fiction that is voice-oriented, told in a fresh way," Upbin stresses. He finds most American writing "small" in focus—it doesn't regard the world in general. For this reason, the magazine's editors have shifted some of their focus internationally; in fact, an issue featured solely bilingual work from Eastern Europe and Latin America.

However, the magazine is not abandoning its roots. An issue entitled "Voices from a Southwestern Land" featured stories about Arizona, New Mexico, Texas and California—"writing with a southwestern, desert spirit," Upbin says.

Each year, one of the two issues of *Sonora Review* is based on a specific theme. The spring/summer 1993 issue will feature a guest editor, a bilingual text and a Native American focus. Contributors to this issue don't have to be "real writers," Upbin says, as long as they are deeply familiar with Native American traditions and lifestyles. Authors interested in the magazine's upcoming themes can find them in newsletters, state arts council bulletins and writing programs around the country.

Upbin, who has been with *Sonora Review* since 1989, feels that a good story must have tight prose, consistency, authority and energy. "Stories should have a point to them," he says. For example, "we like our fiction to look at things on the edge of horror—not Stephen King, but a frightful look at what could happen. Focus it so things are at stake."

He also finds pleasure in writing that considers language as well as plot and characters, "blurring the distinctions between fiction and poetry. I don't subscribe to Ray Carver/Ernest Hemingway stripped-down language," Upbin says. "I like more precise, sensuous use of language.

"All manuscripts are read carefully from cover to cover, so if a story is good, it will catch our attention." Upbin suggests authors polish and rewrite a lot before sending manuscripts, and thinks it's helpful to find someone "brutally honest" to read and critique the manuscript.

"We're not looking for big names," he says. "We publish a lot of emerging writers."

—Suzanne Boggs

How to Contact: Send complete ms with SASE. "We like cover letters that are not boastful and do not attempt to sell the stories but rather provide some personal information about the writer." Photocopied submissions OK if not multiple submission. Reports in 1 month. Publishes ms an average of 1-6 months after acceptance. Sample copy $5.

Payment: Pays 2-4 contributor's copies, depending on length of ms; $3.50 charge for extras.

Terms: Acquires first rights and second serial rights.

Advice: Rejects mss because of "careless writing; often careless typing; stories too personal ('I' confessional), adolescent; working manuscript, not polished; subject matter that editor finds trivial. We are trying to use more fiction and more variety. We would like to see more sophisticated stories. Do not try to outguess editors and give them what you think they want. Write honestly. Be yourself."

THE SOUTH HILL GAZETTE, (II), A.D. Images, P.O. Box 547, Rochester MI 48307. (313)656-9777. Editor: Leigh A. Arrathoon. Newsletter: 8½ × 11; 12 pages; illustrations and b&w photographs. "Upbeat fiction suitable for family reading." Weekly. Circ. 6,000/week.

Needs: Adventure, ethnic, historical (general), humor/satire, prose poem, regional, romance (contemporary and historical), science fiction, suspense/mystery, western, seasonal. "The style must be clear, the words well-chosen (but not affected); the parts of the fiction should work together at the service of the whole. We do use dialect if it is well-done." No erotica, horror, religious, political, juvenile, fantasy, gay, feminist, lesbian or "anything written to shock, impress or horrify—anything illogical." Receives 1 or 2 unsolicited mss/month. Accepts 1 ms/issue; 6-10 4-week pieces (20 pages each). "Our publication reflects the seasons—publication date depends upon how the material fits into that scheme." Published work by Antonia Baquet Cyres, Steve Adolph, Lianna S.M. Wright, Leigh A. Arrathoon. Publishes short shorts. Also publishes poetry.

How to Contact: Query first. "Please call and discuss—9:00 p.m. or later (313)656-9777." SASE. Photocopied submissions OK. Accepts computer printout submissions. Sample copy for 9 × 12 SAE and 3 first class stamps.

Payment: Pays contributor's copies.

Terms: Acquires first rights.

Advice: "The story is the thing. All the devices in the fiction should work together at the service of the statement. If the fiction doesn't have a statement to make, it isn't worth writing. Stories are units of communication that are simply larger constructs than words, sentences and paragraphs. They are a way to teach, amuse or move the reader."

‡SOUTHEASTERN FRONT, (II), Southeastern Front Organization, 565 17th St. NW, Cleveland TN 37311. Editor: Robin Merritt. Magazine: 8½ × 11; 40-60 pages; glossy cover; illustrations and photos. "*Southeastern Front* is an artists and writers representation service, a gallery in a magazine. Our aim is to provide exposure for artists and writers from all over the country. We hope to create an excellent medium of presentation for artists from isolated geographic areas." Estab. 1986. Circ. 1,500.

Needs: "There are no stylistic limitations on submissions or subject matter. We are interested in finding high quality new work by new and/or emerging artists and writers and helping them to obtain exposure. No pieces which are devoid of intellectual or aesthetic merit, nor commercially designed work." Receives 3-5 unsolicited mss/month. Accepts 6-8 mss/issue; 18-20 mss/year. Publishes ms 1-4 months after acceptance. Published new writers within the last year. Length: no restrictions. Publishes short shorts. Critiques rejected mss. Recommends other markets.

How to Contact: Send complete ms with cover letter. Reports in 2-4 months on query and ms. SASE for ms. Simultaneous, photocopied and reprint submissions OK *occasionally*. Accepts computer printout submissions. Sample copy $2.50. Fiction guidelines for SAE and 1 first class postage.

Payment: Pays contributor's copies; charge for extras at wholesale rates for more than 5 copies.

Terms: Writers retain all rights.

Advice: "Allow yourself total creative and intellectual freedom, but never forget to be an artist, a craftsman who is conscious of aesthetic values. Be sure to include substantial human experience in your plots."

SOUTHERN EXPOSURE, (III, IV), Institute for Southern Studies, P.O. Box 531, Durham NC 27702. (919)688-8167. Editor: Eric Bates. Magazine: 8½ × 11; 64 pages. "Southern politics and culture— investigative reporting, oral history, fiction for an audience of Southern changemakers—scholars, journalists, activists." Quarterly. Estab. 1972. Circ. 5,000.

Needs: Contemporary, ethnic, feminist, gay, humor/satire, lesbian, literary, regional. Plans special fiction issue. Receives 50 unsolicited mss/month. Buys 1 mss/issue; 4 mss/year. Publishes ms 3-6 months after acceptance. Agented fiction 25%. Published work by Clyde Egerton, Jill McCorkle and Larry Brown. Length: 3,500 words preferred.
How to Contact: Send complete ms with cover letter. Reports in 4-6 weeks on mss. SASE for ms. Photocopied submissions OK. Accepts computer printout and photocopied submissions. Sample copy for $4, 8½×11 and $1.85 postage. Fiction guidelines for #10 SAE and 1 first class stamp.
Payment: Pays $100, free subscription to magazine and contributor's copies.
Terms: Pays on publication for first rights.

SOUTHERN HUMANITIES REVIEW, (II, IV), Auburn University, 9088 Haley Center, Auburn University AL 36849. Co-Editors: Dan R. Latimer and R.T. Smith. Magazine: 6×9; 96 pages; 60 lb. neutral pH, natural paper, 65 lb. neutral pH med. coated cover stock; occasional illustrations and photos. "We publish essays, poetry, fiction and reviews. Our fiction has ranged from very traditional in form and content to very experimental. Literate, college-educated audience. We hope they read our journal for both enlightenment and pleasure." Quarterly. Estab. 1967. Circ. 800.
Needs: Serious fiction, fantasy, feminist, humor and regional. Receives approximately 25 unsolicited fiction mss each month. Accepts 1-2 mss/issue, 4-6 mss/year. Slower reading time in summer. Published work by Anne Brashler, Heimito von Doderer and Ivo Andric; published new writers within the last year. Length: 3,500-5,000 words. Also publishes literary essays, literary criticism, poetry. Critiques rejected mss when there is time. Sometimes recommends other markets.
How to Contact: Send complete ms with SASE and cover letter with an explanation of topic chosen—special, certain book, etc., a little about author if they have never submitted. Accepts computer printout submissions. Reports in 90 days. Sample copy $4. Reviews novel and short story collections.
Payment: Pays 1 contributor's copy; $4 charge for extras.
Terms: Acquires all rights. Sends galleys to author.
Advice: "Send us the ms with SASE. If we like it, we'll take it or we'll recommend changes. If we don't like it, we'll send it back as promptly as possible. Read the journal. Send a typewritten, clean copy carefully proofread. We also award annually the Hoepfner Prize of $100 for the best published essay or short story of the year. Let someone whose opinion you respect read your story and give you an honest appraisal. Rewrite, if necessary, to get the most from your story."

THE SOUTHERN REVIEW, (II), Louisiana State University, 43 Allen Hall, Baton Rouge LA 70803. (504)388-5108. Editors: James Olney and Dave Smith. Magazine: 6¾×10; 240 pages; 50 lb. Glatfelter paper; 65 lb. #1 grade cover stock; occasional photos. "A literary quarterly publishing critical essays, poetry and fiction for a highly intellectual audience." Quarterly. Published special fiction issue. Estab. 1935. Circ. 3,000.
Needs: Literary and contemporary. "We emphasize style and substantial content. No mystery, fantasy or religious mss." Buys 7-8 mss/issue. Receives approximately 100 unsolicited fiction mss each month. Agented fiction 5%. Published work by William Hoffman, Rick Bass, Jill McCorkle; published new writers within the last year. Length: 2,000-10,000 words. Also publishes literary essays, literary, criticism, poetry. Sometimes recommends other markets.
How to Contact: Send complete ms with cover letter and SASE. "Prefer brief letters giving information on author concerning where he/she has been published before, biographical info and what he/she is doing now." Accepts computer printout submissions. Reports in 2 months on mss. Publishes ms an average of 1-2 years after acceptance. Sample copy $5. Reviews novels and short story collections.
Payment: Pays $12/printed page; 2 contributor's copies.
Terms: Pays on publication for first North American serial rights. "We transfer copyright to author on request." Sends galleys to author.
Advice: "Develop a careful style with characters in depth." Sponsors annual contest for best first collection of short stories published during the calendar year.

SOUTHWEST REVIEW, (II), 307 Fondren Library West, Southern Methodist University, Dallas TX 75275. (214)373-7440. Editor: Willard Spiegelman. Magazine: 6×9; 160 pages. "The majority of our readers are college-educated adults who wish to stay abreast of the latest and best in contemporary fiction, poetry, literary criticism and books in all but the most specialized disciplines." Quarterly. Estab. 1915. Circ. 1,600.
Needs: "High literary quality; no specific requirements as to subject matter, but cannot use sentimental, religious, western, poor science fiction, pornographic, true confession, mystery, juvenile or serialized or condensed novels." Receives approximately 200 unsolicited fiction mss each month. Published

work by Brad Conard, Ellen Akins, Rick Bass and Millicent Dillon. Length: prefers 3,000-5,000 words. Also publishes literary essays, poetry. Occasionally critiques rejected mss. Sometimes recommends other markets.

How to Contact: Send complete ms with SASE. Accepts computer printout submissions. Reports in 3 months on mss. Publishes ms 6 months to 1 year after acceptance. Sample copy $5. Free guidelines for SASE.

Payment: Payment varies; writers receive 3 free author's copies.

Terms: Pays on publication for first North American serial rights. Sends galleys to author.

Advice: "We have become less regional. A lot of time would be saved for us and for the writer if he looked at a copy of the *Southwest Review* before submitting. We like to receive a cover letter because it is some reassurance that the author has taken the time to check a current directory for the editor's name. When there isn't a cover letter, we wonder whether the same story is on 20 other desks around the country."

SOU'WESTER, (II), Southern Illinois University-Edwardsville, Edwardsville IL 62026-1438. (618)692-3190. Managing Editor: Fred W. Robbins. Magazine: 6×9; 88 pages; Warren's Olde Style paper; 60 lb. cover. General magazine of poetry and fiction. Published 3 times/year. Estab. 1960. Circ. 300.

Needs: Receives 40-50 unsolicited fiction mss/month. Accepts 3 mss/issue, 9 mss/year. Published work by Robert Wexelblatt, Robert Solomon; published new writers within the last year. Length: 10,000 words maximum. Also publishes poetry. Occasionally critiques rejected mss.

How to Contact: Send complete ms with SASE. Simultaneous and photocopied submissions OK. Accepts computer printout submissions. Reports in 3 months. Publishes ms an average of 6 months after acceptance. Sample copy $5.

Payment: Pays 2 contributor's copies; $5 charge for extras.

Terms: Acquires first serial rights.

‡SOZORYOKU, Quarterly Journal of the Imagination, (II), Running Dinosaur Press, 265 Fifth Ave., Chula Vista CA 91910. Editor: Ralph E. Vaughan. Magazine: 5½×8½; 36-44+ pages; bond paper; pen & ink illustrations. "Myth, fantasy and science fiction of cosmic import for a highly eclectic and literate audience." Quarterly. Estab. 1990. Circ. 100.

Needs: Adventure, ethnic, experimental, fantasy, feminist, historical, horror, literary, mainstream, prose poem, psychic/supernatural/occult, regional, science fiction, suspense/mystery, western. "No romance, erotica, mundane fiction." Receives 50 unsolicited mss/month. Buys 8-12 mss/issue; 30-50 mss/year. Publishes ms 1-3 months after acceptance. Recently published work by David Barker, Eric Holmes, t. Winter-Damon. Length: 200 words minimum; 2,500 words maximum. Publishes short shorts. Sometimes critiques rejected mss.

How to Contact: Send complete ms with cover letter; ask for guidelines. Reports in 1 week on mss. SASE. Sample copy for $2. Fiction guidelines for #10 SAE and 1 first class stamp.

Payment: Pays ¼-½¢/word.

Terms: Pays on acceptance for one-time rights.

Advice: "I look for a story with sharply drawn characters and plausible settings and conflicts, with a style that draws me into the story and makes me care. I look for stories that stay with me long after the reading, stories with vision and a sense of the cosmic."

SPECTRUM, (II), Anna Maria College, Box 72-C, Sunset Lane, Paxton MA 01612. (617)757-4586. Editor: Robert H. Goepfert. Fiction Editor: Joseph Wilson. Magazine: 6×9; 64 pages; illustrations and photos. "An interdisciplinary publication publishing fiction as well as poetry, scholarly articles, reviews, art and photography. Submissions are especially encouraged from those affiliated with liberal arts colleges." Semiannually. Estab. 1985. Circ. 1,000.

Needs: Contemporary, experimental, historical, literary, mainstream. No western, mystery, erotica, science fiction. Receives an average of 15 unsolicited fiction ms/month. Accepts 4-6 mss/issue. Publishes ms approx. 6 months after acceptance. Length: 2,000-5,0000 words preferred; 3,000 words average; 10,000 words maximum. Publishes short shorts. Also publishes literary essays, literary criticism, poetry. Sometimes critiques rejected mss and recommends other markets.

How to Contact: Send complete ms with cover letter. Reports in 6 weeks. SASE for ms. Photocopied submissions OK. Accepts computer printouts. Sample copy for $3. Fiction guidelines free with SASE.

Payment: Pays $20 and 2 contributor's copies.

Terms: Pays on publication for first North American serial rights. Sends pre-publication galleys to author. Publication not copyrighted.

Advice: "Our chief aim is diversity."

SPINDRIFT, (II), Shoreline Community College, 16101 Greenwood Ave. North, Seattle WA 98133. (206)546-4785. Editor: Carol Orlock, adviser. Magazine: 140 pages; quality paper; photographs; b&w artwork. "We look for fresh, original work that is not forced or 'straining' to be literary." Annually. Estab. around 1967. Circ. 500.

Needs: Contemporary, ethnic, experimental, historical (general), prose poem, regional, science fiction, serialized/excerpted novel, translations. No romance, religious/inspirational. Receives up to 150 mss/year. Accepts up to 20 mss/issue. Does not read during spring/summer. Publishes ms 3-4 months after acceptance. Published work by David Halpern, Jana Harris; published new writers within the last year. Length: 250 words minimum; 3,500-4,500 words maximum. Publishes short shorts.

How to Contact: Send complete ms, and "bio, name, address, phone and list of titles submitted." Reports in 2 weeks on queries; 6 months on mss with SASE. Photocopied submissions OK. Accepts computer printout submissions. Sample copy for $6, 8×10 SAE and $1 postage.

Payment: Pays in contributor's copies; charge for extras.

Terms: Acquires first rights. Publication not copyrighted.

Advice: "The tighter the story the better. The more lyric values in the narrative the better. Read the magazine, keep working on craft. Submit several pieces by February 1."

THE SPIRIT THAT MOVES US, (II), Box 820-W, Jackson Heights NY 11372-0820. (718)426-8788. Editor: Morty Sklar. Publishes fiction, poetry and artwork. "We want feeling and imagination, work coming from the human experience." Semiannually. Estab. 1975. Circ. 1,500-2,000.

Needs: "SASE first to find out what our needs are." Literary and contemporary—"anything goes, if it is fiction, poetry or art." No sensational. Upcoming theme: "The Real Melting Pot of America: Stories and essays from Queens." Buys 5-6 mss/issue and about 15 mss for special fiction issues. Receives approximately 90 unsolicited fiction mss each month. Recently published work by W.P. Kinsella, Julia Alvarez, William S. Burroughs; published new writers within the last year. Length: 10,000 words maximum. Also publishes literary essays, poetry. Critiques rejected mss when there is time.

How to Contact: "A cover letter sort of makes the exchange more personal." Accepts computer printout submissions. Reports in 1 week-1 month on mss. Publishes ms an average of 6 months after acceptance. Sample copy $5 for *Free Parking*, our 15th Anniversay collection.

Payment: Pays free cloth copy, 40% discount for paperbacks; 25% on all other publications.

Terms: Acquires first rights. Buys reprints for anthology issue.

Advice: "We're small but good and well-reviewed. Send the work you love best. Write from yourself and not from what you feel is the fashion or what the editor wants. This editor wants what you want if it has heart, imagination and skill. Aside from the obvious reason for rejection, poor writing, the main reason for rejection is lack of human concerns—that is, the writer seems to be concerned with style more than content. Read a copy of the magazine you'll be submitting work to. Don't rely on your writing for money unless you're in it for the money. Have time to write, as much time as you can get (be anti-social if necessary)."

‡SPIT MAGAZINE, (I), East River SPIT, 529 2nd St., Brooklyn NY 11215. (718)499-7343; (212)673-3546. Magazine: 8½×11; 50-75 pages; illustrations and photographs. "We are a magazine for emerging (new) artists of all kinds. We consider fiction/prose of any style. Audience is varied, though at the moment, mostly youngish; avant-garde." Semiannually. Estab. 1990. Circ. 500.

Needs: Adventure, condensed/excerpted novel, contemporary, erotica, ethnic, experimental, fantasy, feminist, gay, historical (general), horror, humor/satire, lesbian, literary, mainstream, prose poem, psychic/supernatural/occult, regional, science fiction, senior citizen/retirement, serialized novel, sports, suspense/mystery, translations, western. Receives 10 unsolicited mss/month. Accepts 4-5 mss/issue; 8-10 mss/year. Publishes ms 1-2 months after acceptance. Recently published work by Robin Goodman, Barbara Rosenthal, Claas Ehlers. Length: 2,500 words average; 6,000 words maximum. Publishes short shorts. Sometimes critiques rejected mss.

How to Contact: Send complete ms with cover letter. Include a brief biographical statement. Reports in 2 weeks on queries; up to 6 months on mss. SASE. Simultaneous, photocopied and reprint submissions OK. Accepts computer printout submissions. Sample copy for $3. Fiction guidelines for any size SAE and 1 first class stamp.

Payment: Pays in contributor's copies.

Terms: Acquires one-time rights.

Advice: "We are interested in discovering and supporting new writers of all styles, experiences, backgrounds and orientations. It is not necessary that our writers be thoroughly developed or polished; a unique voice, vision or use of language is what will draw our editors to a work of fiction or prose."

SPOOFING!, Yarns and Such, (I, IV), Creative With Words Publications, Box 223226, Carmel CA 93922. (408)649-5627. Editor: Brigitta Geltrich. Booklet: 5½ × 8½; approx. 60 pages; bond paper; illustrations. Folklore. Semiannually. Estab. 1975. Circ. varies.

Needs: Ethnic, humor/satire, juvenile (5-9 years), preschool (1-4 years), regional, young adult/teen (10-18 years), folklore. "Once a year we publish an anthology of the writings of young writers, titled: *We are Writers Too!*" No erotica, religious fiction. Receives 50-100 unsolicited fiction mss/month. Does not read mss July-August. Publishes ms 2-6 months after acceptance. Published new writers within the last year. Length: 1,000 words average. Critiques rejected mss "when requested, *then we charge $20/prose, up to 1,000 words.*"

How to Contact: Query first or send complete ms with cover letter. "Reference has to be made to which project the manuscript is being submitted. Unsolicited mss without SASE will be destroyed after holding them 1 month." Reports in 1 week on queries; 2 months on mss; longer on specific seasonal anthologies. SASE. Photocopied submissions OK. Accepts computer printout submissions. Accepts electronic submissions via Radio Shack Model 4/6 disk. Sample copy price varies. Fiction guidelines for #10 SAE with 2 first class stamps.

Payment: No payment. Charges for contributor's copies; 20% reduction on each copy ordered.

Terms: Acquires one-time rights.

SPSM&H, (II, IV), *Amelia* Magazine, 329 "E" St., Bakersfield CA 93304. (805)323-4064. Editor: Frederick A. Raborg, Jr. Magazine: 5½ × 8¼; 24 pages; Matte cover stock; illustrations and photos. "*SPSM&H* publishes sonnets, sonnet sequences and fiction, articles and reviews related to the form (fiction may be romantic or Gothic) for a general readership and sonnet enthusiasts." Quarterly. Estab. 1985. Circ. 600.

Needs: Adventure, confession, contemporary, erotica, ethnic experimental, fantasy, feminist, gay, historical (general), horror, humor/satire, lesbian, literary, mainstream, regional, contemporary and historical romance, science fiction, senior citizen/retirement, suspense/mystery, translations and western. All should have romantic element. "We look for strong fiction with romantic or Gothic content, or both. Stories need not have 'happy' endings, and we are open to the experimental and/or avant-garde. Erotica is fine; pornography, no." Receives 30+ unsolicited mss/month. Buys 1 ms/issue; 4 mss/year. Publishes ms 6 months-1 year after acceptance. Agented fiction 5%. Published work by Mary Louise R. O'Hara and Clara Castelar Bjorlie. Length: 2,000 words average; 500 words minimum; 3,000 words maximum. When appropriate critiques rejected ms; Recommends other markets.

How to Contact: Send complete ms with cover letter. Should include Social Security number. Reports in 2 weeks. SASE. Photocopied submissions OK. Accepts computer printout submissions. Sample copy $4.50. Fiction guidelines for #10 SAE and 1 first class stamp.

Payment: Pays $10-25; contributor's copies; charge for extras.

Terms: Pays on publication for first North American serial rights.

Advice: "A good story line (plot) and strong characterization are vital. I want to know the writer has done his homework and is striving to become professional."

SQUARE ONE, A Magazine of Fiction, (I, II), Box 11921, Milwaukee WI 53211-0921. Editor: William D. Gagliani. Magazine: 7 × 8½; 75-90 pages; 20 lb. white bond paper; 80 lb. colored linen cover; illustrations; pen and ink drawings or any black on white. "There is no specific theme at *Square One*, but we publish only fiction and illustrations. Aimed at a general literate audience—people who *enjoy* reading fiction." Annually. Estab. 1984. Circ. 250.

Needs: Open to all categories including mainstream, mystery, science fiction, horror, fantasy, suspense, etc. "We like exciting stories in which things happen and characters *exist*." Receives 40-50 unsolicited fiction mss/month. Does not read mss between May and September. Accepts 6-12 mss/issue, depending on lengths; 6-12 mss/year. Publishes ms generally 1-11 months after acceptance. Published new writers within the last year. Length: 3,000 words average; 7,500 words maximum. Publishes short shorts but not vignettes. "It is editorial policy to comment on at least 75% of submissions rejected, but please be patient—we have a very small staff."

How to Contact: Send complete ms with cover letter. "Too many letters explain or describe the story. Let the fiction stand on its own. If it doesn't, the letter won't help. We like a brief bio and a few credits, but some writers get carried away. Use restraint and plain language—don't try to impress (it usually backfires)." Reports in 1-11 months on mss. SASE for ms. Simultaneous (if so labeled), photocopied and reprint submissions OK. Accepts computer printouts. Can accept electronic submissions via disk, "DS/DD, 3½" Atari Mega Disks (using WordPerfect 4.1 for Atari) and HD or DS/DD 3.5 disks (using Microsoft Word 4.0, Works, or WordPerfect 2.0+ for Macintosh). Hard copy should accompany any electronic submissions." Sample copy $3.50, 9×12 SAE, and 6 first class stamps (recent issue). Fiction guidelines for #10 SAE and 1 first class stamp. Please make checks payable to William D. Gagliani.

Payment: Pays 2 contributor's copies.

Terms: Acquires one-time rights.

Advice: "*Square One* is not a journal for beginners, despite what the name may imply. Rather, the name refers to the back-to-basics approach that we take—fiction must first and foremost be compelling. We want to see stories that elicit a response from the reader. We will give slight preference to Wisconsin writers, but will gladly consider submissions from anywhere. We must stress that, since we are an irregular publication, contributors should expect long response lags. Our staff is small and *Square One* is a part-time endeavor. Patience is the best advice we can offer. Also, we oppose the absurdity of asking that writers subscribe to every magazine they would like to write for, especially given most writers' financial state. Check local public and college libraries and bookstores to see what's going on in the small press and literary markets, and—as a matter of dignity—consider carefully before submitting to magazines that routinely charge reading fees."

‡THE STANDING STONE, A Magazine of Fantasy and Horror, (II, IV), Ebenrock Enterprises, #312, 120 Perth Ave., Toronto, Ontario M6P 4E1 Canada. Editor: Gordon R. Menzies. Magazine: 8½×11; 25-40 pages; 100% unbleached recycled paper; 40-70% recycled passport gypsum cover; b&w illustrations. "Fantasy and horror short stories and poetry." Quarterly. Estab. 1990. Circ. 100+.

Needs: Fantasy, horror. Receives 30 unsolicited mss/month. Buys 6-10 mss/issue; 24-40 mss/year. Publishes ms 1-3 months after acceptance. Recently published work by L.K. Rogers, J.P. Reedman, N. Kilpatrick. Length: 2,500 words preferred; 500 words minimum; 3,000 words maximum. Publishes short shorts. Sometimes critiques rejected mss and recommends other markets.

How to Contact: Send complete ms with cover letter. Reports in 1 week on queries; 1 months on mss. SASE (If outside Canada, send IRCs loose American stamps or an American dollar or two which will be exchanged for Canadian postage). Photocopied submission OK. Accepts computer printout submissions. Sample copy for $3. Fiction guidelines for #10 SAE (IRCs, Canadian stamps, loose American stamps or $1-2 American.)

Payment: Pays ½¢/word (Canadian) on acceptance and 1 contributor's copy.

Terms: Pays on acceptance for first north American serial rights.

Advice: Looks for "clean copy and a cover letter about the author, not his publications in the past, always makes us happy. Manuscripts sent on recycled kpaper are nice to see too, but in the end characterization is everything. If your characters are boring, we don't care how imaginative the story is—fiction is about people. Ignore the comments (good and bad) from friends and relatives and just keep sending out your work. If the editors are rejecting you, look at what they are accepting. **Attn: At press time discovered this market no longer published.**

STARLIGHT, Star Books, Inc., 408 Pearson St., Wilson NC 27893. (919)237-1591. Editor: Irene Burk Hrrell. Magazine: Digest-sized 5½×7½; 64 pages; 20 lb. paper; b&w illustrations and photographs. "Christian inspirational material for men and women of all ages, some children." Quarterly. Estab. 1987.

Needs: Religious/inspirational. Wants "Any genre, for any age, as long as it is exciting, God-honoring, in conformity with biblical truth." Publishes ms less than 3 months after acceptance. Published work by Ralph Filicchia. Length: "10-12 double-spaced pages but open to longer or shorter." Also publishes poetry. Sometimes critiques rejected mss.

How to Contact: Send complete manuscript with cover letter. Reports in 1 month on queries. SASE. Photocopied submissions OK. Accepts computer printout submissions. Sample copy $4. Fiction guidelines for #10 SAE and 2 first class stamps.

Payment: Pays 3 contributor's copies.

Terms: Acquires first rights.

STARRY NIGHTS, Merry Men Press, 274 Roanoke Road, El Cajon CA 92020. Editor: Robin Hood. Magazine: 8½×11; 200 pages; 20 lb. paper; 90 lb. cover stock. Erotic science fiction/fantasy, poetry, art "for a mature audience." Estab. 1990.
Needs: Erotica. "See guidelines for definition of erotica. There's a big difference between *E* and *pornography*." Has published special fiction issue in the past. Receives 7 unsolicited mss per month; buys up to 15 mss per issue. Publishes ms 1-11 months after acceptance. "Will accept multiple stories from same author." Also publishes poetry. "Will accept multiple stories from same author." Comments on rejected mss and recommends other markets.
How to Contact: Reports in 1 week on queries; 1 month on mss. SASE. Photocopied and computer printout submissions OK. Accepts electronic submissions, "hard copy must be included." Fiction guidelines for SAE and 1 first class stamp.
Payment: Pays 1¢/word and 1 contributor's copy.
Terms: Pays on publication for first North American serial rights.

STARSONG, A Magazine of Fantasy, Science Fiction and Horror, (I, II), Box 260B, St. Matthews SC 29135. Publisher: Larry D. Kirby III. Editor: Meredith C. Crim. Magazine: 8½×11; 90 pages; Xeroxed paper; heavy cover stock; illustrations. Quarterly. Estab. 1987. Circ. 400.
Needs: Fantasy, horror, humor/satire, prose poem, psychic/supernatural/occult, science fiction. Receives 60 unsolicited fiction mss/month. Accepts 8-12 mss/issue; 32-48 mss/year. Publishes ms within one year of acceptance. Recently published work by John Grey, M.M. LoPiccolo, Don Stockard, Vaugh Heppner; published new writers within the last year. No preferred word length. Publishes short shorts. Also publishes poetry. Sometimes critiques rejected mss.
How to Contact: Send complete ms with cover letter, which should include "bio." SASE. Photocopied submissions OK. Accepts computer printouts. Sample copy $5; fiction guidelines for #10 SAE and 1 first class stamp. Reviews novels and short story collections.
Payment: Pays in contributor's copies.
Terms: Acquires one-time rights.
Advice: "Larger mags won't experiment with style or subject matter. I like new ideas and particularly like new authors. Try new ideas. Experiment. Be willing to rewrite. Pay attention to your dreams. Read small press mags. By the time you change your style to match what's in the big mags, the style will change. Don't send cyberpunk. It's boring. Make me believe your characters. Make me wonder. Make me smile. Make me check the .357 before I turn the lights out."

STONE SOUP, The Magazine By Children, (I, IV), Children's Art Foundation, Box 83, Santa Cruz CA 95063. (408)426-5557. Editor: Gerry Mandel. Magazine: 6×8¾; 48 pages; high quality paper; Sequoia matte cover stock; illustrations; photos. Stories, poems, book reviews and art by children through age 13. Readership: children, librarians, educators. Published 5 times/year. Estab. 1973. Circ. 12,000.
Needs: Fiction by children on themes based on their own experiences, observations or special interests. No clichés, no formulas, no writing exercises; original work only. Receives approximately 500 unsolicited fiction mss each month. Accepts approx. 15 mss/issue. Published new writers within the last year. Length: 150-2,500 words. Also publishes literary essays, poetry. Critiques rejected mss upon request.
How to Contact: Send complete ms with cover letter. "We like to learn a little about our young writers, why they like to write, and how they came to write the story they are submitting." SASE. Accepts computer printout submissions. Reports in 1 month on mss. Publishes ms an average of 1-6 months after acceptance. Sample copy $4. Free guidelines with SASE. Reviews children's books.
Payment: Pays $10 plus 2 free author's copies; $2 charge for extras.
Terms: Buys all rights.
Advice: Mss are rejected because they are "derivatives of movies, TV, comic books; or classroom assignments or other formulas."

STORY, (II), F&W Publications, 1507 Dana Ave., Cincinnati OH 45207. (513)531-2222. Editor: Lois Rosenthal. Magazine: 6¼×9½; 128 pages; uncoated, recycled paper; uncoated index stock. "We publish finest quality short stories. Will consider unpublished novel excerpts if they are self-inclusive." Quarterly. Estab. 1931.
Needs: Literary, experimental, humor, mainstream, translations. No genre fiction—science fiction, detective, young adult, confession, romance, etc. Buys approximately 10 mss/issue. Agented fiction 50-60%. Published work by Joyce Carol Oates, Bobbie Ann Mason, Tobias Wolff, Madison Smartt Bell, Rick DeMarinis, Antonya Nelson, Rick Bass, Charles Baxter, Hortense Calisher, Robert Olmstead,

Melissa Pritchard; published new writers within the last year. Length: 1,000 words minimum; 8,000 words maximum.
How to Contact: Send complete ms with or without cover letter, or submit through agent. SASE necessary for return of ms. Photocopied submissions OK. Accepts computer printout submissions. Sample copy for $5, 9×12 SAE and $2.40 postage. Fiction guidelines for #10 SAE and 1 first class stamp.
Payment: Pays $250 plus 5 contributor's copies.
Terms: Pays on acceptance for first North American serial rights. Sends galleys to author.
Advice: "We only accept fiction of the highest quality, whether by established or lesser-known writers. Since we receive over 250 submissions each week, the competition for space is fierce. We look for original subject matter told through fresh voices. Read issues of *Story* before trying us."

STROKER MAGAZINE, (II), 124 N. Main St., #1, Shakertown PA 18708. Editor: Irving Stettner. Magazine: 5½×8½; average 48 pages; medium paper; 80 lb. good cover stock; illustrations; photos. *"An un-literary* literary review interested in sincerity, verve, anger, humor and beauty. For an intelligent audience—non-academic, non-media dazed in the US and throughout the world." Published 3-4 times/year. Estab. 1974, 48 issues to date. Circ. 600.
Needs: Literary, contemporary. Published new writers within the last year. Also publishes poetry. No academic material. Length: "3-5 pages preferred but not essential."
How to Contact: Send complete ms with SASE. Reports in 6 weeks. Sample copy $4.50.
Payment: Pays 2 contributor's copies; $1 charge for extras.
Terms: Acquires one-time rights.
Advice: "We are interested in fiction. Be sure your name and address are on the manuscript."

STRUGGLE, A Magazine of Proletarian Revolutionary Literature, (IV), Marxist-Leninist Party USA, Detroit Branch, Box 13261, Harper Station, Detroit MI 48213-0261. Editor: Tim Hall. Magazine: 5½×8½; 24-48 pages; 20 lb. white bond paper; colored cover; illustrations; occasional photographs. Publishes material related to "the struggle of the working class and all progressive people against the rule of the rich—including their war policies, racism, exploitation of the workers, oppression of women, etc." Quarterly. Estab. 1985.
Needs: Contemporary, ethnic, experimental, feminist, historical (general), humor/satire, literary, prose poem, regional, science fiction, senior citizen/retirement, suspense/mystery, translations, young adult/teen (10-18). "The theme can be approached in many ways, including plenty of categories not listed here." No romance, psychic, western, erotica, religious. Receives 1-2 unsolicited fiction mss/month. Publishes ms 3 months or less after acceptance. Published work by Leo Paulson, Judy Fitzgerald, R.G. Wilfong; published new writers within the last year. Length: 1,000-3,000 words average; 5,000 words maximum. Publishes short shorts. Normally critiques rejected mss.
How to Contact: Send complete ms; cover letter optional but helpful. "Tries to" report in 3 months. SASE. Simultaneous, photocopied and reprint submissions OK. Accepts computer printout submissions. Sample copy for $1.50. Checks to Tim Hall-Special Account.
Payment: Pays 2 contributor's copies.
Terms: No rights acquired. Publication not copyrighted.
Advice: "Write about the oppression of the working people, the poor, the minorities, women, and if possible, their rebellion against it—we are not interested in anything which accepts the status quo. We are not too worried about plot and advanced technique (fine if we get them!)—we would probably accept things others would call sketches, provided they have life and struggle. Just describe for us a situation in which some real people confront some problem of oppression, however seemingly minor. Observe and put down the real facts. We have increased our fiction portion of our content since last year's listing. We get poetry and songs all the time. We want 1-2 stories per issue."

STUDIO ONE, (II, IV), College of St. Benedict, St. Joseph MN 56374. Editors: Reba Mathern and Kirsten DeVries. Magazine: 7×10; 76-100 pages; illustrations (7-10/issue); photographs (10-15/issue). "Studio One is a regional magazine for literary and visual art. We publish photographs, drawings, paintings, poetry and short fiction for the academic community in the Midwest, particularly for the College of St. Benedict and St. John's University." Annually. Estab. 1976. Circ. 900.
Needs: Contemporary, ethnic, feminist, humor/satire, literary, mainstream, prose poem, regional. "We will consider all work submitted and we welcome submissions. The categories above reflect what we tend to publish annually." No "violent erotica, smut." Receives "maybe 1" unsolicited fiction ms/month. Accepts "5 out of 20" mss/year. Does not read mss in summer. Publishes ms 1-2 months after acceptance. Length: 500-1,000 words preferred; 5,000 words maximum. Publishes short shorts.

How to Contact: Send complete ms with cover letter. Include "return address, phone number and brief history of the work submitted (whether it has be published before)." Reports in 2-3 weeks on queries; 1-6 months on mss. SASE. Simultaneous, photocopied, reprint and computer printout submissions OK.
Payment: Pays in contributor's copies.
Terms: Acquires all rights (or reprint rights).
Advice: "If the story strikes us as interesting, we consider it. But manuscripts that arrest us with their color, word choice, form or message are the manuscripts we publish. It is so difficult to define what we look for in a work other than quality. Usually the work simply tells us that it intends to be published...Please be patient with acceptance letters. If you submitted, we will respond before publication. Our deadline is always in February, so please submit by then."

SUB-TERRAIN (I,IV), Anvil Press, Box 1575, Stn. A, Vancouver, British Columbia V6C 2P7 Canada. (604)876-8700. Editor: B. Kaufman, J.L. McCarthy and P. Pitre. Newspaper: 7 × 10; 16-20 pages; offset printed paper; 60 lb. cover stock; illustrations; photos. "Sub-Terrain functions as a literary magazine with a social conscience. *Sub-Terrain* provides a forum for work that pushes the boundaries in form or content." Estab. 1988.
Needs: "We are looking for work that expresses the experience of urban existence as we approach the closing of the century." Erotica, experimental, humor/satire and literary. Upcoming themes: "Tatooed Women & Tattooed Men," anything on the subject of stigma, branding, being marked; "A Full Frontal," the theme of exposure; "Asleep at the Watchtower," material concerned with the corruption of institutionalized religion. Receives 20-30 unsolicited mss/month. Accepts 3-4 mss/issue. Publishes ms 1-4 months after acceptance. Length: 200-3,000 words; 400-500 average. Publishes short shorts. Length: 200 words. Also publishes literary essays, literary criticism, poetry. Sometimes critiques rejected mss and "at times" recommends other markets.
How to Contact: Send complete ms with cover letter. Reports in 3-4 weeks on queries; 2-3 months on mss. SASE. Sample copy $3. Occasionally reviews novels and short story collections. Send books marked "Review Copy, Managing Editor."
Payment: Pays in contributor's copies.
Terms: Acquires one-time rights.
Advice: "We look for something special in the voice or style. Not simply something that is a well-written story. A new twist, a unique sense or vision of the world. The stuff that every mag is hoping to find. Write about things that are important to you: issues that *must* be talked about; issues that frighten, anger you. The world has all the cute, well-made stories it needs."

THE SUN, (II), The Sun Publishing Company, Inc., 107 N. Roberson St., Chapel Hill NC 27516. (919)942-5282. Editor: Sy Safransky. Magazine: 8½ × 11; 40 pages; offset paper; glossy cover stock; illustrations; photos. "*The Sun* is a magazine of ideas. We publish all kinds of writing—fiction, articles, poetry. Our only criteria are that the writing make sense and enrich our common space. We direct *The Sun* toward interests which move us, and we trust our readers will respond." Monthly. Estab. 1974. Circ. 10,000.
Needs: Open to all fiction. Accepts 3 ms/issue. Receives approximately 150 unsolicited fiction mss each month. Recently published work by Eleanore Devine, Earl C. Pike, Deborah Shouse; published new writers within the last year. Length: 10,000 words maximum. Also publishes poetry.
How to Contact: Send complete ms with SASE. Reports in 3 months. Publishes ms an average of 3-6 months after acceptance. Sample copy $3.
Payment: Pays up to $100 on publication, plus 2 contributor's copies and a complimentary subscription.
Terms: Acquires one-time rights. Publishes reprints.

Market conditions are constantly changing! If you're still using this book and it is 1993 or later, buy the newest edition of Novel & Short Story Writer's Market at your favorite bookstore or order directly from Writer's Digest Books.

SUN DOG: THE SOUTHEAST REVIEW, (II), English Department, 406 Williams, Florida State University, Tallahassee FL 32306. (904)644-4230. Editor: Pat MacEnulty. Magazine: 6×9; 60-100 pages; 70 lb. paper; 10 pt. Krome Kote cover; illustrations; photos. Published biannually. Estab. 1979. Circ. 2,000.
Needs: "We want stories which are well written, beautifully written, with striking images, incidents and characters. We are interested more in quality than in style or genre." Accepts 20 mss/year. Receives approximately 60 unsolicited fiction mss each month. Reads less frequently during summer. Critiques rejected mss when there is time. Occasionally recommends other markets.
How to Contact: Send complete ms with SASE. Typed, double-spaced, on good bond. Clean photocopy acceptable. "Short bio or cover letter would be appreciated." Publishes ms an average of 2-6 months after acceptance. Sample copy $4.
Payment: Pays 2 contributor's copies. $2 charge for extras.
Terms: Acquires first North American serial rights which then revert to author.
Advice: "Avoid trendy experimentation for its own sake (present-tense narration, observation that isn't also revelation). Fresh stories, moving, interesting characters and a sensitivity to language are still fiction mainstays. Also publishes winner and runners up of the World's Best Short Short Story Contest sponsored by the Florida State University English Department."

SWIFT KICK, (II), 1711 Amherst St., Buffalo NY 14214. (716)837-7778. Editor: Robin Kay Willoughby. Magazine: size, number of pages, paper quality, cover stock vary; illustrations; photos, b&w line art, xerographs. "Specializes in unusual formats, hard-to-classify works, visual poetry, found art, etc. for pataphysical, rarified audience." Published special fiction issue; plans another. Estab. 1981. Circ. 100.
Needs: Open. "If it doesn't seem to fit a regular category, it's probably what we'd like! No boring, slipshod, everyday stuff like in mass-market magazines." Receives 5 unsolicited fiction mss/month. Accepts 1-2 mss/issue. Does not read just before Christmas. Publishes ms depending on finances (6 months-1 year) after acceptance. Publishes short shorts of 1,000 words (or 1 picture). Sometimes recommends other markets.
How to Contact: Query first for longer works or send complete ms with cover letter for short work. Reports in 2 months to 1 year. SASE ("or include reply card with OK to toss enclosed work"). Simultaneous and photocopied submissions OK. Will consider reprints of astoundingly good work (out of print). Accepts computer printouts. Sample copy for $7; "sample purchase recommended to best understand magazine's needs."
Payment: Pays in contributor's copies; half price for extras.
Terms: Acquires one-time rights. Rights revert to artists/authors. Sends galleys to author if requested.
Advice: "We always get less fiction than poetry—if a story is good, it has a good chance of publication in little mags. Editorially, I'm a snob, so don't write like anyone else; be *so* literate your writing transcends literature and (almost) literacy. Don't submit over 10 pages first time. Submit a 'grabber' that makes an editor ask for more. Don't neglect the stories in your own life for someone else's castles-in-the-air."

SYCAMORE REVIEW, (II), Department of English, Purdue University, West Lafayette IN 47907. (317)494-3783. Editor: Michael D. Kiser. Fiction Editor: Troy Hickman. Magazine: 5½×8½; 1,000 pages; heavy, textured, uncoated paper; heavy matte uncoated cover. "Journal devoted to contemporary literature. We publish both traditional and experimental fiction, personal essay and poetry." Semiannually. Estab. 1989. Circ. 1,000.
Needs: Contemporary, experimental, historical (general), humor/satire, literary, mainstream, regional, sports, translations. "We generally avoid genre literature, but maintain no formal restrictions on style or subject matter. No science fiction, romance, children's." Publishes ms 3 months-1 year after acceptance. Length: 3,750 words preferred; 250 words minimum. Also publishes poetry. Sometimes critiques rejected mss and recommends other markets.
How to Contact: Send complete ms with cover letter. Cover letter should include previous publications, address changes. Reports in 3 months. SASE. Simultaneous and photocopied submissions OK. Accepts computer printout submissions. Sample copy $4. Fiction guidelines for #10 SAE and 1 first class stamp.
Payment: Pays in contributor's copies; charge for extras.
Terms: Acquires one-time rights.
Advice: "We publish both new and experienced authors but we're always looking for stories with strong emotional appeal, vivid characterization and a distinctive narrative voice; stories that appeal to the heart more than the head. Avoid gimmicks and trite, predictable outcomes. Write stories that have a ring of truth, the impact of felt emotion. Don't be afraid to submit, send your best."

SYZYGY, (I, II), P.O. Box 5975, Chicago IL 60680. (708)690-2577. Fiction Editor: Seth Tisue. Magazine: 7×8½; 50 pages; medium paper; card stock cover; illustrations. "Humor, bizarre fiction, experimental writing, essays." Estab. 1988. Circ. 750.
Needs: Experimental, humor/satire, literary, prose poem, science fiction. Receives 10 unsolicited mss/month. Accepts 5 mss/issue; 10 mss/year. Publishes ms 1-6 months after acceptance. Published work by Geof Huth, John Bergin, Bob Black. Publishes short shorts. Rarely critiques rejected mss.
How to Contact: Send complete manuscript with cover letter. "Tell us about yourself." Reports in 2 weeks on queries; 1 month on mss. Simultaneous, photocopied and reprint submissions OK. Accepts computer printout submissions. Accepts electronic submissions via disk. Sample copy for $1.75.
Payment: Pays free subscription to magazine and contributor's copies.
Terms: Sends galleys to author. Publication not copyrighted.
Advice: "Excellence in form and language; accessibility."

TAMPA REVIEW, (III), Box 19, University of Tampa, Tampa FL 33606-1490. (813)253-3333, ext. 3621. Editor: Richard Mathews. Fiction Editor: Andy Solomon. Magazine: 7½×10½; approximately 100 pages; acid-free paper; visual art; photos. "Interested in fiction of distinctive literary quality." Annually. Estab. 1988.
Needs: Contemporary, ethnic, experimental, fantasy, historical, humor/satire, literary, mainstream, prose poem, translations. "We are far more interested in quality than in genre. No sentimental as opposed to genuinely moving, nor self-conscious style at the expense of human truth." Buys 3-7 mss/issue. Publishes ms within 2 months-1 year of acceptance. Agented fiction 60%. Published work by Lee K. Abbott, Lorrie Moore, Tim O'Connor, Scott Bradfield. Length: 1,000 words minimum; 6,000 words maximum. Publishes short shorts "if the story is good enough." Also publishes literary essays (must be labeled nonfiction), poetry. Sometimes critiques rejected mss and recommends other markets.
How to Contact: Send complete mss with cover letter, which should include brief bio and publishing record. Include Social Security number. Reports within 3 months. SASE. Photocopied submissions OK. Accepts computer printout submissions. Sample copy for $7.50 includes postage, 9×12 SAE. Fiction guidelines for #10 SAE and 1 first class stamp.
Payment: Pays $10 per printed page.
Terms: Pays on publication for first North American serial rights. Sends galleys to author—upon request.
Advice: "There are more good writers publishing in magazines today than there have been in many decades. Unfortunately, there are even more bad ones. In T. Gertler's *Elbowing the Seducer*, an editor advises a young writer that he wants to hear her voice completely, to tell (he means 'show') him in a story the truest thing she knows. We concur. Rather than a trendy workshop story or a minimalism that actually stems from not having much to say, we would like to see stories that make us believe they mattered to the writer and, more importantly, will matter to a reader. Trim until only the essential is left, and don't give up belief in yourself. And it might help to attend a good writers conference, e.g. Wesleyan or Bennington."

TANDAVA, (II), Box 689, East Detroit MI 48021. (313)779-9349. Editor: Tom Blessing. Magazine: 5½×8 or 8×11; 16-50 pages; illustrations. Frequency varies. Estab. 1982. Circ. 100.
Needs: Excerpted novel, contemporary, experimental, fantasy, literary, prose poem, science fiction. Plans special fiction issue. Receives 1 or less unsolicited mss/month. Accepts 2 mss/issue; 5 mss/year. Publishes ms 1½ years after acceptance. Length: 5,000 words maximum. Publishes short shorts. Length: Up to 2 pages. Sometimes critiques rejected mss and recommends other markets.
How to Contact: Send complete ms with cover letter. "Include introduction—where you heard of Tandava, goals, projects." Reports in 2 weeks. SASE. Simultaneous and photocopied submissions OK. Accepts computer printout submissions. Sample copy for $1.50.
Payment: Pays in contributor's copies.
Terms: Publication not copyrighted.

TERROR TIME AGAIN, (II), Nocturnal Publications, 275 W. Stevens, St. Paul MN 55107. (612)227-6958. Editor: Donald L. Miller. Magazine: 5×8; 52-60 pages; 20 lb. paper; 67 lb. cover stock; illustrations. *"Terror Time Again's* objective is to provoke a sense of fear in our readers." Annually. Estab. 1987. Circ. 200.
Needs: Only wants fear-inducing stories. No science fiction or sword and sorcery. Receives up to 35 unsolicited mss/month. Accepts 15-20 mss/issue. Publishes ms in January of following year accepted. Published work by Steve Berman, D.A. Sale, Michael Floyd, Bob Madia and Steve Vernon; published

new writers within the last year. Length: 1,000 words average; 250 words minimum; 2,000 words maximum. Publishes short shorts. Length: 250-700 words. Also publishes poetry. Sometimes critiques rejected mss; recommends other markets.

How to Contact: Send complete ms with brief bio about yourself. Reports in 2-3 weeks on mss. Remember to enclose a SASE. Simultaneous, photocopied and reprint submissions OK. Accepts computer printout submissions. Sample copy $4.50; fiction guidelines free. Reviews novels and short story collections in newsletter (see below).

Payment: Pays 1 contributor's copy.

Terms: Acquires one-time and reprint rights. Sponsors contest for writers through *The Nightmare Express*. "*Terror Time Again* has a cover contest via *The Nightmare Express* in which the cover illustration of the July/August issue of *TNE* is used by the writer to develop a story under 2,000 words. *TNE* is a newsletter for horror writers and is published bi-monthly. A sample copy of *Nightmare Express* is $1.50. A one year subscription is only $10 plus *TTA* is included free."

THE TEXAS REVIEW, (II), Sam Houston State University Press, Huntsville TX 77341. (713)294-1423. Editor: Paul Ruffin. Magazine: 6×9; 148-190 pages; best quality paper; 70 lb. cover stock; illustrations; photos. "We publish top quality poetry, fiction, articles, interviews and reviews for a general audience." Semiannually. Estab. 1976. Circ. 700.

Needs: Literary and contemporary fiction. "We are eager enough to consider fiction of quality, no matter what its theme or subject matter. No juvenile fiction." Accepts 4 mss/issue. Receives approximately 40-60 unsolicited fiction mss each month. Recently published work by George Garnett, Ellen Gilchrist, Fred Chappell; published new writers within the last year. Length: 500-10,000 words. Critiques rejected mss "when there is time." Recommends other markets.

How to Contact: Send complete ms with cover letter. SASE. Reports in 3 months on mss. Sample copy $3.

Payment: Pays contributor's copies plus one year subscription.

Terms: Acquires all rights. Sends galleys to author.

THEMA, (II,IV), Box 74109, Metairie LA 70033-4109. Editor: Virginia Howard. Magazine: 5½×8½; 200 pages; Grandee Strathmore cover stock; b&w illustrations. "Different specified theme for each issue—short stories, poems, b&w artwork must relate to that theme." Quarterly. Estab. 1988.

Needs: Adventure, contemporary, experimental, humor/satire, literary, mainstream, prose poem, psychic/supernatural/occult, regional, science fiction, sports, suspense/mystery, western. "Each issue is based on a specified premise—a different unique theme for each issue. Many types of fiction acceptable, but must fit the premise. No pornographic, scatologic, erotic fiction." Upcoming themes: "Unrecognized at the Airport" (deadline May 1); "Tracks in the Snow" (deadline August 1). Publishes ms within 3-4 months of acceptance. Recently published work by Edith Pearlman, A.L. Sirois, William Luvas. Length: 4,500 words preferred; 2,700 words minimum; 6,000 words maximum. Publishes short shorts "if very clever." Length: 300-500 words. Also publishes poetry. Sometimes critiques rejected mss and recommends other markets.

How to Contact: Send complete ms with cover letter, which should include "name and address, brief introduction, specifying the intended target issue for the mss." Reports on queries in 1 week; on mss in 4-6 weeks after deadline for specified issue. SASE. Photocopied submissions OK. Sample copy $5. Free fiction guidelines.

Payment: Pays $25.

Terms: Pays on acceptance for one-time rights.

Advice: "Do not submit a manuscript unless you have written it for a specified premise. If you don't know the upcoming themes, send for guidelines first, before sending a story. We need more stories told in the Mark Twain/O. Henry tradition in magazine fiction."

THIN ICE, (II), 379 Lincoln Ave., Council Bluffs IA 51503. (712)322-9125. Editor/Publisher: Kathleen Jurgens. Magazine: Digest-sized; 95-110 pages; 16-20 lb. paper; enamel cover; b&w, pen and ink illustrations. "Horror and dark fantasy—short stories, poetry, interviews, art." Triannually. Estab. 1987. Circ. 250.

Needs: Experimental, fantasy (dark), horror, black humor/satire, poetry, psychic/supernatural/occult. No "racist, preachy, straight porn for shock value." Receives 80-120 unsolicited mss/month. Buys approx. 10 mss/issue; approx. 40 mss/year. Publishes ms 1-2 years after acceptance. Published work by Bentley Little, J. N. Williamson, Colleen Drippe, Jeannette Hopper. Length: 1,000-4,000 words preferred. Also publishes poetry. Critiques rejected mss.

How to Contact: Send complete ms with cover letter. Cover letter should include "a personal introduction, mention a few prior 'sales' if desired (though not necessary), where the writers heard of *Thin Ice.*" Reports in 1 week on queries; 1-2 months on mss. SASE. Photocopied submissions preferred. Accepts computer printout submissions. Sample copy for $4.50 to Kathleen Jurgens ($6 outside of the U.S.). Fiction guidelines with #10 SASE.
Payment: Pays in contributor's copies.
Terms: Acquires first North American serial rights.
Advice: "Invest in a copy of our magazine and read it from cover to cover. Get a 'feel' for the overall mood, tone, and subject matter. Don't apologize for misspellings or coffee stains on the manuscript—retype it. While we prefer informal query letters, we become quite irate when potential contributors treat us unprofessionally. We respond to all submissions personally, frequently offering editorial commentary. Always include an SASE with the correct amount of postage. Give us the full 8 weeks to repond. Absolutely no simultaneous or multiple submissions considered. Please, do not summarize the story in your cover letter."

THIRD WOMAN, (II,IV), Chicano Studies Dept., Dwinelle Hall 3412, University of California, Berkeley CA 94720. (415)642-0708 or 642-0240. Editor: Norma Alarcón. Magazine: 5½ × 8½; 100-150 pages; quality paper; glossy color cover; illustrations; photos. "Literature and the arts focusing on the work by/about U.S. Latinas, Hispanic World and Third World Women in general. *Third Woman* is an annual journal of art, essays and criticisms, usually with a theme. Inquire." Semiannually. Estab. 1981. Circ. 1,500.
Needs: Ethnic, feminist, translations. Receives 4 mss/month. Accepts 10 mss/year. Publishes ms within 6 months-2 years of acceptance. Length: 5,000-10,000 words preferred. Publishes short shorts.
How to Contact: Send complete ms with cover letter. Reports on queries in 6-8 weeks; on mss in 6 months. SASE. Simultaneous and photocopied submissions OK. Accepts computer printout submissions. Free sample copy.
Payment: Pays in contributor's copies.
Terms: Acquires first rights. Sends galleys to author.

‡13TH MOON, A Feminist Magazine, (IV), SUNY-Albany, Dept. of English, Albany NY 12222. (518)442-4181. Editor: Judith Johnson. Magazine: 6×9; 200 pages; 50 lb. paper; heavy cover; photographs. "Feminist literary magazine for feminist women and men." Annually. Estab. 1973. Circ. 2,000.
Needs: Excerpted novel, experimental, feminist, lesbian, literary, prose poem, science fiction, translations. No fiction by men. Accepts 1-3 mss/issue. Does not read mss June-Sept. Time varies between acceptance and publication. Recently published work by Meredith Steinbach. Length: Open. Publishes short shorts. Also publishes poetry. Sometimes critiques rejected mss.
How to Contact: Send complete ms with cover letter and SASE. Reports in 1 month on queries; 4 months on mss. SASE. Accepts computer printout submissions. Accepts electronic submissions via disk (WordPerfect 5.1 only). Sample copy for $8.
Payment: Pays 2 contributor's copies.
Terms: Acquires first North American serial rights.
Advice: Looks for "*unusual* fiction with feminist appeal."

THIS MAGAZINE, (II), Red Maple Foundation, 16 Skey Lane, Toronto, Ontario M6J 3S4 Canada. (416)588-6580. Editor: Judy MacDonald. Fiction Editor: Kevin Connolly. Magazine: 8½×11; 42 pages; bond paper; coated cover; illustrations and photographs. "Alternative general interest magazine." Estab. 1973. Circ. 12,000.
Needs: Ethnic, contemporary, experimental, fantasy, feminist, gay, lesbian, literary, mainstream, prose poem, regional. No "commercial/pulp fiction." Receives 15-20 unsolicited mss/month. Buys 1 mss/issue; 8 mss/year. Published work by Margaret Atwood and Peter McGehee. Length: 1,500 words average; 2,500 words maximum. Sometimes critiques rejected mss.
How to Contact: Query with clips of published work. Reports in 3-5 weeks on queries; 8-10 weeks on mss. SASE. Simultaneous and photocopied submissions OK. Accepts computer printout submissions. Sample copy $4 (includes postage and GST). Fiction guidelines for #9 SAE and 46¢ U.S., 40¢ Canadian.

Payment: Pays $100 (Canadian); fiction $25/poem published.
Terms: Buys one-time rights.
Advice: "It's best if you're familiar with the magazine when submitting work; a large number of mss that come into my office are inappropriate. Style guides are available. Manuscripts and queries that are clean and personalized really make a difference. Let your work speak for itself—don't try to convince us."

THUMBPRINTS, (I, IV), Thumb Area Writer's Club, Box 27, Sandusky MI 48471. Editor: Janet Ihle. Newsletter: 8½×11; 6 pages; line drawing illustrations. Material is "primarily on writing and writers." Estab. 1983. Circ. 30.
Needs: Adventure, historical (general), humor/satire, mainstream, prose poem, regional, romance (contemporary, historical and young adult), senior citizen/retirement and sports. Write for list of 1992 themes. Accepts 1 ms/issue; 10-12 mss/year. Publishes ms 3-4 months after acceptance. Length: 750 words maximum; 500 average. Publishes short shorts. Length: 250-400 words. Sometimes critiques rejected mss.
How to Contact: Send complete ms only. Reports in 2 months. SASE. Photocopied submissions OK. Accepts computer printout submissions. Sample copy 75¢, #10 SASE. Guidelines for SASE.
Payment: Pays in contributor's copies; charges for extras.
Terms: Acquires first or one-time rights. Publication not copyrighted.

TICKLED BY THUNDER, (II), A Newsmagazine for Writers, Tickled by Thunder Pub. Co., 7385 129th St., Surrey, British Columbia V3W 7B8 Canada. (604)591-6095. Editor: Larry Lindner. Magazine: Digest-sized; bond paper; bond cover; illustrations and photographs. "Totally open. For writers." Quarterly. Estab. 1990. Circ. 100.
Needs: Adventure, contemporary, fantasy, humor/satire, literary, mainstream, prose poem, psychic/supernatural, religious/inspirational, science fiction, suspense/mystery, western. "No pornography." Receives 40 unsolicited mss/month. Buys 1-4 mss/issue; 4-16 mss/year. Publishes ms next issue after acceptance. Length: 1,500 words average; 2,000 words maximum. Publishes short shorts. Length: No preference. Also publishes poetry. Sometimes critiques rejected mss and recommends other markets.
How to Contact: Query with clips of published work if any including "Brief resume/history of writing experience, photo, credits, etc." Reports in 2 weeks on queries; 1 month on mss. SASE. Photocopied submissions OK. Accepts computer printout submissions. Sample copy $2.50 (Canadian) or 3 IRCs. Fiction guidelines for legal SAE and 1 first class stamp.
Payment: Pays $1 maximum.
Terms: Buys first rights.
Advice: "Send for guidelines, read a sample copy and ask questions."

TOAD HIWAY, (II), Box 44, Universal IN 47884. (317)832-8918. Editor: Doug Martin. Fiction Editor: John Colvin. Magazine: 5½×8½; 24 pages; ink drawing illustrations; b&w photos. "We are especially interested in avant-garde material and quality mainstream fiction." Quarterly. Estab. 1989. Circ. 200.
Needs: Condensed/excerpted novel, contemporary, erotica, experimental, humor/satire, prose poem, science fiction and translations. Plans to publish special fiction or anthology issue in the future. Receives 25 unsolicited mss/month. Accepts 1-2 mss/issue; 4-8 mss/year. Publishes ms 3-6 months after acceptance. Length: 30,000 words maximum; 5,000 average. Publishes short shorts. Sometimes critiques rejected mss and recommends other markets.
How to Contact: Send complete ms with cover letter. "If you've been published before, be specific about magazines and dates." Reports in 6 weeks on queries; 3 months on mss. SASE. Simultaneous submissions OK. Sample copy $2. Fiction guidelines for #10 SAE.
Payment: Pays in contributor's copies.
Terms: Acquires one-time rights.

TRADESWOMEN, A Quarterly Magazine for Women in Blue-Collar Work, (I, IV), Tradeswomen, Inc., P.O. Box 40664, San Francisco CA 94140. (415) 821-7334. Magazine: 8½×11; 40 pages; b&w photographs. Quarterly. Estab. 1981. Circ. 1,500.
Needs: "Looking for fiction about women in blue-collar employment; on-the-job stories, 'what it's like' stories by women and men." Upcoming themes: "Women in Public Works and Utilities (deadline: March 10, 1992); "Pioneering Women," about how our grandmothers did ground-breaking nontraditional work." Receives 1-2 unsolicited mss/month; accepts 1-2 mss/issue. Publishes ms 3-6 months after acceptance. Length: 2,000 words average; 3,000 words maximum. Publishes short shorts. Recommends other markets for rejected mss.

How to Contact: Send complete ms with cover letter. Reports on queries in 1 month; on ms in 2 months. SASE. Simultaneous, photocopied and reprint submissions OK. Accepts computer printout submissions. Sample copy $3. Fiction guidelines free.

TRANSLATION, (II), The Translation Center, Columbia University, 412 Dodge, New York NY 10027. (212)854-2305. Director: Frank MacShane. Magazine: 6 × 9; 200-300 pages; coated cover stock; photos. Semiannually. Estab. 1972. Circ. 1,500.
Needs: Literary translations only. Accepts varying number of mss/year. Receives approximately 20-30 unsolicited fiction mss each month. Length: very short or excerpts; not in excess of 15 mss pages. Critiques rejected mss "rarely, because of time involved."
How to Contact: Send complete translation ms accompanied by original language text, 10-line autobiography, 10-line author's biography and SASE. Note required stating copyright clearance has been obtained. Reports in 3-6 months on mss. Sample copy $9.
Payment: Pays 2 complimentary translator copies.
Terms: Acquires first North American serial rights for that volume publication only.
Advice: "We are particularly interested in translations from the lesser-known languages. Annual awards of $1,000 for outstanding translation of a substantial part of a book-length literary work. Translator must have letter of intent to publish from a publisher. Write for description and application for awards program."

‡TRIBUTARY, (II), The Rockford Writers Guild, Box 858, Rockford IL 61105. Editor: David Ross. Magazine: 5⅜ × 8½; b&w illustrations and photographs. "Devices with a fresh approach to old themes or new insights into the human condition whether prose or poetry." Quarterly. Estab. 1990. Circ. 100.
Needs: Ethnic, experimental, fantasy, feminist, historical (general), humor/satire, literary, regional. Length: 2,500 words maximum. Publishes short shorts.
How to Contact: Send complete ms with cover letter. "Include a short biographical note – no more than four sentences." Reports in 4-6 weeks. SASE. Simultaneous, photocopied and reprint (if indicated) submissions OK. Accepts computer printout submissions. Sample copy for $6. Fiction guidelines for #10 SAE and 1 first class stamp.
Payment: Pays in contributor's copies. Submissions considered for $25 Readers' Poll prize.
Terms: Acquires first North American serial rights.

TRIQUARTERLY, (II), Northwestern University, 2020 Ridge Ave., Evanston IL 60208. (708)491-7614. Fiction Editors: Reginald Gibbons and Susan Hahn. Magazine: 6 × 9¼; 240+ pages; 60 lb. paper; heavy cover stock; illustration; photos. "A general literary quarterly especially devoted to fiction. We publish short stories, novellas or excerpts from novels, by American and foreign writers. Genre or style is not a primary consideration. We aim for the general but serious and sophisticated reader. Many of our readers are also writers." Published 3 times/year. Estab. 1964. Circ. 5,000.
Needs: Literary, contemporary and translations. "No prejudices or preconceptions against anything *except* genre fiction (sci fi, romances, etc.)." Buys 10 mss/issue, 30 mss/year. Receives approximately 500 unsolicited fiction mss each month. Does not read May 1-Sept. 30. Approximately 10% of fiction is agented. Published work by Angela Jackson, Carol Bly, Leon Rooke; published new writers within the last year. Length: no requirement. Publishes short shorts.
How to Contact: Send complete ms with SASE. Reports in 3-4 months on mss. Publishes ms an average of 6 months to 1 year after acceptance. Sample copy $4.
Payment: Pays $100-500, 2 contributor's copies. Cover price less 40% discount for extras.
Terms: Pays on publication for first North American serial rights. Sends galleys to author.

TUCUMCARI LITERARY REVIEW, (I), 3108 W. Bellevue Ave., Los Angeles CA 90026. Editor: Troxey Kemper. Magazine: 5½ × 8½; 32 pages; 20 lb. bond paper; 110 lb. cover; few illustrations; Xerox photographs. "Old-fashioned fiction that can be read and reread for pleasure; no weird, strange pipe dreams." Bimonthly. Estab. 1988. Circ. small.
Needs: Adventure, condensed/excerpted novel, contemporary, ethnic, historical (general), humor/satire, literary, mainstream, regional, (southwest USA), senior citizen/retirement, suspense/mystery, western. No science fiction, sedition, blasphemy, fetishism, drugs/acid rock, pornography, horror, martial arts. "No talking animals or plants. No talking with God or telling what He told you." Accepts 2 or 3 mss/issue; 12-18 mss/year. Publishes ms 2 to 4 months after acceptance. Length: 400-1,200 words preferred. Also publishes poetry. Sometimes critiques rejected mss and recommends other markets.

How to Contact: Send complete ms with or without cover letter. Cover letter should include "anything pertinent to the submission." Reports in 2 weeks. SASE. Simultaneous, photocopied and reprint submissions OK. Accepts computer printout submissions. Sample copy $1.50 plus 50¢ postage. Fiction guidelines for #10 SAE and 1 first class stamp.
Payment: Pays in contributor's copies.
Terms: Acquires one-time rights. Publication not copyrighted.
Advice: "Does the work 'say something' or is it a hodgepodge of sentence fragments and paragraphs, not tied together into a story? No 'it was all a dream' endings."

TURNSTILE, (II), Suite 2348, 175 Fifth Ave., New York NY 10010. Editor: Mitchell Nauffts. Magazine: 6×9; 128 pages; 55 lb. paper; 10 pt. cover; illustrations; photos. "Publishing work by new writers." Biannually. Estab. 1988. Circ. 1,500.
Needs: Contemporary, experimental, humor/satire, literary, regional. No genre fiction. Receives approx. 40 unsolicited fiction mss/month. Publishes approx. 8 short story mss/issue. Recently published work by James Applewhite, Richard Russo; published new writers within the last year. Length: 2,000 words average; 4,000 words maximum. Publishes short shorts. Also publishes poetry. Sometimes comments on rejected mss or recommends other markets.
How to Contact: Query first or send complete ms with cover letter. Reports on queries in 1-2 weeks; on mss in 4-6 weeks. SASE. Simultaneous and photocopied submissions OK. Accepts computer printouts. Sample copy $6.50 and 7×10 SAE; fiction guidelines for #10 SAE and 1 first class stamp.
Payment: Pays in contributor's copies; charge for extras.
Terms: Acquires one-time rights.
Advice: "Also publishes interviews with writers, essays and subjective nonfiction. Also interviews with writers."

2 AM MAGAZINE, (I, II, IV), Box 6754, Rockford IL 61125-1754. Editor: Gretta M. Anderson. Magazine: 8½×11; 60 or more pages; 60 lb. offset paper; 70 lb. offset cover; illustrations; photos occasionally. "Horror, science fiction, fantasy stories, poetry, articles and art for a sophisticated adult audience." Quarterly. Summer fiction issue planned. Estab. 1986. Circ. 1,000.
Needs: Experimental, fantasy, horror, humor/satire, prose poem, psychic/supernatural/occult, science fiction, suspense/mystery. No juvenile. Receives 400 unsolicited mss/month. Buys 12-14 mss/issue; 50 mss/year. Publishes ms an average of 6-9 months after acceptance. Published work by J. N. Williamson, Elizabeth Engstrom, Leonard Carpenter; published new writers within the last year. Length: 1,800 words average; 500 words minimum; 5,000 words maximum. Publishes short shorts. Sometimes critiques rejected mss and recommends other markets.
How to Contact: Send complete ms with cover letter (cover letter optional). Reports in 1 month on queries; 10-12 weeks on mss. SASE. Photocopied submissions OK. Accepts computer printout submissions. Sample copy $4.95 and $1 postage. Fiction guidelines for #10 SAE.
Payment: Pays ½¢/word minimum, negotiable maximum; 1 contributor's copy; 40% discount on additional copies.
Terms: Pays on acceptance for one-time rights with non-exclusive anthology option. Sends prepublication galleys to author.
Advice: "Publishing more pages of fiction, more sf, and mystery, as well as horror. Put name and address on manuscript, double-space, use standard ms format. Pseudonym should appear under title on first manuscript page. True name and address should appear on upper left on first ms page."

‡THE TWOPENNY PORRINGER, (I, II), P.O. Box 1456, Tacoma WA 98401. Editor: Adrian Taylor. Magazine: Digest-sized; 70-80 pages; thick, glossy cover; b&w illustrations and photographs. "General literary and arts (poetry, short stories, photos, artwork)." Quarterly. Estab. 1992. Circ. 2,000.
Needs: Contemporary, experimental, literary, prose poem, translations. Receives 2+ unsolicited mss/ month. Buys a minimum of 4 mss/year. Length: Open. Publishes short shorts. Also accepts poetry. Recommends other markets.
How to Contact: Send complete ms with cover letter. Reports in 3 weeks on mss. SASE. Simultaneous, photocopied submissions OK. Accepts computer printout submissions. Sample copy for $2.
Payment: Pays 2 contributor's copies and 3 subsequent issues.
Terms: Acquires one-time rights. Sends galleys to author.
Advice: "I am very open to all styles. The work should be original and have a captivating quality about it that will keep the interest of the reader. Reality expressed in a creative manner is always best."

TWO-TON SANTA (II), Box 1332, Portsmouth NH 03801. (603)427-0631. Editor: Guy Capecelatro III. Magazine: 5¾ × 8¼; 4 pages. "Because of its size, only four pages, the material must be fairly short. Most tend to be stories and poems about real people dealing with somehow, ironic situations." Weekly. Estab. 1988. Circ. 200.
Needs: Condensed/excerpted novel, contemporary, erotica, experimental, feminist, gay, horror, humor/satire, juvenile (5-9 years), lesbian, preschool (1-4 years), prose poem, religious/inspirational and senior citizen/retirement. "We do not encourage writing styles that tend to alienate people. The language should not detract from or overwhelm the story itself." Publishes annual fiction issue. Receives 400 unsolicited mss/month. Accepts 2 mss/month; 112 mss/year. Publishes ms 2-4 weeks after acceptance. Published work by Russell Edson, Ray Halliday, Nancy Krygowski and Pagan Kennedy. Length: 3-700 words; 100-300 words average. Also publishes poetry. Sometimes critiques rejected mss and recommends other markets.
How to Contact: Query first. Reports in 2-3 weeks. Simultaneous, photocopied and reprint submissions OK. Accepts computer printout submissions.
Payment: Pays in contributor's copies.
Terms: Acquires one-time rights.
Advice: "The stories that stand out are ones that provide a glimpse into real life. They are imaginative in their presentation of how we exist. Stories don't necessarily follow a logical progression, but should invoke some sort of feeling within the reader. Each scene should work at being a part of the whole, if only in setting or voice. The language should not hinder an idea but be used merely as a presentation."

THE ULTIMATE WRITER (I), Perry Terrell Publishing, 4520 Williams Blvd., Box R-328, Kenner LA 70065. (504)465-9412. Editor: Perry Terrell. Magazine: 8½ × 11; bond paper. "Poetry, fiction, essays, articles for an audience of all ages, geared toward creativity in writing and expression." Monthly. Estab. 1990. Circ. 425.
Needs: Adventure, confession, ethnic, experimental, fantasy, historical, humor/satire, juvenile, mainstream, religious/inspirational, romance, science fiction, suspense/mystery, western; also plays, fillers. No pornographic material. Plans special fiction issue. Accepts 48 mss/year. Publishes ms 4-8 months after acceptance, depending on length of ms. Length: 99 words minimum, no maximum, "but more than 5,000 words will be printed in 2 or 3 issues." Also publishes literary essays, literary criticism, poetry.
How to Contact: Query first or send complete ms with cover letter. Reports in 1 week on queries; 2-3 months on mss. SASE. Sample copy for $3.75. Fiction guidelines for #10 SAE and 1 first-class stamp. Reviews novels and short story collections.
Payment: Pays 3 contributor's copies or free three-month subscription.
Advice: Sponsors fiction, essay, poetry, article contest. Write for details.

‡UNCLE, The Magazine for Those Who Have Given Up, (II), Heart's Desire Press, 216 N. Clinton Place, Kansas City MO 64123. (816)483-4227. Editor: John Mort. Fiction Editor: Don Irving Blevins. Newspaper: 6 × 9; 80-120 pages; offset paper; offset cover; line drawings. "Satire and humor for a literary audience. Semiannually. Estab. 1980. Circ. 500.
Needs: Contemporary, erotica, humor/satire, literary, mainstream, prose poem, psychic/supernatura/ occult, regional, science fiction, western, young adult/teen (10-18 years). "Humor is our main concern. When we don't run humor, it's usually offbeat, surreal, deconstructionist and science fiction. But anything is a consideration if it's funny." No "pornography, probably or formula genre stuff." Accepts 10-15 mss/issue; 20-30 mss/year. Publishes ms 6 months to 1 year after acceptance. Recently published work by Rosalind Warren, Eugene Bales, Tom Whalen. Length: 2,000-5,000 words preferred; 8,000 words maximum. Sometimes critiques rejected mss and recommends other markets.
How to Contact: Send complete ms with cover letter. Reports in 1 weeks on queries; 6 weeks on mss. SASE. Photocopied and reprint submissions OK. Accepts computer printout submissions. Accepts electronic submissions via disk. Sample copy for $4. Fiction guidelines for #10 SAE and 1 first class stamp.

The double dagger before a listing indicates that the listing is new in this edition. New markets are often the most receptive to freelance contributions.

Payment: Pays contributor's copies; extra copies at cost.
Terms: Acquires one-time rights. Sends pre-publication galleys to the author on request, or if there's a lot of editing.
Advice: "If we laugh, then it's a good sign. If a manuscript is genuinely funny, we'lltry very hard to print it. Avoid the *New Yorker* model—we, at least, prefer stories to 'casuals.' Don't be afraid to take on difficult subjects to satirize."

UNDERGROUND FOREST/LA SELVE SUBTERRÁNEA, (II), 1701 Bluebell Ave., Boulder CO 80302. Editor: Joseph Richey, Anne Becher. Magazine: 5½×17; 48-64 pages; 50 lb. offset paper; pen and ink illustrations. Our themes are "the American North, Central and South; poetry, culture, politics, the environment, sexuality." For a "hyper-literate, bilingual (Spanish-English) audience." Semiannually. Estab. 1986. Circ. 10,000.
Needs: Condensed/excerpted novel, ethnic, translations. "We publish most pieces in English and Spanish; translations into the other language will be appreciated, though not necessary (we do translating too)." Receives 2 unsolicited mss/month. Accepts 1 ms/year. Publishes ms usually several months after acceptance. Recently published work by Agnes Bushell, Mario Roberto Morales. Length: 2,000-5,000 words preferred; 7,000 words maximum. Publishes short shorts. Sometimes critiques rejected mss.
How to Contact: Query with clips of published work. Reports in 1 month on queries. SASE. Photocopied submissions. Accepts computer printout submissions. Sample copy for $5.
Payment: Pays contributor's copies.
Terms: Not copyrighted.
Advice: Looks for "unselfconscious, confident, yet not presumptious author. Author with strong personal knowledge of subject matter."

UNDERPASS, (II), Underpass Press, #574-21, 10405 Jasper Ave., Edmonton, Alberta T5J 3S2 Canada. Editor: Barry Hammond. Magazine: 5¼×8¼; pages vary; 60 lb. bond paper; Mayfair cover; some illustrations. "Mainly a poetry annual for an adult audience." Annually. Estab. 1987. Circ. 200-300.
Needs: Contemporary, experimental, literary, prose poem. "We have only published a few short stories. We are mainly a poetry annual. No religious or nature poetry." Receives 6 mss/month. Buys 1 or 2 mss/issue. Does not read mss Nov.-Jan. Publishes ms within 6 months after acceptance. Recently published work by Wade Bell. Length: 2,000 words average; 500 words minimum; 6,000 words maximum. Publishes short shorts. Length: No preference. Sometimes critiques rejected mss.
How to Contact: Send complete manuscript with cover letter including "Brief bio. and publishing history (if any)." Reports in 6 weeks. "Our deadline is August 31st each year." SASE. Simultaneous and photocopied submissions OK. Accepts computer printout submissions. Sample copy for $6.95, 6×9 SAE and 2 first class stamps. Fiction guidelines for #10 SAE and 1 first class stamp.
Payment: Pays $10 minimum and contributor's copies.
Terms: Buys one-time rights. Sends galleys to author.
Advice: "Try poetry before submitting prose."

UNIVERSITY OF PORTLAND REVIEW, (II), University of Portland, 5000 N. Willamette Blvd., Portland OR 97203. (503)283-7144. Editor-in-Chief: Thompson M. Faller. Magazine: 5×8; 40-55 pages. "Magazine for the college-educated layman of liberal arts background. Its purpose is to comment on the human condition and to present information in different fields with relevance to the contemporary scene." Published semiannually. Established 1948. Circ. 1,000.
Needs: "Only fiction that makes a significant statement about the contemporary scene will be employed." Receives 4 unsolicited mss/month. Accepts 2-3 mss/issue, 4-6 mss/year. Published new writers within the last year. Length: 1,500 words minimum; 3,500 words maximum; 2,000 words average. Sometimes recommends other markets.
How to Contact: Send complete ms with SASE. Reports in 3 weeks on queries; 6 months on mss. Publishes ms up to 1 year after acceptance. Sample copy 50¢.
Payment: Pays 5 contributor's copies; 50¢ charge for extras.
Terms: Acquires all rights.

UNMUZZLED OX (III), Unmuzzled Ox Foundation Ltd., 105 Hudson St., New York NY 10013. Editor: Michael Andre. Tabloid. "Magazine about life for an intelligent audience." Quarterly. Estab. 1971. Circ. 20,000.

Needs: Contemporary, literary, prose poem and translations. No commercial material. Receives 20-25 unsolicited mss/month. Also publishes poetry. Occasionally critiques rejected mss.
How to Contact: "Cover letter is significant." Reports in 1 month. SASE. Sample copy $7.50.
Payment: Contributor's copies.

‡THE UNSILENCED VOICE, An Anything but Toast Publication, (I), #29, 9333 N. Lombard, Portland OR 97203. (503)240-0120. Editor: Clint C. Wilkinson. Newsletter: 8½ × 11; 4 pages; illustrations. "Leftist, politically and socially oriented also weird, fringe fiction and poetry for an open minded, politically aware audience." Bimonthly. Estab. 1990. Circ. 25.
Needs: Experimental, horror, humor/satire, psychic/supernatural/occult. No erotic, religious, racist material. Plans future special fiction issue. Accepts 2 mss/issue; 20 mss/year. Publishes ms 1 month after acceptance. Recently published work by Clint Wilkinson, Tony Main, Beth Fitzgerald. Length: 150 words preferred; 300 words maximum. Publishes short shorts. Sometimes critiques rejected mss and recommends other markets.
How to Contact: Send complete ms. Reports in 1 month. SASE. Simultaneous, photocopied and reprint submissions OK. Accepts computer printout submissions. Sample copy for $1. Fiction guidelines for #10 SAE and 1 first class stamp.
Payment: Pays in contributor's copies.
Terms: Acquires one-time rights. Publication not copyrighted.
Advice: "I'm just getting into the fiction market, but I look for well-told stories in which well-developed, real characters participate. If it's really weird, that's good too. Send stuff to underground publications to build up credits and confidence for attacking the big leagues. Write what you want to write, not what you think you 'should' write to be successful."

US1 WORKSHEETS, (II), Postings, Box 1, Ringoes NJ 08551. (609)448-5096. Editor: Rotating board. Magazine: 11½ × 17; 20-25 pages. Publishes poetry and fiction. Annually. Estab. 1973.
Needs: "No restrictions on subject matter or style. Good story telling or character deliniation appreciated. Audience does not include children." Publishes ms within 3 months of acceptance. Published work by Alicia Ostriker, Toi Derricotte, J.A. Perkins, Cynthia Goodling, Judith McNally. Publishes short shorts.
How to Contact: Query first. Reports on queries "as soon as possible." SASE. Photocopied submissions OK. Sample copy $4.
Payment: Pays in contributor's copies.
Terms: Acquires one-time rights. Copyright "reverts to author."

VALLEY GRAPEVINE, (I, IV), Seven Buffaloes Press, Box 249, Big Timber MT 59011. Editor/Publisher: Art Cuelho. Theme: "poems, stories, history, folklore, photographs, ink drawings or anything native to the Great Central Valley of California, which includes the San Joaquin and Sacramento valleys. Focus is on land and people and the oil fields, farms, orchards, Okies, small town life, hobos." Readership: "Rural and small town audience, the common man with a rural background, salt-of-the-earth. The working man reads *Valley Grapevine* because it's his personal history recorded." Annually. Estab. 1978. Circ. 500.
Needs: Literary, contemporary, western and ethnic (Okie, Arkie). No academic, religious (unless natural to theme), gay/lesbian or supernatural material. Receives approximately 4-5 unsolicited fiction mss each month. Length: 2,500-10,000 (prefers 5,000) words.
How to Contact: Query. SASE for query, ms. Reports in 1 week. Sample copy available to writers for $4.75.
Payment: Pays 1-2 contributor's copies.
Terms: Acquires first North American serial rights. Returns rights to author after publication, but reserves the right to reprint in an anthology or any future special collection of Seven Buffaloes Press.
Advice: "Buy a copy to get a feel of the professional quality of the writing. Know the theme of a particular issue. Some contributors have 30 years experience as writers; most 15 years. Age does not matter; quality does."

VALLEY WOMEN'S VOICE, Feminist Newsjournal, (II, IV), 321 Student Union, University of Massachusetts, Amherst MA 01002. (413)545-2436. Newspaper: 16 pages. "Feminist analysis, feminist poetry, stories, health articles, revolution-visionary-action oriented, interviews, book reviews, music/art reviews, profiles and ideas for ongoing columns." For women readers. Monthly. Estab. 1979. Circ. 5,000.

Needs: Ethnic, feminist, lesbian, prose poem, spiritual, women's sports. Any subject "as long as it is feminist — especially news and feature articles. Photos with ms a plus." Plans special summer fiction issue (possible). Receives 3-10 mss/month. Publishes new writers regularly. New women writers encouraged to send their best work. Length: no more than five pages. "Fiction accepted up to 20 pages, but the longer it is, the harder it is for us to print it. Please, double spaced." Also publishes literary essays, literary criticism, poetry.

How to Contact: Send complete ms with cover letter. "Cover letter should include short biographical statement which provides a context for work submitted." SASE. Simultaneous, photocopied and reprint submissions OK. Accepts computer printout submissions. Sample copy $1. Reviews novels and short story collections.

Payment: Pays 1 contributor's copy.

VERVE (II), P.O. Box 3205, Simi Valley CA 93093. (805)527-8824. Editor: Ron Reichick. Fiction Editor: Marilyn Hochheiser. Magazine: Digest-sized, 40 pages, 70 lb. paper, 80 lb. cover, cover illustrations or photographs. "Each issue has a theme." Quarterly. Estab. 1989. Circ. 250.

Needs: Contemporary, experimental, fantasy, humor/satire, literary, mainstream, prose poem. No pornographic material. Upcoming themes: "The Other Side of Winter" (deadline: May 1992); "The Stranger Within" (deadline: August 1992); "Reality and Other Myths" (deadline: November 1992). Receives 100 unsolicited fiction mss/month. Accepts 4-6 mss/issue; 16-24 mss/year. Publishes ms 2 months after acceptance. Length: 1,000 words maximum. Publishes short shorts. Also publishes literary criticism, poetry.

How to Contact: "Request guidelines before submitting manuscript." Reports 4-6 weeks after deadline. SASE. Simultaneous, photocopied and computer printout submissions OK. Sample copy for $3.50. Fiction guidelines for #10 SAE and 1 first-class stamp. Reviews short story collections.

Payment: Pays in contributor's copies.

Terms: Acquires one-time rights.

‡A VERY SMALL MAGAZINE, (Perfect for Pocket or Purse), (I), % Blevins, P.O. Box 221, Greenbelt MD 20770. Editor: Beth Blevins. Magazine: 4×5; 24 pages; illustrations. "We usually publish parodies and humorous pieces — also 'theme' issues — myth, travel, etc. For people who like pocket-sized magazines." Frequency varies. Estab. 1989. Circ. 200.

Needs: Adventure, confession (not true stories stuff), erotica, experimental, humor/satire. "Open to anything interesting, concise and well-written. No romance, bad science fiction, stupid erotica." Upcoming themes: "Holy Babel," based on particular books of the Bible (Spring/Summer 1992); "Elvis/Madonna" (1992). Receives 10-15 unsolicited mss/month. Accepts 1-2 mss/issue. Publishes ms 3 months-1 year after acceptance. Recently published work by Adam Katz-Stone, Kim Kupperman. Length: 250-500 words preferred; 2,000 words maximum. Publishes short shorts. Length: 250-500 words. Sometimes critiques rejected mss (especially if writer requests) and recommends other markets.

How to Contact: Send complete ms with cover letter. Reports in 2 months on queries; 1-6 months on mss. SASE. Simultaneous, photocopied and reprint submissions OK. Accepts computer printout submissions. Sample copy for $1.25.

Payment: Pays free subscription to magazine and contributor's copies.

Terms: Publication is not copyrighted. (Copyright statement in each issue though.)

Advice: Looks for material "that's concise, well-written and refreshingly original (or funny). Go ahead — maybe better to send a query and read a sample issue to see what you're getting into."

VIDEOMANIA, The Video Collectors Newspaper, (I, II), LegsOfStone Publishing Co., Box 47, Princeton WI 54968. (414)295-4377. Editor: Bob Katerzynske. Tabloid; 10½×16; 32+ pages; newsprint paper; ground wood cover; b&w/color illustrations and photographs. "Slanted towards the home entertainment buff, individuals with a *real* interest in home video and entertainment. Publishes *anything* we feel is of interest to our readers — fiction and non-fiction. Audience is mostly male (90%), but female readership is always increasing." Bimonthly. Estab. 1982. Circ. 5-6,000.

Needs: Experimental, fantasy, feminist, horror, humor/satire, lesbian, mainstream, video/film. Plans "All Horror" and "All Music" issues. Receives 3-4 unsolicited mss/month. Buys 1-2 mss/issue; 6-9 mss/year. Publishes ms 2-6 months after acceptance. Length: 800 words maximum; 500 words minimum. Publishes short shorts. Length: 500 words. Sometimes critiques rejected mss and recommends other markets.

How to Contact: Send complete ms with cover letter. Reports in 2-4 weeks. SASE. Computer printout submissions are acceptable. Sample copy for $2.50, 9×12 SAE and $1 postage. Fiction guidelines for #10 SAE and 1 first class stamp.

Payment: Pays $2.50 token payment in certain cases; contributor's copies.
Terms: Pays on publication for all rights or as writer prefers.
Advice: "If the editor likes it, it's in. A good manuscript should not be too heavy; a *touch* of humor goes a long way with us. Don't expect to get rich off of us. On the other hand, we're more willing than other publications to look at the first-time, non-published writer. We've published established writers in the past that wanted to use our publication as sort of a sounding board for something experimental."

THE VILLAGE IDIOT, (II), Mother of Ashes Press, Box 66, Harrison ID 83833-0066. Editor: Joe M. Singer. Magazine: 48 pages; illustrations; photos.
Needs: "A good read—stories, essays, articles, some poetry."
How to Contact: Send complete ms with SASE. Photocopied submissions OK. Accepts computer printouts. Sample copy $3. Reviews novels and short story collections. Send books to Art Droll.
Payment: Pays 2 contributor's copies.
Terms: Acquires one-time rights (copyright for author).

THE VILLAGER, (I,II), 135 Midland Ave., Bronxville NY 10707. (914)337-3252. Editor: Amy Murphy. Fiction Editor: Mrs. Anton Tedesko. Magazine: 28-40 pages. "Magazine for a family audience." Publishes monthly, but for 9-months only—October-June. Estab. 1928. Circ. 1,000.
Needs: Adventure, historical, humor/satire, literary, prose poem, romance (historical), suspense/mystery. Length: Open. Publishes short shorts. Also publishes poetry.
How to Contact: Send complete ms with cover letter. SASE. Sample copy for $1.25.
Payment: Pays 2 contributor's copies.

THE VINCENT BROTHERS REVIEW (II), Vincent Brothers Publishing, 4566 Northern Circle, Mad River Twp., Dayton OH 45424. Editor: Kimberly Willardson. Magazine: 5½ × 8½; 64-84 pages; 60 lb. white coated paper; 60 lb. Oxford (matte) cover; b&w illustrations and photographs. "We publish one theme issue per year. Writers must send SASE for information about upcoming theme issues. Each issue of *TVBR* contains poetry, b&w art, at least 2 short stories and usually 1 book review. For a mainstream audience looking for an alternative to the slicks." Publishes 3 times/year. Estab. 1988. Circ. 400.
Needs: Adventure, condensed/excerpted novel, contemporary, ethnic, experimental, feminist, historical (general), humor/satire, literary, mainstream, prose poem, regional, science fiction, senior citizen/retirement, serialized novel, suspense/mystery, translations. "We don't like to exclude any category—we might very much enjoy a fantasy (or western) story if it is well crafted. We focus on the way the story is presented rather than the genre of the story. No racist, sexist, fascist, etc. work." Upcoming theme: "Bus and Train Travel" (Summer 1992); send SASE for other themes. Receives 50-60 unsolicited mss/month. Buys 2-3 mss/issue; 6-9 mss/year. Publishes ms 2-4 months after acceptance. Recently published work by John Shore, Michael Whitley Turner, and Rafael Alvarez. Length: 2,500 words average; 300 words minimum; 3,500 words maximum. Publishes short shorts. Length: 300-1,000 words. Also publishes literary essays, literary criticism, poetry. Sometimes critiques rejected mss and recommends other markets.
How to Contact: Send complete manuscript with cover letter. Include Social Security number. "Previous publications; if the manuscript should be returned (SASE must be included) or if the manuscript is photocopied." Reports in 3-4 weeks on queries; 4-8 months on mss. SASE. Photocopied submissions OK. Accepts electronic submissions. Sample copy $4.50. Fiction guidelines for #10 SAE and 1 first class stamp. Reviews novels and short story collections.
Payment: Pays $10 minimum and 1 contributor's copy. Charge for extras.
Terms: Buys one-time rights.
Advice: "We are average readers—we want to be hooked immediately and rendered unable to put the story down until we've read the last word of it. I strongly recommend that writers read a sample copy *before* submitting stories to us. Blindly submitting stories to *any* magazine is a foolish habit for a writer to have."

VINTAGE NORTHWEST, (I, IV), Northshore Senior Center (Sponsor), Box 193, Bothell WA 98041. (206)487-1201. Editor: Margie Brons. Magazine: 7 × 8½; 64 pages; illustrations. "We are a senior literary magazine, published by and for seniors. All work done by volunteers except printing." For "all ages who are interested in our seniors' experiences." Published winter and summer. Estab. 1980. Circ. 500.

Needs: Adventure, comedy, condensed novel (1,000 words maximum), fantasy, historical, humor/satire, inspirational, poetry, senior citizen/retirement, suspense/mystery. No religious or political mss. Upcoming themes: "Inspirational" (Summer 1992); "Humor" (Winter 1992). Receives 2-3 unsolicited mss/month. Accepts 2 mss/issue. Recently published work by Dave Kneeshaw, Sylvia Tacker; published new writers within the last year. Length: 1,000 words maximum. Also publishes literary essays. Occasionally critiques rejected mss.
How to Contact: Send complete ms. SASE. Simultaneous, photocopied and previously published submissions OK. Accepts computer printout submissions. Sample copy $2.50. Fiction guidelines with SASE.
Payment: Pays 1 contributor's copy.
Advice: "Our only requirement is that the author be over 50 or physically handicapped when submission is written."

VIRGIN MEAT, (I), 2325 West Ave, K-15, Lancaster CA 93536. (805)722-1758. Editor: Steve Blum. Digest: 5 × 8½; 26 pages. Published "about once every 3 months." Estab. 1987. Circ. 350.
Needs: Horror. Receives 3-4 mss/day. Length: 1,000 words maximum. Also publishes poetry.
How to Contact: Send complete ms with cover letter. Reports in 1 week. Simultaneous, photocopied and reprint submissions OK. Accepts computer printout submissions. Sample copy $2. Reviews novels and short story collections.
Payment: Pays in contributor's copies.
Terms: Acquires one-time rights. Publication not copyrighted.
Advice: "Horror fiction should be horrific all the way through, not just at the end. Avoid common settings, senseless violence and humor. Mildly erotic ok. Do not fold in mailing."

VIRGINIA QUARTERLY REVIEW, (III), One West Range, Charlottesville VA 22903. (804)924-3124. Editor: Staige Blackford. "A national magazine of literature and discussion. A lay, intellectual audience, people who are not out-and-out scholars but who are interested in ideas and literature." Quarterly. Estab. 1925. Circ. 4,500.
Needs: Literary, contemporary, feminist, romance, adventure, humor, ethnic, serialized novels (excerpts) and translations. "No pornography." Buys 3 mss/issue, 20 mss/year. Length: 3,000-7,000 words.
How to Contact: Query or send complete ms. SASE. Reports in 2 weeks on queries, 2 months on mss. Sample copy $5.
Payment: Pays $10/printed page. Offers Emily Clark Balch Award for best published short story of the year.
Terms: Pays on publication for all rights. "Will transfer upon request."
Advice: "Because of the competition, it's difficult for a nonpublished writer to break in."

VISIBILITIES, (IV), P.O. Box 1169, Olney MD 20830-1169. (301)774-8591. Editor: Susan T. Chasin. Magazine: 8 × 11; 32+ pages; coated paper; heavy coated cover stock; illustrations and photographs. "We are an international magazine by and for lesbians." Bimonthly. Estab. 1987. Circ. 8,000.
Needs: Lesbian. No "violence, sexist, racist, agist, etc." Accepts 1 ms/issue. Length: 2,000 words average; 1,000 words minimum. Publishes short shorts. Sometimes critiques rejected mss.
How to Contact: Send complete ms with cover letter, which should include "just basics; name, address, telephone and how you heard about us." Reports in 2 weeks on queries; 3 months on mss. SASE. Accepts computer printout submissions. Sample copy $3; fiction guidelines for #10 SASE.
Payment: Pays contributor's copies; $5 charge for extras.
Terms: Acquires first North American serial rights.
Advice: "We are looking for life-affirming fiction—which tells us how people can live healthy, productive lives as lesbians. This does not preclude stories about painful experiences—but tell us how your characters survive and keep going."

‡VISION, Science Fiction Magazine, (II), 561 Dalton Way, Goleta CA 93117. Editor: Steven B. Joy. Fiction Editor: Roy Smith. Magazine: 5¼ × 8½; 38 pages; bond paper; ledger cover; b&w illustrations. "Sci-Fi in 2,000 words or less." Bimonthly. Estab. 1989.
Needs: Adventure, experimental, fantasy, prose poem, science fiction. No sex, violence, war, horror. Receives 30 unsolicited mss/month. Buys 10-13 mss/issue; 72 mss/year. Publishes ms 2-4 months after acceptance. Agented fiction 1%. Recently published work by Herb Kauderer. Length: 2,000 words preferred; 100 words minimum; 3,000 words maximum. Publishes short shorts. Also publishes poetry. Sometimes critiques rejected mss and recommends other markets.

How to Contact: Send complete ms with cover letter. Include "age, some credits, name of story, word count, where you learned of *VISION*." Reports in 2-3 weeks on queries; 3-4 weeks on ms. SASE. Photocopied and reprint submissions OK. Accepts computer printout submissions. Sample copy for $1.75 and 6×9 SAE with 53¢ postage. Fiction guidelines for #10 SAE and 1 first class stamp.
Payment: Pays $15 maximum, contributor's copies, charges $1 for extras.
Terms: Pays on publication for one-time rights. Sends galleys to author.
Advice: Looks for "1. A good ending; 2. Cause an emotion; 3. Was thought provoking. Our magazine is primarily dedicated to the short, short science fiction story. We are looking for mss from new authors who are especially interested in stories about robots, technology, the future, aliens, bioengineering, computers, cyber-punk, space travel, tear-jerkers, time travel, and science fiction art."

If you'd like to tease your brain,
Or wish to visit someone green...
When your day has gone insane,
Dive into Vision Magazine!

And if your brain is twisted as
You wonder what those visions mean,
Read the next story listed in
The latest Vision Magazine!

And if they take your spaceship key,
And repossess your time machine,
May we suggest a remedy?
Subscribe to Vision Magazine!

SPECIALIZING IN ROBOT STORIES • SHORT, SHORT SCIENCE FICTION
ISSUE NUMBER 8 • $1.75

"Our authors look into many possible futures, and we are able to see through the eyes of their visionary characters," says Roy Smith, who serves Vision Magazine *as both editor and cover illustrator. "Robots play a major role in the future as we see it, so we always include stories about robots, and our cover art always includes robots," he explains. "The robot man on the front of this issue represents gravity: He is designed for serious labor. The robot dog on the back is for levity: He is programmed to play." Overall, Smith says, "The stories in* Vision Magazine *contain serious thoughts, ask serious questions, but they're also fun to read."*

WASCANA REVIEW, (II), University of Regina, Regina, Saskatchewan S4S 0A2 Canada. Editor: Joan Givner. "Literary criticism, fiction and poetry for readers of serious fiction." Semiannually. Estab. 1966. Circ. 500.
Needs: Literary and humor. Buys 6 mss/year. Receives approximately 20 unsolicited fiction mss/month. Approximately 5% of fiction is agented. Length: no requirement. Occasionally recommends other markets.
How to Contact: Send complete ms with SASE. Accepts computer printout submissions. Reports in 2 months on mss. Publishes ms an average of 1 year after acceptance. Sample copy $4. Free guidelines with SAE, IRC.
Payment: Pays $3/page for prose; $10/page for poetry; 2 contributor's copies.
Terms: Pays on publication for all rights.
Advice: "Stories are often technically incompetent or deal with trite subjects. Usually stories are longer than necessary by about one-third. Be more ruthless in cutting back on unnecessary verbiage."

WASHINGTON REVIEW, (II, IV), Friends of the Washington Review of the Arts, Box 50132, Washington DC 20091. (202)638-0515. Fiction Editor: Jeff Richards. "We publish fiction, poetry, articles and reviews on all areas of the arts. We have a particular interest in the interrelationships of the arts and emphasize the cultural life of the DC area." Readership: "Artists, writers and those interested in cultural life in this area." Bimonthly. Estab. 1975. Circ. 10,000.
Needs: Literary. Accepts 1-2 mss/issue. Receives approximately 50-100 unsolicited fiction mss each month. Length: Prefers 3,000 words or less. Critiques rejected mss when there is time.
How to Contact: Send complete ms with SASE. Reports in 2 months. Publishes ms an average of 6 months after acceptance. Copy for tabloid-sized SASE and $2.50.
Payment: Pays contributor's copies plus small payment whenever possible.
Terms: Pays on publication for first North American serial rights.
Advice: "Edit your writing for redundant adjectives. Make sure everything makes sense: the plot, character, motivation. Try to avoid clichés."

WEBSTER REVIEW, (II), Webster Review, Inc., Webster University, 470 E. Lockwood, Webster Groves MO 63119. (314)432-2657. Editor: Nancy Schapiro. Magazine: 5×8; 120 pages; 60 lb. white paper; 10pt. C1S; cover illustrations and photographs. "Literary magazine, international, contemporary. We publish many English translations of foreign fiction writers for academics, writers, discriminating readers." Annually. Estab. 1974.
Needs: Contemporary, literary, translations. No erotica, juvenile. Receives 100 unsolicited mss/month. Accepts 3-5 mss/issue; 6-10 mss/year. Publishes ms one year or more after acceptance. Agented fiction less than 1%. Published work by David Williams and Anjana Appachana. Publishes short shorts. Sometimes critiques rejected mss.
How to Contact: Send complete manuscript with cover letter. Reports in 2-4 months on mss. SASE. Simultaneous and photocopied submissions OK. Accepts computer printouts, "if legible." Sample copy for 6×9 SAE and 2 first class stamps.
Payment: Pays contributor's copies.
Terms: Acquires first rights.

WEIRDBOOK, (II), Box 149, Amherst Branch, Buffalo NY 14226. Editor: W. Paul Ganley. Magazine: 8½×11; 64 pages; self cover; illustrations. "Latter day 'pulp magazine' along the lines of the old pulp magazine *Weird Tales*. We tend to use established writers. We look for an audience of fairly literate people who like good writing and good characterization in their fantasy and horror fiction, but are tired of the clichés in the field." Semiannually. Estab. 1968. Circ. 1,000.
Needs: *Presently overstocked. Inquire first.* Psychic/supernatural, fantasy, horror and gothic (not modern). No psychological horror; mystery fiction; physical horror (blood); traditional ghost stories (unless original theme); science fiction; swords and sorcery without a supernatural element; or reincarnation stories that conclude with 'And the doctor patted him on . . . THE END!' " Buys 8-12 mss/issue. Length: 15,000 words maximum. Also publishes poetry. Sometimes recommends other markets.
How to Contact: Send complete ms with SASE. Reports in 3 months on mss. Sample copy $6.80. Guidelines for #10 SASE.
Payment: Pays 1¢/word minimum and 1 contributor's copy.
Terms: Pays on publication ("part on acceptance only for solicited mss") for first North American serial rights plus right to reprint the entire issue.
Advice: "Read a copy and then some of the best anthologies in the field (such as DAW's 'Best Horror of the Year,' Arkham House anthologies, etc.) Occasionally we keep mss longer than planned. When sending a SASE marked 'book rate' (or anything not first class) the writer should add 'Forwarding Postage Guaranteed.' "

WELTER, (I, II), University of Baltimore, 1420 N. Charles St., Baltimore MD 21201-5779. (301)625-3270. Editor: Linda Haller. Magazine: Digest-sized; 75 pages; matte cover; illustrations and photographs. "We publish poetry and fiction. No special theme. We hold a slight bias for local authors, both new and established." Annually. Estab. 1967. Circ. 500 (approx.)
Needs: Contemporary, literary. No genre or category fiction. Accepts 2-3 mss/issue. Does not read mss May-September. Publishes ms approx. 2 months after acceptance. Recently published work by Penny Graf, Stephen Matanle, Sarah Mayfield. Length: 3-5 typed (double-spaced) pages maximum. Publishes short shorts. Also publishes poetry.

How to Contact: Send complete manuscript with cover letter. "Bio (3 lines); SASE always." Reports in 1-3 months. Sample copy $2.
Payment: Pays 2 contributor's copies.
Terms: Acquires one-time rights.
Advice: "We look for fine writing. Send only your best work. We encourage new writers to submit, but don't blow your chances by sending sloppy, unprofessional mss. Revise. Rest, then revise some more. Most of all, have fun doing it. Make us care about your characters. We can't care about them unless you do."

WEST BRANCH, (II), Bucknell Hall, Bucknell University, Lewisburg PA 17837. Editors: K. Patten and R. Taylor. Magazine: 5½ × 8½; 96-120 pages; quality paper; illustrations; photos. Fiction and poetry for readers of contemporary literature. Biannually. Estab. 1977. Circ. 500.
Needs: Literary, contemporary, prose poems and translations. No science fiction. Accepts 3-6 mss/issue. Recently published work by Elaine Menge, John Sandman, Harry Val; published new writers within the last year. No preferred length.
How to Contact: Send complete ms with cover letter, "with information about writer's background, previous publications, etc." SASE. Reports in 6 weeks on mss. Sample copy $3.
Payment: Pays 2 contributor's copies and one-year subscription; cover price less 20% discount charge for extras.
Terms: Acquires first rights.
Advice: "Narrative art fulfills a basic human need—our dreams attest to this—and storytelling is therefore a high calling in any age. Find your own voice and vision. Make a story that speaks to your own mysteries. Cultivate simplicity in form, complexity in theme. Look and listen through your characters."

WESTVIEW, A Journal of Western Oklahoma, (I, II), Southwestern Oklahoma State University, 100 Campus Dr., Weatherford OK 73096. (405)774-3077. Editor: Dr. Leroy Thomas. Magazine: 8½ × 11; up to 44 pages; 24 lb. paper; slick cover; illustrations and photographs. "Various themes for people who like nostalgia." Quarterly. Estab. 1981. Circ. 800.
Needs: Experimental, historical (general), literary, mainstream, western. "The subject must be Western Oklahoma—west of Interstate 35." Upcoming themes: All Western Oklahoma—"Relatives/Kinfolk" (Spring 1992); "Daydreams/Illusions" (Summer 1992); "Dustbowl Days" (Fall 1992); "Colorful Characters" (Winter 1992). Receives 2-5 unsolicited mss/month. Accepts 10 ms/issue; 40 mss/year. Publishes ms 1 month-2 years after acceptance. Published work by Orv Owens, Leroy Thomas and Margie Snowden North. Length: 2,000 words average; 1,000 words minimum; 3,000 words maximum. Publishes short shorts. Length: 400 words. Also publishes literary essays, literary criticism, poetry. Always critiques rejected mss and sometimes recommends other markets.
How to Contact: Query first. Reports in 3 weeks on queries. SASE. Accepts computer printout submissions. Sample copy for $4 and 9 × 12 SAE. Fiction guidelines for #10 SAE and 1 first class stamp. Reviews novels and short story collections.
Payment: Pays contributor's copies.
Terms: Acquires first rights.
Advice: "Write for a copy of our stylesheet and for our list of themes for future issues. Don't neglect the SASE."

WHETSTONE, (II), English Dept., University of Lethbridge, Lethbridge, Alberta T1K 3M4 Canada. (403)329-2367. Contact: Editor. Magazine: approximately 6 × 9; 48-64 pages; superbond paper; photos. Magazine publishing "poetry, prose, drama, prints, photographs and occasional music compositions for a university audience." Twice yearly. Estab. 1971. Circ. 500.
Needs: Experimental, literary and mainstream. "Interested in works by native writers/artists. Interested in multi-media works by individuals or collaborators. Yearly writing contest with cash prizes." Upcoming theme: "Typically marginalized writers will be our focus for upcoming season." Receives 1 unsolicited fiction ms/month. Accepts 1-2 ms/issue, 3-4 mss/year. Does not read May through August. Published new writers within the last year. Length: 12 double-spaced pages maximum. Also publishes literary essays, literary criticism, poetry.
How to Contact: Send complete ms with SASE, or SAE with IRC and cover letter with author's background and experience. Simultaneous and photocopied submissions OK. Accepts computer printout submissions. Reports in 5 months on mss. Publishes ms an average of 3-4 months after acceptance. Sample copy $5 (Canadian) and 7½ × 10½ or larger SAE and 2 Canadian first class stamps or IRCs.

Payment: Pays 2 contributor's copies.
Terms: Acquires no rights.
Advice: "We seek most styles of quality writing. Avoid moralizing."

WHISKEY ISLAND MAGAZINE, University Center 365, Cleveland State University, Cleveland OH 44115. (216)687-2056. Editor: Cynthia Meyer Sabik. Magazine of fiction, poetry, photography with no specific theme. Published 2 times/year. Estab. 1978. Circ. 2,500.
Needs: Receives 20-30 unsolicited fiction mss/month. Acquires 3-4 mss/issue. Length: 5,000 words maximum; 2,000-3,000 words average. Also publishes poetry.
How to Contact: Send complete ms with SASE. No simultaneous or previously published submissions. Reports in 2 months on mss. Sample copy $3.
Payment: Pays 2 contributor's copies.
Terms: Acquires one-time rights.
Advice: "Please include brief bio."

THE JAMES WHITE REVIEW, A Gay Men's Literary Quarterly, (II, IV), The James White Review Association, 3356 Traffic Station, Minneapolis MN 55403. (612)291-2913. Editor: Collective of 3. Tabloid: 17×26; 16 pages; illustrations; photos. "We publish work by *male* gay writers—any subject for primarily gay and/or gay sensitive audience." Quarterly. Estab. 1983. Circ. 3,500.
Needs: Contemporary, adventure, experimental, gay, humor/satire, literary, prose poem, translations. No pornography. Receives 50 unsolicited fiction mss/month. Accepts 3 mss/issue; 12 mss/year. Publishes ms 3 months or sooner after acceptance. Recently published work by Felice Picano, George Stambolian; published new writers within the last year. Length: 22 pages, double spaced. Sometimes critiques rejected mss. Recommends other markets "when we can."
How to Contact: Send complete ms with cover letter with short bio. SASE. Reports in 2-3 months. SASE for ms. Photocopied submissions OK. Sample copy $3. Fiction guidelines $1.
Payment: Pays 3 contributor's copies and $25.
Terms: Buys one-time rights; returns rights to author.

WHITE WALL REVIEW, 63 Gould St., Toronto, Ontario M5B 1E9 Canada. Editor: Changes annually. Magazine: 5¾×8¾; 160 pages; Zephyr Antique paper; soft cover, glossy; two-tone illustrations; b&w photographs. "Book of poetry, prose, art, plays, music and photography. Publishes unknown, international and professional writers. For international audience." Annually. Estab. 1976. Circ. 800.
Needs: "No content 'requirements.' " Must be reasonably short. Nothing "spawning hate, prejudice or obscenity." Accepts 100+ mss/book. Published work by Steven Heighton, Robert Hough, Ruth Olsen Latta; published new writers within the last year. Also publishes poetry.
How to Contact: Send complete ms with cover letter. "The cover letter should contain important information about why the writer is submitting to our publication, where he/she saw our information and some biographical information." Reports on mss "when accepted." SASE or SAE and IRC for ms. Simultaneous and photocopied submissions OK. Accepts computer printout submissions. Sample copy $6 plus $1 for postage and handling.
Payment: Pays 1 contributor's copy.
Terms: Acquires first or one-time rights.
Advice: "Keep it *short*. We look for creativity but not to the point of obscurity."

THE WIDENER REVIEW, (III), Widener University, 14th and Chesnut Sts., Chester PA 19013. (215)499-4341. Fiction editor: Michael Clark. Magazine: 5¼×8½; 80 pages. Fiction, poetry, essays, book reviews for general audience. Annually. Estab. 1984. Circ. 250.
Needs: Contemporary, experimental, literary, mainstream, regional, serialized/excerpted novel. Receives 15 unsolicited mss/month. Publishes 3-4 mss/issue. Does not read mss in summer. Publishes ms 3-9 months after acceptance. Length: 1,000 words minimum; 5,000 words maximum. Occasionally critiques rejected mss.

Market categories: (I) Beginning; (II) General; (III) Prestige; (IV) Specialized.

How to Contact: Send complete ms with cover letter. Reports in 3 months on mss. Deadline for submission: March 15, notification by June 15. SASE for ms. No simultaneous or photocopied submissions or reprints. Accepts computer printouts. Sample copy $4. Fiction guidelines for #10 SAE and first class stamp.
Payment: Pays 1 contributor's copy; charge for extras.
Terms: Acquires first serial rights.

‡THE WILLIAM AND MARY REVIEW, (II), The College of William and Mary, Williamsburg VA 23185. Editor: Alexandra Nemecek. Magazine: 100 pages; graphics; photography. "We publish high quality fiction, poetry, essays, interviews with writers and art. Our audience is primarily academic." Annually. Estab. 1962. Circ. 3,500.
Needs: Literary, contemporary and humor. Receives approximately 90 unsolicited fiction mss each month. Accepts 9 mss/issue. Published work by Paul Wood, W.S. Penn and Dana Gioia; published new writers within the last year. Length: 7,000 words maximum. Also publishes poetry. Usually critiques rejected mss.
How to Contact: Send complete ms with SASE and cover letter with name, address and phone number. "Cover letter should be as brief as possible." Reports in 2 months. Fiction department closed in June, July and August. Sample copy $5. May review novels and short story collections.
Payment: Pays 5 contributor's copies.
Terms: Acquires first rights.
Advice: "We want original, well written stories. Staff requests names be attached separately to individual works. Page allotment to fiction will rise in relation to quality fiction received. The most important aspect of submitting ms is to be familiar with the publication and the types of material it accepts. For this reason, back copies are available."

‡WILLOW REVIEW, (II), College of Lake County, 19351 West Washington St., Grayslake IL 60030. (708)223-6601 ext. 550 or 555. Editor: Paulette Roeske. Magazine: 6×9; 68-76 pages; 70 lb. paper; 80 lb. cover; b&w illustrations and photographs. "*Willow Review* is nonthematic and publishes short fiction, memoir, poetry, photographs and b&w artwork. For a general and literary adult audience." Annually. Estab. 1969. Circ. 1,000.
Needs: Contemporary, ethnic, experimental, feminist, historical, humor/satire, literary, prose poem, regional. "There is no bias against an particular subject matter, although there is a clear editorial preference for literary fiction." No "popular genre fiction; children/young adult." Plans special fiction issue. Receives 50 unsolicited mss/month. Buys 7-8 mss/issue. Does not read mss June-August. Accepted mss published in April of each year. Recently published work by Larry Starzec, Vesle Fenstermaker, Neal Lulofs. Length: 1,500 words minimum; 3,500 words maximum. Publishes short shorts. Length: 500 words. Sometimes comments on rejected mss and recommends other markets.
How to Contact: Send complete ms with cover letter. Include Social Security number, complete mailing address, telephone number, list of several previous publications, other recognition (awards, etc. if applicable). Reports in 1-2 months on mss. SASE (if writer would like it returned). Photocopied submissions OK. Accepts computer printout submissions. Sample copy for $3. Fiction guidelines for #10 SAE and 1 first class stamp.
Payment: Pays contributor's copies to $100 maximum. All manuscripts are automatically considered for the annual *Willow Review* awards: $100 for first place, $50 for second and $25 for third.
Terms: Pays on publication for first North American serial rights. Not copyrighted.
Advice: "*Willow Review*, because of its 68-76 page length, is forced to make word count a factor although we would publish an exceptional story which exceeds our recommended length. Beyond that, literary excellence is our sole criteria. Perhaps voice, more thanany other factor, causes a manuscript to stand out. Study the craft—read the best little magazines, subscribe to them, maintain contact with other writers through writer's groups or informally, attend fiction readings and ask the writers questions in the discussion periods which typically follow,read Eudora Welty's *One Writer's Beginnings* or John Gardner's *On Becoming a Novelist* or Flannery O'Connor on writing fiction or the articles in *Poets & Writers*. Consider writing a discipline, a field of study—it won't kill 'inspiration' or 'creativity' but will augment it to help you write the best story you can write."

WILLOW SPRINGS, (II, III), MS-1, Eastern Washington University, Cheney WA 99004. (509)458-6424. Editor: Nance Van Winckel. Semiannually. Estab. 1977. Circ. 1,000.
Needs: Parts of novels, short stories, literary, prose poems, poems and translations. Receives 70 unsolicited mss/month. Accepts 3-4 mss/issue; 6-8 mss/year. Published work by Brett Lott, Andrea Barrett, Jay Neugeboren; published new writers within the last year. Length: 5,000 words maximum. Rarely critiques rejected mss.

How to Contact: Send complete ms with SASE. Photocopied submissions O[...] submissions. Reports in 2-3 months on mss. Publishes ms an average of 1-6 months a[...] Sample copy for $4.

Payment: Pays 2 contributor's copies; plus small honorarium.

Terms: Acquires first North American rights.

Advice: "We hope to attract good fiction writers to our magazine, and we've made a commitme[...] publish four stories per issue. We like fiction that exhibits a fresh approach to language. Our m[...] recent issues, we feel, indicate the quality and level of our commitment."

WIND MAGAZINE, Rt. 1, Box 809K, Pikeville KY 41501. (606)631-1129. Editor: Quentin R. Howard. Magazine: 5½×8½; 86+ pages. "Literary journal with stories, poems, book reviews from the small presses and some university presses. Readership is students, literary people, professors, housewives and others." Published irregularly. Estab. 1971. Circ. 500.

Needs: Literary and regional. "No restriction on form, content or subject." Published work by Anabel Thomas, Peter LaSalle and Mary Clearman Bleu; published new writers within the last year. Length: no minimum; 5,000 words maximum. Critiques rejected mss when there is time.

How to Contact: Send complete ms with SASE. Photocopied submissions OK. Accepts computer printout submissions. Reports in 1 month. Publishes ms an average of 1 year after acceptance. Sample copy $2.50.

Payment: Pays contributor's copies. $1.50 charge for extras.

Terms: Acquires first rights. Publication not copyrighted.

Advice: "We're constantly looking for beginning fiction writers. Diversity is one of our major editorial goals. No multiple submissions, please. We have no taboos, but set our own standards on reading each ms."

WISCONSIN ACADEMY REVIEW, (II, IV), Wisconsin Academy of Sciences, Arts & Letters, 1922 University Ave., Madison WI 53705. (608)263-1692. Editor-in-Chief: Faith B. Miracle. Magazine: 8½×11; 48-52 pages; 75 lb. coated paper; coated cover stock; illustrations; photos. "The *Review* reflects the focus of the sponsoring institution with its editorial emphasis on Wisconsin's intellectual, cultural, social and physical environment. It features short fiction, poetry, essays and Wisconsin-related book reviews for well-educated, well-traveled people interested in furthering regional arts and literature and disseminating information about sciences." Quarterly. Estab. 1954. Circ. 2,000.

Needs: Experimental, historical (general), humor/satire, literary, mainstream, prose poem. "Author must have lived or be living in Wisconsin or fiction must be set in Wisconsin." Receives 5-6 unsolicited fiction mss/month. Accepts 1-2 mss/issue; 6-8 mss/year. Published new writers within the last year. Length: 1,000 words minimum; 4,000 words maximum; 3,000 words average. Also publishes poetry; "will consider" literary essays, literary criticism.

How to Contact: Send complete ms with SAE and state author's connection to Wisconsin, the prerequisite. Photocopied submissions OK. Accepts computer printout submissions. Publishes ms an average of 6-9 months after acceptance. Sample copy $2. Fiction guidelines for SAE and 1 first class stamp. Reviews books on Wisconsin themes.

Payment: Pays 5 contributor's copies.

Terms: Pays on publication for first rights.

THE WISCONSIN RESTAURATEUR, (I, II), Wisconsin Restaurant Association, 125 W. Doty, Madison WI 53703. (608)251-3663. Editor: Jan LaRue. Magazine: 8½×11; 80 pages; 80 lb. enamel cover stock; illustrations; photos. "Published for foodservice operators in the state of Wisconsin and for suppliers of those operations. Theme is the promotion, protection and improvement of the foodservice industry for foodservice workers, students, operators and suppliers." Monthly except December/January combined. Estab. 1933. Circ. 4,200.

Needs: Literary, contemporary, feminist, science fiction, regional, western, mystery, adventure, humor, juvenile and young adult. "Only exceptional fiction material used. No stories accepted that put down persons in the foodservice business or poke fun at any group of people. No off-color material. No religious, no political." Buys 1-2 mss/issue, 12-24 mss/year. Receives 15-20 unsolicited fiction mss/month. Length: 500-2,500 words. Critiques rejected mss "when there is time."

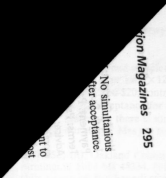

No simultaneous after acceptance.

...th SASE. Accepts computer printout submissions. Reports in ... Guidelines for SASE.

... copy; 50¢ charge for extra copy.

...ts and first North American serial rights.

...of lesson to be learned, a humorous aspect, or some kind of ...ecause they are not written for the restaurateur/reader.

...lege, Orchard Ridge Campus, 27055 Orchard Lake Road, ...32. Editor: Peter Stine. Magazine: 6×9; 160 pages; 60 lb. ...tions and photos. "Fiction, poetry, essays that highlight the ...e times." Tri-annually. Estab. 1987. Circ. 3,000.

...........sed/excerpted novel, contemporary, experimental, fantasy, feminist, literary and sports. "Alternate special or thematic issues: consult back issues or write for themes." Plans to publish a special fiction issue or an anthology in the future. Receives 150 unsolicited mss/month. Buys 10 mss/issue; 40 mss/year. Publishes ms 3 months-1 year after acceptance. Agented fiction 20%. Published work by Joyce Carol Oates, Amy Hempel and Richard Currey. Length: 3,500 words average. Publishes short shorts—500 words. Sometimes critiques mss.

How to Contact: Send complete ms with cover letter. Reports in 3 months on mss. SASE. Simultaneous and photocopied submissions OK. Accepts computer printout submissions. Accepts electronic submissions. Sample copy $5. Fiction guidelines for #10 SAE and 1 first class stamp.

Payment: Pays $6/page minimum and contributor's copies.

Terms: Pays on publication for first North American serial rights.

Advice: Looks for "intelligence, compassion, lucidity, original voice. *Witness* blends features of literary and issue-oriented magazine and highlights the writer as witness. Alternate special issues (*Holocaust, Writings from Prison, Sixties,* etc.)"

WOMAN OF POWER, A Magazine of Feminism, Spirituality, and Politics, (II, IV), P.O. Box 2785, Orleans MA 02653. (508)240-7877. Editor: Char McKee. Magazine: 8½×11; 88 pages; 60 lb. offset stock; 60 lb. glossy cover; illustrations and photos. Quarterly. Estab. 1984. Circ. 15,000.

Needs: Ethnic, experimental, fantasy, feminist, humor/satire, lesbian, literary, psychic/supernatural/occult, religious/inspirational, science fiction, senior citizen/retirement, women's, young adult/teen. "We print works by women only." Upcoming themes: "Women in Community," "Sacred Spaces," "Leadership: Feminist, Spiritual and Political," "Language." Receives 20 unsolicited mss/month. Accepts 1 or 2 mss/issue. Publishes ms 3-6 months after acceptance. Published new writers within the last year. Length: 1,000 words minimum; 3,500 words maximum. Publishes short shorts. Sometimes critiques rejected mss. Sometimes recommends other markets.

How to Contact: Send complete ms with cover letter, which should include "a short biography and reasons for submitting." Reports in 2 weeks on queries; 3 months on mss. SASE. Simultaneous, photocopied and reprint submissions OK. Computer printout submissions acceptable. Sample copy $7. Fiction guidelines for #10 SAE and 1 first class stamp.

Payment: Pays 2 contributor's copies and 1-year subscription.

Terms: Acquires one-time rights. Sends galleys to author on request. Rights revert to authors.

Advice: "It is imperative that women read our magazine before submitting. We have a very *specific* focus which is related to women's spirituality and is best understood by studying past issues. And all materials must directly relate to one of our themes. We print high quality photographs and artwork by women."

THE WORCESTER REVIEW, Worcester Country Poetry Association, Inc., 6 Chatham St., Worcester MA 01609. Editor: Rodger Martin. Magazine: 6×9; 60-100 pages; 60 lb. white offset paper; 10 pt. C1S cover stock; illustrations and photos. "We like high quality, creative poetry, artwork and fiction. Critical articles should be connected to New England." Semiannually. Estab. 1972. Circ. 1,000.

Needs: Literary, prose poem. "We encourage New England writers in the hopes we will publish at least 30% New England but want the other 70% to show the best of writing from across the US." Receives 10-20 unsolicited fiction mss/month. Accepts 2-4 mss/issue. Publishes ms an average of 6 months to 1 year after acceptance. Agented fiction less than 10%. Published work by Debra Friedman, Carol Glickfeld. Length: 2,000 words average; 1,000 words minimum; 4,000 words maximum. Publishes short shorts. Also publishes literary essays, literary criticism, poetry. Sometimes critiques rejected mss and recommends other markets.

How to Contact: Send complete ms with cover letter. Reports in 2 weeks on queries; 4-5 months on mss. SASE. Simultaneous submissions OK if other markets are clearly identified. Accepts computer printout submissions. Sample copy $4; fiction guidelines free.
Payment: Pays 2 contributor's copies and honorarium if possible.
Terms: Acquires one-time rights.
Advice: "Send only one short story—reading editors do not like to read two by the same author at the same time. We will use only one. We generally look for creative work with a blend of craftsmanship, insight and empathy. This does not exclude humor. We won't print work that is shoddy in any of these areas."

WORDS OF WISDOM, (II), 612 Front St., Glendora NJ 08029-1133. (609)863-0610. Editor: J.M. Freiermuth. Newsletter: 5½ × 8½; 20-36 pages; copy paper; some illustrations and photographs. "Fiction, satire, poetry and travel for a general audience —90% of readers have B.A." Monthly. Estab. 1981. Circ. 150.
Needs: Adventure, contemporary, erotica, ethnic, feminist, historical (general), humor/satire, mainstream, regional, suspense/mystery, western. No religion, children's, gay, romance. Plans special West Coast fiction issue. Receives 5-10 unsolicited mss/month. Accepts 2-4 mss/issue; 25-35 mss/year. Publishes ms 2-4 months after acceptance. Recently published work by Jerry Doernberg, Jim Sullivan, Beez Rising. Length: 2,000-3,000 words average; 1,200 words minimum; 6,000 words maximum. Publishes short shorts. Length: "Long enough to develop a good bite." Sometimes critiques rejected mss and recommends other markets.
How to Contact: Send complete manuscript copy and/or DOS floppy with cover letter including "name, address, SASE." Reports in 2-3 weeks on mss. SASE. Simultaneous, photocopied and reprint submissions OK. Accepts computer printout and electronic submissions. Sample copy for $1, 6 × 9 SAE and 75¢ postage. Reviews novels and short story collections.
Payment: Pays free subscription to magazine and contributor's copies.
Terms: Acquires one-time rights. Publication not copyrighted.

‡WORDSMITH, (I), Box 891, Ft. Collins CO 80522-0891. Editor: Brian Kaufman. Magazine: Digest-sized; 40 pages; 60 lb. paper; glossy cover. Annually. Estab. 1992. Circ. 300.
Needs: Adventure, condensed/excerpted novel, contemporary, ethnic, experimental, fantasy, historical (general), horror, humor/satire, literary, mainstream, prose poem, psychic/supernatural/occult, religious/inspirational, romance, science fiction, senior citizen/retirement, serialized novel, sports, suspense/mystery, western, young adult/teen. "We'll look at almost anything. Please, no gay/lesbian, erotica or porno. There are plenty of publications earmarked for those forms." Buys 4-5 mss/issue. Publishes short shorts. Length: 500 words. Always critiques rejected mss and recommends other markets.
How to Contact: Send complete manuscript with cover letter. Include "short bio, credits, (if any)." SASE. Photocopied submissions OK. Accepts computer printout submissions. Sample copy for $3. Fiction guidelines free.
Payment: Pays $10 minimum.
Terms: Pays on publication for one-time rights.
Advice: "Truth strikes us like a hammer. Manuscripts that are poorly prepared, lack spelling skills and punctuation are disqualified and make our editorial task easier. When we read a piece, we want to be amazed. Be it the characters, or the plot, or the rythm of the words, let us see quality in your work."

‡WORM, (I), Macronex, 115 Grand St., Brooklyn NY 11211. Editor: Kit Blake. Newsletter: 8½ × 11; 10 pages; 20 lb. paper; illustrations and photographs. "Cultural magazine for a varied audience." Monthly. Estab. 1991.
Needs: Contemporary, erotica, ethnic, experimental, gay, historical, humor/satire, lesbian, literary, science fiction. No fantasy, romance, sports. Publishes special fiction issue. Receives 2 unsolicited mss/month. Accepts 1 mss/issue; 12 mss/year. Recently published work by Ian Keldoulis, David Brody. Length: 2,000 words preferred; 300 words minimum; 3,000 words maximum. Publishes short shorts. Length: 300-500 words. Recommends other markets.

Read the Business of Fiction section to learn the correct way to prepare and submit a manuscript.

How to Contact: Send complete ms with cover letter. Reports in 3 weeks on queries; 1 month on mss. SASE. Simultaneous, photocopied and reprint submissions OK. Accepts computer printout submissions. Accepts electronic submissions via disk or modem (Mac format preferred). Sample copy for $1.

Payment: Pays contributor's copies.

Terms: Acquires one-time rights. Not copyrighted.

Advice: Looks for "otherworldliness. Write a micro model for a macro world."

THE WORMWOOD REVIEW, (II, IV), P.O. Box 4698, Stockton CA 95204. (209)466-8231. Editor: Marvin Malone. Magazine: 5½×8½; 48 pages; 60 lb. matte paper; 80 lb. matte cover; illustrations. "Concentrated on the prose-poem specifically for literate audience." Quarterly. Estab. 1959. Circ. 700.

Needs: Prose poem. No religious or inspirational. Receives 500-600 unsolicited fiction mss/month. Buys 30-40 mss/issue; 120-160 mss/year. Publishes ms 6-18 months after acceptance. Published work by Charles Bukowski, Dan Lenihan. Length: 300 words preferred; 1,000 words maximum. Publishes short shorts. Critiques or comments on rejected mss. Recommends other markets.

How to Contact: Send complete ms with cover letter. Reports in 1-3 months. SASE. Photocopied submissions OK. Sample copy for $4. Fiction guidelines for #10 SAE and 1 first-class stamp.

Payment: Pays $12-140 or equivalent in contributor's copies.

Terms: Pays on publication for all rights.

Advice: A manuscript that stands out has "economical verbal style coupled with perception and human values. Have something to say—then say it in the most economical way. Do *not* avoid wit and humor."

WRIT MAGAZINE, (II), 2 Sussex Ave., Toronto, Ontario M5S 1J5 Canada. (416)978-4871. Editor: Roger Greenwald. Assoc. Editor: Richard Lush. Magazine: 6×9; 96 pages; Zephyr laid paper; cover stock varies; cover illustrations. "Literary magazine for literate readers interested in the work of new writers." Annually. Publishes occasional special fiction issues. Estab. 1970. Circ. 700.

Needs: Literary, short stories, short shorts, parts of novels, translations. Accepts 10-15 mss/year. Does not read mss in summer. Published fiction by Leon Rooke, Nawal El Saadawi, Michael Stephens; published new writers in the last year. Length: 300-20,000 words. Critiques rejected mss "when there is time. Sometimes recommends other markets."

How to Contact: Send complete ms with SASE (Canadian stamps or IRCs) and brief biographical note on author and/or translator, and a phone number. Translators must send copy of original text. Accepts computer printout submissions. Reports in 2-3 months. Sample copy $7.50.

Payment: Pays 2 contributor's copies. Negotiates charge for extras.

Terms: Acquires first North American serial rights. Copyright reverts to author.

Advice: "Look at your target magazine before submitting."

THE WRITERS' BAR-B-Q (II), 924 Bryn Mawr, Springfield IL 62703. (217)525-6987. Fiction Editors: Tim Osburn, Becky Bradway, Martha Miller, Myra Epping. Magazine: 8½×11; 110 pages; slick cover stock with full-page photo; illustrations and photos. "*The Writers' Bar-B-Q* is a fiction magazine that is looking for unpretentious, fun, exciting writing. A good story with purpose and well-drawn characters is more important to us than clever phrasing. We want writing that shows the author cares, and has something to say." Semiannually. Estab. 1987. Circ. 1,000.

Needs: Adventure, contemporary, erotica, ethnic, experimental, fantasy, feminist, gay, historical (general), horror, humor/satire, lesbian, literary, mainstream, psychic/supernatural/occult, regional, science fiction, serialized/excerpted novel, suspense/mystery, translations. "Display a strong personal voice, a unique view of the world, and a sense of commitment and caring toward the characters and subject. We publish novel excerpts, long stories and plays as well as shorter pieces. We are looking for inventiveness, humor and insight. No formulas—whether they be genre formulas or academic formulas. We do not publish poetry." Receives 150 unsolicited fiction mss/month. Accepts 15-20 mss/issue; 30-40 mss/year. Will not read mss until August 31, 1992. Publishes ms 6 months to 1 year after acceptance. Recently published work by Florri McMillan, David Williams, James Plath; published new writers within the last year. Length: 500-15,000 words. Sometimes critiques rejected mss.

How to Contact: Send complete ms with cover letter. Reports in 6 weeks-4 months on mss. SASE. Simultaneous and photocopied submissions OK. Accepts computer printout submissions. Sample copy $5.

Payment: Pays 3 contributor's copies.
Terms: Acquires first rights. Rights revert upon publication.
Advice: "Please make sure your work is thoughtfully edited. We have returned many stories that would have been good if given more careful attention by the writer. *The Writers' Bar-B-Q* publishes fiction with spirit and energy, with an emphasis on characterization and story over style."

WRITERS' FORUM, (II), University of Colorado at Colorado Springs, Colorado Springs CO 80933-7150. Editor: Dr. Alex Blackburn. "Ten to fifteen short stories or self-contained novel excerpts published once a year along with 25-35 poems. Funded by grants from National Endowment for the Arts, Council for Literary Magazines, University of Colorado and others. Highest literary quality only: mainstream, avant-garde, with preference to western themes. For small press enthusiasts, teachers and students of creative writing, commercial agents/publishers, university libraries and departments interested in contemporary American literature." Estab. 1974.
Needs: Literary, contemporary, ethnic (Native American, Chicano, not excluding others) and regional (West). No "sentimental, over-plotted, pornographic, anecdotal, polemical, trendy, disguised autobiographical, fantasy (sexual, extra-terrestrial), pseudo-philosophical, passionless, placeless, undramatized, etc. material." Accepts 10-12 mss/issue. Receives approximately 40 unsolicited fiction mss each month and will publish new as well as experienced authors. Recently published fiction by Robert Olen Butler, Charles Baxter, Gladys Swan; published many new writers within the last year. Length: 1,500-10,000 words. Also publishes literary essays, literary criticism, poetry. Critiques rejected mss "when there is time and perceived merit."
How to Contact: Send complete ms and letter with relevant career information with SASE. Accepts computer printout submissions. Reports in 3-5 weeks on mss. Publishes ms an average of 6 months after acceptance. Sample back copy $7 to *NSSWM* readers. Current copy $10.
Payment: Pays 1 contributor's copy. Cover price less 60% discount for extras.
Terms: Acquires one-time rights. Rights revert to author.
Advice: "Read our publication. Be prepared for constructive criticism. We especially seek submissions that show immersion in place (trans-Mississippi West) and development of credible characters. Turned off by slick 'decadent' New York-ish content. Probably the TV-influenced fiction is the most quickly rejected. Our format—a 5½ × 8½ professionally edited and printed paperback book—lends credibility to authors published in our imprint."

‡WRITER'S GUIDELINES, A Roundtable for Writers and Editors, (II), Box 608, Pittsburg MO 65724. Editor: Susan Salaki. Magazine: 8½ × 11; 30 pages; 20 lb. paper; 70 lb. cover; illustrations. "We publish all genres of fiction and showcase the story. Fiction published in *WG* is automatically eligible for selection in the Street Songs anthology of 20 best stories published in small press." Bimonthly. Estab. 1988. Circ. 750.
Needs: Adventure, condensed/excerpted novel, confession, contemporary, ethnic, experimental, fantasy, feminist, historical (general), horror, humor/satire, literary, mainstream, prose poem, psychic/supernatural/occult, regional, religious/inspirational, romance, science fiction, senior citizen/retirement, serialized novel, suspense/mystery, western. Receives 30 unsolicited mss/month. Accepts 1 ms/issue; 6 mss/year. Publishes ms 2 months after acceptance. Length: 700 words preferred; 500 words minimum; 800 words maximum. Publishes short shorts. Length: 200-500 words. Sometimes critiques rejected mss and recommends other markets.
How to Contact: Send complete ms with cover letter. Reports in 1 week on queries; 1 month on mss. SASE. Photocopied submissions OK. Accepts computer printout submissions. Sample copy for $4. Fiction guidelines for SASE.
Payment: Pays contributor's copies.
Terms: Acquires one-time rights.
Advice: "At *Writer's Guidelines,* we select our fiction solely on the basis of quality. The instant we become confused as to time, place or character development, the ms is returned as unacceptable. If the author has successfully created a vivid character and through that character elicits an emotional reaction, or comes close to doing so, we either accept the story or offer some tips on how to do another draft that will succeed. One tip we often give is this: When writing fiction, assume your readers are blind. The only way they are going to see what is going on in your story is to describe it for them in

great detail. Some of the best stories we read incorporate all five senses repeatedly throughout the story."

WRITERS' RENDEZVOUS, (I), P.O. Box 105, Sacramento CA 95812. Editor: Karen Campbell. Newsletter: 8½×11; approx. 24 pages; bond paper; no cover; line drawings. "Writer-oriented, publish only work relating to freelance writing and penpalling." Quarterly. Estab. 1986. Circ. 100.
Needs: No fiction "not related to writing/penpalling. No erotica!!" Receives approx. 10 unsolicited fiction mss/month. Publishes approx. 2 mss/issue; approx. 10 mss/year. Publishes ms 6 weeks-1 year after acceptance. Published work by Bettye Griffin, Jan McDaniel, Linda Hutton; published new writers within the last year. Length: 750 words average; 1,500 words maximum. Publishes short shorts. Sometimes comments on rejected mss and recommends other markets. Also publishes literary criticism, poetry.
How to Contact: Send complete ms with cover letter. Reports in 2 months. SASE. Simultaneous, photocopied and reprint submissions OK. Accepts computer printouts. Sample copy for $3.50, #10 SAE and 3 first class stamps; fiction guidelines for #10 SAE and 1 first class stamp. Reviews novels and short story collections.
Payment: Pays in contributor's copies.
Terms: Acquires one-time rights. Publication not copyrighted. Sponsors contests for fiction writers. "SASE for guidelines; $2 entry fee. Cash prize."
Advice: "Proofread. Then proofread again. Then ask a friend or teacher to proofread. Use your dictionary—both for spelling and meaning. Read the guidelines carefully. And, if you want cash for your work, be sure you aren't submitting to markets which pay copies. (I've had several acceptances fall through when I advised the author of our non-payment policy)."

XAVIER REVIEW, (I, II), Xavier University, Box 110C, New Orleans LA 70125. (504)486-7411, ext. 7481. Editor: Thomas Bonner, Jr. Magazine of "poetry/fiction/nonfiction/reviews (contemporary literature) for professional writers/libraries/colleges/universities." Published semiannually. Estab. 1980. Circ. 500.
Needs: Contemporary, ethnic, experimental, historical (general), literary, Latin-American, prose poem, Southern, religious, serialized/excerpted novel, translations. Receives 30 unsolicited fiction mss/month. Buys 2 mss/issue; 4 mss/year. Length: 10-15 pages. Occasionally critiques rejected mss.
How to Contact: Send complete ms. SASE. Sample copy $5.
Payment: Pays 2 contributor's copies.

YELLOW SILK: Journal of Erotic Arts, (II), Verygraphics, Box 6374, Albany CA 94706. Editor/Publisher: Lily Pond. Magazine: 8½×11; 60 pages; matte coated stock; glossy cover stock; 4-color illustrations; photos. "We are interested in nonpornographic erotic literature: joyous, mad, musical, elegant, passionate. 'All persuasions; no brutality' is our editorial policy. Literary excellence is a priority; innovative forms are welcomed, as well as traditional ones." Quarterly. Estab. 1981. Circ. 16,000.
Needs: Comics, erotica, ethnic, experimental, fantasy, feminist/lesbian, gay, humor/satire, literary, prose poem, science fiction and translations. No "blow-by-blow" descriptions. No hackneyed writing except when used for satirical purposes. Nothing containing brutality. Buys 4-5 mss/issue; 16-20 mss/year. Published work by William Kotzwinkle, Gary Soto, published new writers within the last year. Length: no preference. Occasionally critiques rejected ms.
How to Contact: Send complete ms with SASE and include short, *personal* bio notes. No queries. No pre-published material. No simultaneous submissions. Name, address and phone number on each page. Photocopied submissions OK. Accepts computer printout submissions. Submissions on disk OK *with* hard copy only. Reports in 3 months on mss. Publishes ms up to 3 years after acceptance. Sample copy $7.50.

Market conditions are constantly changing! If you're still using this book and it is 1993 or later, buy the newest edition of Novel & Short Story Writer's Market at your favorite bookstore or order directly from Writer's Digest Books.

Payment: Pays 3 contributor's copies plus minimum of $10 per prose item.

Terms: Pays on publication for all periodical and anthology rights for one year following publication, at which time rights revert back to author; and non-exclusive reprint and anthology rights for the duration of the copyright.

Advice: "Read, read, read! Including our magazine—plus Nabokov, Ntozake Shange, Rimbaud, Virginia Woolf, William Kotzwinkle, James Joyce. Then send in your story! Trust that the magazine/editor will not rip you off—they don't. As they say, 'find your own voice,' then trust it. Most manuscripts I reject appear to be written by people without great amounts of writing experience. It takes years (frequently) to develop your work to publishable quality; it can take many re-writes on each individual piece. I also see many approaches to sexuality (for my magazine) that are trite and not fresh. The use of language is not original, and the people do not seem real. However, the gems come too, and what a wonderful moment that is. Please don't send me anything with blue eye shadow."

YESTERDAY'S MAGAZETTE, The Magazine of Memories, (I), Independent Publishing Co., P.O. Box 15126, Sarasota FL 34277. (813)366-9850. Editor: Ned Burke. Magazine: 8½ × 11; 24 pages, 60 lb. paper; glossy cover, illustrations. "Nostalgia themes for adults, 40 and up." Bimonthly. Estab. 1973. Circ. 1,500.

Needs: Historical, humor/satire, mainstream, religious/inspirational, senior citizen/retirement. Published special fiction issue and plans one in the future. Receives 10-30 unsolicited fiction mss/month. Buys 1-3 mss/issue; 10-15 mss/year. Publishes mss 4 months or more after acceptance. Agented fiction 10%. Length: 1,000 words preferred; 500 words minimum; 1,500 words maximum. Publishes short shorts. Length: 250-300 words. Critiques or comments on rejected mss. Recommends other markets.

How to Contact: Send complete ms with cover letter. Reports in 2 months. SASE. Computer printout submissions OK. Sample copy for $2. Fiction guidelines for #10 SAE and 1 first-class stamp.

Payment: Pays $5-25, contributor's copies and free subscription.

Terms: Pays on publication for first rights. Sponsors fiction contest—send for details.

Advice: Looks for "flow--an easy, conversational style that tells a story in much the same way you would tell it to your best friend. Keep it simple, but emotional."

YOUNG JUDAEAN, (IV), Hadassah Zionist Youth Commission, 50 W. 58th St., New York NY 10019. (212)355-7900. Contact: Editor. Magazine: 8½ × 11; 16 pages; illustrations. *"Young Judaean* is for members of the Young Judaea Zionist youth movement, ages 9-12." Quarterly. Estab. 1910. Circ. 4,000.

Needs: Children's fiction including adventure, ethnic, fantasy, historical, humor/satire, juvenile, prose poem, religious, science fiction, suspense/mystery and translations. "All stories must have Jewish relevance." Receives 10-15 unsolicited fiction mss/month. Publishes ms up to 2 years after acceptance. Buys 1-2 mss/issue; 10-20 mss/year. Length: 500 words minimum; 1,500 words maximum; 1,000 words average.

How to Contact: Send complete ms with SASE. Photocopied submissions OK. Reports in 3 months on mss. Sample copy for 75¢. Free fiction guidelines.

Payment: Pays 5¢/word up to $50; 2 free contributor's copies; 75¢ charge for extras.

Terms: Pays on publication for first rights.

Advice: "Stories must be of Jewish interest—lively and accessible to children without being condescending."

YOUNG VOICES MAGAZINE, The Magazine of Young People's Creative Work, (I, II, IV), Box 2321, Olympia WA 98507. (206)357-4863. Editor: Steve Charak. Magazine: "All materials are by elementary and middle school students for children and adults interested in children's work." Bimonthly. Estab. 1988. Circ. 1,000.

Needs: Adventure, experimental, historical (general), humor/satire, juvenile (5-14), literary, mainstream, prose poem, and science fiction. "Everything must be written by elementary or middle school students. (8th grade is the limit)" No excessive violence or sexual content. Plans a special fiction issue or an anthology in the future. Upcoming theme: "Pets and Animals" (May 1992). Receives 50 unsolicited mss/month. Buys 30 mss/issue; 160-200 mss/year. Publishes ms 2-4 months after acceptance. Recently published work by Naehon Weaver, Heather Lint. Length: 500 words average. Publishes short shorts. Also publishes poetry. Always critiques rejected mss and recommends other markets.

How to Contact: Send complete ms with cover letter. Make sure age, grade and school are in the letter. Simultaneous, photocopied and reprint submissions OK. Accepts computer printout submissions. Sample copy $3. Fiction guidelines free.

Payment: Pays $3-5 and contributor's copies.
Terms: Pays on acceptance for one-time rights.

ZERO HOUR, "Where Culture Meets Crime," (I, II, IV), Box 766, Seattle WA 98111. (206)621-8829. Editor: Jim Jones. Tabloid: 11×16; 36 pages; newsprint paper; illustrations and photos. "We are interested in fringe culture. We publish fiction, poetry, essays, confessions, photos, illustrations, interviews, for young, politically left audience interested in current affairs, non-mainstream music, art, culture." Semiannually. Estab. 1988. Circ. 3,000.
Needs: Confessions, erotica, ethnic, experimental, feminist, gay, humor/satire, psychic/supernatural/occult and translations. "Each issue revolves around an issue in contemporary culture: cults and fanaticism, addiction, pornography, etc." No romance, inspirational, juvenile/young, sports. Receives 5 unsolicited mss/month. Accepts 3 mss/issue; 9 mss/year. Publishes ms 2-3 months after acceptance. Published work by Jesse Bernstein and Mike Allmayer. Length: 1,200 words average; 400 words minimum; 1,500 words maximum. Publishes short shorts. Length: 400 words. Also publishes literary essays, literary criticism, poetry. Sometimes critiques rejected mss.
How to Contact: Query first. Reports in 2 weeks on queries; 1 month on mss. SASE. Simultaneous and photocopied submissions OK. Accepts computer printout submissions. Sample copy $3, 9×12 SAE and 5 first class stamps. Fiction guidelines free. Reviews novels and short story collections.
Payment: Pays in contributor's copies.
Terms: Acquires one-time rights. Sends galleys to author.
Advice: "Does it fit our theme? Is it well written, from an unusual point of view or on an unexplored/underexplored topic?"

ZOIKS!, Curdling the Cream of the Mind, (I, II, IV), P.O. Box 33561, Raleigh NC 27636. Editor: Skip Elsheimer. Fiction Editor: David Jordan. Magazine: illustrations and photos. "*Zoiks!* is interested in new ideas and new ways of thinking. Or at least using old ideas in a new way. Exploring the world through innocent absurdism." Plans special fiction issue. Estab. 1986.
Needs: Experimental, humor/satire, psychic/supernatural/occult, translations, underground literature, conspiracy-oriented fiction. "I'm interested in anything that will make you question your surroundings. No fiction that is pretentious, lacking humor." Upcoming theme: "A Salute to Television." Receives 2-3 unsolicited mss/month. Accepts 1-2 mss/issue; 6-12 mss/year. Recently published work by Harrison Nutkins, B.Z. Niditch; published new writers within the last year. Publishes short shorts. Sometimes critiques rejected mss or recommends other markets.
How to Contact: Query first with clips of published work or send complete ms with cover letter, which should include address. Should tell something about the author. Reports in 1 month. Simultaneous, photocopied and reprint submissions OK. Accepts computer submissions. Accepts electronic submissions via Macintosh 800K. Sample copy $1.50. Make checks payable to Skip Elsheimer.
Payment: Pays in contributor's copies; charges for extras at cost plus postage.
Terms: Publication not copyrighted. Work belongs to the author.
Advice: "I feel that magazine fiction is too industry oriented. Everyone should have a shot at getting published. Express *yourself*!"

ZYZZYVA, The Last Word: West Coast Writers and Artists, (II, IV), Suite 1400, 41 Sutter St., San Francisco CA 94104. (415)255-1282. Editor: Howard Junker. Magazine: 6×9; 144 pages; Starwhite Vicksburg smooth paper; graphics; photos. "Literate" magazine. Quarterly. Estab. 1985. Circ. 3,500.
Needs: Contemporary, experimental, literary, prose poem. West Coast writers only. Receives 300 unsolicited mss/month. Buys 5 fiction mss/issue; 20 mss/year. Agented fiction: 10%. Recently published work by Isabel Allende, Dennis Cooper, Elizabeth Tallent; published new writers within the last year. Length: varies. Also publishes literary essays.
How to Contact: Send complete ms. "Cover letters are of minimal importance." Reports in 2 weeks on mss. SASE. No simultaneous submissions or reprints. Accepts computer printouts. Sample copy $8. Fiction guidelines on masthead page.
Payment: Pays $50-250.
Terms: Pays on acceptance for first North American serial rights.
Advice: "Keep the faith."

International literary and small circulation magazines

The following is a list of literary and small circulation publications from countries outside the U.S. and Canada that accept or buy short fiction in English (or in the universal languages of Esperanto or Ido).

Before sending a manuscript to a publication in another country, it's a good idea to query first for information on the magazine's needs and methods of submission. Send for sample copies, or try visiting the main branch of your local library, a nearby college library or bookstore to find a copy.

All correspondence to markets outside your own country must include International Reply Coupons, if you want a reply or material returned. You may find it less expensive to send copies of your manuscript for the publisher to keep and just enclose a return postcard with one IRC for a reply. Keep in mind response time is slow for many overseas publishers, but don't hesitate to send a reply postcard with IRC to check the status of your submission. You can obtain IRCs from the main branch of your local post office. The charge for one in US funds is 95¢.

‡THE ABIKO LITERARY QUARTERLY RAG, 8-1-8 Namiki, Abiko-Shi, Chiba-Ken 270-11 Japan. Tel./ FAX: (0471)84-7904. Editor: Anna Liuia Plurabell. Fiction Editor: D.C. Palter. Quarterly. Circ. 350. Publishes 3 stories/issue. "We are a bilingual (Japanese/English) magazine for Japanese and foreigners living in Japan." Needs: contemporary, erotica, experimental, historical, humor, literary, mainstream, regional, translations. Length: 3,000 average; 5,000 maximum. Send entire manuscript with SAE and IRCs. Pays in contributor's copies. "A story submitted in both English and Japanese receives special consideration, as do stories set in Japan. I look for strong character development as well as a good plot. Most stories I receive are exclusively character development or plot, but both are necessary to stand a good chance of being published. Follow proper format and submission procedures." Sponsors contest. Write for details. Sample copy for 500 yen plus 300 yen postage. Guidelines for IRCs (100 yen).

ACUMEN, 6, The Mount, Furzeham, Brixham, Devon TQ5 8QY England. Fiction Editor: Patricia Oxley. Circ. 500. Semiannual. "Literary magazine with an emphasis on poetry. I use 1-2 short stories/ year (2 issues) which are around 1,500 words, have a clear statement and are written in a literary style. Writers paid in extra copies of *Acumen*. Writers receive copies of the issue containing their work. Send sufficient IRCs to cover return postage. Make sure name and address are on manuscript (not just covering letter or, worse still, on outside of envelope.)"

AQUARIUS, Flat 10, Room-A, 116 Sutherland Ave., Maida-Vale, London W9 England. Fiction Editor: Sean Glackin. Editor: Eddie Lunden. Circ. 5,000. Publishes five stories/issue. Interested in humor/ satire, literary, prose poem and serialized/excerpted novels. "We publish prose and poetry and reviews." Payment is by agreement. "We only suggest changes. Most stories are taken on merit." Price in UK £2 50p. plus postage and packing; in US $18 plus $3 postage. Next issue devoted to women writers.

‡CAMBRENSIS, 41 Heol Fach, Cornelly, Bridgend, Mid-Glamorga, CF33 4LN Wales. Editor: Arthur Smith. Quarterly. Circ. 500. Quarterly. "Devoted solely to the short story form, featuring short stories by writers born or resident in Wales/or with some Welsh connection; receives grants from the Welsh Arts' Council and the Welsh Writers' Trust; uses art-work—cartoons, line-drawings, sketches etc." Length: 2,500 words maximum. Writers receive 3 copies of magazine. Writer has to have some connection with Wales. SAE and International Reply Coupon or similar should be enclosed "Air mail" postage to avoid long delay. Send international reply coupon for a sample copy. Subscriptions via Blackwell's Periodicals, P.O. Box 40, Hythe Bridge Street, Oxford, OX1 2EU, UK or Faxon Europe, P.O. Box 297, 10000A D Amsterdam, Holland.

‡CENCRASTUS, Unit One, Abbeymount Techbase, Edinburgh, EM8 8EJ Scotland. (031)661-5687. FAX: (031)557-8233. Fiction Editor: Ray Ross. Circ. 2,000. Publishes 1 or more short stories per issue. "Scottish literature arts and affairs magazine with international bias. Produced quarterly." Writers are paid for published fiction and receive contributor's copies. "We look at all copy submitted. SAE."

‡CHAPMAN, 4 Broughton Place, Edinburgh EH1 3RX Scotland. Fiction Editor: Joy Hendry. Quarterly. Circ. 2,000. Publishes 4-6 stories/issue. "Scottish literary magazine publishing poetry, short stories, reviews and articles of general interest to culture in Scotland." Length: 1,000 words minimum;

6,000 words maximum. Include SAE and return postage (IRCs) with submissions. Pays £8/page. Sample copy available for £3.

CREATIVE FORUM, Bahri Publications, 997A Gobindpuri Kalkaj, New Delhi 110019 India. Telephones: 011-6445710, 011-6448606. FAX: 91.11-6460796. Fiction Editor: U.S. Bahri. Circ. 1,800. Publishes 8-12 stories annually. "We accept short stories only for our journal, *Creative Forum*. Novels/novellas accepted if suitable subsidy is forthcoming from the author." Length: 2,000-3,000 words. Pays in copies. Manuscripts should be "neatly typed and not beyond 200 sheets." Subscriptions $30 US. "Short stories accompanied with $25 US towards annual subscription of the journal are given preferential treatment and priority."

EDINBURGH REVIEW, 22 George Square, Edinburgh EH8 Scotland. Circ. 2,000. Publishes 16 stories/year. "An international journal of ideas and literature. Interested in all stories, especially the experimental and unorthodox." Pays for published fiction and provides contributor's copies. "We take 5 months to give a decision. We are especially interested in translations and interviews of some length."

‡EOD (The Esoteric Order of Dagon) MAGAZINE, P.O. Box 7545, St., Kilda Rd., Melbourne, Victoria 3004 Australia. Fiction Editor: Chris A. Masters. Bimonthly. Circ. 150. "*EOD* is an amateur, small press magazine, the aim of which is to encourage up-and-coming horror writers, artists and poets in Australia to develop their talents and to promote their work. At the moment *EOD only publishes Australian writers*. This is due to the fact that in Australia there is almost no outlet for horror writers. *EOD* as far as I know, is the only Australian publication that prints regular horror fiction." Length: 10,000 words maximum. Writers receive a copy of the issue in which their story appears. "Unfortunately, I cannot afford to pay for contributions but I do sponsor a short story competition (prizes: $80, $40, $20 Australian) in which the writer's 3 most popular stories receive a small sum for their effort. All contributions to *EOD* should in someway relate to the horror genre and be entertaining. All work should be typed, word processed or on 5¼" disk (360K IBM in ASCII file format). Contributions should also include a SASE for reply or appropriate envelope and postage if work is to be returned. For overseas writers, your best bet would be to seek publication in the much larger British and U.S. market." Sample copy available for $5 (US) or $12 (US) for subscription.

FOOLSCAP, 78 Friars Road, East Ham, London E6 1LL England. Fiction and Poetry Editor: Judi Benson. Quarterly. Publishes 2 stories/issue. "We are primarily poetry though can handle short fiction of up to 5 pages. This could include a scene from a novel. We are looking for strong quality work but will give careful consideration to all submissions. Any subject considered, also nonfiction." Length: 420-2,000 words. Pays 1 contributor's copy. "Do not send work exceeding 5 typed pages as the magazine does not have the space. Send manuscript in typed form with SAE and enough IRCs for return." Sample copy available for $5.

FORESIGHT (IV), 44 Brockhurst Rd., Hodge Hill, Birmingham B36 8JB England. Editor: John Barklam. Fiction Editor: Judy Barklam. Quarterly. Magazine including "new age material, world peace, psychic phenomena, research, occultism, spiritualism, mysticism, UFOs, philosophy, etc. Shorter articles required on a specific theme related to the subject matter of *Foresight* magazine." Length: 300-1,000 words. Pays in contributor's copies. Send SAE with IRC for return of ms. Sample copy for 30p and 25p postage.

FRANK, An International Journal of Contemporary Writing and Art, B.P. 29 94301 Vincennes Cedex, France. US Office: A-L Books, Suite 305, 45 Newbury St., Boston, MA 02116. Editor: David Applefield. Semiannual. "Eclectic, serious fiction, favors innovative works that convey radical social, political, environmental concern — all styles, voices — and translations, novel extracts" for literary international audience. "Send your best work, consult a copy of the journal before submitting." Published work by Raymond Carver, Robert Coover, Rita Dove, Italo Calvino, Vaclav Havel, and Sony Labou Tansi. Length: 3,000 words maximum. Pays 2 copies and $10 (US)/printed page. "Send work that conveys a sense of necessity and soulfulness." Sample copy $8 (US).

GLOBAL TAPESTRY JOURNAL, (II), BB Books, 1 Spring Bank, Longsight Rd., Copster Green, Blackburn, Lancashire BB1 9EU England. Editor: Dave Cunliffe. "Post-underground with avant-garde, experimental, alternative, counterculture, psychedelic, mystical, anarchist etc. fiction for a bohemian and counterculture audience." Recently published fiction by Gregory Stephenson, Arthur Moyse and David Tipton; published work by new writers within the last year. Sample copy $4.

Close-up

David Applefield
Founder and Editor
Frank: An International Journal
of Contemporary Writing & Art

David Applefield moved from Boston to Paris in 1983 to publish his literary magazine, *Frank: An International Journal of Contemporary Writing and Art*. Today, *Frank* has almost tripled in size; its circulation is 3,000. And Applefield has published authors from Kerouac to Coover, Calvino and Burroughs, as well as new voices from many cultures including Nordic, Pakistani, Filipino, Chinese, Turkish and Congolese.

"I wanted to discover and publish voices from many countries and languages with the idea of combatting the ethnocentricity that seemed to affect so much of my American life," he says. "I look at *Frank* as my larger work, each issue a composition whose chemistry belongs to me."

Recently, he's also launched a publishing venture, A-L Books, Inc., in Boston. He teaches at The American University in Paris and at Emerson College's Ploughshares International Fiction Writing Seminar held in Holland each summer. His schedule is punishing by any standards; he works 20-hour days that include editing on a Metro commute from the University to his apartment on the edge of Paris.

Applefield moved to Paris in search of his own voice; he wanted to be part of a "third wave"; he'd been fascinated by Henry Miller's accounts of Bohemian street life and admits he "had to learn the hard way how untrue the myths of the 20s and 30s were, especially in the 80s and 90s."

He began by frequenting readings at The Village Voice Bookstore and Shakespeare & Company. News spread quickly, he says, that a new journal editor in town was looking for manuscripts, and work came pouring in. Poets, writers and translators from many countries dropped by. "I'd wake up in the morning and there'd be a stack of stories outside my door," he says. "After an espresso, I'd clear off the table and start ripping through the pile."

Applefield's advice for American writers seeking publication in *Frank* and other English-speaking foreign magazines is "Read *Novel & Short Story Writer's Market*, and contact each editor by name. Small presses play a smaller role in Europe. Don't be surprised if you don't receive an answer, but don't make the foolish error of sending American return postage on SASEs." (Use International Reply Coupons.)

Frank receives 1,000 submissions each year and publishes two issues annually. Half of each issue is fiction, with both short stories and novel excerpts. "I look for work that takes swipes at social, economic and/or political undercurrents in America," Applefield says. "I don't like stories set in foreign places the writer has only visited. I like work that goes beyond its own craft and style and responds to the contemporary world. I like translations and work that gets beyond ethnocentric barriers and American puritanism."

—Roberta Coffey

GOING DOWN SWINGING, Box 64, Coburg Victoria 3058 Australia. Fiction Editors: Kevin Brophy and Myron Lysenko. Circ. 1,000. Annual. Publishes approx. 80 pages of fiction/year. "We publish short stories, prose poetry, poetry, interviews and reviews. We try to encourage young or new writers as well as established writers. Interested in experimental writing." Payment: $20 (Australian) per contribution. Writers receive 1 contributor's copy. Send ms, 2 International Reply Coupons and a short biographical note." Include 2-3 stories. Deadline: December 15. "We are interested in innovative, contemporary writing with the aim of publishing on equal balance of female and male writers of considerable talent." Sample copies $6 (Australian). Writer's guidelines available. Send SAE and IRC.

GRANTA, 2/3 Hanover Yard, Noel Road, Islington, London N1 8BE England. U.S. Associate Publisher: Anne Kinard. Editor: Bill Buford. U.S. office: 250 W. 57th St., New York NY 10107. Quarterly. "Paperback magazine (256 pages) publishing fiction and cultural and political journalism: fiction (including novellas and works-in progress), essays, political analysis, journalism, etc." Pays in contributor's copies.

HRAFNHOH, 32 Strŷd Ebeneser, Pontypridd Mid Glamorgan CF37 5PB Wales. Fiction Editor: Joseph Biddulph. Circ. 200-500. Published irregularly. "Now worldwide and universal in scope. Suitable: fictionalized history, local history, family history. Explicitly Christian approach. Well-written stories or general prose opposed to abortion and human embryo experimentation particularly welcome. No payment made, but free copies provided. Be brief, use a lot of local colour and nature description, in a controlled, resonant prose or in dialect. Suitable work accepted in Esperanto and other languages, including Creole. Stamps and U.S. currency are no use to me. IRC (International Reply Coupon) will cover a brief response. But mss however small are expensive to return, so please send copy." Sample copy free, but 3 International Reply Coupons would cover real cost of sending it overseas.

‡IMAGO LITERARY MAGAZINE, School of Communication, QUT, GPO Box 2434, Brisbane 4001 Australia. Contact: Dr. Philip Neilsen or Helen Horton. Published 3 times/year. Circ. 750. 30-50% fiction. *Imago* is a literary magazine publishing short stories, poetry articles, interviews and book reviews. "While content of articles and interviews should have some relevance either to Queensland or to writing, stories and poems may be on any subject. The main requirement is good writing." Length: 1,000 words minimum; 3,000 words maximum; approximately 2,000 words preferred. Pays on publication in accordance with Australia Council rates: short stories, $A80 minimum; articles, $A80 minimum; reviews, $A50. Also provides contributor's copy. "Contributions should be typed double-spaced on one side of the paper, each page bearing the title, page number and author's name. Name and address of the writer should appear on a cover page of longer mss, or on the back, or bottom, of single page submissions. A SASE (or SAE and IRCs) with sufficient postage to cover the contents, should be sent for the return of ms or for notification of acceptance or rejection. No responsibility is assumed for the loss of or damage to unsolicited manuscripts." Sample copy available for $A6. Guidelines, as above, available on request.

IRON MAGAZINE (II), Iron Press, 5 Marden Ter., Cullercoats, North Shields, Tyne & Wear NE30 4PD England. Editor: Peter Mortimer. Circ. 800. Published 3 times/year. Publishes 14 stories/year. "Literary magazine of contemporary fiction, poetry, articles and graphics." Length: 6,000 words maximum. Pays approx. £10/page. No simultaneous submissions. Five poems, two stories per submission the limit. Sample copy for $8 (US) (no bills-no checks). "Please see magazine before submitting and don't submit to it before you're ready! Many stories submitted are obviously only of interest to the domestic market of the writer. Always try there first! And do try to find something out about the publication, or better, see a sample copy, before submitting."

‡ISLAND, P.O. Box 207, Sandy Bay 7005 Australia. Fiction Editor: Dr. Cassandra Pybus. Quarterly. Circ. 2,000. Publishes 4 stories/issue. "*Island* is a quarterly of ideas, criticism, fiction and poetry. It features essays on a range of issues (environmental, political, literary, personal) plus short fiction and poetry." Length: 2,000-5,000 words. Pays $80 (Australian) minimum. Send "double-spaced laser print *not* dot matrix. A *small* amount of relevant biographical detail. Only *one* piece at a time. If you are unpublished at home you are unlikely to be published abroad." Sample copy: $10 (Australian).

LA KANCERKLINIKO, (IV), 162 rue Paradis, 13006 Marseille France. Phone: 91-3752-15. Fiction Editor: Laurent Septier. Circ. 300. Quarterly. Publishes 40 pages of fiction annually. "An esperanto magazine which appears 4 times annually. Each issue contains 32 pages. *La Kancerkliniko* is a political and cultural magazine. General fiction, science fiction, etc. Short stories or very short novels. The short story (or the very short novel) must be written only in esperanto, either original or translation from any other language." Length: 15,000 words maximum. Pays in contributor's copies. Sample copy on request with 3 International Reply Coupons from Universal Postal Union.

‡**KRAX MAGAZINE,** 63 Dixon Ln., Leeds LS12 4RR, Yorkshire Britain, U.K. Publishes 9 monthly issues. "*Krax* is a poetry magazine which contains one short story per edition. Usually preferred length is 800-1,500 words." Pays one contributor's copy. "Lighted-hearted material only—no politics not even spoofs." Send IRC's for reply postage (*not* stamps), enquire or send synopsis before sending large manuscripts. Sample copies $1 each, no guidelines.

LONDON MAGAZINE, 30 Thurloe Place, London SW7 England. Editor: Alan Ross. Bimonthly. Circ. 5,000. Publishes 3-4 stories/issue. "Quality is the only criteria." Length: 1,500-5,000 words. Pays £50-100, depending on length, and contributor's copy. "Send only original and literary, rather than commercial, work."

MAELSTROM, 31 Chiltern, Coleman St., Southend-on-Sea SS2 5AE England. Fiction Editor: Malcolm E. Wright. Circ. 300. Publishes 30,000 words/year. "A short-story magazine publishing most types of genre fiction, including science fiction, fantasy, thriller, mystery, horror, etc." Length: 500-5,000 words. British contributors paid $4 per 1,000 words and one contributor copy; American contributors paid contributor copies only. "Send SAE for submission guidelines. Disposable manuscripts are probably best, but a small SAE is still necessary if a reply is required." Sample issues are £1.50 or $5 (U.S.) (cash only—no dollar checks please).

MOMENTUM, % Pamela Goodwin, Almere Farm, Rossett, Wrexham, Clwyd LL12 0BY Wales. Fiction Editor: Jeff Bell. Circ. 350. Published 3 times/year. Publishes an average of 25 stories annually. "*Momentum:* A 'middle-of-the-road' general interest mag with some verse, specializing in new writers—within those parameters anything goes, but no way-out extremes of fantasy or cult stuff, etc. Fiction only. Published 3 times a year (60-page edition)." Writers receive 1 contributor's copy. "Type fairly legibly, 2,500 words maximum and a rough word count is welcome, one side of a sheet please. Address (and name) on copy. Politics *not* barred." Subscription details: £2.40 annually GB. USA add £2, elsewhere add £1. "New subscribers get 1 free back issue."

NEW HOPE INTERNATIONAL, 20 Werneth Ave., Hyde, SK14 5NL England. Fiction Editor: Gerald England. Circ. 750. Publishes 2-6 stories annually. Publishes "mainly poetry. Fiction used must be essentially literary but not pretentious. Only short fiction used (max 2,000 words). Would use more fiction but the standard submitted (in comparison to the poetry) has been rather poor." Payment: 1 complimentary copy. Guidelines available for IRC. Sample copy: $5 (cash, if cheque, send $10, due to bank charges).

NEW OUTLOOK, MIDDLE EAST MONTHLY, (IV), Israel Peace Society, 9 Gordon Street, 63458 Israel. Editor: Chaim Shur. "Middle East peace issues, for a progressive audience." Monthly. Estab. 1957. Circ. 4,500. Needs: ethnic, historical (general), translations, Palestinian literature. Pays in contributor's copies. "We publish Palestinian fiction and controversial Israeli works in English in order to broaden potential audience for these works."

‡**NORTHERN PERSPECTIVE,** Box 40146, Casuarina 0811 Australia. Managing Editor: Dr. Lyn Riddett. Circ. 1,000. Semiannual. Publishes about 200 pages of fiction annually. "Publishes short stories, poems, book reviews, articles. *Northern Perspective* is a liberal arts/literary magazine." Length: 1,500-4,000 words. Writers are paid $10 (Australian)/1,000 words and receive contributor's copies. "Strive for 'form' and style in short story; image in poetry."

NUTSHELL QUARTERLY, 8 George Marston Rd, Binley, Coventry CV3 2HH England. Fiction Editor: Tom Roberts. Circ. 1,000. Accepts 30-40 mss/year. "*Nutshell* is a small press (64-page) magazine featuring short stories, poetry, interviews, articles and reviews. Pleased to receive fiction of any length and of high quality." Pays 1 contributor's copy and choice of payment (nominal) or reduces subscription price. Length: 1,000-3,000 words preferred; 7,000 words maximum. Send SAE with IRCs and a short biography. "We are also interested in hearing about the surroundings in which people work and in receiving correspondence."

PANURGE (I), 15 Westwood Ave., Heaton, Newcastle Upon Tyne, NE6 5QT, U.K. Tel: 091-265-5910. Fiction Editor: David Almond. Circ. 1,000. Published twice/year. Perfect-bound, 120 pages. "Dedicated to short fiction by new and up-and-coming names. Each issue features several previously unpublished names. Several *Panurge* writers have been included in major anthologies, approached by agents, offered contracts by publishers. We seek work that shows vitality of language, command of form, an individual approach." Pays 1 month after publication, 1 contributor's copy. Pays £10/3 printed pages. Overseas subscription $18; Airmail $20. Sample copy $10.

‡**PARIS TRANSCONTINENTAL, A Magazine of Short Stories**, Institut des Pays Anglophones, Sorbonne Nouvelle, 5, rue de l'Ecole de Medecine, 75006 Paris, France. Fiction Editors: Claire Larrière, Albert Russo and Dee Goldberg. Semiannually. Circ. 1,000. Publishes short stories exclusively; no poetry, nonfiction or artwork. "*Paris Transcontinental*, purports to be a forum for writers of excellent stories whose link is the English language, wherever it is spoken. It purports thus to be global in scope and to introduce the best among today's authors, whether they hail from Europe or the Americas, from Oceania, Africa or Asia, for new literatures are evolving that reflect our post-colonial and computerized societies in ways that do not necessarily converge but certainly enrich our common space, hopefully also spurring our mutual understanding." Length: 2,000 words minimum; 4,000 words maximum. "Submitter's should send us no more than 3 stories at a time, along with a few lines about themselves and their work (approx. 100 words), one IRC to let them know of our decision, and *extra* IRCs (at least 3) for the return of their manuscripts. (No stamps please!)" Pays 2 contributor's copies. "Have an authentic voice and be professional. Write with your gut and read from all quarters. Author's featured include Al Brooks, Stephen Dixon, Jayanta Mahapatra, Joyce Carol Oates, Albert Russo, Alan Sillitoe and Michael Wielding." Send IRC for guidelines. For a sample copy, send a check for FF70 (or 70 French Francs) drawn on your own local bank.

PEACE AND FREEDOM, 17 Farrow Rd., Whaplode Drove, Spalding, Lincs. PE12 0TS England. Fiction Editor: Paul Rance. Circ. 500+. Semiannual. Publishes around 6-8 short stories annually. "A mixture of poetry, art, short stories, music and general features. *P and F* has a general humanism slant, as the title suggests, but good literature is judged purely as literature. Anything which is inventive, compelling, compassionate and literate will stand a chance of acceptance. Any racist, sexist, American-Russian tirades will be instantly returned." Pays in copies. "If we have a lot of work to read, of equal merit, then the work sent in by subscribers will be chosen first. No stories over 1,000 words, please. Free gift with every issue. U.S. payment should be either in bills, IRC's or cheque (but for cheques please add $5 to any overall price, due to bankcharges on overseas cheques; 3 IRC's=$1/18 IRC's=$6). *P and F* will also be starting up a service for writers shortly. This merely involves sending details about yourself and your work, together with a story, or stories. We will then pass on to other publishers in the U.K. Writer, as we will send out 1 story for 2 IRC's (not exclusing 1,000 words), and each story thereafter for 2 IRC's each. For airmail replies please double prices." A sample copy of *P and F* costs $2/£1 – U.K.) and is advisable. Subscription – $9 (£4 U.K.) for 4 issues.

‡**PHLOGISTON, (II,IV)**, Burning Tiger Press, Box 11-708 Manners St., Wellington, Aotearoa, New Zealand. Fiction Editor: Alex Heatley. Circ. 100. Quarterly. Publishes 8 stories/year. "Specializes in 'science fiction, fantasy, humor/satire,' but also considers general material." Length: 2,000-10,000 words. Pays in contributor's copies. "Try a copy to get our flavor, take an Alka Seltzer, then send us your best and most unusual work."

‡**PLANET-THE WELSH INTERNATIONALIST**, P.O. Box 44, Aberystwyth, Dyfed, Cymru/ Wales UK. Fiction Editor: John Barnie. Bimonthly. Circ. 1,100. Publishes 1-2 stories/issue. "A literary/cultural/ political journal centered on Welsh affairs but with a strong interest in minority cultures in Europe and elsewhere." Length: 1,500-4,000 words maximum. No submissions returned unless accompanied by an SAE. Writers submitting from abroad should send at least 3 IRCs. Writers receive 1 contributor's copy. Payment is at the rate of £40 per 1,000 words (in the currency of the relevant country if the author lives outside the UK). "We do not look for fiction which necessarily has a 'Welsh' connection, which some writers assume from our title. We try to publish a broad range of fiction and our main criterion is quality. Try to read copies of any magazine you submit to. Don't write out of the blue to a magazine which might be completely inappropriate to your work. Recognize that you are likely to have a high rejection rate, as magazines tend to favor writers from their own countries." Sample copy: cost (to USA & Canada) £2.87. Writers' guidelines for SAE.

‡**THE PLAZA, A Space for Global Human Relations,** U-Kan Inc., Yoyogi 2-32-1, Shibuya-Ku, Tokyo 151, Japan. Tel: (03)3379-3881. Editor: Taylor Mignon. Fiction Editor: F. David Bolton. Quarterly. Circ. 8,000. Publishes 3 stories/issue. "*The Plaza* is an intercultural and bilingual issue in English and Japanese with a focus on the essence of being human. All works will be published simultaneously in English and Japanese in the same issue. The works are translated into Japanese by our editorial staff." Length: 200-2,000 words. "The shorter, the better due to bilingual issue space limit." Send complete ms with cover letter. "The most important criteria is the artistic level. The second, being human, and the third is intercultural relations. These criteria, if followed, make a manuscript stand out. *The Plaza* is devoted to offering a spiritual plaza where people around the world can share their creative work. We are trying to introduce contemporary writers and artists as a human heritage above and beyond intercultural problems. The Plaza is edited with a global view of mankind and focuses on the essence of being human." Sample copy and guidelines free.

‡**PRINTED MATTER,** Hikari Biru 303, 3-7-10 Takadanobaba, Shinjuku-ku, Tokyo 169, Japan. Editor: Stephen Forster. Quarterly. Circ. 600. About 1/3 of each issue is fiction. "*Printed Matter* is an English-language literary journal that features fiction, poetry, reviews, interviews, essays and artwork; now in its fifteenth year of publication. Though based in Japan, the magazine has an international outlook: we are not especially looking for a backdrop of cherry blossoms and Mt. Fuji. Any type of fiction is acceptable; the sole criterion is quality." Length: 5,000-6,000 words. Pays 2 contributor's copies. "As with submissions anywhere, study the magazine first. Submit clearly typed manuscripts together with the usual enclosures (SASE or IRCs)." Sample copy: y600; £3; US $5; Australian $6.

"Printed Matter is the leading English-language literary journal in Japan," says Editor Stephen Forster. It aims to provide "the very best in contemporary poetry and fiction, reviews and essays, news and views from Japan and around the world." In designing a cover, therefore, he looks for something "that can provide maximum impact. We are restricted to black-and-white reproduction, so the graphic has to work well in this medium." Of this particular cover, he says "I was attracted to the tension in the skeleton, the tension in the structure beneath the surface." The photographer is John Einarsen, editor of Kyoto Journal.

‡**ROMANIAN REVIEW,** Redactia Publicatiilor Pentru Strainatate, Piata Presei Libere NR1, 71341 Bucuresti Romania. Fiction Editor: Mrs. Andreea Ionescu. Monthly. Fiction 40%. "Our review is scanning the Romanian history and cultural realities, the cooperation with other countries in the cultural field and it is also a mean of acquaintance with Romanian and overseas writers. We publish the *Romanian Review* in six languages (English, German, French, Spanish, Russian, Chinese). Any kind of well-written fiction may enter the pages of the review, on the sole condition that it would be decent." Length: 2,000 words minimum; 5,000 words maximum. "As we do not have the possibility of payment in foreign currency, we can only offer "lei" 800-2,000/story, depending on its length and qualities. The exchange may be done on the writer's account." Sample copies available; write for information.

SEPIA, Poetry & Prose Magazine, (I), Kawabata Press, Knill Cross House, Higher Anderton Rd., Millbrook, Nr Torpoint, Cornwall England. Editor-in-Chief: Collin David Webb. Published 3 times/year. "Magazine for those interested in modern un-clichéd work." Contains 32 pages/issue. Length:

200-4,000 words (for short stories). Pays 1 contributor's copy. Always include SAE with IRCs. Send $1 for sample copy and guidelines.

‡**THE SMALL HOURS,** (I), Rubber Claw Publications, Sycamore Cottage, Half Moon Lane, Kirkthorpe, Wakefield, West Yorkshire WF1 5SY England. Editor: Porl A. Broome. Annually. Circ. 500. Publishes 5-7 stories/issue. Experimental, horror, science fiction. "All fiction should be hard-hitting, highly original and encourage reaction from the reader." Length: 2,000 words preferred; 2,500 words maximum. Pays contributor's copies. Send complete ms with cover letter which should include "brief literary biography, general niceties/topics of conversation, etc. Don't worry about format. If you think you've written a story worthy of publication, then you may well have. Most of all, *don't hold back.*" Sample copy for $3 ($4 airmail). Writer's guidelines free.

SOCIAL ALTERNATIVES, % Dept. of Government, University of Queensland, St. Lucia, Queensland 4072 Australia. Fiction Editor: John Knight. Circ. 3,000. Quarterly. Publishes 2-3 stories in each quarterly issue. "The journal is socio-political, but stories of any theme or style will be considered. The criterion is excellence." Length: 1,000-3,000 words. Pays writers "if we have money—we usually don't." Writers receive one contributor's copy. Send "3 copies of story, immaculately presented so no sub-editing is necessary. SASE for return."

STAND MAGAZINE, 179 Wingrove Rd., Newcastle Upon Tyne, NE4 9DA England. Fiction Editor: Lorna Tracy. Circ. 4,500. Quarterly. Averages 16-20 stories/year. "*Stand* is an international quarterly publishing poetry, short stories, reviews, criticism and translations." Length: 5,000 words maximum. Payment: £30 per 1,000 words of prose on publication (or in US dollars); contributor's copies. "Read copies of the magazine before submitting. Enclose sufficient IRCs for return of mss/reply. No more than 6 poems or 2 short stories at any one time. Avoid specific genre writing—e.g. science fiction, travel etc. Should not be under consideration elsewhere." Sponsors biennial short competition: First prize, $1,500. Send 2 IRCs for information. Sample copy $6.50. Guidelines on receipt of 2 IRCs/SASE.

‡**STAPLE,** Derbyshire College, Mickleover, Derby DE4 3HD United Kingdom. Fiction Editor: Don Measham. Published 3 times/year. Circ. up to 500. Publishes up to 50% fiction. Staple is "70-80 pages, perfect-bound; beautifully designed and produced. Stories used by *Staple* have ranged from social realism (through autobiography, parody, prequel, parable) to visions and hallucinations. We don't use unmodified genre fiction, i.e. adventure, crime or westerns. We are interested in extracts from larger works—provided author does the extraction." Length: 200 words minimum; 5,000 words maximum. Adequate IRCs and large envelope for return, if return is required. Otherwise IRC for decision only. "UK and European Community writers get £10 for a story of 3 printed pages or more. Otherwise, £5. Get a specimen copy of one of the issues with strong prose representation." Back (double) issues #10 and #11 or #22 (December 1991). Dollar bills or sterling banker's draft only: the former £1.50 or $2; the latter £3 or $5. For guidelines: editorial of *Staple 22* is designed to guide prose writers. Send appropriate cash or draft.

STUDIO: A JOURNAL OF CHRISTIANS WRITING, (II), 727 Peel St., Albury 2640 Australia. Fiction Editor: Paul Grover. Circ. 300. Quarterly. Averages 20-30 stories/year. "*Studio* publishes prose and poetry of literary merit, offers a venue for new and aspiring writers, and seeks to create a sense of community among Christians writing." Length: 500-5,000 words. Pays in copies. Sample copy $8 (Australian). Subscription $39 (Australian) for four issues (one year). International draft in Australian dollars.

‡**SUNK ISLAND REVIEW,** P.O. Box 74, Lincoln LN1 1QG England. Fiction Editor: Michael Blackburn. Biannual. "A biannual magazine of new fiction, poetry, translations. Articles and graphics. Short stories, SF and excerpts from novels, novellas are all welcome not romance, historical fiction etc." Length: Open. Send cover letter and no more than 2 short stories at a time. Pays on publication. "Read the magazine first. We prefer disposable mss. All mss must be accompanied by adequate number of IRS for reply or return."

TAK TAK TAK, P.O. Box 7, Bulwell, Nottingham NG6 OHW England. Fiction Editors: Andrew and Tim Brown. Circ. 500. "An annual anthology on a set theme containing several pieces of fiction. Also several books each year." *Tak Tak Tak* is in paperback book form with cassette for music and the spoken word. We use all sorts of fiction relevant to the theme, but for reasons of space it can't be too long. (2,500 words maximum)." Pays one contributor's copy. "Write for more details, sample copies and guidelines."

‡**TEARS IN THE FENCE, (II)**, 38 Hod View, Stourpaine, Nr. Blandford Forum, Dorset DT11 8TN England. Editor: David Caddy. Semiannual. A magazine of poetry, fiction and graphics, "blended with a conservation section to develop the concepts of ecology and conservation beyond their present narrow usage." Publishes 3-4 stories/issue. Pays £7.50 per story plus complimentary copy of the magazine. Sample copy $4 (US).

THE THIRD HALF MAGAZINE, "Amikeco," 16, Fane Close, Stamford, Lincolnshire PE9 1H9 England. Fiction Editor: Kevin Troop. Quarterly "*The Third Half* literary magazine publishes mostly poetry, but editorial policy is to publish as much *short* short story writing as possible in each issue. Short stories especially for children, for use in the classroom, with 'questions' and 'work to do' are occasionally produced, along with poetry books, as separate editions. I wish to expand on this." Length: 1,800 words maximum. Pays in contributor's copies.

‡**VIGIL, (II)**, Vigil Publications, 12 Priory Mead, Bruton, Somerset BA10 ODZ England. Editor: John Howard Greaves. Estab. 1979. Circ. 250. "Simply the enjoyment of varied forms of poetry and literature with an informed view of poetic technique." Plans special fiction issue. Needs: experimental, literary, regional. Length: 500-1,500 words. Pays in contributor's copies. "Most of the stories we receive are work in progress rather than finished pieces. Well structured, vibrantly expressed work is a delight when it arrives. Freshness and originality must always find an audience." Contributor guidelines available for IRC.

‡**WEBBER'S**, 15 McKillop St., Melbourne, Victoria 3000 Australia. Contact: The Editor. Biannual. "*Webber's* is a relatively new literary magazine specializing in short fiction, poetry, reviews, essays and interviews. It attempts to encourage new writers as well as established ones." Length: 2,000 words maximum. Material submitted must be previously unpublished and include SAE with IRCs. Pays approximately $60-75 (Australian) and 1 contributor's copy. "We are always interested in receiving new manuscripts and consider each contribution carefully. In writing about what *they* know, writers from other countries will be providing Australian readers with material about which they do not know. This is always very positive."

WESTERLY, c/o University of Western Australia, Nedlands, Western Australia 6009 Australia. "A quarterly of poetry, prose and articles of a literary and cultural kind, giving special attention to Australia and Southeast Asia." Length: 1,500-2,000 words. Pays $50 (Australian) minimum and 1 contributor's copy. Sample copy: $5 (Australian).

‡**WESTWORDS**, 15 Trelawney Rd., Peverell, Plymouth, Devon PL3 4JS U.K. Editor: D. Woolley. Semiannual. Circ. 300-400. Publishes 2-3 short stories/issue. "Short stories only so far, but will consider short extracts from novels in progress." Length: 2,500 words maximum. Pays 2 contributor's copies only. Sample copy available for £1 plus IRC equal to £1.

WORKS, 12 Blakestones Rd., Slaithwaite, Huddersfield HD7 5UQ England. Fiction Editor: D. Hughes. Circ. 1,000+. 70%+ of content is fiction. "52 pages speculative and imaginative fiction (SF) with poetry, illustrated." Quarterly. Price: Enclose IRC. $5 *cash only* for 1 issue, $10 *cash only* for 4 issues. Member of the New Science Fiction Alliance. Pays in copies. "All manuscripts should be accompanied by a SASE (in the UK). USA send 2 IRC's with ms, if disposable or 4 IRCs, if not. Usual maximum is 4,500 words."

Other literary and small circulation magazines

The following literary magazines appeared in the 1991 edition of *Novel & Short Story Writer's Market* but are not in the 1992 edition. Those publications whose editors did not respond to our request for an update of their listings may not have done so for a variety of reasons— they may be out of business, for example, or they may be overstocked with submissions. These "no responses" are listed with no additional explanation below. Some responded too late for inclusion and this is indicated. If an explanation was given, it appears in parenthesis next to the listing name. Note that literary magazines from outside the US and Canada appear at the end of this list.

Acta Victoriana
Aerial (asked to be deleted)
After Hours(asked to be deleted)
The Alchemist
Amaranth (ceased publication)
Animal Tales
Apaeros (asked to be deleted)
Art Brigade (ceased publication)
Asymptote (overstocked)
The Asymptotical World
Axe Factory Review (asked to be left out this year)
Big Two-Hearted (ceased publication)
Black Ice (asked to be left out this year)
The Blizzard Rambler (responded late)
The Blue Water Review
Bottomfish Magazine
Cacanadadada Review
Cache Review (asked to be deleted)
Caesura (ceased publication)
Calapooya Collage
California Quarterly (responded late)
Calypso (asked to be left out this year)
Can(n)on Magazine
A Carolina Literary Companion (ceased publication)
Christian Outlook (ceased publication)
The Climbing ArtConverging Paths
Crab Creek Review (asked to be left out this year)
The Creative Woman (suspended publication/may be sold)
Cross Timbers Review (ceased publication)
The Dangerous Times
Dark SideDesert Sun (ceased publication)
Deviance
Door County Almanak (asked to be left out this year)
Eldritch Tales (asked to be left out this year)
The Elephant-Ear

Ellipsis (responded late)
Emerald City Comix & Stories (responded late)
Exit 13 Magazine (no fiction, all poetry)
Experiment in Words (asked to be deleted)
F.O.C. Review (asked to be left out this year)
Fireweed
Four Quarters (asked to be deleted)
Frontiers
Garm Lu (responded late)
Gas (overstocked)
The Gaslight Review
Gauntlet (asked to be deleted)
Gay Chicago Magazine
Gestalt (ceased publication)
Grue Magazine
Haight Ashbury Literary Journal (asked to be deleted)
Heartland Journal (ceased publication)
Heathenzine (see Blue Ryder)
Hemispheres
Hibiscus Magazine (asked to be left out this year)
Hobo Stew Review
Hoofstrikes Newsletter
Imagination
Indigo (ceased publication)
It's a Mad, Mad, Mad . . . World
Jazziminds Magazine
KanaKennebec
Key West Review
Kingfisher
Kola
Late Knocking
Literary Creations (ceased publication)
Living Among Nature Daringly (asked to be deleted)
Living Streams
Loonfeather (asked to be left out this year)
The Mad Engineer (ceased publication)
The Miraculous Medal
Modern Liturgy (asked to be deleted)
Mud Creek (ceased publication)

New Blood Magazine (responded late)
New England Review
New Moon (ceased publication)
NeWest Review
Night Slivers (ceased publication)
The North American Voice of Fatima
The Northern Review (suspended publication,funds cut)
Northwest Writers, Photographers and Design Artists
Nostoc Magazine (responded late)
Obsidian II: Black Literature in Review
Oregon East
Owlflight (asked to be left out this year)
Pacific Review
Para*phrase
Pavor Nocturnus
Pennsylvania Review
Pleiades Magazine/Philae Magazine
Poor Roberts Almanac (ceased publication)
The President Journal
Quintessential Space Debris (ceased publication)
Rafale
Rajah (responded late)
Rambunctious Review (responded late)
The Rampant Guinea Pig (ceased publication)
Realms (ceased publication)
Red Bass
Renaissance Fan
Resurgens
Room of One's Own
Satori (ceased publication)
Scream Magazine (ceased publication)
Shoe Tree (ceased publication)
Six Lakes Arts (asked to be left out this year)
The (something) (ceased publication)
Southern California Anthology
Space and Time (ceased publi

cation)
Spitball
Star Route Journal (asked to be left out this year)
Stone Drum
Storyquarterly
Storyzine (see Blue Ryder)
Strange Plasma
Stunningstories (asked to be deleted)
Summerfield Journal (ceased publication)
Sword of Shahrazad (ceased

publication)
Tabula Rasa
Temm Poetry Magazine (see Blue Ryder)
Terse Tales (ceased publication)
Trajectories
Tramp (ceased publication)
Twisted
Tyro Magazine (ceased publication)
Verdict Magazine
Washington Jewish Singles

Newsletter
The West Texas Sun (ceased publication)
Whispering Wind Magazine (no fiction)
The Wicazo Sa Review (asked to be deleted)
Wide Open Magazine (ceased publication)
Wisconsin Review
Word & Image
Zymergy (suspended publication)

Other international literary and small circulation magazines

Agog & Agog Ago Go
Ambit
Antigruppo
Auguries
Central Coast Courier
Forum Fabulatorum
Hatbox
Hecate
The Honest Ulsterman

Indian Literature
Inkshed
Landfall/Caxton Press (responded late)
Meanjin
New Europe
The New Welsh Review
Nieuwe Koekrand
Nnidnid: Surreality

Slow Dancer
Smoke
Third World
Trapani Nuova
The Writers' Rostrum
Writing Women
Working Classics

Commercial Periodicals

Like the year before it, 1991 was a challenge for those in the commercial magazine industry. Postal rate hikes took affect early on, followed shortly thereafter by the Persian Gulf War. The economy took a turn for the worse as advertisers became more conservative in the midst of prevailing uncertainty. In addition, Canada implemented a 7% goods and services tax (GST), raising the price of reading materials and, ultimately, affecting both Canadian and American publishers.

All of these actions contributed to a downturn in circulation and ad revenues for commercial magazines. Typically, when revenues decline, editorial space does too. For many, this means a reduction in staff. For fiction writers it means little or no space for their work.

Even though preliminary figures released in September by the U.S. Department of Labor indicated that the average number of people employed in the periodicals industry in 1991 would likely be below 1988's figure of 127,600, not all see doom for the industry. In fact, while many were bemoaning their plight, *Folio:* released a special issue celebrating 250 years of magazine publishing. (In case you didn't know, Andrew Bradford and Benjamin Franklin produced America's first two magazines in February 1741.)

Another sign of hope came at the 1991 Fall *Folio:*/MPA Show when, according to *MagazineWeek*, Professor Samir Husni, "one of the reigning gurus on the topic of magazine launches in the United States," predicted that folks would see more than 500 new magazines launched, just as they did in 1990. Though Husni said "50% of all magazines will fail within one year," he also noted that "the survival rate is improving."

Some noteworthy changes

While some launched new magazines last year, others took definite steps to secure their places in the industry. Efforts have included redesigning formats and/or refocusing editorial content—often in conjunction with changing staff—in order to gain readership. *Redbook*, founded in 1903, is just one of those to receive a makeover. The magazine's new focus is "the woman who knows who she is and needs some attention paid to herself," Ellen Levine, new editor-in-chief, explained to *USA Today* prior to the October debut. Others in the group of leading women's service magazines commonly known as the "Seven Sisters," including *Ladies' Home Journal* and *Good Housekeeping*, have also altered their approach to reflect the needs of today's readers.

Amazing Stories, the nation's first science fiction magazine, is another publication to receive a new look—or, actually, revive an "old" one. Originally a 8½×11″ magazine, *Amazing Stories* shrunk to the size of a paperback book after a series of slumps in the market, the most recent being in the early 1980s. Last May, however, it reappeared in its earlier format and is now a monthly, rather than bimonthly, publication.

A number of other changes are revealed in this edition. For starters, some magazines are no longer listed. *Playboy*, for one, declined a listing this year, while *Mother Jones* reported it is no longer publishing fiction. *Wee Wisdom* closed its doors in December, after nearly 100 years. And while *Modern Short Stories* also went out of business, *American Accent Short Story Magazine* has only temporarily suspended publication. You'll find a more complete list at the end of this section.

Although a few periodicals are devoting less space to fiction, most are keeping their space the same. A number of magazines, such as *Arizona Coast* and *Catholic Forester*, are even increasing space for stories. *Boston Review*, believing original fiction is an important part of culture, has a more vigorous approach. "Our 'New Voices' program . . . enables us to work closely with new and promising writers," explains Managing Editor Sophie Glazer.

Adding to the positive side, 16 magazines are new listings this year. Interestingly, most are special-interest publications. *Appalachia Journal*, for one, specializes in backcountry recreation topics, such as hiking, canoeing and cross-country skiing. Another example is *Lethbridge Magazine*, which seeks short stories relevant to Lethbridge and Southern Alberta.

Working with commercial periodicals

Remember, however, that most commercial magazines only use one or two fiction stories in each issue. To make the most of these publishing opportunities, first and foremost, familiarize yourself with the magazines to which you want to submit. Sample copies can be found on many newsstands as well as in bookstores and libraries. In addition, most editors list how copies may be obtained directly from their offices. The importance of reviewing samples cannot be overstated. As R. Murray-O'Hair, editor of *American Atheist*, explains, "We receive a lot of submissions that are entirely inappropriate and this slows down our ability to respond."

Besides reading the magazines you're interested in, write for their specific guidelines. Most publishers gladly provide guidelines for a self-addressed, stamped envelope (SASE) or a self-addressed envelope (SAE) with International Reply Coupons (IRCs) — for use by those outside your own country. This is the best way to discover changes in policy. As of last January, *Mademoiselle*, for example, no longer returns submissions, even if they are accompanied by an appropriately-sized SASE. Also, more and more periodicals are accepting submissions on disk (with a hard copy included, of course), and guidelines often contain specific format requirements.

Above all, follow submission procedures. Send complete manuscripts if listings say editors are open to them. If a magazine here says "query," then send a one-page letter including a brief synopsis of your story and asking whether the editor would like to see the whole manuscript. Always include a SASE (or SAE and IRCs) for a response and/or the return of your material. Also, for information on how to create the most professional presentation, see "The Business of Fiction Writing" on page 71.

In general, editors are looking for short fiction with a unique and/or distinctive voice. And many are seeking work that deals with socially-relevant topics, such as AIDS, the environment, family relationships, multiculturalism and various forms of abuse.

To locate the markets in this section that deal with particular types of fiction, check under Commercial Periodicals in the Category Index beginning on page 603. For listings of commercial periodicals outside the United States and Canada, see pages 390 to 393. Although many of the above comments apply, information particular to these international markets is included there as well.

Besides using listings as markets for your work, you may also find them the source of contests. Some of the contests related to the periodicals here are detailed in the Contests and Awards section. Check the Market Index for specific page numbers. If no other listing exists, send a SASE to obtain further information from the magazine itself.

A new aspect of the listings here, and in Literary and Small Circulation Magazines, is the addition of information regarding book reviews. Although many periodicals simply say they will review published novels or short story collections, consider the focus of the magazine when submitting your work. For example, *Palouse Journal*, a regional general interest publication, will review work "only if author, publisher or subject is of the interior Northwest."

Remember, changes like the ones mentioned earlier often occur between editions of this book. Examining issues of *Writer's Digest* magazine, *MagazineWeek*, *Folio:* and *Folio:'s Publishing News* may help you keep an eye on developments in the industry. Other possible resources include *The New York Times* and the *Wall Street Journal*.

The ranking system for listings in this section follows:

I   **Periodical encourages beginning writers or unpublished writers to submit work for consideration and publishes new writers regularly.**

II **Periodical publishes work by established writers and by new writers of exceptional talent.**

III **Magazine does not encourage beginning writers; prints mostly writers with previous publication credits and very few new writers.**

IV **Special-interest or regional magazine, open only to writers on certain topics or from certain geographical areas.**

ABORIGINAL SCIENCE FICTION, (II, IV), Box 2449, Woburn MA 01888-0849. Editor: Charles C. Ryan. Magazine: 8½×11; 68 pages; 40 lb. paper; 60 lb. cover; 4-color illustrations; photos. *"Aboriginal Science Fiction* is looking for good science fiction stories. While 'hard' science fiction will get the most favorable attention, *Aboriginal Science Fiction* also wants good action-adventure stories, *good* space opera, humor and science fantasy for adult science fiction readers." Bimonthly. Estab. 1986. Circ. 31,000+.
Needs: Science fiction. Original, previously unpublished work only. "No fantasy, sword and sorcery, horror, or Twilight-Zone type stories." Receives 120-140 unsolicited mss/week. Buys 5-7 mss/issue; 30-42 mss/year. Publishes ms 6 months to 1 year after acceptance. Agented fiction 5%. Published work by Larry Niven, David Brin and Walter Jon Williams; published new writers within the last year. Length: 2,500 words minimum; 6,000 words maximum. Some shorter material accepted, but "no shorter than 1,500-2,000 words for fiction. Jokes may be 50-150 words." Sometimes comments on rejected mss.
How to Contact: Send complete ms. Reports in 2-3 months. SASE. Good quality photocopied submissions OK. Accepts computer printout submissions. Sample copy for $3.50 plus $1.05 postage and handling. Fiction guidelines for #10 SAE and 1 first class stamp. Reviews novels and short story collections. Send books to Janice M. Eisen, Apt. 454, 225 State St., Schenectady NY 12305 or Darrell Schweitzer, 113 Deepdale Rd., Strafford PA 19087.
Payment: Pays "$250 flat" and 2 contributor's copies.
Terms: Pays on publication for first North American serial rights and non-exclusive reprint and foreign options.
Advice: "Stories with the best chance of acceptance will make unique use of science ideas; have lively, convincing characters; an ingenious plot; a powerful and well integrated theme, and use an imaginative setting. Read all the science fiction classics and current magazines to understand the field and to avoid clichés."

AIM MAGAZINE, (I, II), 7308 S. Eberhart Ave., Chicago IL 60619. (312)874-6184. Editor: Ruth Apilado. Fiction Editor: Mark Boone. Newspaper: 8½×11; 48 pages; slick paper; photos and illustrations. "Material of social significance: down-to-earth gut. Personal experience, inspirational." For "high school, college and general public." Quarterly. Estab. 1973. Circ. 10,000.
Needs: Open. No "religious" mss. Published special fiction issue last year; plans another. Receives 25 unsolicited mss/month. Buys 15 mss/issue; 60 mss/year. Published work by Thomas J. Cottle, Karl Damgaard, Richie Zeiler; published new writers within the last year. Length: 800-1,000 words average. Publishes short shorts. Sometimes comments on rejected mss.

How to Contact: Send complete ms. SASE with cover letter and author's photograph. Simultaneous submissions OK. Accepts computer printout submissions. Sample copy for $3.50 with SAE (9×12) and $1 postage. Fiction guidelines for #10 envelope and 1 first class stamp. Reviews novels and short story collections occasionally. Send books to fiction editor.
Payment: Pays $15-25.
Terms: Pays on publication for first rights.
Advice: "Search for those who are making unselfish contributions to their community and write about them. Our objective is to purge racism from the human bloodstream. Write about your own experiences."

ALIVE NOW!, (I, II), The Upper Room, Box 189, Nashville TN 37202-0189. (615)340-7218. Magazine of devotional writing and visuals for young adults. Bimonthly. Estab. 1971. Circ. 75,000.
Needs: Religious/inspirational. Buys 4 mss/issue; 12 mss/year. Length: 10 words minimum; 300 words maximum.
How to Contact: Send complete mss with SASE. Photocopied and previously published submissions OK. Accepts computer printout submissions. Reports in 3 months on mss. Sample copy free. Fiction guidelines free. Enclose SASE.
Payment: Pays $25; 12 contributor's copies.
Terms: Pays on publication for first rights, one-time rights, newspaper and periodical rights. Occasionally buys reprints.

ALOHA, The Magazine of Hawaii and the Pacific, (IV), Davick Publishing Co., Suite 309, 49 South Hotel St., Honolulu HI 96813. (808)523-9871. FAX: (808)533-2055. Associate Publisher: Cheryl Tsutsumi. Magazine about the 50th state. Upscale demographics. Bimonthly. Estab. 1979. Circ. 65,000.
Needs: "Only fiction that illuminates the true Hawaiian experience. No stories about tourists in Waikiki or contrived pidgin dialogue." Receives 3-4 unsolicited mss/month. Publishes ms up to 1 year after acceptance. Length: 1,000-2,000 words average.
How to Contact: Send complete ms. Reports in 2 months. SASE. Photocopied submissions OK. Accepts computer printout submissions. Sample copy for $2.95.
Payment: Pays 10¢/word minimum.
Terms: Pays on publication for first-time rights.
Advice: "Submit only fiction that is truly local in character. Do not try to write anything about Hawaii if you have not experienced this culturally different part of America."

AMAZING® STORIES, (II), TSR, Inc., Box 111, Lake Geneva WI 53147. (414)248-3625. Editor: Mr. Kim Mohan. Magazine: 8⅜×10¾; 96 (or more) pages; 80 lb. enamel; 100 lb. Northcote cover stock; perfect-bound; color illustrations; rarely b&w illustrations; rarely photos. Magazine of science fiction, fantasy and horror fiction stories for adults and young adults. Monthly. Estab. 1926. Circ. 20,000.
Needs: Science fiction, fantasy, horror. "We prefer science fiction to dominate our content, but will not turn away a well-written story regardless of genre. Low priority to heroic, pseudo-Medieval fantasy; no hack-'n'-slash or teen exploitation horror." Receives 700-1,000 unsolicited fiction mss/month. Buys 8-10 mss/issue; 100-120 mss/year. Publishes ms 9-18 months after acceptance. Agented fiction approximately 5%. Recently published work by Robert Silverberg, James Morrow, Michael Swanwick; published new writers within the last year. Length: 1,000 words minimum; 25,000 words maximum; will consider serialization of or excerpts from longer works. Usually critiques rejected mss.
How to Contact: Send complete ms with cover letter (list other professional credits in SF, fantasy or horror). Reports in 2 months. SASE. Photocopied submissions OK. No simultaneous submissions. Accepts computer printout submissions. Sample copy for $5. Fiction guidelines for #10 SASE. Reviews novels and short story collections.
Payment: Pays 6-10¢/word.
Terms: Pays on acceptance for first worldwide rights in the English language. Sends prepublication galleys to author.
Advice: "*AMAZING® Stories* is interested in all forms of science fiction, with an emphasis on strong plot lines and believable characterization. Avoid rehashes of old ideas and stereotypical story lines or characters. We encourage writers to experiment with innovative styles and approaches, but not at the expense of comprehensibility. All of that advice holds true for fantasy and horror as well. Read the magazine—at least a couple of issues—before trying to write for it. Send us a story that deserves to be called Amazing, and we'll find a place for it."

AMERICAN ATHEIST, A Journal of Atheist News and Thought, (II, IV), American Atheist Press, Box 140195, Austin TX 78714-0195. Editor: R. Murray-O'Hair. Magazine: 8½×11; 56 pages; 40 lb. offset paper; 80 lb. glossy cover; illustrations and photographs. "The *American Atheist* is devoted to the history and lifestyle of atheism, as well as critiques of religion. It attempts to promote an understanding of atheism, while staying aware of religious intrusions into modern life. Most of its articles are aimed at a general—but atheistic—readership. Most readers are college or self-educated." Monthly. Estab. 1958. Circ. 30,000.
Needs: Contemporary, feminist, historical (general), humor/satire, atheist, anti-religious. "All material should have something of particular interest to atheists." No religious fiction. Receives 0-6 mss/month. "We would like to publish 1 story per issue; we do *not* receive enough quality mss to do so." Publishes ms "1-3 months" after acceptance. Length: 2,000-3,000 words preferred; 800 words minimum; 5,000 words maximum. Sometimes critiques rejected mss.
How to Contact: Send complete ms with cover letter and biographical material. Reports in 3 months. SASE. Photocopied submissions OK. Accepts computer printout submissions. Accepts electronic submissions, "WordPerfect compatible or in ASCII. Should be accompanied by printout." Sample copy for 9×12 SAE or label. Fiction guidelines for #10 SASE. Reviews novels and short story collections. Send books to book review editor.
Payment: Pays $15/1,000 words, free subscription to the magazine and contributor's copies.
Terms: Pays on acceptance for one-time rights.
Advice: "Submit material carefully, after reviewing the publication in question. We receive a lot of submissions that are entirely inappropriate, and this slows down our ability to respond."

THE AMERICAN CITIZEN ITALIAN PRESS, 13681 "V" St., Omaha NE 68137. Editor: Diana C. Failla. Magazine. Quarterly.
Needs: Ethnic, historical (general), sports, celebrity, human interest, mainstream and translations. Receives 4-5 unsolicited mss/month. Buys 1-2 mss/issue. Length: 80 words minimum; 1,200 words maximum. Publishes short shorts.
How to Contact: Send complete ms with cover letter. Reports in 1 month on queries. Simultaneous and photocopied submissions OK. Accepts computer printout submissions. Sample copy and fiction guidelines for 9×12 SAE.
Payment: Pays $20-25.
Terms: Pays on publication for one-time rights.

THE AMERICAN NEWSPAPER CARRIER, (II), Box 2225, Kernersville NC 27285. (919)788-4336. Editor: Will H. Lowry. Newsletter: 9×12; 4 pages; slick paper; b&w illustrations and photos. "A motivational newsletter publishing upbeat articles—mystery, humor, adventure and inspirational material for newspaper carriers (younger teenagers—male and female)." Monthly. Estab. 1927.
Needs: Adventure, comics, humor/satire, inspirational, suspense/mystery and young adult/teen. No erotica, fantasy, feminist, gay, juvenile, lesbian, preschool, psychic/supernatural or serialized/excerpted novel. Receives approximately 12 unsolicited mss/month. Buys 1 ms/issue; 12 mss/year. Publishes ms 3-6 months after acceptance. "About all" of fiction is agented. Published new writers within the last year. Length: approximately 1,000 words average; 800 words minimum; 1,200 words maximum. Rarely critiques rejected mss.
How to Contact: Send complete ms. Reports in 1 month. SASE. Accepts computer printout submissions. Free sample copy and fiction guidelines with #10 SAE and 1 first class stamp for each.
Payment: Pays $25.
Terms: Pays on acceptance for all rights.
Advice: "We could use some stories dealing with motor route carriers and adult carriers."

AMERICAN SQUAREDANCE (IV), Burdick Enterprises, Box 488, Huron OH 44839. (419)433-2188. Editors: Stan and Cathie Burdick. Magazine: 5×8½; 100 pages; 50 lb. offset paper; glossy 60 lb. cover stock; illustrations; photos. Magazine about square dancing. Monthly. Estab. 1945. Circ. 20,000.
Needs: Adventure, fantasy, historical, humor/satire, romance, science fiction and western. Must have square dance theme. Published work by John Heisey, Marilyn Dove, David Stone. Buys 2+ mss/year. Length: 2,500 words average. Publishes short stories of 1,000 words average.
How to Contact: Send complete ms with SASE and cover letter with bio. Reports in 2 weeks on queries. Publishes ms within 6 months after acceptance. Free sample copy and fiction guidelines.
Payment: Pays $2/column inch minimum; free magazine subscription or free contributor's copies.
Terms: Pays on publication for all rights.

ANALOG SCIENCE FICTION & FACT, (II), Davis Publications, Inc., 380 Lexington Ave., New York NY 10168-0035. (212)557-9100. Editor: Stanley Schmidt. Magazine: 5³/₁₆ × 7⅜; 192 pages; illustrations (drawings); photos. "Well-written science fiction based on speculative ideas and fact articles on topics on the present and future frontiers of research. Our readership includes intelligent laymen and/or those professionally active in science and technology." Thirteen times yearly. Estab. 1930. Circ. 85,000.
Needs: Science fiction and serialized novels. "No stories which are not truly science fiction in the sense of having a plausible speculative idea *integral to the story*." We do two double-size issues per year (January and July). Receives 300-500 unsolicited fiction mss/month. Buys 4-8 mss/issue. Agented fiction 30%. Published work by Lois McMaster Bujold, Joe Haldeman, Jerry Oltion, Timothy Zahn and Charles Sheffield; published new writers within the last year. Length: 2,000-80,000 words. Publishes short shorts. Critiques rejected mss "when there is time." Sometimes recommends other markets.
How to Contact: Send complete ms with SASE. Cover letter with "anything that I need to know before reading the story, e.g. that it's a rewrite I suggested or that it incorporates copyrighted material. Otherwise, no cover letter is needed." Query with SASE only on serials. Reports in 1 month on both query and ms. Accepts computer printout submissions. Fiction guidelines for SASE. Sample copy for $2.50. Reviews novels and short story collections. Send books to Tom Easton.
Payment: Pays 5-8¢/word.
Terms: Pays on acceptance for first North American serial rights and nonexclusive foreign rights. Sends galleys to author.
Advice: Mss are rejected because of "inaccurate science; poor plotting, characterization or writing in general. We literally only have room for 1-2% of what we get. Many stories are rejected not because of anything conspicuously *wrong*, but because they lack anything sufficiently *special*. What we buy must stand out from the crowd. Fresh, thought-provoking ideas are important. Familiarize yourself with the magazine – but don't try to imitate what we've already published."

‡APPALACHIA JOURNAL, (II, IV), Appalachian Mountain Club, 5 Joy St., Boston MA 02108. (617)523-0636. Editor: Sandy Stott. Magazine: 6 × 9; 160 pages; 50 lb. recycled paper; 10 pt. C1S cover; 5-10 illustrations; 20-30 photographs. "*Appalachia* is the oldest mountaineering and conservation journal in the country. It specializes in backcountry recreation topics (hiking, canoeing, cross-country skiing, etc.) for outdoor (including armchair) enthusiasts." Semiannually. Estab. 1877. Circ. 10,000.
Needs: Prose poem, sports. Receives 5-10 unsolicited mss/month. Buys 1-4 mss/issue; 2-8 mss/year. Publishes ms 6-12 months after acceptance. Length: 500-1,000 words average. Publishes short shorts.
How to Contact: Send complete ms with cover letter. Reports in 2 weeks on queries; 1 month on mss. SASE for query. Photocopied submissions OK. Accepts computer printout submissions. Sample copy for $5. Fiction guidelines for #10 SAE.
Payment: Pays contributor's copies.
Advice: "All submissions should be related to conservation, mountaineering, and/or backcountry recreation both in the Northeast and throughout the world."

ARIZONA COAST, (II), Hale Communications, Inc., 912 Joshua, Parker AZ 85344. (602)669-6464. Editor: Jerry Hale. Magazine: 5½ × 8½; 40 pages; 70 lb. gloss; illustrations; photos. Publication prints stories about tourism, old West, lifestyle for young travel-oriented family audiences, snowbirds and senior citizens. Bimonthly. Estab. 1988. Circ. 15,000.
Needs: Condensed/excerpted novel, historical (general), senior citizen/retirement, serialized novel, western. Receives 1 unsolicited ms/month. Accepts 1 ms/issue; 6 mss/year. Publishes ms within 6 months after acceptance. Publishes short shorts. Sometimes critiques rejected mss and recommends other markets.
How to Contact: Send complete ms with cover letter. Reports in 2 months. Simultaneous submissions OK. Accepts computer printout submissions. Accepts electronic submissions. Sample copy free. Reviews novels and short story collections.
Payment: Pays free subscription to magazine.
Terms: Acquires one-time rights.
Advice: "Don't give up!"

 The double dagger before a listing indicates that the listing is new in this edition. New markets are often the most receptive to freelance contributions.

ART TIMES, A Cultural and Creative Journal, (II), CSS Publications, Inc., 7484 Fite Rd., Saugerties NY 12477. (914)246-6944. FAX: Same. Editor: Raymond J. Steiner. Magazine: 12 × 15; 20 pages; Jet paper and cover; illustrations; photos. "Arts magazine covering the disciplines for an over 40, affluent, arts-conscious and literate audience." Monthly. Estab. 1984. Circ. 15,000.
Needs: Adventure, contemporary, ethnic, fantasy, feminist, gay, historical, humor/satire, lesbian, literary, mainstream and science fiction. "We seek quality literary pieces. Nothing violent, sexist, erotic, juvenile, racist, romantic, political, etc." Receives 30-50 mss/month. Buys 1 ms/issue; 11 mss/year. Publishes ms within 18-24 months of acceptance. Length: 1,500 words maximum. Publishes short shorts.
How to Contact: Send complete ms with cover letter. Reports in 6 months. SASE. Simultaneous and photocopied submissions OK. Accepts computer printout submissions. Sample copy for $1.75, 9 × 12 SAE and 3 first class stamps. Fiction guidelines for #10 SAE and 1 first class stamp.
Payment: Pays $15, free subscription to magazine (one year); 6 contributor's copies.
Terms: Pays on publication for first North American serial rights.
Advice: "Competition is greater (more submissions received), but keep trying. We print new as well as published writers."

ISAAC ASIMOV'S SCIENCE FICTION MAGAZINE, (II), Davis Publications, Inc., 380 Lexington Ave., New York NY 10168-0035. Editor: Gardner Dozois. Magazine: 5³⁄₁₆ × 7⅜ (trim size); 192 pages; 29 lb. newspaper; 70 lb. to 8 pt. C1S cover stock; illustrations; rarely photos. Magazine consists of science fiction and fantasy stories for adults and young adults. Published 13 issues/year. Estab. 1977. Circ. 120,000.
Needs: Science fiction and fantasy. No horror or psychic/supernatural. "We have two double-issues per year (April and November)." Receives approximately 800 unsolicited fiction mss each month. Buys 10 mss/issue. Publishes ms 6-12 months after acceptance. Agented fiction 30%. Published work by George Alec Effinger, Connie Willis, Walter Jon Williams, Gregory Benford and Judith Moffett; published new writers in the last year. Length: up to 20,000 words. Publishes short shorts. Critiques rejected mss "when there is time." Sometimes recommends other markets.
How to Contact: Send complete ms with SASE. Reports in 1-2 months. Photocopied submissions OK. Accepts computer printout submissions only. Fiction guidelines for #10 SASE. Sample copy for $2.50. Reviews novels and short story collections. Send books to book reviewer.
Payment: Pays 6-8¢/word for stories up to 7,500 words; 5¢/word for stories over 12,500; $450 for stories between those limits.
Terms: Pays on acceptance for first North American serial rights plus specified foreign rights, as explained in contract. Very rarely buys reprints. Sends galleys to author.
Advice: "We are looking for character stories rather than those emphasizing technology or science. New writers will do best with a story under 10,000 words. Every new science fiction or fantasy film seems to 'inspire' writers—and this is not a desirable trend. We consider every submission. We published several first stories last year. Be sure to be familiar with our magazine and the type of story we like; workshops and lots of practice help."

THE ASSOCIATE REFORMED PRESBYTERIAN, (II), The Associate Reformed Presbyterian, Inc., 1 Cleveland St., Greenville SC 29601. (803)232-8297. Editor: Ben Johnston. Magazine: 8½ × 11; 32-48 pages; 50 lb. offset paper; illustrations; photos. "We are the official magazine of our denomination. Articles generally relate to activities within the denomination—conferences, department work, etc., with a few special articles that would be of general interest to readers." Monthly. Estab. 1976. Circ. 6,500.
Needs: Contemporary, juvenile, religious/inspirational, spiritual and young adult/teen. "Stories should portray Christian values. No retelling of Bible stories or 'talking animal' stories. Stories for youth should deal with resolving real issues for young people." Receives 30-40 unsolicited fiction mss/month. Buys 1 ms/some months; 10-12 mss/year. Publishes ms within 1 year after acceptance. Recently published work by Louise Carroll, Stephanie Goldberg and David Willingham. Length: 300-750 words (children); 1,250 words maximum (youth). Sometimes critiques rejected mss. Occasionally recommends other markets.
How to Contact: Query and cover letter preferred. Reports in 6 weeks on queries and mss. Simultaneous submissions OK. Sample copy for $1.50; fiction guidelines for #10 SAE and 1 first class stamp.
Payment: Pays $20-50 and contributor's copies.
Terms: Buys first rights.
Advice: "Know your market! It's good to see more realistic stories about poverty and need. Pollyanna has turned stale."

THE ATLANTIC ADVOCATE (I, II, IV), University Press of New Brunswick Ltd., Box 3370, Fredericton, New Brunswick E3B 5A2 Canada. (506)452-6671. Editor: Marilee Little. Magazine: 8¼×10⅞; 64 pages; coated offset paper and cover; illustrations; photos. Magazine of the Atlantic Provinces of Canada—Nova Scotia, New Brunswick, Prince Edward Island and Newfoundland. For "audience 25 years and over." Monthly. Estab. 1956. Circ. 30,000.
Needs: Historical (general), humor/satire and regional. Nothing "offensive or in poor taste." Published work by Elda Cadogan, Eric Cameron and Muriel Miller. Receives 5 unsolicited mss/month. Buys 20 mss/year. "I plan to publish more short stories—at least one piece of fiction per issue." Length: 1,000-1,200 words average; 1,500 words maximum. Occasionally comments on rejected mss.
How to Contact: Send in mss. Reports in 3-4 weeks. Accepts computer printout submissions. Free fiction guidelines.
Payment: Pays 8-10¢/word and contributor's copies; charge for extras.
Terms: Pays on publication for first North American serial rights.

ATLANTIC MONTHLY, (II), 745 Boylston St., Boston MA 02116. (617)536-9500. FAX: (617)536-3975. Editor: William Whitworth. Senior Editor: Michael Curtis. General magazine for the college educated with broad cultural interests. Monthly. Estab. 1857. Circ. 500,000.
Needs: Literary and contemporary. "Seeks fiction that is clear, tightly written with strong sense of 'story' and well-defined characters." Buys 15-18 stories/year. Receives approximately 1,000 unsolicited fiction mss each month. Published work by Alice Munro, E.S. Goldman, Charles Baxter and T.C. Boyle; published new writers within the last year. Preferred length: 2,000-6,000 words.
How to Contact: Send cover letter and complete ms with SASE. Reports in 2 months on mss.
Payment: Pays $2,500/story.
Terms: Pays on acceptance for first North American serial rights.
Advice: When making first contact, "cover letters are sometimes helpful, particularly if they cite prior publications or involvement in writing programs. Common mistakes: excessive cuteness, too lengthy a list of prior publications."

THE BABY CONNECTION NEWS JOURNAL, (IV), Parent Education for Infant Development, P.O. Drawer 13320, San Antonio TX 78213. Editor: G. Morris-Boyd. Newspaper: 35″ web press; 10¾×16; 16 pages; newsprint paper; newsprint cover; illustrations and photographs. "Material on pregnancy, infant sensory development, birthing and breastfeeding for new and expectant parents, midwives, nurses, ob/gyn's, tots." Bimonthly. Estab. 1986. Circ. 36,000.
Needs: Humor/satire, mainstream, preschool (1-4 years), prose poem, romance (contemporary), pregnancy. "We offer tot pages—fiction for beginner readers—we don't want, 'See Jane run.' No out-of-touch, mystical or crude, rude, demeaning fiction." Receives 6-10 unsolicited mss/month. Accepts 2-3 mss/issue; 18-20 mss/year. Publishes ms 6-8 weeks after acceptance. Published work by Marc Swan, George White. Length: 350 words average; 300 words minimum; 600 words maximum. Publishes short shorts.
How to Contact: Query with clips of published work. Send complete manuscript with cover letter. "Always include a personal bio—not all about works published but info on the writer personally. Married? Children? Hobbies? Our readers like to feel they know the writers personally." SASE. Sample copy for 10×13 SAE with 2 first class stamps. Fiction guidelines for #10 SAE and 1 first class stamp.
Payment: Pays in contributor's copies. Charges for extras.
Terms: Acquires all rights.
Advice: "We especially encourage the male perspective. Everyone knows about kids and babies—so a fiction base should be a breeze for our selected themes of birthing, pregnancy, raising kids, finding time for self and spouse, family values."

BALTIMORE JEWISH TIMES, (II, IV), 2104 N. Charles St., Baltimore MD 21218. (301)752-3504. Local News Editor: Barbara Pash. Magazine: 160 pages a week, average; illustrations; photos. Magazine with subjects of interest to Jewish readers. Weekly. Estab. 1918. Circ. 20,000.
Needs: Contemporary Jewish themes only. Receives 7-10 unsolicited fiction mss/month. Buys 10-15 mss/year. Length: 3,500 words maximum (or 6-15 typed pages). Occasionally critiques rejected mss.
How to Contact: Send complete ms. Simultaneous, photocopied and previously published submissions OK "on occasion." Accepts computer printout submissions. Reports in 2 months on mss. Sample copy $2 and legal-size envelope.
Payment: Pays $35-150.
Terms: Pays on publication.

BECKETT BASEBALL CARD MONTHLY, (IV), Statabase, Suite 200, 4887 Alpha Rd., Dallas TX 75244. (214)991-6657. Editor: Dr. James Beckett. Fiction Editor: Mike Payne. Magazine: 8½×11; 96 pages; coated glossy paper; 8 pt. Sterling cover; 12 illustrations; 100+ photographs. "Collecting baseball cards is a leisure-time avocation. It's wholesome and something the entire family can do together. We emphasize its positive aspects. For card collectors and sports enthusiasts, 6-60." Monthly. Estab. 1984. Circ. 800,000+ paid.
Needs: Humor/satire, sports, young adult/teen (10-18 years). "Sports hero worship; historical fiction involving real baseball figures; fictionalizing specific franchises of national interest such as the Yankees, Dodgers or Mets." No fiction that is "unrealistic sportswise." Publishes ms 4-6 months after acceptance. Length: 1,500 words average; 2,500 words maximum. Publishes short shorts. Sometimes comments on rejected mss or recommends other markets "if we feel we can help the reader close the gap between rejection and acceptance."
How to Contact: Send complete ms with cover letter. Include Social Security number. Reports in 6 weeks. SASE. Will consider reprints "if prior publication is in a very obscure or very prestigious publication." Accepts computer printout submissions. Sample copy for $3. Fiction guidelines free.
Payment: Pays $80-400.
Terms: Pays on acceptance for first rights.
Advice: "Fiction must be baseball oriented and accessible to both pre-teenagers and adults; fiction must stress redeeming social values; fictionalization must involve the heroes of the game (past or present) or a major-league baseball franchise with significant national following. The writer must have a healthy regard for standard English usage. A prospective writer must examine several issues of our publication prior to submission. Our publication is extremely successful in our genre, and our writers must respect the sensitivities of our readers. We are different from other sports publications, and a prospective writer must understand our distinctiveness to make a sale here."

BEPUZZLED, (II, IV), Lombard Marketing, Inc., 45 Wintonbury Ave., Bloomfield CT 06002. (203)286-4222. Editor: Luci Seccareccia. "Mystery jigsaw puzzles ... includes short mystery story with clues contained in puzzle picture to solve the mystery for preschool, 8-12 year olds, adults." Estab. 1987.
Needs: Mystery: Adventure, juvenile, mainstream, preschool, young adult, suspense--all with mystery theme. Receives 3 unsolicited fiction mss/month. Buys 20 mss/year. Publishes ms 6-18 months after acceptance. Recently published work by John Lutz, Matt Christopher, Alan Robbins, Henry Slesar. Length: 4,000 words preferred; 4,000 words minimum; 5,000 words maximum. Sometimes recommends other markets.
How to Contact: Query for submission guidelines. Reports in 2 weeks. SASE. Simultaneous submissions OK. Puzzles range from $10.50 to $18.95 plus postage. Fiction guidelines free.
Payment: Pays $200 minimum.
Terms: Payment is made on delivery of final ms. Buys all rights.
Advice: "Thoughtful, challenging mysteries that can be concluded with a visual element of a puzzle. Many times we select certain subject matter and then send out these specifics to our pool of writers ... Think out the mystery. Work backwards. Think up the solution, list clues and red herrings. Then write the story containing supporting information. Play one of our mystery thrillers so you understand the relationship between the story and the picture."

BIKE REPORT, (I, IV), Bikecentennial, Box 8308, Missoula MT 59807. (406)721-1776. Editor: Daniel D'Ambrosio. Magazine on bicycle touring: 8½×11; 24 pages; coated paper; self cover; illustrations and b&w photos. Published 9 times annually. Estab. 1974. Circ. 18,000.
Needs: Adventure, fantasy, historical (general), humor/satire, regional and senior citizen/retirement with a bicycling theme. Buys variable number of mss/year. Published new writers within the last year. Length: 2,000 words average; 1,000 words minimum; 2,500 words maximum. Publishes short shorts. Occasionally comments on a rejected ms.
How to Contact: Send complete ms with SASE. Reports in 6 weeks. Simultaneous, photocopied and previously published submissions OK. Accepts computer printout submissions. Prefers hard copy with disk submission. Sample copy for $1, 9×12 SAE and 60¢ postage. Fiction guidelines for #10 SAE and 1 first class stamp.
Payment: Pays $25-65/published page.
Terms: Pays on publication for first North American serial rights.

BLACK BELT, (II), Rainbow Publications, Inc., 24715 Ave. Rockefeller, Valencia CA 91355. (818)843-4444. Executive Editor: Jim Coleman. Magazine: 112 pages. Emphasizes "martial arts for both practitioner and layman." Monthly. Circ. 100,000.

Needs: Martial arts-related, historical and modern-day. Buys 1-2 fiction mss/year. Publishes ms 3 months to 1 year after acceptance. Published work by Glenn Yancey.
How to Contact: Query first. Reports in 2-3 weeks. Photocopied submissions OK. Accepts computer printout submissions.
Payment: Pays $100-200.
Terms: Pays on publication for first North American serial rights; retains right to republish.

THE B'NAI B'RITH INTERNATIONAL JEWISH MONTHLY, (IV), 1640 Rhode Island Ave. NW, Washington DC 20036. (202)857-6645. Editor: Jeff Rubin. Magazine: 8⅛ × 10⅞; 48-56 pages; coated stock; illustrations; photos. Subjects of Jewish interest—politics, culture, lifestyle, religion—for a Jewish family audience. Published 10 times annually. Estab. 1886.
Needs: Contemporary, ethnic, historical (general), humor/satire. No immigrant memoirs; holocaust memoirs and fiction discouraged. Receives 2 unsolicited mss/month. Buys 2 mss/year. Publishes ms 6 months to 1 year after acceptance. Length: 2,500 words average; 1,000 words minimum; 5,000 words maximum. Occasionally critiques rejected mss. Recommends other markets.
How to Contact: Reports in 1 month on queries; 6 weeks on mss. Include cover letter and SASE. Accepts computer printout submissions. Accepts electronic submissions via disk or modem. Sample copy $2.
Payment: Pays $100-$750.
Terms: Pays on publication for first North American serial rights. Sends galleys to author.
Advice: "A writer who submits a manuscript without a cover letter doesn't seem to have an awareness of interest in our publication. Cover letters should include a sentence or two of biographical information (publishing credits) and an introduction to the story."

BOMB MAGAZINE, New Art Publications, Suite 1002A, 594 Broadway, New York NY 10012. (212)431-3943. Editor: Betsy Sussler. Magazine: 11 × 14; 100 pages; 70 lb. gloss cover; illustrations and photographs. "Artist-and-writer-edited magazine." Quarterly. Estab. 1981.
Needs: Contemporary, ethnic, experimental, serialized novel. Receives 40 unsolicited mss/month. Buys 6 mss/issue; 24 mss/year. Publishes ms 3-6 months after acceptance. Agented fiction 20%. Recently published work by Patrick McGrath, Lynne Tillman, Kathy Acker. Length: 10-12 pages average. Publishes short interviews.
How to Contact: Send complete manuscript with cover letter. Reports in 6-8 weeks on mss. SASE. Sample copy $5 with $2.50 postage.
Payment: Pays $100 and contributor's copies.
Terms: Pays on publication for first or one-time rights. Sends galleys to author.

BOSTON REVIEW, (II), Boston Critic Inc., 33 Harrison Ave., Boston MA 02111. Publisher/Editor: Joshua Cohen. "A bimonthly magazine of politics, arts and culture." Tabloid: 11 × 17; 24-32 pages; jet paper. Estab. 1975. Circ. 10,000.
Needs: Contemporary, ethnic, experimental, literary, prose poem, regional, and translations. Receives 100+ unsolicited fiction mss/month. Buys 4-6 mss/year. Publishes ms an average of 4 months after acceptance. Published work by Joyce Carol Oates, Yasunari Kawabata, Stephen Dixon. Length: 3,000 words maximum; 2,000 words average. Publishes short shorts. Occasionally critiques rejected ms.
How to Contact: Send complete ms with cover letter and SASE. "You can almost always tell professional writers by the very thought-out way they present themselves in cover letters. But even a beginning writer should find some link between the work (its style, subject, etc.) and the publication—some reason why the editor should consider publishing it." Reports in 2-3 months. Simultaneous and photocopied mss OK. Accepts computer printout submissions. Sample copy for $4. Reviews novels and short story collections. Send books to Sophie Glazer, managing editor.
Payment: Pays $50-200 and 2 contributor's copies.
Terms: Pays on publication for first rights.
Advice: "We believe that original fiction is an important part of our culture—and that this should be represented by the *Boston Review*. Our New Voices program, generously funded by a grant from the Bydale Foundation, enables us to work closely with new and promising writers."

BOSTONIA MAGAZINE, The Magazine of Culture and Ideas, (IV), Boston University, 10 Lenox St., Brookline MA 02146. (617)353-3081/2917. Editor-in-Chief: Keith Botsford. Senior Editor: Janice Friedman. Magazine: 8½ × 11; 72-80 pages; 60 lb. paper; 80 lb. cover stock. "Thoughtful provocative prose for national audience." Quarterly. Estab. 1900. Circ. 140,000.

Needs: Adventure, condensed/excerpted novel, contemporary, ethnic, experimental, horror, humor/satire, literary, mainstream, regional, serialized novel and suspense/mystery. Plans to publish fiction in each issue. Receives 30 unsolicited mss each month. Buys 1 ms/issue; 6 mss/year. Published work by Conall Ryan, John Auerbach and Bette Howland. Length: 3,000 words average; 1,500 words minimum; 4,000-5,000 words maximum.
How to Contact: Send complete ms with cover letter. Reporting time varies. SASE. Sample copy $2.50. Free fiction guidelines.
Payment: Pays $400-700, contributor's copies, charges for extras.
Terms: Pays on acceptance for first North American serial rights.

BOWBENDER, Canada's Archery Magazine, (II, IV), R.R.2, Didsbury, Alberta T0M 0W0 Canada. (403)335-9445. FAX: (403)337-3460. Editor: Kathleen Windsor. Magazine: 8¼ × 10⅞; 48 pages; 60 lb. gloss stock; 100 lb. gloss cover; illustrations; photos. "We publish material dealing with hunting, wildlife, conservation, equipment, nature and Olympic team coverage etc., for outdoorsmen, especially hunters and competitive archers." Published 6 times/year. Estab. 1984. Circ. 45,000.
Needs: Adventure, sports and western. *"Might* publish fiction if it concerns (bow) hunting, archery or traveling in the Canadian outdoors." Does not want to see anything veering off the topic of archery in Canada. Publishes ms within 1 year after acceptance. Length: 1,200 words average; 500 words minimum; 2,000 words maximum.
How to Contact: Query first or send complete manuscript with cover letter, which should include a brief autobiography (archery) to be included in the magazine. Reports in 1 week on queries; 3 weeks on mss. SASE for ms. Photocopied submissions OK. Accepts computer printout submissions. Sample copy for $2.95 (Canadian), 9 × 12 SAE and $1.12 (Canadian postage). Editorial/Photography guidelines for #10 SAE and 40¢ (Canadian), 30¢ (U.S.) postage.
Payment: Pays $300 maximum. (Roughly 10¢/word depending on regularity of submission, quality photo complement, etc.) Free contributor's copies; charge for extras.
Terms: Pays on publication for first North American serial rights, or first Canadian if requested and acceptable.
Advice: "Fiction remains a 'big' maybe. Write for guidelines and review a sample copy first."

BOWHUNTER MAGAZINE, The Magazine for the Hunting Archer, (IV), Cowles Magazines, Inc., Box 8200, Harrisburg PA 17105. (717)657-9555. FAX: (717)657-9526. Editor: M.R. James. Editorial Director: Dave Canfield. Magazine: 8¼ × 10¾; 150 pages; 75 lb. glossy paper; 150 lb. glossy cover stock; illustrations and photographs. "We are a special interest publication for people who hunt with the bow and arrow. We publish hunting adventure and how-to stories. Our audience is predominantly male, 30-50, middle income." Bimonthly. Circ. 230,000.
Needs: Bowhunting, outdoor adventure. "Writers must expect a very limited market. We buy only one or two fiction pieces a year. Writers must know the market—bowhunting—and let that be the theme of their work. No 'me and my dog' types of stories; no stories by people who have obviously never held a bow in their hands." Receives 1-2 unsolicited fiction mss/month. Buys 1-2 mss/year. Publishes ms 3 months to 2 years after acceptance. Length: 1,500 words average; 500 words minimum; 2,000 words maximum. Publishes short shorts. Length: 500 words. Sometimes critiques rejected mss and recommends other markets.
How to Contact: Query first or send complete ms with cover letter. Reports in 2 weeks on queries; 6 weeks on mss. Accepts computer printout submissions. Sample copy for $2 and 8½ × 11 SAE with appropriate postage. Fiction guidelines for #10 SAE and 1 first class stamp.
Payment: Pays $25-250.
Terms: Pays on acceptance for first North American serial rights.
Advice: "We have a resident humorist who supplies us with most of the 'fiction' we need. But if a story comes through the door which captures the essence of bowhunting and we feel it will reach out to our readers, we will buy it. Despite our macho outdoor magazine status, we are a bunch of English majors who love to read. You can't bull your way around real outdoor people—they can spot a phony at 20 paces. If you've never camped out under the stars and listened to an elk bugle and try to relate that experience without really experiencing it, someone's going to know. We are very specialized; we don't want stories about shooting apples off people's heads or of Cupid's arrow finding its mark. James

Market categories: (I) Beginning; (II) General; (III) Prestige; (IV) Specialized.

Dickey's *Deliverance* used bowhunting metaphorically, very effectively . . . while we don't expect that type of writing from everyone, that's the kind of feeling that characterizes a good piece of outdoor fiction."

BOYS' LIFE, For All Boys, (III), Boy Scouts of America, Magazine Division, Box 152079, 1325 Walnut Hill Lane, Irving TX 75015-2079. (214)580-2000. Editor-in-Chief: William B. McMorris. Fiction Editor: Kathleen V. DaGroomes. Magazine: 8 × 11; 68 pages; slick cover stock; illustrations; photos. *"Boys' Life* covers Boy Scout activities and general interest subjects for ages 8 to 18, Boy Scouts, Cub Scouts and others of that age group." Monthly. Estab. 1911. Circ. 1,500,000.
Needs: Adventure, humor/satire, science fiction, suspense/mystery, western and sports. "We publish short stories aimed at a young adult audience and frequently written from the viewpoint of a 10- to 16-year-old boy protagonist." Receives approximately 100 unsolicited mss/month. Buys 12-18 mss/ year. Published work by Donald J. Sobol, Maureen Crane Wartski, Raboo Rodgers; published new writers within the last year. Length: 500 words minimum; 1,200 words maximum; 1,000 words average. "Very rarely" critiques rejected ms.
How to Contact: Send complete ms with SASE. "We'd much rather see manuscripts than queries." Reports in 2 weeks. Simultaneous and photocopied submissions OK. Accepts computer printout submissions. For sample copy "check your local library." Writer's guidelines available; send SASE.
Payment: Pays $500 and up, "depending on length and writer's experience with us."
Terms: Pays on acceptance for one-time rights.
Advice: *"Boys' Life* writers understand the readers. They treat them as intelligent human beings with a thirst for knowledge and entertainment. We tend to use many of the same authors repeatedly because their characters, themes, etc., develop a following among our readers."

BREAD, (II), Church of the Nazarene, 6401 The Paseo, Kansas City MO 64131. (816)333-7000. FAX: (816)333-1683. Editor: Karen De Sollar. Magazine: 8½ × 11; 34 pages; illustrations; photos. Christian leisure reading magazine for junior and senior high students. Monthly. Circ. 18,000.
Needs: Fiction and how-to stories on Christian living. Themes should be school and church oriented, but without sermonizing. Buys 25 mss/year. Recently published work by Alan Cliburn, Jeanette D. Gardner, Betty Everette and Mike LaCrosse; published new writers within the last year.
How to Contact: Send complete ms with SASE. Reports in 6 weeks on mss. Sample copy $1, 9 × 12 SAE and 45¢ postage. Free guidelines for SASE.
Payment: Pays 4¢/word for first rights and 3.5¢/word for second rights.
Terms: Pays on acceptance for first rights and second serial rights. Accepts simultaneous submissions. Byline given.
Advice: "Our readers clamor for fiction."

BUFFALO SPREE MAGAZINE, (II, IV), Spree Publishing Co., Inc., 4511 Harlem Rd., Buffalo NY 14226. (716)839-3405. Editor: Johanna V. Shotell. "City magazine for professional, educated and above-average income people." Quarterly. Estab. 1967. Circ. 21,000.
Needs: Literary, contemporary, feminist, mystery, adventure, humor and ethnic. No pornographic or religious. Buys about 15 mss/issue; 60 mss/year. Length: 2,500 words maximum.
How to Contact: Send complete ms with SASE. Reports within 3-6 months. Sample copy for $2 with 9 × 12 SASE and $2.40 postage.
Payment: Pays $80-150; 1 contributor's copy.
Terms: Pays on publication for first rights.

BUZZWORM: THE ENVIRONMENTAL JOURNAL, (II), Buzzworm, Inc., Suite 206, 2305 Canyon Blvd., Boulder CO 80302. (303)442-1969. Managing Editor: Elizabeth Darby Junkin. Magazine: 8½ × 11; 96 pages; glossy. "Environmental magazine with once-a-year fiction section for outdoor/environment-interested readers, upscale and sophisticated." Bimonthly. Estab. 1988. Circ. 100,000.
Needs: Condensed/excerpted novel, fantasy, literary, "environmental fiction." "All work must have some kind of environmental theme." We plan to publish a special fiction issue other than our regular 'summer reading' issue." Buys 3 mss/year. Publishes ms 6 months after acceptance. Agented fiction 100%. Published work by John Nichols, Edward Abbey and Barbara Kingsolver. Length: 3,500 words preferred; 2,500 words minimum; 5,000 words maximum. Publishes short shorts. Length: 1,000 words.
How to Contact: Send complete ms with cover letter. Submit through agent. Reports on queries in 6 weeks; on mss in 2 months. SASE. Photocopied submissions OK. Sample copy for 9 × 12 SAE and $2.25 postage. Fiction guidelines for #10 SAE and 1 first class stamp. Reviews novels and short story collections. Send books to Ilana Kotin, associate editor.

According to the folks at Buzzworm: The Environmental Journal, the term "buzzworm" means rattlesnake. In a sense, then, Buzzworm strives to "rattle" readers about the condition of the world's environment. The photograph of the she-lion on the cover here "represents the power of the natural environment, and the accessibility of the environmental movement to all people," says Ann Carey, the magazine's photo editor. In particular, she says, "We felt it conveyed the mystery and power of the mountain lion myth described in Charles Bowden's essay, 'Love Among the Lion Killers,' contained within the issue." The photographer is W. Perry Conway.

Payment: "Varies."
Terms: Buys all rights, first North American serial rights.
Advice: "We offer the Edward Abbey Ecofiction award once a year." Write for details.

IL CAFFÉ, The Magazine for the Italian in the U.S., (II, IV), #626, 840 Post St., San Francisco CA 94109. (415)928-4886. Editor: R.T. LoVerso. Magazine: 8×12; 36 pages; illustrations and photos. "Publishes interviews and biographical sketches and articles on all topics (politics, culture, history, fashion, travel, book and film reviews, sports, cuisine) of interest to Italian Americans and Italians." Bimonthly. Estab. 1981. Circ. 20,000.
Needs: Adventure, contemporary, ethnic, humor/satire, literary, mainstream, prose poem, romance (contemporary, historical, young adult), serialized/excerpted novel and translations. Receives 15-20 unsolicited mss/month. Accepts 1-2 mss/issue; 6-12 mss/year. Published new writers within the last year. Length: 1,500-3,000 words. Also publishes short shorts. Occasionally critiques rejected mss.
How to Contact: Send complete ms with SASE. Reports in 1 month. Publishes ms 2-6 months after acceptance. Simultaneous, photocopied and previously published submissions OK. Accepts computer printout submissions. Sample copy $2.25.
Payment: Pays in contributor's copies; $1.25 charge for extras.
Terms: Acquires first rights. Buys reprints.
Advice: "Through primarily interested in articles and stories that are of relevance to the Italian American experience, will consider publishing any story that is of multicultural interest or universal appeal."

CAMPUS LIFE MAGAZINE, (II), Christianity Today, Inc., 465 Gundersen Drive, Carol Stream IL 60188. (312)260-6200. FAX: (708)260-0114. Editor: James Long. Senior Editor: Christopher Lutes. Magazine: 8¼×11¼; 100 pages; 4-color and b&w illustrations; 4-color and b&w photos. "General interest magazine with a religious twist. Not limited strictly to Christian content." Articles "vary from serious to humorous to current trends and issues, for high school and college age readers." Monthly except combined May-June and July-August issues. Estab. 1942. Circ. 130,000.
Needs: Condensed novel, humor/satire, prose poem, serialized/excerpted novel. "All submissions must be contemporary, reflecting the teen experience in the 90s. We are a Christian magazine but are *not* interested in sappy, formulaic, sentimentally religious stories. We *are* interested in well crafted stories that portray life realistically, stories high school and college youth relate to. Nothing contradictory of Christian values. If you don't understand our market and style, don't submit." Buys 5 mss/year. Reading and response time slower in summer. Published work by Barbara Durkin, Christopher Conn; published new writers within the last year. Length: 1,000-3,000 words average, "possibly longer." Publishes short shorts.

How to Contact: Query with short synopsis of work, published samples and SASE. Does not accept unsolicited manuscripts. Reports in 4-6 weeks on queries. Sample copy $2 and 9½×11 envelope.
Payment: Pays "generally" $250-400; 2 contributor's copies.
Terms: Pays on acceptance for one-time rights.
Advice: "We print finely crafted fiction that carries a contemporary teen (older teen) theme. First person fiction often works best. Ask us for sample copy with fiction story. Fiction communicates to our reader. We want experienced fiction writers who have something to say to or about young people without getting propagandistic."

CANADIAN MESSENGER, (IV), Apostleship of Prayer, 661 Greenwood Ave., Toronto, Ontario M4J 4B3 Canada. (416)466-1195. Editors: Rev. F.J. Power, S.J.; Alfred De Manche. Magazine: 7×10; 32 pages; glossy paper; self cover; illustrations; photos. Publishes material with a "religious theme or a moral about people, adventure, heroism and humor, for Roman Catholic adults." Monthly. Estab. 1891. Circ. 17,000.
Needs: Religious/inspirational. Receives 10 mss/month. Buys 1 ms/issue. Publishes ms within 1-1½ years of acceptance. Length: 500 words minimum; 1,500 words maximum.
How to Contact: Send complete ms with cover letter. Reports on mss in "a few" weeks. SASE. Accepts computer printout submissions. Sample copy for $1. Fiction guidelines for $1 and 7½×10½ SAE.
Payment: Pays 4¢/word.
Terms: Pays on acceptance for first North American rights.

CAPPER'S, (II), Stauffer Communications, Inc., 616 Jefferson, Topeka KS 66607. (913)295-1108. Editor: Nancy Peavler. Magazine: 24-48 pages; newsprint paper and cover stock; photos. A "clean, uplifting and nonsensational newspaper for families from children to grandparents." Biweekly. Estab. 1879. Circ. 375,000.
Needs: Serialized novels. "We accept only novel-length stories for serialization. No fiction containing violence, sexual references or obscenity." Receives 2-3 unsolicited fiction mss each month. Buys 2-3 stories/year. Published work by Juanita Urbach, Colleen L. Reece, John E. Stolberg; published new writers within the last year.
How to Contact: Send complete ms with SASE. Cover letter and/or synopsis helpful. Reports in 5-6 months on ms. Sample copy for 85¢.
Payment: Pays $75-250 for one-time serialization and contributor's copies (1-2 copies as needed for copyright).
Terms: Pays on acceptance for second serial (reprint) rights and one-time rights.
Advice: "Please proofread and edit carefully. We've seen major characters change names partway through the manuscript."

CAREER FOCUS, COLLEGE PREVIEW, DIRECT AIM, JOURNEY, VISIONS, Communications Publishing Group, Inc., 3100 Broadway, 225 PennTower, Kansas City MO 64111. Editor: Georgia Clark. Magazines: 70 pages; 50 lb. paper; gloss enamel cover; 8×10 or 5×7 (preferred) illustrations; camera ready photographs. *Career Focus*, "For Today's Professionals" includes career preparation, continuing education and upward mobility skills for advanced Black and Hispanic college students and college graduates. Annually. *College Preview*, "For College-Bound Students" is designed to inform and motivate Black and Hispanic high school students on college preparation and career planning. *Direct Aim*, "A Resource for Career Strategies," is designed for Black and Hispanic college students. Discusses career preparation advancement and management strategies as well as life-enhancement skills. Quarterly. Circ. 600,000. *Journey*, "A Success Guide for College and Career-Bound Students" is for Asian American high school and college students who have indicated a desire to pursue higher education through college, vocational/technical or proprietary schools. Semiannually. *Visions*, "A Success Guide for Career-Bound Students" is designed for Native American students who want to pursue a higher education through college, vocational/technical or proprietary schools. Semiannually. Specialized publication limited to certain subjects or themes.
Needs: Adventure, condensed/excerpted novel, contemporary, ethnic, experimental, historical (general), humor/satire, prose poem, romance (contemporary, historical, young adult), science fiction, sports, suspense/mystery. Receives 2-3 unsolicited mss/month. Buys 2-4 mss/year. After acceptance of ms, time varies before it is published. Length: 1,000 words minimum; 4,000 words maximum. Publishes short shorts. Does not usually comment on rejected ms.

How to Contact: Query with clips of published work (include Social Security number) or send copy of resume and when available to perform. Reports in 4-6 weeks. SASE. Simultaneous, photocopied and reprint submissions OK. Sample copy and fiction guidelines for 9×10 SASE.
Payment: Pays 10¢ per word.
Terms: Pays on acceptance for first rights and second serial (reprint) rights.
Advice: "Today's fiction market is geared toward stories that are generated from real-life events because readers are more sophisticated and aware of current affairs. But because everyday life is quite stressful nowadays, even young adults want to escape into science fiction and fairytales. Fiction should be entertaining and easy to read. Be aware of reader audience. Material should be designed for status-conscious young adults searching for quality and excellence. Do not assume readers are totally unsophisticated and avoid casual mention of drug use, alcohol abuse or sex. Avoid overly ponderous, overly cute writing styles. Query describing the topic and length of proposed article. Include samples of published work if possible. Must be typed, double spaced on white bond paper (clean copy only)."

CAT FANCY, (IV), Fancy Publications, P.O. Box 6050, Mission Viejo CA 92690. (714)855-8822. Editor-in-Chief: K.E. Segnar. General cat and kitten magazine, for "people interested in the responsible care of their pets." Monthly. Circ. 317,000.
Needs: Cat-related themes only. "Stories should focus on a cat or cats, not just be about people who happen to have a cat." Receives approximately 40 unsolicited fiction mss/month. Accepts 12 mss/year. Publishes ms 2-10 months after acceptance. Agented fiction 10%. Published work by Barbara L. Diamond, Edward W. Clarke and Sandi Fisher; published new writers within the last year. Length: 3,000 words maximum. Sometimes recommends other markets.
How to Contact: "Please query first, and enclose copies of published clips, if available." Reports in 2 months. SASE. Simultaneous and photocopied submissions OK. Sample copy for $4. Fiction guidelines for SASE.
Payment: Pays 5¢/word and 2 contributor's copies; $4 charge for extras.
Terms: Rarely buys reprints.
Advice: "Don't let rejections discourage you. We reject many well-written stories because we simply don't have space for them all. At the same time, don't assume your story is beyond reproach. Seek out the opinions of teachers and of writers you respect—and not just those who will be kind to you. Do the best you can to 'develop backbone' and to look hard at your work. Then consider the market of the magazine in which you want to be published. Send out your story and if rejected, revise or choose another market and try, try again. Remember: You never really fail until you stop trying."

CATHOLIC FORESTER, (I, II, III), Catholic Order of Foresters, Box 3012, 425 W. Shuman Blvd., Naperville IL 60566-7012. (708)983-4920. Editor: Barbara Cunningham. Magazine: 8¼×10¾; 40 pages; 45 lb. paper and 60 lb. cover stock; illustrations; photos. "No special theme but we want interesting, lively stories and articles. No true confessions type, no dumb romances. People who have not bothered to study the art of writing need not apply." Bimonthly. Estab. 1884. Circ. 160,000.
Needs: Adventure, contemporary, ethnic, feminist, humor/satire, mainstream, regional, senior citizen/retirement, sports and suspense/mystery. Receives 200 unsolicited fiction mss/month. Buys approximately 7-8 mss/issue; 100 mss/year. "Publication may be immediate or not for 6 months." Agented fiction 5%. Published work by John Keefauver, William Childress and Donald Smith. Length: 2,000 words average; 3,000 words maximum. Also publishes short shorts. Occasionally critiques rejected mss. Sometimes recommends other markets.
How to Contact: Send complete ms. "Cover letters extolling the virtue of the story do not help—manuscripts stand or fall on their own merit. I do not accept queries anymore—too many problems in authors misunderstanding 'speculation,' and it is too time consuming to answer each one." SASE for ms. Simultaneous, photocopied and reprint submissions OK. Sample copy for 8½×11 SASE and 73¢ postage. Fiction guidelines for #10 SASE.
Payment: Pays 10¢/word minimum and one contributor's copy to new author. Sometimes more to frequent contributors. Author may request more copies—no charge.
Advice: "I enjoy a short, friendly cover letter but do not appreciate a long letter telling me the author's personal history, past credits, a complicated synopsis of the story enclosed, and his/her opinion of it. The only thing that counts is the quality and suitability of the story itself. I do make short comments occasionally on rejection slips but cannot go into great detail. Before submitting a story, act out some of your scenes to see if they make sense—speak your dialogue aloud to assure that it is realistic. Ask yourself 'is this how people really talk to each other?' Also, every rejection doesn't mean that the

editor thinks the story is bad. It may just simply not fit the publication's readers, or our space may be limited."

CAVALIER MAGAZINE, (II), Dugent Publishing Corp., Suite 600, 2600 Douglas Rd., Coral Gables FL 33134. (305)443-2378. Editor: Douglas Allen. Fiction Editor: M. DeWalt. Magazine: 8½×11; 103 pages; 60 lb. paper; laminated cover stock; illustrations; photos. Sexually oriented, sophisticated magazine for single men aged 18-35. Published special fiction issue last year; plans another. Monthly. Estab. 1952. Circ. 250,000.
Needs: Adventure, horror and erotica. No material on children, religious subjects or anything that might be libelous. Receives approximately 200 unsolicited fiction mss each month. Buys 3 mss/issue. Published work by Janris Manley, Dillon McGrath, Wayne Rogers; published new writers within the last year. Length: 1,500-3,000 words. Critiques rejected mss "when there is time." Sometimes recommends other markets.
How to Contact: Send complete ms with SASE. A cover letter is not necessary except if ms is a multiple submission or there's special information. Accepts computer printout submissions. Reports in 3-6 weeks on mss. Sample copy for $3. Fiction guidelines for SASE.
Payment: Pays $150-250. Stories sometimes reprinted for ⅓ of original payment.
Terms: Pays on publication for first North American serial rights.
Advice: "We are very strict about stories having a plot . . . i.e., beginning, middle and interesting end. Too many writers send us 'episodes' or sexual streams of consciousness type of material and no matter how titillating the sexual content, if there's no good storyline or if it's too esoteric, forget it. Ask for our guidelines and follow them. Sponsors an annual fiction contest (first prize usually $300) . . . watch publication."

CHESAPEAKE BAY MAGAZINE, (II, IV), Chesapeake Bay Communications, Inc., 1819 Bay Ridge Ave., Annapolis MD 21403. (301)263-2662. Editor: Jean Waller. Magazine: 8½×11½; 88 pages; coated stock paper; coated cover stock; illustrations; photos. "*Chesapeake Bay Magazine* is a regional publication for those who enjoy reading about the Bay and its tributaries. Most of our articles are boating-related. Our readers are yachtsmen, boating families, fishermen, ecologists, anyone who is part of Chesapeake Bay life." Monthly. Estab. 1971. Circ. 32,000.
Needs: Adventure, humor and historical. "Any fiction piece *must* concern the Chesapeake Bay. Only stories done by authors who are familiar with the area are accepted. No general type stories with the Chesapeake Bay superimposed in an attempt to make a sale." Buys 4 short stories/year. Receives approximately 3 unsolicited fiction mss each month. Recently published work by Gilbert Byron and Arline Chase. Published new writers within the last year. Length: 1,250-3,000 words. Publishes short shorts.
How to Contact: Query or send ms, including cover letter with bio information to indicate familiarity with our publication. SASE always. Reports in 1 month on queries, 2 months on mss. Publishes ms an average of 12-14 months after acceptance. Sample copy $2.50. Writer's guidelines for SASE.
Payment: Pays $85-125; 2 contributor's copies.
Terms: Pays on publication for all rights or first North American serial rights.
Advice: "Make sure you have knowledge of the area. Send only material that is related to our market. All manuscripts must be typed, double-spaced, in duplicate. Our readers are interested in any and all material about the Chesapeake Bay area. Thus we use a limited amount of fiction as well as factual material. Work must be fairly short, or have clear break-points for serialization."

CHESS LIFE, (IV), U.S. Chess Federation, 186 Route 9W, New Windsor NY 12553. (914)562-8350. Editor: Glenn Petersen. Magazine: 8¼×10¾; 68 pages; slick paper; illustrations and photos. "Chess: news, theory, human interest, for chess players (mostly male)." Monthly. Circ. 58,000.
Needs: "Chess must be central to story." Receives 3 unsolicited mss/month. Accepts 2 mss/year. Publishes short shorts. Occasionally critiques rejected mss.
How to Contact: Query first. Free sample copy and fiction guidelines.

CHIC, (II), Larry Flynt Publications, Suite 300, 9171 Wilshire Blvd., Beverly Hills CA 90210. Executive Editor: Doug Oliver. Magazine: 100 pages; illustrations; photos. "Men's magazine, for men and women." Monthly. Estab. 1976. Circ. 100,000.

Read the Business of Fiction section to learn the correct way to prepare and submit a manuscript.

Needs: Erotica. Receives 20-30 unsolicited mss/month. Buys 1 ms/issue; 12 mss/year. Publishes ms 1-6 months after acceptance. Published new writers within the last year. Length: 3,000 words average; 2,500 words minimum; 3,500 words maximum. Occasionally critiques rejected mss. Recommends other markets.

How to Contact: Send complete ms with cover letter, which should include "writer's name, address, telephone number and whether the manuscript has been or is being offered elsewhere." Reports in 4-6 weeks. SASE for ms. Photocopied submissions OK. Accepts computer printout submissions. Fiction guidelines for SASE.

Payment: Pays $500.

Terms: Pays on acceptance for all rights.

Advice: "Readers have indicated a desire to read well-written erotic fiction, which we classify as a good story with a sexual undercurrent. The writer should read several published short stories to see the general tone and style that we're looking for. The writer should keep in mind that the first requirement is that the story be a well-written piece of fiction, and secondarily that it deal with sex; we are not interested in 'clinically descriptive' sex accounts."

CHICKADEE, The Magazine for Young Children from OWL, (II), Young Naturalist Foundation, Suite 306, 56 The Esplanade, Toronto, Ontario M5E 1A7 Canada. (416)868-6001. FAX: (416)868-6009. Editor: Catherine Ripley. Magazine: 8½×11¾; 32 pages; glossy paper and cover stock; illustrations and photographs. "*Chickadee* is created to give children under nine a lively, fun-filled look at the world around them. Each issue has a mix of activities, puzzles, games and read-to-me stories." Monthly except July and August. Estab. 1979. Circ. 130,000.

Needs: Juvenile. No fantasy, religious or anthropomorphic material. Buys 1 ms/issue; 10 mss/year. Publishes ms an average of 1 year after acceptance. Published work by Jo Ellen Bogart, Patti Farmer and Marilyn Pond; published new writers within the last year. Length: 200 words minimum; 800 words maximum; 500 words average. Recommends other markets.

How to Contact: Send complete ms and cover letter with $1 to cover postage and handling. Reports in 2 months. Sample copy for $4.50. Free fiction guidelines for SAE.

Payment: Pays $25-350 (Canadian); 2 contributor's copies.

Terms: Pays on acceptance for all rights. Occasionally buys reprints.

Advice: "We are looking for shorter stories that contain a puzzle, mystery, twist or tie-in to a puzzle that follows on the next spread. Make sure the story has a beginning, middle and an end. This seems simple, but it is often a problem for new writers. Read back issues to see what types of fiction we publish."

CHILD LIFE, The Benjamin Franklin Literary & Medical Society, Inc., Box 567, 1100 Waterway Blvd., Indianapolis IN 46206. (317)636-8881. Editor: Steve Charles. Juvenile magazine for youngsters ages 8-11. Looking for adventure, humor, contemporary situations, folk and fairy tales and stories that deal with an aspect of health, nutrition, exercise (sports) or safety.

Needs: Juvenile. No adult or adolescent fiction. Recently published work by Nancy Sweetland, Ben Westfried, Toby Speed and Carole Forman. Published new writers within the last year. Length: 1,200 words maximum.

How to Contact: Send complete ms with SASE. Reports in 8-10 weeks. Sample copy 75¢. Writer's guidelines for SASE.

Payment: Approximately 10¢/word for all rights.

Terms: Pays on publication.

Advice: "Always keep in mind your audience's attention span and interests: grab their attention quickly, be imaginative, and try to make your dialogue free and as natural as possible."

CHILDREN'S DIGEST, (II), Children's Better Health Institute, P.O. Box 567, 1100 Waterway Blvd., Indianapolis IN 46206. Editor: Elizabeth A. Rinck. Magazine: 6½×9; 48 pages; reflective and preseparated illustrations; color and b&w photos. Magazine with special emphasis on health, nutrition, exercise and safety for preteens.

Needs: "Realistic stories, short plays, adventure and mysteries. We would like to see more stories that reflect today's society: concern for the environment, single-parent families and children from diverse backgrounds. Humorous stories are highly desirable. We especially need stories that *subtly* encourage readers to develop better health or safety habits. Stories should not exceed 1,500 words." Receives 40-50 unsolicited fiction mss each month. Published work by Charles Ghigna, Frances Gorman Risser and Julia Lieser; published new writers within the last year.

How to Contact: Send complete ms with SASE. "A cover letter isn't necessary unless an author wishes to include publishing credits and special knowledge of the subject matter." Reports in 10 weeks. Sample copy for 75¢. Free guidelines with SASE.
Payment: Pays approximately 10¢/word with up to 10 contributor's copies.
Terms: Pays on publication for all rights.
Advice: "We try to present our health-related material in a positive—not a negative—light, and we try to incorporate humor and a light approach wherever possible without minimizing the seriousness of what we are saying. Fiction stories that deal with a health theme need not have health as the primary subject but should include it in some way in the course of events. Most rejected health-related manuscripts are too preachy or they lack substance. Children's magazines are not training grounds where authors learn to write 'real' material for 'real' readers. Because our readers frequently have limited attention spans, it is very important that we offer them well-written stories."

CHILDREN'S PLAYMATE, The Benjamin Franklin Literary & Medical Society, Inc., P.O. Box 567, 1100 Waterway Blvd., Indianapolis IN 46206. (317)636-8881. Editor: Elizabeth A. Rinck. Magazine: 6½×9; 48 pages; preseparated and reflective art; b&w and color illustrations. Juvenile magazine for children ages 6-8 years.
Needs: Juvenile with special emphasis on health, nutrition, safety and exercise. "Our present needs are for short, entertaining stories with a subtle health angle. Seasonal material is also always welcome." No adult or adolescent fiction. Receives approximately 150 unsolicited fiction mss each month. Published work by Nancy Gotter Gates, Kathleen Nekich, Jean Leedale Hobson and Marge O'Harra; published new writers within the last year. Length: 700 words or less.
How to Contact: Send complete ms with SASE. Indicate word count on material. Reports in 8-10 weeks. Accepts computer printout submissions. Sample copy for 75¢.
Payment: Pays approximately 10¢/word and up to 10 contributor's copies.
Terms: Pays on publication for all rights.
Advice: "Stories should be kept simple and entertaining. Study past issues of the magazine—be aware of vocabulary limitations of the readers."

CHRISTMAS, The Annual of Christmas Literature and Art, (IV), Augsburg Fortress, Box 1209, 426 S. 5th St., Minneapolis MN 55440. (612)330-3300. Editorial Staff: Gloria Bengtson, Jennifer Huber, Louise Lystig. Annual: 10⅜×13¾; 64 pages; illustrations and photographs. "Christmas—its history, celebration, traditions, music, customs, literature. For anyone who observes Christmas, especially its religious significance." Annually. Estab. 1931.
Needs: Ethnic, historical, literary, mainstream, verse, religious/inspirational, Christmas. Receives 100 unsolicited mss/month. Buys 2-3 mss/issue. Publishes ms 1-3 years after acceptance. Length: around 2,500 words preferred.
How to Contact: Send complete ms with cover letter. Reports in 2-10 weeks. SASE. Simultaneous and reprint submissions OK. Sample copy: Call for current price (plus shipping). Writer guidelines for #10 SAE and 1 first class stamp.
Payment: Pays $150-300; one contributor's copy; charge for extras.
Terms: Pays on acceptance. Purchases all rights, first rights and one-time rights.

THE CHURCH HERALD, (II), 6157 28th St. SE, Grand Rapids MI 49546-6999. (616)957-1351. Editor: Jeffrey Japinga. Magazine: 8½×11; 52 pages. "We deal with religious themes and other reflections of a faith in God for a general audience, most members of the Reformed Church in America." Publishes 11 issues/year. Estab. 1944. Circ. 40,000.
Needs: Prose poem, religious/inspirational, spiritual. Length: 1,200-1,800. Sometimes critiques rejected mss and may recommend other markets. Recently published work by Louis Lotz, James Schaap.
How to Contact: Send query with story synopsis and anticipated length. Reports in 6 weeks on queries. SASE. Accepts computer printout submissions.
Payment: Pay varies according to length.
Terms: Pays on acceptance for all rights, first rights, first North American serial rights and one-time rights.

THE CHURCH MUSICIAN, (IV), The Sunday School Board of the Southern Baptist Convention, 127 9th Ave. N., Nashville TN 37234. (615)251-2961. Editor: William M. Anderson Jr. "*The Church Musician* is for church music leaders in local churches—music directors, pastors, organists, pianists, choir coordinators, and members of music councils and/or other planning committees or groups. Music leaders read the magazine for spiritual enrichment, testimonials, human interest stories and other materials

related to music programs in local churches." Monthly. Estab. 1950. Circ. 20,000.
Needs: Categories related to church music. Receives 1-2 unsolicited fiction mss each month. Length: 750-2,000 words.
How to Contact: Send complete ms with SAE. Reports in 2 months on ms. Free sample copy with SAE and 30¢ postage. No simultaneous submissions.
Payment: Pays maximum 5¢ per word.
Terms: Pays on acceptance for all rights.
Advice: "Avoid mushy sentiment when writing. It must be believable and, of course, practical." Many mss are rejected because they are "too long, too general, too sweet and sentimental, shallow."

CLUBHOUSE, Your Story Hour, (II), Box 15, Berrien Springs MI 49103. (616)471-3701. Editor-in-Chief: Elaine Trumbo. Magazine: 6×9; 32 pages; 60 lb. offset paper; self cover stock; illustrations and some photos. "A Christian magazine designed to help young people feel good about themselves. Our primary goal is to let them know there is a God and that He loves kids. Stories are non-moralistic in tone and full of adventure." Readers are "children 9-14 years old. Stories are selected for the upper end of the age range. Primary audience—kids without church affiliation." Published 6 times/year. Estab. 1951 under former name *The Good Deeder*. Circ. 10,000.
Needs: Adventure, contemporary, historical (general), religious, young adult/teen. No Christmas stories that refer to Santa, elves, reindeer, etc. No Halloween/occult stories. Receives 250+ unsolicited fiction mss/month. Buys 6 mss/issue, 40 mss/year. Reads mss in March-April only. Publishes ms 6-18 months after acceptance. Published new writers within the last year. Length: 1,000-1,200 words. Occasionally critiques rejected mss and recommends other markets.
How to Contact: Send complete ms, in April. Reports in 2 months. SASE always. Simultaneous and photocopied submissions and previously published work OK. Accepts computer printout submissions. Sample copy for 6×9 SAE and 3 first class stamps. Fiction guidelines for #10 SAE and 1 first class stamp.
Payment: Pays $25-35 and contributor's copies.
Terms: Pays within about 6 months for any rights offered. Buys reprints.
Advice: "Especially interested in stories in which children are responsible, heroic, kind, etc., not stories in which children are pushed into admitting that a parent, sibling, friend, etc., was right all along. I want upbeat, fun, exciting stories. Do not mention church, Sunday School, etc., just because this is a Christian magazine. General tone of the magazine is warmth, not criticism. Remember that a story should follow a plot sequence and be properly wrapped up at the end. Most stories I reject involve kids who have regrettable turns of behavior which they finally change, appeal to a too-young age group, are preachy, are the wrong length or lack sparkle. Fiction can be more exact than truths, because details can be fashioned to complete the plot which might by necessity be omitted if the account were strictly factual."

‡THE COMPANION OF ST. FRANCIS AND ST. ANTHONY, (II), Conventual Franciscan Friars, Box 535, Postal Station F, Toronto, Ontario M4Y 2L8 Canada. (416)924-6349. Editor-in-Chief: Friar Philip Kelly, OFM Conv. Magazine. Publishes material "emphasizing religious and human values and stressing Franciscan virtues—peace, simplicity, joy." Monthly. Estab. 1936. Circ. 10,000.
Needs: Adventure, humor, mainstream, religious. Canadian settings preferred. Receives 50 unsolicited fiction mss/month. Buys 2/issue, but "backlogged right now." Time varies between acceptance and publication. Length: 800 words minimum; 1,000 words maximum. Publishes short shorts, 200 words preferred.
How to Contact: Send complete mss. Reports in 3 weeks to 1 month on mss. SASE with "cash to buy stamps" or IRC. Sample copy and fiction guidelines free.
Payment: Pays 6¢/word (Canadian funds).
Terms: Pays on publication for first North American serial rights.

COMPUTOREDGE, San Diego's Free Weekly Computer Magazine, (IV), The Byte Buyer, Inc., Box 83086, San Diego CA 92138. (619)573-0315. FAX: (619)573-0205. Editor: R. Andrew Rathbone. Magazine: 8½×11; 75-100 pages; newsprint paper; 50 lb. bookwrap cover; illustrations and photos. Publishes material relating to "personal computers from a human point of view. For new users/shoppers." Weekly. Estab. 1983. Circ. 80,000.
Needs: Fiction that includes computers. "Keep it short! Can be science fiction including computers or 'future' stories." Receives up to 3 unsolicited fiction mss/month. Buys 3 fiction mss/year. Publishes ms 1-4 months after acceptance. Length: 800 words minimum; 1,200 words maximum.

How to Contact: Send complete ms with cover letter. Include Social Security number and phone number. Reports in 1 month. SASE. Photocopied and reprint submissions OK. Accepts computer printouts. Electronic submission of *accepted* mss *only*. Sample copy for 9 × 12 SAE and $1.50 postage; writer's guidelines for #10 SAE and 1 first class stamp.
Payment: Pays 10¢/word.
Terms: Pays on publication for first rights or first North American serial rights. Offers $15 kill fee.
Advice: Magazine fiction today is "too trendy. Reader should be able to come away from article moved, enlightened, edified."

CONTACT ADVERTISING, Box 3431, Ft. Pierce FL 34948. (407)464-5447. Editor: Herman Nietzche. Magazines and newspapers. Publications vary in size, 40-56 pages. "Group of 14 erotica, soft core publications for swingers, single males, married males." Bimonthly, quarterly and monthly. Estab. 1975. Circ. combined is 60,000.
Needs: Erotica, fantasy, feminist, gay and lesbian. Receives 8-10 unsolicited mss/month. Buys 1-2 mss/issue; 40-50 mss/year. Publishes ms 1-3 months after acceptance. Length: 2,000 words minimum; 3,500 words maximum; 2,500-3,500 words average. Sometimes critiques rejected mss and recommends other markets.
How to Contact: Query first, query with clips of published work or send complete ms with cover letter. Reports in 1-2 weeks on queries; 3-4 weeks on mss. SASE. Simultaneous, photocopied and reprint submissions OK. Accepts computer printout submissions. Sample copy for $6. Fiction guidelines free.
Payment: For 1st submission pays free subscription to magazine; subsequent submissions $25-75; all receive three contributor's copies.
Terms: Pays on publication for all rights or first rights. Sends galleys to author if requested.
Advice: "Know your grammar! Content must be of an adult nature but well within guidelines of the law. Fantasy, unusual sexual encounters, swinging stories or editorials of a sexual bend are acceptable."

COSMOPOLITAN MAGAZINE, (III), The Hearst Corp., 224 W. 57th St., New York NY 10019. (212)649-2000. Editor: Helen Gurley Brown. Fiction Editor: Betty Kelly. Associate Fiction Editor: Jill Herzig. Most stories include male-female relationships, traditional plots, characterizations. Single career women (ages 18-34). Monthly. Circ. just under 3 million.
Needs: Contemporary, romance, mystery and adventure. "Stories should include a romantic relationship and usually a female protagonist. The characters should be in their 20s or 30s (i.e., same ages as our readers). No highly experimental pieces. Upbeat endings." Buys 1 short story plus a novel or book excerpt/issue. Agented fiction 98%. Recently published excerpts by Danielle Steel, Pat Booth and Belva Plain; published new writers within the last year. Length: short shorts (1,500 words); longer (2,000-4,000 words). Occasionally recommends other markets.
How to Contact: Send complete ms with SASE. Accepts computer printout submissions. Guidelines for legal-sized SASE. Publishes ms 6-18 months after acceptance.
Payment: Pays $750-2,000.
Terms: Pays on acceptance for first North American serial rights. Buys reprints.
Advice: "It is rare that unsolicited mss are accepted. We tend to use agented, professional writers. The majority of unsolicited short stories we receive are inappropriate for *Cosmo* in terms of characters used and situations presented, or they just are not well written."

COUNTRY AMERICA, (IV), 1716 Locust St., Des Moines IA 50336. (515)284-3790. Editor: Danita Allen. Magazine: 8¼ × 10½; 100 pages. "*Country America* celebrates and serves the country way of life including country music for an audience who loves rural values and traditions." Monthly. Estab. 1989. Circ. 750,000.
Needs: Receives "very few" unsolicited mss/month. Buys 2 or 3 mss/year. Publishes ms approximately 6 months after acceptance. Published fiction by Charlie Daniels.
How to Contact: Query first. Reports in 1 month. SASE for mss. Sample copy for $3.30.
Payment: Pays 35¢/word minimum, 75¢/word maximum.
Terms: Pays on acceptance. Kill fee negotiable. Buys all rights.

COUNTRY WOMAN, (IV), Reiman Publications, Box 643, Milwaukee WI 53201. (414)423-0100. Editor: Ann Kaiser. Managing Editor: Kathleen Pohl. Magazine: 8½×11; 68 pages; excellent quality paper; excellent cover stock; illustrations and photographs. "Articles should have a rural theme and be of specific interest to women who live on a farm or ranch, or in a small town or country home, and/or are simply interested in country-oriented topics." Bimonthly. Estab. 1971. Circ. 1,000,000.

Needs: Fiction must be upbeat, heartwarming and focus on a country woman as central character. "Many of our stories and articles are written by our readers!" Published work by Lori Ness, Wanda Luttrell and Dixie Laslett Thompson; published new writers within last year. Publishes 1 fiction story per issue and 6-8 profiles per issue. Length: 750-1,000 words.
How to Contact: All manuscripts should be sent to Kathy Pohl, Managing Editor. Query first. Reports in 2-3 months. Include cover letter and SASE. Simultaneous, photocopied and reprint submissions OK. Accepts computer printout submissions. Sample copy and writer's guidelines for $2 and SASE. Guidelines for #10 SASE.
Payment: Pays $90-125.
Terms: Pays on acceptance for one-time rights.
Advice: "Read the magazine to get to know our audience. Send us country-to-the-core fiction, not yuppie-country stories—our readers know the difference!"

CRICKET MAGAZINE, (II), Carus Corporation, Box 300, Peru IL 61354. (815)223-1500. Publisher/Editor-in-Chief: Marianne Carus. Magazine: 7×9; 80 pages; illustrations; photos. Magazine for children, ages 6-14. Monthly. Estab. 1973. Circ. 130,000.
Needs: Juvenile, including literary, contemporary, science fiction, historic fiction, fantasy, western, mystery, adventure, humor, ethnic and translations. No adult articles. All issues have different "mini-themes." Receives approximately 1,100 unsolicited fiction mss each month. Publishes ms 6-24 months or longer after acceptance. Buys 200 mss/year. Agented fiction 1-2%. Published work by Peter Dickinson, Mary Stolz, Jane Yolen; published new writers within the last year. Length: 500-1,500 words.
How to Contact: Do not query first. Send complete ms with SASE. List previous publications. Reports in 3 months on mss. Sample copy for $2; Guidelines for SASE.
Payment: Pays up to 25¢/word; 2 contributor's copies; $1 charge for extras.
Terms: Pays on publication for first North American serial rights and one-time rights. Sends edited mss for approval. Buys reprints.
Advice: "Do not write *down* to children. Write about well-researched subjects you are familiar with and interested in, or about something that concerns you deeply. Children *need* fiction and fantasy. Carefully study several issues of *Cricket* before you submit your manuscript." Sponsors contests for children, ages 5-14.

CRUSADER MAGAZINE, (II), Calvinist Cadet Corps, Box 7259, Grand Rapids MI 49510. (616)241-5616. FAX: (616)241-5558. Editor: G. Richard Broene. Magazine: 8½×11; 24 pages; 50 lb. white paper and cover stock; illustrations; photos. Magazine to help boys ages 9-14 discover how God is at work in their lives and in the world around them. 7 issues/year. Estab. 1958. Circ. 12,000.
Needs: Adventure, comics, confession, ethnic, juvenile, religious/inspirational, science fiction, spiritual and sports. Receives 60 unsolicited fiction mss/month. Buys 3 mss/issue; 18 mss/year. Publishes ms 4-11 months after acceptance. Published work by Sigmund Brouwer, Alan Cliburn and Betty Lou Mell. Length: 800 words minimum; 1,500 words maximum; 1,200 words average. Publishes short shorts.
How to Contact: Send complete ms and SASE with cover letter including theme of story. Reports in 3 weeks. Simultaneous, photocopied and previously published submissions OK. Accepts computer printout submissions. Free sample copy with a 9×12 SAE and 3 first class stamps. Fiction guidelines for #10 SAE and 1 first class stamp.
Payment: Pays 2-5¢/word; 1 contributor's copy.
Terms: Pays on acceptance for one-time rights. Buys reprints.
Advice: "On a cover sheet list the point your story is trying to make. Our magazine has a theme for each issue, and we try to fit the fiction to the theme."

DETROIT JEWISH NEWS, 27676 Franklin Rd., Southfield MI 48034. (313)354-6060. Associate Editor: Alan Hitsky. Newspaper: 120+ pages; illustrations and photos. Jewish news. Weekly. Estab. 1942. Circ. 20,000.

Market conditions are constantly changing! If you're still using this book and it is 1993 or later, buy the newest edition of Novel & Short Story Writer's Market at your favorite bookstore or order directly from Writer's Digest Books.

Needs: "For fiction, we prefer articles on any subject with a Jewish flavor." Receives 3-4 unsolicited mss/month. Buys 6 mss/year. Publishes ms 2-3 months after acceptance. Length: 1,000-2,000 words averge. Publishes short shorts. Sometimes critiques rejected mss.
How to Contact: Send complete ms with cover letter that includes Social Security number. Reports in 1 week on queries; 1 month on mss. SASE. Simultaneous, photocopied and reprint submissions OK. Accepts computer printout submissions. Sample copy for $1.
Payment: Pays $40-100 and contributor's copies; charge for extras.
Terms: Pays on publication for one-time rights. Offers kill fee.

DISCOVERIES, (II), Nazarene Publishing House, 6401 The Paseo, Kansas City MO 64131. Editor: Latta Jo Knapp. Story paper. 5½×8¼; 8 pages; illustrations; color photos. "Committed to reinforce the Bible concept taught in Sunday School curriculum, for ages 8 to 12 (grades 3 to 6)." Weekly.
Needs: Religious, puzzles. Buys 1-2 stories and 1-2 puzzles/issue. Publishes ms 1-2 years after acceptance. Length: 400-800 words.
How to Contact: Send complete ms with cover letter and SASE. Send SASE for sample copy and guidelines.
Payment: Pays 3.5¢/word; .5¢ for multiple rights.
Terms: Pays on acceptance or on publication.
Advice: "Stories should vividly portray definite Christian emphasis or character building values, without being preachy."

DOG FANCY, Fancy Publications, Box 6050, Mission Viejo CA 92690. (714)855-8822. Editor: Kim Thornton. General dog and puppy magazine, consumer-oriented, "for dog and puppy lovers." Monthly. Circ. 150,000.
Needs: Dog-centered theme. Receives approximately 40 unsolicited fiction mss/month. Buys 12 mss/year. Publishes ms an average of 6 months after acceptance. Length: 3,000 words maximum.
How to Contact: Query first or send complete ms. Reports in 1 month on queries; 2 months on mss. SASE always. Photocopied submissions OK. Sample copy for $3. Fiction guidelines for SASE.
Payment: Pays 5¢/word and 2 contributor's copies; $3 charge for extras.
Terms: Buys reprints.
Advice: "Must be about dogs (and people), candid; first person is preferable. Include *brief* cover letter. Write to style of publication so that no rewrite is necessary. Please no stories written 'by the dog' or talking dogs. Dog and dog's experiences must be focus of article; dog shouldn't be incidental character in a 'people' story. We are always especially interested in Christmas stories — something heartwarming for the season, though not necessarily specifically Christmassy in theme."

DRAGON MAGAZINE, The Monthly Adventure Role-Playing Aid, (IV), TSR, Inc., P.O. Box 111, Lake Geneva WI 53147. (414)248-3625. Editor: Roger E. Moore. Fiction Editor: Barbara G. Young. Magazine: 8½×11; 120 pages; 50 penn. plus paper; 80 lb. northcote cover stock; illustrations; rarely photos. "*Dragon* contains primarily nonfiction — articles and essays on various aspects of the hobby of fantasy and science fiction role-playing games. One short fantasy story is published per issue. Readers are mature teens and young adults; over half our readers are under 18 years of age. The majority are male." Monthly. Estab. 1976. Circ. 85,000.
Needs: "We are looking for all types of fantasy (not horror) stories. We are *not* interested in fictionalized accounts of actual role-playing sessions." Receives 50-60 unsolicited fiction mss/month. Buys 10-12 mss/year. Publishes ms 6-12 months after acceptance. Recently published work by eluki bes shahar, M.C. Sumner and Jean Lorrah; published new writers within the last year. Length: 1,500 words minimum; 8,000 words maximum; 3,000-4,000 words average. Occasionally critiques rejected mss.
How to Contact: Send complete ms, estimated word length, SASE. List only credits of professionally published materials within genre. Reports in 4-6 weeks. Photocopied submissions OK. Accepts computer printout submissions. Sample copy for $4.50. Fiction guidelines for #10 SAE and 1 first class stamp. Reviews fantasy and science fiction novels for their application to role-playing games.
Payment: Pays 5-8¢/word; 2 free contributor's copies; $2 charge for extras.
Terms: Pays on acceptance for fiction only for first worldwide English language rights.
Advice: "It is *essential* that you actually see a copy (better, several copies) of the magazine to which you are submitting your work. Do not rely solely on market reports, as stories submitted to the wrong publication waste both your time and the editor's."

DRUMMER, (II, IV), Desmodus, Inc., Box 410390, San Francisco CA 94141. (415)252-1195. Editor: A.F. DeBlase. Magazine: 8½×11; 100 pages; glossy full-color cover; illustrations and photos. "Gay male erotica, fantasy and mystery with a leather, SM or other fetish twist." Monthly. Estab. 1975. Circ. 20,000.
Needs: Adventure, erotica, fantasy, gay, horror, humor/satire, science fiction, suspense/mystery and western. "Fiction must have an appeal to gay men." Receives 20-30 unsolicited fiction mss/month. Accepts 3 mss/issue. Publishes ms 6-8 months after acceptance.
How to Contact: Send complete ms with cover letter. SASE. Photocopied submissions OK; reprints OK "only if previously in foreign or very local publications." Accepts computer printout submissions. Accepts electronic submissions compatible with IBM PC. Sample copy for $5. Fiction guidelines for #10 SASE. Reviews novels and short story collections.
Payment: Pays $100 and contributor's copies.
Terms: Pays on publication for first North American serial rights.

EMERGE MAGAZINE, Our Voice In Today's World, (III), Emerge Communications, 170 Varick St., New York NY 10013. (212)627-4151. Editor: Mr. Wilmer C. Ames, Jr. Fiction Editor: Mr. Roberto Santiago. Magazine; 8⅛×10⅞; 84 pages; 40 lb. paper; 70 lb. cover stock; 5-6 illustrations; 45 photographs. "*Emerge* is an African American news monthly that covers politics, arts and lifestyles for the college educated, middle class African American audience." Estab. 1989.
Needs: Ethnic, fantasy, humor/satire, literary, psychic/supernatural/occult, science fiction, sports, suspense/mystery. "*Emerge* is looking for humorous, tightly written fiction no longer than 3,000 words about African Americans."
How to Contact: Submit ms through agent only. Reviews novels and short story collections. Send to Susan McHenry, executive editor.
Payment: Pays $1,000-3,000 and contributor's copies.
Terms: Pays 25% kill fee. Buys first North American serial rights.
Advice: "*Emerge* stories must accomplish with a fine economy of style what all good fiction must do: make the unusual familiar. The ability to script a compelling story is what has been missing from most of our submissions."

ESQUIRE, Esquire Associates, 179 Broadway, New York NY 10019. Declined listing.

EVANGEL, Light & Life Press, P.O. Box 535002, Indianapolis IN 46253-5002. (317)244-3660. Editor: Vera Bethel. Sunday school take-home paper for distribution to young adults who attend church. Fiction involves young couples and singles coping with everyday crises, making decisions that show growth; for readers ages 25-35. Magazine: 5½×8½; 8 pages; 2-color illustrations; b&w photos. Weekly. Estab. 1896. Circ. 35,000.
Needs: Religious/inspirational. "No fiction without any semblance of Christian message or where the message clobbers the reader." Receives approximately 75 unsolicited fiction mss each month. Buys 1 ms/issue, 52 mss/year. Published work by C. Ellen Watts, Jeanne Zornes and Betty Steele Everett. Length: 1,000-1,200 words.
How to Contact: Send complete ms with SASE. Reports in 1 month. Sample copy and fiction guidelines with 6×9 SASE.
Payment: Pays $45; 2 contributor's copies; charge for extras.
Terms: Pays on publication for simultaneous, first, second serial (reprint), first North American serial or one-time rights.
Advice: "Choose a contemporary situation or conflict and create a good mix for the characters (not all-good or all-bad heroes and villains). Don't spell out everything in detail; let the reader fill in some blanks in the story. Keep him guessing." Rejects mss because of "unbelievable characters and predictable events in the story."

THE FAMILY, (II, IV), Daughters of St. Paul, 50 St. Paul's Ave., Boston MA 02130. (617)522-8911. Editor: Sr. Donna William Giaimo FSP. Magazine: 8½×11; 40 pages; glossy paper; self-cover; illustrations and photos. Family life—themes include parenting issues, human and spiritual development, marital situations for teen-adult, popular audience predominantly Catholic. Monthly, except July-Aug. Estab. 1953. Circ. 10,000.
Needs: Religious/inspirational. "We favor upbeat stories with some sort of practical or moral message." No sex, romance, science fiction, horror, western. Receives about 100 unsolicited mss/month. Buys 3-4 mss/issue; 30-40 mss/year. Publishes ms 4-6 months after acceptance. Length: 800 words minimum; 1,500 words maximum; 1,200 words average.

How to Contact: Send complete ms with cover letter that includes Social Security number and list of previously published works. Reports in 2 months on mss. SASE. Reprint submissions OK. Sample copy for $1.75, 9×12 SAE and 5 first class stamps. Guidelines for #10 SAE and 1 first class stamp.
Payment: Pays $50-150.
Terms: Pays on publication for first North American serial or one-time rights (reprints). Sends galleys to author "only if substantive editing was required."
Advice: "We look for 1) message; 2) clarity of writing; 3) realism of plot and character development. If seasonal material, send at least 7 months in advance. We're eager to receive submissions on family topics. And we love stories that include humor."

FAMILY MAGAZINE, The Magazine for Military Wives, (II), 169 Lexington Ave., New York NY 10016. (212)532-0660. Editor: Susan A. Alberto. Magazine: 80 pages; glossy paper; 65 lb. glossy cover stock; illustrations; photos. Magazine with stories of interest only to military wives. Audience: high school-educated, married women. Monthly. Estab. 1958. Circ. 550,000 worldwide.
Needs: Contemporary. No "singles" stories. Receives 100 unsolicited mss/month. Buys 12-20 mss/year. Published new writers within the last year. Length: 1,000-3,000 words.
How to Contact: Query first. Reports in 2 months only if provided with SASE. Call for information on computer disk submissions. Publishes ms an average of 1 year after acceptance. Sample copy $1.25. Reviews novels and short story collections "only if having to do with the military."
Payment: Pays $75-300; 1 contributor's copy; $1.25 charge for extras.
Terms: Pays on publication for first rights.

FIRST, For Women, (II), Heinrich Bauer North America Inc., 270 Sylvan Ave., Englewood Cliffs NJ 07632. (201)569-6699. Editor: Jackie High. Magazine: 150 pages; slick paper; illustrations and photos. "Women's service magazine for women age 18 up—no upper limit—middle American audience." Monthly. Estab. 1989. Circ. 4 million.
Needs: Contemporary, humor, literary, mainstream and regional. "No experimental, romance, formula fiction, fantasy, sci-fi, or stories with foreign settings." Receives 200 unsolicited mss/month. Buys 1 ms/issue; 12-16 mss/year. Time between acceptance and publication varies. Agented fiction 33⅓%. Published work by Chuck Wachtel, Tima Smith and Paulette Bates Alden. Length: 1,800 words minimum; 2,500 words maximum. "No short shorts." Sometimes critiques rejected mss.
How to Contact: Send complete ms with cover letter. "Cover letter should be brief, mention previous publications and agent if any, and tell us if material is seasonal. No queries please." Reports in 8-10 weeks on mss. SASE for ms. Photocopied and reprint submissions OK. Accepts computer printout submissions. Fiction guidelines for #10 SAE and 1 first class stamp. Send seasonal material 6 months in advance.
Payment: Pays $1,000-1,500 (less for reprinted material).
Terms: Pays on acceptance for first North American serial rights.
Advice: "We especially like a fresh sensibility and a sensitive handling of themes of interest to contemporary women. Read at least 3 issues of the magazine. Send us the story you had to write for yourself, not one you concocted 'especially for *First*.' "

FIRST HAND, Experiences for Loving Men, (II, IV), First Hand Ltd., Box 1314, Teaneck NJ 07666. (201)836-9177. FAX: (201)836-5055. Editor: Bob Harris. Magazine: digest size; 130 pages; illustrations. "Half of the magazine is made up of our readers' own gay sexual experiences. Rest is fiction and columns devoted to health, travel, books, etc." Monthly. Estab. 1980. Circ. 60,000.
Needs: Erotica, gay. "Should be written in first person." No science fiction or fantasy. Erotica should detail experiences based in reality. Receives 75-100 unsolicited mss/month. Buys 6 mss/issue; 72 mss/year. Publishes ms 9-18 months after acceptance. Recently published work by John Hoff, Rick Jackson, Jack Sofelot; published new writers within the last year. Length: 3,000 words preferred; 2,000 words minimum; 3,750 words maximum. Sometimes critiques rejected mss.
How to Contact: Send complete ms with cover letter which should include writer's name, address, telephone and Social Security number and "should advise on use of pseudonym if any. Also whether selling all rights or first North American rights." Reports in 4-6 weeks. SASE. Accepts computer printout submissions. Sample copy for $5. Fiction guidelines for #10 SAE and 1 first class stamp.
Payment: Pays $100-150.
Terms: Pays on publication for all rights or first North American serial rights.
Advice: "Avoid the hackneyed situations. Be original. We like strong plots."

Close-up

Elinor Nauen
Senior Features Editor
First

Before coming to *First* magazine late last year, Elinor Nauen had been an editor for 10 years and spent half of those years as fiction editor for *First*'s sister publication, *Woman's World*. Nauen, whose official title is senior features editor, is responsible for selecting and editing fiction as well as features for *First*. In addition to experience, she brought with her an interest in discovering and working with new writers.

"I'm very willing to work with new writers," says Nauen. "In fact, I don't even look at the credit page—if it's a good story I don't care who wrote it. One day I counted the stories I had accepted for *Woman's World*. I had bought 104 stories from 80 different writers and it was the first publication for many of them."

Nauen is also willing to work with writers whose work is "in the ballpark." At *Woman's World*, she bought stories that were revised two and three times. On the other hand, she says, she expects writers to go that extra step and present a polished story.

"Pay attention to details. It's not my job to remember that Sally has red hair, after you've suddenly changed it to black on page 12." It's those little details—including how you present the work—that can make the difference, she says.

While she admits "plot is the scaffolding on which you hang the story," she says solid characterization is what drives a good story. "My pet peeve is what I call 'television stories.' These are stories where the dialogue seems like canned TV patter and the characters are from nowhere in particular. The dialogue in half of these stories sounds like the same person wrote all of it. Don't get your words out of dictionaries—listen to what people say."

To be a good writer, she says, "you must first have a love of language. You'll learn a lot more about character from reading poetry than you will watching TV.

"Read your story aloud," she suggests. "If it sounds silly, maybe it is. You can tell how the story is working better this way than if you just read it."

Nauen also looks for explicit endings. "Don't let the story drag on, but don't leave the reader hanging either. Try to tie up the loose ends. It's better to err on the side of the obvious."

First publishes one story per issue and Nauen receives 75 to 100 manuscripts each week or 25 a day. The competition is stiff, she says, and writers who send messy, unproofed or otherwise hard-to-read manuscripts will start with two strikes against them. "You don't want to do that when there is so much competition," she warns.

"We're interested in any subject that is of importance or of interest to women," Nauen adds. "We're willing to look at work that pushes the boundaries, that involves exciting issues or settings. For the most part I'd be interested in anything written from a woman's point of view. I might break my rules, however. Nothing is set in stone here. Surprise me."

—Robin Gee

FLORIDA WILDLIFE, Florida Game & Fresh Water Fish Commission, 620 South Meridian St., Talla-hassee FL 32399-1600. (904)488-5563. Editor: Andrea H. Blount. Magazine: 8½×11; 52 pages. "Con-servation-oriented material for an 'outdoor' audience." Bimonthly. Estab. 1947. Circ. 30,000.
Needs: Adventure, sports. "Florida-related adventure or natural history only." Buys 3-4 mss/year. Length: 1,200 words average; 500 words minimum; 1,500 words maximum.
How to Contact: Send complete ms with cover letter including Social Security number. "We prefer to review article. Response varies with amount of material on hand." Sample copy for $1.25.
Payment: Pays $50 per published page.
Terms: Pays on publication for one-time rights.
Advice: "Send your best work."

THE FLYFISHER, (IV), Federation of Flyfishers, 1387 Cambridge Dr., Idaho Falls ID 83401. (208)523-7300. Editor: Dennis Bitton. Magazine: 8½×11; 64 pages; 70 lb. glossy stock; self cover; b&w; illustra-tions; color and b/w photos. Magazine for fly fishermen. "We only publish material directly related to fly fishing." Quarterly. Estab. 1967. Circ. 15,000.
Needs: Fiction related to fly fishing only. Accepts 2 ms/issue, 8 mss/year. Published new writers within the last year. Length: 750 words minimum; 2,500 words maximum; 1,500 words average (preferred).
How to Contact: Query first with SASE. Reports in 1 month on queries and mss. Sample copy $3 with 9×12 SAE and 10 first class stamps. Fiction guidelines for #10 SAE and 1 first class stamp.
Payment: Pays $50-250.
Terms: Pays on publication for first North American serial rights or one-time rights.

FLYFISHING NEWS, VIEWS AND REVIEWS, (II,IV), Bitton Inc., 1387 Cambridge, Idaho Falls ID 83401. (208)523-7300. Editor: Dennis G. Bitton. Newspaper tabloid: 16 pages; good newsprint; b&w illustrations; b&w photos. Publishes information on flyfishing and all related subjects for flyfishermen and women. Bimonthly. Estab. 1986. Circ. 5,000.
Needs: Adventure, condensed novel, confession, historical, humor, regional. "All as flyfishing topics." Receives 20 unsolicited mss/month. Accepts 2 mss/month; 12 mss/year. Length: 1,500-2,000 words average; 250 words minimum; 4,000 words maximum. Occasionally critiques rejected mss. Recom-mends other markets.
How to Contact: Query first. Reports in 2 weeks. SASE.
Payment: Pays $50-250 and 5 contributor's copies. Charge for extras.
Terms: Pays 2-3 weeks after publication for one-time rights.
Advice: "I want to see all good flyfishing fiction. Write like you talk."

FREEWAY, (II), Box 632, Glen Ellyn IL 60138. (708)668-6000 (ext. 216). Editor: Kyle Lennart Olund. Magazine: 8½×11; 4 pages; newsprint paper; illustrations; photos. Weekly Sunday school paper "spe-cializing in first-person true stories about how God has worked in teens' lives," for Christian teens ages 15-21.
Needs: Comics, humor/satire, spiritual, allegories and parables. Length: 1,000 words average; 1,200 words maximum. Occasionally critiques rejected mss.
How to Contact: Send complete ms with SASE. Reports in 2-3 months. Simultaneous and photocop-ied submissions OK. Accepts computer printout submissions. Sample copy or fiction guidelines avail-able for SASE.
Payment: Pays 6-10¢/word.
Terms: Pays on acceptance for one-time rights.
Advice: "Send us humorous fiction (parables, allegories, etc.) with a clever twist and new insight on Christian principles. Do *not* send us typical teenage short stories. Watch out for cliché topics and approaches."

THE FRIEND MAGAZINE, (II), The Church of Jesus Christ of Latter-day Saints, 23rd Floor, 50 E. North Temple, Salt Lake City UT 84150. (801)240-2210. Editor: Vivian Paulsen. Magazine: 8½×10½; 50 pages; 40 lb. coated paper; 70 lb. coated cover stock; illustrations; photos. Publishes for 3-11 year-olds. Monthly. Estab. 1971. Circ. 220,000.
Needs: Adventure, ethnic, some historical, humor, mainstream, religious/inspirational, nature. Length: 1,000 words maximum. Publishes short shorts. Length: 250 words.
How to Contact: Send complete ms. "No query letters please." Reports in 6-8 weeks. SASE. Photo-copied submissions OK. Accepts computer printout submissions. Sample copy for 9½×11 SAE and 98¢ postage.

Payment: Pays 8-11¢/word.
Terms: Pays on acceptance for all rights.
Advice: "The *Friend* is particularly interested in stories with substance for tiny tots. Stories should focus on character-building qualities and should be wholesome without moralizing or preaching. Boys and girls resolving conflicts is a theme of particular merit. Since the magazine is circulated worldwide, the *Friend* is interested in stories and articles with universal settings, conflicts, and character. Other suggestions include rebus, picture, holiday, sports, and photo stories, or manuscripts that portray various cultures. Very short pieces (up to 250 words) are desired for younger readers and preschool children. Appropriate humor is a constant need."

GALLERY MAGAZINE, Montcalm Publishing Corporation, 401 Park Avenue South, New York NY 10016. (212)779-8900. Editor: Marc Lichter. Fiction Editor: John Bowers. Magazine: 112 pages; illustrations and photographs. Magazine for men, 18-34. Monthly. Estab. 1972. Circ. 425,000.
Needs: Adventure, erotica, humor/satire, literary, mainstream, suspense/mystery. Receives 100 unsolicited fiction mss/month. Accepts 1 mss/issue. Publishes ms 2-3 months after acceptance. Less than 10% of fiction is agented. Length: 1,500-3,000 words average; 1,000 words minimum; 3,500 words maximum. Publishes short shorts. Sometimes critiques rejected mss and recommends other markets.
How to Contact: Send complete ms. Reports in 2 months. SASE. Photocopied submissions OK. Accepts computer printout submissions. Sample copy $5. Fiction guidelines for #10 SAE and 1 first class stamp.
Payment: Pays $400-1,000, contributor's copies.
Terms: Pays 50% on acceptance/50% on publication. Buys first North American serial rights.

THE GEM, (II), Churches of God, General Conference, Box 926, Findlay OH 45839. (419)424-1961. Editor: Marilyn Rayle Kern. Magazine: 6×9; 8 pages; 50 lb. uncoated paper; illustrations (clip art). "True-to-life stories of healed relationships and growing maturity in the Christian faith for senior high students through senior citizens who attend Churches of God, General Conference Sunday Schools." Weekly. Estab. 1865. Circ. 8,000.
Needs: Adventure, feminist, humor, mainstream, religious/inspirational, senior citizen/retirement. Nothing that denies or ridicules standard Christian values. Receives 30 unsolicited fiction mss/month. Buys 1 ms every 2-3 issues; 20-25 mss/year. Publishes ms 4-12 months after submission. Published work by Betty Steele Everett, Todd Lee and Betty Lou Mell. Length: 1,500 words average; 1,000 words minimum; 1,700 words maximum.
How to Contact: Send complete ms with cover letter ("letter not essential, unless there is information about author's background which enhances story's credibility or verifies details as being authentic"). Reports in 6 months. SASE for ms. Simultaneous, photocopied and reprint submissions OK. Accepts computer printout submissions. Sample copy and fiction guidelines for #10 SAE and 1 first class stamp. "If more than one sample copy is desired along with the guidelines, will need 2 oz. postage."
Payment: Pays $10-15 and contributor's copies. Charge for extras (postage for mailing more than one).
Terms: Pays on publication for one-time rights.
Advice: "Competition at the mediocre level is fierce. There is a dearth of well-written, relevant fiction which wrestles with real problems involving Christian values applied to the crisis times and 'passages' of life. Humor which puts the daily grind into a fresh perspective and which promises hope for survival is also in short supply. Write from your own experience. Avoid religious jargon and stereotypes. Conclusion must be believable in terms of the story—don't force a 'Christian' ending. Avoid simplistic solutions to complex problems. Listen to the storytelling art of Garrison Keillor. Feel how very particular experiences of small town life in Minnesota become universal."

GENT, (II), Dugent Publishing Corp., Suite 600, 2600 Douglas Rd., Coral Gables FL 33134. (305)443-2378. Editor: Bruce Arthur. "Men's magazine designed to have erotic appeal for the reader. Our publications are directed to a male audience, but we do have a certain percentage of female readers. For the most part, our audience is interested in erotically stimulating material, but not exclusively." Monthly. Estab. 1959. Circ. 175,000.
Needs: Contemporary, science fiction, horror, erotica, mystery, adventure and humor. *Gent* specializes in "D-Cup cheesecake," and fiction should be slanted accordingly. "Most of the fiction published includes several sex scenes. No fiction that concerns children, religious subjects or anything that might be libelous." Receives approximately 30-50 unsolicited fiction mss/month. Buys 2 mss/issue; 24 mss/year. Publishes ms an average of 6 weeks after acceptance. Agented fiction 10%. Published new writers within the last year. Length: 2,000-3,500 words. Critiques rejected mss "when there is time."

How to Contact: Send complete ms with SASE. Reports in 1 month. Sample copy for $5. Fiction guidelines for legal-sized SASE.
Payment: Pay starts at $200; 1 contributor's copy.
Terms: Pays on publication for first North American serial rights.
Advice: "Since *Gent* magazine is the 'Home of the D-Cups,' stories and articles containing either characters or themes with a major emphasis on large breasts will have the best chance for consideration. Study a sample copy first." Mss are rejected because "there are not enough or ineffective erotic sequences, plot is not plausible, wrong length, or not slanted specifically for us."

GEORGIA SPORTSMAN, (II, IV), Game & Fish Publications, P.O. Box 741, Marietta GA 30061. (404)953-9222. Editor: Jimmy Jacobs. Magazine: 8×10¾; 80 pages; slick paper; slick cover; illustrations and photographs. "Adventure, humor and nostalgia dealing with hunting and fishing in Georgia for hunters and fishermen." Monthly. Estab. 1976. Circ. 48,000.
Needs: Adventure, humor/satire. "Fiction must take place in or pertain to Georgia and center on hunting and fishing. Such activities as hiking, camping, canoeing or boating are OK as long as they have a hunting or fishing connection. No strictly camping, hiking, boating or canoeing stories or pieces ascribing human characteristics to animals and fish." Receives 6-8 unsolicited mss/month. Buys 1 ms/issue; 6-12 mss/year. Publishes ms 6 months to 1 year after acceptance. Recently published work by Bob Kornegay, John E. Phillips and Bill Cherry. Length: 1,500 words average; 1,400 words minimum; 1,600 words maximum.
How to Contact: Send complete ms with cover letter including "who the writer is, and how to contact him/her." SASE. Simultaneous and photocopied submissions OK. Accepts computer printout submissions. Sample copy for $2.50. Free fiction guidelines.
Payment: Pays $125.
Terms: Pays 2½ months prior to publication for first North American serial rights. Offers 100% kill fee.

THE GIFTED CHILD TODAY, (IV), GCT Inc., P.O. Box 6448, Mobile AL 36660. (205)478-4700. Editor: Marvin Gold. Magazine: 8½×11; 64 pages; coated paper; self-cover; illustrations and photographs. "Focuses on materials about gifted, creative, and talented children and youth. For parents and professionals." Bimonthly. Estab. 1978. Circ. 10,000.
Needs: "As long as the subject matter deals with gifted, creative, and/or talented individuals in some way, material will be considered." Does not want to see "protagonist(s) and/or antagonist(s) that are not gifted, creative and/or talented individuals." Receives 3-4 unsolicited mss each month. Accepts 1 ms/issue. Publishes ms 1-2 years after acceptance. Length: 1,800 words average; 1,000 words minimum; 5,000 words maximum. Publishes short shorts. Length: 500 words.
How to Contact: Send complete ms with cover letter. Reports in 1 month on queries; 2 months on mss. SASE. Photocopied submissions OK. Sample copy for $5. Reviews novels and short story collections "only if material deals with gifted individuals as subject."
Payment: Pays in contributor's copies. Charges for extras.
Terms: Acquires first rights.

GOLF JOURNAL, (II), United States Golf Assoc., Golf House, Far Hills NJ 07931. (908)234-2300. Editor/Publisher: Robert Sommers. Senior Editor: George Eberl. Managing Editor: David Earl. Magazine: 40-48 pages; self cover stock; illustrations and photos. "The magazine's subject is golf – its history, lore, rules, equipment and general information. The focus is on amateur golf and those things applying to the millions of American golfers. Our audience is generally professional, highly literate and knowledgeable; presumably they read *Golf Journal* because of an interest in the game, its traditions, and its noncommercial aspects." Published 8 times/year. Estab. 1949. Circ. 285,000.
Needs: Humor. "Fiction is very limited. *Golf Journal* has had an occasional humorous story, topical in nature. Generally speaking, short stories are not used. Golf jokes will not be used." Buys 10-12 mss/year. Published new writers within the last year. Length: 1,000-2,000 words. Recommends other markets. Critiques rejected mss "when there is time."
How to Contact: Send complete ms with SASE. Reports in 2 months on mss. Free sample copy with SASE.
Payment: Pays $500-1,000; 1-10 contributor's copies.
Terms: Pays on acceptance.
Advice: "Know your subject (golf); familiarize yourself first with the publication." Rejects mss because "fiction usually does not serve the function of *Golf Journal*, which, as the official magazine of the United States Golf Association, deals chiefly with nonfiction subjects."

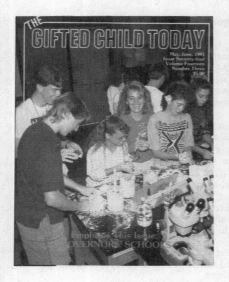

"The theme for this issue was Governors' Schools," says Martha Fagerstrom, assistant editor of The Gifted Child Today. "The activity depicted was one of many in which these youngsters participated at North Carolina Governor's School East. The students here represent the many gifted youth who benefit from governor's school honors programs nationwide," she adds. "All these students—those obviously absorbed in their work as well as those bursting with laughter—exhibit the joy that so often accompanies hands-on learning," making the cover both "interesting and fun!" The photographer is Rooney L. Coffman, director of logistics at St. Andrew's Presbyterian College.

GOOD HOUSEKEEPING, (II), 959 Eighth Ave., New York NY 10019. Editor: John Mack Carter. Fiction Editor: Naome Lewis. Magazine: 8×10; approximately 250 pages; slick paper; thick, high-gloss cover; 4-color illustrations, b&w and color photos. Homemaking magazine of informational articles, how-to's for homemakers of all ages. Monthly. Circ. 20 million.

Needs: "*Good Housekeeping* looks for stories of emotional interest to women—courtship, romance, marriage, family, friendship, personal growth, coming-of-age. The best way to know if your story is appropriate for us is to read several of our recent issues. (We are sorry but we do not furnish free sample copies of the magazine.)" Buys 2 short stories/issue. Agented fiction 75%. Length: 1,000-3,000 words.

How to Contact: Send complete ms with cover letter. Accepts computer printout submissions. *Unsolicited manuscripts will not be returned* (see Advice). Publishes ms an average of 6 months after acceptance.

Payment: Pays standard magazine rates.

Terms: Pays on acceptance for first North American serial rights.

Advice: "It is now our policy that all submissions of unsolicited fiction received in our offices will be read and, if found to be unsuitable for us, discarded. If you wish to introduce your work to us, you will be submitting material that will not be critiqued or returned. The odds are long that we will contact you to inquire about publishing your submission or to invite you to correspond with us directly, so please be sure before you take the time and expense to submit it that it is our type of material."

‡GOREZONE, (II, IV), Starlog Communications, Inc., 475 Park Ave. S., New York NY 10016. (212)689-2830. Editor: Tony Timpone. Fiction Editor: Michael Gingold. Magazine: 8×11; 66 pages; glossy paper; 4-color cover; illustrations; photographs for nonfiction. "We are a horror magazine looking for quality, original and scary short horror stories for teens, mostly male, age 16-22." Quarterly. Estab. 1988. Circ. 180,000.

Needs: Horror only. No "obscenity, 'it was only a dream,' movie-inspired ripoffs, etc." Receives 20 unsolicited mss/month. Buys 1 ms/issue; 4 mss/year ("so it's very competitive."). Publishes ms 4-8 months after acceptance. Agented fiction 10%. Recently published work by Steve Rasnic Tem, Wayne Allen Sallee and Jeffrey Thomas. Length: 2,400 words preferred; 2,000 words minimum; 3,100 words maximum.

How to Contact: Query first with SASE for guidelines or submit through agent. Reports in 3 weeks on queres; 2 months on mss. SASE. Photocopied submissions OK. Sample copy for $4.50, 8½×11 SAE and $1.05 postage. Fiction guidelines for #10 SAE and 1 first class stamp.

Payment: Pays $150-175 and 2 contributor's copies.
Terms: Pays on publication. Buys all rights.
Advice: "Fiction has to be good, presented professionally. Writer must have a strong knowledge of the horror market and our magazine. Read our magazine and back issues to determine what kinds of stories have already been published. Don't call offices ever."

THE GUIDE, Gay Travel, Entertainment, Politics, and Sex, (II, IV), Box 593, Boston MA 02199. (617)266-8557. FAX: (617)266-1125. Editor: French Wall. Magazine: 8×10; 124-156; newsprint; 70 lb. cover stock; photos. "Gay liberation and sex positive information, articles and columns; radical political and radical religious philosophies welcome. Audience is primarily gay men, some lesbians, bar crowd and grassroots politicos." Monthly. Estab. 1981. Circ. 30,000.
Needs: Adventure, erotica, ethnic, experimental, fantasy, feminist, gay, historical (general), humor/satire, lesbian, regional, religious/inspirational romance (contemporary, historical and young adult), science fiction, senior citizen, spiritual, sports, suspense/mystery. "Focus on empowerment—avoidance of 'victim' philosophy appreciated." Receives 4 mss/month. Publishes ms within 3 months to 1 year after acceptance. Length: 1,800 words average; 500 words minimum; 5,000 words maximum. Recently published work by Lars Eighner, John Champagne and A.J. Johnson; published new writers within the last year. Publishes short shorts. Sometimes critiques rejected mss.
How to Contact: Query first. Reports in 2-4 weeks. SASE; include cover letter and phone number. Simultaneous and photocopied submissions OK. Accepts computer printout submissions. Sample copy for 9×13 SAE and 8 first class stamps.
Payment: Pays $50-180.
Terms: Pays on acceptance for all rights or first rights.
Advice: "*The Guide*'s format and extensive distribution in this area makes it an excellent vehicle for writers anxious to be read. *The Guide* has multiplied its press run fourfold in the past years and is committed to continued growth."

GUIDE MAGAZINE, One In Ten Publishing, Box 23070, Seattle WA 98102. (206)323-7374. Editor: Bill Swigart. "We publish articles of current interest news, humor pieces, fiction, poetry, feature stories and interpretive essays examining personalities, politics, science fiction, current events, the arts business and indeed the whole of culture as it relates to gay life." Monthly. Estab. 1986. Circ. 25,000.
Needs: Adventure, condensed novels, ethnic, experimental, historical, horror, humor, mainstream, romance, science fiction, mystery/suspense, western. Publishes 12 fiction mss/year. Length: 800 words minimum; 3,000 words maximum.
How to Contact: Send complete ms. SASE. Photocopied and reprint submissions OK. Accepts computer printout submissions. Accepts electronic submissions via 5¼" disks formatted with MS/DOS files stored in ASCII, WordPerfect or Microsoft Word. Send hard copy with electronic submissions. Sample copy for 9×12 SAE and $1 postage. Writer's guidelines for #10 SAE and 1 first class stamp. Reviews novels and short story collections. Send books to book editor.
Payment: Pays contributor's copies and negotiates payment.
Terms: Pays on publication for first North American serial rights.
Advice: "Well-researched and intellectually challenging pieces get top priority."

‡GULFSHORE LIFE, The Lifestyle Magazine of Southwest Florida, (II, IV), 2975 S. Horseshoe Dr., Naples FL 33942. (813)643-3933. Editor: Janis Lyn Johnson. Magazine: 100 pages; 50 lb. Sommerset paper; 100 lb. Warren Flow cover; photographs. "Lifestyle magazine for older, upscale audience-visitors and residents to southwest Florida." Estab. 1970. Circ. 20,000.
Needs: Literary, mainstream, regional (southwest Florida). No "erotica, gay, preschool." Receives 2-3 unsolicited mss/month. Buys 1 mss/year. Publishes ms 3-6 months after acceptance. Length: 1,800 words preferred; 1,200 words minimum; 3,000 words maximum. Publishes short shorts. Length: 500 words. Sometimes comments on rejected ms.
How to Contact: Send complete ms with cover letter. Reports in 1-2 months. SASE. Simultaneous submissions OK. Accepts electronic submission via disk or modem. Sample copy for $2.95, 8½×11 SAE and $2.50 postage. Fiction guidelines for #10 SAE and 1 first class stamp.

 The double dagger before a listing indicates that the listing is new in this edition. New markets are often the most receptive to freelance contributions.

Payment: Pays 14¢/word.
Terms: Payment is on publication. Offers 30% kill fee. Buys first North American serial rights. Sends galleys to author.
Advice: Looks for writing that "keeps me riveted to the page from word #1! Seldom see enough development of main character(s) or details. Writers try to cover too much with too little detail. Focus everything more!"

GUYS, First Hand Ltd., Box 1314, Teaneck NJ 07666. (201)836-9177. FAX: (201)836-5055. Editor: Brandon Judell. Magazine: digest size; 160 pages; illustrations; photos. "Fiction and informative departments for today's gay man. Fiction is of an erotic nature, and we especially need short shorts and novella-length stories." Published 10 times/year. Estab. 1988.
Needs: Gay. "Should be written in first person. No science fiction or fantasy. No four-legged animals. All characters must be over 18. Stories including members of ethnic groups or the disabled are especially welcome. Erotica should be based on reality." Buys 6 mss/issue; 66 mss/year. Publishes ms 9-18 months after acceptance. Published work by Rick Jackson, Kenn Richie, Jay Shaffer; published new writers within the last year. Length: 3,000 words average; 2,000 words minimum; 3,750 words maximum. For novellas: 7,500-8,600 words. Publishes short shorts. Length: 750-1,250 words. Sometimes critiques rejected mss and recommends other markets.
How to Contact: Send complete ms with cover letter, which should include writer's name, address, telephone and Social Security number and whether selling all rights or first North American serial rights. Reports in 6-8 weeks on ms. SASE. Accepts computer printout submissions. Sample copy for $5. Fiction guidelines for #10 SAE and 1 first class stamp. Reviews novels and short story collections.
Payment: Pays $100-150; $75 for short shorts (all rights); $250 for novellas (all rights).
Terms: Pays on publication or in 240 days, whichever comes first, for all rights or first North American serial rights.
Advice: "Use language that you would normally use. Don't get poetic or rhapsodic. Sex is a basic act. Use basic language."

HADASSAH MAGAZINE, (IV), 50 W. 58th St., New York NY 10019. Executive Editor: Alan M. Tigay. Senior Editor: Zelda Shluker. General interest magazine: 8½×11; 48-70 pages; coated and uncoated paper; slick, medium weight coated cover; drawings and cartoons; photos. Primarily concerned with Israel, the American Jewish community, Jewish communities around the world and American current affairs. Monthly except combined June/July and August/September issues. Circ. 375,000.
Needs: Ethnic (Jewish). Receives 20-25 unsolicited fiction mss each month. Recently published fiction by Anita Desai and Lori Ubell; published new writers within the last year. Length: 3,000 words maximum. Also publishes short stories 1,500-2,000 words.
How to Contact: Send complete ms with SASE. Accepts computer printout submissions. Reports in 6 weeks on mss. "Not interested in multiple submissions or previously published articles."
Payment: Pays $300 minimum. Offers $50 kill fee for assigned mss not published.
Terms: Pays on publication for U.S. publication rights.
Advice: "Stories on a Jewish theme should be neither self-hating nor schmaltzy."

HARPER'S MAGAZINE, (II, III), 11th Floor, 666 Broadway, New York NY 10012. (212)614-6500. Editor: Lewis H. Lapham. Magazine: 8×10¾; 80 pages; illustrations. Magazine for well educated, widely read and socially concerned readers, college-aged and older, those active in political and community affairs. Monthly. Circ. 200,000.
Needs: Contemporary and humor. Stories on contemporary life and its problems. Receives approximately 300 unsolicited fiction mss/month. Published new writers within the last year. Length: 1,000-5,000 words.
How to Contact: Query to managing editor, or through agent. Reports in 6 weeks on queries.
Payment: Pays $500-1,000.
Terms: Pays on acceptance for rights, which vary on each author and material. Negotiable kill fee. Sends galleys to author.
Advice: "Buys very little fiction but *Harper's* has published short stories traditionally."

HI-CALL, (II), Gospel Publishing House, 1445 Boonville Ave., Springfield MO 65802-1894. (417)862-2781. Editor: Deanna S. Harris. Take-home Sunday school paper for teenagers (ages 12-17). Weekly. Estab. 1936. Circ. 80,000.

Needs: Religious/inspirational, mystery/suspense, adventure, humor, spiritual and young adult, "with a strong but not preachy Biblical emphasis." Receives approximately 100 unsolicited fiction mss/ month. Published work by Betty Steele Everett, Alan Cliburn and Michelle Starr. Published new writers within the last year. Length: up to 1,500 words.

How to Contact: Send complete ms with SASE. Reports in 1-3 months. Simultaneous and previously published submissions OK. Accepts computer printout submissions. Free sample copy and guidelines.

Payment: Pays 2-3¢/word.

Terms: Pays on acceptance for one-time rights.

Advice: "Most manuscripts are rejected because of shallow characters, shallow or predictable plots, and/or a lack of spiritual emphasis. Send seasonal material approximately 18 months in advance."

HIGH ADVENTURE, (II), General Council Assemblies of God (Gospel Publishing Co.), 1445 Boonville, Springfield MO 65802. (417)862-2781, ext. 4178. Editor: Marshall Bruner. Magazine: 8⁵⁄₁₆ × 11⅛; 16 pages; lancer paper; self cover; illustrations; photos. Magazine for adolescent boys. "Designed to provide boys with worthwhile, enjoyable, leisure reading; to challenge them in narrative form to higher ideals and greater spiritual dedication; and to perpetuate the spirit of the Royal Rangers program through stories, ideas and illustrations." Quarterly. Estab. 1971. Circ. 86,000.

Needs: Adventure, historical (general), religious/inspirational, suspense/mystery and western. Published new writers within the last year. Length: 1,200 words minimum. Publishes short shorts to 1,000 words. Occasionally critiques rejected mss.

How to Contact: Send ms with SASE. Include Social Security number. Reports in 8 weeks. Simultaneous, photocopied and previously published submissions OK. Free sample copy and fiction guidelines for 9 × 12 SASE.

Payment: Pays 2-3¢/word (base) and 3 contributor's copies.

Terms: Pays on acceptance for first rights and one-time rights.

Advice: "Ask for list of upcoming themes."

HIGHLIGHTS FOR CHILDREN, 803 Church St., Honesdale PA 18431. (717)253-1080. Editor: Kent L. Brown, Jr. Address fiction to: Beth Troop, Manuscript Coordinator. Magazine: 8½ × 11; 42 pages; uncoated paper; coated cover stock; illustrations; photos. Published 11 times/year. Circ. 2.8 million.

Needs: Juvenile (ages 2-12). Unusual stories appealing to both girls and boys; stories with good characterization, strong emotional appeal, vivid, full of action. "Begin with action rather than description, have strong plot, believable setting, suspense from start to finish." Length: 400-900 words. "We also need easy stories for very young readers (100-400 words)." No war, crime or violence. Receives 600-800 unsolicited fiction mss/month. Buys 6-7 mss/issue. Also publishes rebus (picture) stories of 125 words or under for the 3-to 7-year-old child. Recently published work by Nancy West, Cris Peterson and Trinka Enell; published new writers within the last year. Critiques rejected mss occasionally, "especially when editors see possibilities in story."

How to Contact: Send complete ms with SASE and include a rough word count and cover letter "with any previous acceptances by our magazine; any other published work anywhere." Reports in 1 month. Accepts computer printout submissions. Free guidelines on request.

Payment: Pays 14¢ and up per word.

Terms: Pays on acceptance for all rights. Sends galleys to author.

Advice: "We accept a story on its merit whether written by an unpublished or an experienced writer. Mss are rejected because of poor writing, lack of plot, trite or worn-out plot, or poor characterization. Children *like* stories and learn about life from stories. Children learn to become lifelong fiction readers by enjoying stories." Sponsors occasional contests. Write for information.

ALFRED HITCHCOCK'S MYSTERY MAGAZINE, (I, II), Davis Publications, Inc., 380 Lexington Ave., New York NY 10017. (212)557-9100. Editor: Cathleen Jordan. Mystery fiction magazine: 5¹⁄₁₆ × 7⅜; 160 pages; 28 lb. newsprint paper; 60 lb. machine-/coated cover stock; illustrations; photos. Published 13 times/year. Estab. 1956. Circ. 225,000.

Needs: Mystery and detection. No sensationalism. Number of mss/issue varies with length of mss. Length: up to 14,000 words. Also publishes short shorts.

How to Contact: Send complete ms and SASE. Accepts computer printout submissions. Reports in 2 months. Guideline sheet for SASE.

Payment: Pays 5¢/word on acceptance.

THE HOME ALTAR, Meditations for Families with Children, (II), P.O. Box 590179, San Francisco CA 94159-0179. Editor: M. Elaine Dunham. Magazine: 5¼×7¼; 64 pages; newsprint paper; coated 4-color cover; 2-color illustrations. *"The Home Altar* is a magazine of daily devotions. For each day, there is a designated Bible reading, a short story (fiction or nonfiction) which reflects the central message of the biblical passage, and a concluding prayer." Readers are "primarily Lutheran (ELCA) families—with children between 6 and 14 years of age." Quarterly. Estab. 1940. Circ. 75,000.
Needs: Juvenile (5-9 years) and religious/inspirational. "No unsolicited manuscripts are accepted for publication in *The Home Altar.* All writing is done on assignment, to reflect specific Bible readings and themes." Accepts up to 90 mss/issue; approximately 200 mss/year. Publishes ms an average of 6-12 months after acceptance. Recently published work by Barbra Minar, Normajean Matzke and Jerome Koch. Length: 150 words average; 125 words minimum; 170 words maximum. Sometimes critiques rejected mss.
How to Contact: Query with clips of published or unpublished work. Reports on queries in 3 months; on mss in 2 weeks. Photocopied submissions OK. Accepts computer printout submissions. Sample copy and fiction guidelines free.
Payment: Pays $10/"story"; contributor's copies.
Terms: Pays on acceptance for all rights.
Advice: "We're trying to serve a diverse group of readers—children of all ages as well as adults. A well-written story often has several levels of meaning and will touch people of different ages and experiences in different ways. Write stories in which children are the protagonists. Keep your sentences short. Use inclusive language when referring to human beings or to God."

HOME LIFE, (II), The Sunday School Board of the Southern Baptist Convention, 127 9th Ave. N., Nashville TN 37234. (615)251-2271. Editor: Charlie Warren. A Christian family magazine: 8⅛×11; 66 pages; coated paper; separate cover stock; illustrations; photos. "Top priorities are strengthening and enriching marriage; parenthood; family concerns and problems; and spiritual and personal growth. Most of our readers are married couples and parents between the ages of 25-50. They read it out of denominational loyalty and desire for Christian growth and discipleship." Monthly. Estab. 1947. Circ. 680,000.
Needs: Contemporary, prose poem, religious/inspirational, spiritual, humor and young adult. "We do not want distasteful, risqué or raunchy fiction. Nor should it be too fanciful or far-fetched." Receives approximately 100-200 unsolicited fiction mss/month. Buys 1-2 mss/issue; 12-24 mss/year. Publishes ms 12-20 months after acceptance. Published work by Irene J. Kutz, Mary C. Perham, Ann Beacham; published new writers within the last year. Length: 750-1,800 words. Publishes short shorts of 500+ words. Recommends other markets.
How to Contact: Query or send complete ms. Reports in 1 month on queries; 2 months on mss. SASE always. Simultaneous submissions OK. Accepts computer printout submissions. Sample copy for $1.
Payment: Pays up to 5½¢/word for unsolicited mss; 3 contributor's copies.
Terms: Pays on acceptance for all rights, first rights or first North American serial rights. Rarely buys reprints.
Advice: "Work must be believable."

HORSE ILLUSTRATED, Fancy Publications, Box 6050, Mission Viejo CA 92690. (714)855-8822. FAX: (714)855-3045. Editor: Sharon Ralls Lemon. Associate Editor: Kathryn Shayman. "General all-breed horse magazine for horse lovers of all ages but mainly women riding for show and pleasure. All material is centered around horses; both English and western riding styles are profiled." Monthly. Estab. 1982. Circ. 120,000.
Needs: Adventure, humor and suspense/mystery. "Must concern horses. Liberal—nothing unsuitable to a younger audience, although we do not want mss aimed directly at young readers." Receives 3-5 unsolicited mss/month. Buys 5-6 mss/year. Publishes ms 4-10 months after acceptance. Published work by Cooky McClung, Elizabeth Vaugh; published new writers within the last year. Length: 1,500-2,000 words average; 1,000 words minimum; 2,500 words maximum. Occasionally critiques rejected mss if asked to do so.
How to Contact: Query first or send complete ms. Reports in 2 months on queries; 3 months on mss. SASE. Photocopied submissions OK. Accepts computer printout submissions. Sample copy for $3.25. Fiction guidelines for SASE.

Payment: Pays $50-150; 2 contributor's copies; $2 charge for extras ("free if request is for a reasonable number of copies").
Terms: Pays on publication for one-time rights.
Advice: "Write about adult women—*no* little girl, wild stallion or cowboy and Indian stories, please."

HUMPTY DUMPTY'S MAGAZINE, (II), Children's Better Health Institute, Benjamin Franklin Literary & Medical Society, Inc., Box 567, 1100 Waterway Blvd., Indianapolis IN 46206. Editor: Christine French Clark. Magazine: 6½×9⅛; 48 pages; 35 lb. paper; coated cover; illustrations; rarely photos. Children's magazine stressing health, nutrition, hygiene, exercise and safety for children ages 4-6. Publishes 8 issues/year.
Needs: Juvenile health-related material and material of a more general nature. No inanimate talking objects. Rhyming stories should flow easily with no contrived rhymes. Receives 250-300 unsolicited fiction mss/month. Buys 3-5 mss/issue. Length: 600 words maximum.
How to Contact: Send complete ms with SASE. No queries. Reports in 8-10 weeks. Sample copy for 75¢. Editorial guidelines for SASE.
Payment: Pays minimum 10¢/word for stories plus 2 contributor's copies (more upon request).
Terms: Pays on publication for all rights. (One-time book rights returned when requested for specific publication.)
Advice: "In contemporary stories, characters should be up-to-date, with realistic dialogue. We're looking for health-related stories with unusual twists or surprise endings. We want to avoid stories and poems that 'preach.' We try to present the health material in a positive way, utilizing a light humorous approach wherever possible." Most rejected mss "are too wordy. Cover letters should be included only if they give pertinent information—list of credits, bibliography, or mention of any special training or qualifications that make author an authority."

HUSTLER BUSTY BEAUTIES, (II), HG Publications, Inc., Suite 300, 9171 Wilshire Blvd., Beverly Hills CA 90210. (213)858-7100. Editor: N. Morgen Hagen. Magazine: 8×11; 100 pages; 60 lb. paper; 80 lb. cover; illustrations and photographs. "Adult entertainment and reading centered around large-breasted women for an over-18 audience, mostly male." Monthly. Estab. 1988. Circ. 150,000.
Needs: Adventure, erotica, fantasy, suspense/mystery. All must have erotic theme. Receives 25 unsolicited fiction mss/month. Buys 1 ms/issue; 6-12 mss/year. Publishes mss 3-6 months after acceptance. Published work by Mike Dillon, H.H. Morris. Length: 1,600 words preferred; 1,000 words minimum; 2,000 words maximum.
How to Contact: Query first. Then send complete ms with cover letter. Reports in 1 week on queries; in 2-4 weeks on mss. SASE. Sample copy for $5. Fiction guidelines free.
Payment: Pays $80-500.
Terms: Pays on acceptance for all rights.
Advice: Looks for "1. Plausible plot, well-defined characters, literary ingenuity. 2. Hot sex scenes. 3. Readable, coherent, grammatically sound prose."

I.D., (IV), David C. Cook Publishing Co., 850 N. Grove, Elgin IL 60120. (708)741-2400. Editor: Douglas Schmidt. A take-home Sunday school paper: 5½×8½; 8 pages; Penegra paper and cover; full color illustrations and photos. For senior high classes. Weekly.
Needs: Christian spiritual. Writers work mostly on assignment. "Each piece must present some aspect of the Christian life without being preachy. No closing sermons and no pat answers. Any topic appropriate to senior high is acceptable." Buys 5-10 mss/year. Length: 900-1,200 words.
How to Contact: Send complete ms with SASE. No queries please. Cover letter with brief bio, religious credentials and experience with senior highs. Reports in 2 months on mss. Guidelines for SASE.
Payment: Pays $100-125.
Terms: Pays on acceptance for all rights.
Advice: "You've got to know kids and be aware of the struggles Christian kids are facing today. Don't write about how things were when you were a teenager—kids don't want to hear it."

IDEALS MAGAZINE, (II), Ideals Publishing Corp., Suite 890, 565 Marriott Dr., Nashville TN 37210. (615)885-8270. Associate Editor: D. Fran Morley. Vice President of Publishing: Patricia Pingry. Magazine: 8⅛₆×10⅞; 80 pages; 60 lb Cougarpaper; 12 pt C1S cover; illustrations; photos. "*Ideals* is a family-oriented magazine with issues corresponding to seasons and based on traditional values." Published 8 times a year. Estab. 1944.

Needs: Seasonal, inspirational, spiritual, or humorous short, short fiction or prose poem. Length: 700 words maximum.
How to Contact: Send complete ms with SASE. Reports in 12-16 weeks on mss.
Payment: Varies.
Terms: Pays on publication for one-time rights.
Advice: "We publish fiction that is appropriate to the theme of the issue and to our audience."

IN TOUCH FOR MEN, (IV), 7216 Varna St., North Hollywood CA 91605. (818)764-2288. Editor: Alec Wagner. Magazine: 8 × 10¾; 100 pages; glossy paper; coated cover; illustrations and photographs. "*In Touch* is a magazine for gay men. It features five to six nude male centerfolds in each issue, but is erotic rather than pornographic. We include fiction." Monthly. Estab. 1973. Circ. 70,000.
Needs: Confession, gay, erotica, romance (contemporary, historical). All characters must be over 18 years old. Stories must have an explicit erotic content. No heterosexual or internalized homophobic fiction. Buys 3 mss/month; 36 mss/year. Publishes ms 3 months after acceptance. Published work by Chuck Fallon, Christopher H. Allenson and Addison Whitney. Length: 2,500 words average; up to 3,500 words maximum. Sometimes critiques rejected mss and recommends other markets.
How to Contact: Send complete ms with cover letter, name, address and Social Security number. Reports in 1 week on queries; 2 months on mss. SASE. Simultaneous, photocopied and reprint submissions, if from local publication, OK. Accepts computer printout submissions. Sample copy for $5.95. Fiction guidelines free. Reviews novels and short story collections.
Payment: Pays $25-75 (except on rare occasions for a longer piece).
Terms: Pays on acceptance for one-time rights.
Advice: "Fiction is the most popular feature of our magazine. Our magazine features erotic fiction— remember *both* words. To be published, it must have some *storyline* ('fiction'), as well as sexual activity ('erotic')."

INDIA CURRENTS, California's Guide to Indian Arts, Entertainment and Dining, (II, IV), Box 21285, San Jose CA 95151. (408)274-6966. FAX: (408)274-2733. Editor: Arvind Kumar. Magazine: 8½ × 11; 72 pages; newsprint paper; illustrations and photographs. "The arts and culture of India as seen in America for Indians and non-Indians with a common interest in India." Monthly. Estab. 1987. Circ. 25,000.
Needs: All Indian content: contemporary, ethnic, feminist, historical (general), humor/satire, literary, mainstream, prose poem, psychic/supernatural/occult, regional, religious/inspirational, romance, translations (from Indian languages). "We seek material with insight into Indian culture, American culture and the crossing from one to another." Receives 12 unsolicited mss/month. Buys 6 ms/issue; 72 mss/year. Publishes ms 2-6 months after acceptance. Published work by Chitra Divakaruni, C.J. Wallia, Javaid Qazi; published new writers within the last year. Length: 2,000 words average; 1,000 words minimum; 3,000 words maximum. Publishes short shorts. Length: 500 words.
How to Contact: Send complete ms with cover letter and clips of published work. Reports in 1 month on queries; 2 months on mss. SASE. Simultaneous, photocopied and reprint submissions OK. Accepts computer printout submissions. Accepts electronic submissions. Sample copy $2.
Payment: Pays $25/1,000 words.
Terms: Pays on publication for one-time rights.
Advice: "Story must be related to India and subcontinent in some meaningful way. The best stories are those which document some deep transformation as a result of an Indian experience, or those which show the humanity of Indians as the world's most ancient citizens."

INDIAN LIFE MAGAZINE, (II, IV), Intertribal Christian Communications, Box 3765, Station B, Winnipeg, Manitoba R2W 3R6 Canada. (204)661-9333 or (800)665-9275 in Canada only. FAX: (204)661-3982. Editor: Jim Uttley. Magazine: 8½ × 11; 24 pages; newsprint paper and cover stock; illustrations; photos. A nondenominational Christian magazine written and read mostly by North American Indians. Bimonthly. Estab. 1979. Circ. 65,000.
Needs: Adventure, confession, ethnic (Indian), historical (general), juvenile, men's, religious/inspirational, women's and young adult/teen. Receives 10 unsolicited mss/month. Buys 1 ms/issue; 4-5 mss/ year. Recently published work by Chief Billy Diamond and Kari Hill. Published new writers within

Market categories: (I) Beginning; (II) General; (III) Prestige; (IV) Specialized.

the last year. Length: 1,000-1,200 words average. Publishes short shorts of 600-900 words. Occasionally comments on rejected mss.

How to Contact: Query first, send complete ms (with cover letter, bio and published clips), or query with clips of published work. Reports in 1 month on queries; in 2 months on mss. IRC or SASE ("US stamps no good up here"). Accepts computer printout submissions. Sample copy $1 and 8½ × 11 SAE. Fiction guidelines for $1 and #10 SAE.

Payment: Pays 4-5¢/word and 3 contributor's copies; 50¢ charge for extras.

Terms: Pays on publication for first rights.

Advice: "Keep it simple with an Indian viewpoint at about a 7th grade reading level. Read story out loud. Have someone else read it to you. If it doesn't come across smoothly and naturally, it needs work."

"Many of our cover photos do not necessarily relate to the issues," says Jim Uttley, Jr., editor of Indian Life, *a nondenominational Christian magazine for North American Indians. "Rather, we think the covers speak for themselves," he says. The photograph here is of a Cree girl from Northern Manitoba. "We choose it for its brilliant color and for the way it portrays Indian youth," Uttley explains. He says those seeking to publish in* Indian Life *should "write through the eyes of a Native American." The cover photo is courtesy of Travel Manitoba, the travel and tourist department of the province of Manitoba. The cover design is by Don Monkman.*

‡INIQUITIES, The Magazine of Great Wickedness & Wonder, (I, II), Suite 1346, 235 E. Colorado Blvd., Pasadena CA 91101. Editors: J.F. Gonzalez and Buddy Martinez. Magazine: 8½ × 11; 96 pages; slick glossy paper; illustrations and photographs. "Horror fiction, nonfiction in relation to horror and relating subjects (see guidelines) for anybody who has an interest in horror (books, film, etc.)." Quarterly. Estab. 1990. Circ. 10,000.

Needs: Horror, psychic/supernatural/occult; science fiction and suspense/mystery. No sword and sorcery, romance, confessional, pornography. Receives 100 unsolicited mss/month. Buys 6-8 mss/issue; 30-35 mss/year. Publishes ms 6 months-1½ years after acceptance. Recently published work by Peter Straub, Clive Barker, Ray Bradlow. Length: 4,000-6,000 words preferred; 10,000 words maximum. Publishes short shorts. Sometimes critiques rejected mss and recommends other markets.

How to Contact: Send complete ms with cover letter. Include "credits, if any, name, address and phone number. I don't want the writer to tell me about the story in the cover letter." Reports in 1-3 weeks on queries; 3 months on mss. SASE. Simultaneous, photocopied and reprint submissions OK. Accepts computer printout submissions. Sample copy for $4.95. Fiction guidelines for #10 SAE and 1 first class stamp.

Payment: Pays 3¢-5¢/word.

Terms: Offers kill fee of half the amount. Buys first North American serial rights. Sends galleys to author.

Advice: Looks for "believable characters and original ideas. Good writing. Fantastic writing. Make the words flow and count for the story. If the story keeps us turning the pages with bated breath. It has a great chance. If we get through the first two pages and it's sloppy, displays weak, or uninteresting characters or a contrived plot, we won't even finish it. Chances are the reader won't either. Know the genre and what's been done. *Invest in a sample copy.* While we are open to different styles of horror.

We have high expectations for the fiction we publish. The only way a beginner will know what we expect is to buy the magazine and read what we've published."

INSIDE, The Magazine of the Jewish Exponent, (II), Jewish Federation, 226 S. 16th St., Philadelphia PA 19102. (215)893-5700. Editor-in-Chief: Jane Biberman. Magazine: 175-225 pages; glossy paper; illustrations; photos. Aimed at middle- and upper-middle-class audience, Jewish-oriented articles and fiction. Quarterly. Estab. 1980. Circ. 80,000.
Needs: Contemporary, ethnic, humor/satire, literary and translations. No erotica. Receives approximately 10 unsolicited fiction mss/month. Buys 1-2 mss/issue; 4-8 mss/year. Published new writers within the last year. Length: 1,500 words minimum; 3,000 words maximum; 2,000 words average. Occasionally critiques rejected mss.
How to Contact: Query first with clips of published work. Reports on queries in 3 weeks. SASE. Simultaneous and photocopied submissions OK. Accepts computer printouts. Sample copy for $3. Fiction guidelines for SASE.
Payment: Pays $100-600.
Terms: Pays on acceptance for first rights. Sometimes buys reprints. Sends galleys to author.
Advice: "We're looking for original, avant-garde, stylish writing."

INSIDE TEXAS RUNNING, The Tabloid Magazine That Runs Texas, (II, IV), 9514 Bristlebrook, Houston TX 77083. (713)498-3208. Publisher/Editor: Joanne Schmidt. Specialized tabloid for Texas joggers/runners—novice to marathoner, bicycling, aerobics and general fitness. Monthly. Estab. 1977. Circ. 10,000; overall readers 30,000.
Needs: Historical (general), humor/satire, literary, and serialized/excerpted books on running and general fitness. "Nothing sexually explicit—we're family-oriented." Texas-oriented mss preferred. Buys 1 ms/issue. Length: 500 words minimum; 2,000 words maximum. Occasionally critiques rejected mss.
How to Contact: *Query only*. "We're overrun with too much to read. Not accepting manuscripts at this time." Simultaneous, photocopied and previously published submissions OK. Reports in 1 month on mss. Sample copy $2.50. Free fiction guidelines with SASE.
Payment: Pays $25-100.
Terms: Pays on acceptance for one-time rights.
Advice: "If a writer has something useful and original to convey, editors will want to buy his work. Period. A writer should ask himself if he, as a reader, would find the story worth reading. Too many writers can't look beyond their own experiences and relate every boring detail of some personal incident, which they disguise as fiction."

INSIGHTS, NRA News for Young Shooters, (II, IV), National Rifle Association of America, 1600 Rhode Island Ave. NW, Washington DC 20036. (202)828-6075. Editor: John Robbins. Magazine: 8⅛×10⅞; 24 pages; 60 lb. Midset paper and cover; illustrations and photos."*InSights* publishes educational yet entertaining articles, teaching young hunters and shooters ways to improve their performance. For boys and girls ages eight to 20." Monthly. Estab. 1981. Circ. 30,000.
Needs: Hunting or competition shooting. No "anti-hunting, anti-firearms." Receives 5-10 unsolicited mss/month. Accepts 1 ms/issue; 12 mss/year. Publishes ms an average of 1 month to 1 year after acceptance. Published work by Dan Anderson, Michael Manley and John Robbins; published new writers within the last year. Length: 1,000 words minimum; 1,500 words maximum. Publishes short shorts. Sometimes critiques rejected ms; occasionally recommends other markets.
How to Contact: Query with clips of published work and cover letter. Reports in 1 month on query; 6-8 weeks on mss. SASE. Photocopied submissions OK. Accepts computer printout submissions. Free sample copy and fiction guidelines.
Payment: Pays up to $250.
Terms: Pays on acceptance.
Advice: "Writing is an art but publishing is a business—a big business. Any writer who understands his market place has an edge over a writer who isn't familiar with the publications that want his kind of writing. We have become more discriminating in the fiction that we buy. Story has to have a strong plot and must present a lesson, whether it is gun safety, ethics or hunting knowledge."

INTERNATIONAL BOWHUNTER, (I, II, IV), P.O. Box 67, Pillager MN 56473-0067. (218)746-3333. Editor: Johnny Boatner. Magazine: 8¼×10¾; 68 pages; enamel paper; illustrations and photographs. "Bowhunting articles only for bowhunters." Published 7 times/year. Estab. 1990. Circ. 50,000+.

Needs: Adventure and sports. "We want articles by people who are actually bowhunters writing about their experience." Receives 30 unsolicited mss/month. Buys 7-12 mss/issue; 49-84/year. Publishes ms 1-6 months after acceptance. Length: 1,200 words preferred; 600 words minimum; 4,000 words maximum. Publishes short shorts. Length: 500 words. Sometimes critiques rejected mss and recommends other markets.
How to Contact: Send complete ms with cover letter. Include Social Security number and bio. Reports on queries in 2 weeks. SASE. Accepts computer printout submissions. Sample copy for $2, #10 SAE and 1 first class stamp. Fiction guidelines for #10 SAE and 1 first class stamp.
Payment: Pays $25-150 and contributor's copies; charge for extras.
Terms: Buys first rights.
Advice: "Read your guidelines."

JACK AND JILL, The Benjamin Franklin Literary & Medical Society, Inc., Box 567, 1100 Waterway Blvd., Indianapolis IN 46206. (317)636-8881. Editor: Steve Charles. Children's magazine of articles, stories and activities many with a health, safety, exercise or nutritional-oriented theme, ages 6-8 years. Monthly except January/February, March/April, May/June, July/August. Estab. 1938.
Needs: Science fiction, mystery, sports, adventure, historical fiction and humor. Health-related stories with a subtle lesson. Published work by Peter Fernandez, Adriana Devoy and Myra Schomberg; published new writers within the last year. Length: 500-1,500 words.
How to Contact: Send complete ms with SASE. Reports in 10 weeks on mss. Sample copy 75¢. Fiction guidelines for SASE.
Payment: Pays 8¢/word.
Terms: Pays on publication for all rights.
Advice: "Try to present health material in a positive—not a negative—light. Use humor and a light approach wherever possible without minimizing the seriousness of the subject. We need more humor and adventure stories."

JIVE, BLACK CONFESSIONS, BLACK ROMANCE, BRONZE THRILLS, BLACK SECRETS, (I, II), Sterling's Magazines/Lexington Library, 355 Lexington Ave., New York NY 10017. (212)949-6850. Editor: Angela Sang. Magazine: 8½×11; 72 pages; newsprint paper; glossy cover; 8×10 photographs. "We publish stories that are ultra romantic and have romantic lovemaking scenes in them. Our audience is basically young and in high school and college. However, we have a significant audience base of divorcees and housewives. The age range is from 18-49." Bimonthly (*Jive* and *Black Romance* in odd-numbered months; *Black Confessions* and *Bronze Thrills* in even-numbered months). 6 issues per year. Estab. 1962. Circ. 100,000.
Needs: Confession, romance (contemporary, young adult). No "stories that are stereotypical to black people, ones that do not follow the basic rules of writing, or ones that are too graphic in content and lack a romantic element." Receives 200 or more unsolicited fiction mss/month. Buys 6 mss/issue (2 issues/month); 144 mss/year. Publishes ms an average of 3-6 months after acceptance. Recently published work by Linda Smith; published new writers within the last year. Length: 15-19 pages. Always critiques rejected mss; recommends other markets.
How to Contact: Query with clips of published work or send complete ms with cover letter. "A cover letter should include an author's bio and what he or she proposes to do. Of course, address and phone number." Reports in 3-6 months. SASE. Simultaneous and photocopied submissions OK. "Please contact me if simultaneously submitted work has been accepted elsewhere." Accepts computer printout submissions. Sample copy for 9×12 SAE and 5 first class stamps; fiction guidelines for #10 SAE and 2 first class stamps.
Payment: Pays $75-100.
Terms: Pays on publication for first rights or one-time rights.
Advice: "Our four magazines are a great starting point for new writers. We accept work from beginners as well as established writers. Please study and research black culture and lifestyles if you are not a black writer. Stereotypical stories are not acceptable. Set the stories all over the world and all over the USA—not just down south. We are not looking for 'the runaway who gets turned out by a sweet-talking pimp' stories. We are looking for stories about all types of female characters. Any writer should not be afraid to communicate with us if he or she is having some difficulty with writing a story. We are available to help at any stage of the submission process. Also, writers should practice patience. If we do not contact the writer, that means that the story is being read or is being held on file for future publication. If we get in touch with the writer, it usually means a request for revision and resubmission. Do the best work possible and don't let rejection slips send you off 'the deep end.' Don't take everything that is said about your work so personally. We are buying all of our work from freelance writers."

JUGGLER'S WORLD, (IV), International Juggler's Association, Box 443, Davidson NC 28036. (704)892-1296. Editor: Bill Giduz. Fiction Editor: Ken Letko. Magazine: 8½×11; 44 pages; 70 lb. paper and cover stock; illustrations and photos. For and about jugglers and juggling. Quarterly.
Needs: Historical (general), humor/satire, science fiction. No stories "that don't include juggling as a central theme." Receives "very few" unsolicited mss/month. Accepts 2 mss/year. Publishes ms an average of 6-12 months to 1 year after acceptance. Length: 1,000 words average; 500 words minimum; 2,000 words maximum. Sometimes critiques rejected mss.
How to Contact: Query first. Reports in 1 week. Simultaneous and photocopied submissions OK. Accepts computer printout submissions. Prefers electronic submissions via IBM or Macintosh compatible disk. Sample copy for $2.
Payment: Pays $25-50, free subscription to magazine and 5 contributor's copies.
Terms: Pays on acceptance for first rights.

JUNIOR TRAILS, (I, II), Gospel Publishing House, 1445 Boonville Ave., Springfield MO 65802. (417)862-2781. Elementary Editor: Sinda S. Zinn. Magazine: 5½×8½; 8 pages; 36 lb. coated offset paper; art illustrations; photos. "A Sunday school take-home paper of nature articles and fictional stories that apply Christian principles to everyday living for 9-to 12-year-old children." Weekly. Estab. 1954. Circ. 70,000.
Needs: Contemporary, religious/inspirational, spiritual, sports and juvenile. Adventure stories are welcome. No Biblical fiction or science fiction. Buys 2 mss/issue. Published work by Betty Lou Mell, Mason M. Smith, Nanette L. Dunford; published new writers within the last year. Length: 1,200-1,500 words. Publishes short shorts.
How to Contact: Send complete ms with SASE. Reports in 6-8 weeks. Accepts computer printout submissions. Free sample copy and guidelines.
Payment: Pays 3¢/word. 3 free author's copies.
Terms: Pays on acceptance.
Advice: "Know the age level and direct stories relevant to that age group. Since junior-age children (grades 5 and 6) enjoy action, fiction provides a vehicle for communicating moral/spiritual principles in a dramatic framework. Fiction, if well done, can be a powerful tool for relating Christian principles. It must, however, be realistic and believable in its development. Make your children be children, not overly mature for their age. We would like more stories with a *city* setting."

KID CITY, (II), Children's Television Workshop, 1 Lincoln Plaza, New York NY 10023. (212)595-3456. Editor-in-Chief: Maureen Hunter-Bone. Magazine: 8½×11; 32 pages; glossy cover; illustrations; photos. General interest for children 6-10 "devoted to sparking kids' interest in reading and writing about the world around them." Published 10 times/year. Estab. 1974. Circ. 350,000.
Needs: Adventure, mystery, juvenile (6-10 years), science fiction. Publishes ms "at least" 6 months after acceptance. Length: 600-750 words average; 1,000 words maximum.
How to Contact: Send complete ms with cover letter. Reports in 1-2 months on mss. SASE. Photocopied submissions OK. Accepts computer printout submissions. Sample copy for $1.50 and 9×12 SAE with 75¢ postage. Writers' guidelines for 9×12 SAE with 75¢ postage.
Payment: Pays $200-400 and contributor's copies.
Terms: Pays on acceptance for all rights (some negotiable).
Advice: "We look for bright and sparkling prose. Don't talk down. Don't stereotype. Don't use cutesy names, animals or plots. No heavy moralizing or pat dilemmas."

KINDERGARTEN LISTEN, (IV), WordAction Publishing Company, 6401 The Paseo, Kansas City MO 64109. (816)931-1900 or (816)333-7000 (editorial). Editor: Janet Sawyer. Fiction Editor: Janet R. Reeves. Tabloid: 4-page story paper; 8½×11; newsprint; newsprint cover; b&w and 4-color illustrations; 4-color photos. Stories follow a 2-year topic cycle. Readers are kindergarten 4s, 5s and early 6s. Weekly. Estab. 1981. Circ. 45,000.
Needs: Contemporary, prose poem, religious/inspirational, spiritual, Christian topic themes. Published work by Katharine Ruth Adams, Helen Ott, Minnie Wells. Length: 300 words minimum; 400 words maximum. Sometimes critiques rejected mss and recommends other markets.
How to Contact: Query first "if unfamiliar with 2-year topic cycle" or send complete mss. Writers must include SASE for each submission. Reports in 3 weeks on queries; in 1 month on mss. SASE. Photocopied submissions OK. Accepts computer printout submissions. Accepts electronic submissions via disk or modem in ASCII text only. Sample copy and fiction guidelines for 8½×11 SAE and 1 first class stamp.

Payment: Pays 5¢/word or $25 for stories (whichever is greater) and 4 contributor's copies. Charges for extra copies.
Terms: Pays on acceptance for multiple use rights. No remuneration for reprinting stories when issues are recycled. Authors are free to submit to other publications whose audiences do not overlap that of *Listen*.
Advice: "A majority of submissions we've received lately are of poor quality. Dialogue and actions of main child characters are unrealistic to the young age group our magazine ministers to. Actions and dialogue of parent characters is often too unrealistic as well. They're either too good to be true or very stilted in actions and speech. Because today's children are growing up in a rough world, we seek to help them deal with a variety of situations from divorce to the simple worries of a young child, like being left with a new babysitter. We seek to portray fictional children finding real solutions in the love and guidance of Christ, assisted by parent and other adult figures. Too many submissions appear to come from writers who don't take the children's market seriously or view it as an easy area to write prose for. In fact, children's stories require research and realism, and much effort in writing and rewriting. Writers have to know the audience well, not just guess or try to recall what it was like to be a pre-K child. Few writers can relate well enough to produce good manuscripts without these efforts." Criteria used in choosing fiction: "(1) Does it relate to our theme titles for the 2-year cycle? (2) Is the story interesting to children? (3) Does it assist them in understanding some vital area of the Christian life, God's love, etc.? (4) Is it realistic in portrayal of all characters? (5) Does it flow naturally and make for good reading? (6) Does the story line progress logically? (7) Does it include any references to inappropriate parent behavior, or unacceptable practices, or doctrines, of the Church of the Nazarene. Ex: We've had a hair-raising number of writers portraying scenes where children are left unattended in shopping malls or some other public place—which is highly inappropriate parental behavior considering the abduction situation that has terrorized our country's parents and families. The portrayal shows little insight on the writer's part."

LADIES' HOME JOURNAL, (III), Published by Meredith Corporation, 100 Park Ave., New York NY 10017. Editor-in-Chief: Myrna Blyth. Fiction/Books Editor: Sofia Marchant. Magazine: 190 pages; 34-38 lb. coated paper; 65 lb. coated cover; illustrations and photos.
Needs: Book mss and short stories, *accepted only through an agent*. Return of unsolicited material cannot be guaranteed. Recently published work by Fay Weldon, Anita Shreve, Rosamunde Pilcher. Length: approximately 3,500 words.
How to Contact: Cover letter with ms (credits). Publishes ms 4-12 months after acceptance.
Terms: Buys First North American rights.
Advice: "Our readers like stories, especially those that have emotional impact. We are using fiction every month, whether it's an excerpt from a novel or a short story. Stories about relationships between people—husband/wife—mother/son—seem to be subjects that can be explored effectively in short stories. Our reader's mail and surveys attest to this fact: Readers enjoy our fiction, and are most keenly tuned to stories dealing with children. Fiction today is stronger than ever. Beginners can be optimistic; if they have talent, I do believe that talent will be discovered."

LADYBUG, (II, IV), Carus Publishing, P.O. Box 300, Peru IL 61354. Editor-in-Chief: Marianne Carus. Contact: Submissions Editor. Magazine: 8×9¼; 36 pages plus 4-page pullout section; illustrations. "*Ladybug* publishes original stories and poems and reprints written by the world's best children's authors. For young children, ages 2-7." Monthly. Estab. 1990.
Needs: Juvenile, fantasy (children's), preschool, read-out-loud stories, picture stories, folk tales, fairy tales. Length: 300-750 words preferred. Publishes short shorts.
How to Contact: Send complete ms with cover letter. Include word count on ms (do not count title). Reports in 3 months. SASE. Reprints are OK. Fiction guidelines for #10 SAE and 1 first class stamp. Sample copy: $2.
Payment: Pays up to 25¢/word (less for reprints).
Terms: Pays on publication for first North American serial rights or second North American rights. For recurring features, pays flat fee and copyright becomes property of Carus Publishing.

LADY'S CIRCLE, (II), Lopez Publications, 111 East 35th St., New York NY 10016. (212)689-3933. Editor: Mary Bemis. Magazine: "A lot of our readers are in Midwestern states." Bimonthly. Estab. 1963. Circ. 200,000.
Needs: Confession, historical, humor/satire, mainstream, religious/inspirational, romance (contemporary, historical, young adult), senior citizen/retirement. Receives 100 unsolicited fiction mss/month. Buys about 6-7 fiction mss/year. Time between acceptance and publication "varies, usually works 6

months ahead." Length: 3,000 words preferred; 1,000 words minimum; 3,000 words maximum. Accepts short shorts "for fillers." Sometimes critiques rejected ms.

How to Contact: Query first. Reports in 3 months on queries. SASE. Simultaneous, photocopied and reprint submissions OK. Accepts electronic submissions via disk or modem. Sample copy for $1.95; fiction guidelines for SAE.

Payment: Pay varies, depending on ms.

Terms: Pays on publication for first North American serial rights.

‡**LETHBRIDGE MAGAZINE, (I, II),** 248684 Alberta Ltd., P.O. Box 1203, Lethbridge, Alberta T1J 4A4 Canada. (403)327-3200. Editor: Richard Burke. Magazine: 8 ½ × 11; 48 pages; glossy paper; illustrations and photos. "*Lethbridge Magazine* prints general interest topics relating to Lethbridge and Southern Alberta for an audience of all ages. Bimonthly. Estab. 1981. Circ. 17,218.

Needs: Adventure, historical (general), humor/satire, literary, regional. Receives 10 unsolicited mss/month. Buys 1 ms/year. Publishes ms 2 months after acceptance. Length: 1,500 words preferred; 1,000 words minimum; 2,000 words maximum. Publishes short shorts.

How to Contact: Query first with clips of published work or send complete ms with cover letter. Reports in 2 months. SASE. Simultaneous, photocopied and reprint submissions OK. Accepts computer printout and electronic submissions. Sample copy for $2. Fiction guidelines for SASE.

Payment: Pays 5¢/word minimum; 12¢/word maximum. Provides contributor's copies.

Terms: Pays on publication for first North American serial rights.

Advice: "Space requirements usually dictate if we can use a submission. Originality and quality of writing make a manuscript stand out. Keep the length short (800 words)."

LIGUORIAN, "A Leading Catholic Magazine," (I, IV),Liguori Publications, 1 Liguori Dr., Liguori MO 63057. (314)464-2500. Editor-in-Chief: Allan Weinert, CSS.R. Managing Editor: Francine M. O'Connor. Magazine: 5 × 8½; 64 pages; b&w illustrations and photographs. "*Liguorian* is a Catholic magazine aimed at helping our readers to live a full Christian life. We publish articles for families, young people, children, religious and singles—all with the same aim." Monthly. Estab. 1913. Circ. 430,000.

Needs: Religious/inspirational, young adult and senior citizen/retirement (with moral Christian thrust), spiritual. "Stories submitted to *Liguorian* must have as their goal the lifting up of the reader to a higher Christian view of values and goals. We are not interested in contemporary works that lack purpose or are of questionable moral value." Receives approximately 25 unsolicited fiction mss/month. Buys 12 mss/year. Recently published work by Tom Dowling, Sharon Helgens, Jim Auer, Ann Urrein and Jon A. Ripslinger; published new writers within the last year. Length: 1,500-2,000 words preferred. Also publishes short shorts. Occasionally critiques rejected mss "if we feel the author is capable of giving us something we need even though this story did not suit us." Occasionally recommends other markets.

How to Contact: Send complete ms with SASE. Accepts computer printout submissions. Accepts disk submissions compatible with TRS-80 Model III. Prefers hard copy with disk submission. Reports in 6 weeks on mss. Sample copy and free fiction guidelines for 6 × 9 SASE.

Payment: Pays 10-12¢/word and 6 contributor's copies. Offers 50% kill fee for assigned mss not published.

Terms: Pays on acceptance for all rights.

Advice: "First read several issues containing short stories. We look for originality and creative input in each story we read. Since most editors must wade through mounds of manuscripts each month, consideration for the editor requires that the market be studied, the manuscript be carefully presented and polished before submitting. Our publication uses only one story a month. Compare this with the 25 or more we receive over the transom each month. Also, many fiction mss are written without a specific goal or thrust, i.e., an interesting incident that goes nowhere is *not a story*. We believe fiction is a highly effective mode for transmitting the Christian message and also provides a good balance in an unusually heavy issue."

‡**LILITH MAGAZINE, The Jewish Women's Magazine, (I, II, IV),** Suite 2432, 250 W. 57th St., New York NY 10107. (212)757-0818. Editor: Susan Weidman Schneider. Fiction Editor: Julia Wolf Mazow. Magazine: 8½ × 11; 32 pages; 80 lb. cover; b&w illustrations; b&w and color photos. Publishes work relating to Jewish feminism, for Jewish feminists, feminists and Jewish households. Quarterly. Estab. 1975. Circ. 10,000.

Needs: Ethnic, feminist, lesbian, literary, prose poem, psychic/supernatural/occult, religious/inspirational, senior citizen/retirement, spiritual, translation, young adult. "Nothing that does not in any way relate to Jews, women or Jewish women." Receives 15 unsolicited mss/month. Accepts 1 ms/issue; 3 mss/year. Publishes ms 2-6 months after acceptance. Published work by Leslea Newman and Fredelle Maynard. Publishes short shorts.
How to Contact: Send complete ms with cover letter, which should include a 2-line bio. Reports in 2 months on queries; 2-6 months on mss. SASE. Simultaneous, photocopied and reprint submissions OK. Accepts computer printout submissions. Sample copy for $5. Fiction guidelines for #10 SAE and 1 first class stamp. Reviews novels and short story collections. Send books to Rachel Dobkin.
Payment: Varies.
Terms: Acquires first rights.

LIVE, Assemblies of God, 1445 Boonville, Springfield MO 65802. (417)862-2781. Editor: Lorraine Mastrorio. "A take-home story paper distributed weekly in young adult/adult Sunday school classes. *Live* is a fictional story paper primarily. True stories in narrative style are welcome. Articles are acceptable. Poems, first-person anecdotes and humor are used as fillers. The purpose of *Live* is to present in short story form realistic characters who utilize biblical principles. We hope to challenge readers to take risks for God and to resolve their problems scripturally." Weekly. Circ. 180,000.
Needs: Religious/inspirational, prose poem and spiritual. No controversial stories about such subjects as feminism, war or capital punishment. Buys 2 mss/issue. Published work by Maxine F. Dennis, E. Ruth Glover and Larry Clark; published new writers within the last year. Length: 500-2,000 words.
How to Contact: Send complete ms. Social Security number and word count must be included. Free sample copy and guidelines only for SASE.
Payment: Pays 3¢/word (first rights); 2¢/word (second rights).
Terms: Pays on acceptance.
Advice: "Stories should go somewhere! Action, not just thought-life; interaction, not just insights. Heroes and heroines, suspense and conflict. Avoid simplistic, pietistic conclusions, preachy, critical or moralizing." Reserves the right to change titles, abbreviate length and clarify flashbacks in stories for publication.

LIVING WITH TEENAGERS, (II), Baptist Sunday School Board, MSN 140, 127 9th Ave. North, Nashville TN 37234. (615)251-2273. Editor: Jimmy Hester. Magazine: 10⅜ × 8⅛; 50 pages; illustrations; photos. Magazine especially designed "to enrich the parent-teen relationship, with reading material from a Christian perspective" for parents of teenagers. Quarterly. Estab. 1978. Circ. 50,000.
Needs: Religious/inspirational, spiritual and parent-teen relationships. Nothing not related to parent-teen relationships or not from a Christian perspective. Receives approximately 50 unsolicited fiction mss/month. Buys 2-5 mss/issue. Length: 600-1,200 words (short shorts).
How to Contact: Query with clips of published work or send complete ms. Cover letter with reason for writing article; credentials for writing. Reports in 2 months on both queries and mss. SASE always. Sample copy for 9 × 12 SAE and proper postage.
Payment: Pays 5½¢/published word and 3 contributor's copies for all rights.
Terms: Pays on acceptance for all and first rights.
Advice: "Sometimes a fictitious story can communicate a principle in the parent-youth relationship quite well."

LOLLIPOPS MAGAZINE, (II), Good Apple, Inc., Box 299, Carthage IL 62321. (217)357-3981. Editor: Jerry Aten. Magazine: 8½ × 11; 64 pages; illustrations. "Preschool-2nd grade publication for teachers and their students. All educational material. Short stories, poems, activities, math, gameboards." Published 5 times/year. Circ. 18,000.
Needs: Preschool-grade 2. Submissions cover all areas of the curriculum. Seasonal materials considered. Receives 40-50 unsolicited mss/month. Number of fiction mss bought varies per issue. Published new writers within the last year. Occasionally accepts short stories (500-750 words).

Read the Business of Fiction section to learn the correct way to prepare and submit a manuscript.

How to Contact: Query first or write for guidelines and a free sample copy. Reports in 1 week on queries. SASE for ms. Accepts computer printout submissions.
Payment: Payment varies; depends on story.
Terms: Pays on publication for all rights.

THE LOOKOUT, (II), Standard Publishing, 8121 Hamilton Ave., Cincinnati OH 45231. (513)931-4050. FAX: (513)931-0904. Editor: Simon J. Dahlman. Magazine: 8½×11; 16 pages; newsprint paper; newsprint cover stock; illustrations; photos. "Conservative Christian magazine for adults and young adults." Weekly. Estab. 1894. Circ. 125,000.
Needs: Religious/inspirational. No predictable, preachy material. Taboos are blatant sex, swear words and drinking alcohol. Receives 50 unsolicited mss/month. Buys 1 fiction ms/issue; 45-50 mss/year. Publishes ms 2-12 months after acceptance. Published work by Bob Hartman, June Rae Wood, Wanda Trawick and Daniel Schantz; published new writers within the last year. Length: 1,200-2,000 words.
How to Contact: Send complete ms with SASE. "No queries please." Reports in 2-3 months on ms. Simultaneous, photocopied and reprint submissions OK. Accepts computer printout submissions. Sample copy for 50¢. Guidelines for #10 SASE.
Payment: Pays 5-7¢/word for first rights; 4-5¢/word for other rights and contributor's copies.
Terms: Pays on acceptance for one-time rights. Buys reprints.
Advice: "We would like to see a better balance between stories that focus on external struggles (our usual fare in the past) and those that focus on internal (spiritual, emotional, psychological) struggles. Send us good stories—not good sermons dressed up as stories."

THE LUTHERAN JOURNAL, Outlook Publications, Inc., 7317 Cahill Rd., Minneapolis MN 55435. (612)941-6830. Editor: Rev. A.U. Deye. "A family magazine providing wholesome and inspirational reading material for the enjoyment and enrichment of Lutherans." Quarterly. Estab. 1936. Circ. 136,000.
Needs: Literary, contemporary, religious/inspirational, romance (historical), senior citizen/retirement and young adult. Must be appropriate for distribution in the churches. Buys 2-4 mss/issue. Length: 1,000-1,500 words.
How to Contact: Send complete ms with SASE. Accepts computer printout submissions. Sample copy for SASE with 59¢ postage.
Payment: Pays $10-25 and 6 free author's copies.
Terms: Pays on publication for all and first rights.

LUTHERAN WOMAN TODAY, (IV), Published by Augsburg Fortress, Box 1209, Minneapolis MN 55440. LWT editorial offices: 8765 West Higgins Rd., Chicago IL 60631. (312)380-2743. Editor: Nancy Stelling. Associate Editor: Sue Edison-Swift. Magazine: 5⅜×8⅜; 48 pages; 40 lb. paper; illustrations; photos. Publishes solicited and freelance theological articles, fiction, good devotional pieces, articles of interest to women. "A magazine for women of the Evangelical Lutheran Church in America 'for growth in faith and mission.' " Monthly. Estab. 1988. Circ. 300,000.
Needs: Faith-related-to-life, religious/inspirational, advocacy/peace and justice, feminist. "We look for short (700-1,000 words), well-written work of special interest to Christian women." Receives 100-150 mss/month. Buys 5-10 mss/year. Publishes ms within 1 year of acceptance. Published work by Carol Bly, Joyce Ditmanson. Length: 700 words average; 1,200 words maximum. Publishes short shorts. Length: 350 words.
How to Contact: Send complete ms with cover letter which should include name, address, phone, word count and *rights offered*. Reports on mss in 2 months. SASE. Accepts computer printout submissions. Sample copy for $1 and 5×7 SAE. Fiction guidelines for #10 SAE and 1 first class stamp.
Payment: Pays per printed page rate.
Terms: Pays on acceptance for first rights and one-time rights. Sometimes offers kill fee.

MCCALL'S, The New York Times Company, 230 Park Ave., New York NY 10169. Declined listing.

MADEMOISELLE MAGAZINE, Condé Nast Publications, Inc., 350 Madison Ave., New York NY 10017. (212)880-8690. Fiction Editor: Eileen Schnurr. Fashion magazine for women from ages 18-34 with articles of interest to women: beauty and health tips, features, home and food, fiction. Audience interested in self-improvement, curious about trends, interested in updating lifestyle and pursuing a career. Monthly. Estab. 1935. Circ. 1.1 million.

Needs: Literary and contemporary short stories. Publishes 1-2 ms/issue; 12-20 mss/year. Length: 7-25 pages.
How to Contact: Send complete ms. Reports in 2-3 months. "Manuscripts will not be returned even if accompanied by SASE." Fiction guidelines for SASE.
Payment: Pays $1,000 minimum for short shorts; $1,500-2,500 for short stories.
Terms: Pays on acceptance for first North American serial rights.
Advice: "We are particularly interested in stories of relevance to young single women, and we continue in the *Mademoiselle* tradition of publishing fiction of literary quality." See the listing in Contest and Awards section for guidelines for *Mademoiselle's* Fiction Writers Contest.

THE MAGAZINE FOR CHRISTIAN YOUTH!, (II, IV), The United Methodist Publishing House, 201 8th Avenue S., Nashville TN 37202. (615)749-6463. Editor: Christopher B. Hughes. Magazine: 8½×11; 52 pages; slick, matte finish paper. *"The Magazine for Christian Youth!* tries to help teenagers develop Christian identity and live their faith in contemporary culture. Fiction and nonfiction which contributes to this purpose are welcome." Monthly. Estab. 1985. Circ. 45,000.
Needs: Adventure, contemporary, ethnic, fantasy, humor/satire, prose poem, religious/inspirational, science fiction, spiritual, suspense/mystery, translations, young adult/teen (10-18 years). "Don't preach; but story should have a message to help teenagers in some way or to make them think more deeply about an issue. No Sunday school lessons like those found in curriculum." Receives 50-75 unsolicited mss/month. Buys 1-2 mss/issue; 12-24 mss/year. Publishes ms 9-12 months after acceptance. Length: 700-2,000 words. Publishes short shorts.
How to Contact: Send complete ms with cover letter. Reports in 3-6 months. SASE. Simultaneous and reprint submissions OK. Accepts computer printout submissions. Sample copy and fiction guidelines for 9½×12½ SASE. Preference given to teenaged writers.
Payment: Pays $1.50 minimum, 4¢/word.
Terms: Pays on acceptance for first North American serial rights or one-time rights.
Advice: "Get a feel for our magazine first. Don't send in the types of fiction that would appear in Sunday school curriculum just because it's a Christian publication. Reflect the real world of teens in contemporary fiction." Writing contest announced in March issue. Deadline is early April.

MAGAZINE OF FANTASY AND SCIENCE FICTION, Box 56, Cornwall CT 06753. Unable to contact for information.

MANSCAPE, (II, IV), First Hand Ltd., Box 1314, Teaneck NJ 07666. (201)836-9177. Editor: Dave Babbitt. Magazine: digest sized; 130 pages; illustrations. "Magazine is devoted to gay male sexual fetishes; publishes fiction and readers' letters devoted to this theme." Monthly. Estab. 1985. Circ. 60,000.
Needs: Erotica, gay. Should be written in first person. No science fiction or fantasy. Erotica must be based on real life. Receives 25 unsolicited fiction mss/month. Accepts 5 mss/issue; 60 mss/year. Publishes ms an average of 12-18 months after acceptance. Published new writers within the last year. Length: 3,000 words average; 2,000 words minimum; 3,750 words maximum. Sometimes critiques rejected ms.
How to Contact: Send complete ms with cover letter. SASE. Accepts computer printout submissions. Sample copy for $5; fiction guidelines for #10 SASE.
Payment: Pays $100-150.
Terms: Pays on publication or in 240 days, whichever comes first, for all rights or first North American serial rights.

MATURE LIVING, (II), Sunday School Board of the Southern Baptist Convention, MSN 140, 127 Ninth Ave. N., Nashville TN 37234. (615)251-2191. Acting Editor: Judy Pregel. Magazine: 8½×11; 48 pages; non-glare paper; slick cover stock; illustrations; photos. "Our magazine is Christian in content and the material required is what would appeal to 60+ age group: inspirational, informational, nostalgic, humorous. Our magazine is distributed mainly through churches (especially Southern Baptist churches) that buy the magazine in bulk and distribute it to members in this age group." Monthly. Estab. 1977. Circ. 360,000.
Needs: Contemporary, religious/inspirational, humor, prose poem, spiritual and senior citizen/retirement. Avoid all types of pornography, drugs, liquor, horror, science fiction and stories demeaning to the elderly. Buys 1 ms/issue. Publishes ms an average of 1 year after acceptance. Published work by Burndean N. Sheffy, Pearl E. Trigg, Joyce M. Sixberry; published new writers within the last year. Length: 425-900 words (prefers 900). "Also, please use 42 characters per line."

How to Contact: Send complete ms with SASE. Reports in 2 months. Sample copy for $1. Guidelines for SASE.

Payment: Pays $21-73; 3 contributor's copies. 85¢ charge for extras.

Terms: Pays on acceptance. First rights 15% less than all rights, reprint rights 25% less. Rarely buys reprints.

Advice: Mss are rejected because they are too long or subject matter unsuitable. "Our readers seem to enjoy an occasional short piece of fiction. It must be believable, however, and present senior adults in a favorable light."

MATURE YEARS, (II), United Methodist Publishing House, 201 Eighth Ave. S., Nashville TN 37202. (615)749-6468. Editor: Marvin W. Cropsey. Magazine: 8½×11; 112 pages; illustrations and photos. Magazine "helps persons in and nearing retirement to appropriate the resources of the Christian faith as they seek to face the problems and opportunities related to aging." Quarterly. Estab. 1953.

Needs: Religious/inspirational, nostalgia, humor, intergenerational relationships, prose poem, spiritual (for older adults). "We don't want anything poking fun at old age, saccharine stories or anything not for older adults." Buys 3-4 mss/issue, 12-16 mss/year. Usually publishes ms 12-18 months after acceptance. Published new writers within the last year. Length: 1,000-1,800 words.

How to Contact: Send complete ms with SASE and Social Security number. Reports in 2 months. Sample copy for 10½×11 SAE and $2.50 postage.

Payment: Pays 4¢/word.

Terms: Pays on acceptance for all and first rights.

Advice: "Practice writing dialogue! Listen to people talk; take notes; master dialogue writing! Not easy, but well worth it! Most inquiry letters are far too long. If you can't sell me an idea in a brief paragraph, you're not going to sell the reader on reading your finished article or story."

MESSENGER OF THE SACRED HEART, (II), Apostleship of Prayer, 661 Greenwood Ave., Toronto, Ontario M4J 4B3 Canada. (416)466-1195. Editors: Rev. F.J. Power, S.J. and Alfred DeManche. Magazine: 7×10; 32 pages; coated paper; self-cover; illustrations; photos. Magazine for "Canadian and U.S. Catholics interested in developing a life of prayer and spirituality; stresses the great value of our ordinary actions and lives." Monthly. Estab. 1891. Circ. 18,000.

Needs: Religious/inspirational. Stories about people, adventure, heroism, humor, drama. No poetry. Buys 1 ms/issue. Recently published work by Ken Thoren, Rev. Charles Dickson, Ph.D., and Rev. John M. Scott, S.J.; published new writers within the last year. Length: 750-1,500 words. Recommends other markets.

How to Contact: Send complete ms with SAE or IRC. Reports in 1 month. Sample copy for $1.50.

Payment: Pays 4¢/word, 3 free author's copies.

Terms: Pays on acceptance for first North American serial rights. Rarely buys reprints.

Advice: "Develop a story that sustains interest to the end. Do not preach, but use plot and characters to convey the message or theme. Aim to move the heart as well as the mind. If you can, add a light touch or a sense of humor to the story. Your ending should have impact, leaving a moral or faith message for the reader."

METRO SINGLES LIFESTYLES, (II), Metro Publications, Box 28203, Kansas City MO 64118. (816)436-8424. Editor: Robert L. Huffstutter. Fiction Editor: Earl R. Stonebridge. Tabloid: 36 pages; 30. lb newspaper stock; 30 lb. cover; illustrations; photos. "Positive, uplifting, original, semi-literary material for all singles: widowed, divorced, never-married, of all ages 18 and over." Bimonthly. Estab. 1984. Circ. 25,000.

Needs: Humor/satire, literary, prose poem, religious/inspirational, romance (contemporary), special interest, spiritual, single parents. No erotic, political, moralistic fiction. Receives 2-3 unsolicited mss/month. Buys 1-2 mss/issue; 12-18 mss/year. Publishes ms 2 months after acceptance. Length: 1,500 words average; 1,200 words minimum; 4,000 words maximum. Publishes short shorts. Published work by Patricia Castle, Libby Floyd, Donald G. Smith; published new writers within the last year. Length: 1,200. Occasionally critiques rejected mss. Recommends other markets.

How to Contact: Send complete ms with cover letter. Include short paragraph/bio listing credits (if any), current profession or job. Reports in 3 weeks on queries. SASE. Accepts computer printout submissions. Sample copy $3.

Payment: Pays $25-50, free subscription to magazine and contributor's copies.
Terms: Payment on publication.
Advice: "A question I ask myself about my own writing is: will the reader feel the time spent reading the story or article was worth the effort? Personally, I enjoy stories and articles which will create a particular emotion, build suspense, or offer excitement or entertainment. Features accompanied by photos receive special attention."

MIDSTREAM, A Monthly Jewish Review, (II, IV), Theodor Herzl Foundation, 110 E. 59th St., New York NY 10022. (212)752-0600. Editor: Joel Carmichael. Magazine: 8½ × 11; 48 pages; 50 lb. paper; 65 lb. white smooth cover stock. "We are a Zionist journal; we publish material with Jewish themes or that would appeal to a Jewish readership." Monthly. Estab. 1955. Circ. 10,000.
Needs: Historical (general), humor/satire, literary, mainstream, translations. Receives 15-20 unsolicited mss/month. Accepts 1 mss/issue; 10 mss/year. Publishes ms 6-18 months after acceptance. Agented fiction 10%. Published work by I. B. Singer, Anita Jackson, Enid Shomer. Length: 2,500 words average; 1,500 words minimum; 3,000 words maximum. Sometimes critiques rejected mss.
How to Contact: Send complete ms with cover letter, which should include "address, telephone, identification or affiliation of author; state that the ms is fiction." Reports in 1-2 weeks. SASE. Photocopied submissions OK. Accepts computer printout submissions. Sample copy for 9 × 12 SAE. Fiction guidelines for #10 SASE.
Payment: Pays 5¢/word and contributor's copies.
Terms: Pays on publication for first rights.
Advice: "Always include a cover letter and double space."

MILITARY LIFESTYLE, (II), Downey Communications, Inc., Suite 710, 4800 Montgomery Lane, Bethesda MD 20814. Editor: Hope M. Daniels. Magazine: 8½ × 11; 80-100 pages; coated paper; illustrations and photos. Monthly magazine for military families worldwide. Publishes 10 issues per year. Estab. 1969. Circ. 520,000.
Needs: Contemporary. "Fiction must deal with lifestyle or issues of particular concern to our specific military families audience." Receives 50 unsolicited mss/month. Buys 1-2 mss/issue; 10-15 mss/year. Publishes ms 2-6 months after acceptance. Published new writers within the last year. Length: 1,500 words average. Generally critiques rejected mss. Recommends other markets if applicable.
How to Contact: Send complete ms with cover letter, which should include info on writer and writing credits and history. Reports in 6-8 weeks on mss. SASE. Photocopied submissions OK. Accepts computer printout submissions. Sample copy for $1.50, 9 × 12 SAE and 4 first class stamps. Fiction guidelines for #10 SASE and 1 first class stamp. Reviews novels and short story collections.
Payment: Pays $400 minimum and 2 contributor's copies.
Terms: Pays generally on publication unless held more than 6 months; then on acceptance for first North American serial rights.
Advice: "Fiction is slice-of-life reading for our audience. Primarily written by military wives or military members themselves, the stories deal with subjects very close to our readers: prolonged absences by spouses, the necessity of handling child-raising alone, the fear of accidents while spouses are on maneuvers or in dangerous situations, etc. The important point: Target the material to our audience — military families — and make the characters real, empathetic and believable. Read your copy over as an objective reader rather than as its author before submission. Better yet, read it aloud!"

MODERN GOLD MINER AND TREASURE HUNTER, (II), P.O. Box 47, Happy Camp CA 96039. (916)493-2029. Editor: Dave McCracken. Fiction Editor: Gary Brooks. Magazine: 8 × 10⅞; 48 pages; 50 lb. coated #5 paper; 80 lb. Sterling Web cover; pen-and-ink illustrations; photographs. "Recreational and small-scale gold mining, treasure and relic hunting. All stories must be related to these topics. For recreational hobbyists, adventure loving, outdoor people." Bimonthly. Estab. 1988. Circ. 50,000.
Needs: Adventure, experimental, historical, humor, senior citizen/retirement, suspense/mystery. "Futuristic stories OK, but not sci-fi. No erotica, gay, lesbian--absolutely no 'cussing!' " Buys 1-2 mss/issue; 6-16 mss/year. Publishes ms 4-6 months after acceptance. Published work by Ken Hodgson and Michael Clark. Length: 2,000 words preferred; 900 words minimum; 2,700 words maximum. Publishes short shorts. Length: 400-500 words. Sometimes critiques or comments on rejected mss.
How to Contact: Send complete ms with cover letter. Include Social Security number, "brief outline of the story and something about the author." Reports in 2 weeks on queries; 4-6 weeks on mss. SASE for mss. Photocopied submissions OK. Accepts electronic submissions. Sample copy for $2.95 (U.S.), $3.50 (Canada). Free fiction guidelines.

Payment: Pays 3¢/word minimum and contributor's copies.
Terms: Pays on publication for all rights.
Advice: Looks for "as always, quality writing. We can edit small changes but the story has to grab us. Our readers love 'real life' fiction. They love exploring the 'that could happen' realm of a good fiction story. Keep your story geared to gold mining or treasure hunting. Know something about your subject so the story doesn't appear ridiculous. Don't try to dazzle readers with outlandish adjectives and keep slang to a minimum." Sponsors fiction contest—look for rules in upcoming issues.

THE MODERN WOODMEN, (II), Modern Woodmen of America, 1701 1st Ave., Rock Island IL 61201. (309)786-6481. Editor: Gloria Bergh. Fiction Editor: Beth T. Fratzke. Magazine: 8½×11; 24 pages; 50 lb. paper; self cover; illustrations and photos. "We want articles that appeal to families, emphasize family interaction, for the family audience including all age groups from children to the elderly." Quarterly. Circ. 350,000.
Needs: Adventure, contemporary, historical (general), juvenile (5-9 years), mainstream, senior citizen/retirement, young adult/teen (10-18 years). Receives approximately 35 unsolicited fiction mss/month. Accepts 1-2 mss/month; 12-24 mss/year. Length: 1,200 words preferred. Sometimes critiques rejected mss, "but very seldom."
How to Contact: Send complete ms with cover letter. Reports in 2 months. SASE. Simultaneous, photocopied and reprint submissions OK. Accepts computer printout submissions. Sample copy for 8½×11 SAE with 2 first class stamps. Fiction guidelines for #10 SASE.
Payment: Pays $50 and up.
Terms: Pays on acceptance for one-time rights.
Advice: "A well-written short story is a drawing card to interest our readers."

MOMENT MAGAZINE, (II, IV), Suite 300, 3000 Connecticut Ave. NW, Washington DC 20008. (202)387-8888. Publisher/Editor: Hershel Shanks. Managing Editor: Suzanne F. Singer. Magazine: 8½×11; 64 pages; 60 lb. coated paper; 80 lb. cover stock; illustrations and photos. Modern, historical magazine publishing material on intellectual, cultural and political issues of interest to the Jewish community. Audience is college-educated, liberal, concerned with Jewish affairs. Bimonthly. Estab. 1975. Circ. 30,000.
Needs: Contemporary, ethnic, historical, religious, excerpted novel and translations. "All fiction should have Jewish content. No sentimental stories about 'Grandma' etc. Do not encourage Holocaust themes." Receives 60-80 unsolicited fiction mss/month. Buys 2-3 mss/year. Publishes ms 1-24 months after acceptance. Length: 2,000 words minimum; 4,000 words maximum; 3,000 words average. Publishes short shorts.
How to Contact: Query first or send complete ms. Cover letter with bio. Reports in 1 month on queries; 2 months on mss. SASE always. Photocopied submissions OK. No multiple submissions. Accepts computer printout submissions. Sample copy for $4. Fiction guidelines for #10 SAE and 1 first class stamp.
Payment: Varies.
Terms: Pays on publication for first rights.
Advice: "We caution against over-sentimentalized writing which we get way too much of all the time. Query first is helpful; reading stories we've published a must."

MONTANA SENIOR CITIZENS NEWS, (II,IV), Barrett-Whitman Co., Box 3363, Great Falls MT 59403. (406)761-0305. Editor: Jack Love. Tabloid: 11×17; 50-60 pages; newsprint paper and cover; illustrations; photos. Publishes "everything of interest to seniors, except most day-to-day political items like Social Security and topics covered in the daily news. Personal profiles of seniors, their lives, times and reminiscences." Bimonthly. Estab. 1984. Circ. 23,000.
Needs: Historical, senior citizen/retirement, western (historical or contemporary). No fiction "unrelated to experiences to which seniors can relate." Buys 1 or fewer mss/issue; 4-5 mss/year. Publishes ms within 6 months of acceptance. Published work by Anne Norris, Helen Clark, Juni Dunklin. Length: 500-800 words preferred. Publishes short shorts. Length: under 500 words.
How to Contact: Send complete ms with cover letter and phone number. Only responds to selected mss. SASE. Simultaneous, photocopied and reprint submissions OK. Accepts computer printout submissions. Accepts electronic submission via WordPerfect disk. Sample copy for 9×12 SAE and $2 postage and handling.
Payment: Pays $2/column inch.
Terms: Pays on publication for first rights or one-time rights.

MOTHER JONES MAGAZINE, Foundation for National Progress, 1663 Mission St., San Francisco CA 94103. *No longer publishing fiction.*

MY FRIEND, The Catholic Magazine for Kids, (II), Daughters of St. Paul, 50 St. Paul's Ave., Boston MA 02130. (617)522-8911. Editor: Sister Anne Joan. Magazine: 8½×11; 32 pages; smooth, glossy paper and cover stock; illustrations; photos. Magazine of "religious truths and positive values for children in a format which is enjoyable and attractive. Each issue contains Bible stories, lives of saints and famous people, short stories, science corner, contests, projects, etc." Monthly during school year (September-June). Estab. 1979. Circ. 10,000.
Needs: Juvenile, prose poem, religious/inspirational, spiritual (children), sports (children). Receives 30 unsolicited fiction mss/month. Accepts 3-4 mss/issue; 30-40 mss/year. Recently published work by Eileen Spinelli, Virginia Kroll and M. Donaleen Howitt; published new writers within the past year. Length: 200 words minimum; 900 words maximum; 600 words average.
How to Contact: Send complete ms with SASE. Accepts computer printout submissions. Reports in 1-2 months on mss. Publishes ms an average of 1 year after acceptance. Sample copy for 10×14 SAE and 60¢ postage.
Payment: Pays $20-150 (stories, articles).
Advice: "We prefer child-centered stories in a real-world setting. Children enjoy fiction. They can relate to the characters and learn lessons that they might not derive from a more 'preachy' article. We accept only stories that teach wholesome, positive values. We are particularly interested in material for boys aged 8-10."

NA'AMAT WOMAN, Magazine of Na'amat USA, The Women's Labor Zionist Organization of America, 200 Madison Ave., New York NY 10016. (212)725-8010. Editor: Judith A. Sokoloff. "Magazine covering a wide variety of subjects of interest to the Jewish community—including political and social issues, arts, profiles; many articles about Israel; and women's issues. Fiction must have a Jewish theme. Readers are the American Jewish community." Published 5 times/year. Estab. 1926. Circ. 30,000.
Needs: Contemporary, literary. Receives 10 unsolicited fiction mss/month. Buys 3-5 fiction mss/year. Length: 1,500 words minimum; 3,000 words maximum. Also buys nonfiction.
How to Contact: Query first or send complete ms with SASE. Photocopied submissions OK. Accepts computer printout submissions. Reports in 3 months on mss. Free sample copy for 9×11½ SAE and 98¢ postage.
Payment: Pays 8¢/word; 2 contributor's copies.
Terms: Pays on publication for first North American serial rights; assignments on work-for-hire basis.
Advice: "No maudlin nostalgia or romance; no hackneyed Jewish humor and no poetry."

NATIONAL LAMPOON, (II), 155 Avenue of the Americas, New York NY 10013. (212)645-5040. Editor: Sam Johnson. Magazine. "We publish humor and satire." Bimonthly. Estab. 1970. Circ. 250,000.
Needs: Receives 200 unsolicited fiction mss/month. Buys 2 mss/issue. Publishes ms 2-3 months after acceptance. Short shorts preferred. Length: 50-100 words. Longer ms, 1,000-2,000 words maximum. Publishes short shorts.
How to Contact: Query first. Reports in 1-2 months. SASE required. Simultaneous and photocopied submissions OK. Accepts electronic submissions via disk or modem. Fiction guidelines free.
Payment: Payment is negotiated.
Terms: Pays on publication for first North American serial rights and anthology rights. Offers varying kill fee.

NEW ERA MAGAZINE, (II, IV), The Church of Jesus Christ of Latter-day Saints, 50 E. North Temple St., Salt Lake City UT 84150. (801)532-2951. Editor: Richard M. Romney. Magazine: 8×10½; 51 pages; 40 lb. coated paper; illustrations and photos. "We will publish fiction on any theme that

Market conditions are constantly changing! If you're still using this book and it is 1993 or later, buy the newest edition of Novel & Short Story Writer's Market at your favorite bookstore or order directly from Writer's Digest Books.

strengthens and builds the standards and convictions of teenage Latter-day Saints ('Mormons')."
Monthly. Estab. 1971. Circ. 200,000.

Needs: Stories on family relationships, self-esteem, dealing with loneliness, resisting peer pressure
and all aspects of maintaining Christian values in the modern world. "All material must be written
from a Latter-day Saint ('Mormon') point of view—or at least from a generally Christian point of
view, reflecting LDS life and values." Receives 30-35 unsolicited mss/month. Accepts 1 ms/issue; 12
mss/year. Publishes ms 3 months to 5 years after acceptance. Length: 1,500 words average; 250 words
minimum; 2,000 words maximum.

How to Contact: Query letter preferred; send complete ms. Reports in 6-8 weeks. SASE. Photocopied submissions OK. Accepts computer printout submissions. Sample copy for $1 and 9 × 12 SAE with
2 first class stamps. Fiction guidelines for #10 SASE.

Payment: Pays $50-375 and contributor's copies.

Terms: Pays on acceptance for all rights (reassign to author on request).

Advice: "Each magazine has its own personality—you wouldn't write the same style of fiction for
Seventeen that you would write for *Omni*. Very few writers who are not of our faith have been able to
write for us successfully, and the reason usually is that they don't know what it's like to be a member
of our church. You must study and research and know those you are writing about. We love to work
with beginning authors, and we're a great place to break in if you can understand us." Sponsors
contests and awards for LDS fiction writers. "We have an annual contest; entry forms are in each
September issue. Deadline is January; winners published in August."

NEW HAMPSHIRE LIFE, (II, IV), Masthead Communications, Inc., Box 1200, North Hampton NH
03862. (603)964-2121. Fiction Editor: John A. Meng. Magazine: 8½ × 11; 100 pages; coated freesheet
paper; 65 lb. coated cover stock; color photographs, 75/issue. "Lifestyle magazine for and about New
Hampshire. We publish fiction each issue plus regional events, investigative journalism, recipes, business, health, fashion and people articles for an upscale, well-educated audience, 25-50." Bimonthly.
Estab. (as *Seacoast Life*) 1985. Circ. 20,000.

Needs: Adventure, contemporary, fantasy, humor/satire, literary, mainstream, regional, science fiction, senior citizen/retirement, serialized/excerpted novel, suspense/mystery and translations. "No radical fiction, i.e. homosexual, pornographic, etc. We promote literature that elicits an emotional response—not the type with a purpose to horrify or impress." Receives 20-30 unsolicited fiction mss/
month. Accepts 1 mss/issue; 6 mss/year (including a holiday issue). Publishes ms 3-6 months after
acceptance. Published work by Jules Archer, Sharon Helgens, Lawrence Millman and Robert Baldwin;
published new writers within the last year. Length: 1,500-3,000 words average. Sometimes critiques
rejected ms.

How to Contact: "Subject must be regional in order to submit—New Hampshire." Send complete
ms with cover letter, writer's bio. Reports in 1 month. SASE. Simultaneous and photocopied submissions OK. Accepts computer printout submissions. Sample copy for $2.50 and 9 × 12 SAE with $2.40
postage. Fiction guidelines for #10 SAE and 40¢ postage.

Payment: Pays $100 minimum; varies according to individual circumstances.

Terms: Pays 30 days after publication. Rights purchased negotiated with each individual writer.

Advice: "Our readership is highly educated, critical of shabby work and loves good fiction. Our readers
love to read. Writers should be patient. We will read and reply to all submissions."

NEW MYSTERY, The Best New Mystery Stories, (III), #2001, 175 Fifth Ave., New York NY 10010.
(212)353-1582. Editor: Charles Raisch. Magazine: 5 × 8; 96 pages; illustrations and photographs. "Mystery, suspense and crime." Bimonthly. Estab. 1990. Circ. 50,000.

Needs: Suspense/mystery. Plans special annual anthology. Receives 150+ unsolicited mss/month.
Buys 6-10 ms/issue. Agented fiction 50%. Published work by Lawrence Block, Herb Resnicow, Michael
Avallone, Stu Kaminsky. Length: 3,000-5,000 words preferred. Sometimes critiques rejected mss and
recommends other markets.

How to Contact: Send complete ms with cover letter. Reports on ms in 1 month. SASE. Accepts
electronic submissions. Sample copy for $5, 9 × 12 SAE and 4 first class stamps.

Payment: Pays $25-500.

Terms: Pays on publication for all rights.

Advice: *Note: at press time unable to reach this magazine. Query before sending mss or before requesting
a sample copy.*

NEW YORK RUNNING NEWS, (IV), New York Road Runners Club, 9 East 89 St., New York NY 10128. Editor: Don Mogelefsky. Magazine: 8×11; 80+ pages; illustrations; b&w and color photos. "Regional running magazine, local event coverage and membership (NY Road Runners Club) profiles, for serious and recreational runners, and road racers." Bimonthly. Estab. 1958. Circ. 40,000.
Needs: "Only running-related" fiction (and nonfiction). Receives "several dozen" unsolicited fiction mss/month. Accepts "one or less" ms/issue. Publishes ms 1-6 months after acceptance. Length: 1,000 words average; 500 words minimum; 1,500 words maximum. Publishes short shorts. Length: 500 words. Occasionally critiques rejected mss.
How to Contact: Send complete ms with cover letter. Reports in "a few" weeks. SASE. Photocopied and reprint submissions OK. Accepts computer printout submissions. Sample copy $3 and 2 first class stamps. Writer's guidelines for #10 SASE.
Payment: Pays $50-150; charges for extra copies.
Terms: Pays on publication for first rights.
Advice: "Anything well done is publishable. Be funny. Be sophisticated. Be natural."

THE NEW YORKER, (III), The New Yorker, Inc., 20 W. 43rd St., New York NY 10036. (212)840-3800. Fiction Department. A quality magazine of interesting, well written stories, articles, essays and poems for a literate audience. Weekly. Estab. 1925. Circ. 622,000.
How to Contact: Send complete ms with SASE. Reports in 2 months on mss. Publishes 2 mss/issue.
Payment: Varies.
Terms: Pays on acceptance.
Advice: "Be lively, original, not overly literary. Write what you want to write, not what you think the editor would like."

NORTHEAST, the Sunday Magazine of the Hartford Courant, 285 Broad St., Hartford CT 06115. (203)241-3700. Editor: Lary Bloom. Magazine: 10×11½; 32-100 pages; illustrations; photos. "A regional (New England, specifically Connecticut) magazine, we publish stories of varied subjects of interest to our Connecticut audience" for a general audience. Weekly. Published special fiction issue and a special college writing issue for fiction and poetry. Estab. 1981. Circ. 300,000.
Needs: Contemporary and regional. No children's stories or stories with distinct setting outside Connecticut. Receives 60 unsolicited mss/month. Buys 1 ms/issue. Publishes short shorts. Length: 750 words minimum; 3,500 words maximum.
How to Contact: Send complete ms with SASE. Reports in 3 weeks. Simultaneous and photocopied submissions OK. No reprints or previously published work. Accepts computer printout submissions. Sample copy and fiction guidelines for 10×12 or larger SASE.
Payment: Pays $250-1,000.
Terms: Pays on acceptance for one-time rights.

NUGGET, (II), Dugent Publishing Corp., Suite 600, 2600 Douglas Rd., Coral Gables FL 33134. (305)443-2378. Editor: Jerome Slaughter. A newsstand magazine designed to have erotic appeal for a fetish-oriented audience. Bimonthly. Estab. 1956. Circ. 100,000.
Needs: Offbeat, fetish-oriented material encompassing a variety of subjects. Most of fiction includes several sex scenes. No fiction that concerns children or religious subjects. Buys 3 mss/issue. Agented fiction 5%. Length: 2,000-3,500 words.
How to Contact: Send complete ms with SASE. Reports in 1 month. Sample copy for $5. Guidelines for legal-sized SASE.
Payment: Pay starts at $200. Free author's copy.
Terms: Pays on publication for first rights.
Advice: "Keep in mind the nature of the publication, which is fetish erotica. Subject matter can vary, but we prefer fetish themes."

OH! IDAHO, The Idaho State Magazine, (IV), Peak Media, Box 925, Hailey ID 83333. Editor: Laurie Sammis. Magazine: 80-96 pages; high quality paper; some illustrations and photographs. Publishes material on "Idaho, for Idahoans and people across the nation." Quarterly. Estab. 1988. Circ. 20,000.
Needs: Humor/satire. "Must relate specifically to Idaho, without being denigrating to the potato state. Easy on the peeve, long on the humor. Adventure—stories with information in a fictional format." Receives 4-5 unsolicited mss/month. Publishes ms 6 months after acceptance. Length: 1,200 words preferred. Sometimes critiques rejected mss and recommends other markets.

"Oh! Idaho is known for high quality photography and enlightening articles of special people and places in Idaho," says Art Director Joan Donnelly. "Each issue reveals something interesting and beautiful about the state," she says. Pictured here is a small toad nestled in a water lily at Lily Lake in the Sawtooths. Donnelly says she chose this photograph because of "its boldness and surprise element. It's an unforgettable image," she adds. The photographer, Scott Spiker, lives in Moscow, Idaho, and is a frequent contributor to the magazine.

How to Contact: Query with clips of published work. Include Social Security number with ms. Reports in 4-6 weeks on queries. SASE. Simultaneous, photocopied and reprint submissions OK. Accepts computer printout submissions. Accepts electronic submissions via WordPerfect or MS-DOS ASCII only. Sample copy for $3. Guidelines for #10 SAE and 1 first class stamp.
Payment: Pays 10¢/word.
Terms: Pays on publication for first North American serial rights.
Advice: "All articles must relate specifically to Idaho and should convey all or part of this idea: Idaho is a beautiful place to live and vacation in, there are many fun and interesting activities here and the people of Idaho are fascinating. Articles should be timeless, upscale and positive. The subject matter should focus on all facets of Idaho and/or her people."

OMNI, (II), General Media, 1965 Broadway, New York NY 10023. Fiction Editor: Ellen Datlow. Magazine: 8½×11; 114-182 pages; 40-50 lb. stock paper; 100 lb. Mead off cover stock; illustrations; photos. "Magazine of science and science fiction with an interest in near future; stories of what science holds, what life and lifestyles will be like in areas affected by science for a young, bright and well-educated audience between ages 18-45." Monthly. Estab. 1978. Circ. 1,000,000.
Needs: Science fiction, contemporary fantasy and technological horror. No sword and sorcery or space opera. Buys 20 mss/year. Receives approximately 400 unsolicited fiction mss/month. Agented fiction 5%. Published work by Joyce Carol Oates, Pat Cadigan and Michael Bishop. Length: 2,000 words minimum, 10,000 words maximum. Critiques rejected mss that interest me "when there is time." Sometimes recommends other markets.
How to Contact: Send complete ms with SASE. Accepts computer printout submissions. Reports within 3 weeks. Publishes ms 3 months to 2 years after acceptance.
Payment: Pays $1,250-2,250; 3 free author's copies.
Terms: Pays on acceptance for first North American serial rights with exclusive worldwide English language periodical rights and nonexclusive anthology rights.
Advice: "Beginning writers should read a lot of the best science fiction short stories today. We are looking for strong, well written stories dealing with the next 100 years. Don't give up on a market just because you've been rejected several times. If you're good, you'll get published eventually. Don't ever call an editor on the phone and ask why he/she rejected a story. You'll either find out in a personal rejection letter (which means the editor liked it or thought enough of your writing to comment) or you won't find out at all (most likely the editor won't remember a form-rejected story)." Recent award winners and nominees: "Tower of Babylon," by Ted Chiang won the Nebula award for novelette and has been nominated for a Hugo. Ellen Datlow has been nominated in Best Professional editor category of the Hugos 2 years running.

ON OUR BACKS, Entertainment for the Adventurous Lesbian, (II, IV), Blush Productions, 526 Castro St., San Francisco CA 94114. (415)861-4723. Editor: Debi Sundahl. Magazine: 8½×11; 50 pages; slick paper; illustrations; photos. "Lesbian erotica, short stories, nonfiction, commentary, news clips, photos." Bimonthly. Estab. 1984. Circ. 15,000.
Needs: Erotica, fantasy, humor/satire, lesbian. No "non-erotic, heterosexual" fiction. Receives 20 mss/month. Buys 2-3 mss/issue. Publishes ms within 1 year of acceptance. Published new writers within the last year. Length: 3,500 words preferred; 2,500 words minimum; 5,000 words maximum.
How to Contact: Query with clips of published work. Include Social Security number. Reports in 6 weeks. No simultaneous submissions. Accepts computer printout submissions. Accepts electronic submissions via disk. Sample copy for $6. Fiction guidelines for #10 SAE and 1 first class stamp.
Payment: Pays $20-100 and contributor's copies.
Terms: Pays on publication for first North American serial rights.
Advice: "Ask yourself—does it turn me on? Ask a friend to read it—does it turn her on as well? Is it as well-written as any well-crafted non-erotic story? We love to read things that we don't see all the time—originality is definitely a plus!" Sponsors awards for fiction writers.

ON THE LINE, (II), Mennonite Publishing House, 616 Walnut Ave., Scottdale PA 15683-1999. (412)887-8500. Editor: Mary Meyer. Magazine: 7×10; 8 pages; illustrations; b&w photos. "A religious take-home paper with the goal of helping children grow in their understanding and appreciation of God, the created world, themselves and other people." For children ages 10-14. Weekly. Estab. 1970. Circ. 10,000.
Needs: Adventure and religious/inspirational for older children and young teens (10-14 years). Receives 50-100 unsolicited mss/month. Buys 1 ms/issue; 52 mss/year. Recently published work by Michael LaCross, Betty Lou Mell, Virginia Kroll; published new writers within the last year. Length: 750-1,000 words.
How to Contact: Send complete ms noting whether author is offering first-time or reprint rights. Reports in 1 month. SASE. Simultaneous, photocopied and previously published work OK. Accepts computer printout submissions. Free sample copy and fiction guidelines.
Payment: Pays on acceptance for one-time rights.
Advice: "We believe in the power of story to entertain, inspire and challenge the reader to new growth. Know children and their thoughts, feelings and interests. Be realistic with characters and events in the fiction. Stories do not need to be true, but need to *feel* true."

OPTIONS, The *Bi*-Monthly, (I, II), AJA Publishing, Box 470, Port Chester NY 10573. Associate Editor: Diana Sheridan. Magazine: Digest-sized; 114 pages; newsprint paper; glossy cover stock; illustrations and photos. Sexually explicit magazine for and about bisexuals. 10 issues/year. Estab. 1982. Circ. 100,000.
Needs: Erotica, gay, lesbian. "First person as-if-true experiences." Accepts 5 unsolicited fiction mss/month. "Very little" of fiction is agented. Published new writers within the last year. Length: 2,000-3,000 words average; 2,000 words minimum. Sometimes critiques rejected mss.
How to Contact: Send complete ms with cover letter. Reports in approximately 3 weeks. SASE. Photocopied submissions OK, if clearly marked "not a simultaneous submission." Accepts computer printout submissions. "Submissions on Macintosh disk welcome, but please include hard copy too." Sample copy for $2.95 and 6×9 SAE with 5 first class stamps. Fiction guidelines for SASE.
Payment: Pays $100.
Terms: Pays on publication for all rights.
Advice: "Read a copy of *Options* carefully and look at our spec sheet before writing anything for us. That's not new advice, but to judge from some of what we get in the mail, it's necessary to repeat. We only buy 2 bi/lesbian pieces per issue; need is greater for bi/gay male mss. Though we're a bi rather than gay magazine, the emphasis is on same-sex relationships. If the readers want to read about a male/female couple, they'll buy another magazine. Gay male stories sent to *Options* will also be considered for publication in *Beau*, our gay male magazine. *Most important:* We *only* publish male/male stories that feature 'safe sex' practices unless the story is clearly something that took place pre-AIDS."

ORANGE COAST MAGAZINE, The Magazine of Orange County, (II), Suite 8, 245-D Fischer Ave., Costa Mesa CA 92626. (714)545-1900. Editor: Palmer Thomason Jones. Managing Editor: Erik Himmelsbach. Magazine: 8½×11; 200 pages; 50 lb. Sonoma gloss paper; 10. Warrenflo cover; illustrations and photographs. *Orange Coast* publishes articles offering local insight to its affluent, well-educated Orange County readers. Monthly. Estab. 1974. Circ. 35,000.

Needs: Contemporary, humor/satire, suspense/mystery. Receives 10 unsolicited mss/month. Buys 4 mss/year. Publishes ms 4-6 months after acceptance. Published work by Robert Ray. Length: 2,500 words average; 1,500 words minimum; 4,000 words maximum.
How to Contact: Send complete ms with cover letter that includes Social Security number. Reports in 2 months. SASE. Simultaneous submissions OK. Sample copy for SASE.
Payment: Pays $250.
Terms: Pays on acceptance for first North American serial rights.

ORGANICA QUARTERLY, (II), Organica Press, 4419 N. Manhattan Ave., Tampa FL 33614. (813)876-4879. Editor: Susan Hussey. Fiction Editor: Silvia Curbelo. Tabloid: 28 pages. "Intelligent, literary." Quarterly. Circ. 200,000.
Needs: Contemporary, ethnic, experimental, humor/satire, literary. "Have strong aversion to 'New Age' genre; to self-indulgent writing of all kinds." Buys 1-2 mss/year. Time from acceptance to publishing varies. Recently published work by Ann Darby and Renée Ashley. Length: 2,500-3,000 words average; 5,000 words maximum. Publishes short shorts. Recommends other markets.
How to Contact: Send complete ms with cover letter. "Not necessary; previous publications might be listed if cover letter is enclosed." Reports in 4-6 weeks on mss. Sample copy $1.
Payment: Varies.
Terms: Pays on publication for first North American serial rights. Sends galleys to author.
Advice: "Our only criteria is quality. We are looking for intelligent fiction and a fresh approach to language."

THE OTHER SIDE, (III), 300 W. Apsley St., Philadelphia PA 19144-4221. (215)849-2178. Editor: Mark Olson. Fiction Editor: Barbara Moorman. Magazine: 8½ × 11; 64 pages; illustrations and photographs. Magazine of justice rooted in discipleship for Christians with a strong interest in peace, social and economic justice. Bimonthly. Estab. 1965. Circ. 14,000.
Needs: Contemporary, ethnic, experimental, feminist, humor/satire, literary, mainstream, spiritual and suspense/mystery. Receives 30 unsolicited fiction mss/month. Buys 6 mss/year. Publishes ms 3-9 months after acceptance. Published work by Laurie Skiba, James Schaap and Shirley Pendlebury. Length: 1,500 words minimum; 5,000 words maximum; 3,500 words average.
How to Contact: Send complete ms with SASE. Reports in 6-8 weeks. No simultaneous submissions or pre-published material. Accepts computer printout submissions. Sample copy for $4.50.
Payment: Pays $50-250; free subscription to magazine; 6 free contributor's copies.
Terms: Pays on acceptance for all or first rights.

OUI MAGAZINE, (II), 15th Floor, 519 8th Ave., New York NY 10018. (212)967-6262. Editor: Richard Kidd. Magazine: 8 × 11; 112 pages; illustrations; photos. Magazine for college-age males and older. Monthly. Estab. 1972. Circ. 1 million.
Needs: Contemporary, fantasy, lesbian, men's, mystery and humor. Buys 1 ms/issue; 12 mss/year. Receives 200-300 unsolicited fiction mss/month. Published new writers within the last year. Length: 1,500-3,000 words.
How to Contact: Cover letter with author background, previous publications, etc. Send complete ms with SASE. Accepts computer printout submissions. Reports in 6-8 weeks on mss.
Payment: Pays $250 and up.
Terms: Pays on publication for first rights.
Advice: "Many mss are rejected because writers have not studied the market or the magazine. We want writers to take chances and offer us something out of the ordinary. Look at several recent issues to see what direction our fiction is headed."

OUT MAGAZINE, (II, IV), YOU the Publications, Box 5, 359 Davenport Rd., Toronto, Ontario M5R 1K5 Canada. Editor: Shawn Venasse. Tabloid: 11 × 17; 16 pages; newsprint; illustrations and photographs. "*By* and *for gay men* — short fiction, essays, poetry, interviews, photos, illustrations for gay men, age 18-54." Monthly. Estab. 1986. Circ, 20,000+.
Needs: Gay: Adventure, condensed/excerpted novel, erotica, ethnic, experimental, fantasy, historical (general), humor/satire, literary, prose poem, suspense/mystery, translations. "We are looking for 'original' bold, innovative, distinctive writing that both explores and celebrates the *gay male* spirit. We are not particularly interested in clichéd work, i.e. 70's porn, 'coming out' stories (unless they are really good) nor AIDS stories (again, not unless they are exceptional)." Nothing homophobic, sexist, racist nor *porn* written in a clichéd manner. Plans special fiction issue. Receives 10 unsolicited mss/month. Accepts 2 mss/issue; 12 mss/year. Publishes ms up to 2 months after acceptance. Agented

fiction 10%. Published work by Peter Crossley, Jim Nason. Length: 1,500 words average; 1,000 words minimum; 2,000 words maximum. Publishes short shorts. Length: 400-500 words. Sometimes critiques rejected mss and recommends other markets.
How to Contact: Send complete manuscript with cover letter. Include bio material, intent of story, why writer chose *Out!* Reports in 2 weeks on queries; 4-6 weeks on mss. SASE. Photocopied submissions OK. Accepts computer printout submissions. Accepts electronic submissions via disk (Word Perfect 5.0 preferred). Sample copy $2.
Payment: Pays free subscription and contributor's copies.
Terms: Acquires one-time rights.
Advice: "We look for bold, innovative words coupled with a strong voice. A writer who is not afraid to challenge his readers. A strong visual/descriptive sense. 'Passionate, honest, thoughtful' — key words."

OUTLAW BIKER, (II, IV), Outlaw Biker Enterprises, #2305, 450 7th Ave., New York NY 10123. (212)564-0112. FAX: (212)465-8350. Publisher/Editor: Casey Exton. Magazine: 8½×11; 96 pages; 50 lb. color paper; 80 lb. cover stock; illustrations; photos. Publication for hard-core bikers, their partners and for tattoo enthusiasts. Monthly. Special issue 6 times/year, *Tattoo Review*. Estab. 1984. Circ. 225,000.
Needs: Biker fiction and humor. Receives 20 unsolicited mss/month. Accepts 3 fiction mss/issue. Publishes ms 4 months after acceptance. Length: 1,000 words minimum; 2,500 words maximum.
How to Contact: Send complete ms with cover letter. SASE very important. Reports on queries in 1 month. Sample copy $3.50.
Payment: Pays $50-150.
Terms: Pays on publication for all rights.
Advice: "Timely biker events with photos used constantly. Photos do not have to be professionally taken. Clear snapshots of events with the short story usually accepted. Send to: Casey Exton, Attention."

PALOUSE JOURNAL, (II, IV), North Country Book Express, Box 9632, Moscow ID 83843. (208)882-0888. Editor: Ed Hughes. Tabloid: 11×17; 24-40 pages; 34 lb. stock; illustrations; photos. "We are a regional general interest magazine, for an educated, literate audience." Bimonthly. Estab. 1981.
Needs: Regional. "We will consider good writing about our region." Buys 1 ms/issue at most; 2-6 mss/year. Recently published work by Robert Wrigley, Pat McManus, Mary Blew; published new writers within the last year. Length: 1,500 words maximum. Will consider short shorts as columns, up to 800 words. Occasionally critiques rejected mss.
How to Contact: Send complete ms with cover letter. Reports in 2-3 months. SASE. Photocopied submissions OK. Accepts computer printout submissions. Sample copy for $2. Writers' guidelines for SASE. Reviews novels and short story collections "only if author, publisher or subject is of the interior Northwest."
Payment: Pays $25-75 for a full feature story.
Terms: Pays on publication for first North American serial rights.
Advice: "We look for good clean writing, a regional relevance. Manuscripts are often rejected because writer is obviously not familiar with the magazine and story lacks regional flavor. Read the publication first to see if your story fits! We only publish work about the Pacific and Intermountain West."

PEN SYNDICATED FICTION PROJECT, (I), P.O. Box 15650, Washington DC 20003. (203)543-6322. Director: Caroline Marshall. "Fiction syndicate created to market quality short fiction to a broad, national audience via radio (The Sound of Writing, co-produced with NPR), newspaper Sunday magazines and regional magazines (a varying group) and literary publications, including *American Short Fiction* published by the University of Texas Press."
Needs: Literary. Receives 2,500-5,000 submissions/year. Buys 50 mss/year. Only reads in January. Length: 2,500 words maximum. Publishes short shorts.
How to Contact: Send 2 copies of complete ms with cover letter and brief bio. Up to 5 stories may be submitted at one time, but no one story may exceed 2,500 words. Decisions made by May. SASE. Fiction guidelines for #10 SAE and 1 first class stamp.

Payment: Pays $500 plus $100 per publication by participating newspapers (plus tearsheets). "Realistic possible potential: $1,000-1,500."
Terms: Pays $500 on return of contract; syndication fees paid on semiannual basis. Buys worldwide serial rights, audio and anthology rights.
Advice: "Newspaper and radio audiences prefer short pieces of general, topical or family interest. Submitters are encouraged to imagine seeing their work in a Sunday magazine with accompanying illustration or hearing it on the air to judge a story's suitability."

PILLOW TALK, (II), 801 2nd Ave., New York NY 10017. Editor: Asia Fraser. Magazine: digest-sized; 98 pages; photos. Bimonthly erotic letters magazine.
Needs: "We use approximately 20 short letters of no more than five manuscript pages per issue, and five long letters of between seven and nine manuscript pages." Published new writers within the last year. Recommends other markets.
How to Contact: "We encourage unsolicited manuscripts. Writers who have proven reliable will receive assignments."
Payment: Pays $5 per page for short letters and a $75 flat rate for long letters and articles.
Terms: Pays on acceptance.
Advice: "Keep it short and sensual. We buy many more short letters than long ones. This is a 'couples-oriented' book; the sex should be a natural outgrowth of a relationship, the characters should be believable, and both male and female characters should be treated with respect. No S&M, bondage, male homosexuality, incest, underage characters or anal sex—not even in dialogue, not even in implication. No language that even implies sexual violence—not even in metaphor. No ejaculation on any part of a person's body. Romance is a big plus."

THE PLAIN DEALER MAGAZINE, (II), 1801 Superior Ave., Cleveland OH 44114. (216)344-4546. Editor: Clint O'Connor. Magazine: 10 × 11½; 20-64 pages; color and b&w illustrations and photos. Regional magazine, Sunday supplement to The Plain Dealer newspaper for our readers (Cleveland and state). Weekly. Circ. 575,000.
Needs: Adventure, contemporary, ethnic, historical (general), humor/satire, literary, mainstream, psychic/supernatural/occult, regional, science fiction, sports, suspense/mystery. "Regional preferred." Publishes annual special summer fiction issue. Receives 10-20 unsolicited mss/month. Number of mss accepted per issue "depends on quality." Publishes ms 2-3 months after acceptance. Length: 2,000 words maximum. Occasionally comments on rejected mss.
How to Contact: Send complete ms with cover letter, include Social Security number. Reports in 1 month on mss. SASE for ms, not needed for query. Sample copy $1 and 7½ × 10½ SAE.
Payment: Pays $500 maximum; 2 contributor's copies.
Terms: Pays on publication for one-time rights.

PLAYBOY MAGAZINE, Playboy Enterprises, Inc., 680 N. Lake Shore Dr., Chicago IL 60611. Declined listing.

POCKETS, Devotional Magazine for Children, (II), The Upper Room, Box 189, 1908 Grand Ave., Nashville TN 37202. (615)340-7333. Editor-in-Chief: Janet R. McNish. Magazine: 7 × 9; 32 pages; 50 lb. white econowrite paper; 80 lb. white coated, heavy cover stock; color and 2-color illustrations; some photos. Magazine for children ages 6-12, with articles specifically geared for ages 8 to 11. "The magazine offers stories, activities, prayers, poems—all geared to giving children a better understanding of themselves as children of God." Published monthly except for January. Estab. 1981. Estimated circ. 68,000.
Needs: Adventure, contemporary, ethnic, fantasy, historical (general), juvenile, religious/inspirational and suspense/mystery. "All submissions should address the broad theme of the magazine. Each issue will be built around several themes with material which can be used by children in a variety of ways. Scripture stories, fiction, poetry, prayers, art, graphics, puzzles and activities will all be included. Submissions do not need to be overtly religious. They should help children experience a Christian lifestyle that is not always a neatly wrapped moral package, but is open to the continuing revelation of God's will. Seasonal material, both secular and liturgical, is desired. No violence, horror, sexual and racial stereotyping or fiction containing heavy moralizing." Receives approximately 120 unsolicited fiction mss/month. Buys 2-3 mss/issue; 22-33 mss/year. Publishes short shorts. A peace-with-justice theme will run throughout the magazine. Agented fiction 50%. Published work by Peggy King Anderson, Angela Gibson and John Steptoe; published new writers last year. Length: 600 words minimum; 1,500 words maximum; 1,200 words average.

How to Contact: Send complete ms with SASE. Photocopied and previously published submissions OK, but no simultaneous submissions. Accepts computer printout submissions. Reports in 2 months on mss. Publishes ms 1 year to 18 months after acceptance. Sample copy for $1.95. Fiction guidelines and themes for SASE. "Strongly advise sending for themes before submitting."
Payment: Pays 12¢/word and up and 2-5 contributor's copies. $1.95 charge for extras; $1 each for 10 or more.
Terms: Pays on acceptance for newspaper and periodical rights. Buys reprints.
Advice: "Do not write *down* to children." Rejects mss because "we receive far more submissions than we can use. If all were of high quality, we still would purchase only a few. The most common problems are overworked story lines and flat, unrealistic characters. Most stories simply do not 'ring true', and children know that. Each issue is theme-related. Please send for list of themes. Include SASE." Sponsors fiction writing contest. Deadline: Oct. 1, 1992. 1,000-1,600 words.

PORTLAND MAGAZINE, (II), 578 Congress St., Portland ME 04101. (207)773-5250. Editor: Colin Sargent. Magazine: 68 pages; 60 lb. paper; 80 lb. cover stock; illustrations and photographs. "City lifestyle magazine — style, business, real estate, controversy, fashion, cuisine, interviews, art." Monthly. Estab. 1986. Circ. 22,000.
Needs: Contemporary, historical, literary. Receives 20 unsolicited fiction mss/month. Buys 1 mss/issue; 12 mss/year. Publishes short shorts. Recently published work by David Ray, Lewis Simpson, Michael Kimball. Length: 3 double-spaced typed pages. Query first.
How to Contact: "Fiction below 700 words, please." Send complete ms with cover letter. Reports in 3 months. SASE. Accepts computer printout and electronic submissions.
Terms: Pays on publication for first North American serial rights.
Advice: "We publish ambitious short fiction featuring everyone from Frederick Barthelme to newly discovered fiction by Edna St. Vincent Millay."

PRIVATE LETTERS, (I, II), 801 2nd Ave., New York NY 10017. Editor: Asia Fraser. Magazine: digest-sized; 98 pages; illustrations; photographs. Bimonthly letters magazine.
Needs: Erotica, written in letter form. No S&M, incest, homosexuality, anal sex or sex-crazed women and macho, women-conquering studs. "We use approximately 40 short letters per issue of no more than four double-spaced manuscript pages and five long letters of about 10 double-spaced manuscript pages." Published work by Diana Shamblin, Frank Lee and Shirley LeRoy; published new writers within the last year. Recommends other markets.
How to Contact: Send complete ms. "The majority of the material is assigned to people whose writing has proven consistently top-notch. They usually reach this level by sending us unsolicited material which impresses us. We invite them to send us some more on spec, and we're impressed again. Then a long and fruitful relationship is hopefully established. We greatly encourage unsolicited submissions. We are now printing two additional issues each year, so naturally the demand for stories is higher."
Payment: Pays $5 per page for short letters; $75 for long (7-10 page) letters.
Terms: Pays on acceptance.
Advice: "If you base your writing on erotic magazines other than our own, then we'll probably find your material too gross. We want good characterization, believable plots, a little romance, with sex being a natural outgrowth of a relationship. (Yes, it can be done. Read our magazine.) Portray sex as an emotionally-charged, romantic experience — not an animalistic ritual. *Never* give up, except if you die. In which case, if you haven't succeeded as a writer yet, you probably never will. (Though there have been exceptions.) Potential writers should be advised that each issue has certain themes and topics we try to adhere to. It would be greatly to one's benefit to write to ask for a copy of the writer's guidelines *and* a list of themes and topics for upcoming issues. Also, while the longer stories of more than 7 pages pay more, there are only about five of them accepted for each issue. We buy far more 4-6 page mss."

PURPOSE, (II), Mennonite Publishing House, 616 Walnut Ave., Scottdale PA 15683-1999. (412)887-8500. Editor: James E. Horsch. Magazine: 5⅜ × 8⅜; 8 pages; illustrations; photos. "Magazine focuses on Christian discipleship — how to be a faithful Christian in the midst of tough everyday life complexities. Use story form to present models and examples to encourage Christians in living a life of faithful discipleship." Weekly. Estab. 1969. Circ. 18,350.

Needs: Historical, religious/inspirational. No militaristic/narrow patriotism or racism. Receives 100 unsolicited mss/month. Buys 3 mss/issue; 40 mss/year. Recently published work by Mary Cotton, Glenna F. Hartley and Pauline Spray. Length: 700 words average; 1,000 words maximum. Occasionally comments on rejected mss.
How to Contact: Prefers full manuscript to queries. Reports in 6 weeks. Simultaneous, photocopied and previously published work OK. Accepts computer printout submissions. Sample copy for 6×9 SAE and 2 first class stamps. Writer's guidelines free with sample copy only.
Payment: Pays up to 5¢/word for stories and 2 contributor's copies.
Terms: Pays on acceptance for one-time rights.
Advice: Many stories are "situational—how to respond to dilemmas. Write crisp, action moving, personal style, focused upon an individual, a group of people, or an organization. The story form is an excellent literary device to use in exploring discipleship issues. There are many issues to explore. Each writer brings a unique solution. Let's hear them. The first two paragraphs are crucial in establishing the mood/issue to be resolved in the story. Work hard on developing these."

ELLERY QUEEN'S MYSTERY MAGAZINE, (II), Davis Publications, Inc., 380 Lexington Ave., New York NY 10017. (212)557-9100. Editor: Janet Hutchings. Magazine: Digest-sized; 160 pages with special 288-page issues in March and October. Magazine for lovers of mystery fiction. Published 13 times/year. Estab. 1941. Circ. 350,000.
Needs: "We accept only mystery, crime and detective fiction." Receives approximately 250 unsolicited fiction mss each month. Buys 10-15 mss/issue. Publishes ms 6-12 months after acceptance. Agented fiction 50%. Published work by Clark Howard, Robert Barnard and Ruth Rendell; published new writers within the last year. Length: up to 9,000 words. Critiques rejected mss "only when a story might be a possibility for us if revised." Sometimes recommends other markets.
How to Contact: Send complete ms with SASE. Cover letter should include publishing credits and brief biographical sketch. Reports in 1 month or sooner on mss. Fiction guidelines for SASE. Sample copy for $2.75.
Payment: Pays 3¢/word and up.
Terms: Pays on acceptance for first North American serial rights. Occasionally buys reprints.
Advice: "We have a Department of First Stories and usually publish at least one first story an issue— i.e., the author's first published fiction. We select stories that are fresh and of the kind our readers have expressed a liking for. In writing a detective story, you must play fair with the reader re clues and necessary information. Otherwise you have a better chance of publishing if you avoid writing to formula."

R-A-D-A-R, (II), Standard Publishing, 8121 Hamilton Ave., Cincinnati OH 45231. (513)931-4050. Editor: Margaret Williams. Magazine: 12 pages; newsprint; illustrations; a few photos. "*R-A-D-A-R* is a take-home paper, distributed in Sunday school classes for children in grades 3-6. The stories and other features reinforce the Bible lesson taught in class. Boys and girls who attend Sunday school make up the audience. The fiction stories, Bible picture stories and other special features appeal to their interests." Weekly. Estab. 1978.
Needs: Fiction—The hero of the story should be an 11- or 12-year-old in a situation involving one or more of the following: history, mystery, animals (preferably horses or dogs), prose poem, spiritual, sports, adventure, school, travel, relationships with parents, friends and others. Stories should have believable plots and be wholesome, Christian character-building, but not "preachy." No science fiction. Receives approximately 75-100 unsolicited mss/month. Published work by Betty Lou Mell, Betty Steele Everett and Alan Cliburn; published new writers within the last year. Length: 900-1,000 words average; 400 words minimum; 1,200 words maximum. Publishes short shorts.
How to Contact: Send complete ms. Reports in 2 weeks on queries; 6-8 weeks on mss. SASE for ms. No simultaneous submissions; photocopied and reprint submissions OK. Accepts computer printout submissions. Free sample copy and guidelines.
Payment: Pays 3-7¢/word; contributor's copy.
Terms: Pays on acceptance for first rights, reprints, etc.
Advice: "Send for sample copy, guidesheet, and theme list. Follow the specifics of guidelines. Keep your writing current with the times and happenings of our world."

RADIANCE, The Magazine for Large Women, (II), Box 30246, Oakland CA 94604. (510)482-0680. Editor: Alice Ansfield. Fiction Editors: Alice Ansfield and Carol Squires. Magazine: 8½×11; 48-52 pages; glossy/coated paper; 70 lb. cover stock; illustrations; photos. "Theme is to encourage women to live fully now, whatever their body size. To stop waiting to live or feel good about themselves until they lose weight." Quarterly. Estab. 1984. Circ. 35,000.

Needs: Adventure, contemporary, erotica, ethnic, fantasy, feminist, historical, humor/satire, mainstream, prose poem, science fiction, spiritual, sports, suspense, young adult/teen. "Would prefer fiction to have in it a larger-bodied character; living in a positive, upbeat way. Our goal is to empower women." Receives 30-50 mss/month. Buys 15 mss/year. Publishes ms within 1 year of acceptance. Published work by Marla Zarrow and Dan Davis. Length: 1,800 words preferred; 800 words minimum; 2,500 words maximum. Publishes short shorts. Sometimes critiques rejected mss and recommends other markets.

How to Contact: Query with clips of published work and send complete mss with cover letter. Reports in 1-2 months. SASE. Simultaneous, photocopied and reprint submissions OK. Accepts computer printout submissions. Sample copy for $3.50. Fiction guidelines for #10 SASE. Reviews novels and short story collections ("with at least 1 large-size heroine.")

Payment: Pays $50-100 and contributor's copies.

Terms: Pays on publication for one-time rights. Sends galleys to the author if requested.

Advice: "Read our magazine before sending anything to us. Know what our philosophy and points of view are before sending a manuscript. Look around within your community for inspiring, successful and unique large women doing things worth writing about. At this time, prefer fiction having to do with a larger woman (man, child). *Radiance* is one of the leading resources in the size acceptance movement. Each issue profiles dynamic large women from all walks of life, along with articles on health, media, fashion and politics. Our audience is the 30 million American women who wear a size 16 or over. Feminist, emotionally-supportive, quarterly magazine."

RANGER RICK MAGAZINE, (II), National Wildlife Federation, 1400 16th St. NW, Washington DC 20036-2266. (703)790-4278. Editor: Gerald Bishop. Fiction Editor: Deborah Churchman. Magazine: 8 × 10; 48 pages; glossy paper; 60 lb. cover stock; illustrations; photos. "*Ranger Rick* emphasizes conservation and the enjoyment of nature through full-color photos and art, fiction and nonfiction articles, games and puzzles, and special columns. Our audience ranges in ages from 6-12, with the greatest number in the 7 to 10 group. We aim for a fourth grade reading level. They read for fun and information." Monthly. Estab. 1967. Circ. 900,000+.

Needs: Fantasy, mystery, adventure, science fiction, sports, and humor. "Interesting stories for kids focusing directly on nature or related subjects. Fiction that carries a conservation message is always needed, as are adventure stories involving kids with nature or the outdoors. Moralistic 'lessons' taught children by parents or teachers are not accepted. Human qualities are attributed to animals only in our regular feature, 'Adventures of Ranger Rick.' " Receives about 150-200 unsolicited fiction mss each month. Buys about 6 mss/year. Published fiction by Judy Braus. Length: 900 words maximum. Critiques rejected mss "when there is time."

How to Contact: Query with sample lead and any clips of published work with SASE. Reports in 3 weeks on queries, 2 months on mss. Publishes ms 8 months to 1 year after acceptance, but sometimes longer. Sample copy for $2. Guidelines for legal-sized SASE. Sometimes reviews short story collections. Send books to fiction editor.

Payment: Pays $550 maximum/full-length ms.

Terms: Pays on acceptance for all rights. Very rarely buys reprints. Sends galleys to author.

Advice: "For our magazine, the writer needs to understand kids and that aspect of nature he or she is writing about—a difficult combination! Mss are rejected because they are contrived and/or condescending—often overwritten. Some mss are anthropomorphic, others are above our readers' level. We find that fiction stories help children understand the natural world and the environmental problems it faces. Beginning writers have a chance equal to that of established authors *provided* the quality is there."

REDBOOK, (II), The Hearst Corporation, 224 W. 57th St., New York NY 10019. Fiction Editor: Dawn Raffel. Magazine: 8 × 10¾; 150-250 pages; 34 lb. paper; 70 lb. cover; illustrations; photos. "*Redbook*'s readership consists of American women, ages 25-44. Most are well-educated, married, have children and also work outside the home." Monthly. Estab. 1903. Circ. 4,000,000.

Needs: "*Redbook* generally publishes two short stories per issue. We are looking for fiction that will appeal to active, thinking, contemporary women. Stories need not be about women exclusively; we also look for fiction reflecting the broad range of human experience. We are interested in new voices and buy up to a quarter of our stories from unsolicited submissions. Standards are high: Stories must be fresh, felt and intelligent; no straight formula fiction, pat endings, highly oblique or symbolic stories

without conclusions." Receives up to 3,000 unsolicited fiction mss each month; published new writers within the last year. Length: up to 22 ms pages.
How to Contact: Send complete ms with 9 × 12 SASE. No queries, please. Reports in 6-8 weeks.
Terms: Pays on acceptance for first North American serial rights.
Advice: "Superior craftsmanship is of paramount importance: Pay keen attention to character development and a strong and engaging storyline. Please read a few issues to get a sense of what we're looking for."

REFORM JUDAISM, (II), Union of American Hebrew Congregations, 838 5th Ave., New York NY 10021. (212)249-0100, ext. 400. Editor: Aron Hirt-Manheimer. Managing Editor: Joy Weinberg. Fiction Editor: Steven Schnur. Magazine: 8½ × 11; 32 or 48 pages; illustrations; photos. "We cover subjects of Jewish interest in general and Reform Jewish in particular, for members of Reform Jewish congregations in the United States and Canada." Quarterly. Estab. 1972. Circ. 295,000.
Needs: Humor/satire, religious/inspirational. Receives 30 unsolicited mss/month. Buys 3 mss/year. Publishes ms 3 months after acceptance. Length: 1,000 words average; 700 words minimum; 2,000 words maximum. Sometimes recommends other markets.
How to Contact: Send complete ms with cover letter. Reports in 3 weeks. SASE for ms. Simultaneous and photocopied submissions OK. Accepts computer printout submissions. Sample copy for $1 and SAE. Fiction guidelines for SAE.
Payment: Pays 10¢/word.
Terms: Pays on publication for first North American serial rights.

ROAD KING MAGAZINE, (I), William A. Coop, Inc., Box 250, Park Forest IL 60466. (708)481-9240. Magazine: 5¾ × 8; 48-88 pages; 60 lb. enamel paper; 60 lb. enamel cover stock; illustrations; photos. "Bimonthly leisure-reading magazine for long-haul, over-the-road professional truckers. Contains short articles, short fiction, some product news, games, puzzles and industry news. Truck drivers read it while eating, fueling, during layovers and at other similar times while they are en route."
Needs: Truck-related, western, mystery, adventure and humor. "Remember that our magazine gets into the home and that some truckers tend to be Bible Belt types. No erotica or violence." Receives 200 unsolicited fiction mss each year. Buys 1 ms/issue; 6 mss/year. Publishes ms 1-2 months after acceptance. Published work by Forrest Grove and Dan Anderson. Length: 1,200 words, maximum.
How to Contact: Send complete ms with SASE. Reports in 3-6 months. Sample copy with 6 × 9 SASE.
Payment: Pays $400 maximum.
Terms: Pays on acceptance for all rights.
Advice: "Don't phone. Don't send mss by registered or insured mail or they will be returned unopened by post office. Don't try to get us involved in lengthy correspondence. Be patient. We have a small staff and we are slow." Mss are rejected because "most don't fit our format . . . they are too long; they do not have enough knowledge of trucking; there is too much violence. Our readers like fiction. We are a leisure reading publication with a wide variety of themes and articles in each issue. Truckers can read a bit over coffee, in the washroom, etc., then save the rest of the magazine for the next stop. Know the trucker market. We are not interested in stereotypical image of truckers as macho, beer guzzling, women-chasing cowboys."

ST. ANTHONY MESSENGER, (II), 1615 Republic St., Cincinnati OH 45210. Editor: Norman Perry, O.F.M. Magazine: 8 × 10¾; 56 pages; illustrations; photos. "*St. Anthony Messenger* is a Catholic family magazine which aims to help its readers lead more fully human and Christian lives. We publish articles which report on a changing church and world, opinion pieces written from the perspective of Christian faith and values, personality profiles, and fiction which entertains and informs." Monthly. Estab. 1893. Circ. 360,000.
Needs: Contemporary, religious/inspirational, romance, senior citizen/retirement and spiritual. "We do not want mawkishly sentimental or preachy fiction. Stories are most often rejected for poor plotting and characterization; bad dialogue—listen to how people talk; inadequate motivation. Many stories say nothing, are 'happenings' rather than stories." No fetal journals, no rewritten Bible stories. Receives 70-80 unsolicited fiction mss/month. Buys 1 ms/issue; 12 mss/year. Publishes ms up to 1 year after acceptance. Published work by Marjorie Franco, Joseph Pici, Joan Savro and Philip Gambone. Length: 2,000-2,500 words. Critiques rejected mss "when there is time." Sometimes recommends other markets.

How to Contact: Send complete ms with SASE. Reports in 6-8 weeks. Accepts computer printout submissions. Sample copy and guidelines for #10 SASE. Reviews novels and short story collections. Send books to Barbara Beckwith, book review editor.

Payment: Pays 14¢/word maximum; 2 contributor's copies; $1 charge for extras.

Terms: Pays on acceptance for first North American serial rights.

Advice: "We publish one story a month and we get up to 1,000 a year. Too many offer simplistic 'solutions' or answers. Pay attention to endings. Easy, simplistic, deus ex machina endings don't work. People have to feel characters in the stories are real and have a reason to care about them and what happens to them. Fiction entertains but can also convey a point in a very telling way just as the Bible uses stories to teach."

"We are a general interest, family-oriented Catholic magazine interested in promoting sound married and family life with religious values," says Norman Perry, editor of St. Anthony Messenger. With this in mind, the cover of last February's issue featured April and Ralph Bolton walking on the grounds of St. Anne's Covenant in Melbourne, Kentucky. "The picture was commissioned to illustrate the article on 'Prescription for a Healthy, Holy Marriage' by Mitch Finley," Perry says. The photographer is Brad Smith/Photosmith.

ST. JOSEPH'S MESSENGER AND ADVOCATE OF THE BLIND, (II), Sisters of St. Joseph of Peace, 541 Pavonia Ave., Jersey City NJ 07306. (201)798-4141. Magazine: 8½×11; 16 pages; illustrations; photos. For Catholics generally but not exclusively. Theme is "religious—relevant—real." Quarterly. Estab. 1903. Circ. 20,000.

Needs: Contemporary, humor/satire, mainstream, religious/inspirational, romance and senior citizen/ retirement. Receives 30-40 unsolicited fiction mss/month. Buys 3 mss/issue; 20 mss/year. Publishes ms an average of 1 year after acceptance. Published work by Eileen W. Strauch; published new writers within the last year. Length: 800 words minimum; 1,800 words maximum; 1,500 words average. Occasionally critiques rejected mss.

How to Contact: Send complete ms with SASE. Simultaneous, photocopied and previously published submissions OK. Sample copy for #10 SAE and 1 first class stamp. Fiction guidelines for SASE.

Payment: Pays $10-25 and 2 contributor's copies.

Terms: Pays on acceptance for one-time rights.

Advice: Rejects mss because of "vague focus or theme. Write to be read—keep material current and of interest. *Do not preach*—the story will tell the message. Keep the ending from being too obvious. Fiction is the greatest area of interest to our particular reading public."

SASSY MAGAZINE, (II), Lang Communications, 230 Park Ave., New York NY 10169. (212)552-9500. Editor: Jane Pratt. Fiction Editor: Christina Kelly. Magazine; 9½×11; 100-130 pages; glossy 40 lb. stock paper and cover; illustrations and photographs. "Lifestyle magazine for girls, ages 14-19, covering entertainment, fashion as well as serious subjects." Monthly. Estab. 1988. Circ. 650,000.

Needs: Contemporary, ethnic, experimental, feminist, gay, humor/satire, literary, mainstream, prose poem, regional, young adult/teen (10-18 years). "No typical teenage romance." Publishes annual special fiction issue. Receives 300 unsolicited mss/month. Buys 1 ms/issue; 12 mss/year. Publishes ms 3-6 months after publication. Published Christina Kelly, John Elder, Elizabeth Mosier. Length: 2,000 words; 1,000 words minimum; 3,500 words maximum. Sometimes critiques rejected mss and recommends other markets.

How to Contact: Send complete manuscript with cover letter. Include social security number and address, brief background, perhaps one sentence on what story is about or like. Reports in 3 months. SASE. Simultaneous and photocopied submissions OK. Computer printout submissions are acceptable. Sample copy for $2. Fiction guidelines are free.

Payment: Pays $1,000 and contributor's copies.

Terms: Pays on acceptance. Offers 20% kill fee. Buys all rights or first North American serial rights. Send galleys to author (if requested).

Advice: "We look for unusual new ways to write for teenagers. It helps if the story has a quirky, vernacular style that we use throughout the magazine. Generally our stories have to have a teenage protagonist but they are not typical teen fiction. In the end, our only real criterion is that a story is original, intelligent, well-crafted and moves us."

SCHOLASTIC SCOPE, 730 Broadway, New York NY 10003. No longer taking queries or unsolicited submissions.

‡SCREW MAGAZINE, The Sex Review, (II), Milky Way Productions, Box 432, Old Chelsea Station, New York NY 10011. (212)989-8001. Editor: Al Goldstein. Fiction Editor: Manny Neuhaus. Tabloid: 64 pages; pulp paper; 2-color pulp cover stock; illustrations; photos. Humor, sex, satire, parody, first-person erotica stories for adult males. Weekly. Estab. 1968. Circ. 150,000.

Needs: Confession, erotica, ethnic, experimental, feminist, gay, humor/satire, lesbian. Nothing nonsexual. Receives 5-15 unsolicited fiction mss/month. Buys 1-3 mss/issue. Publishes ms 1-6 months after acceptance. Length: 1,300 words average; 1,000 words minimum; 2,500 words maximum. Occasionally critiques rejected mss. Recommends other markets.

How to Contact: Send complete ms with cover letter. Reports in 1-2 months. Photocopied submissions OK. Accepts computer printouts. Free sample copy and fiction guidelines. Reviews novels and short story collections. Send books to Michael Perkins, contributing editor.

Payment: Pays $40-150; contributor's copies.

Terms: Pays on publication for all rights.

SEEK, (II), Standard Publishing, 8121 Hamilton Ave., Cincinnati OH 45231. Editor: Eileen H. Wilmoth. Magazine: 5½×8½; 8 pages; newsprint paper; art and photos in each issue. "Inspirational stories of faith-in-action for Christian young adults; a Sunday School take-home paper." Weekly. Estab. 1970. Circ. 75,000.

Needs: Religious/inspirational. Buys 150 mss/year. Publishes ms an average of 1 year after acceptance. Published new writers within the last year. Length: 500-1,200 words.

How to Contact: Send complete ms with SASE. Reports in 4-6 weeks. Accepts computer printout submissions. Free sample copy and guidelines. Reviews "some" novels and short story collections.

Payment: Pays 5-7¢/word.

Terms: Pays on acceptance. Buys reprints.

Advice: "Write a credible story with Christian slant—no preachments; avoid overworked themes such as joy in suffering, generation gaps, etc. Most mss are rejected by us because of irrelevant topic or message, unrealistic story, or poor character and/or plot development. We use fiction stories that are believable."

SEVENTEEN, (II), News America, Inc., 850 3rd Ave., New York NY 10022. (212)759-8100. Fiction Editor: Adrian Nicole LeBlanc. Magazine: 8½×11; 125-400 pages; 40 lb. coated paper; 80 lb. coated cover stock; illustrations; photos. A general interest magazine with fashion, beauty care, pertinent topics such as current issues, attitudes, experiences and concerns during the teenage years. Monthly. Estab. 1944. Circ. 1.7 million.

Needs: High-quality literary fiction. Receives 300 unsolicited fiction mss/month. Buys 1 mss/issue. Agented fiction 50%. Published work by Margaret Atwood, Joyce Carol Oates; published new writers within the last year. Length: approximately 1,500-3,500 words. Also publishes short shorts.

How to Contact: Send complete ms with SASE and cover letter with relevant credits. Reports in 2 months on mss. Guidelines for with SASE.
Payment: Pays $700-2,500.
Terms: Pays on acceptance for one-time rights.
Advice: "Respect the intelligence and sophistication of teenagers. *Seventeen* remains open to the surprise of new voices. Our commitment to publishing the work of new writers remains strong; we continue to read every submission we receive. We believe that good fiction can move the reader toward thoughtful examination of her own life as well as the lives of others—providing her ultimately with a fuller appreciation of what it means to be human. While stories which focus on female teenage experience continue to be of interest, the less obvious possibilities are equally welcome. We encourage writers to submit literary short stories concerning subjects that may not be immediately identifiable as 'teenage,' with narrative styles that are experimental and challenging. Too often, unsolicited submissions possess voices and themes condescending and unsophisticated. Also, writers hesitate to send stories to *Seventeen* which they think too violent or risqué. Good writing holds the imaginable and then some, and if it doesn't find its home here, we're always grateful for the introduction to a writer's work."

SHINING STAR, Practical Teaching Magazine for Christian Educators and Parents, (II), Box 299, Carthage IL 62321. Editor: Becky Daniel. Magazine: 8½ × 11; 80 pages; illustrations. "Biblical stories only for teachers and parents of children K-8th graders." Quarterly. Estab. 1982. Circ. 20,000.
Needs: Looking for ideas to teach scripture to children age 4-12. Receives 100 unsolicited mss/month. Buys 3 mss/issue; 12 mss/year. Publishes ms 9-12 months after acceptance. Published new writers within the last year. Length: 500-1,000 words. Publishes short shorts.
How to Contact: Send complete ms with cover letter. Reports in 1 month. SASE for ms. Simultaneous and photocopied submissions OK. Accepts computer printouts. Sample copy $2. Fiction guidelines free with SASE.
Payment: Pays $20-50 and contributor's copies.
Terms: Pays on publication for all rights.
Advice: "Know the scriptures and be a teacher or person that has worked with and understands young children. Work should place emphasis on building positive self-concepts in children in Christian setting. Stories should be set in Biblical times and include characters and stories from the Bible."

‡SHOFAR, For Jewish Kids On The Move, (I, II, IV), Senior Publications, Ltd., 43 Northcote Dr., Melville NY 11747. (914)634-9423. Editor: Gerald H. Grayson, Ph.D. Magazine: 8½ × 11; 32-48 pages; 60 lb. paper; 80 lb. cover; illustration; photos. Audience: Jewish children in fourth through eighth grades. Monthly (October-May). Estab. 1984. Circ. 10,000.
Needs: Adventure, contemporary, ethnic, fantasy, humor, juvenile (5-9 years), prose poem, religious/inspirational, spiritual, sports, suspense/mystery, translations, young adult/teen (10-18 years) and Jewish. Receives 12-24 unsolicited mss/month. Buys 3-5 mss/issue; 24-40 mss/year. Published work by Caryn Huberman, Diane Claerbout and Rabbi Sheldon Lewis. Length: 750-1,000 words. Occasionally critiques rejected mss. Recommends other markets.
How to Contact: Send complete ms with cover letter. Reports in 6-8 weeks. SASE. Simultaneous, photocopied and reprint submissions OK. Accepts computer printout submissions. Sample copy for 9 × 12 SAE and 5 first class stamps. Fiction guidelines for 3½ × 6½ SAE and 1 first class stamp.
Payment: Pays 7¢/word.
Terms: Pays on publication for first North American serial rights.
Advice: "Know the magazine and the religious-education needs of Jewish elementary-school-age children. If you are a Jewish educator, what has worked for you in the classroom? Write it out; send it on to me; I'll help you develop the idea into a short piece of fiction. A beginning fiction writer eager to break into *Shofar* will find an eager editor willing to help."

THE SINGLE PARENT, Journal of Parents Without Partners, (IV), Parents Without Partners, Inc., 8807 Colesville Rd., Silver Spring MD 20910. (301)588-9354. FAX: (301)588-9216. Editor: Rene McDonald. Magazine: 8 × 10¾; 48 pages; 40 lb. glossy paper; illustrations; photos. Publication for di-

The double dagger before a listing indicates that the listing is new in this edition. New markets are often the most receptive to freelance contributions.

vorced, separated, widowed or never-married parents and their children. Published 6 times/year. Estab. 1957. Circ. 115,000.

Needs: Short stories for *children only*, not adults. Stories should deal with issues that children from one-parent families might face. Buys 2 mss/issue. Recently published work by Nancy Martin, Diane Getson, Deborah Wilkes; published new writers within the last year. Length: 1,500 words maximum.

How to Contact: Send complete ms with SASE. Reports within 2 months. Sample copy for $1 or 10 × 12 manila SAE with 75¢ postage. Reviews novels and short story collections occasionally.

Payment: Pays up to $75; 2 contributor's copies.

Terms: Pays on publication.

Advice: "Write about real children facing (and coping with) the real problems that crop up in single parent households."

THE SINGLE SCENE, (II, IV), (formerly *Columbus Single Scene*), Box 30856, Gahanna OH 43230. (614)476-8802. Editor: Jeanne Marlowe. Magazine: 8 × 11; 40 pages; illustrations; photos. Single living, male-female relationship topics covered for single adults. Monthly. Estab. 1985. Circ. 30,000.

Needs: Confession, contemporary, experimental, fantasy, humor/satire, mainstream, suspense/mystery. Buys 12 mss/year. Publication time varies "now that I have a backlog." Recently published work by Alan Selk, Arthur Bently; published new writers within the last year. Length: 5,000 words maximum; "shorter mss more likely to be accepted." Publishes short shorts. Occasionally critiques rejected mss.

How to Contact: Send complete ms with a statement granting one-time rights in exchange for copies. Reports in 1 week on queries; 2-4 weeks on mss. SASE for ms, "unless you don't want ms returned." Simultaneous, photocopied and reprint submissions OK, "if not from regional publications (OH, WV, KY)." Accepts computer printout submissions. Sample copy for $2. Reviews novels and short story collections.

Payment: Contributor's copies and advertising trade for most; $25 plus advertising trade maximum.

Terms: Pays on acceptance for one-time rights.

Advice: "My readers are primarily interested in meeting people, dating/relating to the other sex. I like to include a biographical note about my contributors' relation to singles. Although I have little space, I like to tackle tough problems and integrate fiction with editorial and personal experience. I don't shy away from the controversial, but reject the superficial."

SINGLELIFE MAGAZINE, (II), Single Life Enterprises, Inc., Suite 703, 606 W. Wisconsin Ave., Milwaukee WI 53203. (414)271-9700. FAX: (414)271-5263. Editor: Jeff White. Magazine: 8 × 11; 64 pages; slick paper; illustrations; photos. "Material deals with concerns of single persons of 24-60 age group." Primarily a nonfiction magazine. Bimonthly. Estab. 1982. Circ. 25,000.

Needs: Humor/satire, literary, travel, relationships, self-help, seasonal food and entertaining. Receives 50 unsolicited mss/month. Recently published work by Pamela Schweppe, Deborah Shouse and Christina Zawadiwsky. Publishes ms 2-4 months after acceptance. Length: 1,000 words minimum; 3,500 words maximum. Also publishes short shorts. Occasionally critiques rejected mss.

How to Contact: Send complete ms. Reports in 1 week, "depends on production schedule." SASE for ms. Simultaneous, photocopied and reprint submissions OK. Accepts computer printout submissions. Accepts electronic submissions via disk or modem. Sample copy $3.50. Fiction guidelines for SAE and 1 first class stamp.

Payment: Pays $50-150 and contributor's copies.

Terms: Pays on publication for one-time rights.

SOJOURNER, A Women's Forum, (II,IV), 42 Seaverns, Jamaica Plain MA 02130. (617)524-0415. Editor: Karen Kahn. Magazine: 11 × 17; 48 pages; newsprint paper; illustrations; photos. "Feminist journal publishing interviews, nonfiction features, news, viewpoints, poetry, reviews (music, cinema, books) and fiction for women." Published monthly. Estab. 1975. Circ. 33,000.

Needs: Contemporary, ethnic, experimental, fantasy, feminist, lesbian, humor/satire, literary, prose poem and women's. Upcoming themes: "Annual Health Supplement" (March); "Gay, Lesbian, Bisexual Pride" (June). Receives 20 unsolicited fiction mss/month. Accepts 10 mss/year. Agented fiction 10%. Published new writers within the last year. Length: 1,000 words minimum; 4,000 words maximum; 2,500 words average. Recommends other markets.

How to Contact: Send complete ms with SASE and cover letter with description of previous publications; current works. Photocopied submissions OK. Publishes ms an average of 6 months after acceptance. Sample copy $2 with 10 × 13 SASE and 86¢ postage. Fiction guidelines for SASE.

Payment: Pays subscription to magazine and 2 contributor's copies, $15. No extra charge up to 5; $1 charge each thereafter.
Terms: Buys first rights only.
Advice: "Pay attention to appearance of manuscript! Very difficult to wade through sloppily presented fiction, however good. Do write a cover letter. If not cute, it can't hurt and may help. Mention previous publication(s)."

SPORTING TIMES, (II,IV), Whitehouse Publishing, Box 1778, Vernon, British Columbia V1T 8C3 Canada. (604)545-9896. Editor: Geoff White. Tabloid: 10¼×12½; 24-28 pages; Electrabrite paper; illustrations and 85 screen photos. "For horsepersons." Estab. 1979. Circ. 17,000.
Needs: Adventure, juvenile (5-9 years), sports (horses) and young adult/teen (10-18). Receives 1-2 unsolicited mss/month. Buys 6-9 mss/year. Publishes ms 1-3 months after acceptance.
How to Contact: Send complete ms with cover letter. Reports in 1 month on queries. SASE. Sample copy for $1, 8×10 SAE. Fiction guidelines for #10 SAE.
Payment: Pay varies.
Terms: Pays on publication for first rights.

SPORTS AFIELD, (II, IV), Hearst Magazine, 250 W. 55th St., New York NY 10019. (212)649-4000. Editor: Tom Paugh. Magazine: 8×11; "the best paper"; 70 lb. cover stock; illustrations; photos. "This is an outdoor magazine: hunting, fishing, camping, boating, conservation, etc." for men and women who take an active interest in their sport. Monthly. Estab. 1887. Circ. 524,000.
Needs: Adventure, humor/satire when related to hunting and freshwater fishing, sports (fishing, hunting, camping). No old-fashioned me-and-Joe yarns. Receives 20 unsolicited mss/week. Buys a few mss each year. Publishes ms up to 2 years after acceptance. Agented fiction 5%. Length: 2,500 words or less. Also publishes short shorts of 200-250 words.
How to Contact: Query first; include name, address, a little background and credits, *brief* synopsis of story. Reports in 6 weeks on queries and mss. SASE for query. Accepts computer printout submissions. Reviews novels and short story collections occasionally.
Payment: Pays $850.
Terms: Pays on acceptance for first rights.
Advice: "Fiction is a very tough market—and not just in the outdoor field. Know the market. Don't give up!"

STANDARD, (II, IV), Nazarene International Headquarters, 6401 The Paseo, Kansas City MO 64131. (816)333-7000. Editor: Beth A. Watkins. Magazine: 8½×11; 8 pages; illustrations; photos. Inspirational reading for adults. Weekly. Estab. 1936. Circ. 172,000.
Needs: Religious/inspirational, spiritual. Receives 350 unsolicited mss/month (both fiction and nonfiction). Accepts 60 mss/year. Publishes ms 9-24 months after acceptance. Published work by Todd Lee, Floyd Allen, Jeanne Hill and Mark Littleton; published new writers within the last year. Length: 1,000 words average; 300 words minimum; 1,500 words maximum. Also publishes short shorts of 300-350 words.
How to Contact: Send complete ms with name, address and phone number. Reports in 1-2 months on mss. SASE. Simultaneous submissions OK but will pay only reprint rates. Accepts computer printout submissions. Sample copy and guidelines for SAE and 1 first class stamp.
Payment: Pays 3½¢/word; 2¢/word (reprint); contributor's copies.
Terms: Pays on acceptance for one-time rights.
Advice: "Too much is superficial; containing the same story lines. Give me something original, humorous, yet helpful. I'm also looking for more stories on current social issues. Make plot, characters realistic. Contrived articles are quick to spot and reject."

STORY FRIENDS, (II), Mennonite Publishing House, 616 Walnut Ave., Scottdale PA 15683. (412)887-8500. Editor: Marjorie Waybill. Sunday school publication which portrays Jesus as a friend and helper. Nonfiction and fiction for children 4-9 years of age. Weekly.
Needs: Juvenile. Stories of everyday experiences at home, in church, in school or at play, which provide models of Christian values. Length: 300-800 words.
How to Contact: Send complete ms with SASE. Seasonal or holiday material should be submitted 6 months in advance. Free sample copy.
Payment: Pays 3-5¢/word.
Terms: Pays on acceptance for one-time rights. Buys reprints. Not copyrighted.
Advice: "It is important to include relationships, patterns of forgiveness, respect, honesty, trust and caring. Prefer exciting yet plausible short stories which offer different settings, introduce children to wide ranges of friends and demonstrate joys, fears, temptations and successes of the readers."

STRAIGHT, (II), Standard Publishing Co., 8121 Hamilton Ave., Cincinnati OH 45231. (513)931-4050. Editor: Carla Crane. "Publication helping and encouraging teens to live a victorious, fulfilling Christian life. Distributed through churches and some private subscriptions." Magazine: 6½ × 7½; 12 pages; newsprint paper and cover; illustrations (color); photos. Quarterly in weekly parts. Estab. 1951. Circ. 75,000.
Needs: Contemporary, religious/inspirational, romance, spiritual, mystery, adventure and humor—all with Christian emphasis. "Stories dealing with teens and teen life, with a positive message or theme. Topics that interest teenagers include school, family life, recreation, friends, church, part-time jobs, dating and music. Main character should be a 15- or 16-year-old boy or girl, a Christian and regular churchgoer, who faces situations using Bible principles." Receives approximately 100 unsolicited fiction mss/month. Buys 1-2 mss/issue; 75-100 mss/year. Publishes ms an average of 1 year after acceptance. Less than 1% of fiction is agented. Published work by Alan Cliburn, Marian Bray, Teresa Cleary; published new writers within the last year. Length: 800-1,200 words. Recommends other markets.
How to Contact: Send complete ms with SASE and cover letter (experience with teens especially preferred from new writers). Reports in 1 month. Accepts computer printout submissions. Sample copy and guidelines for SASE.
Payment: Pays 3-7¢/word.
Terms: Pays on acceptance for first and one-time rights. Buys reprints.
Advice: "Get to know us before submitting, through guidelines and sample issues (free with a SASE). And get to know teenagers. A writer must know what today's teens are like, and what kinds of conflicts they experience. In writing a short fiction piece for the teen reader, don't try to accomplish too much. If your character is dealing with the problem of prejudice, don't also deal with his/her fights with sister, desire for a bicycle, or anything else that is not absolutely essential to the reader's understanding of the major conflict."

THE STUDENT, (I, II), A Christian Collegiate Magazine, Student Ministry Department of the Baptist Sunday School Board, 127 Ninth Ave. North, Nashville TN 37234. (615)251-2788. Editor: Milt Hughes. Magazine: 8¼ × 11; 50 pages; uncoated paper; coated cover stock; illustrations; photos. Magazine for Christians and non-Christians about life and work with Christian students on campus and related articles on living in dorm setting, dating life, missions activities, Bible study, and church ministry to students. Monthly. Estab. 1922. Circ. 40,000.
Needs: Adventure, humor, comics, confession, contemporary, ethnic, and religious/inspirational. Does not want to see mss "without purpose or without moral tone." Receives approximately 25 unsolicited fiction mss/month. Buys 1-2 mss/issue; 12-24 mss/year. Length: 300 words minimum (or less, depending on treatment); 1,500 words maximum; 750 words average.
How to Contact: Cover letter with bio and description of published works. Query first with SASE. Simultaneous, photocopied and previously published submissions OK. Reports in 3 weeks on queries; 6 weeks on mss. Sample copy 75¢. Free fiction guidelines for SASE.
Payment: Pays 5¢/word and 3 contributor's copies.
Terms: Pays on publication for all rights, first rights, one-time rights, and assignments for work-for-hire basis.
Advice: "Fit writing to format and concept of the piece. View many issues of the magazine before you write. Our readers demand fiction which conveys our message in an interesting way."

STUDENT LAWYER, (II, IV), American Bar Association, 750 N. Lake Shore Dr., Chicago IL 60611. (312)988-6048. Editor: Sarah Hoban. Managing Editor: Miriam Krasno. Magazine: 8½ × 10¾; 48 pages; glossy paper and cover; illustrations; photos. "Magazine for law students as part of their Law Student Division/ABA membership. Features legal aspects, trends in the law, social/legal issues, and lawyer profiles." Monthly (September-May). Circ. 35,000.
Needs: "All stories have to have a legal/law/lawyer/law-school element to them. No science fiction." Buys 1 full-length or 2-3 short humorous pieces/year. Publishes ms 1-6 months after acceptance. Length: 1,000-3,000 words. Sometimes recommends other markets.
How to Contact: Send complete ms with SASE. Reports in 1 month. Accepts computer printout submissions. Sample copy for $4; contact Order Fulfillment at above address.
Payment: Pays $75-500.
Terms: Pays on acceptance for first rights. Buys very few reprints.
Advice: "Rejects mss because "usually, the stories are of mediocre quality. Because we favor nonfiction pieces, the fiction we do publish has to be outstanding or at least very original. Keep trying—and *know* the magazine you're submitting to."

STUDENT LEADERSHIP JOURNAL, (IV), InterVarsity Christian Fellowship, P.O. Box 7895, 6400 Schroeder Rd., Madison WI 53707-7895. (608)274-9001. Managing Editor: Jeff Yourison. "The journal is a networking and leadership development tool for audience described below. We publish articles on leadership, spiritual growth and evangelism. We publish occasional poetry, short stories and allegories. The audience is Christian student leaders on secular college campuses." Quarterly. Estab. 1988. Circ. 8,000.

Needs: Religious/inspirational, prose poem. "The form of fiction is not nearly as important as its quality and content. Fiction published by *Student Leadership* will always reflect a Christian worldview." No romance or children's fiction. Receives 10-15 unsolicited fiction mss/month. Buys up to 1 ms/issue; 4 ms/year. Publishes ms up to 2 years after acceptance. Published work by H. Edgar Hix. Length: 2,000 words preferred; 200 words minimum; 2,500 words maximum.

How to Contact: Query first with clips of published work. "A good cover letter will demonstrate familiarity with the magazine and its needs and will briefly describe the submission and any relevant information." Reports in up to 2 months on queries; up to 3 months on mss. SASE. Simultaneous, photocopied, reprint and computer printout submissions OK. Sample copy for $2, 9 × 12 SAE and $2.40 postage. Fiction guidelines for #10 SAE and 1 first class stamp. Reviews novels and short story collections "if they address our audience *and* contemporary cultures."

Payment: Pays $25-200.

Terms: Pays on acceptance for first or one-time rights. Sends pre-publication galleys to author.

Advice: "Read! Read! Read! The short story author must be an *artist* with words in so short a space. *Read* the best work of others. Observe it; get it into your bones. Just like a picture, a story must be vivid, colorful, well-balanced and eye-catching. Write! Write! Write! Don't be afraid to have at it! Picasso pitched many of his sketches. You'll pitch most of yours. But it's good practice, and it keeps your creative mind flowing."

SUNDAY JOURNAL MAGAZINE, *The Providence Journal-Bulletin*, 75 Fountain St., Providence RI 02902. (401)277-7349. Editor: Elliot Krieger. Magazine: 10 × 11½; 28 pages; coated newsprint paper; illustrations; photos. "Magazine which has appeared weekly for 40 years in the *Providence Sunday Journal*." Circ. 280,000.

Needs: Regional. Recently published fiction by Paul Watkins and Ann Hood; published new writers within the last year.

How to Contact: Submit with SASE.

Payment: Pays $175 minimum; $400 maximum.

Terms: Buys one-time rights. Sponsors short-story contest for New England writers.

Advice: New England, especially Rhode Island, fiction only.

SUNSHINE MAGAZINE, (II), Henrichs Publications, Box 40, Sunshine Park, Litchfield IL 62056. Magazine: 5¼ × 7¼; 48 pages; matte paper and cover stock; illustrations. "To promote goodwill for the betterment of our society. We publish short, nondenominational, inspirational material." Monthly. Estab. 1924. Circ. 60,000.

Needs: "Light" fiction, humor, juvenile (5-9 years), preschool (0-4 years), senior citizen/retirement. No fiction that is lengthy, fantasy, sexual, specifically religious, violent or dealing with death, drugs, divorce or alcohol. Receives 500 unsolicited fiction mss/month. Buys 12 mss/issue; 140 mss/year. Publishes ms within a year of acceptance. Published work by Robert Tefertillar, Gail Geddes, Joanna Captain; published new writers within the last year. Length: 750 words average; 100 words minimum; 1,250 words maximum. Publishes short shorts. Sometimes critiques rejected ms and recommends other markets.

How to Contact: Send complete ms with SASE and cover letter with name, address, rights offered. Reports in 2 months on mss. SASE. Photocopied submissions OK. Accepts computer printout submissions. Sample copy for 50¢ or 6 × 8 SAE with 2 first class stamps. Fiction guidelines for #10 SASE.

Payment: Pays $10-100, contributor's copies; charge for extras.

Terms: Pays on acceptance for first North American serial rights.

Advice: "Always know the magazine you're submitting to. Read the guidelines *thoroughly* and examine one or two sample copies."

SURFING MAGAZINE, (IV), Western Empire, Box 3010, San Clemente CA 92672. (714)492-7873. Editor: Nick Carroll. Editorial Director/Dept. Manager: David Gilovich. Magazine: 8 × 11; 140 pages; 45 lb. free sheet paper; 80 lb. cover stock; photos. Magazine covering "all aspects of the sport of surfing for young, active surfing enthusiasts." Monthly. Estab. 1964. Circ. 92,000.

Needs: Surfing-related fiction. Receives 2 unsolicited mss/month. Buys 3 mss/year. Length: 2,000-3,000 words average. Occasionally critiques rejected mss. Also publishes short shorts.
How to Contact: Cover letter with background on surfing. Query first. Reports in 2 weeks. SASE. Photocopied submissions OK. Accepts computer printout submissions. Free sample copy and fiction guidelines.
Payment: Pays 15-20¢/word.
Terms: Pays on publication for one-time rights.
Advice: "Establish yourself as a *Surfing* general contributor before tackling fiction."

'TEEN MAGAZINE, (II), Petersen Publishing Co., 8490 Sunset Blvd., Los Angeles CA 90069. Editor: Roxanne Camron. Magazine: 100-150 pages; 34 lb. paper; 60 lb. cover; illustrations and photos. "The magazine contains fashion, beauty and features for the young teenage girl. The median age of our readers is 16. Our success stems from our dealing with relevant issues teens face, printing recent entertainment news and showing the latest fashions and beauty looks." Monthly. Estab. 1957. Circ. 1.1 million.
Needs: Romance, adventure, mystery, humor and young adult. Every story, whether romance, mystery, humor, etc., must be aimed for teenage girls. The protagonist should be a teenager, preferably female. No experimental, science fiction, fantasy or horror. Buys 1 ms/issue; 12 mss/year. Generally publishes ms 3-5 months after acceptance. Published work by Emily Ormand, Louise Carroll and Linda Bernson; published new writers within the last year. Length: 2,500-4,000 words. Publishes short shorts.
How to Contact: Send complete ms and short cover letter with SASE. Reports in 10 weeks on mss. Sample copy for $2.50. Guidelines for SASE.
Payment: Pays $100.
Terms: Pays on acceptance for all rights.
Advice: "Try to find themes that suit the modern teen. We need innovative ways of looking at the age-old problems of young love, parental pressures, making friends, being left out, etc. '*TEEN* would prefer to have romance balanced with a plot, re: a girl's inner development and search for self. Handwritten mss will not be read."

TEEN POWER, Scripture Press Publications, Inc., Box 632, Glen Ellyn IL 60138. (312)668-6000. Editor: Amy Cox. Magazine: 5⅜×8⅜; 8 pages; non-glossy paper and cover; illustrations and photographs. "*Teen Power* publishes true stories and fiction with a conservative Christian slant—must help readers see how principles for Christian living can be applied to everyday life; for young teens (11-14 years); many small town and rural; includes large readerships in Canada, England and other countries in addition to U.S." Estab. 1966.
Needs: Adventure, humor/satire, religious/inspirational, young adult/teen (10-18 years). "All must have spiritual emphasis of some sort." Receives approximately 50-75 unsolicited mss/month. Buys 1 ms/issue; about 50 mss/year. Publishes ms at least 1 year after acceptance. Published work by Alan Cliburn, Betty Steele Everett, Randy Southern and Michael La Cross; published new writers within the last year. Length: 1,000 words preferred; 250 words minimum; 1,100 words maximum. Publishes short shorts. Length: 300-500 words. Sometimes critiques rejected mss and recommends other markets.
How to Contact: Send complete ms with cover letter. Reports in 6-8 weeks. SASE. Simultaneous, photocopied and reprint submissions OK. Accepts computer printout submissions. Sample copy and fiction guidelines for #10 SAE and 1 first class stamp.
Payment: Pays $20 minimum; $120 maximum; contributor's copies.
Terms: Pays on acceptance. Buys first rights and one-time rights.
Advice: "We look for spiritual emphasis (strong but not preachy), writing style, age appropriateness, creativity in topic choice and presentation. A writer for *Teen Power* must know something about young teens and what is important to them, plus have a working knowledge of basic principles for Christian living, and be able to weave the two together."

TEENS TODAY, (II), Church of the Nazarene, 6401 The Paseo, Kansas City MO 64131. (816)333-7000. Editor: Karen DeSollar. Sunday school take-home paper: 8½×11; 8 pages; illustrations; photos. "For junior and senior high students involved with the Church of the Nazarene who find it interesting and helpful to their areas of life." Weekly. Circ. 60,000.

Market categories: (I) Beginning; (II) General; (III) Prestige; (IV) Specialized.

Close-up

Anne Roiphe
Fiction Editor
Tikkun

© Sigrid Estrada

Tikkun, in Hebrew, means to mend, repair and transform the world. *Tikkun*, the magazine, sets out to accomplish this by offering a bimonthly Jewish critique of politics, culture and society. It offers thoughtful and probing discussion through its journalism, poetry and fiction and speaks to its community of readers urgently and sincerely as intellectual equals. So, it is not surprising that when Anne Roiphe, the magazine's fiction editor, is asked how she envisions the reader, she says, "Like myself. That's all." The selection of fiction, she says, is "simply based on what I want to read."

Roiphe is a writer herself. In her late 20s, she submitted her first novel for publication to McGraw Hill. It was accepted, and she has been writing ever since—books of fiction and nonfiction and articles for such major publications as *The New York Times* Magazine, *The Washington Post*, *Mirabella* and *Vogue*.

She brings a writer's perspective to the manuscripts she reads for *Tikkun* and dislikes all academic and formal attempts at defining what makes a good short story. She is interested, she says, in "anything under the sun that's well written—real storytelling," which she hazards, "does not mean plot." Good writers, she says, "speak their minds and their souls in the story. I look for what moves and speaks to me."

Her goal as fiction editor, simply stated, is "to involve new talent and to provide a place for gifted writers of every generation on Jewish and non-Jewish themes." She has held the position since July of 1991, and she has had her "ear to the ground for word of mouth on talented writers," calling those she knows in writing programs and contacting various agents. "Often," she says, "by the time people have material that we would want to print, they are at least known to a few of their colleagues, and the word is out a little bit."

Based in New York, while the magazine is in Oakland, California, Roiphe relies on two to three readers there to screen the unsolicited submissions and is sent three to four to consider for each issue. These, she says, get a thorough read and are often critiqued. Yet "you don't tell writers what to do," she says, "I only discuss what I don't think works."

Roiphe has always been an avid reader and calls the question of who her favorite writers are an absurd one. After mentioning Woolf, Salinger, Lessing, Roth and Joyce, she stops and says, "There are too many. I can't begin to unravel it."

With so much to read, her only stipulation in submitting to *Tikkun* is that the manuscript be typed and in good condition so that she doesn't have to spend more time than is necessary reading it. A cover letter, she says, is unnecessary, while inclusion of name and phone number is imperative. "If I need to know anything," she says, "I'll find out when I call them."

—Lauri Miller

Needs: Contemporary, religious/inspirational, romance, humor, juvenile, young adult and ethnic. "Nothing that puts teens down or endorses lifestyles not in keeping with the denomination's beliefs and standards." Buys 1-2 mss/issue. Published new writers within the last year. Length: 1,000-1,500 words.
How to Contact: Send complete ms with SASE. Reports in 6 weeks on mss. Publishes ms 8-10 months after acceptance. Sample copy and guidelines for SASE.
Payment: Pays 4¢/word and 3½¢/word on second reprint.
Terms: Pays on acceptance for first and second serial rights. Buys reprints.
Advice: "Don't be too juvenile."

‡TEXAS CONNECTION MAGAZINE, (IV), Box 541805, Dallas TX 75220. (214)241-8350. Editor: Alan Miles. Magazine: 8½×11; 152 pages; book offset paper; 100 lb. enamel cover; illustrations and photographs. "Adult erotica, for adults only." Monthly. Estab. 1985. Circ. 15,000.
Needs: Erotica, erotic cartooning, sexual fantasy, feminist, gay, humor/satire and lesbian. Receives 20-30 unsolicited mss/month. Buys 2-3 mss/issue. Publishes ms 2-3 months after acceptance. Length: 1,750 words preferred; 1,000 words minimum; 2,500 words maximum.
How to Contact: Send complete ms with cover letter. Cover letter must state writer/author's age (18 yrs. minimum). Reports in 3 weeks. SASE for ms, not needed for query. Simultaneous, photocopied and reprint submissions OK. Accepts computer printout submissions. Sample copy for $7.50. Free fiction guidelines. Reviews erotic fiction only.
Payment: Pays $25-200, free subscription to magazine and contributor's copies.
Terms: Pays on publication. Purchases all rights on some, first rights on most.
Advice: "We publish an adult, alternative lifestyle magazine that is (uniquely) distributed both in the adult store market and mass-market outlets (convenience stores) throughout 5 states: Texas (main), Oklahoma, Arkansas, Louisiana, New Mexico. We are, of course, interested in fresh, erotic fiction only."

TIKKUN, (III), A Bimonthly Jewish Critique of Politics, Culture and Society, Institute for Labor and Mental Health, 5100 Leona St., Oakland CA 94619. (415)482-0805. Editor: Michael Lerner. Fiction Editor: Anne Roiphe. Magazine: 8×11; 96 pages; high quality paper. "*Tikkun* was created as the liberal alternative to *Commentary Magazine* and the voices of Jewish conservatism, but is not aimed just at a Jewish audience. Readers are intellectuals, political activists, Washington policy circles, writers, poets." Bimonthly.
Needs: Condensed/excerpted novel, contemporary, feminist, gay, historical (general), humor/satire, lesbian, literary, mainstream, translations, Jewish political. "No narrowly Jewish fiction. At least half of our readers are not Jewish. Or anything that is not of highest quality." Receives 150 unsolicited mss/month. Buys 1 ms/issue. Publishes ms 6-9 months after acceptance. Agented fiction 50%. Published work by Amos Oz, Lynne Sharon Schwartz, E.M. Broner. Length: 4,000 words preferred. Publishes short shorts. Almost always critiques rejected mss.
How to Contact: Send complete ms with cover letter. Reports in 2-3 months. SASE. Accepts computer printout submissions. Sample copy for $7.50.
Payment: Pays $100-250.
Terms: Pays on publication for first rights.
Advice: Looks for creativity, sensitivity, intelligence, originality, profundity of insight. "Read *Tikkun*, at least 3-4 issues worth, understand the kinds of issues that interest our readers, and then imagine yourself trying to write fiction that delights, surprises and intrigues this kind of an audience. Do not write what you think will feel sweet or appealing to this audience—but rather that which will provoke, bring to life and engage them."

TOUCH, (II), Calvinettes, Box 7259, Grand Rapids MI 49510. (616)241-5616. Editor: Joanne Ilbrink. Magazine: 8½×11; 24 pages; 50 lb. paper; 50 lb. cover stock; illustrations and photos. "Our purpose is to lead girls into a living relationship with Jesus Christ. Puzzles, poetry, crafts, stories, articles, and club input for girls ages 9-14." Monthly. Circ. 16,000.
Needs: Adventure, ethnic, juvenile and religious/inspirational. "Articles must help girls discover how God is at work in their world and the world around them." Each issue has a theme; write for biannual update. Receives 50 unsolicited fiction mss/month. Buys 3 mss/issue; 30 mss/year. Usually does not read during February, March, September and October. Published work by Ida Mae Petsock; published new writers within the last year. Length: 500 words minimum; 1,000 words maximum; 1,000 words average.

How to Contact: Send complete ms with 8 × 10 SASE. Prefers no cover letter. Reports in 2 months. Simultaneous, photocopied and previously published submissions OK. Sample copy for 8 × 10 SASE. Free guidelines.
Payment: Pays 3¢/word.
Terms: Pays on acceptance for simultaneous, first or second serial rights.
Advice: "Try new and refreshing approaches. The one-parent, new girl at school is a bit overdone in our market. We have been dealing with issues like AIDS, abuse, drugs, and family relationships in our stories—more awareness-type articles."

TQ (TEENQUEST), (II), Good News Broadcasting Co., Box 82808, Lincoln NE 68501. (402)474-4567. FAX: (402)474-4519. Managing Editor: Lisa Thompson. Magazine: 8 × 10¾; 48 pages; illustrations; photos. "*TQ* is designed to aid the spiritual growth of young teen Christian readers by presenting Biblical principles." Publishes 11 issues/year. Estab. 1946. Circ. 60,000.
Needs: Religious/inspirational, regional, romance, adventure, fantasy, science fiction and mystery. "Stories must be grounded in Biblical Christianity and should feature teens in the 14-17 year range." Buys 3-4 mss/issue; 35-40 mss/year. Receives 50-60 unsolicited fiction mss/month. Published work by Nancy Rue, Stephen Bly, Marian Bray, Scott Pinzon; published new writers within the last year. Length: up to 2,000 words.
How to Contact: Managing editor reads all query letters. All other mss screened. Send SASE and cover letter. Accepts computer printout submissions. Reports in 2 months. Publishes ms 6 months to 2 years after acceptance. Free sample copy and guidelines for 9 × 12 SASE.
Payment: Pays 7-10¢/word for unassigned fiction. More for assignments. Pays 3¢/word for reprints.
Terms: Pays on acceptance for first or reprint rights.
Advice: "The most common problem is that writers don't understand the limitations of stories under 2,500 words and try to cram a 6,000-word plot into 2,000 words at the expense of characterization, pacing and mood. We feel that fiction communicates well to our teenage readers. They consistently rank fiction as their favorite part of the magazine. We get hundreds of stories on 'big issues' (death, drugs, etc). Choose less dramatic subjects that are important to teenagers and give us a new storyline that has a Biblical emphasis, but isn't preachy. Although our magazine is based on Christian principles, we do not want fiction where the lesson learned is blatantly obvious. We're looking for subtlety. Before you try to write for teens, get to know some—talk to them, watch their TV shows, read their magazines. You'll get ideas for stories and you'll be able to write for our audience with accurate and up-to-date knowledge." Teen fiction writers under age 20 may enter annual contest.

TRAILER BOATS MAGAZINE, (II, IV), Poole Publications Inc., 20700 Belshaw Ave., Carson CA 90246. Editor-in-Chief: Wiley Poole. Magazine: 100 pages; high quality paper; 100 lb. cover stock. "Our magazine covers boats of 26 feet and shorter, (trailerable size limits) and related activities; skiing, fishing, cruising, travel, racing, etc. We publish how-to articles on boat and trailer maintenance, travel, skiing, boat tests and evaluations of new products." Audience: owners and prospective owners of trailerable-size boats. Monthly. Estab. 1971. Circ. 80,000.
Needs: Adventure, contemporary, fantasy, humor/satire, science fiction, and suspense/mystery. "Must meet general guidelines of the magazine regarding boats and related activities." Receives very few unsolicited fiction mss/month. Buys 1-3 mss/year. Publishes ms 1-6 months after acceptance. Length: 200 words minimum; 1,000 words maximum. Publishes short shorts of 500 words. Occasionally critiques rejected mss. Sometimes recommends other markets.
How to Contact: Query first with SASE. Reports in 1 month on queries; 4-6 weeks on mss. Accepts computer printout submissions. Free general guidelines. Sample copy for $1.50.
Payment: Pays 7-10¢/word.
Terms: Pays on publication for all rights.
Advice: "In our case, knowing the audience is of prime importance. Our readership and experience with fiction is limited. We are a consumer magazine with an audience of dedicated boaters. My suggestion is to know the audience and write for it specifically."

TURN-ON LETTERS, (I, II), AJA Publishing, Box 470, Port Chester NY 10573. Editor: Julie Silver. Magazine: digest-size; 114 pages; newsprint paper; glossy cover; illustrations; photos. "Sexually explicit. Publishing first person 'letters' written as if true." Published 8 times/year. Estab. 1982. Circ. 100,000.
Needs: Erotica. Buys approx. 42 "letters"/issue; 400 "letters"/year. Publishes ms 4-8 months after acceptance. Very little agented fiction. Length: 2-3 typed, double-spaced pages average. Occasionally critiques rejected mss.

How to Contact: Send complete ms with or without cover letter. Reports in an average of 3 weeks on mss. SASE. Photocopied submissions OK if clearly marked "not simultaneous submissions." Accepts computer printout submissions. "Submissions on Macintosh disk welcome, but please include hard copy too." Sample copy for $2.95 and 6×9 SAE with 4 first class stamps. Fiction guidelines for #10 SAE with 1 first class stamp.

Payment: Pays $15.

Terms: Pays on publication for all rights.

Advice: "Letters must be hot and must 'read real.' Our sister publication, *Uncensored Letters* will automatically be considered for both. It is requested that you do not send to both. Guidelines are the same."

TURTLE MAGAZINE FOR PRESCHOOL KIDS, (I, II), Children's Better Health Institute, Benjamin Franklin Literary & Medical Society, Inc., Box 567, 1100 Waterway Blvd., Indianapolis IN 46206. Editor: Christine French Clark. Magazine of picture stories and articles for preschool children 2-5 years old.

Needs: Juvenile (preschool). Special emphasis on health, nutrition, exercise and safety. Also has need for "action rhymes to foster creative movement and retold folktales for use in 'Pokey Toes Theatre.' " Receives approximately 100 unsolicited fiction mss/month. Published work by Ginny Winter, Robin Krautbauer and Ann Devendorf; published new writers within the last year. Length: 8-24 lines for picture stories; 500 words for bedtime or naptime stories.

How to Contact: Send complete ms with SASE. No queries. Reports in 8-10 weeks. Send SASE for Editorial Guidelines. Sample copy for 75¢.

Payment: Pays 10¢/word (approximate). Payment varies for poetry and activities.

Terms: Pays on acceptance for all rights.

Advice: "Become familiar with past issues of the magazine and have a thorough understanding of the preschool child. You'll find we are catering more to our youngest readers, so think simply. Also, avoid being too heavy-handed with health-related material. First and foremost, health features should be fun! Because we have developed our own turtle character ('Pokey Toes'), we are not interested in fiction stories featuring other turtles."

THE VANCOUVER CHILD, (II), 757 Union St., Vancouver, British Columbia V6A 2C3 Canada. (604)251-1760. Editor: Wendy Wilkins. Tabloid: 10¼×15½; 12 or 16 pages; newsprint paper; newsprint cover; illustrations and b&w photographs. "*The Vancouver Child* celebrates children and families, and we primarily publish nonfiction articles on issues affecting children's daily lives for parents in the Lower Mainland (Vancouver and suburbs); children also read our kids' pages but most of our readers are parents." Monthly. Estab. 1988. Circ. 30,000.

Needs: Feminist, juvenile (5-9 years), literary, mainstream, preschool (1-4 years), regional. "Short stories should have something to do with family life or children. It is possible that we would print a short story for children on our kids' pages, if the story were very short and of good quality. No foul language, please." No confession, erotica, romance, religious. Receives 1 or 2 unsolicited mss/month. Buys 10 mss/year. Publishes ms 1-5 months after acceptance. Recently published work by Robert Stelnach, Dolores Wilkins, Tiffany Stone. Length: 750 words average; 1,000 words maximum. Publishes short shorts. Sometimes critiques rejected mss and recommends other markets.

How to Contact: Send complete ms with cover letter. "Complete manuscript more important than cover letter. We will read the story and judge it on its merits." Reports in 3-5 weeks. Send SAE with International Reply Coupon. Photocopied submissions OK. Accepts electronic submissions via disk. Sample copy for 10×13 SAE and 2 first class stamps or IRC. Free fiction guidelines. Reviews only children's stories.

Payment: Pays 5¢/word.

Terms: Pays on publication for one-time rights.

Advice: "For our publication we favor writing that is 'tight'—i.e. every word counts. The language, however, should remain rich and evocative. We also prefer a good story to a specifically moralistic or socially relevant story. Thus if a writer has a point to make, we prefer the point of view to be embedded in the story and subtle rather than leaving nothing to the imagination and intelligence of the reader. Although we do not have a policy to print only Canadian authors, we prefer stories which make reference to Canadian locations rather than American locations. In some stories, it's not a problem, but a manuscript may be rejected on those grounds."

VIRTUE, The Christian Magazine for Women, (II), Virtue Ministries, Inc., Box 850, Sisters OR 97759. (503)549-8261. Editor: Marlee Alex. Magazine: 8⅛×10⅞; 80 pages; illustrations; photos. Christian women's magazine featuring food, fashion, family, etc.—"real women with everyday problems, etc." Published 6 times/year. Estab. 1978. Circ. 150,000.

Needs: Condensed novel, contemporary, humor, religious/inspirational and romance. "Must have Christian slant." Buys 1 ms/issue; 6 mss/year (maximum). Length: 1,200 words minimum; 2,000 words maximum; 1,200 words average. Publishes short shorts.

How to Contact: Reports in 6-8 weeks on ms. Accepts computer printout submissions. Sample copy for $3, 9×13 SAE and 90¢ postage. Writer's guidelines for SASE. Reviews novels and short story collections.

Payment: Pays 15-25¢/published word.

Terms: Pays on publication for first rights or reprint rights.

Advice: "Send us descriptive, colorful writing with good style. *Please*—no simplistic, unrealistic pat endings or dialogue. We like the story's message to be implicit as opposed to explicit. Show us, inspire us—don't spell it out or preach it to us."

VISION, (II,IV), Box 7259, Grand Rapids MI 45910. (616)241-5616. Editor: Dale Dieleman. Magazine: 8½×11; 16-20 pages; 60 lb. paper; 60 lb. cover; photos. *Vision*'s readers are young adults in their 20s in the U.S. and Canada. Bimonthly. Circ. 3,500.

Needs: Stories exploring values, lifestyles, relationships as young adults in workplace, campus, social settings—cultural, ethnic variety a plus. Christian perspective but no preachy, pious platitudes. Recently published work by Lonni Collins Pratt, Nancy Eastridge and Mark Littleton. Length: 1,500 words maximum.

How to Contact: Send ms plus SASE for return. Reports in 1 month on mss. Simultaneous submissions OK (specify other submission periodicals). Sample copy for 9×12 and 56¢ postage.

Payment: Pays $35-75.

Terms: Pays on publication.

‡VISIONS MAGAZINE: The Intercollegiate Magazine of Speculative Fiction and Fantasy, (IV), P.O. Box 6695, Ithaca NY 14851-6695. (607)272-2000. Editor: Steven Kurtz. Fiction Editor: Andrew Sewell. Magazine: 7¼×11¼; 72 pages; 50 lb. Finch White Opaque paper; 80 lb. enamel cover; b&w illustrations. "We only publish fiction and art produced by college and grad students for a general audience." Published 3 times/year. Estab. 1986. Circ. 12,000.

Needs: Open. Receives 50-100 unsolicited mss/month. Buys 12-14 mss/issue; 36 mss/year. Publishes ms 1-3 months after acceptance. Recently published work by Jeff VanderMeer and Matt Ruff. Length: 4,000 preferred; 400 words minimum; 12,000 words maximum. Comments on or critiques rejected ms and recommends other markets.

How to Contact: Send complete ms with cover letter. "Include a short biographical paragraph, part of which will be included with the story if it is published." Reports in 1 month on queries; 1-3 months on mss. SASE. Simultaneous, photocopied, reprints and computer printout submissions. Accepts electronic submissions "or E-mail, address JMTY@CORNELLF." Sample copy for $3.50. Fiction guidelines for #10 SAE and 1 first class stamp.

Payment: Pays $6/page in printed magazine, payable within 60 days of publication.

Terms: Buys one-time rights.

Advice: "*Visions* was founded and is operated by college students for the sole purpose of introducing new authors to publication in a professional media. Since everyone on staff is a full-time student, replies to submissions might not come for a few months, but please be patient. Most returned submissions have been heavily marked with comments for improvements." Sponsors a yearly contest, announced in each spring issue.

VISTA, (II), Wesley Press, Box 50434, Indianapolis IN 46953. (317)842-0444. Editor: Regina A. Lawton. Magazine: 8½×11; 8 pages; offset paper and cover; illustrations and photos. "*Vista* is our adult take-home paper and is published in conjunction with the Wesley Biblical Series adult Sunday school lesson." Weekly. Estab. 1906. Circ. 50,000.

Needs: Humor/satire, religious/inspirational, senior citizen/retirement. "We are not looking for 'Sunday Soap Opera,' romance, stories with pat or easy outs, or incidents that wouldn't feasibly happen to members of your own church." Receives 100 unsolicited mss/month. Buys 1 ms/issue. Publishes ms 10 months after acceptance. Length: 500 words minimum; 1,300 words maximum.

How to Contact: Send complete ms with cover letter. Reports in 4-6 weeks. SASE. Simultaneous, photocopied and reprint submissions OK. Accepts computer printout submissions. Sample copy for 9×12 SAE.
Payment: Pays $10-60.
Terms: Pays on acceptance for one-time rights.
Advice: "Manuscripts for all publications must be in keeping with early Methodist teachings that people have a free will to personally accept or reject Christ. Wesleyanism also stresses a transformed life, holiness of heart and social responsibility. I like true-to-life fiction . . . not necessarily a 'happily ever after' ending. Also, keep within the previously published guidelines."

THE WASHINGTONIAN, (IV), Washington Magazine Co., Suite 200, 1828 L St. NW, Washington DC 20036. (202)296-3600. Editor: John A. Limpert. General interest, regional magazine. Magazine: 8¼×10⅞; 200 pages; 40 lb. paper; 80 lb. cover; illustrations; photos. Monthly. Estab. 1965. Circ. 166,000.
Needs: Short pieces set in Washington. Receives 8-10 unsolicited fiction mss/month. Buys 3 fiction mss/year. Length: 1,000 words minimum; 10,000 words maximum. Occasionally critiques rejected mss.
How to Contact: Send complete ms with SASE. Reports in 2 months. Simultaneous and photocopied submissions OK. Sample copy for $3.
Payment: Pays $100-2,000.
Terms: Pays on publication for first North American rights. Negotiates kill fee for assigned mss not published.

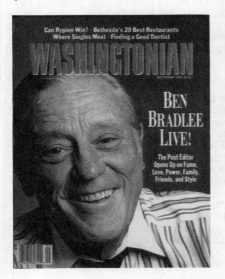

The **Washingtonian** *is a general interest, regional magazine, covering a wide variety of events in the nation's capitol. Associate Editor Diane Lazarus says, however, the monthly is now devoting "less space to everything, including fiction." She stresses that writers interested in submitting to this magazine should focus on short pieces set in the Washington area. Pictured on the cover here is Ben Bradlee, who retired from his position as executive editor of the Washington Post last September. The photographer is Breton Littlehales.*

WEIRD TALES, The Unique Magazine, (I, IV), Terminus Publishing Company, Inc., Box 13418, Philadelphia PA 19101. Editors: George Scithers and Darrell Schweitzer. Magazine: 6½×9½; 148 pages; acid-free book paper; pen and ink illustrations. "This is a professional fantasy-fiction and horror-fiction magazine." Quarterly. Estab. 1923. Circ. 10,000.
Needs: Fantasy, horror, supernatural/occult. "Writers should be familiar with the fantasy/horror genres; the editors are well read in the field and want fresh ideas rather than tired old retreads. To paraphrase Ursula K. LeGuin, 'If you want to write it, you gotta read it!' " Receives 400-500 unsolicited fiction mss/month. Buys 3-4 fiction mss/month; 48-80 mss/year. Publishes ms usually less than 2 years after acceptance. Published work by Gene Wolfe, Ramsey Campbell and Nancy Springer; published new writers within the last year. Length: 20,000 words maximum. Publishes short shorts. Always comments on rejected mss.
How to Contact: Send complete ms, which should include return address. Reports within 1 month. SASE. Accepts photocopied submissions. Sample copy for $5. Fiction guidelines for #10 SAE and 1 first class stamp.

Payment: Pays 3-5¢/word, depending on length of story, plus 3 contributor's copies.
Terms: Pays on acceptance for first North American serial rights. Sends galleys to author.
Advice: *"Weird Tales* is a revival of a famous old 'pulp' magazine, published in the original format, but with new fiction by many top writers and talented newcomers to the field. Basically, we're trying to make this *Weird Tales* as it would be today had it continued uninterrupted to the present. Know the field. Know manuscript format. Be familiar with the magazine, its contents and its markets. Send only your best work."

WESTERN PEOPLE, (II), Western Producer Publications, Box 2500, Saskatoon, Saskatchewan S7K 2C4 Canada. (306)665-3500. FAX: (306)653-1255. Editor: Keith Dryden. Managing Editor: Michael Gillgannon. Tabloid: 10¼×14½; 8 pages; newsprint paper and cover stock; illustrations and photos. *"Western People* is for and about western Canadians, a supplement of the region's foremost weekly agricultural newspaper. Includes fiction, nonfiction (contemporary and history) and poetry. Readership is mainly rural and western Canadian." Weekly. Published special fiction issue last year; plans another. Estab. 1978. Circ. 130,000.
Needs: Contemporary, adventure and humor. Buys 20 mss/year. Publishes short shorts. Published new writers within the last year. Length: 750-2,000 words.
How to Contact: Send complete ms with SAE, IRC (or $1 without IRC). Reports in 3 weeks on mss. Free sample copy with 9×12 SAE, IRC. Free general guidelines with legal-sized SAE, IRC.
Payment: Pays $150 (Canadian) maximum (more for serials).
Terms: Pays on acceptance for first North American rights.
Advice: "The story should be lively, not long, related in some way to the experience of rural western Canadians. We believe our readers enjoy a good story, particularly when it has some relevance to their own lives. Although most of the stories in *Western People* are nonfictional, we offer variety to our readers, including fiction and poetry. Write about what could happen, not what did happen. We find that beginning writers try to fictionalize actual events with a result that is neither fish nor fowl."

WITH MAGAZINE, (II, IV), Faith & Life Press and Mennonite Publishing House, Box 347, Newton KS 67114. (316)283-5100. Magazine: 8½×11; 32 pages; 60 lb. coated paper and cover; illustrations and photos. "Our purpose is to help teenagers understand the issues that impact them and to help them make choices that reflect Mennonite-Anabaptist understandings of living by the Spirit of Christ. We publish all types of material—fiction, nonfiction, poetry, prose poem, spiritual, sports, features, 'think' pieces, etc." Published 8 times/year. Estab. 1968. Circ. 5,000.
Needs: Contemporary, ethnic, humor/satire, literary, mainstream, religious, translations, young adult/teen (13-18 years). "We accept issue-oriented pieces as well as religious pieces. No religious fiction that gives 'pat' answers to serious situations." Receives about 50 unsolicited mss/month. Buys 1-2 mss/issue; 8-10 mss/year. Publishes ms up to 1 year after acceptance. Published new writers within the last year. Length: 1,500 words preferred; 400 words minimum; 2,000 words maximum. Sometimes critiques rejected mss and recommends other markets.
How to Contact: Send complete ms with cover letter, which should include short summary of author's credits and what rights they are selling. Reports in 2-3 weeks on queries; 3 months on mss. SASE. Simultaneous, photocopied and reprint submissions OK. Accepts computer printout submissions. Accepts electronic submissions via DOS (IBM compatible) disk, preferably in Wordstar. Sample copy for 9×12 SAE and $1.21 postage. Fiction guidelines for #10 SAE and 1 first class stamp.
Payment: Pays 2¢/word for reprints; 4¢/word for simultaneous rights (one-time rights to an unpublished story). Supplies contributor's copies; charge for extras.
Terms: Pays on acceptance for one-time rights.
Advice: "Write with a teenage audience in mind, but don't talk down to them. Treat the audience with respect. Don't expect to make a sale with the usual 'I've-got-a-problem-give-it-all-to-Jesus-and-everything-will-turn-out-fine' story. Real life isn't always like that and teens will perceive the story as unbelievable. Do include ethnic minorities in your stories; our audience is both rural and urban."

Market conditions are constantly changing! If you're still using this book and it is 1993 or later, buy the newest edition of Novel & Short Story Writer's Market at your favorite bookstore or order directly from Writer's Digest Books.

WOMAN'S DAY, (II), 1633 Broadway, New York NY 10019. (212)767-6000. Editor-in-Chief: Jane Chesnutt. "A strong service magazine geared to women, with a wide variety of well written subjects (foods, crafts, beauty, medical, etc.)." Publishes 17 issues/year. Estab. 1939. Circ. 7½ million; readership 20 million.
Needs: Literary, contemporary, fantasy, women's. No violence, crime or totally male-oriented stories. *Woman's Day* does not accept any unsolicited short fiction. Length: 2,000-3,000 words average.
How to Contact: Send complete ms with SASE. Guidelines for SASE.
Payment: Pays top rates.
Terms: Pays on acceptance for first North American serial rights. Occasionally buys reprints.
Advice: "Read the magazine and keep trying."

WOMAN'S WORLD MAGAZINE, The Woman's Weekly, (II), Heinrich Bauer North America, 270 Sylvan Ave., Englewood Cliffs NJ 07632. (201)569-0006. Editor: Dena Vane. Fiction Editor: Jeanne Muchnick. Magazine; 9½×11; 54 pages; newspaper quality. "The magazine for 'Mrs. Middle America.' We publish short romances and mini-mysteries for all women, ages 18-68." Weekly. Estab. 1980. Circ. 1.5 million.
Needs: Romance (contemporary), suspense/mystery. No humour, erotica. Receives 50 unsolicited mss/month. Buys 2 mss/issue; 104 mss/year. Publishes mss 6-10 weeks after acceptance. Agented fiction 2%. Recently published work by Tina Smith, P.J. Platz, Lisa Albert, Fay Thompson. Length: romances—3,200 words; mysteries—1,100 words. Publishes short shorts. Sometimes critiques rejected mss and recommends other markets.
How to Contact: Send complete manuscript with cover letter. "*No queries.*" Reports in 6-8 weeks. SASE. Accepts computer printout submissions. Sample copy for $1. Fiction guidelines free.
Payment: Romances—$1,000, mysteries—$500.
Terms: Pays on acceptance. Buys first North American serial rights only.

‡WOMEN'S GLIBBER, A Collection of Women's Humor, (IV), Women's Glib™, P.O. Box 259, Bala Cynwyd PA 19004. (215)668-4252. Editor: Rosalind Warren. Annual trade paperback book. 6×9; 200 pages; 60 lb. paper; (cartoons) and (photoessays). "Women's humor—humor written/drawn by women. Stories, essays, cartoons, photoessays—short, hilarious feminist material." For "anybody who appreciates feminist humor." Annually. Estab. 1990. Circ. 20,000 in print.
Needs: Women's humor: Contemporary, ethnic, feminist, gay, humor/satire, lesbian, literary, mainstream. "I need mostly short, hilariously (laugh-out-loud) funny material—don't be safe, be outrageous!—*by women only*. No domestic humor. No diet or weight loss humor or material about how svelte a girl should be. No stories in which aliens land on planet earth to share their intergalactic diet secrets with us. Nothing about how to catch or keep a man or about how men can't cook or do laundry. Nothing homophobic or racist or sexist. Female protagonists preferred." Receives 150 unsolicited mss/month. Buys 20 mss/issue. Publishes ms within a year after acceptance. Agented fiction 5%. Recently published work by Nora Ephron, Alice Kahn, Lynda Barry. Length: 1,000 words preferred; 3,000 words maximum. Publishes short shorts. Usually critiques rejected mss and recommends other markets.
How to Contact: Query with clips of published work or send complete ms with cover letter. Reports in 2 weeks. SASE. Simultaneous, photocopied and reprint submissions OK. Accepts computer printout submissions. Sample copy for $10.95 (includes postage). Fiction guidelines for #10 SAE and 1 first class stamp.
Payment: Pays $5/page and 2 contributor's copies.
Terms: Pays on publication for one-time, nonexclusiverights.
Advice: "If it makes me laugh I publish it. Don't be safe—be outrageous! Challenge the status quo! I prefer short (2-10 pages) material. Some of the most popular material in the first book (*Women's Glib*) was by previously unpublished writers. Read the first book in the series."

WONDER TIME, (II), Beacon Hill, Press of Kansas City, 6401 Paseo, Kansas City MO 64131. (816)333-7000. Editor: Evelyn Beals. Magazine: 8¼×11; 4 pages; self cover; color illustrations; photos. Handout story paper published through the Church of the Nazarene Sunday school; stories should follow outline of Sunday school lesson for 6-7 year-olds. Weekly. Circ. 45,000.
Needs: Religious/inspirational and juvenile. Stories must have controlled vocabulary and be easy to read. No fairy tales or science fiction. Receives 50-75 unsolicited fiction mss/month. Buys 1 ms/issue. Publishes ms an average of 1 year after acceptance. Agented fiction 25%. Published works by Eleanor P. Anderson, Jane Landreth and Virginia Brossirt. Length: 300-550 words. Recommends other markets.

How to Contact: Send complete ms with SASE. Reports in 6 weeks. Free sample copy and curriculum guide with SASE.

Payment: Pays $25 minimum.

Terms: Pays on acceptance for rights which allow the publisher to print and reprint the story in the same publication in subsequent years without additional payment. Buys reprints.

Advice: "Control vocabulary. Start with action—not description. Include an element of suspense. Don't just relate happenings. Study children to know what children are interested in; stories should deal with children's problems of today and must be tastefully handled. Know your readership."

‡**WY'EAST HISTORICAL JOURNAL, (II)**, Crumb Elbow Publishing, P.O. Box 294, Rhododendron OR 97049. (503)622-4798. Editor: Michael P. Jones. Newspaper: 8½×11; 60 pages; top-notch paper; hardcover; illustrations and photographs. "Publishes historical or contemporary articles on the history of Oregon's Mt. Hood, the Columbia River, the Pacific NW, or the Old Oregon Country that includes Oregon, Washington, Idaho, Wyoming, Montana, Alaska, Northern California and British Columbia. For young adults to elderly." Quarterly. Estab. 1992. Circ. 10,000.

Needs: Open. Special interests include wildlife and fisheries, history of fur trade in Pacific Northwest, the Oregon Trail and Indians. "All materials should relate—somehow—to the region the publication is interested in." Plans to publish annual special fiction issue. Receives 10 unsolicited mss/month. Buys 1-2 mss/issue; 22-24 mss/year. Publishes ms up to one year after acceptance. Recently published work by Joel Palmer. Publishes short shorts. Recommends other markets. "We have several other publications through Crumb Elbow Publishing where we can redirect the material."

How to Contact: Query with clips of published work or send complete ms with cover letter. Reports in 2 months "depending upon work load." SASE. Simultaneous, photocopied and reprint submissions OK. Accepts computer printout submissions. Sample copy $5. Fiction guidelines for #10 SAE and 1 first class stamp.

Payment: Pays contributor's copies.

Terms: Pays on publication. Buys one-time rights.

Advice: "A ms has to have a historical or contemporary tie to the Old Oregon Country, which was the lands that lay west of the Rocky Mountains to the Pacific Ocean, south to Northern California, and North to Alaska. It has to be about such things as nature, fish and wildlife, the Oregon Trail, pioneer settlement and homesteading, the Indian wars, gold mining, wild horses—which are only a few ideas. It has to be written·in a non-offensive style, meaning please remove all four-letter words or passages dealing with loose sex. Do not be afraid to try something a little different. No prima donnas, please! We wish to work with writers who are professionals, even if they haven't had any of their works published before. This is a great place to break into the publishing world as long as you are an adult who acts like an adult. Send copies only! And please note that we cannot be responsible for the U.S. Postal Service once you mail something to us, or we mail something to you. We are looking forward to working with those who love history and nature as much as we do."

XTRA MAGAZINE, Church-Wellesley Review (Literary Supplement), (IV), Pink Triangle Press, Box 7289, Stn. A, Toronto, Ontario M5W 1X9 Canada. (416)925-6665. Editor: Ken Popert. Fiction Editor: Dayne Ogilvie. Tabloid: 11½×17; 44-60 pages; newsprint paper; illustrations and photographs. "Gay/lesbian magazine, but fiction/poetry does not have to be about sexual orientation." Fiction supplement is annual. Estab. 1990 (supplement only). Circ. 20,000.

Needs: Gay, lesbian. Publishes annual special fiction issue. Receives 4-5 unsolicited mss/month. Buys up to 20 mss/year. Publishes mss spring after acceptance. Recently published work by Antler (American poet) Sky Gilbert (Canadian playwright). Length: 1,500 words maximum. Publishes short shorts. Sometimes critiques rejected mss and recommends other markets.

How to Contact: Send complete manuscript with cover letter. Reports in 1-2 months on mss. SASE. If notified, simultaneous, photocopied and reprint submissions OK. Accepts computer printout submissions. Sample copy free.

Payment: Pays 70¢/word (slightly more for poetry) up to $150 maximum.

YANKEE MAGAZINE, (II, III), Yankee, Inc., Dublin NH 03444. Editor: Judson D. Hale. Fiction Editor: Edie Clark. Magazine: 6×9; 176+ pages; glossy paper; 4-color glossy cover stock; illustrations; color photos. "Entertaining and informative New England regional on current issues, people, history, antiques and crafts for general reading audience." Monthly. Estab. 1935. Circ. 1,000,000.

Needs: Literary. Fiction is to be set in New England or compatible with the area. No religious/ inspirational, formula fiction or stereotypical dialect, novels or novellas. Buys 1 ms/issue; 12 mss/year. Published work by Andre Dubus, H. L. Mountzoures and Fred Bonnie; published new writers within the last year. Length: 2,000 words. Recommends other markets.

How to Contact: Send complete ms with SASE and previous publications. "Cover letters are important if they provide relevant information: previous publications or awards; special courses taken; special references (e.g. 'William Shakespeare suggested I send this to you . . . .')" Reports in 3-6 weeks.

Payment: Pays $1,000.

Terms: Pays on acceptance; rights negotiable. Sends galleys to author.

Advice: "Read previous 10 stories in *Yankee* for style and content. Fiction must be realistic and reflect life as it is—complexities and ambiguities inherent. Our fiction adds to the 'complete menu'—the magazine includes many categories—humor, profiles, straight journalism, essays, etc. Listen to the advice of any editor who takes the time to write a personal letter. Go to workshops; get advice and other readings before sending story out cold."

YM, Gruner and Jahr USA, Inc., 685 3rd Ave., New York NY 10017. Declined listing.

THE YOUNG CRUSADER, National Woman's Christian Temperance Union, 1730 Chicago Ave., Evanston IL 60201. (708)864-1396. Editor-in-Chief: Mrs. Rachel Bubar Kelly. Managing Editor: Michael C. Vitucci. "Character building material showing high morals and sound values; inspirational, informational nature articles and stories for 6-12 year olds." Monthly. Estab. 1887. Circ. 10,000.

Needs: Juvenile. Stories should be naturally written pieces, not saccharine or preachy. Buys 3-4 mss/ issue; 60 mss/year. Length: 600-650 words. Also prose and poetry. Published work by Nadine L. Mellott, William R. Barrow, Gloria L. Sollid and Veronica McClearin.

How to Contact: Send complete ms with SASE. Reports in 6 months or longer on mss. Free sample copy with SASE.

Payment: Pays ½¢/word and contributor's copy.

Terms: "If I like the story and use it, I'm very lenient and allow the author to use it elsewhere." Mss/ prose/poetry, if used, pays on publication. If not used mss/prose/poetry will be destroyed.

YOUNG SALVATIONIST/YOUNG SOLDIER, (II, IV), The Salvation Army, P.O. Box 269, 615 Slaters Lane, Alexandria VA 22313. (703)684-5500. Editor: Capt. Robert Hostetler. Magazine: 8×11; 16 pages (*Young Salvationist*), 8 pages (*Young Soldier*); illustrations and photos. Christian emphasis articles for youth members of the Salvation Army. Monthly. Estab. 1984. Circ. 50,000.

Needs: Religious/inspirational, young adult/teen. Receives 150 unsolicited mss/month. Buys 9-10 ms/ issue; 90-100 mss/year. Publishes ms 3-4 months after acceptance. Length: 1,000 words preferred; 750 words minimum; 1,200 words maximum. Publishes short shorts. Sometimes critiques rejected mss and recommends other markets.

How to Contact: Send complete ms. Reports in 1-2 weeks on queries; 2-4 weeks on mss. SASE. Simultaneous, photocopied and reprint submissions OK. Accepts computer printout submissions. Sample copy for 9×12 SAE and 3 first class stamps. Fiction guidelines for #10 SAE with 1 first class stamp.

Payment: Pays 3-5¢/word.

Terms: Pays on acceptance for all rights, first rights, first North American serial rights and one-time rights.

International commercial periodicals

The following commercial magazines, all located outside the United States and Canada, also accept work from fiction writers. Countries represented here range from England, Ireland and Scotland to Czechoslovakia, Germany and Italy. Also included are South Africa, Australia and China.

As with other publications, try to read sample copies. While some of these may be available at large newsstands, most can be obtained directly from the publishers. Write for guidelines as well. Whereas one editor may want fiction with some connection to his or her own country, another may seek more universal settings and themes. Watch, too, for payment policies. Many publications pay only in their own currencies.

In all correspondence, use self-addressed envelopes (SAEs) with International Reply

Coupons (IRCs) for magazines outside your own country. IRCs may be purchased at the main branch of your local post office. In general, send IRCs in amounts roughly equivalent to return postage. When submitting work to these international publications, you may find it easier to include a disposable copy of your manuscript and only one IRC with a self-addressed postcard for a reply. This is preferred by many editors, and it saves you the added cost of having your work returned.

‡FAIR LADY, (III), National Magazine, Box 1802, Cape Town 8000 South Africa. Editor: Liz Butler. "Women's glossy magazine with regular fashion, features, beauty, cooking, parenting section, competitions, fiction, book reviews, interviews (especially celebrity), serious articles in general on self-help, and current affairs for a very broad spectrum of population, including men. More interested in quality writing than ever." Sample copy available for 35 Rand.

‡FANTASY TALES, The Paperback Magazine of Fantasy and Terror, Robinson Publishing/Carroll & Graff, 194 Station Rd., Kings Heath, Birmingham B14 7TE England. Fiction Editor: David A. Sutton. Semiannually. Circ. 30,000. Publishes 10 stories/issue. "*Fantasy Tales* is a paperback magazine that publishes fantasy, horror and some science fiction. Authors include Clive Barker, Ramsey Campbell, Charles L. Grant, Robert Bloch, etc. We are looking for well-written contemporary horror, fantasy and low-tech SF." Length: 1,000-7,000 words. Pays 2 contributor's copies. "We are not interested in run-of-the-mill plotting. If you expect a reply, ensure you enclose self-addressed envelope and three IRCs. (US stamps *don't* work in Britain). Writers should send a disposable copy of their ms, and only single ms should be sent—not batches. Back issue list available for ordering sample copies. Guidelines sent on receipt of IRC."

FORUM, Northern and Shell Building, Box 381, Mill Harbour, London E14 9TW England. Fiction Editor: Elizabeth Coldwell. Circ. 30,000. Publishes 13 stories/year. "*Forum* is the international magazine of human relations, dealing with all aspects of relationships, sexuality and sexual health. We are looking for erotic stories in which the plot and characterisation are as important as the erotic content." Length: 2,000-3,000 words. Pays contributor's copy. "Try not to ask for the ms to be returned, just a letter of acceptance/rejection as this saves on your return postage. Anything which is very 'American' in language or content might not be as interesting to readers outside America. Writers can obtain a sample copy by saying they saw our listing. We don't have any formal guidelines."

GUIDE PATROL, (formerly *Today's Guide*), 17-19 Buckingham Palace Rd., London SW1W OPT England. Editor: Deborah Fulham. Circ. 25,000. Publishes 12 short stories annually. "Magazine aimed at girls aged 10-14. The official magazine for the Girl Guides Association. Stories need to be 1,000-1,500 words long with a Guiding background." Payment is £40 per 1,000 words plus contributor copy. "We would be interested in stories with a North American Guiding background."

‡INTERZONE: Science Fiction and Fantasy, 217 Preston Drove, Brighton BN1 6FL England. Editor: David Pringle. Monthly. Circ. 10,000. Publishes 5-6 stories/issue. "We're looking for intelligent science fiction in the 2,000-7,000 word range. Send 2 IRCs with 'overseas' submissions and a *disposable* ms." Pays £30 per 1,000 words on publication and 2 free copies of magazine. "Please *read the magazine*— available through speclialist science-fiction dealers or direct by subscription." Sample copies to USA: $5. Write for guidelines.

‡IRELAND'S OWN, 1 North Main St., Wexford Ireland. Fiction Editor: Austin Channing. Weekly. Circ. 56,000. Publishes 3 stories/issue. "*Ireland's Own* is a homely family-oriented weekly magazine with a story emphasis on the traditional values of Irish society. Short stories must be written in a straightforward nonexperimental manner with an Irish orientation." Length: 2,000-3,000 words. Pays £20-25 on publication and contributor's copies. "Study and know the magazine's requirements, orientation and target market. Guidelines and copies sent out on request."

‡LOVING MAGAZINE, Room 2735, IPC, King's Reach Tower, Stamford St., London SE1 9LS England. Editor: Lorna Read. Monthly. Circ. 50,000. Publishes 17 stories/issue. Needs "romantic fiction in first or third person, from male or female point of view. No school stories, no heroes/heroines under 16. We also have a 'Something Different' section for historical, crime or even science fiction stories, provided they have a romance at the core. Stories must be typed and double-spaced, and a word count

must be given. Please advise if story is available on disk." Length: 1,000 words minimum; 5,000 words maximum. Writers receive a contributor's copy. Payment is in authors' own currency and is on a sliding scale from £25-£50/1,000 words, according to how much editing work the story needs. Make plot universal enough to interest people in other countries and cultures. If a story is too parochial, it will alienate a foreign reader. We will sometimes send out a sample copy but cannot do it as a matter of course because we are only given a limited supply of each issue for distribution from our office." Write for guidelines.

‡NEW WOMAN, 15-19 Golderbrode House, Great Titchfield St., London W1P 7FB England. Fiction Editor: Samantha Harrison. Monthly. Circ. 233,000. Publishes 1 story/issue. "Mainstream quality women's magazine usually featuring established writers, but occasionally run outstanding submissions from unknown authors." Length: 1,500-3,500 words.

NOVA SF, Perseo Libri srl, Box 1240, I-40100 Bologna Italy. Fiction Editor: Ugo Malaguti. Bimonthly. Circ. 5,000. "Science fiction and fantasy short stories and short novels." Pays $100-600, depending on length, and 2 contributor's copies on publication. "No formalities required, we read all submissions and give an answer in about 20 weeks. Buys first Italian serial rights on stories."

OVERSEAS!, (II), Kolpingstr. 1, Leimen 6906 Germany. Editor: Greg Ballinger. Published 10 times/ year. "*Overseas!* is published for the US military personnel stationed in Europe. It is the leading military magazine in Europe, directed to all members of the military." Needs humorous but factual trave-in-Europe stories. Length: 1,000-2,000 words maximum. Writers receive contributor's copies. Pay is negotiated. Sample copy and writer's guidelines available. "Send query and IRCs. No American postage."

PEOPLE'S FRIEND, 80 Kingsway East, Dundee Scotland. Fiction Editor: W. Balnave. Weekly. Circ. 566,000. Publishes 5 stories/issue. Length: 1,000-3,000 words. Pays $40-45 and contributor's copies. "British backgrounds preferred by our readership." Sample copy and guidelines available on application.

REALITY MAGAZINE, 75 Orwell Rd., Rathgar, Dublin 6 Ireland. Fiction Editor: Fr. Kevin H. Donlon. Monthly. Circ. 25,000. Publishes an average of 11 short stories annually. Length: 900-1,200 words. Pays £25-£35 (Ireland)/1,000 words and 2 contributor's copies. "Be clear, brief, to the point and practical. Write only about your own country. Sample copies supplied on request."

‡THE SCOTS MAGAZINE, 7-25 Bank Street, Dundee DD1 9HU Scotland. Editor: John Rundle. Monthly. Circ. 85,000. "World's oldest popular periodical. We use well-written fiction in a Scottish setting." Length: 1,000-4,000 words. Payment made in pounds sterling, also contributor's copies. "No ghosts of Culloden or Glencoe, no haggis and no phoney Scotts dialogue." Guidelines available on request.

‡SVET FANTASTIKY, Talpress, Smirnovova 2041, 155 00 Parha5-Stodulky Czechoslovakia. Editor: Vlastimir Talas. Circ. 20,000-40,000. Publishes 25 short stories/year (mainly translations). "*Svet Fantastiky* is a quarterly short story anthology in magazine form. Each issue contains 100,000 words." Authors receive royalties in non-transferable Czechoslovak currency deposited into a special account, but in mid-1992, we may be able to send U.S. dollars. Also pays 1 contributor's copy.

‡WOMAN'S DAY, G.P.O. Box 5245, Sydney NSW 2001 Australia. "*Woman's Day* looks for two types of short stories: first for Five Minute Fiction page at the back of the magazine, length usually between 1,000 and 1,200 words long; longer short stories, between 2,500 and 4,000 words in length, are used less frequently. Manuscripts should be typed with double spacing and sufficient margins on either side of the text for notes and editing. They should be sent to the Fiction Editor with SAE and IRC." Payment is usually about $200 (Australian) for the Five Minute Fiction, from $250 for longer stories. *Woman's Day* purchases the first Australian and New Zealand rights. After publication, these revert to the author. "We accept unsolicited manuscripts, but must point out that we receive around 100 of these in the fiction department each week, and obviously, are limited in the number we can accept."

WOMAN'S REALM, IPC Magazines, King's Reach Tower, Stamford St., London SE1 9LS England. Fiction Editor: Nick Vermuth. Weekly. Circ. 530,000. Publishes 2 stories/issue. Appeals to practical, intelligent, family-minded women, age 40 upwards. High standard of writing required. Originality

important. "Nearest US equivalent to our kind of fiction is probably *Redbook*." Length: 800-1,000 words and 1,500-2,000 words. Payment starts from approximately £150 and includes contributor's copy. "We do not accept unsolicited fiction. However, if writers are interested, they can contact us with their idea. On the whole, we don't send out sample copies. However, if someone lives so far away that they cannot receive a copy, we'll send one. Guidelines are available for established writers."
ally. "Publishes a wide range of love stories including humorous, first- or third-person, single, divorcée, second marriage, perhaps with kids, career/home conflicts, 20s-30s. Stories narrated by men also welcome. Avoid doom and gloom. Length: 1,500-6,000 words." Writers paid for published fiction. "Write for tip sheet."

WOMAN'S WEEKLY, IPC Magazines, King's Reach, Stamford St., London SE1 9LS England. Fiction Editor: Gaynor Davies. Circ. 1.9 million. Publishes 2 serials and at least one short story/week. "Short stories can be on any theme, but must have love as the central core of the plot, whether in a specific romantic context, within the family or mankind in general. Serials need not be written in installments. They are submitted as complete manuscripts and we split them up. Send first installment of serial (8,000 words) and synopsis of the rest." Length: 1,000-5,000 words for short stories; $1,000-41,000 words for serials. Short story payment starts at £220 and rises as writer becomes a more regular contributor. Serial payments start at around £400/installment. Writers also receive contributor's copies. "Read the magazine concerned and try to understand who the publication is aimed at." Writers' guidelines available. Write to "fiction department."

THE WORLD OF ENGLISH, Box 1504, Beijing China. Fiction Editor: Chen Yu-lun. Bimonthly. Circ. 300,000+. "We welcome contributions of short articles that would cater to the interest of our reading public, new and knowledgeable writings on technological finds, especially interesting stories and novels, etc. We can only pay in our currency which regrettably is inconvertible or in contributor copies." Length: 500-4,000 words.

Other commercial periodicals

Most of the following commercial magazines appeared in the 1991 edition of *Novel & Short Story Writer's Market* but are not in the 1992 edition. Those publications whose editors did not respond this year to our request for an update are listed below without further explanation. They may have done so for a variety of reasons—they may be out of business, they are no longer taking fiction or they may be overstocked with submissions. They may have responded too late for inclusion in this edition.

If we received information about why a publication would not appear, we included the explanation next to its name below. International commercial periodicals that are not included this year follow.

American Accent Short Story Magazine
Atlanta Singles Magazine (no fiction)
Atlantic Salmon Journal
Balloon Life (responded late)
Bear (responded late)
Changes (asked to be left out this year)
Dialogue
Futurific Magazine (no fiction)
Genesis Magazine
Gentleman's Companion
Harvey for Loving People
High Times (no fiction)

Horror
Hot Shots
Hustler
In Touch (ceased publication)
Mainstreet USA (no fiction)
Modern Short Stories (ceased publication)
Noah's Ark
Northcoast View (asked to be deleted)
Northwest Magazine (ceased publication)
Ocean Sports International (no fiction)
Pennywhistle Press (now Kids

Today, no freelance)
Prime Time
Prime Times Sports and Fitness
Senior Life Magazine (ceased publication)
Sun and Sonlight Christian Newspaper
Swank Magazine
Wee Wisdom Magazine (ceased publication)
Wigwag (ceased publication)
Women's American ORT Reporter
Young American

Other international commercial periodicals

Encounter
Fear
Ikarie

Israel-Al
London Review of Books
My Weekly

R&R Entertainment Digest
Superbike

Small Press

Last year was a fairly good year for small publishers. Independent and small presses—especially literary presses—continued to gain ground in both respect and prestige within the publishing community. One proof of this was the inclusion of several small presses on the main floor of the year's big publishing convention, sponsored by the American Booksellers Association. For the first time, instead of being relegated to the small press wing, some of the more established small publishers, including Coffee House, Graywolf and Milkweed stood right next to the "big boys." The ABA also honored a small press book, *When I Am an Old Woman I Shall Wear Purple*, published by Papier Mache, with a nomination for the group's ABBY award, given to books booksellers have the most pleasure selling.

Two generous grants were awarded to small presses for the first time last year. Thanks to The Lila Wallace-Reader's Digest Fund and the Andrew W. Mellon Foundation several million dollars were made available through the Council of Literary Magazines and Small Presses to support literary and nonprofit presses.

The role of the small press

What does all this mean to writers? Coffee House Press Publisher Allan Kornblum answered this question best in a recent *Publishers Weekly* article. He said, "It's almost frightening when I consider how few opportunities there are for new writers to break into print. There is a real role to be played by small presses and with the money now available, we have a great obligation to use it wisely."

It's true that with the emphasis on "big" books and the current tight economic climate, it's been increasingly difficult for new writers—especially those whose work is literary or experimental—to get published. Introducing interesting new writers to the reading public, therefore, has become the most important role played by the small press today.

Actually, small presses have been introducing some of the world's finest writers for a long time now. Yet the biggest change comes more in the public's recognition of this role. Readers interested in discovering new, talented authors are turning to the small press to find them.

Even though small presses have received a boost in new funding and recognition, they are still unable to pay six-figure advances and treat their authors to lavish parties and promotional tours. Yet small presses continue to offer opportunities to writers who would otherwise have only a slim chance at publication by larger houses.

Reasons to work with small press publishers

Although most small presses cannot offer big advances, small press publishing can still be profitable for writers. For one thing, smaller houses tend to keep books in print much longer than their commercial counterparts. Many belong to cooperative marketing and distribution networks, increasing their sales through group catalogs and advertising. This can actually mean more money for writers over time.

Another reason many writers say they prefer working with small publishers is the relationship they have with these publishers. Most cite a good, stable editor/writer relationship as the main reason they've stayed with the small press. Editors at small presses tend to stay longer because they have more stake in the business—in fact, many actually own the press. And many small press owners are also writers.

Types of small presses

We use the term "small press" in the broadest sense here. Included in our definition are publishers who are not backed by large corporations and who do not publish more than 10-20 books each year. This section includes very small operations, nonprofit presses, university publishers and small- to mid-size independent presses.

The very small presses are owned and operated by one or two people—usually friends or family members. They may have started by publishing their own books and the books of a few friends but now take on one or two additional titles each year. These presses can be easily swamped with submissions. Writers who have been published by these very small presses, however, say they are often treated as "one of the family."

Nonprofit presses must depend on grants and donations. Many were hurt in recent years by state and federal funding cutbacks, so overall they may be doing fewer titles in the coming year. If a nonprofit is funded by a private organization such as a church or club, books that reflect the backers' views or beliefs are most likely to be considered for publication.

Funding for university presses is often tied to government and private grants as well. Traditionally, universities tend to publish writers who are either affiliated in some way with the school or have a connection to the region.

Independent literary and regional presses make up a large group of publishers in this section. Some are doing quite well and have gained a clear understanding of how to survive in the market and how to compete successfully with larger houses.

Working with small presses

Although smaller publishers may operate informally, editors at these houses expect the same professional presentation as editors at larger houses. This means a good, brief cover letter and a neatly typed or computer-printed manuscript is appreciated. As with large publishers, be sure to include a self-addressed, stamped envelope in an appropriate size with all correspondence.

Since many small press publishers have succeeded by carving out a niche or specialty in the market, it's a good idea to familiarize yourself with the press' focus and line. Visit independent and college bookstores and libraries to find their books. Write away for catalogs to those presses that interest you most.

For small presses listed in this section, check the Category Index located just before the Markets Index at the back of this book. Check under the subject categories in the Small Press portion to find presses most interested in your type of work. Then look them up in this section and carefully read the listings to find the right press or presses for you.

Another way to find small publishers who handle work similar to your own is to check for similar books in the subject area of the *Small Press Record of Books in Print*, published by Dustbooks (P.O. Box 100, Paradise CA 95967). This book is available at most libraries and includes subject, author, title and publisher indexes.

While most presses in this section welcome unsolicited submissions, many publishers say they look for new writers in literary journals. Publication in small magazines and journals gives new writers experience and demonstrates they are familiar with the publishing process. Also many small presses publish anthologies and are always looking for new stories to include.

Following the listings of small North American presses, you'll find another list of small publishers from most English-speaking countries around the world. When dealing with publishers outside your country, be sure to use International Reply Coupons for return postage and write first to make sure the publisher is open to new submissions.

The following are the codes we've used to classify the small presses listed in this section:

I   **Publisher encourages beginning or unpublished writers to submit work for consideration and publishes new writers frequently.**

II **Publisher accepts work by established writers and by occasional new writers of unusual talent.**

III **Publisher does not encourage beginning, unagented writers; publishes mainly writers with extensive previous publication credits and a very few new writers.**

IV **Special-interest or regional publisher open only to writers on certain subjects or from certain geographic areas.**

ACADIA PUBLISHING CO., (II,IV), Subsidiary of World Three, Inc., Box 170, Bar Harbor ME 04609. (207)288-9025. President: Frank J. Matter. Fiction Editor: Christina Carter. Estab. 1980. "Small independent publisher." Publishes hardcover and paperback originals and reprints. Books: offset printing; case, paperback or spiral binding; line art, photographs; average print order: 2,500; first novel print order: 2,000. Published new writers within the last year. Plans 2 first novels this year. Averages 6 total titles, 4 fiction titles each year. Sometimes comments on rejected mss; $50 charge for critiques.
Needs: Historical, juvenile (5-9 yrs.) including: animal, historical and ethnic; young adult/teen (10-18 years). No erotica, gay, romance, science fiction. Published *My Dear Sarah Anne*, by T. Smedstad and *Aguahega*, by K. Snow.
How to Contact: Query first or submit complete ms with cover letter. SASE. Cover letter should include Social Security number. Reports on queries in 3 weeks; on mss in 3 months. Simultaneous and photocopied submissions OK. Accepts computer printout submissions.
Terms: Pays standard royalties. Advance is negotiable. Sends galleys to author. Publishes ms within 12-18 months of acceptance. "We will produce a work under contract. Rate depends on condition of the manuscript, final quality required, etc. We are very selective (2-3 titles a year)." Subsidy titles "do not bear our imprint." Book catalog: for #10 SAE and 1 first class stamp.
Advice: "We like quality regardless of the author's past publishing history. Please, do not send a manuscript in its 'working stage.' We need to see what you *can do* – not what you only think you can do. Please be professional, neat and reasonable. Research, research, research. This is a very competitive business and each work we publish must be the best we can acquire. If the work is right we will work with the author."

ADVOCACY PRESS, (IV), Box 236, Santa Barbara CA 93102. Publisher: Mindy Bingham. Estab. 1983. Small publisher with 3-5 titles/year. Hardcover and paperback originals. Books: perfect or Smythe-sewn binding; illustrations; average print order: 10,000 copies; first novel print order: 10,000. Plans 2 first novels this year; 2 children's fiction (32-48 pg.) titles per year.
Needs: Juvenile (5-9 years); preschool/picture book. New series: 32 page picturebook of stories of little known influential women in history. Wants only feminist/nontraditional messages to boys or girls – picture books; self-esteem issues. Published *Father Gander Nursery Rhymes*, by Dr. Doug Larch (picture book); *Berta Benz and the Motorwagon*, by Mindy Bingham (picture book); *Mimi*, by Agnes Rosenstiehl (series).
How to Contact: Submit complete manuscript with SASE for return. Reports in 10 weeks on queries. Simultaneous submissions OK. No photocopies. Accepts computer printouts. Request editorial policy.
Terms: Pays in royalties of 5-10%. Sends pre-publication galleys to the author. Book catalog free on request with SASE.
Advice: "We are looking for fictional stories for children 4-8 years old that give messages of self sufficiency for little girls; little boys can nurture and little girls can be anything they want to be, etc. Looking for talented writers/artists. Please review some of our publications *before* you submit to us."

*AEGINA PRESS, INC., (I,II), 59 Oak Lane, Spring Valley, Huntington WV 25704. (304)429-7204. Imprint is University Editions, Inc. Managing Editor: Ira Herman. Estab. 1984. Independent small press. Publishes paperback and hardcover originals and reprints. Books: 50 lb. white text/10 point high gloss covers; photo-offset printing; perfect binding, illustrations; average print order: 500-1,000. Published new writers within the last year. Plans 5-10 first novels this year. Averages 30 total titles, 15 fiction titles each year. Sometimes comments on rejected ms.
Needs: Adventure, contemporary, experimental, faction, fantasy, historical, horror, literary, main-stream, regional, science fiction, short story collections, suspense/mystery. No racist, sexist, or obscene materials. Recently published *Circle of Blood*, by Margery La Porte (novel); *Dream Demon*, by Clark R. Schmidt (novel); and *A Journey into Mystery*, by Richard Lazarus (short stories).
How to Contact: Accepts unsolicited mss. Send outline/synopsis and 3 sample chapters or complete ms with cover letter. SASE. Agented fiction 5%. Reports in 3 weeks on queries; 1-2 months on mss. Simultaneous and photocopied submissions OK. Accepts computer printout submissions.
Terms: Pays 15% royalties. *Subsidy publishes most new authors.* "If the manuscript meets our quality standards but is financially high risk, self-publishing through the University Editions imprint is offered. All sales proceeds go to the author until the subsidy is repaid. The author receives a 40% royalty thereafter. Remaining unsold copies belong to the author." Sends galleys to author. Publishes ms 6-9 months after acceptance. Writer's guidelines for #10 SASE. Book catalog for 9 × 12 SAE, 4 first class stamps and $2.

ALASKA NATIVE LANGUAGE CENTER, (IV), University of Alaska, Box 900111, Fairbanks AK 99775-0120. (907)474-6577. Editor: Tom Alton. Estab. 1972. Small education publisher limited to books in and about Alaska native languages. Generally nonfiction. Publishes hardcover and paperback origi-nals. Books: 60 lb. book paper; offset printing; perfect binding; photos, line art illustrations; average print order: 500-1,000 copies. Averages 6-8 total titles each year.
Needs: Ethnic. Publishes original fiction only in native language and English by Alaska native writers. Recently published *Aleut Tales*, edited by Knut Bergsland and Moses Dirks; *K'Etetaalkanee*, by Cather-ine Attla; *Elngua*, by Anna Jacobson.
How to Contact: Does not accept unsolicited mss. Photocopied submissions OK. Accepts computer printout submissions. Electronic submissions via ASCII for modem transmissions or Macintosh com-patible files on 3½" disk.
Terms: Does not pay. Sends galleys to author.

ALYSON PUBLICATIONS, INC., (II), 40 Plympton St., Boston MA 02118. (617)542-5679. Fiction Edi-tor: Sasha Alyson. Estab. 1977. Medium-sized publisher specializing in lesbian- and gay-related mate-rial. Publishes paperback originals and reprints. Books: paper and printing varies; trade paper, perfect-bound; average print order: 8,000; first novel print order: 6,000. Published new writers within the last year; plans 4 first novels this year. Averages 15 total titles, 8 fiction titles each year.
Needs: "We are interested in all categories; *all* materials must be geared toward lesbian and/or gay readers." Recently published *Oil and Gasoline*, by Billi Gordon and Taylor-Anne Wentworth; *The Crystal Cage*, by Sandy Bayer; *Masters' Counterpoints*, by Larry Townsend.
How to Contact: Query first with SASE. Reports in 3 weeks on queries; 2 months on mss. Photocop-ied submissions OK but not preferable.
Terms: "We prefer to discuss terms with the author." Sends galleys to author. Book catalog for SAE and 52¢ postage.

AMERICAN ATHEIST PRESS, (IV), Gustav Broukal Press, Box 140195, Austin TX 78714-0195. Editor: Robin Murray-O'Hair, Estab. 1960. Paperback originals and reprints. Books: bond and other paper; offset printing; perfect binding; illustrations "if pertinent." Averages 6 total titles/year. Occasionally critiques or comments on rejected mss.

The asterisk indicates a publisher who sometimes offers subsidy arrangements. Authors are asked to subsidize part of the cost of book production. See the introduction to Commercial Publishers for more information.

Close-up

Robert Pope
Author

© Larry Naymik

"Both archetypal and stereotypical stories that seem to be infinitely reproducible (and infinitely reproduced!) are important to know because then you have some knowledge of reader expectation," says Robert Pope, author of *Private Acts*, a collection of stories published by Another Chicago Press. "But a story doesn't take off until you *surprise* the reader and the only way to do that is to surprise yourself. You have to be a bit of an explorer at this point.

"Early writers tend to create stories in the form of what they think a story should be," says Pope. "True surprise comes when a character does something you never expected and yet it is absolutely within character. It's the old adage of discovering a shape within the stone rather than imposing a shap on the stone.

"For me, the center of writing is character. Ideas, language and telling my own story really pushed me, but over the years I've found that character includes all these things. Forget plot. Plot will lead you astray. Show us characters and they will find the plot and a series of events that have causation."

This approach to writing has paid off for Pope. His stories have appeared in *Denver Quarterly*, *The Missouri Review*, *The Georgia Review* and other fine literary magazines. His novel, *Jack's Universe*, has been published by Another Chicago Press.

A professor of creative writing at the University of Akron, Pope graduated from the University of Iowa Writer's Workshop and often speaks at writers' conferences, including the Akron Manuscript Club's Annual May Conference, cosponsored by the university.

"I'm often asked my opinion on books on writing. I think people who want to write turn to these books for inspiration. All the little things in these books become magical details, part of the incantation, and people cling to them. 'Only use #2 pencils or yellow legal pads. Write two hours in the morning and one in the evening.' Are these things necessary? No, they aren't. But any advice that *helps* somebody is good advice."

Pope writes "whenever I can, as much as I possibly can, until I finish something. Then I'm blown out. Exhausted." After completing a project, he recharges anywhere from two weeks to a month or more, depending on the project's length. During this time he thinks of new ideas and takes notes, none of which, he says, he actually uses. Why? "Because nothing happens until I sit down to write. The natural world, the natural play of the mind, works back and forth and the story—the *characters*—dictate the shape.

"The longer a person writes, the more individual their work is because they pass through all the phases of 'What I think writing is.' Each writer has a rhythm," Pope adds. "Over the years you discover it, any way you can."

—Michelle Cowx

Needs: Contemporary, humor/satire, literary, science fiction. No "religious/spiritual/occult."
How to Contact: Query with sample chapters and outline. SASE. Reports in 2 months on queries; 3 months on mss. Simultaneous and photocopied submissions OK. Accepts computer printout submissions. Accepts electronic submissions via IBM-PC/Word-Perfect on disk.
Terms: Pays 8-11% royalties. Writers guidelines for #9 SAE and 1 first class stamp. Book catalog free on request.
Advice: "We only publish fiction which relates to Atheism; we receive many queries for general interest fiction, which we do not publish."

ANDROGYNE, 930 Shields St., San Francisco CA 94132. (415)586-2697. Contact: Ken Weichel. Estab. 1971. "Independent press working within the cultural coincidence of San Francisco." Publishes books and a periodical, *Androgyne*. Publishes paperback originals. Averages 3 total titles, 1 fiction title each year. Average first novel print order 500 copies.
Needs: Contemporary, experimental, and literary.
How to Contact: Does not accept unsolicited mss. Query. SASE. Reports in 1 month on queries; 2 months on mss. Simultaneous and photocopied submissions OK. Accepts computer printout submissions.
Terms: Pays in contributor's copies (10%). See magazine for writer's guidelines. Free book catalog.

ANNICK PRESS LTD., (IV), 15 Patricia Ave., Willowdale, Ontario M2M 1H9 Canada. (416)221-4802. Publisher of children's books. Publishes hardcover and paperback originals. Books: offset paper; full-color offset printing; perfect and library binding; full-color illustrations; average print order: 9,000; first novel print order: 7,000. Plans 18 first picture books this year. Averages approximately 20 titles each year, all fiction. Average first picture book print order 2,000 cloth, 9,000 paper copies. Occasionally critiques rejected ms.
Needs: Children's books only.
How to Contact: "Annick Press publishes only work by Canadian citizens or residents." Does not accept unsolicited mss. Query with SASE. Free book catalog.
Terms: Sends galleys to author.
Advice: "Publishing more fiction this year, because our company is growing. But our publishing program is currently full."

ANOTHER CHICAGO PRESS, (II), Box 11223, Chicago IL 60611. (708)848-6333. Senior Editor: Lee Webster. Estab 1976. Small literary press, non-profit. Books: offset printing; perfect-bound, occasional illustrations; average print order 2,000. Averages 4 total titles, 3 fiction titles each year. Occasionally critiques or comments on rejected ms.
Needs: Literary. No inspirational religious fiction. Recently published *Jack's Universe*, by Robert Pope (novel); *What I Think I Know: New & Selected Poems*, by Robert Dana; *Here Lies the Water*, by Meredith Steinbach (novel); published fiction by previously unpublished writers within the last year.
How to Contact: Does not accept or return unsolicited mss. Query first for books, then submit outline/synopsis and sample chapters. SASE. Agented fiction 10%. Reports in 3-6 weeks on queries; 8-12 weeks on mss. Simultaneous and photocopied submissions OK. Accepts computer printout submissions.
Terms: Advance negotiable; pays royalties of 10%. Sends galleys to author.
Advice: "We publish novels and collections of short stories and poetry as our funds and time permit— and then probably only by solicitation. We publish literary fiction and poetry of substance and quality. We publish books that will entertain, enlighten or disturb. Our books, our authors will be read well into the 21st Century."

APPLEZABA PRESS, Box 4134, Long Beach CA 90804. Editorial Director: Shelley Hellen. Estab. 1977. "We are a family-operated publishing house, working on a part-time basis. We plan to expand over the years." Publishes paperback originals. Averages 1 fiction title each year.
Needs: Contemporary, literary, experimental, feminist, gay, lesbian, fantasy, humor/satire, translations, and short story collections. No gothic, romance, confession, inspirational, satirical, black humor or slapstick. Recently published *Horse Medicine and Other Stories*, by Raephael Zepecha; *Nude*, by Judson Jerome.
How to Contact: Accepts unsolicited mss. Submit complete ms with SASE. No simultaneous submissions; photocopied submissions OK. Accepts computer printout submissions. Reports in 2 months. Publishes ms 2-3 years after acceptance.

Terms: Pays in author's copies and 8-15% royalties; no advance. Free book catalog.

Advice: "Cover letter with previous publications, etc. is OK. Each book, first or twentieth, has to stand on its own. If a first-time novelist has had shorter works published in magazines, it makes it somewhat easier for us to market the book. We publish only book-length material."

ARIADNE PRESS, (I), 4817 Tallahassee Ave., Rockville MD 20853. (301)949-2514. President: Carol Hoover. Estab. 1976. Shoestring operation—corporation with 4 directors who also act as editors. Publishes hardcover and paperback originals. Books: 50 lb. alkaline paper; offset printing; Smyth-sewn binding. Average print order 1,000; average first novel print order 1,000. Plans 1 first novel this year. Averages 1 total title each year; only fiction. Sometimes critiques rejected mss. "We comment on selected mss of superior writing quality, even when rejected."

Needs: Adventure, contemporary, feminist, historical, humor/satire, literary, mainstream, suspense, psychological, family relations and marital, war. Looking for "literary-mainstream" fiction. No short stories, no science fiction, horror or mystery. Published *How to Write an Uncommonly Good Novel*, (nonfiction).

How to Contact: *Query first.* SASE. Agented fiction 5%. Reports in 1 month on queries; 2 months on mss. Simultaneous and photocopied submissions OK. Accepts computer printout submissions.

Terms: Pays royalties of 10%. No advance. Sends pre-publication galleys to author. Writer's guidelines not available. List of books in stock for #10 SASE.

Advice: "We exist primarily for non-established writers. Try large, commercial presses first."

‡ARROWOOD BOOKS, (II), Box 2100, Corvallis OR 97330. (503)753-9539. Editor: Lex Runciman. Estab. 1985. Small, part-time, 2-person operation. Publishes hardcover and paperback originals. Books: acid free paper. Average print order 1,000; first novel print order varies. Averages 2 titles/year.

Needs: Contemporary, literary, mainstream. Recently published *Sorrowful Mysteries and Other Stories*, by Normandi Ellis.

How to Contact: Accepts unsolicited mss. Query first. Reports on queries in 3 weeks; 3 months on mss. Photocopied submissions OK. Accepts computer printout submissions.

Terms: Advance is negotiable. Sends pre-publication galleys to author.

ARTE PUBLICO PRESS, (II, IV), University of Houston, Houston TX 77004. (713)749-4768. Publisher: Dr. Nicolas Kanellos. Estab. 1979. "Small press devoted to the publication of contemporary U.S. Hispanic literature." Publishes paperback originals and occasionally reprints. Average print order 2,000-5,000; first novel print order 2,500-5,000. Sometimes critiques rejected mss.

Needs: Contemporary, ethnic, feminist, literary, short story collections. Published *A Shroud in the Family*, by Lionel Garcia (satire); *This Migrant Earth*, by Rolando Hinojosa; and *Taking Control*, by Mary Helen Ponce (short stories).

How to Contact: Accepts unsolicited mss. Submit outline/synopsis and sample chapters or complete ms with cover letter. Agented fiction 1%. Accepts computer printout submissions.

Terms: Pays $1,000 average advance; 20 author's copies. Sends pre-publication galleys to author. Book catalog free on request.

Advice: "All fiction, all paperback."

‡THE AUTHORS CONNECTION PRESS, (I, II), P.O. Box 40, 1 NW Alto Ave., Waldo FL 32694. (904)468-2939. Fiction Editor: Ron Willett. Estab. 1986. Publishes hardcover and paperback originals. Books: 50 lb. bond paper; offset printing; print order varies. Published new writers within the last year. Plans 3 first novels this year. Averages 3-10 total titles/year. Sometimes critiques rejected mss.

Needs: Adventure, contemporary, juvenile (5-9 years), preschool/picture book, short story collections, suspense/mystery, western, young adult/teen (10-18 years). Looking for children's and young adult novels, adventures for all ages. No "gay, religious or erotic work."

How to Contact: Sometimes accepts unsolicited ms. Query first. SASE. Agented fiction 1%. Reports in 1-3 weeks on queries; 1-2 months on mss. Photocopied submissions OK. Accepts computer printout submissions. Accepts electronic submissions via disk (MS DOS only).

Terms: Pays 15% royalties. "We may consider other publishing/payment arrangements at times but we use standard publishing contract/royalty 98% of the time." Sends galleys to author. Publishes ms 6-12 months after acceptance. Writer's guidelines for #10 SAE and 2 first class stamps. Book catalog for #10 SAE and 2 first class stamps.

‡AUTHORS UNLIMITED, (II), Imprints include Authors Unlimited and Military Literary Guild, 3324 Barham Blvd., Los Angeles CA 90068. (213)874-0902. Senior Editor: Renais J. Hill. Estab. 1983. Midsize independent publisher with plans to expand. Publishes hardcover and paperback originals. Books: 60 lb. paper; trade paper and hard cover binding; illustrations; average print order: 2,000. Published new writers within the last year. Plans 10 first novels this year. Averages 30 total titles, 15 fiction titles each year.
Needs: Adventure, contemporary, ethnic, faction, fantasy, feminist, gay, historical, horror, humor/satire, lesbian, literary, mainstream, military/war, psychic/supernatural/occult, regional, religious/inspirational, romance, science fiction, short story collections, spiritual, suspense/mystery, western. No pornography. Recently published *God*, by Bill Idelson (satire); *The Butcher*, by Lynn Gravbelle (mystery); *Against Her Will*, by Denise Henderson (adventure).
How to Contact: Accepts unsolicited mss. Submit complete ms with cover letter. SASE (IRC). Reports in 1 month. Simultaneous and photocopied submissions OK. Accepts computer printout submissions.
Terms: *Subsidy publishes 10% of books* (cooperative terms, approx. 60/40%). No advance. Provides 50 author's copies. Sends galleys to author. Publishes ms 9 months after acceptance. Writer's guidelines for 9 × 12 SAE and $1.25 postage. Book catalog for 9 × 12 SAE and $1.25 postage.

‡BAMBOO RIDGE PRESS, (IV), P.O. Box 61781, Honolulu HI 96839-1781. (808)599-4823. Editors: Darrell Lum and Eric Chock. Estab. 1978. "Bamboo Ridge Press publishes *Bamboo Ridge: The Hawaii Writers' Quarterly*, a journal of fiction and poetry with special issues devoted to the work of one writer—fiction or poetry." Publishes paperback originals and reprints. Books: 60 lb. natural; perfect-bound; illustrations; average print order: 2,000. Published new writers within the last year. Plans 10 first novels this year. Averages 2-4 total titles.
Needs: Ethnic, literary and short story collections. "Interested in writing that reflects Hawaii's multicultural ethnic mix. No psuedo-Hawaiiana myths or Hawaii-Five-O type of mentality—stereotypical portrayals of Hawaii and its people." Recently published *Pass On, No Pass Back*, by Darrll Lum (short story collection).
How to Contact: Accepts unsolicited mss. Query first. SASE. Reports in 4-6 weeks on queries; 3-6 months on mss. Simultaneous and photocopied submissions OK.
Terms: Payment depends on grant/award money. Sends galleys to author. Publishes ms 6 months-1 year after acceptance. Writer's guidelines for #10 SAE and 1 first class stamp. Book catalog for #10 SASE or IRC and 52¢ postage.

BARLOW PRESS, (I,II), Box 5403, Helena MT 59604. (406)449-7310. Fiction Editor: Russell B. Hill. Estab. 1987. One-person publishing/printing company which produces titles both by offset and letterpress (hand-set) printing. Publishes hardcover and paperback originals and reprints. Books: acid-free letterpress stock (i.e. Mohawk, Superfine); usually letterpress printing, occasionally offset, hand-sewn binding with end papers, heavier cover stock, sometimes leather; woodcuts, line-art plates or one-color artwork. Average print order: 500-1,000 letterpress; 2,000-3,000 offset. Publishes 2 total titles/year; plans 0-1 first fiction title this year. Sometimes critiques rejected mss.
Needs: Adventure, contemporary, historical, humor/satire, literary, mainstream, regional, short story collections.
How to Contact: Query first. SASE. Reports in 2 months.
Terms: Payment by individual arrangement, depending on the book. Publishes ms 6 months-2 years after acceptance. Rarely subsidy, but "publication by Barlow Press usually involves a joint effort—Barlow Press contributes the time and expenses, author contributes mss, with particular terms of reimbursement subject to negotiation."
Advice: "Frankly, a publisher like Barlow Press can't compete with larger publishers for manuscripts they want, and we encourage authors to submit material to potentially lucrative publishers first. But we are convinced too many manuscripts deserve one more reading, one more potential outlet. We don't publish most manuscripts we read, but we have never regretted reading a manuscript. And because Barlow Press handles every publication by individual arrangement with the author, we aren't shy about proposing to edit manuscripts to fit our needs."

 The double dagger before a listing indicates that the listing is new in this edition. New markets are often the most receptive to freelance contributions.

‡BARN OWL BOOKS, (I, IV), Box 226, Vallecitos NM 87581. (505)582-4226. Imprints include Amazon Press. Publisher: Gina Covina. Estab. 1983. Two-person small publisher; "author participation in publishing process encouraged." Publishes paperback originals. Books: quality paperback standard paper; offset litho printing; perfect binding; illustrations "if appropriate"; average print order: 2,000-5,000; first novel print order: 2,000. Averages 1 total title/year. Occasionally critiques or comments on rejected ms.
Needs: Contemporary, ethnic, feminist, gay, lesbian, literary, regional.
How to Contact: Accepts unsolicited mss. Query first. SASE. Reports in 1 month on queries; 2 months on mss. Photocopied submissions OK. Accepts computer printout submissions.
Terms: Pays royalties of 7-12%. Sends galleys to authors.

FREDERIC C. BEIL, PUBLISHER, INC., (II), 414 Tattnall St., Savannah GA 31401. Imprints include The Sandstone Press. President: Frederic C. Beil III. Estab. 1983. General trade publisher. Publishes hardcover originals and reprints. Books: acid-free paper; letterpress and offset printing; Smythe-sewn, hardcover binding; illustrations; average print order: 3,000; first novel print order: 3,000. Plans 2 first novels this year. Averages 10 total titles, 2 fiction titles each year.
Needs: Historical, literary, regional, short story collections, translations. Published *A Woman of Means*, by Peter Taylor.
How to Contact: Does not accept unsolicited mss. Query first. Reports in 1 week on queries. Accepts computer printout submissions.
Terms: Payment "all negotiable." Sends galleys to author. Book catalog free on request.

BETHEL PUBLISHING, (IV), 1819 S.Main, Elkhart IN 46516.(219)293-8585. Contact: Senior Editor. Estab. 1975. Mid-size Christian book publisher. Publishes paperback originals and reprints. Averages 3-5 total titles per year. Occasionally critiques or comments on rejected manuscripts.
Needs: Religious/inspirational, young adult/teen. No "workbooks, cookbooks, coloring books, theological studies, pre-school or elementary-age stories."
How to Contact: Accepts unsolicited manuscripts. Query first. Reports in 2 weeks on queries; 3 months on mss. Accepts simultaneous submissions. Publishes manuscripts 8-16 months after acceptance.
Terms: Pays royalties of 10% and 12 author's copies. Writer's guidelines and book catalog free on request.

BILINGUAL PRESS/EDITORIAL BILINGÜE, (II, IV), Hispanic Research Center, Arizona State University, Tempe AZ 85287-2702. (602)965-3867. Editor: Gary Keller. Estab. 1973. "University affiliated." Publishes hardcover and paperback originals, and reprints. Books: 60 lb. acid free paper; single sheet or web press printing; case-bound and perfect-bound; illustrations sometimes; average print order: 4,000 copies (1,000 case-bound, 3,000 soft cover). Published new writers within the last year. Plans 2 first novels this year. Averages 12 total titles, 6 fiction each year. Sometimes comments on rejected ms.
Needs: Ethnic, literary, short story collections and translations. "We are always on the lookout for Chicano, Puerto Rican, Cuban-American or other U.S. Hispanic themes with strong and serious literary qualities and distinctive and intellectually important themes. We have been receiving a lot of fiction set in Latin America (usually Mexico or Central America) where the main character is either an ingenue to the culture or spy, adventurer, or mercenary. We don't publish this sort of 'Look, I'm in an exotic land' type of thing. Also, novels about the Aztecs or other pre-Columbians are very iffy." Recently published *Distant Journeys*, by Rafael Castillo (short stories); *Peregrinos de Aztlán*, by Miguel Mèndez (novel); *Lenor Park*, by Nash Candelaria (novel).
How to Contact: Query first. SASE. Include Social Security number with submission. Reports in 3 weeks on queries, 2 months on mss. Simultaneous and photocopied submissions OK. Accepts computer printout submissions.
Terms: Pays royalties of 10%. Average advance $300. Provides 10 author's copies. Sends galleys to author. Publishes ms 1 year after acceptance. Writer's guidelines not available. Book catalog free.
Advice: "Writers should take the utmost care in assuring that their manuscripts are clean, grammatically impeccable, and have perfect spelling. This is true not only of the English but the Spanish as well. All accent marks need to be in place as well as diacritical marks. When these are missing it's an immediate first indication that the author does not really know Hispanic culture and is not equipped to write about it. We are interested in publishing creative literature that treats the U.S. Hispanic experience in a distinctive, creative, revealing way. The kinds of books that we publish we keep in

print for a very long time (certainly into the next century) irrespective of sales. We are busy establishing and preserving a U.S. Hispanic canon of creative literature."

BLACK HERON PRESS, (I, II), P.O. Box 95676, Seattle WA 98145. Publisher: Jerry Gold. Estab. 1984. One-person operation; no immediate plans to expand. Publishes paperback and hardback originals. Average print order: 1,000; first novel print order: 500-1,500. Averages 2 fiction titles each year.
Needs: Adventure, contemporary, experimental, humor/satire, literary, science fiction. Vietnam war novel—literary. "We don't want to see fiction written for the mass market. If it sells to the mass market, fine, but we don't see ourselves as a commercial press." Recently published *The Confession of Jack Straw*, by Simone Zelitch; *Newt*, by Ron Dakrow; *The Inquisitor*, by Jerome Gold.
How to Contact: Query only. Will not accept unsolicited manuscripts until 1993. Reports in 2 months on queries; 3 months on mss. Simultaneous and photocopied submissions OK.
Terms: Pays standard royalty rates. No advance.
Advice: "I prefer a query, but I'll look at an unsolicited ms anyway. A query letter should tell me: 1) number of words, 2) number of pages, 3) if ms is available on floppy disk, 4) if parts of novel been published? 5) where? If you're going to submit to *Black Heron*, make the work as good as you can. I'm a good editor but I don't have the time to solve major problems with a manuscript."

BLACK MOSS PRESS, (II), Box 143, Station A, Windsor Ontario N9A 6L7 Canada. (519)252-2551. Editorial Contact Person: Kristina Russelo. Fiction Editor: Marty Gervais. Estab. 1969. "Small independent publisher assisted by government grants." Publishes paperback originals. Books: Zephyr paper; offset printing; perfect binding; 4-color cover, b&w interior illustrations; average print order: 500. Averages 10-14 total titles, 7 fiction titles each year. Sometimes comments on rejected mss.
Needs: Humor/satire, juvenile (5-9 years, including easy-to-read, contemporary), literary, preschool/ picture book," short story collections. "Usually open to children's material. Nothing religious, moralistic, romance." Recently published *The Failure of Love*, by Paul Vasey; *Ethel on Fire*, by Heleh Humphreys; *The Gospel According to Mary Magdalene*, by Clive Doucet.
How to Contact: Accepts unsolicited mss. Submit outline/synopsis and 2 sample chapters. SASE. Reports in 1-3 months. Photocopied submissions OK. Accepts computer printout submissions. *Canadian authors only*.
Terms: Pays for children's in royalties; literary in author's copies. Sends galleys to author. Publishes ms 1 year after acceptance. Book catalog for SASE.
Advice: "Generally, originality, well developed plots, strong, multi-dimensional characters and some unusual element catch my interest. It's rare that we publish new authors' works, but when we do, that's what we want. (We do publish short story collections of authors who have had some stories in lit mags.) Because we are assisted by government grants which place certain restrictions on us, we are unable to publish any material by anyone other than a Canadian citizen or immigrant landed in Canada. We've just begun a new series, The Young Reader's Library Series, for young adults but not currently accepting unsolicited mss for this series."

BLACK TIE PRESS, (I, II), Box 440004, 12655 Whittington Dr., Houston TX 77244. (713)789-5119. Publisher/Editor: Peter Gravis. Estab. 1986. "We are a tiny press interested in contemporary poetry and short fiction." Publishes hardcover and paperback originals. Books: Mohawk vellum, Glatfelter paper; combination offset and letter press printing; Smythe sewn; illustrations; average print order: varies.
Needs: Contemporary and experimental. "Our current aim is to publish an anthology of short fiction (4-6,000 words). No science fiction, romance, spiritual, religious, juvenile, historical."
How to Contact: Query or submit complete ms (with proper postage) with cover letter. SASE necessary for returns. Reporting time varies. Photocopied submission OK. Accepts computer printout submissions.
Terms: Usually pays in copies. "Payment will be determined on individual basis." Publishes ms one year after acceptance. Writer's guidelines free for SASE or IRC.

BLIND BEGGAR PRESS, Box 437, Bronx NY 10467. Imprint: LampLight Editions. Fiction Editors: Gary Johnston, C.D. Grant. Estab. 1975. Small press with plans to expand. Publishes paperback originals. Plans to publish first novels "dependent upon budget." Averages 2-3 total titles each year; "no fiction titles thus far." Average print order 2,000 copies. Occasionally critiques rejected ms.

Needs: Ethnic (Third World), experimental, juvenile (animal, easy-to-read, fantasy, historical), preschool/picture book, short story collections, translations and young adult/teen (historical).
How to Contact: Query first with SASE. Reports in 1 month on queries; 2 months on mss. Simultaneous and photocopied submissions OK. Publishes ms 12-18 months after acceptance.
Terms: Pays in author's copies (10-15% of run). "If author wishes to pay all or part of production costs, we work out individual arrangements directly." Book catalog free on request.
Advice: Recent trends include ethnic historical (biographies, political history, etc.). In first novels interested in high quality, relevancy to Third World readers. "Within two years we plan to publish children's books, short stories and *maybe* a small novel."

BOOKS FOR ALL TIMES, INC., Box 2, Alexandria VA 22313. Publisher/Editor: Joe David. Estab. 1981. One-man operation. Publishes hardcover and paperback originals. Books: 60 lb. paper; offset printing; perfect binding; average print order: 1,000. "No plans for new writers at present." Has published 1 fiction title to date. Occasionally critiques rejected mss.
Needs: Contemporary, literary and short story collections. "No novels at the moment; hopeful, though, of someday soon publishing a collection of quality short stories. No popular fiction or material easily published by the major or minor houses specializing in mindless entertainment. Only interested in stories of the Victor Hugo or Sinclair Lewis quality." Published *The Fire Within*, by Joe David (literary); *Glad You Asked!*, by Joe David (non-fiction).
How to Contact: Query first with SASE. Simultaneous and photocopied submission OK. Reports in 1 month on queries.
Terms: Pays negotiable advance. "Publishing/payment arrangement will depend on plans for the book." Book catalog free on request.
Advice: Interested in "controversial, honest books which satisfy the reader's curiosity to know. Read Victor Hugo, Fyodor Dostoyevsky and Sinclair Lewis, for example."

BOREALIS PRESS, (IV), 9 Ashburn Dr., Ottawa, Ontario K2E 6N4 Canada. Imprint includes *Journal of Canadian Poetry*. Editor: Frank Tierney. Fiction Editor: Glenn Clever. Estab. 1970. Publishes hardcover and paperback originals and reprints. Books: standard book-quality paper; offset printing; perfect and cloth binding; average print order: 1,000. Buys juvenile mss with b&w illustrations. Average number of titles: 4.
Needs: Contemporary, literary, adventure, historical, juvenile and young adult. "Must have a Canadian content or author; query first." Accepts short stories. Recently published *Annie*, by Carl Hortie (novel); *The Exotic Canadians*, by Jan Drabek (stories); *Black Forest Secret*, by Janice Cowan (juvenile).
How to Contact: Submit query with SASE (Canadian postage) or IRCs. No simultaneous submissions. Reports in 2 weeks on queries, 3-4 months on mss. Publishes ms 1-2 years after acceptance.
Terms: Pays 10% royalties and 3 free author's copies; no advance. Sends galleys to author. Free book catalog with SASE or IRC.
Advice: " Have your work professionally edited. We generally publish only material with a Canadian content or by a Canadian writer."

***BOTTOM DOG PRESS, (IV),** Firelands College, Huron OH 44839. (419)433-5560. Editor/Publisher: Dr. Larry Smith. Estab. 1984. Four-person part-time operation assisted by grants from Ohio Arts Council. Publishes paperback originals. Books: fine paper; perfect binding; cover art illustrations; average print order: 1,500 fiction. Averages 3 total titles, 1-2 fiction titles each year. Always critiques or comments on rejected mss.
Needs: Literary, mainstream. Midwest life. Published *Best Ohio Fiction* collection (160 pages) with work by Jack Matthews, Robert Flanagan, Philip F. O'Connor, Robert Fox; *Loving Power: Stories by Robert Flanagan*.
How to Contact: Accepts unsolicited mss. Query first. Submit complete ms with cover letter. SASE. Reports on queries in 2 weeks; 2 months on mss. Accepts computer printout submissions.
Terms: Pays royalties of 10-15% minimum and 20 author's copies. Sends galleys to author. Has done 2 books co-operatively—50/50. Book catalog free on request.
Advice: "We do an 'Ohio Writers Series' specializing in chapbook collection of stories or novellas—emphasis on sense of place and strong human characters. All submissions must fall within the 40,000 word limit. We also do a 'Contemporary Midwest Fiction Series' of stories or novel (160 pgs.)."

‡BRITISH AMERICAN PUBLISHING, LTD., (III), Subsidiary of British American (distributed by Simon & Schuster), 19 British American Blvd., Latham NY 12110. (518)786-6000. Imprint includes Paris Review Editions. Managing Editor: Kathleen A. Murphy. Estab. 1988. Midsize independent publisher

with plans to expand. Publishes hardcover originals and reprints and paperback originals. Published new writers within the last year. Plans 1 first novel this year. Averages 10 total titles, 5 fiction, this year. Sometimes comments on rejected ms.
Needs: "General—all genres." Recently published *Portable People*, by Paul West (biographical sketches); *Miracle Cure*, by Harlan Coken (suspense); *Boiling Rock*, by Remar Sutton (suspense mystery); *Frog*, by Stephen Dixon (1991 National Book Award finalist).
How to Contact: Accepts unsolicited mss. Submit complete ms with cover letter. SASE (IRC). Agented fiction 90%. Reports in 4-6 weeks. Simultaneous and photocopied submissions OK.
Terms: Pays royalties, negotiable advance. Sends pre-publication galleys to author. Publishes ms 1 year after a acceptance. Book catalog free.

■BRYANS & BRYANS, (Book Packager and Editorial Consultant), (I), Box 121, Fairfield CT 06430. (203)454-2051. President: John B. Bryans. Fiction Editor: James A. Bryans. Arranges publication of paperback originals (packages). Books: paperback/mass market. *Critiques mss: $200 charge* "for 2-page evaluation only when this has been agreed upon in advance. Often I will offer comments and criticism at no charge where, based on a query, we have encouraged submission. Line-editing and ongoing consulting services to author and publishers."
Needs: Adventure, contemporary, historical, horror, humor/satire, literary, mainstream, romance (contemporary, historical). Recently produced *Baton Rouge* (historical with romance elements); *Portland* and *Omaha*, by Lee Davis Willoughby (packaged by us for Knightsbridge Publishing, Los Angeles).
How to Contact: Does not accept unsolicited mss. Query first. SASE. Agented fiction 50-90%. Reports in 2 weeks on queries; 1 month on mss. Electronic submissions OK via Microsoft Word on Macintosh disk.
Terms: Pays in royalties of 6-10%. Negotiable advance.
Advice: "Send us a letter, maximum 2 pages, describing the project and giving pertinent background info on yourself. Include an SASE and we will reply to let you know if we find the idea intriguing enough to see 3 sample chapters (the *first* three) and a detailed synopsis."

BURNING BOOKS, (IV), Suite 1501, 690 Market St., San Francisco CA 94104. (415)788-7480. Publishers: Kathleen Burch, Michael Sumner. Estab. 1979. Three-person part-time operation. Publishes paperback originals. Books: acid-free paper; offset and letterpress printing; spiral or signature sewn binding; illustrations; average print order: 1,000-3,000. Averages 1 title/year; 1 fiction title every 2 years. *Will provide detailed critique of ms for $100.*
Needs: Literary. No "commercially inspired" fiction. Published *Moment of Silence*, by Toma Longinovic.
How to Contact: Does not accept unsolicited mss. Query first. Reports on queries in 6 weeks.
Terms: Pays in author's copies. Sends galleys to author. Book catalog free on request.

CACANADADADA, (I, II, IV), 3350 West 21 Ave., Vancouver, British Columbia V6S 1G7 Canada. (604)738-1195. President: Ronald B. Hatch. Fiction Editor: J. Michael Yates. Estab. 1988. Publishes paperback originals. Books: 60 lb. paper; photo offset printing; perfect binding; average print order: 1,000; first novel print order: 1,000. Plans 1 first novel this year. Averages 6 total titles, 1 or 2 fiction this year. Sometimes comments on rejected ms.
Needs: Experimental and literary. Recently published *Torpor*, by J. Michael Yates (experimental, prose fiction); *Daymares*, by Robert Zend; *A Devious Dictionary*, by Robin Skelton.
How to Contact: *Canadian authors only.* Accepts unsolicited mss. Submit outline/synopsis and 1 or 2 sample chapters. SASE. Reports in 1 week on queries; 1 month on mss. Photocopied submissions OK. Accepts computer printout submissions.
Terms: Pays royalties of 10%. Provides author's copies. Sends galleys to author. Publishes ms 6 months after acceptance.
Advice: "We publish mostly poetry, but plan to do one or two fiction books each year. We are a Canadian publishing house and depend on a partial government subsidy to publish books. Thus, authors *must* be Canadian."

Listings marked with a solid box [■] are book packagers. See the introduction to Commercial Publishers for more information.

CADMUS EDITIONS, (III), Box 687, Tiburon CA 94920. (707)431-8527. Editor: Jeffrey Miller. Estab. 1979. Emphasis on quality literature. Publishes hardcover and paperback originals. Books: Approximately 25% letterpress; 70% offset printing; perfect and case binding; average print order: 2,000; first novel print order: 2,000. Averages 3-5 total titles, 3 fiction titles each year.
Needs: Literary. Published *The Wandering Fool*, by Yunus Emre, translated by Edouard Roditi and Guzin Dino; *The Hungry Girls*, by Patricia Eakins; *Zig-Zag*, by Richard Thornley.
How to Contact: Does not accept or return unsolicited mss. Query first. SASE. Photocopied submissions OK.
Terms: Royalties negotiated per book. Sends galleys to author.

CALYX BOOKS, (II,IV), Box B, Corvallis OR 97339. (503)753-9384. Editor: M. Donnelly. Estab. 1986. "We publish fine literature and art by women." Publishes hardcover and paperback originals. Books: offset printing; paper and cloth binding; average print order: 5,000-10,000 copies; first novel print order: 5,000. Published new writers within the last year. Plans 2 short story collection. Averages 2-4 total titles, 2 fiction, this year.
Needs: Contemporary, ethnic, experimental, feminist, lesbian, literary, short story collections and translations. Recently published *The Riverhouse Stories*, by Andrea Carlisle (literary); *Ginseng and Other Tales from Manila*, by Marianne Villanueva (short stories); *Killing Color*, by Charlotte Watson Sherman (short stories).
How to Contact: Query first or submit outline/synopsis and 3 sample chapters. Include SASE (IRC). *Closed to submissions until January 1993.* Reports in 1 month on queries; 6 months on mss. Photocopied submissions OK. Accepts computer printout submissions.
Terms: Pays royalties of 10% minimum, author's copies, (depends on grant/award money). Sends galleys to author. Publishes ms 2 years after acceptance. Writer's guidelines for #10 SAE and 1 first class stamp or IRC. Book catalog free on request.

‡CANE HILL PRESS, 225 Varick St., 11th Floor, New York NY 10014. (212)316-5513. Publisher: Steve Schrader. Estab. 1988. "Literary press—contemporary fiction." Publishes paperback originals. Average print order: 2,000. Published new writers within the last year. Plans 1 first novel this year. Averages 2-3 total titles, all fiction, this year. Sometimes comments on rejected ms.
Needs: Literary, short story collections. No genre. Recently published *Getting Jesus in the Mood*, by Anne Brashler (story collection); *Phoenix*, by Melissa Pritchard (novel); and *All Backs Were Turned*, by Marek Hlasko (translation from a Polish novel).
How to Contact: Accepts unsolicited mss. Query first. Agented fiction 50%. Reports in 1 week on queries; 1 month on mss. Simultaneous and photocopied submissions OK.
Terms: Pays in advance; $2,000-3,000. Also 50 author's copies. Sends galleys to author. Publishes ms 18 months after acceptance. Book catalog free on request.

‡CARAVAN PRESS, (III), 15445 Ventura Bl., #279, Sherman Oaks CA 91403. (818)377-4301. Publisher: Jana Cain. Estab. 1979. "Small three-person publisher with expansion goals." Publishes hardcover and paperback originals, especially poetry collections. Plans 1-2 novels this year. Averages 6 total titles. Occasionally critiques or comments on rejected ms; fee varies.
Needs: Erotica, historical, humor/satire, literary, short story collections. *List for novels filled for next year or two.* Recently published *Litany*, by Scott Sonders (poems).
How to Contact: Query through agent only. SASE. Agented fiction 90%. Reports in 2 months on queries. Simultaneous and photocopied submissions OK. Accepts computer printout submissions.
Terms: Payment rate is "very variable." Sends galleys to author.
Advice: "Be competent, be solvent. Know who you are. Target your market."

*CAROLINA WREN PRESS, (II,IV), Box 277, Carrboro NC 27510. (919)560-2738. Imprints are Lollipop Power Books. Editor-in-Chief: Elaine Goolsby. Fiction Editor: Kathryn Lovatt. "Small non-profit independent publishing company which specializes in women's and minority work and non-sexist, multi-racial children's books." Publishes paperback originals. Books: off-set printing; perfect and saddle-stitching binding; illustrations mainly in children's; average print order: 1,000 adult, 3,000 children; first novel print order: 1,000. Published new writers within the last year. Plans 2 first novels this year. Averages 2-3 total titles each year. Sometimes comments on rejected mss.
Needs: Contemporary, ethnic, experimental, feminist, gay, juvenile (easy-to-read, fantasy, contemporary), lesbian, literary, preschool/picture book, regional, short story collections, translations. No standard clichéd stuff, romances, etc. No animals (children's books). "We are currently looking for short stories by women, in particular, Southern and minority writers are *especially* encouraged to apply."

Published *Love, Or a Reasonable Facsimile*, by Gloree Rogers (ethnic); *Brother and Keeper, Sister's Child*, by Margaret Stephens (literary).
How to Contact: Accepts unsolicited mss. Submit outline/synopsis and 1 or 2 sample chapters. SASE. Reports in 6 months. Photocopied submissions OK. Computer printout submissions are acceptable.
Terms: Pays in copies (10% of print run for adults, 5% for children's books). Pays cash advance and royalties if grants are available. Sends galleys to author. Publishes ms 2-3 years after acceptance. Writer's guidelines for #10 SAE and 2 first class stamps. Book catalog for #10 SAE and 2 first class stamps.
Advice: "We would like to see work from more black women writers."

CARPENTER PRESS, (I, II), Box 14387, Columbus OH 43214. Editorial Director: Robert Fox. Estab. 1973. One-man operation on part-time basis. Publishes paperback originals. Books: alkaline paper; offset printing; perfect or saddle stapled binding; illustrations sometimes; average print order: 500-2,500; first novel print order: 1,000.
Needs: Contemporary, literary, experimental, fantastical. "Literary rather than genre science fiction and fantasy." Published *Song for Three Voices*, by Curt Johnson (novel); and the 10th anniversary first novel contest winner, *The Three-Week Trance Diet*, by Jane Pirto. "Do not plan to publish more than one book/year including chapbooks, and this depends upon funding, which is erratic. Contemplating future competitions in the novel and short story."
How to Contact: Accepts unsolicited mss. Query. SASE. Simultaneous and photocopied submissions OK. Accepts computer printout submissions. Reports promptly.
Terms: Pays in author's copies or 10% royalties. "Terms vary according to contract." No cash advance. Free book catalog with #10 SASE.
Advice: "Know what we've published. Don't try to impress us with whom you've studied or where you've published. Read as much as you can so you're not unwittingly repeating what's already been done. I look for freshness and originality. I wouldn't say that I favor experimental over traditional writing. Rather, I'm interested in seeing how recent experimentation is tying tradition to the future and to the work of writers in other countries. We encourage first novelists."

*CATBIRD PRESS, (II), 44 N. 6th Ave., Highland Park NJ 08904. Publisher: Robert Wechsler. Estab. 1987. Small independent trade publisher. Publishes hardcover and paperback originals and reprints. Books: acid-free paper; offset printing; cloth/paper binding; illustrations (where relevant). Average print order: 4,000; first novel print order: 3,000. Averages 5 total titles, 1-2 fiction titles each year.
Needs: Contemporary, humor (specialty); literary, mainstream, translations (specialty Czech, French and German read in-house). Recently published *The Four Arrows Fe-As-Ko*, by Randall Beth Platt; *War with the Newts*, by Karel Zapek (trans. E. Osers); *Three Novels*, by Karel Zapek (trans. M. and R. Weatherall).
How to Contact: Accepts unsolicited mss but no queries. Submit outline/synopsis with sample chapters. SASE. Reports in 4-6 weeks on mss. Simultaneous and photocopied submissions OK, but let us know if simultaneous.
Terms: Pays royalties of 7½-15%. Average advance: $1,000; offers negotiable advance. Pays in 10 author's copies. Sends prepublication galleys to author. Publishes ms approx. 1 year after acceptance. *Some subsidy publishing;* terms depend on particular book. Writer's guidelines for #10 SAE with 1 first class stamp.
Advice: "We are a new publisher interested in quality fiction particularly with a comic vision. We are definitely interested in unpublished novelists who combine a sense of humor with a true knowledge of and love for literature, a lack of ideology, care for craft and self-criticism."

‡CENTER PRESS, 307 Johnson St., Santa Fe NM 87501. (505)986-1774. Publisher: Carol Bergé. Estab. 1970. "Innovative fiction for a highly well-read and literate audience." Publishes book series, chapbooks. Publishes new writers within the last year. Averages 3 total titles/year. Sometimes comments on rejected ms; $25 charge for critiques.
Needs: Contemporary, erotica, experimental, humor/satire, translations. "No crystals, Gurdjieff, mythos, first-person narratives (unless clearly not from the point of view of the author). No journals; no poetry; no kid-lit of any kind."
How to Contact: Charges $10 reading fee for works longer than 5 pages. Query first. Reports in 2 weeks on queries; 3 weeks on mss.
Terms: Pays in author's copies; ½ of print run and some cash. Sends galleys to authors. Book catalog for 9×12 SASE or IRC and $1.05 postage (book rate).

CHELSEA GREEN PUBLISHING CO., Route 113, P.O. Box 130, Post Mills VT 05058. (802)333-9073. Editor: Ian Baldwin. Estab. 1985. "Small independent trade publisher with plans to expand." Publishes hardcover and paperback originals. Averages 8-10 total titles, 1-2 fiction titles each year.
Needs: Serious fiction only . . . no genre fiction (ie. romance, spy, sci fi) or mainstream." Published *The Automotive History of Lucky Kellerman*, by Steve Heller (literary); *The Eight Corners of the World*, by Gordon Weaver (lit/comedy).
How to Contact: Query first. Prefers no unsolicited submissions. SASE.
Terms: Royalties to trade standards; small advances on royalties negotiable.

CHILD WELFARE LEAGUE OF AMERICA, (IV), Suite 310, 440 First St. NW, Washington DC 20001. (202)638-2952. Director of Publications: Susan Brite. Estab. 1920. Nonprofit association with publishing arm. Publishes hardcover and paperback originals. Books: average print order 3,000. Publishes 1 or 2 fiction titles/year.
Needs: Published *Floating*, by Mark Krueger, PhD (stories about youth-care workers in residential homes for children).
How to Contact: Query first with SASE.
Terms: Payment varies. Book catalog free.

*CHINA BOOKS, (IV), 2929 24th St., San Francisco CA 94110. (415)282-2994. Senior Editor: Bob Schildgen. Estab. 1959. "Publishes books about China or things Chinese." Publishes hardcover and paperback originals. Books: Letterpress, offset printing; perfect-bound; b&w illustrations; average print order: 5,000. Published new writers within the past year. Averages 12 total titles, 3 fiction titles each year. Sometimes critiques rejected mss.
Needs: Ethnic, subjects relating to China and translations from Chinese. Published *The Piano Tuner*, by Cheng Naishan; *6 Tanyin Alley*, by Liu Zongren; *Old Well*, by Zheng Yi.
How to Contact: Query first or submit outline/synopsis and 2 sample chapters. Reports in 2 weeks on queries; in 1 month on mss. Simultaneous and photocopied submissions OK.
Terms: Pays royalties of 5-8%. Sends galleys to author. Publishes ms 1 year after acceptance. *Subsidy publishes 1%/year.* Writer's guidelines and book catalog free on request.

‡CLEAR LIGHT PUBLISHERS, (IV), 823 Don Diego, Santa Fe NM 87501. (505)989-9590. Publisher: Harmon Houghton. Estab. 1980. "Publish primarily on Southwest, traditional cultures." Publishes hardcover originals. Plans 3 first novels this year. Averages 10-12 total titles, 3 fiction titles each year. Sometimes comments on rejected ms.
Needs: Faction, historical, humor/satire, regional, spiritual, western. Looking for "Southwest, western, native American."
How to Contact: Query first or submit outline/synopsis and sample chapters or sample of writing. SASE. Reports in 6-9 weeks on queries. Simultaneous, photocopied submissions OK. Accepts computer printout submissions.
Terms: Pays 10-12.5% royalties, negotiable advance. Sends galleys to author. Publishes ms 3-6 months after acceptance. Book catalog free.

CLIFFHANGER PRESS, (II), Box 29527, Oakland CA 94604-9527. (415)763-3510. Editor: Nancy Chirich. Estab. 1986. Publishes trade paperback originals. Books: 60 lb. recycled paper; offset printing; perfect binding; average print order: 2,500; first novel print order: 2,500. Published all new writers within the last year; goal is 10 novels a year.
Needs: Suspense/mystery. "Need mystery/suspense (approximately 75,000 words); heavy on the American regional or foreign background. No grossly hardboiled detectives and no spies." (Send SASE for guidelines for specific needs.) Recently published *Beecher*, by Virginia O'Neal; *The Third Letter*, by Frank Ramirez; *Three to Get Ready*, by Hans Ostrom; and *Beyond Saru*, by T.A. Roberts.
How to Contact: Please first send for writer's guidelines, free on request for SASE. Query first with outline/synopsis and first three chapters as sample. SASE. If sample appears to be our style, we will request complete ms. Reports in 3 weeks on queries; approx. 12 weeks on requested mss. Unsolicited mss are piled up until we can get to them; sometimes for over a year. Simultaneous and photocopied submissions OK, but please let us know. Accepts computer printout submissions, but no justified type.
Terms: No advances. Pays royalties of 8-15%. Sends galleys to author.
Advice: "No clones, please. We publish good writers with original ideas who express themselves in their own individual and original ways."

Close-up

Frank Chin
Author

Author and playwright Frank Chin is known for his strong opinions regarding the treatment and role of work by Chinese-American writers. He rejects the idea that immigrant fiction is about the assimilation of different cultures into the mainstream. Instead Chin's work celebrates the culture of the Chinese community and he vehemently refuses, he says, to write material to be more commercially palatable.

Too much of the writing published by the larger houses, he asserts, seems to be written to fit a misguided idea of what will sell with little regard for reflecting the true culture. "They tend to see literature as a commodity." He feels many good writers are considered risks because their work does not fit a mainstream ideal.

He also says quite often commercial publishers are afraid readers will not want to buy books that challenge commonly-held beliefs. Yet, he believes strongly that the reading public will accept, and is in fact hungry for, information that challenges stereotypes. "People are just as open to real information as they are false," he says.

While he doesn't believe work written outside the mainstream viewpoint is unmarketable, he does believe the small press offers more opportunities for writers who do not write "commercial fiction."

Chin's latest novel, *Donald Duk*, and a much-acclaimed collection of short stories, *The Chinaman & Pacific Frisco R.R. Co.*, were both published by Coffee House Press. "You might say the small press is guided by 'literary visionaries' — people who have definite ideas about which books they'd like to publish. They have very strong ideas about the impact they want to make on the way the world views literature and books," he says. "I was lucky to publish with a small press like Coffee House. They've been very hospitable to Asian-American writers."

Chin's publication with Coffee House illustrates his point about success and commercial viability. He had been writing for several years when he sent his short story collection to an agent. By that time he had some success with two of his plays produced off-Broadway, *The Chickencoop Chinaman* and *The Year of the Dragon*, but his collection was ultimately rejected by the agency as "not commercial enough." An agent working there disagreed with her company's decision and when she later left to become an editor at Coffee House, she brought his manuscript with her. His short story collection has since received an American Book Award and *Donald Duk* went back to press twice in its first year.

Although he started as a playwright Chin says he works with all forms of writing — essays, plays, stories and novels. Most recently he was one of four editors for Plume's *The Big Aiiieeeee: An Anthology of Chinese-American and Japanese-American Literature*.

"I write full time, all the time. I write for fun," says Chin. "When I'm not writing, I'm researching." His advice: Stay true to your vision and "pay careful attention to content."

—Robin Gee

*CLOTHESPIN FEVER PRESS, (I), 5529 N. Figueroa, Los Angeles CA 90042. (213)254-1373. Publisher: Jenny Wrenn. Estab. 1986. Small two-person operation with plans to expand. Books: offset printing; perfect binding, comb or saddlestitched binding; graphics of 2 or 3 colors, photos etc., average print order: 2,000 copies. Published new writers within the last year. Averages 2 total titles, 0-1 fiction title each year.
Needs: Experimental, feminist, lesbian, literary, short story collections. "Looking for literary work by lesbian writers. No male stories by male writers." Recently published *Shitkickers and Other Texas Stories*, by Carolyn Weathers; *In A Different Light: An Anthology of Lesbian Writers*, by Jenny Wrenn and Carolyn Weathers; *Crazy*, by Carolyn Weathers (novel).
How to Contact: Accepts unsolicited mss. Query first with cover letter that includes summary or topic plus sample short story or chapter. SASE. Reports in 3 weeks on queries; 3 months on mss. Simultaneous and photocopied submissions OK. Accepts computer printout submissions.
Terms: Payment is negotiable. Sends galleys to author. Writer's guidelines free for SASE. Book catalog on request.
Advice: "A writer should be open to rewrite suggestions that a publisher might suggest without taking offense. Spelling and correct grammar should be strived for above all. Keep writing and rewriting but don't despair if you think your work is unmarketable. Keep in mind that the right publisher for you may be hard to find."

COFFEE HOUSE PRESS, (II), 27 N. 4th St., Minneapolis MN 55401. (612)338-0125. Editorial Assistant: Michael L. Wiegers. Fiction Editor: Allan Kornblum. Estab. 1984. "Nonprofit publisher with a small staff. We publish literary titles: fiction and poetry." Publishes paperback originals. Books: acid-free paper; offset and letterpress printing; Smythe sewn binding; cover illustrations; average print order: 2,500; first novel print order: 3,000-4,000. Published new writers within the last year. Plans one first novel this year. Averages 10 total titles, 5-6 fiction titles each year. Sometimes critiques rejected mss.
Needs: Contemporary, ethnic, experimental, humor/satire, literary, short story collections. Looking for "non-genre, contemporary, high quality, unique material." No westerns, romance, erotica, mainstream, sci-fi, mystery. Recently published *Donald Duk*, by Frank Chin; *Survival*, by Nancy Lord; and *Woman Who Read Novels & Peacetime*, by Constance Urdang.
How to Contact: Accepts unsolicited mss. Submit samples or complete manuscript with cover letter. SASE. Agented fiction 10%. Reports in 3 months on queries; 9 months on mss. Photocopied submissions OK. Accepts computer printout submissions.
Terms: Pays royalties of 8%. Average advance $500. Provides 15 author's copies. Writer's guidelines for #10 SASE or IRC.
Advice: "Be brilliant."

CONFLUENCE PRESS INC., (II), Spalding Hall, Lewis-Clark State College, Lewiston ID 83501. (208)799-2336. Imprints: James R. Hepworth Books and Blue Moon Press. Fiction Editors: James R. Hepworth and Shirley McGeoghegan. Estab. 1976. Small trade publisher. Publishes hardcover and paperback originals and reprints. Books: 60 lb. paper; photo offset printing; Smythe-sewn binding; average print order: 1,500-5,000 copies. Published new writers this year. Averages 8 total titles/year. Critiques rejected mss for $25/hour.
Needs: Contemporary, historical, literary, mainstream, short story collections, translations. "Our needs favor serious fiction, 1 novel and 1 short fiction collection a year, with preference going to work set in the contemporary western United States." Recently published *Angels and Others*, by Ken Smith; *Runaway*, by Mary Clearman Blew; *Passages West*, edited by Hugh Nichols.
How to Contact: Query first. SASE for query and ms. Agented fiction 50%. Reports in 6-8 weeks on queries and mss. Simultaneous and photocopied submissions OK. Accepts computer printouts.
Terms: Pays in royalties of 10%; advance is negotiable; 10 author's copies; payment depends on grant/ award money. Sends galleys to author. Book catalog for 6x9 SASE.
Advice: "We are very interested in seeing first novels from promising writers emerging from writers' workshops who wish to break into serious print. We are also particularly keen to publish the best short story writers we can find. We are also interested in seeing volume editors for our American authors series. Prospective editors should send proposals."

‡COTEAU BOOKS, (IV), Thunder Creek Publishing Co-operative Ltd., 401-2206 Dewdney Ave., Regina, Saskatchewan S4R 1H3 Canada. (306)777-0170. Managing Editor: Shelley Sopher. Estab. 1975. Small, independent publisher; focus on first-time published works. Publishes hardcover and paperback originals. Books: #2 offset or 60 lb. hi-bulk paper; offset printing; perfect and Smythe-sewn binding; 4 color illustrations; average print order: 1,500-3,000; first novel print order: approx. 1,500. Published

new writers within this year. Plans 1 first novel this year. Publishes 9-11 total titles, 5-6 fiction titles each year. Sometimes comments on rejected mss.
Needs: No science fiction. Recently published *A Celibate Season*, by Carol Shields and Blanche Howard; *The I.Q. Zoo*, by Peter McGehee.
How to Contact: *Canadian writers only.* Query first, then submit complete ms with cover letter. SASE. Agented fiction 10%. Reports on queries in 2 weeks; on mss in 3 months. Photocopied submissions OK. Accepts computer printout submissions "if they are in good shape."
Terms: "We're a co-operative who receives subsidies from the Canadian, provincial and local governments. We do not accept payments from authors to publish their works." Sends galleys to author. Publishes ms 1-2 years after acceptance. Book catalog for 8½×11 SASE.
Advice: "We publish short-story collections, novels and poetry collections, as well as literary interviews and children's books. This is part of our mandate."

COUNCIL FOR INDIAN EDUCATION, (I,IV), 517 Rimrock Rd., Billings MT 59102. (406)252-7451. Editor: Hap Gilliland. Estab. 1963. Small, non-profit organization publishing Native American materials for schools. Publishes hardcover and paperback originals. Books: offset printing; perfect bound or saddle stitched binding; b&w illustrations; average print order: 1,000; first novel print order: 1,000. Published new writers within the last year; plans 3 first novels this year. Averages 5 total titles, 4 fiction titles each year. Usually critiques rejected ms.
Needs: Adventure, ethnic, historical, juvenile (historical, adventure and others), preschool/picture book, regional, western, young adult/teen (easy-to-read, and historical). Especially needs "short novels, and short stories accurately portraying American Indian life past or present—fast moving with high interest." No sex emphasis. Published *Chief Stephen's Parky*, by Ann Chandonnet; *Sun Dance for Andy Horn*, by Shelly Frome (novel); *Charlie Young Bear*, by Katherine Van Ahren and Joan Young Bear; *Search for Identity* (short stories).
How to Contact: Accepts unsolicited mss. Submit complete ms with SASE. Reports in 4 months. Simultaneous and photocopied submissions OK. Accepts computer printout submissions.
Terms: Pays 10% of wholesale price or 1½¢/word. Sends galleys to author. Free writer's guidelines and book catalog.
Advice: Mostly publishes original fiction in paperback. "Be sure material is culturally authentic and good for the self-concept of the group about whom it is written. Send us only material on Native Americans, make sure it is true to the culture and way of life of a particular tribe at a particular time, and that you don't downgrade any group."

CREATIVE ARTS BOOK CO., (II), 833 Bancroft Way, Berkeley CA 94710. (415)848-4777. Imprint: Creative Arts Communications Books. Editorial Production Manager: Donald Ellis. Estab. 1975. Small independent trade publisher. Publishes hardcover originals and paperback originals and reprints. Average print order: 2,500-10,000; average first novel print order: 2,500-10,000. Published new writers within the last year. Plans 3 first novels this year. Averages 10-20 titles each year.
Needs: Contemporary, erotica (literary), feminist, historical, literary, regional, short story collections, suspense/mystery (Black Lizard Crime Fiction), translations, western. Published *Russia*, by Nikos Kazantzakis (first English translation, travel journal/literature); *A Butterfly Net And A Kingdom and other stories*, by Blair Fuller; *Driving Under the Carboard Pines*, by Colleen McElroy.
How to Contact: Accepts unsolicited ms. Submit outline/synopsis and 3 sample chapters (approx. 50 pages). SASE (IRC). Agented fiction 50%. Reports in 2 weeks on queries; 1 month on mss. Simultaneous and photocopied submissions OK. Accepts computer printout submissions.
Terms: Pays royalties of 6-10%; average advance of $500-1,000; 10 author's copies. Sends galleys to author. Writers guidelines and book catalog for SASE or IRC.

CREATIVE WITH WORDS PUBLICATIONS, (II, III), Box 223226, Carmel CA 93922. Editor-in-Chief: Brigitta Geltrich. Estab. 1975. One-woman operation on part-time basis. Books: bond and stock paper; mimeographed printing; saddle stitch binding; illustrations; average print order varies. Publishes paperback anthologies of new and established writers. Averages 2 anthologies each year. *Critiques rejected mss; $10 for short stories; $20 for longer stories, folklore items, $5 for poetry.*
Needs: Humor/satire, juvenile (animal, easy-to-read, fantasy). "Editorial needs center on folkloristic items (according to themes): tall tales and such for biannual anthologies." Needs seasonal short stories appealing to general public; "tales" of folklore nature, appealing to all ages, poetry and prose written by children. Recently published anthologies, "Rural America," "Native Americans" and "The Slavic People." Prose not to exceed 1,000 words.

How to Contact: Accepts unsolicited mss. Query first; submit complete ms with SASE and cover letter. Photocopied submissions OK. Accepts computer printout submissions. Reports in 1 month on queries; 2 months on mss. Publishes ms 1-6 months after acceptance. Writer's guidelines and catalog sheet (2 oz.) for SASE. No simultaneous submissions.
Terms: Pays in 20% reduced author copies.
Advice: "Our fiction appeals to general public: children-senior citizens. Follow guidelines and rules of *Creative With Words* publications and not those the writer feels CWW should have. We only consider fiction along the lines of folklore or seasonal genres. Be brief, sincere, well-informed and proficient!"

CREATIVITY UNLIMITED PRESS, (II), 30819 Casilina, Rancho Palos Verdes CA 90274. (213)377-7908. Contact: Rochelle Stockwell. Estab. 1980. One-person operation with plans to expand. Publishes paperback originals and self-hypnosis cassette tapes. Books: perfect binding; illustrations; average print order: 1,000; first novel print order 1,000 copies. Averages 1 title (fiction) each year.
Needs: Published *Insides Out*, by Shelley Stockwell (plain talk poetry); *Sex and Other Touchy Subjects*, (poetry and short stories): and *Timetravel: Do-It Yourself Past Life Regression Handbook*.
Advice: Write for more information.

CROSS-CULTURAL COMMUNICATIONS, (IV), 239 Wynsum Ave., Merrick NY 11566-4725. (516)868-5635. Editorial Director: Stanley H. Barkan. Estab. 1971. "Small/alternative literary arts publisher focusing on the traditionally neglected languages and cultures in bilingual and multimedia format." Publishes chapbooks, magazines, anthologies, novels, audio cassettes (talking books) and video cassettes (video books, video mags); hardcover and paperback originals. Publishes new women writers series, Holocaust series, Israeli writers series, Dutch writers series, Asian-American writers series.
Needs: Contemporary, literary, experimental, ethnic, humor/satire, juvenile and young adult folktales, and translations. "Main interests: bilingual short stories and children's folktales, parts of novels of authors of other cultures, translations; some American fiction. No fiction that is not directed toward other cultures. For an annual anthology of authors writing in other languages (primarily), we will be seeking very short stories with original-language copy (other than Latin script should be print quality 10/12) on good paper. Title: *Cross Cultural Review Anthology: International Fiction 1*. We expect to extend our *CCR* series to include 10 fiction issues: *Five Contemporary* (Dutch, Swedish, Yiddish, Norwegian, Danish, Yugoslav, Sicilian, Greek, Israeli, etc.) *Fiction Writers*." Recently published *Sicilian Origin of the Odyssey*, by L.G. Pocock (bilingual English-Italian translations by Nat Scamacca); *Sikano Americano!* and *Bye Bye America*, by Nat Scammacca.
How to Contact: Accepts unsolicited mss. Query with SAE with $1 postage to include book catalog. "Note: Original language ms should accompany translations." Simultaneous and photocopied submissions "of good quality" OK. Accepts computer printout submissions. Reports in 1 month.
Terms: Pays "sometimes" 10-25% in royalties and "occasionally" by outright purchase, in author's copies—"10% of run for chapbook series," and "by arrangement for other publications." No advance.
Advice: "Write because you want to or you must; satisfy yourself. If you've done the best you can, then you've succeeded. You will find a publisher and an audience eventually. Generally, we have a greater interest in nonfiction novels and translations. Short stories and excerpts from novels written in one of the traditional neglected languages are preferred—with the original version (i.e., bilingual). Our kinderbook series will soon be in production with a similar bilingual emphasis, especially for folktales, fairy tales, and fables."

HARRY CUFF PUBLICATIONS LTD., (IV), 94 LeMarchant Rd., St. John's, Newfoundland A1C 2H2 Canada. (709)726-6590. Editor: Harry Cuff. Estab. 1981. "Small regional publisher specializing in Newfoundlandia." Publishes paperback originals. Books: offset printing; perfect binding; average print order: 1,000; first novel print order: 800. Averages 12 total titles, 1 fiction each year.

Market conditions are constantly changing! If you're still using this book and it is 1993 or later, buy the newest edition of Novel & Short Story Writer's Market at your favorite bookstore or order directly from Writer's Digest Books.

Needs: "Either about Newfoundland, or by a Newfoundlander, or both. No mainstream or ᵥ Published *Collected Works of A.R. Scammell* (short story collection) and *Princes*, by Tom Finn (sᵢ story collection).
How to Contact: Accepts unsolicited mss. Submit outline/synopsis and 3 sample chapters. SASE (IRC) necessary for return of ms. Reports in 1 month on queries; 3-5 months on mss. Photocopied submissions OK. Accepts computer printout submissions. Accepts electronic submissions via disk (query first).
Terms: Pays royalties of 10% minimum. Sends galleys to author. Publishes ms 6-18 months after acceptance. Writer's guidelines and book catalog free.
Advice: "I would like to see more good fiction, period, but it *has* to be about Newfoundland or by a Newfoundlander (note that these are entirely discrete categories) I don't want any more mss about the Vietnam War or running a radio station in Kansas City or the like! Our readers will not buy that from us."

*DAN RIVER PRESS, (I,II), Conservatory of American Letters, Box 88, Thomaston ME 04861. (207)354-6550. President: Robert Olmsted. Fiction Editor: R.S. Danbury III. Estab. 1976. Publishes hardcover and paperback originals. Books: 60 lb. offset paper; offset printing; perfect (paperback); hardcover binding; illustrations; average print order: 1,000; first novel print order: 1,000. Published new writers within the past year. Averages 4-5 total titles; 3 fiction titles last year.
Needs: Adventure, contemporary, experimental, fantasy, historical, horror, humor/satire, literary, mainstream, military/war, psychic/supernatural/occult, regional, science fiction, short story collections, western. "We want good fiction that can't find a home in the big press world. No mindless stuff written flawlessly." Recently published *Bound*, by William Hoffman, (novel); *Blue Collar and Other Stories*, by Tom Laird (short story collection); *Tales of the Furtakers*, by Tom Eberhard (short story collection).
How to Contact: Accepts unsolicited mss. Reports in 2 weeks. Simultaneous and photocopied submissions OK, plain paper only. Accepts computer printout submissions. "Guidelines help. Large SASE please."
Terms: Pays $250 cash advance (minimum) on acceptance; 10% royalties on 1,000 copies, then 15%. Sends galleys to author. After acceptance, publication "depends on many things (funding, etc.). Probably in six months once funding is achieved." Writer's guidelines for #10 SAE and 2 first class stamps. Book catalog for 6x9 SAE and 2 first class stamps.
Advice: "Submit to us (and any other small press) when you have exhausted all hope for big press publication. Then, do not expect the small press to be a big press. We lack the resources to do things like 'promotion,' 'author's tours.' These things either go undone or are done by the author. When you give up on marketability of any novel submitted to small press, adopt a different attitude. Become humble, as you get to work on your second/next novel, grow, correct mistakes and create an audience."

JOHN DANIEL AND COMPANY, PUBLISHERS, (I, II), Box 21922, Santa Barbara CA 93121. (805)962-1780. Fiction Editor: John Daniel. Estab. 1980/reestablished 1985. Small publisher with plans to expand. Publishes paperback originals. Books: 55-65 lb. book text paper; offset printing; perfect bound paperbacks; illustrations sometimes; average print order: 2,000; first novel print order: 2,000. Plans 2 first novels this year. Averages 10 total titles, 3-4 fiction titles each year. Critiques rejected ms.
Needs: "I'm open to all subjects (including nonfiction)." Literary, mainstream, short story collections. No pornographic, exploitive, illegal, or badly written fiction. Recently published *Rats in the Trees*, stories by Jess Mowry; and *The Balancing Pole*, a novel by Ann L. McLaughlin; *Out of a Forest Clearing*, by Randall Beth Platt (an environmental fable); published new writers within the last year.
How to Contact: Accepts unsolicited mss. Query first. SASE. Submit outline/synopsis and 2 sample chapters. Reports in 3 weeks on queries; 2 months on mss. Simultaneous and photocopied submissions OK. Accepts computer printouts.
Terms: Pays in royalties of 10% of net minimum. Sends galleys to author.
Advice: Encourages first novelists. "As an acquiring editor, I would never sign a book unless I were willing to publish it in its present state. Once the book is signed, though, I, as a developmental editor, would do hard labor to make the book everything it could become. Read a lot, write a lot, and stay in contact with other artists so you won't burn out from this, the loneliest profession in the world."

*MAY DAVENPORT PUBLISHERS, (I, II, IV), 26313 Purissima Rd., Los Altos Hills CA 94022. (415)948-6499. Editor/Publisher: May Davenport. Estab. 1975. One-person operation with independent subcontractors. Publishes hardcover and paperback originals. Books: 65-80 lb. paper; off-set printing; perfect binding/saddle stitch/plastic spirals; line drawing illustrations; average print order 500-3,000; average first novel print order: 3,000. Plans 1-3 first novels this year. Averages 3-5 total titles/year (including coloring books/reprints); 2-5 fiction titles/year. Sometimes critiques rejected mss.

Needs: "Overstocked with picture book mss. Prefer drama for junior and senior high students. Don't preach. Entertain!" Recently published *Creeps*, by Shelly Fredman; *The Chase of the Sorceress*, by Philip K. Johnson; *All About Turtles*, by Andrea Ross (coloring book with read-along cassette.); *I Told the Spotted Fish*, by James D. Warrick.

How to Contact: Query first with SASE. Agented fiction 2%. Reports in 2-3 weeks.

Terms: Pays royalties of 10-15%; no advance. Sends galleys to author. "Partial subsidy whenever possible in advance sales of 3,000 copies, which usually covers the printing and binding costs only. The authors are usually teachers in school districts who have a special book of fiction or textbook relating to literature." Writer's guidelines free with your SASE.

Advice: "If you are print-oriented, remember the TV-oriented are not literate. They prefer visuals and verbalizing to writing. Personal tip: Combat illiteracy by creating material which will motivate children/young adults to enjoy words and actions. Write a play for this junior/senior high age. They will read anything which they think they can participate in dramatically for themselves."

DAWNWOOD PRESS, (II, IV), Fifth Floor, 387 Park Ave. South, New York NY 10016-8810. (212)532-7160. FAX: (212)213-2495. President: Kathryn Drayton. Fiction Editor: John Welch. Estab. 1984. Publishes hardcover originals. Books: 60 lb. Lakewood-white paper; offset litho printing; adhesive case binding; average print order: 5,000. Averages 1 fiction title each year.

Needs: Contemporary. "Our needs are taken care of for the next 2 years." No experimental. Published *History's Trickiest Questions*, by Paul Kuttner (history); *Artful Questions*, by Paul Kuttner (non-trivia about entertainment, literature, art, music); *Killing Love*, by Paul Kuttner.

How to Contact: Does not accept unsolicited mss. Submit through agent only. Reports in 2 weeks on queries; 2 weeks on mss. Simultaneous and photocopied submissions OK.

Terms: Advance negotiable. Sends galleys to author.

Advice: "Same advice since Dickens's days: Tell a story from the opening sentence in easily understood English, and if you must philosophize do so through action and colloquial dialogue."

*DAYSPRING PRESS, INC., (I,II), Box 135, Golden CO 80401. (303)279-2462. Editor: John C. Brainerd. Estab. 1984. "One-person 'little literary' and 'religious' operation on part-time basis; 3 periodicals, tracts and paperbacks." Books: 20 lb. Cascade Bond Xerographic; photo offset printing; staple, spiral, perfect-bound; b&w illustrations; average print order: 1,000; first novel print order: 500. Published new writers within the last year. Plans 2 first novels this year. Plans 3-4 fiction titles this year. Sometimes critiques rejected mss. "I would not reject any material categorically. Purposefully violent, scandalous and pejorative material would have to have very definite counter values."

Needs: Sci-fi, period, and contemporary genre. Published *The Final Love Story*, by Bea Halperin; *The Faerie Way*, by Josie Lightman and *The Incorrupti*, by Amanda Crannech.

How to Contact: Accepts unsolicited mss. Submit complete ms with cover letter. Include SASE and Social Security number with submission. Reports in 1 month. Photocopied submissions OK. Accepts computer printout submissions.

Terms: Usually payment, may negotiate. *Subsidy publishes 30% of books*. Sends galleys to author (books only). Publishes ms 90 days after acceptance. Writer's guidelines for #10 SAE and 1 first class stamp. Book catalog for 6×9 SAE and 2 first class stamps.

Advice: "I would like to see more poignant trading in the hardcore human issues and less detraction in the trivial."

THE DRAGONSBREATH PRESS, (IV), 10905 Bay Shore Dr., Sister Bay WI 54234. Editor: Fred Johnson. Estab. 1973. One-man operation on part-time basis. Publishes paperback and hardback originals in small editions as handmade books. Books: varied paper; letterpress printing; hand binding; illustrations.

The asterisk indicates a publisher who sometimes offers subsidy arrangements. Authors are asked to subsidize part of the cost of book production. See the introduction to Commercial Publishers for more information.

Needs: Contemporary, literary, experimental, erotica, science fiction, fantasy, and humor/satire. "NO NOVELS, but rather single short stories."
How to Contact: "We are not currently accepting any unsolicited mss." Query and when requested send complete ms with SASE. Simultaneous and photocopied submissions OK. Accepts computer printout submissions. Reports in 1 month on queries, 2 months on mss. "Always include a cover letter and SASE."
Terms: Negotiates terms. No advance. "Since we are a small press, we prefer to work cooperatively, sharing the work and expenses between the author and the press. We are not a 'vanity press'."
Advice: "This is a small press working with the book as an art form producing handmade limited-edition books combining original artwork with original writing. Since we work with hand-set type and have limited time and money, we prefer shorter writing suited to handwork and illustrating. We are not a typical publishing house; books would have limited distribution, mainly to art and book collectors. We are now also looking for regional (Wisconsin) writing for a regional magazine the press has begun publishing entitled *The Door County Alamanak*. Always include cover letter with brief description of story."

DUNDURN PRESS, (II), 2181 Queen St. E., #301, Toronto, Ontario M4L 1E5 Canada. (416)698-0454. Editorial Contact Person: Kirk Howard. Estab. 1972. Midsize independent publisher with plans to expand. Publishes hardcover and paperback originals. "We do not as yet publish fiction, but intend to start in 1992 or 1993."
Needs: Contemporary.
How to Contact: Accepts unsolicited mss. Submit outline/synopsis and sample chapters. SASE for ms. Simultaneous and photocopied submissions OK. Accepts computer printout submissions. Accepts electronic submissions.
Terms: Pays royalties of 10-15%; $1,000 average advance; 10 author's copies. Sends galleys to author. Publishes ms 6-9 months after acceptance. Writer's guidelines not available. Book catalog free on request for SASE.

THE ECCO PRESS, (II), 100 West Broad St., Hopewell NJ 08525. (609)466-4748. Editor-in-Chief: Daniel Halpern. Estab. 1970. Small publisher. Publishes hardcover and paperback originals and reprints. Books: acid-free paper; offset printing; Smythe-sewn binding; occasional illustrations. Averages 25 total titles, 10 fiction titles each year. Average first novel print order 3,000 copies.
Needs: Literary and short story collections. "We can publish possibly one or two original novels a year." No science fiction, romantic novels, western (cowboy). Published: *The Assignation*, by Joyce Carol Oates (stories); *In the Music Library*, by Ellen Hunnicutt; *A Distant Episode*, by Paul Bowles.
How to Contact: Accepts unsolicited mss. Query first, especially on novels, with SASE. Photocopied submissions OK. Accepts computer printout submissions. Reports in 2 to 3 months, depending on the season.
Terms: Pays in royalties. Advance is negotiable. Writer's guidelines for SASE. Book catalog free on request.
Advice: "We are always interested in first novels and feel it's important that they be brought to the attention of the reading public."

THE EIGHTH MT. PRESS, (II, IV), 624 SE 29th Ave., Portland OR 97214. (503)233-3936. Publisher: Ruth Gundle. Estab. 1984. One-person operation on full-time basis. Publishes paperback originals. Books: acid-free paper, perfect-bound; average print order: 5,000. Averages 2 total titles, 1 fiction title, each year.
Needs: Books by women. Ethnic, feminist, lesbian, literary, short story collections. Published *Cows and Horses*, by Barbara Wilson (feminist/literary).
How to Contact: Accepts unsolicited mss. Query first. SASE. Reports on queries in 2 weeks; on mss in 3 weeks.
Terms: Pays royalties of 8-10%. Sends galleys to author. Publishes ms within 1 year of acceptance.

ESOTERICA PRESS, (I, II, IV), Also publishes *Notebook/Cuaderno: A Literary Journal*, Box 15607, Rio Rancho NM 87174. Editor: Ms. Yoly Zentella. Estab. 1983. One-person operation on a part-time basis. Publishes paperback originals. Books: 50 lb. white/neutral paper; offset printing; saddle stitch and perfect binding; black and white illustrations and photos; average print order: 200-300; first novel print order: 150-200. Plans more than 1 first novel this year. Averages 1-2 total titles each year. Sometimes comments on rejected ms.

Needs: Contemporary, ethnic (especially Chicano), historical, juvenile (5-9, including: historical), literary, short story collections, translations (Spanish-English/English-Spanish); women's issues. Published *Blood at the Root*, by Aisha Eshe (novella). Looking for "fiction, nonfiction based on Latino-American experience, Black-American, Arab-American, also humanist experience. No mystery, frivolity."
How to Contact: Accepts unsolicited mss with SASE and self addressed stamped postcard. Submit complete ms with cover letter. SASE (IRC) necessary for return of ms. Agented fiction 1%. Reports in 2-3 months on mss. Simultaneous and photocopied submissions OK. Accepts computer printout submissions.
Terms: Provides author's copies. Contract expenses paid first, then profits split between author/publisher. Sends pre-publication galleys to author. Publishes ms 6 months to 1 year after acceptance. Writer's guidelines and book catalog for #10 SAE and 1 first class stamp.

FABER AND FABER, INC., (I, II), 50 Cross St., Winchester MA 01890. Small trade house which publishes literary fiction and collections. Averages 5-10 total titles each year.
Needs: Literary. Recently published *Higher Math*, by Jennifer Ball; *Flying Lessons*, by Susan Johnson; *Life After Death and Other Stories*, by Susan Compo.
How to Contact: "Prefer query and one or two sample chapters with SASE for reply. Require synopsis/description—cannot consider ms without this. Many beginning writers make the mistake of submitting entire ms without even a cover letter."
Advice: "Accepting very little original fiction at present."

FASA CORPORATION, (II, IV), 1026 West Van Buren, Chicago IL 60607. Editor: L. Ross Babcock III. "Company responsible for science fiction, adventure games, to include adventures, scenarios, game designs and novels, for an audience high school age and up." Published new writers within the last year.
Needs: Adventure, science fiction. Publishes ms an average of 9 months to 1 year after acceptance. Occasionally critiques or comments on rejected ms. Recommends other markets.
How to Contact: Query first. Reports in 2-6 weeks. Simultaneous and photocopied submissions OK. Accepts computer printout submissions. Accepts electronic submissions via IBM ASCII or MacIntosh disks.
Terms: Pays on publication for all rights. Sends galleys to author.
Advice: "Be familiar with our product and always ask about suitability before plunging into a big piece of work that I may not be able to use."

THE FEMINIST PRESS AT THE CITY UNIVERSITY OF NEW YORK, 311 East 94 St., New York NY 10128. (212)360-5790. Publisher: Florence Howe. Estab. 1970. "Nonprofit, tax-exempt, education organization interested in changing the curriculum, the classroom and consciousness." Publishes hardcover and paperback reprints. "We use a fine quality paper, perfect bind our books, four color covers; and some cloth for library sales if the book has been out of print for some time; we shoot from the original text when possible. We always include a scholarly and literary afterword, since we are introducing a text to a new audience; average print run: 4,000." Publishes no original fiction. Averages 12 total titles/year; 4-6 fiction titles/year (reprints of feminist classics only).
Needs: Contemporary, ethnic, experimental, feminist, gay, historical, lesbian, literary, regional, science fiction, short story collections, translations, women's.
How to Contact: Accepts unsolicited mss. Query first. Submit outline/synopsis and 1 sample chapter. SASE (IRC). Reports in 2 weeks on queries; 2 months on mss. Simultaneous and photocopied submissions OK. Accepts computer printout submissions.
Terms: Pays royalties of 10% of net sales; $100 advance; 10 author's copies. Sends galleys to author. Book catalog free on request.

FIREBRAND BOOKS, (II), 141 The Commons, Ithaca NY 14850. (607)272-0000. Contact: Nancy K. Bereano. Estab. 1985. Publishes quality trade paperback originals. Averages 8-10 total titles each year.
Needs: Feminist, lesbian. Recently published *Cecile*, by Ruthann Robson (short stories); *Just Say Yes*, by Judith McDaniel (novel).
How to Contact: Accepts unsolicited mss. Submit outline/synopsis and sample chapters or send complete ms with cover letter. SASE. Reports in 2 weeks on queries; 2 months on mss. Simultaneous and photocopied submissions OK with notification. Accepts computer printouts.
Terms: Pays royalties.

1st AMENDMENT PUBLISHERS INC. (IV), P.O. Box 9222, Santa Fe NM 87504. (505)988-4838. Editor: Allen A. Nysse. Fiction Editor: Dawn-Marie Peterson. Estab. 1989. New mid-size independent publisher with plans to expand. Publishes hardcover and paperback originals and paperback reprints. Books: 50 lb. Lakewood, 444PPI paper; belt press printing; adhesive case binding; b&w illustrations; average print order: 3,000; first novel print order: 3,000. Published new writers within the last year. Plans 1 first novel this year. Averages 3 total titles, 2 fiction titles per year. Sometimes comments on rejected manuscripts.
Needs: Historical, literary, mainstream, military/war. Looking for novels that "encourage the reader to think about moral, social and philosophical problems; those that point out evils in society and challenge the reader to seek social and /or political reforms." Does not want to see "anything negative or with degenerating moral tendency, and all self-serving fiction." Published *America Within*, by Allen Nysse (psychological novel).
How to Contact: Accepts unsolicited manuscripts. Query first, then send outline/synopsis and 3 sample chapters. SASE. Reports in 6 weeks on queries; 3 months on mss. Accepts simultaneous and photocopied submissions.
Terms: Pays royalties of 2-10%; 100 contributor's copies. Publishes manuscripts 6-18 months after acceptance.

‡*FLORIDA LITERARY FOUNDATION PRESS, (II), distributed by Woldt Corp., 2516 Ridge Ave., Sarasota FL 34235. (813)388-2378. Chairman: Virginia G. McClintock. Fiction Editor: John Crook. Estab. 1989. "Nonprofit literary foundation." Publishes paperback originals. Books: quality trade paper. Averages 1-2 total titles, 1 anthology fiction title each year. Sometimes comments on rejected ms.
Needs: Literary. "Quality work on any subject—nothing clichéd." Recently published *Shells: Monuments to Life*, by M. John Childrey (anthology of short stories and poetry).
How to Contact: SASE. Submit outline/synopsis and sample chapters. SASE. Reports in 1 month on queries; 6 weeks on mss. Simultaneous and photocopied submissions OK. Accepts computer printout submissions. Accepts electronic submissions.
Terms: Provides 10-50 author's copies, honorarium; payment depends on grant/award money. Individual arrangement with author depending on the book. Will consider subsidy publishing. Sends galleys to author. Publishes ms 6-8 months after acceptance. Writer's guidelines free.

FOUR WALLS EIGHT WINDOWS, Box 548, Village Station, New York NY 10014. (212)206-8965. Co-Publishers: John Oakes/Dan Simon. Estab. 1986. "We are a small independent publisher." Publishes hardcover and paperback originals and paperback reprints. Books: quality paper; paper or cloth binding; illustrations sometimes; average print order: 3,000-5,000; first novel print order: 3,000-5,000. Averages 20 total titles/year; approximately 7-8 fiction titles/year.
How to Contact: "Query letter accompanied by sample chapter and SASE is best. Useful to know if writer has published elsewhere, and if so, where." Accepts unsolicited mss. Submit outline/synopsis and 1 sample chapter. SASE (IRC). Agented fiction 70%. Reports in 2 months on mss. Simultaneous and photocopied submissions OK. Accepts computer printout submissions.
Terms: Pays standard royalties; advance varies. Sends galleys to author. Book catalog free on request.

FROG IN THE WELL, (I, II, IV), Box 170052, San Francisco CA 94117. (415)431-2113. Fiction Editor: Susan Hester. Estab. 1980. One-woman operation. Publishes paperback originals. Books: 50 lb. off-white paper; web/offset printing; perfect-bound; illustrations; average print order: 2,500; first novel print run: 2,500. Averages 2-3 total titles, 1-3 fiction titles each year. Occasionally critiques rejected mss.
Needs: Feminist, lesbian, regional, short story collections (about women), and women's. Published *The Honesty Tree*, by Carole Spearon McCauley; *For Nights Like This One*, by Becky Birtha; *The New Women's Broken Heart*, by Andrea Dworkin.
How to Contact: Submit outline/synopsis and 3 sample chapters with SASE. Simultaneous (if noted) and photocopied submissions OK. Accepts computer printout submissions. Reports in 2-3 months on mss.
Terms: Pays in royalties (varies); 12 author's copies. Sends galleys to author. Free book catalog on request.
Advice: "Write well—write from personal experience. Develop your own style. We like to publish first novels by serious writers. We consider our publishing house a place for writers to publish works which may not be placed elsewhere. We regard the author/editor relationship as very important. Go out and meet people in the book world, and do readings/events. Get known in your community—build a following."

FROMM INTERNATIONAL PUBLISHING CORPORATION, (III), 560 Lexington Ave., New York NY 10022. (212)308-4010. Managing Editor: Thomas Thornton. Estab. 1981. "Small independent publisher of quality fiction, cultural history and history." Publishes hardcover originals and paperback reprints. Books: acid-free paper; burst-hardcover, 1-piece cloth binding; illustrations; average print order: 5,000; first novel print order: 4,000. Averages 10 total titles; 3-4 fiction titles each year. Usually comments on rejected ms.

Needs: Contemporary, faction, historical, literary, short story collections, translations. Published *Farewell Sidonia*, by Erich Hackl (literary); *Laura's Skin*, by J.F. Federspiel (literary); and *The Couple*, by Thomas Huerlimann (literary).

How to Contact: Query first, then submit outline/synopsis and sample chapters. SASE. Agented fiction 80%. Reports on queries in 6 weeks; on mss in 3 months. Photocopied submissions OK. Accepts computer printout submissions.

Terms: Pays negotiable royalties; advance is more for agented ms. Sends galleys to author. Publishes ms 9 months after acceptance. Writer's guidelines not available. Book catalog free on request.

GAY SUNSHINE PRESS AND LEYLAND PUBLICATIONS, (IV), P.O. Box 410690, San Francisco CA 94141. (415)824-3184. Editor: Winston Leyland. Estab. 1970. Publishes hardcover and paperback originals. Books: natural paper; perfect-bound; illustrations; average print order: 5,000-10,000.

Needs: Literary, experimental and translations—all gay material only. "We desire fiction on gay themes of *high* literary quality and prefer writers who have already had work published in literary magazines. We also publish erotica—short stories and novels." Published *Crystal Boys*, by Pai Hsien-yung (novel).

How to Contact: "Do not send an unsolicited manuscript." Query with SASE. Reports in 3 weeks on queries, 2 months on mss.

Terms: Negotiates terms with author. Sends galleys to author. Royalties or outright purchase.

Advice: "We continue to be interested in receiving queries from authors who have manuscripts of high literary quality. We feel it is important that an author know exactly what to expect from our press (promotion, distribution etc.) before a contract is signed. Before submitting a query or manuscript to a particular press, obtain critical feedback from knowledgeable people on your manuscript, e.g. a friend who teaches college English. If you alienate a publisher by submitting a manuscript shoddily prepared/typed, or one needing very extensive re-writing, you will surely not get a second chance with that press."

*GMS PUBLICATIONS, (II, IV), (formerly Dragon's Den Publishing), 11659 Doverwood Drive, Riverside CA 92505. President: G. Michael Short. Estab. 1988. Small, part-time press. Publishes hardcover and paperback originals. Books: usually paperback binding; cover artwork only; average print order 1,000; first novel print order 500-1,000. Plans 2 first novels this year. Sometimes comments on rejected mss.

Needs: Fantasy, historical, horror, psychic/supernatural/occult, science fiction, short story collections, spiritual, suspense/mystery. Needs "novels dealing with the paranormal, extraordinary, etc.; also fantasy (especially sword and sorcery); historical novels dealing with the war periods." No "fiction giving ESP a bad name; make-overs of Conan; unbelievable horror (such as *Nightmare on Elm Street* or *Friday the 13th*)."

How to Contact: Accepts unsolicited mss. Submit complete ms with synopsis and SASE. Agented fiction 5%. Reports in 3-4 weeks on queries; 6-9 months on mss. Photocopied submissions OK.

Terms: Pays in royalties of 5-15%. Publishes ms 9 months after acceptance. *Subsidy publishes* "only at author's request upon receipt of rejection. Author pays 100% of production cost." Writer's guidelines for #10 SASE.

Advice: "A cover letter is a must! We need to know the author's background. A résumé is not necessary for fiction. We encourage agented work. Keep cover letters short (no more than a page if possible) but interesting—even entertaining. Do not include synopsis within your cover letter; keep it separate. Be patient."

Market categories: (I) Beginning; (II) General; (III) Prestige; (IV) Specialized.

GOOSE LANE EDITIONS, (I, II, IV), 361 Queen St., Fredericton, New Brunswick E3B 1B1 Canada. (506)450-4251. Acquisitions Editor: Laurel Boone. Estab. 1957. Publishes hardcover and paperback originals and occasional reprints. Books: some illustrations, average print run: 2,000; first novel print order: 1,500. Averages 12 total titles, 2-4 fiction, each year. Sometimes critiques rejected mss.
Needs: Contemporary, historical, literary, short story collections. "Not suitable for mainstream or mass-market submissions." Recently published *Samara the Wholehearted*, by Nancy Bauer (novel); *A Guide to Animal Behavior*, by Douglas Glover (stories); *Eyemouth*, by Keith Harrison (historical novel).
How to Contact: Accepts unsolicited mss; complete work, no "samples." Query first. SASE "with Canadian stamps, International Reply Coupons, cash, check or money order. No US stamps please." Reports in 2-3 months. Simultaneous and photocopied submissions OK. Accepts computer printout submissions.
Terms: *"Only mss from Canada."* Pays royalties of 8% minimum; 12% maximum. Average advance: $100-200, negotiable. Sends galleys to author. Writers guidelines for 9x12 SAE and IRCs.

GRAYWOLF PRESS, (III), 2402 University Ave., St. Paul MN 55114. (612)641-0077. Publisher: Scott Walker. Estab. 1974. Growing small press, nonprofit corporation. Publishes hardcover and paperback originals and paperback reprints. Books: acid-free quality paper; offset printing; hardcover and soft binding; illustrations occasionally; average print order: 3,000-10,000; first novel print order: 2,000-6,000. Averages 14-16 total titles, 6-8 fiction titles each year. Occasionally critiques rejected ms. No genre books (romance, western, suspense).
Needs: Literary, and short story collections. Published *Skywater*, by Melinda Worth Popham; *A Farm Under a Lake*, by Martha Bergland; and *A Gravestone Made of Wheat*, by Will Weaver.
How to Contact: Query with SASE. Reports in 2 weeks. Simultaneous and photocopied submissions OK.
Terms: Pays in royalties of 7½-10%; negotiates advance and number of author's copies. Sends galleys to author. Free book catalog.

GRIFFON HOUSE PUBLICATIONS, Box 81, Whitestone NY 11357. (212)767-8380. President: Frank D. Grande. Estab. 1976. Small press. Publishes paperback originals and reprints.
Needs: Contemporary, literary, experimental, ethnic (open), translations, reprints, and multinational theory.
How to Contact: Query with SASE. No simultaneous submissions; photocopied submissions OK. Accepts computer printout submissions. Reports in 1 month on queries, 6 weeks on mss.
Terms: Pays in 6 free author's copies. No advance.

GUERNICA EDITIONS, (III, IV), 3160 Avenue de Carignan, Montréal, Québec H1N 2Y5 Canada. Editor: Antonio D'Alfonso. Fiction Editor: Umberto Claudio. Editor for women's books: Julia Gualtierri. Estab. 1978. Publishes paperback originals. Books: offset printing; perfect/sewn binding; average print order: 1,000; average first novel print order: 1,000. Plans to publish 1 first novel this year. Publishes 16-20 total titles each year.
Needs: Contemporary, ethnic, literary, translations of foreign novels. Looking for novels about women and ethnic subjects. No unsolicited works. Recently published *Bittersweet Pieces: Dutch Short Stories*, edited by Gernt Bussink; *Infertility Rites*, by Mary Meljo; *The Tangible Word*, by France Théoret.
How to Contact: Does not accept or return unsolicited mss. Query first. IRC. 100% of fiction is agented. Reports in 6 months. Photocopied submissions OK. Accepts computer printout submissions. Electronic submissions via IBM WordPerfect disks.
Terms: Pays royalties of 7-9% and 10 author's copies. Book catalog for SAE and $1 postage. (Canadian stamps only).
Advice: Publishing "more pocket books."

‡*GUYASUTA PUBLISHER, (I,II), Subsidiary of Lee Shore Agency, Sterling Bldg., 440 Friday Rd., Pittsburgh PA 15209. (412)821-6211. Imprint is One Foot on the Mountain Press. Acquisitions Manager: Anna Aivaliotis. Fiction Editor: Trinette Kern. Estab. 1988. Publishes paperback originals. Books: offset printing; perfect-bound; illustrations; average print order: 750. Published new writers within the last year. Plans 4 first novels this year. Averages 30 total titles, 2 fiction titles each year. Sometimes comments on rejected ms.
Needs: Contemporary, erotica, short story collections. No "historical romances, experimental fiction, anything over 65,000 words." Recently published *Waltzing Through the Forbidden Forest*, by Tony Bowler (humor/satire).

How to Contact: Accepts unsolicited mss. Query first. SASE. Reports in 2 weeks on queries; 3 months on mss. Simultaneous and photocopied submissions OK.

Terms: Pays royalties of 7% maximum. "We make individual arrangements with authors depending on the book. We do straight publishing and cooperative publishing. We send out press releases, include books in catalog, market mainly through mail and book conventions." Sends galleys to author. Publishes ms 6-9 months after acceptance. Writer's guidelines and book catalog for 4 × 9 SAE and 1 first class stamp.

Advice: "When submitting a manuscript do not send us your first draft. We will reject it. Work on your story, give it time to evolve. Read fiction and how-to books. Please type, double space and use healthy margins."

*HAYPENNY PRESS, (I), 211 New St., West Paterson NJ 07424. Estab. 1988. "Small independent publisher with plans to expand." Publishes paperback originals. Books: offset and/or mimeo printing; perfect binding. Published new writers within the last year. Plans 2-4 first novels this year. Averages 2-3 titles (all fiction). Sometimes comments on rejected ms. "No charge for comments . . . *for detailed (separate) critique: $25 (for ms under 200 pages.)*"

Needs: Contemporary, ethnic, experimental, fantasy, humor/satire, literary, mainstream, military/war, regional, science fiction, short story collections, young adult/teen (10-18 years) easy-to-read and problem novels. No horror, pornography or formula stories. Published *Cooper Street*, by P.D. Jordan (y/a).

How to Contact: Does not accept unsolicited mss. Query first (always!!). Include SASE. Reports in 2 weeks on queries; 1 month on ms. Photocopied submissions OK. Accepts computer printout submissions.

Terms: Pays by "individual arrangement. Cooperative situations possible." Sends galleys to author. Publishes ms up to 1 year after acceptance. Writer's guidelines for #10 SASE and 1 first class stamp.

Advice: "Prefer to work with authors who have a specific purpose/market/audience (ie: counselors at runaway shelters; teachers of literacy programs; etc.). The competition in 'general' markets is fierce and authors are expected to do all they can to help promote their work. We are open to suggestions/ arrangements, if the work merits publication. Y/A writers: project something useful to your teen audience without being "preachy." Others: offbeat, unusual is fine . . . main criteria is to be good/ original enough to stand out . . . Please no five-step plots or outlines."

‡HELICON NINE EDITIONS, (II), Subsidiary of Helicon Nine, Inc., P.O. Box 22412, Kansas City KS 66208. (913)722-2999. Publisher/Editor: Gloria Vando Hickok. Estab. 1990. Small press publishing poetry, fiction, creative nonfiction and anthologies. Publishes paperback originals. Books: 70 lb. Vellum paper; offset printing; perfect-bound; 4-color cover; average print order: 1,000-5,000. Published new writers within the last year. Plans 8 total titles, 2-4 fiction titles this year.

Needs: Contemporary, ethnic, experimental, literary, short story collections, translations. "We're only interested in fine literature." Nothing "commercial." Recently published *Sweet Angel Band*, by R.M. Kinder (short story collection).

How to Contact: Does not accept unsolicited mss. Query first or submit outline/synopsis and sample chapter. SASE. Reports in 1 week on queries; 3 months on mss. Photocopied submissions OK.

Terms: Pays royalties, author's copies or honorarium. "Individual arrangement with author." Sends galleys to author. Publishes ms 1-6 months after acceptance. Writer's guidelines for SASE.

Advice: "Make it good. Check spelling and grammar before submitting. Be proud of your work. Submit a clean, readable copy in a folder or box—paginated with title and name on each page. Also, do not pre-design book, i.e. no illustrations—it's very amateurish. We'd like to see books that will be read 50-100 years from now. New classics."

‡HERBOOKS, (II,IV), P.O. Box 7467, Santa Cruz CA 95061. (408)425-7493. Contact: Irene Reti. Estab. 1984. "One-person lesbian feminist press, part-time basis." Publishes paperback originals. Books: 60 lb. paper; offset printing; perfect-bound; b&w photos and line drawings; average print order: 2,000; first novel print order: 1,500. Published new writers within the last year "in anthology form." Plans 2 total titles each year, 1 fiction title every other year. Sometimes comments on rejected ms "briefly."

 The double dagger before a listing indicates that the listing is new in this edition. New markets are often the most receptive to freelance contributions.

Needs: Contemporary, ethnic, feminist, historical, lesbian, religious (Jewish). Looking for "Native American lesbian fiction." No "sadomasochistic content; no work by men."
How to Contact: Accepts unsolicited mss. Query first. Reports in 2 weeks. Simultaneous and photo-copied submissions OK. Accepts electronic submissions via "Word 4.0 on disk for Mac."
Terms: Pays royalties of 10% minimum. Author's copies negotiable. Publishes ms 6-12 months after acceptance. Writer's guidelines and book catalog for #10 SAE with 45¢ postage.
Advice: "We primarily publish fiction in subject-oriented anthologies. Books by previously unpub-lished authors have not done well for us, and we can't afford to do many of them. Write for guidelines of current projects/anthologies. Look at other books published by HerBooks to see if you fit in our list."

*HERITAGE PRESS, (II, IV), Box 18625, Baltimore MD 21216. (301)383-9330. President: Wilbert L. Walker. Estab. 1979. One-man operation, full-time basis; uses contractual staff as needed. Publishes hardcover originals. Books: 60 lb. white offset paper; offset printing; sewn hardcover binding; average print order: 2,000; first novel print order: 1,000. Averages 2 total titles, 1-2 fiction titles each year.
Needs: Ethnic (black). Interested in "fiction that presents a balanced portrayal of the black experience in America, from the black perspective. No fiction not dealing with blacks, or which views blacks as inferior." Published *Stalemate at Panmunjon* (the Korean War), and *Servants of All*, by Wilbert L. Walker.
How to Contact: Does not accept unsolicited mss. Query first with SASE. Simultaneous and photo-copied submissions OK. Reports in 2 weeks on queries, 2 months on mss. Publishes ms an average of 9 months after acceptance.
Terms: Must return advance if book is not completed or is unacceptable. *"We plan to subsidy publish only those works that meet our standards for approval.* No more than 1 or 2 a year. Payment for publica-tion is based on individual arrangement with author." Book catalog free on request.
Advice: "Write what you know about. No one else can know and feel what it is like to be black in America better than one who has experienced our dichotomy on race." Would like to see new ideas with broad appeal. "First novels must contain previously unexplored areas on the black experience in America. We regard the author/editor relationship as open, one of mutual respect. Editor has final decision, but listens to author's views."

HERMES HOUSE PRESS, (II), 52 Lanark Rd., Brookline MA 02146. (617)566-9766. Publisher: Richard Mandell. Estab. 1980. Small press operation. Publishes paperback originals and reprints. Books: 70 lb. paper; offset printing; paper binding; illustrations; average print order: 1,000; first novel print order: 1,000. Plans 1-2 first novels this year. Averages 2 total titles, 1-2 fiction titles each year. Generally critiques rejected mss.
Needs: Contemporary, experimental, feminist, literary, short story collections, novellas and transla-tions. No sexist, erotica, horror. Recently published *Three Stories*, by R.V. Cassill (short stories), *The Deadly Swarm & Other Stories*, by LaVerne Harrell Clark, *Bella B's Fantasy and Other Stories*, by Raymond Jean; and *O Loma! Constituting a Self*, by Kurt H. Wolff.
How to Contact: Not currently reading manuscripts. Reports in 3 weeks on queries; 2 months on mss. Photocopied submissions OK. Accepts computer printout submissions. Publishes ms within 1 year after acceptance.
Terms: Pays in author's copies plus percentage above costs. Sends galleys to author.
Advice: Encourages first novelists. "We regard the author/editor relationship as open communication/ free dialogue. Be persistent."

*HOMESTEAD PUBLISHING, (I, II), Box 227, Moose WY 83012. (406)538-8960. Editor: Carl Schreier. Estab. 1980. Regional publishers for the Rocky Mountains, midsize firm. Publishes hardcover and paperback originals and reprints. Books: natural stock to enamel paper; web, sheet-feed printing; perfect or smythe-sewn binding; b&w or color illustrations; average print order: 10,000; first novel print order: 2,000-5,000. Plans 1-2 first novels this year. Averages 8-10 total titles; 1-2 fiction each year. Sometimes critiques rejected mss.
Needs: Historical, juvenile (wildlife, historical), literary, preschool/picture book, short story collection, western, young adult/teen (10-18 years, historical). Looking for "good quality, well written and contem-porary" fiction. Published *The Great Plains: A Young Reader's Journal*, by Bullock (children's natural history-adventure).

How to Contact: Accepts unsolicited mss. Query first. SASE. Reports in 1 month. Sends galleys to author. Simultaneous and photocopied submissions OK. Accepts computer printout submissions.
Terms: Pays royalties of 6-10%. Provides 6 author's copies. Subsidy publishes "occasionally, depending on project."

‡**INFINITE SAVANT PUBLISHING, (I, II),** P.O. Box 2321, Van Nuys CA 91404. (213)293-7767. Editor/Owner: James C. Jones II. Estab. 1990. "Two-person operation on part-time basis with plans to expand." Publishes paperback originals. Books: perfect binding; average print order: 2,000-5,000; first novel print order: 1,000-3,000. Plans 5 first novels this year. Averages 6 total titles, all fiction this year. Sometimes comments on rejected ms.
Needs: Adventure, erotica, fantasy, feminist, gay, horror, lesbian, psychic/supernatural/occult, science fiction, suspense/mystery. Recently published *Landfill*, by James C. Jones II (mystery/adventure); *Terminal Frost*, by T. LeRoy Birdine (mystery); *Manana*, by Harriet Nelson-Jones (play).
How to Contact: Accepts unsolicited mss. Query first, then submit complete ms with cover letter. SASE (IRC). Reports in 2 weeks on queries; 2 months on mss. Simultaneous, photocopied submissions OK. Accepts computer printout submissions. Accepts electronic submissions via (IBM PC-ASCII—5¼ or 3½; Commodore 128-ASCII—3½; Amiga-ASCII—3½.)
Terms: Pays royalties of 8-10%. Provides 10 author's copies. Publishes ms 1-2 years after acceptance. Writer's guidelines for SASE, #10 envelope and 1 first class stamp.

INVERTED-A, INC., (II), 401 Forrest Hill, Grand Prairie TX 75051. (214)264-0066. Editors: Amnon or Aya Katz. Estab. 1977. A small press which evolved from publishing technical manuals for other products. "Publishing is a small part of our business." Publishes paperback originals. Books: bond paper; offset printing; illustrations; average print order: 250; first novel print order: 250. Publishes 2 titles a year, in recent years mostly poetry, fiction is now about every other year. Also publishes a periodical *Inverted-A, Horn*, which appears irregularly and is open to very short fiction as well as excerpts from unpublished longer fiction. Comments on rejected mss.
Needs: "We are interested in justice and freedom approached from a positive and romantic perspective." Published *The Few Who Count*, by Aya Katz (novel); *Damned in Hell*, by A.A. Wilson (novella); *Inverted Blake* (collection); and *Inverted Blake #2* (collection).
How to Contact: Submit query with sample. SASE. Reports in 6 weeks on queries; 3 months on mss. Simultaneous and photocopied submissions OK. Accepts computer printouts. Accepts electronic submissions via modem or ASCII file on a pc MSDOS diskette. Electronic submission mandatory for final ms of accepted longer work.
Terms: We do not pay except for author copies. Sends galleys to author. For current list send SAE and 1 first class stamp.
Advice: "Deal with more than personal problems. Project hope. We are planning a collection of short stories which is open for submissions."

ISLAND HOUSE, (IV), 731 Treat Ave., San Francisco CA 94110. (415)826-7113. Imprint: Cottage Books. Senior Editor: Susan Sullivan. Fiction Editor: Pat Healy. Estab. 1987. "Small Press, four person, full time." Publishes paperback originals. Books: acid-free paper; offset printing; perfect-bound; average print order: 2-3,000. Published new writers within the last year. Averages 3 total titles, 2 fiction titles each year. Sometimes comments on rejected ms; *$75 charge for critiques*.
Needs: Ethnic, experimental, faction, literary and short story collections. Looking for Irish-Celtic themes and quality. Published *The West*, by Ed Stack (short stories).
How to Contact: No unsolicited mss. Query first. Agented fiction 50%. Reports in 2 weeks on queries; 3 months on mss. Simultaneous and photocopied submissions OK. Accepts computer printout submissions.
Terms: Pays royalties of 6-10%; offers negotiable advance. Sends galleys to author. Publishes ms 6-9 months after acceptance. Book catalog free.

ITALICA PRESS, (IV), 595 Main St., #605, New York NY 10044. (212)935-4230. Publishers: Eileen Gardiner and Ronald G. Musto. Estab. 1985. Small independent publisher. Publishes paperback originals. Books: 50-60 lb. natural paper; offset printing; Smythe-sewn binding; illustrations; average print order: 1,000. "First time translators published. We would like to see translations of well-known Italian writers in Italy who are not yet translated for an American audience." Publishes 6 total titles each year; 2 fiction titles. Sometimes critiques rejected mss.

Needs: Translations from Italian. Looking for "4 novels over next two years—particularly translations of 20th Century Italian literature." Recently published *Dolcissimo*, by Giuseppe Bonaviri; *The Fat Woodworker*, by Antonio Manetti.
How to Contact: Accepts unsolicited mss. Query first. Reports in 3 weeks on queries; 2 months on mss. Simultaneous and photocopied submissions OK. Accepts computer printout submissions. Electronic submissions via Macintosh disk.
Terms: Pays in royalties of 5-15% and 10 author's copies. Sends pre-publication galleys to author. Book catalog free on request.

JAYELL ENTERPRISES, (IV), Box 2616, Dearborn MI 48124. (313)565-9687. President: James L. Limbacher. Estab. 1983. One-person operation on a part-time basis; also produces TV cable programs. Publishes paperback originals. Books: average print order: 500. Averages 1 fiction title each year. Sometimes comments on rejected mss; *$50 charge for critiques*.
Needs: No "badly written, amateurish works."
How to Contact: Does not accept unsolicited mss. Query first. Reports in 3 weeks on queries; in 1 month on mss. Photocopied submissions OK. Accepts computer printout submissions.
Terms: Pays royalties of 25% minimum. Provides 6 author's copies. Sends galleys to author.
Advice: Publishing "less fiction. Nonfiction sells better."

JESPERSON PRESS LTD., (I), 39 James Lane, St. John's, Newfoundland A1E 3H3 Canada. (709)753-0633. Trade Editor: Shelly Dawe. Midsize independent publisher. Publishes hardcover and paperback originals. Published new writers within the last year. Averages 7-10 total titles, 1-2 fiction titles each year. Sometimes comments on rejected mss.
Needs: Adventure, fantasy, humor/satire, juvenile (5-9 yrs.) including: animal easy-to-read, fantasy, historical, sports, spy/adventure and contemporary. Published *Black Light*, by Ishmael Baksh (first novel).
How to Contact: Accepts unsolicited mss. Submit complete manuscript with cover letter. SASE. Reports in 3 months on mss. Photocopied submissions OK.
Terms: Pays negotiable royalties. Sends galleys to author. Book catalog free.

KAR-BEN COPIES, INC., (II, IV), 6800 Tildenwood Lane, Rockville MD 20852. (301)984-8733. President: Judye Groner. Estab. 1974. Small publisher specializing in juvenile Judaica. Publishes hardcover and paperback originals. Books: 70-80 lb. patina paper; offset printing; perfect and case binding; 2-4 color illustrations; average print order: 5,000-10,000. Averages 8-10 total titles, 6-8 fiction titles each year. Published new writers within the last year.
Needs: Juvenile (3-10 years). Recently published *Two by Two, Favorite Bible Stories*, by Harry Arater; *Daddy's Chair*, by Sandy Lantor and four new board books for toddlers.
How to Contact: Accepts unsolicited mss. Submit outline/synopsis and sample chapters or complete ms with cover letter. SASE. Reports in 1 week on queries; 1 month on mss. Simultaneous and photocopied submissions OK. Accepts computer printouts.
Terms: Pays in royalties of 5-10%; average advance: $1,000; 12 author's copies. Sends galleys to author. Writer's guidelines for SASE. Book catalog free on request.

KNIGHTS PRESS, (II, IV), P.O. Box 6737, Stamford CT 06901. (203)969-1699. Publisher: Elizabeth G. Gershman. Estab. 1983. Small press publishing only gay male fiction and non-fiction. Publishes trade paperback originals. Published new writers in the last year. Plans 4 first novels this year. Averages 12 total titles each year.
Needs: "Fiction must have a gay theme (not lesbian or non-gay). We publish on literary merit." No gratuitous erotica. No pornography. Published *Boys In the Bars*, by Christopher Davis; *Some Dance to Remember*, by Jack Fritscher; and *Families*, by David Watmaugh.
How to Contact: Accepts unsolicited mss. Query first. SASE. Agented fiction: 50%. Reports in 3 weeks on queries; 3 months on mss. No simultaneous submissions. Photocopied submissions OK. Accepts computer printouts.
Terms: Pays in royalties with advance. Sends galleys to author. Writer's guidelines for #10 SASE and 1 first class stamp. Book catalog for #10 SASE and 1 first class stamp.
Advice: "Write about people, places, events you know. Then plot and define characters. Story must have a positive gay lifestyle or relationship. Consider that a book costs money to buy and to produce. Would *you* spend *your* money on your submission? Would you spend thousands of dollars to produce it? If you wouldn't, neither would the book buyer or the publisher."

KRUZA KALEIDOSCOPIX, INC., (IV), Box 389, Franklin MA 02038. (508)528-6211. Editor/President: J.A. Kruza. Fiction Editor: R. Burbank. Estab. 1976. Publishes hardcover and paperback originals. Books: 60-80 lb. coated paper; offset printing; saddle and perfect binding; illustrations; average print order: 10,000. Averages 12 total titles each year. Sometimes critiques rejected mss.
Needs: Historical (nautical); juvenile (5-9 yrs.) including: animal, lesson teachings about work ethic, historical. "Stories for children, ages 3-7, with problem and characters who work out solution to problem, i.e. work ethic."
How to Contact: Accepts and returns unsolicited mss. Submit complete ms with cover letter. SASE. Reports in 3 weeks on queries; 3 months on mss. Simultaneous and photocopied submissions OK. Accepts computer printout submissions.
Terms: *Charges $3 reading fee.* Pays in royalties of 3-5% "or flat fee, depending on strength of story. Length of royalties are usually limited to a specific time, usually 4 to 7 years." Provides 10 author's copies. Writer's guidelines for #10 SAE with 1 first class stamp.

*LIBRA PUBLISHERS, INC., (II), Suite 383, 3089C Clairemont Dr., San Diego CA 92117. (619)581-9449. President: William Kroll. Estab. 1960. Small independent publisher. Hardcover and paperback originals. Books: 60 lb. offset paper; offset printing; hardcover—Smythe sewn binding; paperback—perfect binding; illustrations occasionally; average print order 3,000; first novel print order 1,000+. Plans to publish 3 first novels this year. Averages approximately 15 titles/year; 3-4 fiction titles/year.
Needs: "We consider all categories." Published *All God's Children*, by Alex LaPerchia (inspirational); *Seed of the Divine Fruit*, by Enrico Rinaldi (multi-generational about founding of Atlantic City); and *Caveat Emptor*, by William Attias (racist takeover of a city).
How to Contact: Accepts unsolicited mss. Send complete ms with cover letter. SASE. Reports on queries in 1 week; on mss in 2-3 weeks. Simultaneous and photocopied submissions OK. Computer printout submissions OK.
Terms: Pays 10-40% royalties. Sends pre-publication galleys to author. Publishes ms an average of 6-12 months after acceptance. Book catalog for SASE with 5 first class stamps.
Advice: "Libra publishes nonfiction books in all fields, specializing in the behavioral sciences. We also publish two professional journals: *Adolescence* and *Family Therapy*. We have published fiction on a royalty basis but because of the difficulty in marketing works by unknown writers, we are not optimistic about the chances of offering a standard contract. However, we shall continue to consider fiction in the hope of publishing on a standard basis books that we like and believe have good marketing potential. In addition, our procedure is as follows: Manuscripts we do not consider publishable are returned to the author. When we receive manuscripts which we feel are publishable but are uncertain of the marketability, we suggest that the author continue to try other houses. If they have already done so and are interested in self-publishing, we offer two types of services: (1) we provide editing, proofreading, book and cover design, copyrighting and production of the book; copies are then shipped to the author. (2) We provide these services plus promotion and distribution. In all cases, the problems and risks are spelled out."

LOLLIPOP POWER BOOKS, (II), Box 277, Carrboro NC 27510. (919)376-8152. Editor: Elizabeth Core. Estab. 1970. New children's division of the Carolina Wren Press; publishes non-sexist, multi-racial "alternative" children's books. Publishes paperback originals. Buys juvenile mss with or without illustrations. Averages 1 title (fiction) each year. Average first book run 2,500 copies. Usually critiques rejected ms "unless completely inappropriate submission for our purpose."
Needs: Juvenile. "We are currently looking for well-written stories with strong plots which deal with issues of race or sex-role stereotyping or with contemporary family problems, especially divorce. We would like to see ms about a realistic black child or family or ms dealing with handicapped children." Published *Brother's Keeper, Sister's Child* by Margaret Stephens; *Love, or a Reasonable Facsimile*, by Gloree Rogers; *The Boy Toy*, by Phyllis Johnson.
How to Contact: Send complete manuscript with SASE. Reports in 2 months on mss. Simultaneous and photocopied submissions OK. Publishes ms from 1-2 years after acceptance.
Terms: Pays royalties of 10%.
Advice: "Know what the publisher's specialty is. Though we want books with a strong message, we also want strong and appealing characters, and plots which children will want to return to again and again. We are particularly interested in works by women and minorities!"

HENDRICK LONG PUBLISHING CO., (IV), Box 25123, Dallas TX 75225. (214)358-4677. Vice President: Joann Long. Estab. 1969. "Independent publisher focusing on Texas material geared primarily to a young audience. (K through high school). Cornerstone of company is a Texas history seventh grade textbook (state adopted)." Publishes hardcover and paperback originals and hardcover reprints. Books: average print order: 2,000 (except textbooks which have a much longer run.) Published new writers within the last year. Averages 8 total titles, 4 fiction titles each year. Sometimes comments on rejected ms.

Needs: Texas themes: historical, regional, for juvenile, young adult, teen. "No material not suitable for junior high/high school audience." Recently published *Tilli Comes to Texas*, by Oppenheimer (Christmas fantasy); *Cowboy Stories from East Texas*, by John Lash (juvenile); *The Mystery of Y'Barbos' Tunnel*, by Mary Tanner Jones (juvenile/ya).

How to Contact: Accepts unsolicited mss, but prefer query. Query first or submit outline/synopsis and sample chapters (at least 2—no more than 3). SASE. Reports in 2 weeks on queries; 2 months on ms. Photocopied submissions OK. Accepts computer printout submissions.

Terms: Offers negotiable advance. Sends galleys to author. Publishes ms 18 months after acceptance. Writer's guidelines for SASE. Book catalog for $1.

LONGSTREET PRESS, (II), Suite 102, 2150 Newmarket Parkway, Marietta GA 30067. (404)980-1488. Associate Editor: John Yow. Estab. 1988. "Small independent publisher with plans to grow." Publishes hardcover and paperback originals. Published new writers within the last year. Averages 20-25 total titles, 2-3 fiction titles each year. Sometimes comments on rejected ms.

Needs: Literary, mainstream, short story collections. "Quality fiction." No "genre fiction, highly experimental work, ya, juvenile." Recently published *Chattering Man*, by Merrill Joan Gerber (literary); *When All the World Was Young*, by Ferrol Sams (literary).

How to Contact: Accepts unsolicited mss. Submit outline/synopsis and sample chapters. SASE. Agented fiction 50%. Reports on queries in 6 weeks; on mss in 3 months. Simultaneous (if told) and photocopied submissions OK. Accepts computer printout submissions.

Terms: Pays in royalties; advance is negotiable; author's copies. Sends galleys to author. Publishes ms 6 months-1 year after acceptance. Writer's guidelines for #10 SASE and 1 first class stamp. Book catalog free on request.

Advice: "Read good contemporary literary fiction—know the field."

LOS HOMBRES PRESS, (II,IV), Box 632729, San Diego CA 92163-2729. (619)234-6710. Publisher: James D. Kitchen. Estab. 1989. Small publisher with plans to do 5 books in 1992. Publishes paperback originals. Books: 60 lb. paper; offset printing; perfect-bound; average print order: 2,000; first novel print order: 2,000. Published new writers within the last year. Plans 2 first novels this year. Averages 4-5 total titles, 3 fiction titles each year. Sometimes comments on rejected mss.

Needs: Gay and lesbian. "Novels including mainstream, literary, science fiction, mystery, fantasy, futuristic, adventure. Open to most categories with a gay theme; short story collections." No men's action, pornography. Recently published *The Search for Sebastion* by Judston Crown (gay-comedy-adventure) and *The Road to AJ*, by Sean Martin (illustrated gay, send-up of the OZ story).

How to Contact: Accepts unsolicited mss. Query first or submit 3 sample chapters. SASE. Include social security number with submission. Agented fiction 50%. Reports on queries in 2 weeks; mss in 2 months. Simultaneous and photocopied submissions OK. Computer printout submissions are acceptable.

Terms: Pays 10-15% royalties and 10 author's copies. Sends galleys to author. Publishes ms 1 year after acceptance. Writer's guidelines for #10 SASE and 1 first class stamp.

LUCKY HEART BOOKS, (I), Subsidiary of Salt Lick Foundation, 1909 Sunny Brook Dr., Austin TX 78723-3449. Editor/Publisher: James Haining. Estab. 1969. Small press with significant work reviews in several national publications. Publishes paperback originals and reprints. Books: offset/bond paper; offset printing; stitch, perfect bound; illustrations; average print order: 500; first novel print order: 500. Sometimes comments on rejected mss.

Needs: Open to all fiction categories.

How to Contact: Accepts unsolicited mss. SASE. Agented fiction 1%. Reports in 2 weeks to 4 months on mss. Photocopied submissions OK. Accepts computer printout submissions.

Terms: Pays 10 author's copies. Sends pre-publication galleys to author.

‡MADWOMAN PRESS, (I, IV), P.O. Box 690, Northboro MA 01532. (508)393-3447. Editor/Publisher: Diane Benison. Estab. 1991. "Independent small press publishing lesbian fiction. Two-person operation. Our first two books will be published in the fall of 1992." Publishes paperback originals. Books: perfect binding; average print order: 4,000-6,000; first novel print order: 5,000. Averages 2-4 total titles, 2 fiction titles each year. Sometimes comments on rejected ms.

Needs: "All must have lesbian themes: adventure, erotica, ethnic, feminist, romance, science fiction, short story collection, suspense/mystery, western. Especially looking for lesbian romance." No horror. No gratuitous violence.
How to Contact: Does not accept unsolicited mss. Query first. Include brief statement of name, address, phone, previous publication and a 1-2 page precis of the plot. SASE. Reports in 1 month. Simultaneous, photocopied submissions OK. Accepts computer printout submissions.
Terms: Pays royalties of 8-15% "after recovery of publications costs." Provides 20 author's copies. Sometimes sends galleys to author. Publishes ms 1-2 years after acceptance. Writer's guidelines for #10 SAE and 1 first class stamp.
Advice: "We're looking to form long-term relationships with writers, so talented first novelists are ideal for us. We want to publish an author regularly over the years, build an audience for her and keep her in print. We're interested in books by, for and about lesbians. Books that are affirming for lesbian readers and authors. Would like to see more romances."

‡**MAGE PUBLISHERS, (IV)**, 1032 29th St. NW, Washington DC 20007. (202)342-1642. Editorial Contact: Scott Ripley. Estab. 1985. "Small independent publisher." Publishes hardcover originals. Averages 4 total titles, 1 fiction title each year.
Needs: We publish *only* books on Iran. Ethnic (Iran) fiction.
How to Contact: Query first. SASE (IRC). Reports in 3 months on queries. Simultaneous, photocopies submissions OK. Accepts computer printout submissions.
Terms: Pays royalties. Publishes ms 6-9 months after acceptance. Writer's guidelines for SASE. Book catalog free.

‡**MANIC D PRESS, (II)**, P.O. Box 410804, San Francisco CA 94141. Editor: Jennifer Joseph. Estab. 1984. Small independent publisher. Publishes paperback originals. Books: 50 lb. paper; offset printing; perfect binding; average print order: 1,000. Averages 5 total titles, 2 fiction titles each year.
Needs: Literary. No military, western, religious, romance. Recently published *Bricks and Anchors*, by Jon Longhi (cyperpunk short stories); and *Graveyard Golf and Other Stories*, by Vampyre Mike Kassel (fantasy/horror short stories).
How to Contact: Accepts unsolicited mss. Query first. SASE. Reports in 1 month on queries; 1-2 months on mss. Simultaneous and photocopied submissions OK. Accepts computer printout submissions.
Terms: Pays author's copies. Sends galleys to author. Publishes ms 6-24 months after acceptance. Writer's guidelines and book catalog for #10 SAE and 1 first class stamp.
Advice: "Don't send the whole novel. Always query first."

MARRON PUBLISHERS, INC., (II), Dark Secrets, Romance In Black, P.O. Box 756, Yonkers NY 10703. (718)481-9599. Co-owner: Marquita Guerra. Fiction Editor: Sharon A. Ortiz. Estab. 1988. "Marron Publishers is a small, growing independent publisher dedicated to printing quality works which celebrate ethnic and cultural diversity." Publishes paperback originals. Books: illustrations on newsletter (Dark Secrets); average print order: 10,000; first novel print order: 10,000. Plans 8 first novels this year. Averages 8-10 total titles each year (all fiction). Sometimes comments on rejected mss.
Needs: Adventure, contemporary, historical, mainstream, romance (contemporary, historical), suspense/mystery, young adult/teen (romance/ya). Looking for "romance for the *Romance In Black* line."
How to Contact: Accepts unsolicited mss (no queries). Submit outline/synopsis and 3 sample chapters, or complete ms with cover letter. SASE. Agented fiction 25%. Reports on queries in 2 weeks; on mss in 1 month. Photocopied submissions OK. Accepts computer printout submissions. Accepts electronic submissions with prior approval.
Terms: Depends on experience of author and previous track record. "Individual arrangement with author depending on the book." Sends galleys to author. Publication time "depends on the book" (approximately 2 to 18 months). Writer's guidelines for 8½×11 SASE and 45¢ postage. Book catalog for SASE.

Market categories: (I) Beginning; (II) General; (III) Prestige; (IV) Specialized.

Advice: "Be honest and forthright in your cover letters without gushing. State your case—don't be shy about what you feel are your positive points. Always remember that you have to sell yourself to the publisher and don't back down on questions of quality—your name will appear on the book or the publication. Be open to criticism and flexible when it comes to certain changes. But be wary of changing your original concept to one that is foreign to your creative intent."

MERCURY HOUSE, (III), Suite 400, 201 Filbert St., San Francisco CA 94133. Executive Editor: Tom Christensen. Publisher: William Brinton. Submissions Editor: Alison Macondray. Small, independent publisher of quality fiction and nonfiction. Publishes hardcovers and some paperback originals and reprints. Averages 20 titles annually. 25% of books from first-time authors.
Needs: Literary adult fiction, nonfiction and translations.
How to Contact: No unsolicited mss. Submit query letter, 3 sample chapters, synopsis and SASE. Reports in 3 months. Book catalog for 8½ × 11 SAE and 65¢. Simultaneous submissions OK.

*MEY-HOUSE BOOKS, (II), Box 794, Stroudsburg PA 18360. (717)646-9556. Editorial contact person: Ted Meyer. Estab. 1983. One-person operation part-time with plans for at least 2 novels shortly. Publishes hardcover and paperback originals. Averages 1 title/year. Occasionally critiques or comments on rejected ms, "cost varies."
Needs: Adventure, contemporary, ethnic, science fiction. "No gay, erotic or lesbian fiction."
How to Contact: Accepts unsolicited mss. Query first. SASE. Reports in 1 month on queries. Simultaneous, photocopied submissions OK.
Terms: Payment "varies." Sends galleys to author. *Subsidy publishes "on an individual basis."*

MILKWEED EDITIONS, Suite 505, 528 Hennepin Ave., Minneapolis MN 55403. (612)332-3192. Editor: Emilie Buchwald. Estab. 1980—*Milkweed Chronicle*/1984—*Milkweed Editions*. Small press with emphasis on literary and visual arts work. Publishes hardcover and paperback originals. Books: book text quality—acid-free paper; offset printing; perfect or hardcover binding; illustrations in all books; average print order: 2,000; first novel print order depends on book. Averages 12 total titles/year. Number of fiction titles "depends on mss."
Needs: Contemporary, experimental, literary. Looking for excellent writing. No romance, mysteries, science fiction. Recently published *Aquaboogie*, by Susan Straight; *Agassiz*, by Sandra Birdsell; and *Cracking India*, by Bapsi Sidhwa.
How to Contact: Accepts unsolicited mss. Submit outline/synopsis and 2 sample chapters. SASE. Reports in 1 month on queries; 2 months on mss. Simultaneous and photocopied submissions OK. Accepts computer printouts. "Please send for guidelines. Must enclose SASE."
Terms: Authors are paid in royalties of 10%; advance is negotiable; 10 author's copies. Sends galleys to author. Book catalog for 3 first class stamps.
Advice: "Read good contemporary fiction; find your own voice. Do not send us pornographic work, or work in which violence is done to women or children or men."

*MOSAIC PRESS, Fine Miniature Books, (II, IV), 358 Oliver Rd., Cincinnati OH 45215. (513)761-5977. Publisher: Miriam Irwin. Estab. 1977. Publishes hardcover originals in miniature format. Books: acid-free archival paper; litho or letter press printing; hardbound, cloth, leather or half-leather binding; illustrations; average print order: 2,000. Plans to publish 2 new authors this year. Averages 4 total titles, 1 fiction title each year. Occasionally buys juvenile mss with or without illustrations.
Needs: Comics, historical, humor/satire, literary, regional, religious/inspirational, romance, and young adult (historical, sports). "Our books are short (3,500 words maximum). No fantasy, science fiction or occult." Published *Scrimshaw*, by Carolyn G. Orr.
How to Contact: Accepts unsolicited mss. Query first or submit complete ms. SASE always. Simultaneous and photocopied submissions OK. Accepts computer printout submissions. Reports in 2 weeks. Publishes ms an average of 2 years after acceptance.
Terms: Pays in outright purchase of $50 and 5 author's copies. "We also do subsidy publishing of private editions. Negotiable arrangements." Book catalog $3. Free writer's guidelines with SASE.
Advice: "We want a good topic, beautifully written, in very few words; no full-length novel submissions. Regarding the author/editor relationship, the writer should trust editor; editor should trust designer. Read the publisher's stated purpose carefully."

MOTHER COURAGE PRESS, (II), 1533 Illinois St., Racine WI 53405. (414)634-1047. Executive Editor: Barbara Lindquist. Estab. 1981. Small feminist press. Publishes paperback originals. Books: perfect binding; sometimes illustrations; average print order: 3,000; first novel print order: 3,000. Averages 4 total titles, 1 fiction title each year.

Needs: Lesbian adventure, lesbian feminist/humor/satire, lesbian romance, lesbian science fiction, lesbian suspense/mystery. "Need strongly feminist, lesbian or women oriented, nothing written by men." Recently published *Mega*, by B.L. Holmes (science fiction lesbian); *Hodag Winter*, by Deborah Wiese.
How to Contact: Accepts unsolicited mss. Query first then submit outline/synopsis and 2 sample chapters. SAE. Reports in 6 weeks on queries; 3 months on mss. Simultaneous and photocopied submissions OK. Accepts computer printout submissions. Accepts electronic submissions via Macintosh.
Terms: Pays in royalties of 10-15%. Average advance: $250. Sends galleys to author. Book catalog free on request.
Advice: "Write a good query letter, including, the plot of the novel, main characters, possible markets, etc."

MOYER BELL LIMITED, Colonial Hill, RFD #1, Mt. Kisco NY 10549. (914)666-0084. President: Jennifer Moyer. Fiction Editor: Britt Bell. Estab. 1984. "Small publisher established to publish literature, reference and art books." Publishes hardcover and paperback originals and reprints. Books: Average print order 2,500; first novel print order: 2,500. Averages 14 total titles, 1 fiction title each year. Sometimes comments on rejected ms.
Needs: Serious literary fiction. No genre fiction. Published *The Other Garden*, by Francis Wyndham (literary).
How to Contact: Accepts unsolicited mss. Submit outline/synopsis and 2 sample chapters. SASE. Reports in 2 weeks on queries; 2 months on mss. Simultaneous submissions OK. Accepts electronic submissions.
Terms: Pays royalties of 10% minimum. Average advance $1,000. Sends galleys to author. Publishes ms 9-18 months after acceptance. Book catalog free.

THE NAIAD PRESS, INC., (I, II, IV), Box 10543, Tallahassee FL 32302. (904)539-5965. FAX: (904)539-9731. Editorial Director: Barbara Grier. Estab. 1973. Books: 55 lb. offset paper; sheet-fed offset; perfect-bound; average print order: 12,000; first novel print order: 12,000. Published new writers within the last year. Publishes 24 total books/year.
Needs: Lesbian fiction, all genres. Recently published *Murder by Tradition* (a Kate Delafield mystery), by Katherine V. Forrest; *Cop Out* (a Detective Inspector Carol Ashton mystery), by Claire McNab; and *Side by Side*, by Isabel Miller (author of *Patience and Sarah*).
How to Contact: Query first only. SASE. Reports in 3 weeks on queries; 3 months on mss. No simultaneous submissions; photocopied submissions OK "but we prefer original mss."
Terms: Pays 15% royalties using a standard recovery contract. Occasionally pays 7½% royalties against cover price. "Seldom gives advances and has never seen a first novel worthy of one. Believes authors are investments in their own and the company's future—that the best author is the author who produces a book every 12-18 months forever and knows that there is a *home* for that book." Publishes ms 1-2 years after acceptance. Book catalog for legal-sized SASE.
Advice: "We publish lesbian fiction primarily and prefer honest work (i.e., positive, upbeat lesbian characters). Lesbian content must be accurate . . . a lot of earlier lesbian novels were less than honest. No breast beating or complaining. Our fiction titles are becoming increasingly *genre* fiction, which we encourage. Original fiction in paperback is our main field, and its popularity increases. First novels are where the world is . . . really. Don't be a smart aleck. Send a simple letter, who, what, why, where, when, about yourself and a single page with at most a 2 paragraph precis of your book . . . not how good but WHAT IT IS ABOUT. Remember that no editor has time to waste, and the more accurate your self-description is, the more chance you have of getting a reader who will READ your book. Include telephone numbers, day and evening if possible. Get your homework done, be sure you are sending out the best book you can produce. Publishers are not sitting around waiting to help you write your book. Make it VERY easy for the editor to deal with you. The concise, smart, savvy, self-serving author wins the glass doughnut . . . every time."

Read the Business of Fiction section to learn the correct way to prepare and submit a manuscript.

THE NAUTICAL & AVIATION PUBLISHING CO. OF AMERICA INC., (II), 8 W. Madison St., Baltimore MD 21201. (301)659-0220. Publisher: Jan Snouck-Hurgronje. Estab. 1979. Small publisher interested in quality military history and literature. Publishes hardcover originals and reprints. Averages 10 total titles, 1-4 fiction titles each year. Sometimes comments on rejected mss.
Needs: Military/war (especially military history and Civil War). Looks for "novels with a strong military history orientation." Published *South to Java*, by Adm. William P. Mack and William Mack, Jr., (historical fiction); *The Captain*, Hartog (reprint); *Greenmantle*, John Buchan (reprint).
How to Contact: Accepts unsolicited mss. Query first or submit complete mss with cover letter. SASE necessary for return of mss. Agented fiction "miniscule." Reports on queries in 2-3 weeks; on mss in 3 weeks. Simultaneous and photocopied submissions OK. Accepts computer printout submissions.
Terms: Pays royalties of 15%. Advance negotiable. After acceptance publishes ms "as quickly as possible—next season." Book catalog free on request.
Advice: Publishing more fiction. Encourages first novelists. "We're interested in good writing—first novel or last novel. Keep it historical, put characters in a historical context. Professionalism counts. Know your subject. *Convince us.*"

NEW DIRECTIONS, (I, II), 80 Eighth Ave., New York NY 10011. (212)255-0230. Editor-in-Chief: Peter Glassgold. Small independent publisher. Publishes hardcover and paperback originals and reprints. Average print order: 1,000 hardback; 3,000 paperback. Sometimes critiques rejected ms.
Needs: "Mostly avant-garde; will look at everything, including poetry."
How to Contact: Accepts unsolicited mss. Query first with outline/synopsis and sample chapters. SASE. Reports in 6-8 weeks on queries; 3-4 months on mss. Photocopied submissions OK. Accepts computer printout submissions.
Terms: Pays royalties. Offers advance. Publishes ms at least 1 year after acceptance, "depends on type of book."
Advice: "Try to get published in a literary magazine first to establish a writing reputation and for the experience."

NEW RIVERS PRESS, Suite 910, 420 North 5th St., Minneapolis MN 55401. Publisher: C.W. Truesdale. Estab. 1968. Plans 5 fiction titles in 1992.
Needs: Contemporary, literary, experimental, translations. "No popular fantasy/romance. Nothing pious, polemical (unless very good other redeeming qualities). We are interested in only quality literature and always have been (though our concentration in the past has been poetry)." Published *Out Far, in Deep*, by Alvin Handleman (short stories); *Borrowed Voices*, by Roger Sheffer (short stories); and *Suburban Metaphysics*, by Ronald J. Rindo (short stories).
How to Contact: Query. SASE. Reports in 2 months on queries; within 2 months of query approval on mss. Photocopied submissions OK. "No multiple submissions tolerated."
Terms: Pays 100 author's copies; also pays royalties; no advance. Minnesota Voices Series pays authors $500 plus 15% royalties on list price for second and subsequent printings. Free book catalog.
Advice: "We are not really concerned with trends. We read for quality, which experience has taught can be very eclectic and can come sometimes from out of nowhere. We are interested in publishing short fiction (as well as poetry and translations) because it is and has been a great indigenous American form and is almost completely ignored by the commercial houses. Find a *real* subject, something that belongs to you and not what you think or surmise that you should be doing by current standards and fads."

NEW VICTORIA PUBLISHERS, Box 27, Norwich VT 05055. (802)649-5297. Editor: Claudia Lamperti. Publishes trade paperback originals. Averages 4-5 titles/year.
Needs: Adventure, erotica, ethnic, fantasy, lesbian, historical, humor, feminist, mystery, romance, science fiction and western. Looking for "strong feminist characters, also strong plot and action. We will consider most anything if it is well written and appeals to a lesbian/feminist audience." Publishes anthologies or special editions. Recently published *Cody Angel*, by Joanne Whitfield; *Woman with Red Hair*, by Sigrid Brunel; and *Death by the Riverside*, by Jean Redmann.
How to Contact: Submit outline/synopsis and sample chapters. SASE. Reports in 2 weeks on queries; 1 month on mss. Photocopied and disk submissions OK.
Terms: Pays royalties of 10%.
Advice: "We would particularly enjoy a humorous novel."

NEWEST PUBLISHERS LTD., (IV), #310, 10359 Whyte Ave., Edmonton, Alberta T6E 1Z9 Canada. General Manager: Liz Grieve. Estab. 1977. Publishes paperback originals. Published new writers within the last year. Plans 1 first novel this year. Averages 7 total titles, 2 fiction titles each year. Sometimes offers brief comments on rejected ms.
Needs: Literary. "Our press is most interested in western Canadian literature." Recently published *Breathing Water*, by Joan Crate; *Last One Home*, by Fred Stenson; *Grace Lake*, by Glen Huser; *Mostly Country*, by Rosemary Nixon; all literary.
How to Contact: Accepts unsolicited mss. Query first or submit outline/synopsis and 3 sample chapters. SASE (IRC) necessary for return of manuscript. Reports in 2 weeks on queries; 3 months on mss. Accepts computer printouts, photocopied and electronic submissions.
Terms: Pays royalties of 10% minimum. Sends galleys to author. Publishes ms at least 1 year after acceptance. Book catalog for 9 × 12 SASE or IRC.

‡NIGHTSHADE PRESS, (II), Ward Hill, Troy ME 04987. (207)948-3427. Contact: Carolyn Page or Ted Holmes. Estab. 1988. "Fulltime small press publishing literary magazine, poetry chapbooks and one short story reader. Short stories *only*, no novels." Publishes paperback originals. Books: 60 lb. paper; offset printing; saddle-stitched or perfect-bound; illustrations; average print order: 400. Published new writers within the last year. Averages about 20 total titles, 1 fiction title (short story reader) each year. Sometimes comments on rejected ms.
Needs: Contemporary, humor/satire, literary, mainstream, regional. No religious, romance, preschool, juvenile, young adult, fantasy, faction, horror, psychic/occult.
How to Contact: Accepts unsolicited mss—short stories only. Will not read agented material. Reports in 2 weeks on queries; 1-2 months on mss. Photocopied submissions OK. Accepts computer printout and electronic submissions.
Terms: Pays 2 author's copies. Publishes ms about 1 year after acceptance. Writer's guidelines and book catalog for SASE.
Advice: "Would like to see more real humor; less gratuitous violence—the opposite of TV."

OMMATION PRESS, (II, IV), 5548 N. Sawyer, Chicago IL 60625. Imprints include *Mati Magazine, Ditto Rations Chapbook Series, Offset Offshoot Series, Salome: A Journal for the Performing Arts, Dialogues on Dance Series.* Editorial Director: Effie Mihopoulos. Estab. 1975. Rarely comments on rejected mss.
Needs: Contemporary, literary, experimental, feminist, prose poetry. "For the Dialogues on Dance Series, dance-related fiction; for the Offset Offshoot Series, poetry mss, including prose poems." Published *Victims Of The Latest Dance Craze*, by Cornelius Eady (1985 Lamont Selection by Academy of American Poets); *Invisible Mirror*, by Michael Cadnum.
How to Contact: Submit complete ms with SASE. Simultaneous, if so indicated, and photocopied submissions OK. Reports in 1 month.
Terms: Pays 50 author's copies (and $100 honorarium if grant money available). Book catalog for #10 SASE.

OPEN HAND PUBLISHING, INC., P.O. Box 22048, Seattle WA 98122. (206)323-3868. Manuscript Editor: Pat Andrus. Estab. 1981. Small publisher of books. Publishes hardcover and paperback originals and reprints. Books: 55 or 60 lb. paper; offset printing; perfect-bound and case-bound; average print order: 5,000; first novel print order: 3,500. Published new writers within the last year. Plans 1 first novel this year. Averages 4 total titles/year. Sometimes comments on rejected mss.
Needs: Ethnic, juvenile (historical), young adult/teen (historical). Published *Love, Debra*, by Fritz Hamilton (human interest).
How to Contact: Accepts unsolicited mss. Query first or submit outline/synopsis and 2 sample chapters. SASE. Reports in 3 weeks on queries; 6 weeks on mss. Simultaneous and photocopied submissions OK. Accepts computer printout submissions. Must be double-spaced.
Terms: Pays royalties (negotiable). "Reports in sales and royalty sent out at 6-month intervals." Sends galleys to author. Publishes ms 1-2 years after acceptance. Writer's guidelines available upon request.

 The double dagger before a listing indicates that the listing is new in this edition. New markets are often the most receptive to freelance contributions.

ORCA BOOK PUBLISHERS LTD., (I, IV), P.O. Box 5626, Sta. B, Victoria, British Columbia V8R 6S4 Canada. (604)380-1229. Publisher: R.J. Tyrrell. Estab. 1984. "Regional publisher of West Coast-oriented titles." Publishes hardcover and paperback originals. Books: quality 60 lb. book stock paper; illustrations; average print order: 3,000-5,000; first novel print order: 2,000-3,000. Plans 1-2 first novels this year. Averages 12 total titles, 2-3 fiction titles each year. Sometimes comments on rejected ms.
Needs: Contemporary, juvenile (5-9 years), literary, mainstream, young adult/teen (10-18 years). Looking for "contemporary fiction." No "romance, science fiction."
How to Contact: Query first, then submit outline/synopsis and 1 or 2 sample chapters. SASE. Agented fiction 20%. Reports in 2 weeks on queries; 1-2 months on mss. Photocopied submissions OK. Accepts computer printout submissions.
Terms: Pays royalties of 10%; $500 average advance. Sends galleys to author. Publishes ms 6 months-1 year after acceptance. Writer's guidelines for SASE (IRC). Book catalog for 8½×11 SASE (IRC).
Advice: "We are looking to promote and publish new West Coast writers, especially Canadians."

OUR CHILD PRESS, 800 Maple Glen Lane, Wayne PA 19087. (215)964-0606. CEO: Carol Hallenbeck. Estab. 1984. Publishes hardcover and paperback originals and reprints. Published new writers within the last year. Plans 2 first novels this year. Plans 2 titles this year. Sometimes comments on rejected ms.
Needs: Adventure, contemporary, fantasy, juvenile (5-9 yrs.), preschool/picture book and young adult/teen (10-18 years). Especially interested in books on adoption or learning disabilities. Published *Don't Call Me Marda*, by Sheila Welch (juvenile); and *Oliver—An Adoption Story*, by Lois Wickstrom.
How to Contact: Does not accept unsolicited mss. Query first. Reports in 2 weeks on queries; 2 months on mss. Simultaneous and photocopied submissions OK. Accepts computer printout submissions.
Terms: Pays royalties of 5% minimum. Publishes ms up to 6 months after acceptance. Book catalog free.

THE OVERLOOK PRESS, 149 Wooster St., New York NY 10012. (212)477-7162. Estab. 1972. Small-staffed, full-time operation. Publishes hardcover and paperback originals and reprints. Averages 30 total titles; 7 fiction titles each year. Occasionally critiques rejected mss.
Needs: Fantasy, juvenile (fantasy, historical, sports, contemporary), literary, psychic/supernatural/occult, regional (Hudson Valley), science fiction, translations. No romance or horror. Recently published *The Book of the Beast*, by Tanith Lee (science fiction); *Klee*, by Phillipe Compte (art); *The Very Rich Hours of Count von Stauffenberg*, by Paul West (novel).
How to Contact: Query first or submit outline/synopsis. SASE. Allow up to 6 months for reports on queries. Simultaneous and photocopied submissions OK.
Terms: Vary.

PADRE PRODUCTIONS, (II), Box 840, Arroyo Grande CA 93421-0840. (805)473-1947. Accepts fiction and poetry. See The Press of MacDonald and Reinecke.

PANDO PUBLICATIONS, (II), 540 Longleaf Dr., Roswell GA 30075. (404)587-3363. Editorial Contact Person: Andrew Bernstein. Estab. 1987. "Two person, full-time book publisher." Publishes hardcover and paperback originals. Books: 60 lb. paper; perfect-bound, Smythe-sewn or hardcover binding; average print order: 3,000-9,000. Averages 6-10 total titles each year. Rarely comments on rejected mss.
Needs: Adventure, historical, humor/satire, juvenile (animal, easy-to-read, historical, sports, spy/adventure, contemporary), mainstream, military/war, regional, science fiction, suspense/mystery, young adult/teen (easy-to-read, fantasy/science fiction, historical, problem novels, sports, spy/adventure).
How to Contact: Accepts unsolicited mss. Submit outline/synopsis and 3 sample chapters. SASE for ms. Reports in 1 month on queries; 3-4 months on ms. Simultaneous and photocopied submissions OK. Computer printout submissions are acceptable. Accepts electronic submissions via WordPerfect.
Terms: Pays royalties of 6-12½%. Average advance is about ⅓ of royalty of 1st run; negotiable. Sends galleys to author. Publishes ms 6 months after acceptance.
Advice: Would like to see "more children's stories based on myth and legend, current happenings (world events, politics, demographic movements, social problems, ecological concerns, medical problems, growing up in a TV-VCR-cable-computer world, and so on)."

THE PAPER BAG PRESS, (I, II), P.O. Box 268805, Chicago IL 60626-8805. (312)285-7972. Editor: Michael H. Brownstein. Estab. 1988. "Small press with a small staff." Publishes paperback originals. Books: regular paper; Xerox printing; saddle stapled binding; photocopy illustrations; average print order: 200. Published new writers within the last year. Averages 2 total titles, 1 fiction title each year. Always comments on rejected mss.
Needs: Adventure, contemporary, erotica, ethnic, experimental, fantasy, feminist, historical, horror, humor/satire, literary, mainstream, military/war, science fiction, short story collection, suspense/mystery, western. "We will only consider collections of short fiction. We never take short stories longer than 500 words."
How to Contact: Accepts unsolicited mss. Submit complete manuscript with cover letter. SASE. Reports in 1 week to 2 months on queries; 1 week to 3 months on mss. Photocopied submissions OK. Accepts computer printout submissions.
Terms: Provides author's copies "depends on press run;" honorarium; payment depends on grant/award money. Sometimes sends galleys to author. Writer's guidlines free for SASE.
Advice: "Too often the fiction we get is sloppy, needs tremendous editing and does not follow our guidelines that all short stories be under 500 words."

PAPIER-MACHE PRESS, (IV), 795 Via Manzana, Watsonville CA 95076. (408)726-2933. Editor/Publisher: Sandra Martz. Estab. 1984. Three-person operation on a full-time basis. Publishes anthologies and "poetry and fiction" originals. Books: 60-70 lb. offset paper; perfect-bound or case-bound; photographs; average print order: 3,000-6,000 copies. Published new writers within the last year. Publishes 4-6 total titles/year; 4-6 fiction/poetry titles/year.
Needs: Contemporary, feminist, short story collections, women's. Recently published fiction by Mary Ann Ashley, Molly Martin, Ruthann Robson; and *Merle's and Marilyn's Mink Ranch*, by Randeane Tetu.
How to Contact: Query first. SASE. Reports in 2 months on queries; 6 months on mss. Simultaneous and photocopied submissions OK. Accepts computer printouts.
Terms: Standard royalty agreements for novels/fiction collections. Complimentary copies for anthology contributors; honorarium for contributors when anthologies go into second printings.
Advice: "Indicate with your manuscript whether or not you are open to revision suggestions. Always indicate on original submission if this is a simultaneous submission or a previously published work. We can handle either, but only if we know in advance. Absolutely essential to query first."

PATH PRESS, INC., (II), Suite 724, 53 W. Jackson, Chicago IL 60604. (312)663-0167. FAX: (312)663-0318. Editorial Director: Herman C. Gilbert. "Small independent publisher which specializes in books by, for and about Black Americans and Third World Peoples." Published new writers within the last year. Averages 6 total titles, 3 fiction titles each year. Occasionally critiques rejected ms.
Needs: Ethnic, historical, sports, and short story collections. Needs for novels include "black or minority-oriented novels of any genre, style or subject." Published *Brown Sky*, by David Covin (a novel of World War II); *Congo Crew*, by William Goodlett (a novel set in Africa during 1960-61).
How to Contact: Accepts unsolicited mss. Query first or submit outline/synopsis and 5 sample chapters with SASE. Reports in 2 months on queries; 4 months on mss. Simultaneous and photocopied submissions OK. Accepts computer printout submissions.
Terms: Pays in royalties.
Advice: "Deal honestly with your subject matter and with your characters. Dig deeply into the motivations of your characters, regardless how painful it might be to you personally."

PAYCOCK PRESS, (II), Apt. #1, 5025 Bradley Blvd., Chevy Chase MD 20815. (301)656-5146. Editor/Publisher: Richard Peabody. Estab. 1976. Small independent publisher with international distribution. Publishes paperback originals and reprints. Books: 55 lb. natural paper; offset printing; perfect-bound; some illustrations; average print order: 1,000; first novel print order: 1,000. Encourages new writers. Averages 1 title each year. Occasionally comments on rejected mss. "Recently started producing audio tapes of music/spoken-word material."
Needs: Contemporary, literary, experimental, humor/satire and translations. "No tedious AWP résumé-conscious writing or NEA-funded minimalism. We'd be interested in a good first novel that deals with the musical changes of the past few years." Recently published *The Love Letter Hack*, by Michael Brondoli (contemporary/literary); *Natural History*, by George Myers, Jr. (poems and stories); and *The Walking Rain*, by Fortune Nagle (poems and stories).

Close-up

Sandra Martz
Publisher/Editor
Papier-Mache Press

Although Papier-Mache Press receives 15 to 45 queries a day, Publisher/Editor Sandra Martz reads every one. "You never know, it could be the last one you look at that really fits," says Martz.

In 1984 Martz and some members of her writing group made a call for entries for an anthology with a theme of women's participation in the Olympics. Although the original project never made it to press, the response helped convince Martz that there was a real need for a press devoted to developing new women writers and poets who write about traditional women's issues. She established Papier-Mache in the same year.

"Women need a place and an audience to push the boundaries," she says.

Essential to Martz and Papier-Mache is maintaining strong, long-lasting relationships with authors. "I'd never ask someone to change something more than they felt comfortable with . . . I don't believe in compromise; collaboration, yes; but compromise, no."

Papier-Mache is not strictly a literary or feminist press—it's mainstream, too, says Martz. About her upcoming projects she says she wants them " . . . radical yet accessible."

Today, Martz can't imagine not being completely immersed in her small press, but someday she might look into other projects. Such as? "Possibly an annual literary review, or relocating someday to Nevada and having a retreat—to have people visit with a focus on mid-life or older women." She's also thought about creating The Papier-Mache Foundation, a nonprofit organization for literary publications.

"Because I'm 46 and am concerned about issues facing older women, that's what I'm focusing on right now," says Martz. Her anthology of writings for and about women and aging, *When I Am an Old Woman I Shall Wear Purple*, has sold more than 150,000 copies and was nominated for the ABBY Award by the American Booksellers Association. The ABBY stands for American Booksellers Book of the Year and is given to the book booksellers had the most fun selling. "It verified to me that there's an issue around mid-life women and men as well. It also told me that booksellers appreciated this material."

The celebratory treatment of aging has struck a chord in readers young and old alike. The overwhelming success of the anthology has helped establish an editorial philosophy that aging is of concern to women, and it is a niche that Papier-Mache can fill.

"It's been suggested to me to include some of the feelings of men on aging, but I'm not quite comfortable with that. I may be someday, but I'm not looking into that area right now," Martz says. An area she may look into is women's attitudes toward work.

Because of the success of *When I Am an Old Woman*, this is the first year Martz has actually be able to hire staff. Yet she's firmly committed to keeping the press a home-based business. She's also committed to her authors and to reading every manuscript she receives.

—Donna Collingwood

How to Contact: Query with SASE. Reports in 1 week on queries; 1 month on mss. Photocopied submissions OK. Accepts computer printout submissions.
Terms: Pays in author's copies—10% of print run plus 50% of all sales "after/if we break even on book." No advance. Sends galleys to author.
Advice: "Keep trying. Many good writers simply quit. Many mediocre writers keep writing, eventually get published, and become better writers. If the big magazines won't publish you, try the small magazines, try the local newspaper. Always read your fiction aloud. If you think something is *silly*, no doubt we'd be embarrassed too. Write the kind of stories you'd like to read and can't seem to find. We are more concerned with *how* a novelist says what he/she says, than with *what* he/she says. We are more interested in *right now* than in books about the '50s, '60s, '70s, etc. We are publishing more in anthology format, and encourage first novelists."

PEACHTREE PUBLISHERS, LTD., (II), 494 Armour Circle NE, Atlanta GA 30324. (404)876-8761. President: Margaret Quinlin. Estab. 1977. Small, independent publisher specializing in general interest publications, particularly of Southern origin. Publishes hardcover and paperback originals and hardcover reprints. Averages 20 total titles, 4 fiction titles each year. Average first novel print order 10,000-15,000 copies.
Needs: Contemporary, literary, mainstream, regional, and short story collections. "We are primarily seeking Southern fiction: Southern themes, characters, and/or locales." No science fiction/fantasy, children's/young adult, horror, religious, romance, historical or mystery/suspense. Published *The Blue Valleys,* by Robert Morgan (stories); *The Song of Daniel,* by Philip Lee Williams; and *To Dance with the White Dog,* by Terry Kay.
How to Contact: Accepts unsolicited mss. Query, submit outline/synopsis and 50 pages, or submit complete ms with SASE. Reports in 1 month on queries; 3 months on mss. Simultaneous and photocopied submissions OK. Accepts computer printout submissions.
Terms: Pays in royalties. Sends galleys to author. Free writer's guidelines and book catalog.
Advice: "We encourage original efforts in first novels."

‡PERMEABLE PRESS, (I), Suite 409-A, 350 Townsend St., San Francisco CA 94107. (415)978-9737. Imprints are Xerotic Ephemera, Puck! Publisher: Brian Clark. Editor: Kurt Putnam. Estab. 1984. "Small literary press with inhouse design and typesetting." Publishes hardcover and paperback originals and paperback reprints. Books: 60 lb. paper; offset printing; perfect-bound; illustrations; average print order: 3,500. Published new writers within the last year. Plans 1 first novel this year. Averages 3 total titles, all fiction, each year. Sometimes comments on rejected ms.
Needs: Erotica, experimental, feminist, gay, historical, juvenile, lesbian, literary, preschool/picture book, psychic/supernatural/occult, science fiction, short story collections. Looking for "cyberpunk; conspiracy. Should be challenging to read." No romance. Recently published *Shaman,* by Hugh Fox (experimental memoir); and *The Royal Elephant,* by Lorraine Morrison (children's).
How to Contact: Accepts unsolicited mss. Query first or submit outline/synopsis and 3 sample chapters. SASE. Reports in 4-6 weeks on queries; 3 months on mss. Photocopied submissions OK. Accepts computer printout submissions "if laser." Accepts electronic submissions.
Terms: Pays royalties of 5-20%. Author's copies vary. Honorarium depends on grant/award money. Sends galleys to author. Writer's guidelines and book catalog for 9×12 SAE and 4 first class stamps.
Advice: "As a design firm our business has grown rapidly in several areas. Consequently we are currently looking for hot new titles as well as bargain reprint rights."

PIKESTAFF PUBLICATIONS, INC., (I, II), Box 127, Normal IL 61761. (309)452-4831. Imprints include The Pikestaff Press: Pikestaff Fiction Chapbooks; *The Pikestaff Forum,* general literary magazine. Editorial Directors: Robert D. Sutherland and James R. Scrimgeour. Estab. 1977. Small independent publisher with plans to expand gradually. Publishes hardcover and paperback originals. Books: paper varies; offset printing; b&w illustrations; average print order: 500-2,000. "One of the purposes of the press is to encourage new talent." Occasionally comments on rejected mss.
Needs: Contemporary, literary, and experimental. "No slick formula writing written with an eye to the commercial mass market or pure entertainment that does not provide insights into the human condition. Not interested in heroic fantasy (dungeons & dragons, swords & sorcery); science fiction

Market categories: (I) Beginning; (II) General; (III) Prestige; (IV) Specialized.

of the space-opera variety; westerns; mysteries; love-romance; gothic adventure; or pornography (sex-ploitation)." Published fiction by Constance Pierce and Linnea Johnson.

How to Contact: Query or submit outline/synopsis and 1-2 sample chapters. "Anyone may inquire; affirmative responses may submit ms." SASE. Reports in 1 month on queries; 3 months on mss. No simultaneous or photocopied submissions. Accepts computer printout submissions.

Terms: Negotiates terms with author. Sends galleys to author. Publishes ms within 1 year after acceptance.

Advice: "Have fictional characters we can really *care* about; we are tired of disembodied characters wandering about in their heads unable to relate to other people or the world about them. Avoid too much TELLING; let the reader participate by leaving something for him or her to do. Yet avoid vagueness, opaqueness, personal or 'private' symbolisms and allusions. Here we regard the relationship between the writer and editor as a cooperative relationship—we are colleagues in getting the book out. The writer has an obligation to do the best self-editing job of which he or she is capable; writers should not rely on editors to make their books presentable. Don't give up easily; understand your reasons for wanting the work published (personal satisfaction? money? fame? to 'prove' something? to 'be a novelist'? etc.). Ask yourself honestly, Should it be published? What can it provide for a reader that makes it worth part of that reader's *lifetime* to read? Be prepared for shocks and disappointments; study contracts carefully and retain as many rights and as much control over the book's appearance as possible. Be prepared to learn how to be your own best promoter and publicist."

PINEAPPLE PRESS, (II), P.O. Drawer 16008, Southside Station, Sarasota FL 34239. (813)952-1085. Executive Editor: June Cussen. Estab. 1982. Small independent trade publisher. Publishes hardcover and paperback originals and paperback reprints. Books: quality paper; offset printing; Smythe-sewn or perfect-bound; illustrations occasionally; average print order: 5,000; first novel print order: 2,000-5,000. Published new writers within the last year. Averages 12 total titles each year. Occasionally critiques rejected ms.

Needs: Contemporary, experimental, historical, environmental, regional, how-to and reference. Recently published *Princess of the Everglades*, by Charles Mink (novel).

How to Contact: Prefers query, outline or one-page synopsis with sample chapters (including the first) and SASE. Then if requested, submit complete ms with SASE. Reports in 6 weeks. Simultaneous and photocopied submissions OK. Accepts computer printout submissions.

Terms: Pays royalties of 7½-15%. Advance is not usually offered. "Basically, it is an individual agreement with each author depending on the book." Sends galleys to author. Book catalog sent if label and 52¢ postage enclosed.

Advice: "We publish both Florida regional books and general trade fiction and nonfiction. Quality first novels will be published. We regard the author/editor relationship as a trusting relationship with communication open both ways. Learn all you can about the publishing process and about how to promote your book once it is published."

PIPPIN PRESS, 229 East 85th Street, Gracie Station Box 92, New York NY 10028. (212)288-4920. Publisher: Barbara Francis. Estab. 1987. "Small, independent children's book company, formed by the former editor-in-chief of Prentice Hall's juvenile division." Publishes hardcover originals. Books: 135-150 GSM offset-semi-matte paper (for picture books); offset, sheet-fed printing; Smythe-sewn binding; full color, black and white line illustrations and half tone, b&w and full color photographs. Averages 8-12 titles each year. Sometimes comments on rejected mss.

Needs: Juvenile only (5-9 yrs. including animal, easy-to-read, fantasy, science, humorous, spy/adventure). "I am interested in humorous novels for children of about 7-12 and in picture books with the focus on humor."

How to Contact: Accepts unsolicited mss. Query first or submit outline/synopsis and 2 sample chapters. SASE. Reports in 2-3 weeks on queries; 3 months on mss. Simultaneous submissions OK. Accepts computer printout submissions.

Terms: Pays royalties. Sends galleys to author. Publication time after ms is accepted "depends on the amount of revision required, type of illustration, etc."

*POCAHONTAS PRESS, INC., (II, IV), Manuscript Memories, 832 Hulcheson Rd., Blacksburg VA 24060. (703)951-0467. Editorial contact person: Mary C. Holliman. Estab. 1984. "One-person operation on part-time basis, with several part-time colleagues. Subjects not limited, but stories about real people are almost always required. Main intended audience is youth—young adults, ages 10-18." Books: 70 lb. white offset paper; offset litho printing; perfect binding; illustrations; average print order:

3,000-5,000. Averages 4 total titles, 2-3 fiction titles each year. Usually critiques or comments on rejected mss.

Needs: "Stories based on historical facts about real people." Contemporary, ethnic, historical, sports, regional, translations, western. "I will treat a short story as a book, with illustrations and a translation into Spanish or French and also Chinese someday." No fantasy or horror. Published *From Lions to Lincoln*, by Fran Hartman; and *Mountain Summer*, by Bill Mashburn.

How to Contact: Accepts unsolicited mss. Query first. "I don't expect to be considering any new material until mid-1992. I need to complete current projects first." Reports in 1 month on queries; 1-2 months on mss. "I try to meet these deadlines but seldom succeed." Simultaneous, photocopied submissions OK. "If simultaneous, I would need to know up front what other options the author is considering." Accepts computer printout submissions.

Terms: Pays royalties of 10% maximum. $50 advance negotiable. Sends galleys to author. "I will subsidy publish—but expect book and author to meet the same qualifications as a regular author, and will pay royalties on all copies sold as well as pay back the author's investment as books are sold."

Advice: "Get an unbiased, non-friend editor and follow his or her suggestions. There's more good, publishable material out there than can ever all get published—don't get discouraged but keep trying—and keep revising."

‡POLESTAR BOOK PUBLISHERS, (I, II), P.O. Box 69382, Station K, Vancouver, British Columbia V5K 4W6 Canada. (604)251-9718. Publisher: Michelle Benjamin. Estab. 1983. "Small literary press with eclectic list of fiction, poetry, nonfiction and hockey books." Publishes paperback originals. Published new writers within the last year. Plans 2 first novels this year. Averages 10 total titles, 4-6 fiction titles each year. Sometimes comments on rejected ms.

Needs: Open. "No racist, sexist, violent themes/issues." Recently published *Rapid Transits*, by Holley Rubinsky (short stories); and *Disturbing the Peace*, by Caroline Woodward (short stories).

How to Contact: Accepts unsolicited mss. Submit outline/synopsis and 3 sample chapters. SASE. Agented fiction 10%. Reports in 1 month on queries; 6-8 weeks on mss. Simultaneous, photocopied submissions OK. Accepts computer printout submissions.

Terms: Pays royalties of 10-12%; and 10 author's copies. Advance negotiable; $400 average. Sends galleys to author. Publication time after acceptance varies. Book catalog free.

Advice: "We have a Polestar First Fiction Series. We like the excitement of discovering new writers ... feel *somewhat* that this is the role of the small press. We would like to see more passionate writing, less excess words."

THE POST-APOLLO PRESS, (I), 35 Marie St., Sausalito CA 94965. (415)332-1458. Publisher: Simone Fattal. Estab. 1982. Publishes paperback originals. Book: acid-free paper; lithography printing; perfect-bound; average print order: 3,000; first novel print order: 3,000. Published new writers within the last year. Averages 2 total titles, 1 fiction title each year. Sometimes comments on rejected ms.

Needs: Feminist, lesbian, literary, short story collections, spiritual and translations. No juvenile, horror, sports or romance. Recently published *Sitt Marie-Rose*, by Etel Adnan; *Home For The Summer*, by Georgina Kleege (psychological thriller); *Josef is Dying*, by Ulla Berkewicz.

How to Contact: Send query or complete ms with SASE. Reports in 3 months.

Terms: Pays royalties of 6½% minimum or by individual arrangement. Sends galleys to author. Publishes ms 1½ years after acceptance. Book catalog free.

PRAIRIE JOURNAL PRESS, (II, IV), Prairie Journal Trust, Box 997, Station G, Calgary, Alberta T3A 3G2 Canada. Estab. 1983. Small-press, noncommercial literary publisher. Publishes paperback originals. Books: bond paper; offset printing; stapled binding; b&w line drawings. Averages 2 total titles or anthologies/year. Occasionally critiques or comments on rejected ms if requested.

Needs: Literary. No romance, horror, pulp, erotica, magazine type, children's, adventure, formula, "western." Published *Prairie Journal Fiction, Prairie Journal Fiction II* (anthologies of short stories) and *Solstice* (short fiction on the theme of aging).

How to Contact: Accepts unsolicited mss. Query first and send Canadian postage or IRCs and $3 for sample copy, then submit outline/synopsis and 1-2 stories with SASE (IRC). Reports in 2 weeks. Photocopied submissions OK. Accepts computer printout submissions.

Terms: Pays 1 author's copy; honorarium depends on grant/award provided by the government or private/corporate donations. Sometimes sends galleys to author. Book catalog free on request to institutions; SAE with IRC for individuals. "No U.S. stamps!"

Advice: "We wish we had the means to promote more new writers. We often are seeking theme-related stories. We look for something different each time and try not to repeat types of stories."

THE PRAIRIE PUBLISHING COMPANY, Box 2997, Winnipeg, Manitoba R3C 4B5 Canada. (204)885-6496. Publisher: Ralph Watkins. Estab. 1969. Buys juvenile mss with illustrations. Books: 60 lb. high-bulk paper; offset printing; perfect-bound; line-drawings; average print order: 2,000; first novel print order: 2,000.
Needs: Open. Recently published: *The Homeplace*, (historical novel); *My Name is Marie Anne Gaboury*, (first French-Canadian woman in the Northwest); and *The Tale of Jonathan Thimblemouse*. Published work by previously unpublished writers within the last year.
How to Contact: Query with SASE or IRC. No simultaneous submissions; photocopied submissions OK. Reports in 1 month on queries, 6 weeks on mss. Publishes ms 4-6 months after acceptance.
Terms: Pays 10% in royalties. No advance. Free book catalog.
Advice: "We work on a manuscript with the intensity of a Max Perkins of Charles Scribner's Sons of New York. A clean, well-prepared manuscript can go a long way toward making an editor's job easier. On the other hand, the author should not attempt to anticipate the format of the book, which is a decision for the publisher to make. In order to succeed in today's market, the story must be tight, well written and to the point. Do not be discouraged by rejections."

PRESS GANG PUBLISHERS, (II, IV), 603 Powell St., Vancouver, British Columbia V6A 1H2 Canada. (604)253-2537. Estab. 1974. Feminist press, 2 full-time staff, 1 half-time staff. Publishes paperback originals and reprints. Books: paperback; offset printing; perfect-bound; average print order: 3,500; first novel print order: 2,500. Plans 4 first novels this year. Sometimes critiques rejected mss.
Needs: Looking for "feminist, mystery/suspense, short stories." Also accepts contemporary, erotica, ethnic (native women especially), humor/satire, lesbian, literary, science fiction. No children's/young adult/teen. Recently published *Sojourner's Truth*, by Lee Maracle; *Food and Spirits*, by Beth Brant (Canadian edition); and *Scuttlebutt*, by Jana Williams (Canadian edition).
How to Contact: Accepts unsolicited mss. Query first. SASE (IRC). Reports in 1 month on queries; 2-3 months on mss. Simultaneous and photocopied submissions OK. Accepts computer printout submissions. Accepts AT compatible discs.
Terms: Pays 8-10% royalties. Sends galleys to author. Book catalog free on request.

THE PRESS OF MACDONALD AND REINECKE (II,III), Padre Productions, Box 840, Arroyo Grande CA 93421-0840. (805)473-1947. Publisher: Lachlan P. MacDonald. Fiction Editor: Mack Sullivan. Estab. 1974. "Literary imprint of a small independent press." Publishes hardcover and paperback originals. Books: book paper; offset printing; Smythe case-bound and perfect-bound; illustrations; average print order: 3,000; first novel print order: 500-3,000. Publishes fiction by a previously unpublished writer "every 2-3 years." Plans 1 first novel this year. Averages 6 total titles, 1-2 fiction titles each year. Sometimes comments on rejected mss.
Needs: Historical, humor/satire, literary, mainstream, short story collections. Currently overstocked. No mystery, suspense, western, religious, military, adventure, fantasy, romance categories. Published *Joel in Tananar*, by Robert M. Walton (juvenile); *Contemporary Insanities*, by Charles Broshew (short fiction).
How to Contact: Accepts unsolicited mss. Submit outline/synopsis and 1-2 sample chapters. SASE. Agented fiction 5%. Reports on queries in 2 weeks; on mss in 2 months. Simultaneous and photocopied submissions OK.
Terms: Pays in royalties. Sends galleys to author. "Unfortunately, it may be 2 years" before publication after acceptance. Writer's guidelines for SASE. Book catalog for 6×9 SAE.
Advice: "Publishing less fiction than in the past. Demonstrate a following by documenting publication in literary magazines, general magazines or anthologies."

PUCKERBRUSH PRESS, (I,II), 76 Main St., Orono ME 04473. (207)581-3832. Publisher/Editor: Constance Hunting. Estab. 1979. One-person operation on part-time basis. Publishes paperback originals. Books: laser printing; perfect-bound; sometimes illustrations; average print order: 1,000; first novel print order: 1,000. Published new writers within the last year. Plans 1 first novel this year. Averages 3 total titles, 2 fiction titles each year. Sometimes comments on rejected ms. *If detailed comment, $500.*

Read the Business of Fiction section to learn the correct way to prepare and submit a manuscript.

Needs: Contemporary, experimental, literary.
How to Contact: Accepts unsolicited mss. Submit complete ms with cover letter. SASE. Reports in 2 weeks on queries; 2 months on mss.
Terms: Pays royalties of 10%; 10 author's copies. Sends galleys to author. Publishes ms usually 1 year after acceptance. Writer's guidelines for #10 SAE and 1 first class stamp. "I have a book list and flyers."

‡*Q.E.D. PRESS, (II), Subsidiary of Comp-Type, Inc., 155 Cypress St., Ft. Bragg CA 95437. (707)964-9520. Senior Editor: John Fremont. Estab. 1985. "Small press publisher subsidiary of mid-size production house." Publishes hardcover and paperback originals. Books: acid free recycled 60 lb. paper; offset or Cameron Belt printing; perfect or Smythe-sewn binding; average print order: 3,000; first novel print order: 1,000. Plans 1 first novel this year. Averages 10 total titles, 2-3 fiction titles each year.
Needs: Experimental, faction, literary, suspense/mystery, translations. "Our needs are minimal, but we'll jump on something we think is hot. No formula anything." Recently published *Tales From the Mountain*, by Miguel Torga (short story collection); *Weitchie*, by David Coe (environmental novel).
How to Contact: Accepts unsolicited mss. Submit outline/synopsis with 3 sample chapters. SASE. Agented fiction 10%. Reports in 3 weeks on queries; 5 weeks on mss. Photocopied submissions OK. Accepts computer printout submissions.
Terms: Pays royalties of 8-15%. *Subsidy publishes under another imprint.* Publishes ms 6 months to 2 years after acceptance. Writer's guidelines not available. Book catalog free.

QUARRY PRESS, (I,II), Box 1061, Kingston, Ontario K7L 4Y5 Canada. (613)548-8429. Managing Editor: Melanie Dugan. Estab. 1965. Small independent publisher with plans to expand. Publishes paperback originals. Books: Rolland tint paper; offset printing; perfect-bound; illustrations; average print order: 1,200; first novel print order: 1,200. Published new writers within the past year. Plans 1 first novel this year. Averages 20 total titles, 4 fiction titles each year. Sometimes comments on rejected mss.
Needs: Experimental, feminist, historical, literary, short story collections. Published *Ritual Slaughter,* by Sharon Drache; *Engaged Elsewhere,* edited by Kent Thompson (includes work by Mavis Gallant, Margaret Laurence, Dougles Glover, Ray Smitz, Keath Fraser and others); published fiction by previously unpublished writers within the last year.
How to Contact: Accepts unsolicited mss. Query first. SASE for query and ms. Reports in 4 months. Simultaneous and photocopied submissions OK. Accepts computer printout submissions.
Terms: Pays royalties of 7-10%. Advance: negotiable. Provides 5-10 author's copies. Sends galleys to author. Publishes ms 6-8 months after acceptance. Book catalog free on request.
Advice: "Publishing more fiction than in the past. Encourages first novelists. Canadian authors only for New Canadian Novelists Series. If mailing from US, need SAE with IRC (a must)."

*READ 'N RUN BOOKS, Subsidiary of Crumb Elbow Publishing, (I), Box 294, Rhododendron OR 97049. (503)622-4798. Imprints are Elbow Books, Research Centrex, Wind Flow Press, Silhouette Imprints, Tyre Press, Oregon Fever Books and Trillium Art Productions. Publisher: Michael P. Jones. Estab. 1978. Small independent publisher with three on staff. Publishes hardcover and paperback originals and reprints. Books: special order paper; offset printing; "usually a lot" of illustrations; average print order: varies. Published new writers within the last year. Plans 1 first novel this year. Averages 10 titles, 2 fiction titles each year. Sometimes comments on rejected ms; *$75 charge for critiques depending upon length. May be less or more.*
Needs: Adventure, contemporary, ethnic, experimental, fantasy, feminist, historical, horror, humor/satire, juvenile (animal, easy-to-read, fantasy, historical, sports, spy/adventure, contemporary), literary, mainstream, military/war, preschool/picture book, psychic/supernatural/occult, regional, religious/

The asterisk indicates a publisher who sometimes offers subsidy arrangements. Authors are asked to subsidize part of the cost of book production. See the introduction to Commercial Publishers for more information.

inspirational, romance (contemporary, historical), science fiction, short story collections, spiritual, suspense/mystery, translations, western, young adult/teen (easy-to-read, fantasy/science fiction, historical, problem novels, romance, sports, spy/adventure). Looking for fiction on "historical and wildlife" subjects. "Also, some creative short stories would be nice to see for a change. No pornography." Recently published *Umpqua Agriculture, 1851,* by Jesse Applegate; *Life on the Oregon,* by Alfred Setan; *Samuel Kimbrough Barlow: A Pioneer Road Builder of Oregon,* by Mary Barlow Wilkins. This year starting anthology to give writers a chance to express themselves about nature and the environment.
How to Contact: Accepts unsolicited ms. Query first. Submit outline/synopsis and complete ms with cover letter. SASE. Reports in 1 month on queries; 1-2 months on mss. Simultaneous and photocopied submissions OK. Accepts computer printout submissions.
Terms: Provides 5+ author's copies (negotiated). Sends galleys to author. Publishes ms 10-12 months after acceptance. *Subsidy publishes two books or more/year.* Terms vary from book to book. Writer's guidelines for 45¢ postage. Book catalog for SASE or IRC and $1.25 postage.
Advice: Publishing "more hardcover fiction books based on real-life events. They are in demand by libraries. Submit everything you have—even artwork. Also, if you have ideas for layout, provide those also. If you have an illustrator that you're working with, be sure to get them in touch with us. Do not by pushy! We are very busy and deal with a lot of people, which means you and your needs are equal to everyone else's. We are a great place for writers to get started if they have a professional working attitude and manner."

RED ALDER BOOKS, (IV), Box 2992, Santa Cruz CA 95063. (408)426-7082. Editorial Contact Person: David Steinberg, owner. Imprint: Pan-Erotic Review. Estab. 1974. Small, independent publisher. Publishes hardcover and paperback originals. Books: offset printing, case/perfect binding; some illustrations; average print order: 5,000. Averages 1 total title, 1 fiction title each year.
Needs: "Quality-conscious, provocative erotica." Erotica, feminist, lesbian, literary, short story collections. "Short stories only. No pornography, cliché sexual stories." Published *Erotic by Nature,* by Steinberg, editor (collection of erotic stories, poems, photographs).
How to Contact: Accepts and returns unsolicited mss. Query first. SASE for query and ms. Reports on queries in 6-8 weeks. Simultaneous and photocopied submissions OK. Accepts computer printout submissions.
Terms: Pays royalties of 8% minimum. Sends galleys to author.

RED DEER COLLEGE PRESS, (I, IV), Box 5005, Red Deer, Alberta T4N 5H5 Canada. (403)342-3321. Managing Editor: Dennis Johnson. Estab. 1975. Publishes hardcover and paperback originals. Books: offset paper; offset printing; hardcover/perfect-bound; average print order: 1,000-4,000; first novel print order: 2,500. Plans 2 first novels this year. Averages 10-12 total titles, 2 fiction titles each year. Sometimes comments on rejected mss.
Needs: Contemporary, experimental, literary, short story collections. No romance, sci-fi.
How to Contact: *Canadian authors only.* Does not accept unsolicited mss. Query first or submit outline/synopsis and 2 sample chapters. SASE. Agented fiction 10%. Reports in 1 month on queries; in 3 months on mss. Simultaneous and photocopied submissions OK. Accepts computer printout submissions.
Terms: Pays royalties of 8-10%. Advance is negotiable. Sends galleys to author. Publishes ms 1 year after acceptance. Book catalog for 9×12 SASE (IRC).
Advice: "Final manuscripts must be submitted on Mac disk in MS Word. Absolutely *no* unsolicited mss. Query first."

REFERENCE PRESS, (IV), Box 70, Teeswater, Ontario N0G 2S0 Canada. (519)392-6634. Imprints are RP Large Print Books. Editor: Gordon Ripley. Estab. 1982. Small independent Canadian publisher of library reference material, computer software and large print books. Hardcover and paperback originals and hardcover reprints. Books: 70 lb. Zepher laid paper; offset printing; casebound, some perfect-bound; average print order: 1,000. Published new writers within the last year. Averages 10 total titles, 4 fiction titles each year. Always comments on rejected mss.
Needs: Sports. Published *Canadian Sports Stories* (fiction, anthology); *Dance Me Outside* and *Born Indian,* by W.P. Kinsella (large print).
Terms: Pays in royalties of 10%; 5 author's copies. Writer's guidelines and book catalog free. Accepts unsolicited mss. Accepts electronic submissions.

‡RIO GRANDE PRESS, (I), Imprints include *Se La Vie Writer's Journal*, P.O. Box 371371, El Paso TX 79937. (915)595-2625. Publisher: Rosalie Avara. Estab. 1989. "One person operation on a half-time basis. Planning to expand to story anthologies and/or novelettes in 1992." Publishes paperback originals. Books: offset printing; saddle stitching binding; average print order: 50-75. Published new writers within the last year. Plans 2-3 first novels this year. Averages 10 total titles, 4 fiction titles each year. Sometimes comments on rejected ms.

Needs: Adventure, contemporary, ethnic, fantasy, humor/satire, literary, regional, short story collections, suspense/mystery. Looking for "general interest, slice of life stories; good, clean, wholesome stories about everyday people. No sex, nor porn, no science fiction (although I may consider flights of fantasy, day dreams, etc.), no religious. Any subject within the 'wholesome' limits. No experimental styles, just good conventional plot, characters, dialogue."

How to Contact: Query first then submit outline/synopsis and 1st/last sample chapters or 2 stories in a collection. SASE. Reports in 2 weeks on queries; 3-4 weeks on mss. Photocopied submissions OK. Accepts computer printout submissions.

Terms: Pays 1 author's copy, depends on grant/award money (if contest is involved, up to $25.) "Short story collections and/or novelettes—individual arrangements with author, depending on ms—probably a contributor's copy plus publication and review in *Se La Vie Writer's Journal*." Sends galleys to author (once only). Publishes ms 2-4 months after acceptance. Writer's guidelines for #10 SAE and 2 first class stamps. Book catalog for #10 SAE and 2 first class stamps.

Advice: "I enjoy working with writers new to fiction, especially when I see that they have really worked hard on their craft, i.e., cutting out all unnecessary words, action dialogue, interesting descriptive scenes, thought-out plots and well rounded characters that are believable. Please read listing carefully noting what type and subject of fiction is desired. Don't send the entire ms (book) packed in a heavy (costly) book box. Please send me a short cover letter giving brief history of your writing experience or credits. If none, just say so. Or, send me the first and last chapters, and one central character description (a short synopsis, may)." Would like to see more stories or novelettes with a Southwestern flavor; story collections centered around a central theme; novelettes that give a personal insight into age old problems of life."

RISING TIDE PRESS, (II), 5 Kivy St., Huntington Station NY 11746. (516)427-1289. Editor: Lee Boojamra. Estab. 1988. "Small, independent press, publishing lesbian fiction—novels only—no short stories." Publishes paperback trade originals. Books: 50-60 lb. offset paper; web printing; perfect-bound; average print order: 5,000; first novel print order: 4,000-6,000. Plans 4 first novels this year. Averages 4-6 total titles. Comments on rejected ms.

Needs: Lesbian adventure, contemporary, erotica, fantasy, feminist, lesbian, romance, science fiction, suspense/mystery, western. Looking for romance and mystery. "Nothing with heterosexual content." Recently published *Romancing The Dream*, by H.H. Johanna; *Edge of Passion*, by Shelley Smith.

How to Contact: Accept unsolicited mss with SASE. Photocopied submissions OK. Reports in 1 week on queries; 3-4 months on mss. Accepts computer printout submissions.

Terms: Pays 10-15% royalties. "We will assist writers who wish to self-publish for a nominal fee." Sends galleys to author. Publishes ms 6-18 months after acceptance. Writer's guidelines free for #10 SAE and 1 first class stamp.

‡RYDAL PRESS, (III, IV), P.O. Box 2247, Santa Fe NM 87504. (505)983-1680. Publisher: Clark Kimball. Estab. 1930. "Small fine press which resells its titles to larger houses." Publishes hardcover originals, "signed, limited fine editions in slipcase." Averages 2 total titles, both fiction, each year. *Will critique ms for $100 fee.*

Needs: Literary, regional, western. Looking for "thoughtful, important, polished novels, short short and essay collections." Nothing "non-redeeming; without value; hackneyed; amateurish." Recently published *Shields*, by N. Scott Momaday (Indian); and *Bear*, by John L. Sinclair (western).

How to Contact: Does not accept or return unsolicted mss. Query first with sample chapter. SASE. Include Social Security number with submission. Reports in 2 weeks on queries; 1 month on mss. Simultaneous and photocopied submissions OK. Accepts computer printout submissions.

Terms: Pays 10% author's copies plus royalty on reprint. "This is not self-publish; once our fine edition is published, we resell hard and soft rights to larger publishers." Sends galleys to author. Publishes ms 1 year after acceptance.

Advice: "Get someone who is not family or particular friend to critically read work. Listen to them." Would like to see more "finished, letter-perfect mss." Less "overdone themes with poor structure."

*SAMISDAT, (II), 456 Monroe Turnpike, Monroe CT 06468. Imprint: *Samisdat Magazine.* Editor/ Publisher: Merritt Clifton. Estab. 1973. Publishes paperback originals. Books: standard bond paper; offset printing; saddle-stitch or square-back binding; some illustrations; average print order: 300-500. Encourages new writers. "Over 60% of our titles are first books—about 1 first novel per year." Comments on rejected mss.
Needs: Short stories, novellas, literary, feminist, gay, lesbian, and regional. Published *An American Love Story*, by Robert Swisher (novel).
How to Contact: Query or submit complete ms. SASE always. Reports in 1 week on queries; time varies on mss.
Terms: No advance. Free book catalog with SASE. "Our author payments for books are a paradox: At this writing, we've published over 220 titles over the past 18 years, about 85% of which have earned the authors a profit. On the other hand, we've relatively seldom issued royalty checks—maybe 20 or 30 in all this time, and all for small amounts. We're also paradoxical in our modus operandi: *Authors cover our cash expenses* (this comes to about a third of the total publishing cost—we're supplying equipment and labor) in exchange for half of the press run, but we make no money from authors, and if we don't promote a book successfully, we still lose." Publishes ms from 2-6 months after acceptance.
Advice: "We do not wish to see *any* book-length ms submissions from anyone who has not already either published in our annual magazine, *Samisdat*, or at least subscribed for about a year to find out who we are and what we're doing. We are not a 'market' engaged in handling books as commodities. Submissions are getting much slicker, with a lot less guts to them. This is precisely the opposite of what we're after. Read the magazine. Submit stories or poems or chapters to it. When familiar with us, and our subscribers, query about an appropriate book ms. We don't publish books except as special issues of the magazine, and blind submissions stand absolutely no chance of acceptance at all. Go deep. Involve your characters with the outside world, as well as with each other. Use the most compact structure possible, bearing in mind that fiction is essentially drama without a stage. I no longer wish to see novels or queries about novels at all. My patience has been too severely abused by would-be novelists. I am still interested in the occasional chapbook-length short story or novella (up to about 10,000 words)."

SANDPIPER PRESS, (IV), Box 286, Brookings OR 97415. (503)469-5588. Owner: Marilyn Reed Riddle. Estab. 1979. One-person operation specializing in low-cost large-print 18 pt. books. Publishes paperback originals. Books: 70 lb. paper; saddle stitch binding, perfect-bound, 84 pages maximum; leatherette cover; b&w sketches or photos; average print order 2,000; no novels. Averages 1 title every 2 years. Occasionally critiques or comments on rejected mss.
Needs: From Native American "Indian" writers only, *true* visions and prophesies; from general public writers, unusual quotations, sayings.
How to Contact: Does not accept unsolicited mss. Query first or submit outline/synopsis. SASE. Reports in 1 month on queries; 1 month on mss. Simultaneous and photocopied submissions OK. Accepts computer printout submissions.
Terms: Pays 2 author's copies and $10 Native American. Publisher buys true story and owns copyright. Author may buy any number of copies at 40% discount and postage. Book catalog for #10 SAE and 1 first class stamp.

‡THE SAVANT GARDE WORKSHOP, (III, IV), a privately-owned affiliate of The Savant Garde Institute, Ltd., P.O. Box 1650, Sag Harbor NY 11963. (516)725-1414. Publisher: Vilna Jorgen II. Estab. 1953. "Midsize multiple-media publisher." Publishes hardcover and paperback originals and reprints. Averages 2 total titles. Sometimes comments on rejected ms.
Needs: Contemporary, fantasy, feminist, humanist, literary, philosophical, science fiction, spiritual, suspense/mystery. "We are open to the best, whatever it is." No "mediocrity, pot boilers, sadism or horror or erotica with no redeeming message." Recently published *SKEETS: The New Frankenstein Chronicles*, by Artemis Smith (avant garde).

 The double dagger before a listing indicates that the listing is new in this edition. New markets are often the most receptive to freelance contributions.

How to Contact: Query first with SASE. Agented fiction 50%. Reports in 1 week on queries; 3 weeks on mss. Simultaneous, photocopied submissions OK. Accepts computer printout submissions. Accepts electronic submissions.

Terms: Average advance: $500, provides author's copies, honorarium (depends on grant/award money). Terms set by individual arrangement with author depending on the book and previous professional experience. Sends galleys to author. Publishes ms 18 months after acceptance. Writer's guidelines free.

Advice: "Most of the time we recommend authors to literary agents who can get better deals for them with other publishers, since we are looking for extremely rare offerings. We are not interested in the usual commercial submissions. Convince us you are a real artist, not a hacker." Would like to see more "thinking for the 21st Century of Nobel Prize calibre."

SCARE WARE, (I,IV), P.O. Box 705, Salem OR 97308. Editorial Contact Person: Michelle Marr. Estab. 1990. "One-person operation publishing books on disks." Books: 5¼" computer disks for IBM and compatible computers. Plans 10 first novels this year. Plans for 12+ total titles, all fiction, each year. Sometimes comments on rejected ms.

Needs: Horror, psychic/supernatural/occult. "I plan to use horror novels and story collections, probably none over 75,000 words. No juvenile, romance, science fiction, etc."

How to Contact: Accepts unsolicited mss. Query first, then submit outline/synopsis and sample chapters or completed ms. SASE. Reports in 2 weeks on queries; 2 months on mss. Photocopied submissions OK. Accepts computer printouts. Accepts electronic submissions.

Terms: Pays royalties of 25%, and 1 author's copy. No advances at this time. Sends galleys to author. Publishes ms 2 months after acceptance. Writer's guidelines for #10 SASE. Book catalog free on request (when available). A sample novella is now available for $1, check payable to Michelle Marr.

Advice: "I would like to work with new novelists; I feel that the electronic market is easier to break into as there is less expense involved."

SEAL PRESS, (IV), 3131 Western Ave., Seattle WA 98121. (206)283-7844. President: Faith Conlon. Estab. 1976. Publishes hardcover and paperback originals. Books: acid-free paper; offset printing; perfect or cloth binding; average print order: 4,000. Averages 8-12 total titles, including 5-6 fiction titles each year. Sometimes critiques rejected ms "very briefly."

Needs: Ethnic, feminist, lesbian, literary, mystery, young adult, short story collections. "We publish women only. Work must be feminist, non-racist, non-homophobic." Recently published *Disappearing Moon Cafe*, by Sky Lee (literary novel); *No Forwarding Address*, by Elisabeth Bowers (mystery novel); *No More Secrets*, by Nina Weinstein (young adult novel).

How to Contact: Query first. SASE. Reports in 1-2 months. Accepts "readable" computer printouts.

Terms: "Standard publishing practices; do not wish to disclose specifics." Sends galleys to author. Book catalog for SAE and 65¢ postage.

SECOND CHANCE PRESS AND THE PERMANENT PRESS, (II), Noyac Rd., Sag Harbor NY 11963. (516)725-1101. Co-publisher: Judith Shepard. Estab. 1977. Mid-size, independent publisher. Publishes hardcover originals and reprints. Books: hardcover; average print order: 1,500-2,000; first novel print order: 1,500-2,000. Published new writers within the last year. Plans 4 first novels this year. Averages 10 total titles; all fiction, each year.

Needs: Contemporary, humor/satire, literary, supsense/mystery. "I like novels that have a unique point of view and have a high quality of writing." No gothic, romance, horror, science fiction, pulp. Published *Dies Irae*, by Ruby Spinell (literary/mystery); *The Affair at Honey Hill*, by Berry Fleming (literary/historical); and *Zulus*, by Percival Everett (literary/futuristic).

How to Contact: Query first. Submit outline and no more than 2 chapters. SASE. Agented fiction 15%. Reports in 6 weeks on queries; 3 months on mss. Photocopied submissions OK.

Terms: Pays royalties of 10-15%. Advance to $1,000. Sends galleys to author. Book catalog for $3.

Advice: "We are looking for good books, be they tenth novels or first novels, it makes little difference. The fiction is more important than the track record."

SEVEN BUFFALOES PRESS, (II), Box 249, Big Timber MT 59011. Editor/Publisher: Art Cuelho. Estab. 1975. Publishes paperback originals. Averages 4-5 total titles each year.

Needs: Contemporary, short story collections, "rural, American Hobo, Okies, American Indian, Southern Appalachia, Arkansas and the Ozarks. Wants farm- and ranch-based stories." Published *Rig Nine*, by William Rintoul (collection of oilfield short stories).

How to Contact: Query first with SASE. Reports in 1 week on queries; 2 weeks on mss. Photocopied submissions OK.

Terms: Pays royalties of 10% minimum; 15% on second edition or in author's copies (10% of edition). No advance. Writer's guidelines and book catalog for SASE.

Advice: "There's too much influence from TV and Hollywood, media writing I call it. We need to get back to the people, to those who built and are still building this nation with sweat, blood, and brains. More people are into it for the money, instead of for the good writing that is still to be cranked out by isolated writers. Remember, I was a writer for 10 years before I became a publisher."

HAROLD SHAW PUBLISHERS, (II), Box 567, 388 Gundersen Dr., Wheaton IL 60189. (708)665-6700. Director of Editorial Services: Ramona Cramer Tucker. Estab. 1968. "Small, independent religious publisher with expanding fiction line." Publishes paperback originals and reprints. Books: 35 lb. Mando Supreme paper; sheet-fed printing; perfect-bound; average print order: 5,000. Published new writers within the last year. Plans 1 novel per year in Northcote Books (our literary/academic fiction subsidiary). Averages 30 total titles, 3-4 fiction titles each year. Sometimes critiques on rejected mss.

Needs: Literary, religious/inspirational, young adult/teen (13-18 years) problem novels. Looking for religious literary novels or young adult fiction (religious). No short stories, romances, children's fiction. Recently published *A Land of Heart's Desire, Lee William's Quest, A Waiting Legacy,* by Joy Pennock Gage (books one, two and three of the Seventh Child Series); *Absolutely Perfect Summer,* by Jeffrey Asher Nesbit (young adult fiction); *Hoverlight,* by Fay S. Lapka (young adult fiction).

How to Contact: Accepts unsolicited mss. Query first. Submit outline/synopsis and 2-3 sample chapters. SASE. Reports in 2 weeks on queries; 2-4 weeks on mss. Simultaneous and photocopied submissions OK. Accepts computer printout submissions.

Terms: Pays royalties of 10%, Average advance $1,000. Provides 10 author's copies. Sends pages to author. Publishes ms 12-18 months after acceptance. Free writer's guidelines. Book catalog for 9 × 12 SAE and $1.25 postage.

Advice: "Character and plot development are important to us. We look for quality writing in word and in thought. 'Sappiness' and 'pop-writing' don't go over well at all with our editorial department."

SHOE TREE PRESS, Box 219, Crozet VA 22932. An Imprint of Betterway Publications Inc. Editor: Susan Lewis. Estab. 1984. Publishes juvenile hardcover and paperback originals and reprints. Books: generally 70 lb. vellum paper; offset printing; reinforced binding; occasionally uses illustrations for middle years books; average print order: 5,000; first novel print order: 5,000. Published new writers within the last year. Plans 3 first novels this year. Averages 5 fiction titles each year. Rarely critiques or comments on rejected mss.

Needs: Young adult, middle years fiction. "No formula or genre fiction please." Recently published *With Secrets to Keep,* by Rose Levit; and *The Admiral and the Deck Boy,* by Genevieve O'Connor.

How to Contact: Please query. SASE. Agented fiction 33%. Reports in 2-4 weeks on queries; 10-12 weeks on mss. Simultaneous and photocopied submissions OK. Accepts computer printout submissions.

Terms: Pays royalties on graduating scale, beginning at 12% of wholesale price. Advance varies and is negotiable. Sends galleys to author.

Advice: "We publish juvenile fiction and nonfiction only. Our primary focus is on historical fiction for middle years and on nonfiction. We do *not* publish picture books. Don't get caught up in trying to follow 'market trends.' Write about what you know, and write it from the heart. We publish books that children, ages 10 and up, will enjoy but also learn from. We are also interested in 'problem' novels that confront issues kids must deal with today."

SILVERLEAF PRESS, INC., (I, II), Box 70189, Seattle WA 98107. Editor: Ann Larson. Estab. 1985. Publishes paperback originals. Books: 50 lb. book stock; offset printing; perfect-bound; no illustrations; average print order: 1,600; first novel print order: 1,600. Published new writers within the last year. Plans 1-2 first novels this year. Averages 2 total titles/year; 2 fiction titles/year. Sometimes critiques or comments on rejected mss.

Needs: Feminist, humor/satire, lesbian, short story collections. "Must be feminist or lesbian." Published *Three Glasses of Wine Have Been Removed From This Story,* by Marian Michener; *The Blessed,* by Nona Caspers; *Silverleaf's Choice: An Anthology of Lesbian Humor.*

How to Contact: Accepts unsolicited mss. Submit complete ms with cover letter. SASE (IRC). Reports in 2-3 months. Photocopied submissions OK. Accepts computer printout submissions.
Terms: Pays negotiable royalties and advance; author's copies. Sends galleys to author. Book catalog free on request.
Advice: "Try the small presses—they are more likely to give you a chance."

SIMON & PIERRE PUBLISHING COMPANY LIMITED, (II), Box 280, Adelaide St. Postal Stn., Toronto, Ontario M5C 2J4 Canada. Imprints include Bastet Books, Canplay Series, Canadian Theatre History Series and The Canadian Dramatist. Contact: Editors. Estab. 1972. Publishes hardcover and paperback originals. Books: 55 lb. hi bulk web printing; perfect-bound; line drawings; average print order: 2,000. Published new writers within the last year. Averages 10-12 titles/year.
Needs: Contemporary, literary, mystery, spy, historical, humor/satire, juvenile, young adult and translations. No romance, erotica, horror, science fiction. Recently published *An Emerald for Iamanja*, by Michael Jacot; and *Sherlock Holmes & The Mark of the Beast*, by Ronald C. Weyman.
How to Contact: *We publish only Canadian authors.* Query, submit complete ms, submit outline/synopsis and sample chapter or submit through agent with SASE (Canadian stamps) or IRCs. Reports in 1 month on queries, 4 months on mss. Simultaneous and photocopied submissions OK.
Terms: Pays royalties; small advance. Sends galleys to author. Free book catalog.
Advice: "Include with submissions: professional résumé listing previous publications, detailed outline of proposed work and sample chapters. We publish novelists who are good at proofing themselves and not afraid of being involved in their own marketing, but the fiction must be based on current topics or themes."

SOHO PRESS, 853 Broadway, New York NY 10003. (212)260-1900. Publisher: Juris Jurjevics. Publishes hardcover originals and trade paperback reprints. Published new writers within the last year. Averages 14 titles/year.
Needs: Adventure, ethnic, historical, literary, mainstream, mystery/espionage, suspense. "We do novels that are the very best in their genres." Recently published *Shadow Catcher*, by Charles Fergus; *Meridian 144*, by Meg Files; and *Gerontius*, by James Hamilton-Paterson.
How to Contact: Submit query or complete ms with SASE. Reports in 1 month on queries; 6 weeks on mss. Photocopied and simultaneous submissions OK.
Terms: Pays royalties of 10-15% on retail price. For trade paperbacks pays 7½% royalties to 10,000 copies; 10% after. Offers advance. Book catalog for SASE.
Advice: "There aren't any tricks (to writing a good query letter)—just say what the book is. Don't analyze the market for it. Don't take writing courses too seriously, and *read* the best people in whatever genre you are working. We are looking for those who have taught themselves or otherwise mastered the craft."

SOLEIL PRESS, (IV), R.F.D. #1, Box 452, Lisbon Falls ME 04252. (207)353-5454. Editor: Denis Ledoux. Estab. 1988. "Soleil Press publishes writing by and/or about Franco-Americans (French-Canadian-American). SP has *no* interest in the European French experience." Publishes paperback originals. Average print order: 2,000. Published new writers within the last year. Averages 1-2 total titles, 0-1 fiction titles/year. Occasionally comments on rejected ms.
Needs: Ethnic (Franco-American). "No interest at all in exploring the French of France."
How to Contact: Does not accept unsolicited mss. Query. SASE. Reports in 1 month on queries; 1-2 months on mss. Simultaneous and photocopied submissions OK. Accepts computer printout submissions.
Terms: Pays in author's copies. Writer's guidelines and book catalog for SASE.

‡SOUTHERN METHODIST UNIVERSITY PRESS, (I), P.O. Box 415, Dallas TX 75275. (214)739-5959. Senior Editor: Kathryn M. Lang. Estab. 1936. "Small university press publishing in areas of composition/rhetoric, film/theater, Southwest life and letters, religion/medical ethics and contemporary fiction." Publishes hardcover and paperback originals and reprints. Books: acid-free paper; perfect-bound; some illustrations; average print order 2,000. Published new writers within the last year. Plans 1 first novel this year. Averages 15 total titles; 5 fiction titles each year. Sometimes comments on rejected ms.
Needs: Contemporary, ethnic, experimental, historical, literary, mainstream, regional, short story collections. "We are booked for the next year or two; we always are willing to look at 'serious' or 'literary' fiction." No "mass market, sci fi, thriller, romance." Recently published *Common Bonds: Stories By and About Modern Texas Women*, edited by Suzanne Comer (collection of stories); *Red Wolf,*

Red Wolf, by W.P. Kinsella (collection of stories); *The Laying Out of Gussie Hoot*, by Margot Fraser (comedy of manners/mystery).
How to Contact: Accepts unsolicited mss. Query first. Submit outline/synopsis and 3 sample chapters. SASE. Agented fiction 10%. Reports in 3 weeks on queries; 3 months on mss. Simultaneous, photocopied submissions OK.
Terms: Pays royalties of 10% of net, negotiable advance, 10 author's copies. Publishes ms 1 year after acceptance. Book catalog free.
Advice: "We view encouraging first time authors as part of the mission of a university press. Send a clean (legible, grammatically correct), interesting query letter describing the project and your own background." Looks for "quality fiction from new or established writers."

SPACE AND TIME, (IV), 138 W. 70th St. (4-B), New York NY 10023-4432. Book Editor: Jani Anderson. Estab. 1966—book line 1984. Two-person operation on part-time basis. Publishes paperback originals. Books: 50 lb. Lakewood white 512PPi paper; offset Litho printing; perfect-bound; illustrations on cover and frontispiece; average print order: 1,000; first novel print order: 1,000. Averages 8 total titles, 1 fiction title each year. Critiques or comments on rejected ms.
Needs: Fantasy, horror, psychic/supernatural/occult, science fiction. Wants to see "cross-genre material, such as horror-western, sf-mystery, occult-spy adventure, etc." Does not want "anything *without* some element of fantasy or sf (or at least the 'feel' of same)." Published *The Wall*, by Ardath Mayhar (horror-mystery); *Vanitas*, by Jeffrey Ford (sci-fantasy-horror); *The Gift*, by Scott Edelman (gay-horror).
How to Contact: *No unsolicited mss.* Query first or submit outline/synopsis and 2 sample chapters. Reports in 4-6 weeks on queries; 3-4 months on mss. Simultaneous and photocopied submissions OK. "Prefer photocopies. Prefer around 50,000 words."
Terms: Pays royalties of 10% based on cover price and print run, within 60 days of publication (additional royalties, if going back to press). Average advance $100, negotiable. Sends galleys to author. Book catalog free on request.
Advice: "We are actively interested in publishing new authors, though at present have enough on hand to last us through 1992."

‡SPECTRUM PRESS, (I, II), Box 109, 3023 N. Clark St., Chicago IL 60657. (312)281-9223. Editor D.P. Agin. Estab. 1991. "Small independent electronic publisher." Publishes computer disks only. Published new writers within the last year. Plans 5 first novels this year. Averages 30 total titles, 25 fiction titles each year. Sometimes comments on rejected ms.
Needs: Adventure, contemporary, erotica, ethnic, experimental, fantasy, feminist, gay, historical, lesbian, literary, mainstream, science fiction, short story collections, suspense/mystery, translations, western. "Quality lesbian fiction of all kinds, feminist writing, literary novels." No juvenile or young adult. Recently published *The Cage*, by Daniel Vian (literary); *Linda Baby*, by Rachel Perez (lesbian).
How to Contact: Accepts unsolicited mss. Query first. Submit outline/synopsis and sample chapters or complete ms with cover letter. Prefer submission on IBM/MSDOS computer disk. Reports in 2 weeks on queries; 1 month on mss. Simultaneous, photocopied submissions OK. Accepts computer printout submissions. Accepts electronic submissions on disk only.
Terms: Pays royalties of 10-15%. Sends disk to author. Publishes within 2 months after acceptance. Writer's guidelines available. Book catalog free.
Advice: "We are interested in new voices and new attitudes. We prefer disk submissions in ASCII code or WordPerfect 5.1 format. Contact us first for other formats. Disks can be any size, any density, provided they are IBM/MSDOS."

THE SPEECH BIN, INC., (IV), 1766 20th Ave., Vero Beach FL 32960. (407)770-0007. FAX: (407)770-0006. Senior Editor: Jan J. Binney. Estab. 1984. Small independent publisher and major national and international distributor of books and material for speech-language pathologists, audiologists, special

Market conditions are constantly changing! If you're still using this book and it is 1993 or later, buy the newest edition of Novel & Short Story Writer's Market at your favorite bookstore or order directly from Writer's Digest Books.

educators and caregivers. Publishes hardcover and paperback originals. Averages 6-10 total titles/year. "No fiction at present time, but we are very interested in publishing fiction relevant to our specialties."
Needs: "We are most interested in seeing fiction, including books for children, dealing with individuals experiencing communication disorders, other handicaps, and their families and caregivers, particularly their parents, or family members dealing with individuals who have strokes, physical disability, hearing loss, Alzheimer's and so forth."
How to Contact: Accepts unsolicited mss. Query first. SASE. Agented fiction 10%. Reports in 4-6 weeks on queries; 1-3 months on mss. Simultaneous and photocopied submissions OK. Accepts computer printout submissions.
Terms: Pays royalties of 8%+. Sends galleys to author. Writer's guidelines for #10 SASE. Book catalog for 9×12 SAE with 3 first class stamps.
Advice: "We are most interested in publishing fiction about individuals who have speech, hearing and other handicaps."

‡**SPINSTERS BOOK CO., (IV),** Box 410687, San Francisco CA 94141. (415)558-9655. Editor: Sherilyn Thomas. Estab. 1978. Moderate size women's publishing company growing steadily. Publishes paperback originals and reprints. Books: 55 lb. acid-free natural paper; photo offset printing; perfect-bound; illustrations when appropriate; average print order: 5,000. Published new writers within the last year. Plans 3 first novels this year. Averages 6 total titles, 3-5 fiction titles each year. Occasionally critiques rejected ms.
Needs: Feminist, lesbian. Wants "full-length quality fiction—thoroughly revised novels which display deep characterization, theme and style. We *only* consider books by women. No books by men, or books with sexist, racist or ageist content." Recently published *Final Session*, by Mary Morell (mystery); *Being Someone*, by Ann MacLeod; and *Love and Memory*, by Amy Oleson.
How to Contact: Accepts unsolicited mss. Query or submit outline/synopsis and 3 sample chapters with SASE. Reports in 1 month on queries; 2 months on mss. Simultaneous submissions discouraged; photocopied submissions OK. Accepts computer printout submissions. Disk submissions OK (DOS format—MS Word or WP 5.0). Prefers hard copy with disk submission.
Terms: Pays royalties of 7-10%, plus 25 author's copies; unlimited extra copies at 45% discount. Free book catalog.
Advice: "In the past, lesbian fiction has been largely 'escape fiction' with sex and romance as the only required ingredients; however, we encourage more complex work that treats the lesbian lifestyle with the honesty it deserves. We run an annual Lesbian Fiction Contest designed to increase the body of quality literature about the lesbian lifestyle. The prize is $1,000."

***STAR BOOKS, INC.,** 408 Pearson St., Wilson NC 27893. (919)237-1591. President: Irene Burk Harrell. Estab. 1983. "Small but growing" publisher. Publishes paperback originals. Books: offset paper; offset printing; perfect-bound; some illustrations; average print order: 1,000; first novel print order: 1,000. Plans 1 first novel this year. Expects to publish 20 titles this year. Sometimes comments on rejected mss, "comment no charge; critique $1/ms page, $25 minimum."
Needs: Religious/inspirational, young adult/teen. "Strongly and specifically Christian." Recently published *Shatterings*, by Ralph Fillichia (short stories); *Apes and Peacocks*, by Rosalind Marshall (biblical novel about King Solomon).
How to Contact: Accepts unsolicited mss. Submit complete ms with cover letter. SASE. Reports in 2 weeks. Photocopied submissions OK. No simultaneous submissions. Accepts computer printout submissions.
Terms: Pays royalties of 10-15%. Sends page proofs to author. Publishing of ms after acceptance "depends on our situation. *Sometimes*, (not always) we need author to buy prepub copies (at 50% off list) to help with first printing costs." Guidelines and book catalog for #10 SAE and 2 first class stamps.
Advice: "Make sure that for us the book is in line with Biblical principles and powerful enough to cause the reader to make an initial commitment of his/her life to Jesus Christ, or if the reader is already a Christian, to strengthen his/her walk with Him."

‡***STARBOOKS PRESS,** Subsidiary of Woldt Corp., 601 S. Tyler Dr., Sarasota FL 34236. (813)388-2378. Vice President: Michael Powers. Estab. 1979. "Small press specializing in mature adult fiction and nonfiction, including mainly titles of gay orientation." Publishes paperback originals. Books: Perfect-bound; average print order: 1,000-5,000. Published new writers within the last year. Plans 1 first novel this year. Averages 6-8 total titles, 4-5 fiction titles each year. Sometimes comments on rejected ms.

Needs: Gay. Also erotica, lesbian, short story collections. Recently published *Randy*, by Joe Leslie (gay); *Angel: The Complete Quintet*, by John Patrick (gay); *Deadly Minute*, by John Patrick (gay).
How to Contact: Accepts unsolicited mss. Submit outline/synopsis and sample chapters. SASE. Reports in 1 week on queries; 2 weeks on mss. Photocopied submissions OK. Accepts computer printout submissions. Accepts electronic submissions.
Terms: Pays royalties of 15-20%; offers negotiable advance. Provides 10-50 contributor's copies. Individual arrangement with author depending on the book. *May consider subsidy publishing.* Sends galleys to author. Publishes ms 3-4 months after acceptance. Writers guidelines for SASE. Book catalog free.

*STARBURST PUBLISHERS, (IV), P.O. Box 4123, Lancaster PA 17604. (717)293-0939. Managing Editor: Ellen. Estab. 1977. Publishes paperback and hardcover originals. Books: paper varies; offset printing; perfect-bound; line art(text), full-color cover. Average print order 10,000; first novel print order 5,000 to 10,000. Published new writers within the last year. Plans 4-6 new novels this year. Averages 15 total titles, 6-7 fiction titles per year. Charges for critique of rejected manuscript.
Needs: Religious/inspirational: Adventure, contemporary, fantasy, historical, horror, military/war, psychic/supernatural/occult (with Judeo-Christian solution), romance (contemporary, historical), spiritual, suspense/mystery, western. Wants "inspirational material similar to Frank Peretti's *This Present Darkness*." Published *A Candle in Darkness* and *While They Sleep*, by June Livesay and *The Quest for Truth*, by Ken Johnson.
How to Contact: Query first, then submit outline/synopsis and 3-4 sample chapters. SASE. Include Social Security number with submission. Agented fiction less than 10%. Reports in 6-8 weeks on manuscripts. Accepts computer printouts and electronic submissions via disk and modem, "but also wants clean double-spaced typewritten or computer printout manuscript."
Terms: Pays in variable royalties. "Individual arrangement with writer depending on the manuscript as well as writer's experience as a published author." *Subsidy publishes "occasionally."* Sends galleys to author. Publishes ms up to one year after acceptance. Writer's guidelines for SAE and 1 first class stamp.

*STATION HILL PRESS (II, III), Station Hill Rd., Barrytown NY 12507. (914)758-5840. Imprint: Pulse. Publishers: George Quasha and Susan Quasha. Estab. 1978. Publishes paperback and cloth originals. Averages 20 total titles, 5-7 fiction titles each year.
Needs: Contemporary, experimental, literary, translations, and new age. Published *Operas and Plays*, by Gertrude Stein; *Narrative Unbound*, by Donald Ault.
How to Contact: Query first with SASE before sending ms. No unsolicited mss.
Terms: Pays in author's copies (10% of print run) or by standard royalty, depending on the nature of the material. *Occasional subsidy publishing.* "Co-venture arrangements are possible with higher royalty." Book catalog free on request.

‡STONE BRIDGE PRESS, (IV), P.O. Box 8208, Berkeley CA 94707. (510)524-8732. FAX: (510)524-8711. Publisher: Peter Goodman. Estab. 1989. "Small press focusing on books about Japan in English (business, language, culture, literature)." Publishes paperback originals and reprints. Books: 60-70 lb. offset paper; web and sheet paper; perfect-bound; some illustrations; average print order: 3,000; first novel print order: 2,000-2,500. Averages 6 total titles, 2 fiction titles, each year. Sometimes comments on rejected ms.
Needs: Japan-themed. If not translation, interested in the expatriate experience—all categories welcome: contemporary, erotica, ethnic, experimental, faction, literary, science fiction, short story collections, translations (from Japanese). "Primarily looking at material relating to Japan. Mostly translations, but we'd like to see samples of work dealing with the expatriate experience. Also Asian and Japanese-American. Recently published *Death March on Mount Hakkoda*, by Jiro Nitta (translation-

The asterisk indicates a publisher who sometimes offers subsidy arrangements. Authors are asked to subsidize part of the cost of book production. See the introduction to Commercial Publishers for more information.

faction); *Wind and Stone*, by Masaaki Tachihara (translation-literary); *Still Life and Other Stories*, by Junzo Shono (translation-literary).

How to Contact: Accepts unsolicited mss. Query first. Submit outline/synopsis and 3 sample chapters. SASE. Agented fiction 25%. Reports in 2 weeks on queries; 2 months on mss. Simultaneous, photocopied submissions OK. Accepts computer printout submissions.

Terms: Pays royalties, offers negotiable advance. Publishes ms 18 months after acceptance. Writer's guidelines for #10 SAE and 1 first class stamp. Book catalog for #10 SAE and 2 first class stamps.

Advice: "As we focus on Japan-related material there is no point in approaching us unless you are very familiar with Japan as a flesh-and-bones nation with real people – not European-style exotica or 'orientalia.' No silly portrayals of subservient women or inscrutable polite ninja masters. We'd like to see more submissions dealing with the expatriate experience. More investigations of contemporary Japan. Love to see fantasy and science fiction on Japanese themes as well, but with a decided literary tone, not mass market."

SUNSTONE PRESS, (IV), Box 2321, Santa Fe NM 87504-2321. (505)988-4418. Contact: James C. Smith, Jr. Estab. 1971. Midsize publisher. Publishes paperback originals. Average first novel print order: 2,000 copies. Published new writers within the last year. Plans 2 first novels this year. Averages 16 total titles, 2-3 fiction titles, each year.

Needs: Western. "We have a Southwestern theme emphasis. Sometimes buys juvenile mss with illustrations." No science fiction, romance or occult. Published *Apache: The Long Ride Home*, by Grant Gall (Indian/Western); *Border Patrol*, by Cmdr. Alvin E. Moore; and *The Last Narrow Gauge Train Robbery*, by Robert K. Swisher, Jr.

How to Contact: Accepts unsolicited mss. Query first or submit outline/synopsis and 2 sample chapters with SASE. Reports in 2 weeks. Simultaneous and photocopied submissions OK. Accepts computer printout submissions. Publishes ms 9-12 months after acceptance.

Terms: Pays royalties, 10% maximum, and 10 author's copies.

‡SWAMP PRESS, 323 Pelham Rd., Amherst MA 01002. Chief Editor: Ed Rayher. Estab. 1977. One-person part-time. Publishes hardcover originals and paperback originals. Books: hardcover/mould-made paper; letterpress printing; hard/soft binding; illustrations; average print order: 200 softcovers, 100 hardbound. Averages 3 total titles, 1 fiction title each year. Critiques or comments on rejected ms.

Needs: Literary, experimental, short story collections, translations. Recently published *Thus May be Figured in Numberless Ways*, by Bonnie Gordon (short-story narrative).

How to Contact: Accepts unsolicited mss. SASE. Query first or submit outline/synopsis and 1 or 2 sample chapters or complete ms with cover letter. SASE. Reports in 2 months on queries; 2 months on mss. Photocopied submissions OK. Accepts computer printouts including dot-matrix.

Terms: Pays in author's copies 10% of run, depending on grant/award money. Individual arrangement with author. Writer's guidelines for SAE and 1 first class stamp. Book catalog free on request.

TEXTILE BRIDGE PRESS, (II), Subsidiary of Moody Street Irregulars, Inc., Box 157, Clarence Center NY 14032. (716)741-3393. Imprints include The Jack Kerouac Living Writers Reading Series. President/Editor: Joy Walsh. Fiction Editor: Marion Perry. Estab. 1978. "We publish a magazine on and about the work of Jack Kerouac. We also publish book length manuscripts in the spirit of Kerouac when available." Publishes paperback originals. Books: bond paper; offset printing; saddle or perfect binding; average print order: 300-500; first novel print order: 500. Plans 1 first novel this year. Averages 5 total titles each year, 2 fiction titles each year. Sometimes comments on rejected ms; charges for critiques.

Needs: Experimental, literary, short story collections. No romance, gothic. Published *Big Ben Hood*, by Emmanual Freed (literary); *Links of the Chain*, by William Harnock (short story collection); and *Walk With Me*, by Dorothy Smith (literary); published new writers within last year.

How to Contact: Accepts unsolicited mss. Submit complete ms with cover letter. SASE. Agented fiction 1%. Reports in 1 week on queries; 1 month on mss. Simultaneous and photocopied submissions OK. Accepts computer printout submissions.

Terms: Pays in author's copies "if run 300, 30 copies/if 500, 50 copies." Sends galleys to author. Publishes ms 1 year after acceptance. Writers guidelines not available. Book catalog free, if available.

Read the Business of Fiction section to learn the correct way to prepare and submit a manuscript.

Close-up

Patrick O'Rourke
Editor-in-Chief
Thistledown Press

"The spirit that initiated the press was something that nagged at me. That's why I thought of starting a new series," says Patrick O'Rourke, editor-in-chief of Thistledown Press in Saskatoon, Saskatchewan.

"Regional literary presses were established to afford opportunities for new voices," he explains. "Now that we've been around as long as we have, one of the great dilemmas is: How do you juggle both those people you've published over the years and newer authors or authors coming from a different angle?"

O'Rourke's answer is New Leaf Editions, a "more or less no-frills series" for new authors. Books are produced at a minimal cost and printed in short runs. A similar format — 64 pages, generic design — translates into savings on printing costs. This allows O'Rourke to put more new writers into print.

The series, launched in 1990 with two books of poetry and two of fiction, was temporarily suspended last year "because there wasn't money in the budget," O'Rourke explains.

"To a large extent, literary publishing in Canada is heavily subsidized," he says. "A tremendous amount of funding has to go into it from The Canada Council. Also, the Saskatchewan Arts Board has long been a solid supporter of Thistledown Press. When these people start feeling the pinch, they pass it on; and we're left to cut corners."

Now, New Leaf Editions is back in place. "It's an open invitation to submit," O'Rourke says, "but we will not deal with submissions per se — only queries." He is excited about the program because "it has the flexibility to deal with both traditional and experimental writing." He stresses, however, that he only accepts submissions from Canadians.

The press seeks to publish provincial writers first, regional writers next, then national writers, says O'Rourke. "We are trying to publish high quality literature in all veins — poetry, short fiction, novels, young adult material and children's literature. In all cases, the final determinant is the author's merit as a writer."

In general, "we try to personalize the whole process as much as we can," O'Rourke says. If possible, authors are involved in development and copyediting. "We inform them about the stages of production, and they get to see the typeface and everything else we choose for the work," he says. "About twice a year we send out a newsletter, so everyone gets to know what everyone else in the stable is doing.

"We also personalize the process by sending authors a handbook that we put together to give some pointers that might lead to the effective marketing of their work," he says.

"Overall," says O'Rourke, "we've found books that are truly successful are usually books by authors who put tremendous effort themselves into selling and promoting their work and being available for readings and signings. We do whatever we can to help them."

— Christine Martin

THIRD WORLD PRESS, 7524 S. Cottage Grove Ave., Chicago IL 60619. (312)651-0700. Assistant Editor: Dana L. Reid. Estab. 1967. Small independent publisher with plans to expand. Publishes paperback originals. Plans 2 first novels this year. Averages 10 total titles, 3 fiction titles each year. Average first novel print order 15,000 copies.
Needs: Ethnic, historical, juvenile (animal, easy-to-read, fantasy, historical, contemporary), preschool/ picture book, science fiction, short story collections, and young adult/teen (easy-to-read/teen, fantasy/ science fiction, historical). "We primarily publish nonfiction, but will consider fiction by and about Blacks."
How to Contact: Accepts unsolicited mss. Query or submit outline/synopsis and 1 sample chapter with SASE. Reports in 6 weeks on queries; 5 months on mss. Simultaneous and photocopied submissions OK. Accepts computer printout submissions.
Terms: Individual arrangement with author depending on the book, etc.

THISTLEDOWN PRESS, (II, IV), 668 East Place, Saskatoon, Saskatchewan S7J 2Z5 Canada. (306)244-1722. Editor-in-Chief: Patrick O'Rourke. Estab. 1975. Publishes paperback originals. Books: Quality stock paper; offset printing; perfect-bound; occasional illustrations; average print order 1,500-2,000; first novel print order: 1,000-1,500. Plans 1 first novel and 3 collections of stories. Publishes 12 titles/ year, 6 or 7 fiction. Occasionally critiques rejected mss.
Needs: Literary, experimental, short story collections and novels.
How to Contact: "We *only* want to see Canadian-authored submissions. We will *not* consider multiple submissions." No unsolicited mss. Query first with SASE. Photocopied submissions OK. Reports in 2 months on queries. Recently published *Yuletide Blues*, by R.P. MacIntyre (young adult novel); *After Sixty: Going Home*, by Gertrude Story (short stories); *Sick Pigeon*, by M.A.C. Farrant (short fictions).
Advice: "We are primarily looking for quality writing that is original and innovative in its perspective and/or use of language. Thistledown would like to receive queries first before submission—perhaps with novel outline, some indication of previous publications, periodicals your work has appeared in. We publish Canadian authors only. We are continuing to publish more fiction and are looking for new fiction writers to add to our list. New Leaf Editions line is first books of poetry or fiction by emerging Western Canadian authors. Familiarize yourself with some of our books before submitting a query or manuscript to the press."

THREE CONTINENTS PRESS, (II, IV), Suite 407, 1901 Pennsylvania Ave. N.W., Washington DC 20006. (202)223-2554. Fiction Editor: Donald Herdeck. Estab. 1973. Small independent publisher with expanding list. Publishes hardcover and paperback originals and reprints. Books: library binding; illustrations; average print order: 1,000-1,500; first novel print order: 1,000. Averages 15 total titles, 6-8 fiction titles each year. Average first novel print order: 1,000 copies. Occasionally critiques ("a few sentences") rejected mss.
Needs: "We publish original fiction only by writers from Africa, the Caribbean, the Middle East, Asia and the Pacific. No fiction by writers from North America or Western Europe." Published *Kaidara*, by Mamadou Bah, translated by Daniel Whitman; *Fountain and Tomb* by Naguib Mahfous, translated by James Kennison. Also, short-story collections by established writers.
How to Contact: Query with outline/synopsis and sample pages and SAE, IRC. State "origins (non-Western), education and previous publications." Reports in 1 month on queries; 2 months on mss. Simultaneous and photocopied submissions OK. Computer printout submissions OK.
Terms: "We are not a subsidy publisher, but do a few specialized titles a year with subsidy. In those cases we accept grants or institutional subventions. Foundation or institution receives 20-30 copies of book and at times royalty on first printing. We pay royalties twice yearly (against advance) as a percentage of net paid receipts." Royalties of 5% minimum, 10% maximum; 10 author's copies; offers negotiable advance, $300 average. Depends on grant/award money. Sends galleys to author. Free book catalog.

THRESHOLD BOOKS, RD 4, Box 600, Dusty Ridge Rd., Putney VT 05346. (802)254-8300. Director: Edmund Helminski. Estab. 1981. Small independent publisher with plans for gradual expansion. Publishes paperback originals. Books: 60 lb. natural paper; offset litho printing; sew-wrap binding; average print order: 2,500. Averages 2-3 total titles each year. Occasionally critiques rejected ms.
Needs: Spiritual literature and translations of sacred texts. Published *Lineage*, by Bo Lozzoff (short stories); and *Toward the Fullness of Life, The Fullness of Love*, by Arnaud Desjardin (nonfiction on male-female relationships).

How to Contact: Accepts unsolicited mss. Query first, submit outline/synopsis and sample chapters or complete ms with SASE. Reports in 2 months. Simultaneous and photocopied submissions OK. Accepts computer printout submissions. Publishes ms an average of 18 months after acceptance.
Terms: Pays in royalties of 10% of net. Sometimes sends galleys to author. Book catalog free on request.
Advice: "We are still small and publishing little fiction." Publishing "less fiction, more paperbacks due to our particular area of concentration and our size."

‡*TIDE BOOK PUBLISHING COMPANY, Box 101, York Harbor ME 03911. Subsidiary of Tide Media. President: Rose Safran. Estab. 1979. Independent, small publisher. Publishes paperback originals. Averages 1 title each year. Occasionally critiques rejected mss.
Needs: Contemporary, feminist, historical, humor/satire, literary, mainstream, regional. Needs "women's novels with a social service thrust. No gothic, trash."
How to Contact: Query first or submit outline/synopsis and 1-2 sample chapters with SASE. Reports in 1 month. Simultaneous submissions OK. Accepts computer printout submissions.
Terms: Pays 100 author's copies. *Considering cost plus subsidy arrangements* –will advertise.

TIMES EAGLE BOOKS, P.O. Box 2441, Berkeley CA 94702. Fiction Editor: Mark Hurst. Estab. 1971. "Small operation on part-time basis." Specialized publisher limited to contributors from West Coast region. First novel print order: 2,500. Plans 2 first novels this year. Averages 2 titles/year, all fiction.
Needs: Contemporary. "Graphic descriptions of teenage life by West Coast youth, such as Bret Easton Ellis's *Less than Zero*." Recently published *Equator: The Story and the Letters*, by V.O. Blum (erotic/philosophical novel).
How to Contact: Does not accept or return unsolicited mss. Query first in one paragraph. Reports in 2 weeks.
Terms: Pays 10-15% royalties.
Advice: "Times Eagle Books prefers first novelists."

THE TRANSLATION CENTER, (II), 412 Dodge Hall, Columbia University, New York NY 10027. (212)854-2305. Editors: Frank MacShane, Lori Carlson. Estab. 1972. Publishes paperback originals. Books: 6 × 9; perfect bound; high-quality paper. Averages 2 total titles/year.
Needs: Translations.
How to Contact: Accepts unsolicited ms. Submit complete ms with cover letter and SASE. Photocopied submissions OK. Accepts computer printouts.
Terms: Pays in 2 translator's copies.

TURNSTONE PRESS, (II), 607-100 Arthur St., Winnipeg, Manitoba R3B 1H3 Canada. (204)947-1555. Managing Editor: Marilyn Morton. Estab. 1976. Books: Offset paper; perfect-bound; average first novel print order: 1,500. Published new writers within the last year. Averages 8 total titles/year. Occasionally critiques rejected ms.
Needs: Experimental and literary. "We will be doing only 2-3 fiction titles a year. Interested in new work exploring new narrative/fiction forms. We publish some anthologies (e.g. *Made in Manitoba*, edited by Wayne Tefs). Stories are nominated." Recently published *Fox*, by Margaret Sweatman; *Murder in Gutenthal*, by Armin Wiebe; and *Black Tulips*, by Bruce Eason.
How to Contact: *Canadian authors only.* Send SASE or SAE and IRC. Reports in 1 month on queries; 2-4 months on mss. Photocopied submissions OK.
Terms: Pays royalties of 10%; 10 author's copies. Book catalog free on request.
Advice: "Like most Canadian literary presses, we depend heavily on government grants which are not available for books by non-Canadians. Do some homework before submitting work to make sure your subject matter/genre/writing style falls within the publishers area of interest."

ULTRAMARINE PUBLISHING CO., INC., (III), Box 303, Hastings-on-the-Hudson NY 10706. (914)478-2522. Publisher: Christopher P. Stephens. Estab. 1973. Small publisher. "We have 150 titles in print. We also distribute for authors where a major publisher has dropped a title." Encourages new writers. Averages 15 total titles, 12 fiction titles each year. Buys 90% agented fiction. Occasionally critiques rejected ms.
Needs: Experimental, fantasy, mainstream, science fiction, and short story collections. No romance, westerns, mysteries.
How to Contact: Prefers agented ms. Does not accept unsolicited mss. Submit outline/synopsis and 2 sample chapters with SASE. Reports in 6 weeks. Simultaneous and photocopied submissions OK. Accepts computer printout submissions.

Terms: Pays royalties of 10% minimum; advance is negotiable. Publishes ms an average of 8 months after acceptance. Free book catalog.

*UNIVERSITY EDITIONS, (I, II), 59 Oak Lane, Spring Valley, Huntington WV 25704. Imprint of Aegina Press. Managing Editor: Ira Herman. Estab. 1983. Independent publisher presently expanding. Publishes hardcover and paperback originals and reprints. Books: 50 lb. library-weight paper; litho offset printing; most are perfect-bound; illustrations; average print order: 500-1,000; first novel print order: 500-1,000. Plans 10 first novels this year. "We strongly encourage new writers." Averages 25 total titles, approximately 15 fiction titles each year. Often critiques rejected ms.
Needs: Adventure, contemporary, ethnic, experimental, faction, fantasy, feminist, historical, romance, horror, humor/satire, juvenile (all types), literary, mainstream, regional, science fiction, short story collections, translations and war. "Historical, literary, and regional fiction are our main areas of emphasis." Recently published *The Doc Poe Reader*, by W.S. Furie (short stories); *Sunrise at Ten*, by Marie Morgart (novel); and *Medusa Etude*, by John Myrl Apple (novel).
How to Contact: Accepts unsolicited mss. "We depend upon manuscripts that arrive unsolicited." Query or submit outline/synopsis and 3 or more sample chapters or complete ms. "We prefer to see entire manuscripts; we will consider queries and partials as well." SASE. Reports in 1 week on queries; 1 month on mss. Simultaneous and photocopied submissions OK. Accepts computer printout submissions.
Terms: Payment is negotiated individually for each book. Depends upon author and subject. *Subsidy publishes most new titles.* Sends galleys to author.
Advice: "We attempt to encourage and establish new authors. Editorial tastes in fiction are eclectic. We try to be open to any type of fiction that is well written. We are publishing more fiction now that the very large publishers are getting harder to break into. We publish softcovers primarily, in order to keep books affordable."

THE UNIVERSITY OF ARKANSAS PRESS, (I), Fayetteville AR 72701. (501)575-3246. Director: Miller Williams. Acquisitions Editor: James Twiggs. Estab. 1980. Small university press. Publishes hardcover and paperback originals. Average print order 750 cloth and 2,000 paper copies. Averages 40 total titles, 2 short fiction titles (rarely a novel), each year.
Needs: Literary, mainstream, novels, short story collections, and translations. Publishes anthologies or special editions. Stories are usually selected by the editor. Recently published *Writing for Love and Money*, by Katherin Perutz (novel); *Jonah and the Pink Whale*, by Jose Wolfango Montes Vannuci (novel), translated by Kay Pritchett; *Plato at Scratch Daniel's and Other Stories*, by Edward Falco.
How to Contact: Accepts unsolicited mss. Query first with SASE. Reports in 2 weeks. Simultaneous and photocopied submissions OK "if very clean." Accepts computer printout submissions.
Terms: Pays royalties of 10%; 10 author's copies. Publishes ms an average of 1 year after acceptance. Writer's guidelines and book catalog for 9×12 SASE.
Advice: "We are looking for fiction written with energy, clarity and economy. Apart from this, we have no predisposition concerning style or subject matter. The University of Arkansas Press does not respond to queries or proposals not accompanied by SASE."

UNIVERSITY OF IDAHO PRESS, (IV), 16 Brink Hall, University of Idaho, Moscow ID 83843. (208)885-7564. Director: James J. Heaney. Estab. 1972. "Small university press with combined scholarly and regional emphasis." Publishes hardcover and paperback originals and paperback reprints. Averages 8-10 total titles, 1-2 fiction titles each year. Sometimes comments on rejected ms.
Needs: Regional, short story collections. "We would like to publish some Western fictional works of suitable stylistic competence for a primarily regional market in Idaho and the inland Northwest. No fictionalized memoirs of pioneers, pony express riders, and so on." Published *Unearned Pleasures*, by Ursula Hegi (short story collection). Recently developed Northwest Folklife Series.
How to Contact: Accepts unsolicited mss. Query first. Reports in 1 month on queries; 4 months on mss. Photocopied submissions OK. Accepts computer printout submissions. Accepts electronic submissions via disk.

Market categories: (I) Beginning; (II) General; (III) Prestige; (IV) Specialized.

Terms: Pays royalties. "Contracts are always negotiated individually. The small size of the regional fiction market makes less than luxurious terms a necessity for the publisher." Sends galleys to author. Writer's guidelines and book catalog free.

UNIVERSITY OF ILLINOIS PRESS, (I), 54 E. Gregory, Champaign IL 61820. (217)333-0950. Senior Editor: Ann Lowry. Estab. 1918. Not-for-profit university press. Publishes clothbound originals. Books: acid free paper; cloth binding; average print order: 1,500-2,000. Number of titles: 2-4 per year. Encourages new writers who have journal publications. Occasionally comments on rejected mss.
Needs: Contemporary, literary, and experimental. Story collections only. "No novels." Published *Man Without Memory*, by Richard Burgin; *The People Down South*, by Cary C. Holladay; *Bodies at Sea*, by Erin McGraw.
How to Contact: Accepts unsolicited mss. Query or submit complete ms. SASE. Simultaneous and photocopied submissions OK. Accepts computer printout submissions. Reports in 1 week on queries, 2-4 months on mss.
Terms: Pays 7½% net of all copies sold. No advance. Free book catalog.
Advice: "We do not publish novels, and we have no outlet for individual short stories. We publish collections of short fiction by authors who've usually established their credentials by being accepted for publication in periodicals, generally literary periodicals."

W.W. PUBLICATIONS, (IV), Subsidiary of A.T.S., Box 373, Highland MI 48357-0373. (813)585-0985. Also publishes *Minas Tirith Evening Star*. Editor: Philip Helms. Estab. 1967. One-man operation on part-time basis. Publishes paperback originals and reprints. Books: typing paper; offset printing; staple-bound; black ink illustrations; average print order: 500+; first novel print order: 500. Averages 1 title (fiction) each year. Occasionally critiques rejected ms.
Needs: Fantasy, science fiction, and young adult/teen (fantasy/science fiction). Novel needs: "Tolkien-related mainly, some fantasy." Recently published *The New Hobbit*, by Dave Dettman.
How to Contact: Accepts unsolicited mss. Submit complete ms with SASE. Reports in 1 month. Simultaneous and photocopied submissions OK. Accepts computer printout submissions.
Terms: Individual arrangement with author depending on book, etc.; provides 5 author's copies. Free book catalog.
Advice: "We are publishing more fiction and more paperbacks. The author/editor relationship: a friend and helper."

*WATERFRONT PRESS, (IV), 52 Maple Ave., Maplewood NJ 07040. (201)762-1565. President: Kal Wagenheim. Estab. 1982. Two persons, active part-time small press. Hardcover and paperback originals and reprints. Books: standard trade and textbook formats, illustrations occasionally; average print order: 1,000-1,500; first novel print order: 500-1,000. Averages 4 total titles/year; 1 or 2 fiction titles/year. Occasionally critiques rejected mss.
Needs: Ethnic, translations. "Our main focus is Puerto Rico and Hispanics in the US. We may consider other Caribbean nations." Published *The Labyrinth*, by Enrique A. Laguerre (translation from Spanish of book first published 1959); and *La Charca*, by Manuel Zeno-Gandia (translation from Spanish of 19th century novel).
How to Contact: Does not accept unsolicited mss. Query first or submit outline/synopsis and sample chapters. SASE for query and ms. Reports in 1 month on queries; 2 months on mss. Simultaneous and photocopied submissions OK. Accepts computer printouts.
Terms: Pays in royalties of 10-15%; $250-500 advance; advance is negotiable. Sends galleys to author. "On a few occasions, with books of great merit, *we have co-published with author*, who provided part of costs (in cases where our budget did not permit us to proceed quickly with the project)."
Advice: "We will endorse or support grant applications made by writers to foundations, if we believe the work has merit."

WATERMARK PRESS, INC., (I,II,IV), Suite 201, 149 N. Broadway, Wichita KS 67202. (316)263-8951. Editor: Gaylord L. Dold. Estab. 1988. Regional independent publisher, planning to expand. Publishes hardcover originals.

Needs: "We seek quality literary manuscripts." Recently published *Leaving Las Vegas*, by John O'Brien.

How to Contact: Accepts unsolicited mss. Query first. Reports 3 months. Simultaneous and photocopied submissions OK.

Terms: Sends prepublication galleys to author. Publishes ms an average of 1 year after acceptance.

Advice: "We encourage writers, agented or not, to submit highly original manuscripts. No genre work accepted, no poetry, no esoterica. We are seeking hard, lucid work on the post-modern scene."

WILLOWISP PRESS, INC., (II), Subsidiary of SBF Services, Inc., 10100 SBF Dr., Pinellas Park FL 34666. (813)578-7600. Imprints include Worthington Press, Hamburger Press. Editorial contact person: Hannah M. Murphy. Estab. 1984. Publishes paperback originals. Published new writers within the last year. Sometimes critiques rejected mss.

Needs: "Children's fiction and nonfiction, K-middle school." Adventure, contemporary, horror, juvenile (5-9 yrs.), preschool/picture book, young adult. No "violence, sex; romance must be very lightly treated." Recently published *Sister vs. Sister*, by Carol Perry; and *So Much To Live For*, by Lurlene McDaniel.

How to Contact: Accepts unsolicited mss. Query (except picture books) with outline/synopsis and 3 sample chapters. SASE. Report on queries varies; 2 months on mss. Simultaneous and photocopied submissions OK. Accepts computer printout submissions. "Prefer hard copy for original submissions; prefer disk for publication."

Terms: Pay "varies." Publishes ms 6-12 months after acceptance. Writer's guidelines for #10 SAE and 1 first class stamp. Book catalog for 9×12 SAE with $1.25 postage.

Advice: "We publish what *kids* want to read, so tell your story in a straightforward way with 'kid-like' language that doesn't convey an adult tone or sentence structure."

WOMAN IN THE MOON PUBLICATIONS, (I,IV), 2215-R Market St., Box 137-WDB, San Francisco CA 94110. (408)253-3329. Publisher: Dr. SDiane A. Bogus. Estab. 1979. "We are a small press with a primary publishing agenda for poetry. We accept short story manuscripts infrequently but are open to them." Publishes paperback originals. Books: 60 lb. acid-free paper; off-set/web press printing; perfect binding preferred, sometimes saddle, Smythe sewn; occasional illustrations; average print order: 1,000. Averages 2-4 total titles each year. Sometimes comments on rejected mss.

Needs: Contemporary, ethnic, fantasy, gay, lesbian, psychic/supernatural/occult, prisoner's stories, short story collections.

How to Contact: Accepts unsolicited mss between April 1 and June 31 only up to 100 mss.. Query first or submit outline/synopsis and sample chapters. SASE for query. Acknowledges in 1 week; reports in 3 months on queries. Simultaneous submissions OK.

Terms: *$5 reading fee required.* Pays in author's copies (half of press run). Publishes ms within 2 years after acceptance. Writer's guidelines for #10 SAE and 1 first class stamp. Book catalog for 6×9 SAE and 98¢ postage.

Advice: "To the short story writer, write us a real life lesbian gay set of stories. Tell us how life is for a Black person in an enlightened world. Create a possibility, an ideal that humanity can live toward. Write a set of stories that will free, redeem and instruct humanity. The trends in fiction by women have to do with the heroine as physical and capable and not necessarily defended by or romantically linked to a male." Sending out calls for submissions for prison anthology called *Steel Mirrors*; it will include fiction. Authors in prison may submit. Deadline: November 1992.

WOMEN'S PRESS, (I, II, IV), Suite 233, 517 College St., Toronto, Ontario M6G 4A2 Canada. (416)921-2425. Estab. 1972. Publishes paperback originals. Books: Web coat paper; web printing; perfect-bound; average print order: 2,000; first novel print order: 1,500. Plans 2 first novels this year. Published new writers within the last year. Averages 8 total titles each year. Sometimes "briefly" critiques rejected ms.

Needs: Contemporary, feminist, lesbian, juvenile and adolescent (fantasy, historical, contemporary), literary, preschool/picture book, short story collections, mysteries, women's and young adult/teen (problem novels). Nothing sexist, pornographic, racist. Recently published *S.P. Likes A.D.*, by Catherine Brett; *Catherine, Catherine*, by Ingrid MacDonald; *Harriet's Daughter*, by Marlene Nourbese Philip.

How to Contact: Submit complete ms with SAE and "Canadian stamps or a check. Our mandate is to publish Canadian women or landed immigrants." Reports in 3 months. Simultaneous or photocopied submissions OK. Accepts computer printout submissions.

Terms: Pays in royalties of 10% maximum; small advance. Sends galleys to author. Free book catalog.
Advice: "We publish feminist, lesbian and adolescent novels, anthologies of short stories and single-author story collections. We encourage women of all races and ethnicities to submit work and we have a particular interest in publishing writers of colour."

WOODLEY MEMORIAL PRESS, (IV), English Dept. Washburn University, Topeka KS 66621. (913)295-6448. Editor: Dr. Robert Lawson. Estab. 1980. "Woodley Memorial Press is a small press organization which publishes book-length poetry and fiction collections by Kansas writers only; by 'Kansas writers' we mean writers who reside in Kansas or have a Kansas connection." Publishes paperback originals. Averages varying number of total titles each year. Sometimes comments on rejected ms.
Needs: Contemporary, experimental, literary, mainstream, short story collection. "We do not want to see genre fiction, juvenile, or young adult." Publishes anthologies or special editions occasionally. "We have contests."
How to Contact: *Charges $5 reading fee.* Accepts unsolicited mss. Submit outline/synopsis and 2 sample chapters. SASE. Reports in 2 weeks on queries; 2 months on mss. Photocopied submissions OK. Accepts computer printout submissions.
Terms: "Terms are individually arranged with author after acceptance of manuscript." Sends galleys to author. Publishes ms one year after acceptance. Writer's guidelines for #10 SAE and 1 first class stamp. Book catalog for #10 SAE and 2 first-class stamps.

WOODSONG GRAPHICS INC., (II), P.O. Box 304, Lahaska PA 18931-0304. (215)794-8321. Editor: Ellen Bordner. Estab. 1977. "Small publishing firm dedicated to printing quality books and marketing them creatively." Publishes paperback and hardcover originals. Books: Standard or coated stock paper; photo offset printing; GBC or standard binding; illustrations; average print order: 5,000; first novel print order; 2,500. Averages 6-8 total titles each year. "Sometimes" buys juvenile mss with illustrations. Occasionally critiques rejected mss.
Needs: Adventure, contemporary, gothic/historical and contemporary romance, historical (general), humor/satire, juvenile (animal, easy-to-read, fantasy, historical, picture book, spy/adventure, contemporary), literary, mainstream, psychic/supernatural/occult, science fiction, suspense/mystery, war, western, and young adult (easy-to-read/teen, fantasy/science fiction, historical, problem novels, spy/adventure). No deviant sex of any kind or pornography.
How to Contact: Accepts unsolicited mss. Query first or submit complete ms. SASE always. Simultaneous and photocopied submissions OK. Accepts computer printout submissions. Reports in 3 weeks on queries, longer on mss. "We do everything possible to get replies out promptly, but do read everything we're sent . . . and that takes time." Publishes ms 6-12 months after acceptance.
Terms: Pays in royalties; negotiates advance. Sends galleys to author. "Arrangements will depend totally on the author and manuscript."
Advice: "If first novels are good, we have no problem with them, and we're always happy to look. Along with queries, send at least a few pages of actual ms text, since quality of writing is more important than topic where fiction is concerned. If you believe in what you've written, stick with it. There is so much good material that we must reject simply because we can't afford to do everything. Others must have the same problem, and it's a matter of being on the right desk on the right day to finally succeed."

WYRICK & COMPANY, 12 Exchange St., Box 89, Charleston SC 29402. (803)722-0881. Editor-in-Chief: Charles L. Wyrick, Jr. Publishes hardcover and trade paperback originals and reprints. Published new writers within the last year. Averages 8-12 titles/year.
Needs: Adventure, southern regional, experimental, humor, mainstream. "We seek exemplary works of fiction, particularly those by southern writers. We welcome submissions by unpublished authors. We are not normally interested in sci-fi, western or romance." Published *Things Undone*, by Max Childers.
How to Contact: Submit outline/synopsis with a "clear, concise" cover letter and sample chapters or complete ms. SASE. Reports in 2-3 weeks on queries; 8-12 weeks on mss. Simultaneous and photocopied submissions OK.
Terms: Pays royalties of 8-12% on retail price. Average advance: $500.
Advice: "By publishing quality works of fiction and nonfiction, Wyrick & Company hopes to sell to knowledgeable readers of all ages—those who seek well written, well designed and well produced books of all types. Overemphasis by major houses and the media on blockbusters has created a greater, rather than a lesser, opportunity for small and medium-sized publishers to find and publish tomorrow's great books."

‡**YARROW PRESS, (II),** #312, 225 Lafayette St., New York NY 10012. (212)941-1275. Publishers: Michael J. Miller and Anne Yarowsky. Estab. 1990. Small, independent publisher with plans to expand. Publishes hardcover and paperback originals and reprints. Averages 6-8 total titles. Sometimes comments on rejected mss.
Needs: Adventure, contemporary, humor/satire, literary, mainstream, preschool/picture book, short story collections. Recently published *I Am Thinking of My Darling*, by Vincent McHugh (adventure); *A Time To Be Born*, by Dawn Powell (satire); and *The Locusts Have No King*, by Dawn Powell.
How to Contact: Accepts unsolicited mss. Query first or submit outline/synopsis and 3 sample chapters. SASE. Reports in 1-2 months on queries; 3-4 months on mss. Simultaneous, photocopied submissions OK. Accepts computer printout submissions.
Terms: Offers negotiable advance. Sends galleys to author. Publishes ms 10-12 months after acceptance. Writer's guidelines not available. Book catalog free.
Advice: "Don't make a synopsis so lengthy and detailed that there is no need to read the book. It should leave us hungry to fill in the information. Also, self-deprecating cover letters, or those making grandiose claims (sell jobs) — don't work for us."

YITH PRESS, (I, IV), 1051 Wellington Rd., Lawrence KS 66049. (913)843-4341. Subsidiary: *Eldritch Tales Magazine*. Editor/Publisher: Crispin Burnham. Estab. 1984. One-man operation on part-time basis. Publishes paperback originals and reprints. Books: offset printing; perfect binding; illustrations; average print order: 500-1,000. Averages 1-2 titles each year. Average first novel print order: 500-1,000 (depending pre-publication orders). Occasionally critiques rejected ms.
Needs: Fantasy and horror. Accepts short stories for collections only. Novel needs include "anything in the supernatural horror category." No "mad slasher or sword and sorcery."
How to Contact: Accepts unsolicited mss. Submit complete ms with SASE. Reports in 2 months. Simultaneous and photocopied submissions OK. Accepts computer printout submissions. Prefers letter-quality. Disk submissions OK with MacIntosh II system.
Terms: Individual arrangement with author depending on the book. Sends galleys to author. Pays in royalties of 25% minimum; 35% maximum.
Advice: "Be original, don't try to be the next Lovecraft or Stephen King. Currently, I plan to publish one or two books/year, along with *Eldritch Tales*. The author/editor relationship should be give and take on both sides. I will try *not* to rewrite the author's work. If I feel that it needs some changes then I'll suggest them to the author. We are currently on hold with the book line as we are trying to get *Eldritch Tales* out on a quarterly schedule. Any potential submitter should send a card to inquire as to status."

YORK PRESS, Box 1172, Fredericton, New Brunswick E3B 5C8 Canada. (506)458-8748. Editorial Director: Dr. S. Elkhadem. Estab. 1975. Midsize independent publisher with plans to expand. Publishes hardcover and paperback originals. Publishes in English and other languages. Average first novel print order: 1,000 copies. Number of titles: 68 in 1991.
Needs: Contemporary, experimental, and translations by established writers. "No mss written mainly for entertainment, i.e., those without literary or artistic merit." Published *Three Pioneering Egyptian Novels*, translated and edited by Saad El-Gabalawy; Michel Butor's *Description of San Marco*, translated by Barbara Mason; and *Missing in Action* by W. Van Wert.
How to Contact: Accepts unsolicited mss, "although an initial query is appreciated." Query with SASE or SAE and IRC. No simultaneous submissions; photocopied submissions OK. Reports in 1 week on queries; 1 month on mss.
Terms: Pays 10% in royalties; no advance. Free book catalog.
Advice: "We are devoted to the promotion of scholarly publications; areas of special interest include general and comparative literature, literary criticism, translations of important works of fiction and creative writing of an experimental nature."

ZEPHYR PRESS, (III), 13 Robinson St., Somerville MA 02145. Subsidiary of Aspect, Inc. Editorial Directors: Ed Hogan and Leora Zeitlin. Estab. 1980. Publishes hardcover and paperback originals. Books: acid-free paper; offset printing; Smythe-sewn binding; some illustrations; average print order: 1,500-2,000; first novel print order: 1,000-1,500. Averages 5 total titles, 1-2 fiction titles each year.
Needs: Contemporary, ethnic, experimental, feminist/lesbian, gay, historical, humor/satire, literary, mainstream, regional, short story collections. Published *Two Novels*, by Philip Whalen; and *The St. Veronica Gig Stories*, by Jack Pulaski.

How to Contact: "We no longer read unsolicited mss. We read small press and literary magazines to find promising writers. We accept queries from agents, and from authors whose previous publications and professional credits (you must include a summary of these), demonstrate work of exceptional talent and vision. Queries should include vita, list of publications, and up to 10 samples pages, photocopies only. If we are interested, we will request the full manuscript. Otherwise, we will make no response."
Terms: Pays royalties approximately 10% of publisher's net for first edition. "There can be some flexibility of terms, based on mutual arrangements, if desired by author and publisher." Sends galleys to author. Book catalog for SASE.
Advice: "Seek well qualified feedback from literary magazine editors or agents and/or professionally established writers before submitting manuscripts to publishers. We regard the author/editor relationship as one of close cooperation, from editing through promotion."

ZOLAND BOOKS, INC., (II), Box 2766, Cambridge MA 02238. (617)864-6252. Publisher: Roland Pease. Managing Editor: Peter Nielson. Marketing Director: Alice Maurice. Estab. 1987. "We are a literary press, publishing poetry, fiction, photography, and other titles of literary interest." Publishes hardcover and paperback originals. Books: acid-free paper; sewn binding; some with illustrations; average print order: 2,000-5,000. Averages 6 total titles each year.
Needs: Contemporary, feminist, literary, short story collections, translations. Recently published *Small Victories*, by Sallie Bingham (novel); *Secret Words*, by Jonathan Strong (novel); and *Natural Light*, by Ethel Gorham.
How to Contact: Accepts unsolicited mss. Query first, then send complete ms with cover letter. SASE. Reports in 2-4 weeks on queries; 4-6 weeks on mss. Photocopied submissions OK. Accepts computer printout submissions.
Terms: Pays royalties of 5-8%. Average advance: $1,500; negotiable (also pays author's copies). Sends galleys to author. Publishes ms 1-2 years after acceptance. Book catalog for 6×9 SAE and 2 first class stamps.

International small press

The following small presses from countries outside the U.S. and Canada will consider novels or short stories in English. Some of the countries represented here include Australia, England, India, Ireland, Italy, Malawi, New Zealand, Nigeria, Sweden, West Germany and Zimbabwe. Many of these markets do not pay in cash, but may provide author copies. Always include a self-addressed envelope with International Reply Coupons to ensure a response or the return of your manuscript. International Reply Coupons are available at the main branch of your local post office. To save the cost of return postage on your manuscript, you may want to send a copy of your manuscript for the publisher to keep or throw away and enclose a return postcard with one IRC for a reply.

‡**AFRICA CHRISTIAN PRESS**, P.O. Box 30, Achimota, Ghana, West Africa. Fiction Editor: Mr. Raymond Mills-Tetteh. Averages 6 fiction titles/year. "We are a Christian publishing house specializing in Christian fiction works by Africans or expariates with a long association with Africa." Length: 15,000 words minimum. Send: Cover letter, synopsis, brief summary, sample chapter/s and/or entire manuscript. Pays royalties. Mss should be "typewritten, double spaced, with generous margins." Send 2 copies and a SAE with IRCs for response/return. Write for catalog and/or writer's guidelines.

‡**ANOWUO EDUCATIONAL PUBLICATIONS**, P.O. Box 3918, 2R McCarthy Hill, Accra, Ghana. Fiction Editor: Samuel Asare Konadu. Average 5-10 fiction titles/year. "Publication development organization for Ghanaian, African and world literature: novels, workbooks, language development, etc." Length: 80 typed pages minimum; 250 maximum. Send brief summary and first and last chapter. Pays advance and royalties. Looks for cultural development, romance.

ASHTON SCHOLASTIC LTD., Private Bag 1, Penrose, Auckland, New Zealand. Fiction Editor: Penny Scown. Publishes 20 fiction titles annually. "Educational publishing with a focus on books for the teaching of language arts and children's literature for all ages from picture books to teen novels." Pays royalties. "Do not 'write down' to children—write the story you want to tell using the best language— i.e., most appropriate vocabulary, letting the story only dictate the length."

‡ATTIC PRESS, 4 Upper Mount St., Dublin Ireland. Managing Editor: Grainne Healy. Averages 6-8 fiction titles/year. "Attic Press is an independent, export-oriented, Irish-owned publishing house with a strong international profile. The press specializes in the publication of fiction and nonfiction books for and about women by Irish and international authors." Send cover letter, synopsis, brief summary, 3 samples chapters or entire manuscript. Pays advance on signing contract and royalties. "Please ensure that your book is by/about/for women; that it is properly laid out for reading—double-spaced typewritten etc." Write for catalog.

BIBLIOTECA DI NOVA SF, FUTURO, GREAT WORKS OF SF, Perseo Libri srl, Box 1240, I-40100 Bologna Italy. Fiction Editor: Ugo Malaguti. "Science fiction and fantasy; novels and/or collections of stories." Pays 7% royalties on cover price; advance: $800-1,000 on signing contract. Buys Italian book rights; other rights remain with author. "While preferring published writers, we also consider new writers."

‡JONATHAN CAPE, 20 Vauxhall Bridge Rd., London SW1V 2SA England. Fiction Editor: David Godwin. Averages 20-25 fiction titles/year. Send a cover letter, synopsis, 2-3 sample chapters. Pays advance and royalties. "Send sample chapters first, not the whole ms." Our catalog is available on demand from our publicity dept.

‡CHRISTCHURCH PUBLISHERS LTD., 2 Caversham St., London S.W.3, 4AH UK. Fiction Editor: James Hughes. Averges 25 fiction titles/year. "Miscellaneous fiction, also poetry. More 'literary' style of fiction, but also thrillers, crime fiction etc." Length: 30,000 words minimum. Send a cover letter, synopsis, brief summary. "Preliminary letter and *brief* synopsis favored." Pays advance and royalties. "We have contacts and agents worldwide." Write for catalog.

‡CHRISTIAN LITERATURE ASSOCIATION IN MALAWI, P.O. Box 503, Blantyre, Malawi. Contact: Willie T. Zingani or Anderson J. Fumulani. Averages 5-10 fiction titles/year. "All fiction with Christian theme." Length: 10,000-50,000 words. "First contact us to find out our requirements." Send cover letter and outine or entire ms. Pays royalties.

EASTERN CARIBBEAN INSTITUTE (ECI) (IV), Box 1338, Frederiksted, Virgin Islands 00841. Editor/President: S.B. Jones-Hendrickson, PhD. Estab. 1982. Small press with plans to expand. Publishes hardcover originals and paperback originals. Regional. Needs for novels include Caribbean issues and settings. No religious. Length: 10,000 words minimum. Send cover letter with synopsis and 1 sample chapter. Reports in 1 week on queries; 1 month for mss. Write for catalog.

‡AIDAN ELLIS PUBLISHING, Cobb House, Nuffield, Henley-on-Thames, Oxon RG9 5RT England. Fiction Editor: Aidan Ellis. Averages 12 fiction titles/year. "Founded in 1971, with an annual turnover of around £250,000 we are a small publishing house publishing fiction and general trade books." Send a cover letter, synopsis, brief summary, sample chapter/s or entire manuscript. Pays advance on publication, royalties twice yearly. Write for catalog.

‡FOURTH ESTATE, Classic House, 289 Westbourne Grove, London W11 2QA England. Editorial Director: Giles O'Bryen. Publishes 50 books/year. "Small general publisher. Modern fiction, mostly young writers. Strong storyline but often a new or different way of telling it." Writers paid advance against royalties. "Submit only cover letter, a synopsis and 2 sample chapters in the first instance." Length: 40,000 words minimum.

HEMKUNT, Publishers A-78 Naraina Industrial Area Ph.I, New Delhi India 110028. Managing Director: G.P. Singh. "We would be interested in novels, preferably by authors with a published work. Would like to have distribution rights for US, Canada and UK beside India." Send a cover letter, brief summary, 3 sample chapters (first, last and one other chapter). "Writer should have at least 1-2 published novels to his/her eredit." Catalog on request.

‡HERITAGE BOOKS, 2-8 Calcutta Crescent, Gate 4, P.O. Box 610, Apapa, Lagos Nigeria. Fiction Editor: Bakin Kunama. "The type of fiction we are interested in: Must be from black writers; must be strongly Afrocentric; broadly Pan African; must enhance black image; must be trail blazing. Length: 40,000-60,000 words. Send a cover letter, brief summary, 1 sample chapter. Pays royalties.

KAWABATA PRESS, (II), Knill Crass House, HR Anderton Rd., Millbrook, Torpoint, Cornwall PL10 1DX England. Fiction Editor: C. Webb. "Mostly poetry—but prose should be realistic, free of genre writing and clichés and above all original in ideas and content." Length: 200-4,000 words (for stories); 30,000-100,000 words (for novels). Send cover letter, synopsis and 1 sample chapter. "Don't forget return postage (IRCs)." Writers receive half of profits after print costs are covered. Write for guidelines and book list.

KINGSWAY PUBLICATIONS, 1 St. Anne's Road, Eastbourne, E. Sussex BN21 3UN England. Contact: Carolyn Owen. Publishes "Christian books; children's fiction, but not short stories. Does not publish adult fiction. Books on leadership, discipleship, devotional, biography, music, the church, currrent issues from a Christian perspective." Length: 25,000-75,000 words. Payment varies "according to whether writer has an agent or not, and whether we negotiate contract directly or through a US publisher. Submit synopsis and one sample chapter, double-spaced, typed with adequate margins. Allow 6-8 weeks for response. "The writer should understand the international market. Do not send anything without specifically Christian content. Include return postage, but not U.S. stamps. A knowledge of the differences in culture and language would be useful."

‡THE LITERATURE BUREAU, P.O. Box 8137 Causeway, Harare Zimbabwe. Fiction Editor: B.C. Chitsike. Averages 12 fiction titles/year. "All types of fiction from the old world novels to the modern ones with current issues. We publish these books in association with commercial publishers but we also publish in our own right." Length: 7,000-30,000 words maximum. Send entire manuscript. Pays royalties. "Send the complete manuscript for assessment. If it is a good one it is either published by the Bureau or sponsored for publication. If it needs any correction a full report will be sent to the author." Obtain guidelines by writing to the Bureau. We have 'Hints to New Authors' a pamphlet for aspiring authors. These can be obtained on request.

MAROVERLAG, Riedingerstrasse 24, D-8900, Augsburg West Germany. Editor: Benno Käsmayr. Publishes 4-6 novels or story collections/year. Publishes "exciting American authors in excellent translations; e.g. Charles Bukowski, Jack Kerouac, William Burroughs, Paul Bowles, Gerald Locklin, Keith Abbott and Gilbert Sorrentino." Send a cover letter, synopsis, brief summary and 2 sample chapters. Writers paid for published fiction. "Please include SAE and postage. Our books and catalogs can be ordered at every German bookstore. Most of them send to the US too."

MONARCH PUBLICATIONS LIMITED, 1 St. Anne's Road, Eastbourne, E. Sussex, BN21 3UN England. Contact: Carolyn Owen. Publishes up to 12 novels per year. "We are Christian publishers and are only interested in full-length works of fiction with a Christian slant. Length: 30,000-80,000 words. Pays in advanced royalty and standard royalties based on sales. "Send a synopsis and two sample chapters. Please do not send entire manuscripts. International Reply Coupons are not essential but appreciated. Manuscripts should be typed double-spaced with generous margins. Authors should keep a copy of any material sent. US writers should be aware of barriers created by the use of what is strictly US idiom, and of fiction which is exclusive to the US culture."

‡OBOBO BOOKS, 2-8 Calcutta Crescent, Gate 4, P.O. Box 610, APAPA, Lagos Nigeria. Fiction Editor: Ms. Obobo Osahon. "Positive image forming works for African kids." Length: 3,000-5,000 words maximum. Send a cover letter, brief summary, 1 sample chapter. Pays royalties.

‡PUBLISHERS GROUP SOUTH WEST (IRELAND), Allihies, Bantry, County Cork IP2 91 Ireland. Executive Editor: Peter Haston. Averages 6-10 fiction titles/year. "Experimental fiction of all kinds, including audiobooks." Send synopsis and sample chapter, typed and posted registered airmail. Payment by agreement. Advice: "Contact publishers associations and research a publishing house that already produces work of the same kind. Determine which editor there has on his list the works most akin to yours. Do your research. Follow up." Send postcard of inquiry for catalog.

‡STAPLE FIRST EDITIONS, Derbyshire College of HE,Western Rd., Mickleover, Derby DE3 56X UK. Fiction Editor: Don Meatham. Averages 2 fiction titles/year. "Unpublished, original typescripts in one of the following categories: poetry (single, long cycle poem, group of poems); prose (single story, section or sections of a novel, group of stories)." Length: 28-40 pages (of published text). Send entire manuscript. Each script must be accompanied by the statement overleaf and a reading fee of £5 or £10, if author wishes a 250-word report. Fee is refunded if work is published. Pays 10% royalties on cover price plus £75 advance and 6 author's copies. Overall closing date for submissions is July 31, 1992.

‡**TEMPLE PRESS**, P.O. Box 227, Brighton, Sussex BN2 3GL England. Averages 3 fiction titles/year. "Radical press dealing in new writings. We specialize in avant garde material unsuited to the major publishing houses. We have published fiction works on the occult and sexual deviation." Length: 10,000-100,000 words. Send a cover letter, synopsis, 3 sample chapters or entire manuscript. Pays mix of royalty and advances. "Clear presentation. Writers must be offering a new angle/vision. 80% of our writers are based overseas." Send 3 IRCs for information.

‡**UNIVERSITY PRESS**, Three Crowns Building, Jericho, P.M.B. 5095, Ibadan Nigeria. Contact: Editorial Controller. Averages 12-30 fiction titles/year. "University Press PLC is an offshoot of Oxford University Press Oxford, UK. It is the only book publishing company quoted under the Nigerian Stock Exchange. Nigerians own 60% of its share capital while Oxford University Press Oxford owns 40%. Educational fiction is poetry, novel and drama (not romance) in the three Nigerian major languages (Igbo, Yoruba, Hausa) apart from English." Length: 10,000-20,000 words. Send entire manuscript. Pays advance and royalty. Catalog and other information on request.

THE VANITAS PRESS, Plaatslagarevägen 4 E 1, 22230 Lund Sweden. Fiction Editor: Mr. March Laumer. "One-person full-time operation publishing for prestige, not cash profit motives. At present exclusively interested in promising 'Oz' novels. Very actively interested in attracting writers/illustrators who would care to *collaborate* in the creation of 'latter-day' Oz novels. Best is for writers to send a first enquiry letter. We are glad to send advice on what/how to submit."

Other small press

The following small presses appeared in the 1991 edition of *Novel & Short Story Writer's Market* but are not in the 1992 edition. Those presses whose editors did not respond to our request for an update are listed below without explanation. There are several reasons why a small press did not respond—they may be out of business, or overstocked with submissions. If an explanation was given, it is included next to the listing name. Note presses from outside of the US and Canada appear at the end of the list.

Another Way
Ansuda Publications (asked to be left out this year)
Banned Books (asked to be deleted)
Breitenbush Books (out of business)
Carlton Books
Cave Books
Clarity Press (asked to be deleted)
Double M Press (asked to be left out this year)
Fiction Collective Two (asked to be deleted)
Green Tiger Press
Max Hardy-Publisher (sold, asked to be left out this year)
Hyperion Press Limited (no longer publishing fiction)
Intertext (overstocked until at least 1994)
Kitchen Table: Women of Color
Kubicek & Associates
Library Research Associates (no fiction in 1992)
Lincoln Springs Press
Misty Hill Press
New Seed Press (asked to be deleted)
Owl Creek Press
Papyrus Publishers (asked to be left out this year)
Perspectives Press (no fiction)
Porcupine's Quill (asked to be deleted)
Primal Publishing (not reading until 1994)
Ramalo Publications (asked to be left out this year)
Re/Search Publishing (asked to be deleted)
Satchell's Publishing
Scojtia, Publishing Company (responded late)
The Smith
Stormline Press (asked to be deleted)
Teal Press
Tudor Publishers (asked to be left out this year)
University of Utah Press (asked to be deleted)
Vehicule Press
The Woman Sleuth Mystery Press (series no longer published)

Other international small press
GMP Publisher
Handshake Editions
Karnak House
Settle Press (no fiction)

Commercial Publishers

World events affected the publishing industry's pocketbook during the past year, but the forecast for 1992 is encouraging as many publishers make changes to capture more readers' interest—as well as profits.

For 1990, the Association of American Publishers reported a 5.3% increase in sales, including a 7.4% increase in trade books and a 4.9% increase in mass market paperbacks. The result was more than $15.4 billion for the book publishing industry.

Unfortunately, publishers may not see similar revenues when final figures are tallied for 1991. The industry expected to see increases in postage as well as demands for printing on recycled and acid-free paper, but it was also dealt blows from the economic recession and the Persian Gulf War. With uncertainty reigning nationwide, consumers cut back their spending, causing worried booksellers to cut staff and inventory, process returns more quickly and make purchases in smaller amounts.

Even though the war ended relatively quickly, consumer confidence has remained low. In September 1991, Cahners Economics predicted a sales gain of just 4.7% for publishers in 1991, but their outlook for 1992 is stronger, with a predicted 8.3% sales gain.

Internationally, sales were a mixed bag, with drops in the Middle East but strong increases in the former Eastern Bloc. The result was a 2.3% gain in overall exports for the first half of the year and a better outlook for the future.

Hard and soft deals

Although fiction publishing is often the first to suffer during tight times, writers may be heartened by Cahners' predictions—and the knowledge that fiction sales were much stronger than nonfiction sales in 1990. New writers may also find comfort in the knowledge that many publishers are still investing strongly in first fiction. A recent issue of *Publishers Weekly* includes a list of more than 125 first novels set for release between Fall 1991 and Fall 1992.

A related development is that, more and more, publishers are not just signing authors to hardcover contracts. With many hardcover houses now having their own paperback counterparts, "hard-soft deals" are increasing. These deals include provisions for an author's book to be published first in hardcover and then later in paperback by divisions of the same publisher. As agent Aaron Priest explained in an issue of *Publishers Weekly*, "Ten years ago the hard-soft deal was an exception. Five years ago it was 50/50. Today, in terms of big books, it's 85% to 90% of the business." Although primarily offered to proven authors, hard-soft deals are now occasionally presented to first novelists as well.

Changes in paperbacks

Paperback publishing itself is also seeing some changes. Many publishers continue to release both novels and short story collections in trade paperback, giving books a place next to hardcover titles without incurring the same publication costs. This format often works well with "literary" titles and titles by emerging writers.

Bantam, however, is now taking a more innovative approach with its literary fiction. Last fall, a selection of the work that would have normally appeared in trade paperback appeared in quality books the same width but slightly taller than standard mass market paperbacks. These "Tracks," a nickname for trade paper/rack size, are the publisher's means of making an impression in a trade paperback fiction market which has become glutted.

In general, mass market paperbacks are either reprints of hardcover titles or releases of original category fiction. Not only are mass market paperbacks the least expensive format in which to publish, but they also have the widest distribution. They can be found anywhere from the local drugstore to the retail outlets of national bookstore chains. The problem many mass market publishers face, however, is how to gain additional space on paperback racks. Dell is meeting this challenge by developing a new imprint.

Following in the footsteps of Pocket Books' Star imprint, Ballantine's Ivy and Penguin's Onyx line, Dell has created Island Books, a new list of top-of-the-line releases. The list made its debut in February with a reprint of *The Firm* by John Grisham. Original novels, such as Meagan McKinney's *Lions and Lace* which is due out this May, are included in the list as well.

A growing format

Perhaps another format for authors to note is spoken-word audio, which has grown from only a sideline market to a publishing enterprise all its own. At last year's American Booksellers Association, the Audio Publishers Association estimated industry-wide sales of spoken-word audio at $850 million. In general, however, only bestselling authors and titles are making it onto audiotapes. Yet, with some houses having their own audio divisions, many tapes are published at the same time as books. Recent developments include the release of both abridged and unabridged works. Unabridged tapes for Stephen King's *Needful Things*, for example, were released simultaneously with the hardcover edition last November.

Trends and new listings

A different vision of spoken-word audio is presented by one of the 11 new listings in this section: Books in Motion. As President Gary Challender explains, Books in Motion is an "audiobook" company, meaning that original work is published in cassette form only. Challender's needs for fiction include mysteries and action-adventure stories.

One trend readers will find among the other listings in this section is an increased interest in Christian fiction. This includes not only historical, romance and biblical novels, but also "mainstream" novels, which may simply be considered Christian in perspectives or themes. As Jane Dekker, assistant to the director of publications at Baker Book House explains, "[We are] a publisher just breaking into adult fiction . . . We're doing so because interest in fiction continues to increase in the Christian market, several niches in the market are waiting to be filled and some of this fiction can cross over into the secular market." Along with listings for Accent Books, Bethany House Publishers, Crossway Books and Zondervan, all of which seek Christian fiction, you will now find listings for Baker Book House, Bridge Publishing, Inc. and the David C. Cook Publishing Company.

Two other new listings are devoted to fiction for children. The first, Lerner Publications Company, would like to see children's fiction with "less gender and racial stereotyping" and "more protagonists from ethnic minority groups." The second, Philomel Books, an imprint of the Putnam & Grosset Book Group, seeks "ethnic novels with a strong cultural voice but which speak universally."

Indeed, the desire for more multicultural works is growing, even in adult fiction. Now included among publishers' offerings are works by and/or about not only African Americans but also Asian Americans, Hispanic Americans and Native Americans. Last spring, five Chinese-American works were released by five different publishers. Since 1990, when Oscar Hijuelos received a Pulitzer Prize for *The Mambo Kings Play Songs of Love*, Hispanic writers have been receiving more attention. And, over the course of the past few years, the number of Native-American novels has grown considerably.

Finally, the listings in this section continue to include a variety of publishers seeking category fiction, such as romances, mysteries and westerns. For more complete details on trends in each of these genres, and others, see the "Popular Fiction Market Report" beginning on page 36.

How to submit

When it comes to deciding where to submit your novel or short story collection, start by checking under Commercial Publishers in the Category Index on page 603. There you will find publishers classified by the particular types of fiction they seek most often.

After you have narrowed down your options, review the individual listings and request catalogs from the publishers that interest you to see how your work compares to their line of books. Many of the publishers in the listings explain how catalogs and writer's guidelines may be obtained. Often, writers are asked to send self-addressed, stamped envelopes (SASEs) for these materials. If a publisher is located outside your country, send a self-addressed envelope (SAE) and International Reply Coupons (IRCs).

Once you have decided where you would like to submit your work, study the publisher's submission procedures. Most commercial publishers do not accept unsolicited manuscripts. Rather, writers should send queries, usually consisting of a cover letter, brief synopsis or outline, and three consecutive sample chapters, in the case of novels. Publishers who prefer queries to complete manuscripts often say in their listings exactly what they would like to see. Again, include SASEs or SAEs with IRCs for replies.

It is important to note, however, that more and more commercial publishers prefer contacts through agents over queries directly from writers. Many agents specialize in certain areas and are quite familiar with the needs of related publishing houses. Consequently, many publishers are relying on agents to do the initial screening of submissions and present only what is most appropriate for their lines. For more information about how agents function and to locate an agent compatible with your type of fiction, consult the *1992 Guide to Literary Agents & Art/Photo Reps* (Writer's Digest Books).

Whether you are submitting a query or a complete manuscript to either an editor or agent, you must present your material in a professional manner. For details about proper submission formats, see "The Business of Fiction Writing" on page 71.

Other options

Besides commercial publishers, this section also includes both book packagers and subsidy publishers. Book packagers, such as Cloverdale Press, are designated by a filled-in box (■) at the beginning of their listings. They are best described as companies that produce books for publishers, often at the request of the publishers themselves. Here's how it works: A publisher contacts a book packager when he has an idea for a book to fit the needs of a particular line (or even an idea for a whole line of books) but lacks a potential writer. He gives the book packager an outline of the developed idea, including descriptions of characters, setting and story. The book packager, then, is responsible for hiring a writer and overseeing the completion, and sometimes the production, of the manuscript.

While commercial publishers pay their authors in advances and royalties, book packagers most often use work-for-hire arrangements where writers receive payment in one large sum. Under these arrangements, writers are not generally given credit for their work nor do they have any claim to the copyright. However, writers may benefit by working closely with the editors at book packagers and by attaining publication.

Subsidy publishing is another option open to writers seeking publication, and you will find such publishers designated by an asterisk (*) at the beginning of their listings. In subsidy publishing, though, writers are asked to pay for all or part of the costs of producing the book. In return, subsidy publishers offer assistance in the book's marketing and distribution.

Although new writers or writers of experimental works may find such arrangements useful, subsidy publishing should be considered only after more conventional means have been exhausted. Writers should also be wary of subsidy publishers requiring excessive fees. Always find out exactly how many copies of the book will be printed and what types of paper, printing and binding will be used. Compare the subsidy publisher's price with that of a local printer willing to offer the same number of copies in a similar manner. If the difference is considerable, ask yourself whether or not the assistance in marketing and distribution is worth the extra cost. Also, see if you can find one of the publisher's previous books in a local bookstore. Checking the true availability of the finished work may aid your decision.

Further information

For more information about the publishing industry in the United States, Canada and other countries, read *Publishers Weekly*. Also, The Book Industry Study Group (BISG) releases various reports to its members throughout the year. Nonmembers may want to check the availability of the BISG's reports at the local library or contact the group itself (160 Fifth Ave., New York NY 10010). Finally, for listings of commercial publishers outside of the United States and Canada see pages 507-509.

The ranking system for listings in this section follows:

   I **Publisher encourages beginning or unpublished writers to submit work for consideration and publishes new writers frequently.**

  II **Publisher accepts work by established writers and by occasional new writers of unusual talent.**

 III **Publisher does not encourage beginning, unagented writers; publishes mainly writers with extensive previous publication credits and a very few new writers.**

  IV **Special-interest or regional publisher open only to writers on certain subjects or from certain geographic areas.**

ACADEMY CHICAGO PUBLISHERS, (I), 213 W. Institute Place, Chicago IL 60610. (312)751-7302. Imprints carrying fiction include Cassandra Editions, Academy Mystery, Academy Travel Classic and Academy Firsts. Senior Editor: Anita Miller. Estab. 1975. Midsize independent publisher. Publishes hardcover and paperback originals and paperback reprints. Books: 55 lb. Glatfelter; mostly sheet fed; perfect, sometimes Smythe-sewn for hardcovers; b&w illustrations; average print order for paperback 5,000; for hardcover 1,500-3,000. Buys 20% agented fiction for reprints only. Average first novel print order 5,000 copies paper, 1,500 copies hardbound. Occasionally comments on rejected mss.
Needs: Mystery, historical, feminist and translations. No experimental, religious, romance or children's. Published *The Scarlet City: A Novel of 16th-Century Italy*, by Hella S. Haasse; *Tales for a Winter's Night*, by Arthur Conan Doyle; and *Miss Read's Christmas*, by Miss Read (psuedonym).

How to Contact: Accepts unsolicited mss. Query and submit first three chapters with SASE. No simultaneous submissions; photocopied submissions OK. Reports in 2 weeks on queries, 6 weeks on mss. *"No* micro-dot printer. Manuscripts without envelopes will be discarded. *Mailers* are a *must."* Publishes ms an average of 1 year after acceptance.
Terms: Pays 5-10% on net in royalties; no advance. Sends galleys to author.
Advice: "The relationship between novelist and editor should be close; the manuscript is gone over line by line, word by word. An aspiring novelist should submit manuscripts directly to publishers and avoid agents. If the big houses turn it down there are many smaller independent presses which will read everything that comes in a bound manuscript. We do not like to receive postage and label *without* a mailing envelope — it prejudices us against the work from the outset."

ACCENT BOOKS, (II), A Division of Accent Publications, Box 15337, Denver CO 80215. (303)988-5300. Executive Editor: Mary B. Nelson. Estab. 1975. Growing midsize independent publisher of Christian books. Publishes paperback originals. Books: type of paper varies; established book printers; average print order varies. Will publish new writers this year. Averages 10-12 total titles, 4 fiction titles per year. Occasionally critiques rejected mss.
Needs: "Christian novels in these categories only: contemporary, mystery/romance and frontier romance. All must have strong, evangelical, Christian storylines showing how Christ makes a difference in a person's life." Recently published *Shadow Wind*, by Diane Todd; *The Fire Within*, by B.J. Hansen; *A Deadly Snare*, by Sara Mitchell; and *Cry on Desert Winds*, by Bea Carlton.
How to Contact: Submit outline/synopsis and 3-4 sample chapters with SASE. Reports in 5 weeks on queries, 2 months on proposals. Simultaneous submissions and clear photocopied submissions accepted. Accepts computer printout submissions.
Terms: Pays royalties. Sends galleys to author. Writer's guidelines for SASE; book catalog for 9 × 12 SASE with $1.25 postage.
Advice: "We are looking for fiction with a solid evangelical message. People are realizing that important truths as well as clean entertainment can be provided through quality Christian fiction. Know the publishing house standards. Be sure to enclose SASE with every submission. Don't take shortcuts. Write it, then rewrite it. Be willing to keep reworking the same proposal until it is absolutely tight, top-notch entertainment. Be unique, not trite. Be aware of the world and people around you."

ACE SCIENCE FICTION, (formerly Ace Charter Books), Berkley Publishing Group, 200 Madison Ave., New York NY 10016. (212)951-8800. Estab. 1977. Publishes paperback originals and reprints. See Berkley Ace Science Fiction.

APPLE BOOKS, Scholastic, Inc., 730 Broadway, New York NY 10003. (212)505-3000. Senior Editor: Regina Griffin. Children's imprint. See Scholastic Inc.
Needs: "Apple books are generally contemporary. There are no restrictions as to length or subject matter, but all Apple Books are geared toward the capacities and interests of 8-12 year olds." Published *Fourth Graders Don't Believe in Witches*, by Terri Fields; *I Spent My Summer Vacation Kidnapped Into Space*, by Martyn Godfrey; and *The Broccoli Tapes*, by Jan Slepian.
How to Contact: Accepts unsolicited mss. Submit outline/synopsis and 3 sample chapters. Reports in 3 weeks on queries; 8 weeks on mss. Single submissions only. Accepts computer printout submissions.
Terms: Pays an advance against royalties.

ARCHWAY PAPERBACKS, 1230 Avenue of the Americas, New York NY 10020. (212)698-7000. Executive Editor: Patricia MacDonald. Published by Pocket Books. Imprints: Minstrel Books (ages 7-11); and Archway (ages 11 and up). Publishes paperback originals and reprints.
Needs: Young adult (mystery, suspense/adventure, thrillers, young readers (short, 64 pages and up), animals, themes: friends, adventure, mystery, school, fantasy, family, etc.). No picture books. Recently published *My Heart Belongs to That Boy*, by Linda Lewis; *Scavenger Hunt*, by Christopher Pike; and the *Fear Street Series*, by R.L. Stine. Published new writers this year.
How to Contact: Submit query first with outline; SASE "mandatory. If SASE not attached, query letter will not be answered."

ATHENEUM BOOKS FOR CHILDREN, (II), Imprint of the Macmillan Children's Book Group, 866 Third Ave., New York NY 10022. (212)702-7894. Editorial Director: Jonathan J. Lanman. Fiction Editors: Gail Paris or Marcia Marshall (especially sf/fantasy). Midsize imprint of large publisher/corporation. Publishes hardcover originals. Books: Illustrations for picture books, some illustrated short novels; average print order: 6,000-7,500; first novel print order: 6,000. Averages 70 total titles, 55 fiction titles each year. Very rarely critiques rejected mss.

Needs: Juvenile (animal, fantasy, historical, sports, adventure, contemporary), preschool/picture book, young adult/teen (fantasy/science fiction, historical, problem novels, sports, spy/adventure, mystery). No "paperback romance type" fiction. Published books include *The Good-bye Book*, by Judith Viorst (3-6, picture book); *Tree by Leaf*, by Cynthia I. Voigt (9-13, preteen "problem"); and *Maudie in the Middle*, by Phyllis Reynolds Naylor (7-11, preteen illustrated novel).

How to Contact: Accepts unsolicited mss "if novel length; we want outline and 3 sample chapters." SASE. Agented fiction 40%. Reports in 3-4 weeks on queries; 6-8 weeks on mss. Simultaneous submissions OK "if we are so informed"; photocopied submissions OK "if clear and legible." Accepts computer printout submissions.

Terms: Pays in royalties of 10-12%. Average advance: $3,000 "along with advance and royalties, authors standardly receive ten free copies of their book and can purchase more at a special discount." Sends galleys to author. Writer's guidelines for #10 SAE and 1 first class stamp. Book catalog for 9 × 12 SAE and 6 first class stamps.

Advice: "We publish all hardcover originals, occasionally an American edition of a British publication. Our fiction needs have not varied in terms of quantity—of the 60-70 titles we do each year, 50-60 are fiction in different age levels. We are less interested in specific topics or subject matter than in overall quality of craftsmanship. First, know your market thoroughly. We publish only children's books, so caring for and *respecting* children is of utmost importance. Also, fad topics are dangerous, as are works you haven't polished to the best of your ability. (Why should we choose a 'jewel in the rough' when we can get a manuscript a professional has polished to be ready for publication.) The juvenile market is not one in which a writer can 'practice' to become an adult writer. In general, be professional. We appreciate the writers who take the time to find out what type of books we publish by visiting the libraries and reading the books. Neatness is a pleasure, too."

AVALON BOOKS, (II, IV), 401 Lafayette St., New York NY 10003. Vice President/Publisher: Barbara J. Brett. Imprint of Thomas Bouregy Company, Inc. Publishes hardcover originals. Average print order for all books (including first novels): 2,100. Averages 60 titles/year. Buys very little agented fiction. Recently published *Heart Games*, by Lynn Bulock (romance); *Prescription For Love*, by Anne Ladley (career romance); *Annabelle's Secret*, by Alice Sharpe (mystery romance); *Raid at Black Persimmon Bluff*, by Howard Pelham (western).

Needs: "Avalon Books publishes wholesome romances and westerns that are sold to libraries throughout the country. Intended for family reading, our books are read by adults as well as teenagers, and their characters are all adults: The heroines of the romances are all young (mid-twenties) single (no divorcees or widows, please!) women, and the heroes of the westerns range in age from late twenties to early thirties. There is no graphic sex in any of our novels; kisses and embraces are as far as our characters go. The heroines of the romances and the heroes of the westerns and adventures should all be looking forward to marriage at the end of the book. Currently, we publish five books a month: two romances, one mystery romance, one career romance and one western; we publish only three adventures a year. All the romances are contemporary; all the westerns are historical. The important action in all our novels takes place over a short period of time, ranging from days to no longer than a year." Books range in length from a minimum of 40,000 words to a maximum of 50,000 words.

How to Contact: Submit the first chapter and a brief, but complete, summary of the book, or submit complete manuscript. Publishes many first novels and very little agented fiction. Enclose ms-size SASE. Reports in about three months. "Send SASE for a copy of our tip sheet."

Terms: Pays $600 for the first book, $800 for the second, $1,000 thereafter, against the first 3,500 copies sold. (Initial run is 2,100.) A royalty of 10% is paid on any additional sales. The first half of the advance is paid upon signing of the contract; the second within 30 days after publication. Usually publishes within six to eight months.

AVON BOOKS, (II), The Hearst Corporation, 1350 Avenue of the Americas, New York NY 10019. (212)261-6800. Imprints include Avon, Camelot and Flare. Associate Publisher Trade Division: Mark Gonpertz. Editor-in-Chief Avon Books: Robert Mecoy. Estab. 1941. Large paperback publisher. Publishes paperback originals and reprints. Averages 300 titles a year.

Market categories: (I) Beginning; (II) General; (III) Prestige; (IV) Specialized.

Needs: Fantasy, historical romance, mainstream, occult/horror, science fiction, medical thrillers, intrigue, war, western and young adult/teen. No poetry, mystery, short story collections, religious, limited literary or esoteric nonfiction. Published *Butterfly*, by Kathryn Harvey; *So Worthy My Love*, by Kathleen Woodiwiss.

How to Contact: Query letters only. SASE to insure response.

Terms: Vary. Book catalog for SASE. Sponsors Flare Novel competition.

BAEN BOOKS, (II), P.O. Box 1403, Riverdale NY 10471. (212)548-3100. Baen Science Fiction, Baen Fantasy. Publisher and Editor: Jim Baen. Executive Editor: Toni Weisskopf. Consulting Editor: Josepha Sherman. Estab. 1983. Independent publisher; books are distributed by Simon & Schuster. Publishes hardcover and paperback originals and paperback reprints. Published new writers within the last year. Plans 6-10 first novels this year. Averages 60 fiction titles each year. Occasionally critiques rejected mss.

Needs: Fantasy and science fiction. Interested in science fiction novels (generally "hard" science fiction) and fantasy novels "that are not rewrites of last year's bestsellers." Recently published *Generation Warriors*, by Anne McCaffrey and Elizabeth Moon (science fiction); *The Man-Kzin Wars IV*, by Larry Niven (science fiction); and *The Wizardry Cursed*, by Rick Cook (fantasy).

How to Contact: Accepts unsolicited mss. Submit ms or outline/synopsis and 3 consecutive sample chapters with SASE. Reports in 2-3 weeks on partials; 4-8 weeks on mss. Will consider simultaneous submissions, "but grudgingly and not as seriously as exclusives." Accepts computer printout submissions.

Terms: Pays in royalties; offers advance. Sends galleys to author. Writer's guidelines for SASE.

Advice: "Keep an eye and a firm hand on the overall story you are telling. Style is important but less important than plot. We like to maintain long-term relationships with authors."

‡BAKER BOOK HOUSE, (II), P.O. Box 6287, Grand Rapids MI 49516. (616)676-9185. Assistant to Director of Publications: Jane Dekker. Estab. 1939. "Midsize Evangelical publisher." Publishes hardcover and paperback originals. Books: Web offset print; average print order: 5,000-10,000; first novel print order: 5,000. Plans 1 first novel this year. Averages 130 total titles. "In 1992, the first year in which we will publish fiction, we will do at least 3 such titles." Sometimes comments on rejected ms.

Needs: "We are mainly seeking Christian fiction of two genres: Contemporary women's fiction and mystery." No fiction that is not written from a Christian perspective or of a genre not specified.

How to Contact: Does not accept unsolicited mss. Submit outline/synopsis and sample chapters. SASE. Agented fiction 100% (so far). Reports in 3-4 weeks on queries. Simultaneous, photocopied submissions OK. Accepts computer printout submissions.

Terms: Pays royalties of 14% (of net). Sometimes offers advance. Sends galleys to author. Publishes ms 1 year after acceptance. Writer's guidelines for #10 SAE and 1 first class stamp. Book catalog for 9½ × 12½ SAE and 3 first class stamps.

Advice: "I would suggest that authors interested in writing contemporary women's fiction write us for more information regarding this genre."

BALLANTINE BOOKS, 201 E. 50th St., New York NY 10022. Subsidiary of Random House. Vice Pres. and Senior Editor: Pamela D. Strickler. Publishes originals (general fiction, mass-market, trade paperback and hardcover). Averages over 120 total titles each year.

Needs: Major historical fiction, women's mainstream and general contemporary fiction. Manuscripts can be submitted unsolicited to Pamela D. Strickler. Recently published *The Tokaido Road*, by Lucia St. Clair Robson; *The Expendables*, by Leonard Scott; and *For All Their Lives*, by Fern Michaels. Published new writers this year.

How to Contact: Submit brief outline/synopsis and complete ms. SASE required. Photocopied submissions OK. Reports in 2 months on queries; 4-5 months on mss.

Terms: Pays in royalties and advance.

BANTAM SPECTRA BOOKS, (II, IV), Subsidiary of Bantam Doubleday Dell Publishing Group, 666 5th Ave., New York NY 10103. (212)765-6500. Vice-President and Publisher: Lou Aronica. Executive Editor: Amy Stout. Associate Publisher: Betsy Mitchell. Editor: Janna Silverstein. Estab. 1985. Large science fiction, fantasy and speculative fiction line. Publishes hardcover originals, paperback originals and trade paperbacks. Averages 60 total titles each year, all fiction.

Needs: Fantasy, literary, science fiction. Needs include novels that attempt to broaden the traditional range of science fiction and fantasy. Strong emphasis on characterization. Especially well written traditional science fiction and fantasy will be considered. No fiction that doesn't have at least some element of speculation or the fantastic.
How to Contact: Does not accept unsolicited mss. Query first with 3 chapters and a synopsis. SASE. Agented fiction 90%. Reports in 6-8 weeks on queries. Photocopied submissions OK. Accepts computer printouts.
Terms: Pays in royalties; negotiable advance. Sends galleys to author.

THE BERKLEY PUBLISHING GROUP, (III), Subsidiary of G.P. Putnam's Sons, 200 Madison Ave., New York NY 10016. (212)951-8800. Imprints are Berkley, Jove, Diamond, Ace Science Fiction, Pacer. Editor-in-Chief: Leslie Gelbman. Senior Editor: Elizabeth Beier. Fiction Editors: Natalee Rosenstein, Judith Stern, John Talbot, Melinda Metz, Susan Allison, Peter Heck, Ginger Buchanan, Carrie Feron, Gail Fortune, Hillary Cige, Andy Zack. Nonfiction: Open. Large commercial category line. Publishes paperback originals and hardcover and paperback reprints. Books: Paperbound printing; perfect binding; average print order: "depends on position in list." Plans approx. 10 first novels this year. Averages 1,180 total titles, 1,000 fiction titles each year. Sometimes critiques rejected mss.
Needs: Fantasy, horror, humor/satire, literary, mainstream, psychic/supernatural/occult, religious/inspirational, romance (contemporary, historical), science fiction, short story collections (by established authors, but rarely), suspense/mystery, war, western, young adult/teen (problem novels). "We are looking for strong horror and contemporary romance/mainstream fiction titles. Because we are a mass market publishing house, we publish a vast array of genres. We do short story collections, except for the rare collection by an established author." Published *Springfancy*, by LaVyrle Spencer (historical romance); *The Cardinal and the Kremlin*, by Tom Clancy (fiction/military); and *Midnight*, by Dean Koontz (horror).
How to Contact: Accepts no unsolicited mss. Submit through agent only. Agented fiction 98%. Reports in 1 month on mss. Simultaneous and photocopied submissions OK. Accepts computer printout submissions.
Terms: Pays royalties of 4-10%. Provides 25 author's copies. Writer's guidelines and book catalog not available.
Advice: "Aspiring novelists should keep abreast of the current trends in publishing by reading the New York Times Bestseller Lists, trade magazines for their desired genre and *Publishers Weekly*."

BERKLEY/ACE SCIENCE FICTION, (II), Berkley Publishing Group, 200 Madison Ave., New York NY 10016. (212)951-8800. Editor-in-Chief: Susan Allison. Estab. 1948. Publishes paperback originals and reprints. Number of titles: 10/month. Buys 85-95% agented fiction.
Needs: Science fiction and fantasy. No other genre accepted. No short stories. Published *The Cat Who Walks Through Walls*, by Robert Heinlein; *Neuromancer*, by William Gibson.
How to Contact: Submit outline/synopsis and 3 sample chapters with SASE. No simultaneous submissions; photocopied submissions OK. Reports in 2 months minimum on mss. "Queries answered immediately if SASE enclosed." Publishes ms an average of 18 months after acceptance.
Terms: Standard for the field. Sends galleys to author.
Advice: "Good science fiction and fantasy are almost always written by people who have read and loved a lot of it. We are looking for knowledgeable science or magic, as well as sympathetic characters with recognizable motivation. We need less fantasy and more science fiction. We are looking for solid, well-plotted SF: good action adventure, well-researched hard science with good characterization and books that emphasize characterization without sacrificing plot. In fantasy, again, we are looking for all types of work, from high fantasy to sword and sorcery." Submit fantasy and science fiction to Susan Allison, Ginjer Buchanan and Beth Fleisher.

BETHANY HOUSE PUBLISHERS, (II), 6820 Auto Club Rd., Minneapolis MN 55438. (612)829-2500. Fiction lines include: Prairie Love Stories, The Stonewyck Trilogy, George MacDonald Classics, Canadian West, The Zion Chronicles, The Zion Covenant. Editorial Director: Carol Johnson. Manuscript Reviews: Sharon Madison. Estab. 1956. Midsize independent religious publisher with plans to expand; publishing in a variety of categories from theological to fiction. Publishes paperback and hardcover originals. Books: Type of paper varies; offset printing; average print order: 20,000; first novel print order average: 15,000.
Needs: Religious/inspirational, adventure, mystery, regional, romance (historical and young adult), gothic and juvenile. Published *Love Takes Wing*, by Janette Oke (prairie romance); *Key to Zion*, by Bodie Thoene (historical); *Code of Honor*, by Sandy Dengler (historical).

How to Contact: Query or submit outline/synopsis and 2-3 sample chapters with SASE. Simultaneous and photocopied submissions OK. Accepts computer printout submissions. Reports in 1 month on queries, 6 weeks on mss. Publishes ms an average of 1 year after acceptance.
Terms: Pays in royalties. Sends galleys to author. Book catalog and fiction guidelines with 8½×11 SASE.
Advice: "Prairie romances are *very* strong in our line, as well as historical fiction. We look at everything that is submitted; a first novel has a chance with us, especially if it has series possibilities. We do *not* recommend an agent—this puts an unnecessary barrier between publisher and author (chances for misunderstanding, mistrust). Send queries and proposals around till you have raised some interest; work with the editor to fit it to a publisher's needs."

JOHN F. BLAIR, PUBLISHER, (II, IV), 1406 Plaza Dr., Winston-Salem NC 27103. (919)768-1374. President: Margaret Couch. Editor: Stephen Kirk. Estab. 1954. Small independent publisher. Publishes hardcover and paperback originals. Books: Acid-free paper; offset printing; illustrations; average print order 2,500-5,000. Number of titles: 6 in 1991. Encourages new writers. Occasionally comments on rejected mss.
Needs: Contemporary, literary and regional. Generally prefers regional material dealing with southeastern U.S. No confessions or erotica. "We do not limit our consideration of manuscripts to those representing specific genres or styles. Our primary concern is that anything we publish be of high literary quality." Published works include *Blackbeard's Cup and Stories of the Outer Banks*, by Charles Harry Whedbee (folklore); and *The Legend of Nance Dude*, by Maurice Stanley (novel).
How to Contact: Query or submit with SASE. Simultaneous and photocopied submissions OK. Accepts computer printout submissions. Reports in 1 month on queries, 3 months on mss. Publishes ms 1-2 years after acceptance. Free book catalog.
Terms: Pays 10% standard royalties, 7% on paperback royalties.
Advice: "We are primarily interested in serious adult novels of high literary quality. Most of our titles have a tie-in with North Carolina or the southeastern United States. Please enclose a cover letter and outline with the manuscript. We prefer to review queries before we are sent complete manuscripts. Queries should include an approximate word count."

BOOKCRAFT, INC., 1848 W. 2300 South, Salt Lake City UT 84119. (801)972-6180. Editorial Manager: Cory H. Maxwell. Publishes hardcover originals. Books: 60 lb. stock paper; sheet-fed and web press; average print order: 5,000-7,000; 3,000 for reprints. Published new writers within the last year. "We are always open for creative, fresh ideas."
Needs: Contemporary, historical, western, romance and religious/inspirational. Recently published *The Burning Bush Patrol*, by Richard Marshall; *The Work and the Glory: Pillar of Light*, by Gerald N. Lund.
How to Contact: Query, submit outline/synopsis and sample chapters, or submit complete ms with SASE. Photocopied submissions OK. Reports in 2 months.
Terms: Pays royalties; no advance. Sends galleys to author. Free book catalog and writer's guidelines.
Advice: "Read our fiction. Our market is the membership of The Church of Jesus Christ of Latter-Day Saints (Mormons), and all stories must be related to the background, doctrines or practices of that church. No preaching, but tone should be fresh, positive and motivational. No anti-Mormon works. The amount of fiction we publish has remained the same the last three or four years. We publish little in the way of paperback; given regional nature of our market, it is difficult to price paperbacks competitively."

‡BOOKS IN MOTION, (I), Suite #501, 9212 E. Montgomery, Spokane WA 99206. (509)922-1646. President: Gary Challender. Estab. 1980. "Audiobook company, national marketer. Publishes novels, novellas and short stories in audiobook form *only*." Published new writers within the last year. Plans 12 first novels this year. Averages 70 total titles, 65 fiction titles each year.
Needs: Open. "We accept full-length novels, and since we publish works in audio cassette form only, we need plots that move, characterizations that are vivid and stories that capture the *ear* as well as the imagination. Our current priorities are mysteries, action/adventure and humor." No "introspective fiction (i.e. notes from the underground) or erotic fiction or pointed political fiction." Recently published *Cow County Law*, by M & M Lehman (western); *By A Promise Bound*, by Barbara Francis (historical drama/romance); and *Flight of the White Horse*, by Todd S. Moffett (fantasy).

How to Contact: Accepts unsolicted mss. Submit outline/synopsis and 4 sample chapters. SASE for ms. Reports within 3 weeks to 3 months. Simultaneous and photocopied submissions OK.
Terms: Pays royalties of 10%. "We pay royalties every 6 months. Royalties that are received are based on the gross sales that any given title generates during the 6-month interval. Authors must be patient since it usually takes a minimum of one year before new titles will have significant sales." Publishes ms 6-12 months after acceptance. Book catalog free on request.
Advice: "We would like to see more short works, less than 700 pages. We are currently looking for works from 55 to 100 double-spaced, typed pages."

THOMAS BOUREGY & COMPANY, INC., 401 Lafayette St., New York NY 10003. See Avalon Books. Small category line.

BOYDS MILLS PRESS, (II, IV), Subsidiary of Highlights for Children, 910 Church St., Honesdale PA 18431. (717)253-1164. Manuscript Coordinator: Juanita Galuska. Estab. 1990. "Independent publisher of quality books for children of all ages." Publishes hardcover and paperback originals. Books: Coated paper; offset printing; case binding; 4-color illustrations; average print order varies. Plans 36 titles, 2 fiction titles. Critiques or comments on rejected mss.
Needs: Juvenile, young adult (adventure, contemporary, ethnic, fantasy, historical, animal, easy-to-read, sports, preschool/picture book, science fiction). Recently published *Pedro's Journal*, by Pam Conrad; *The Violin Man*, by Maureen Brett Hooper; *Matie's Whisper*, by Alice de LaCroix.
How to Contact: Accepts unsolicited mss. Send complete ms with cover letter. Reports in 1 month. Simultaneous and photocopied submissions OK.
Terms: Pays standard rates. Sends pre-publication galleys to author. Time between acceptance and publication depends on "what season it is scheduled for." Writer's guidelines for #10 SAE and 1 first class stamp.
Advice: "We're interested in young adult novels of real literary quality as well as middle grade fiction that's imaginative with fresh ideas. Getting into the mode of thinking like a child is important."

BRADBURY PRESS, INC., (I, II), Affiliate of Macmillan, Inc., 866 3rd Ave., New York NY 10022. (212)702-9809. Vice President and Editorial Director: Barbara Lalicki. Publishes juvenile hardcover originals. Books: Excellent quality paper printing and binding; full-color or black-and-white illustrations—depends on what the book needs. Encourages new writers. Seldom comments on rejected mss.
Needs: Juvenile and young adult: contemporary, adventure, science fiction. Recently published *Woodsong*, by Gary Paulsen; *Windcatcher*, by Avi; and *Cricket and the Crackerbox Kid*, by Alane Ferguson.
How to Contact: Query first on novels. Send complete picture book ms with SASE. Specify simultaneous submissions; photocopied submissions OK. Reports in 3 months on mss.
Terms: Pays royalty based on retail price. Advance negotiable.

BRANDEN PUBLISHING CO., (I, II), Subsidiary of Branden Press, Box 843, 17 Station St., Brookline Village MA 02147. Imprint: I.P.L. Estab. 1967. Publishes hardcover and paperback originals and reprints. Books: 55-60 lb. acid-free paper; case- or perfect-bound; illustrations; average print order: 5,000. Plans 5 first novels this year. Averages 15 total titles, 5 fiction titles each year.
Needs: Adventure, contemporary, ethnic, historical, literary, mainstream, military/war, short story collections, suspense/mystery and translations. Looking for "contemporary, fast pace, modern society." No porno, experimental or horror. Published *Payola!*, by Gerry Cagle; *Miss Emily Martine*, by Lynn Thorsen; *Tales of Suicide*, by Luigi Pirandello; and *The Saving Rain*, by Elsie Webber; published new writers within the last year.
How to Contact: Does not accept unsolicited mss. Query *only* with SASE. Reports in 1 week on queries. Accepts computer printout submissions.
Terms: Pays royalties of 10% minimum. Advance negotiable. Provides 10 author's copies. Sends galleys to author. Publishes ms "several months" after acceptance.
Advice: "Publishing more fiction because of demand. Do not oversubmit; try single submissions; do not procrastinate if contract is offered."

 The double dagger before a listing indicates that the listing is new in this edition. New markets are often the most receptive to freelance contributions.

*GEORGE BRAZILLER, INC., (III), 60 Madison Ave., New York NY 10010. (212)889-0909. President: George Braziller. Fiction Editor: Christiane Neumayer. Estab. 1955. Publishes hardcover originals and paperback reprints. Books: Cloth binding; illustrations sometimes; average print order: 4,000. Average first novel print order: 3,000. Buys 10% agented fiction. Averages 25 total titles, 6 fiction titles each year. Occasionally critiques rejected mss.
Needs: Art, feminist, literary, short story collections and translations. Recently published *You Don't Love Yourself*, by Nathalie Sarraute (literary); *The White Castle*, by Orhan Pamuk (literary); *And They Didn't Die*, by Lauretta Ngcobo (ethnic/feminist).
How to Contact: Query first with SASE. Photocopied submissions OK. Reports in 2 weeks on queries. Publishes ms an average of 1 year after acceptance.
Terms: *Some subsidy publishing.* Negotiates advance. Must return advance if book is not completed or is not acceptable. Sends galleys to author. Free book catalog on request with oversized SASE.

‡*BRIDGE PUBLISHING, INC., (III, IV), 2500 Hamilton Blvd., South Plainfield NJ 07080. (201)754-0745. Editor: Raymond Stanbury. Estab. 1981. Midsize independent publisher of Christian literature. Publishes cloth and paperback originals and reprints. Averages 20 total titles/year.
Needs: "We want quality, literary Christian fiction, written in the style of Frederick Buechner, John Cheever, and John Updike. *No* "genre" fiction (romance, biblical novels, gothics, sci-fi, etc.). We want well written fiction that shows believable characters struggling to 'work out their salvations' in believable situations. Books that exhibit real human drama and stylistic craftsmanship." Published *Getting Them Sober*, by Toby Drews; *Help for the Battered Woman*, by Dr. Lydia Savina; and *The Teen Sex Survival Manual*, by Watkins.
How to Contact: Accepts unsolicited mss. Submit complete ms with cover letter. SASE required. Reports in 1 month. Simultaneous or photocopied submissions OK. Accepts computer printouts.
Terms: *Offers self/cooperative publishing services.* Writer's guidelines for #10 SAE and 1 first class stamp. Book catalog for $2.
Advice: "While we are not generally accepting fiction, we will consider manuscripts of exceptional merit. Authors must already have material published and/or other books published by reputable publishers. The work must be written from a biblical Christian worldview but does not necessarily need to be explicitly religious in nature. Only completed manuscripts will be considered."

BROADMAN PRESS, (II), 127 9th Ave. N., Nashville TN 37234. (615)251-2433. Editorial Director: Harold S. Smith. Religious publisher associated with the Southern Baptist Convention. Publishes hardcover and paperback originals. Books: Offset paper stock; offset printing; perfect or Smythe sewn binding; illustrations possible; average print order depends on forecast. Average number of titles: 3/ year.
Needs: Adventure, historical, religious/inspirational, humor/satire, juvenile, and young adult. Will accept no other genre. Recently published: *Recovery of the Lost Sword*, L.L. Chaikin; *Mary of Magdala*, by Anne C. Williman; *Journey to Amanah: The Beginning*, by Colleen K. Snyder.
How to Contact: Query, but decision is not made until ms is reviewed. No simultaneous submissions; photocopied submissions OK. Reports in 2 months on queries and mss.
Terms: Pays 10% in royalties; no advance. Sends galleys to author if requested.
Advice: "We publish very few fiction works, but we encourage first novelists. We encourage a close working relationship with the author to develop the best possible product."

CAMELOT BOOKS, (II), Imprint of Avon Books, (Division of the Hearst Corporation), 1350 Avenue of the Americas, New York NY 10019. (212)261-6816. Editorial Director: Ellen E. Krieger. Estab. 1961. Publishes paperback originals and reprints for middle-grade juvenile list. Books: 6-10 line drawings in a few of the younger books. No color.

The asterisk indicates a publisher who sometimes offers subsidy arrangements. Authors are asked to subsidize part of the cost of book production. See the introduction to Commercial Publishers for more information.

Needs: Juvenile (fantasy—"very selective," contemporary—"selective"). Looking for "contemporary, humorous books about real kids in real-life situations." No "science fiction, animal stories, picture books." Published *Haunting in Williamsburg*, by Lou Kassem; *The Return of the Plant that Ate Dirty Socks*, by Nancy McArthur; and *The Secret of the Indian*, by Lynne Reid Banks.
How to Contact: Accepts unsolicited mss. Submit complete ms with cover letter (preferred) or outline/synopsis and 3 sample chapters. Agented fiction 75%. Reports in 3-4 weeks on queries; 6-10 weeks on mss. Simultaneous and photocopied submissions OK. Accepts computer printout submissions.
Terms: Royalties and advance negotiable. Sends galleys to author. Writer's guidelines for #10 SAE and 1 first class stamp. Book catalog for 9×11 SAE and 98¢ postage.

CARROLL & GRAF PUBLISHERS, INC., (III), 260 5th Ave., New York NY 10001. (212)889-8772. Contact: Editor. Estab. 1983. Publishes hardcover and paperback originals and paperback reprints. Plans 5 first novels this year. Averages 120 total titles, 75 fiction titles each year. Average first novel print order 7,500 copies. Occasionally critiques rejected mss.
Needs: Contemporary, erotica, fantasy, science fiction, literary, mainstream and suspense/mystery. No romance.
How to Contact: Does not accept unsolicited mss. Query first or submit outline/synopsis and sample chapters. SASE. Reports in 2 weeks. Photocopied submissions OK. Accepts computer printout submissions.
Terms: Pays in royalties of 6-15%; advance negotiable. Sends galleys to author. Free book-catalog on request.

CITADEL PRESS, (II), Lyle Stuart Inc., 120 Enterprise Ave., Secaucus NJ 07094. (201)866-4199. Vice President: Allan J. Wilson. Estab. 1942. Publishes hardcover and paperback originals and paperback reprints. Averages 65 total titles, 4-7 fiction titles each year. Occasionally critiques rejected mss.
Needs: No religious, romantic or detective. Published *The Rain Maiden*, by Jill M. Phillips and *Human Oddities*, by Martin Monestiere.
How to Contact: Accepts unsolicited mss. Query first with SASE. Reports in 6 weeks on queries; 2 months on mss. Simultaneous and photocopied submissions OK.
Terms: Pays in royalties of 10-15%; 12-25 author's copies. Advance is more for agented ms; depends on grant/award money.

CLARION BOOKS: A Houghton Mifflin Company, (II), 215 Park Ave. South, New York NY 10003. (212)420-5800. Editor/Publisher: Dorothy Briley. Executive Editor: Dinah Stevenson. Estab. 1965 "as the children's book division of Seabury Press; 1979 as a new children's book imprint of Houghton Mifflin Company." Midsize children's book imprint of a major publishing company. Publishes hardcover originals and paperback reprints from its own backlist. Number of titles: 50 in 1991. Average print order: 8,000-10,000. Published new writers within the last year. Buys 10-15% agented fiction. Comments on rejected mss "only if we're encouraging a revision."
Needs: Juvenile and young adult: adventure, suspense and humorous contemporary stories for ages 6-10, 8-12 and 10-14; "fresh, personal stories that capture our attention, and that we think young readers would enjoy." Published *Always and Forever Friends*, by C. S. Adler; *Saying Good-bye to Grandma*, by Jane Resh Thomas; *December Stillness*, by Mary Downing Hahn. Especially interested in humorous stories for ages 8 to 12.
How to Contact: Accepts unsolicited mss. Query with sample chapter/s on mss of more than 50 pages. SASE. "We like queries to be straightforward—no dramatic teaser openings—and to contain a description of the story, plus any relevant writing credits. It's good if they can be kept to a page, or at most two pages." Reluctantly considers simultaneous submissions; photocopied submissions OK. Accepts computer printout submissions. Reports in 2 weeks on queries, 8 weeks on mss. Publishes ms 1½-2 years after acceptance.
Terms: Pays 5% royalties on picture books; 10% on other books; offers $3,000+ advances. Writer must return advance if book is not completed or is not acceptable. Free book catalog and guidelines.
Advice: "I really believe that the best novels come out of the author's self-knowledge of his or her own experience and background. Don't send us imitations of other writers' successes. We're always open to first novelists in the hope that they'll become regular contributors to our list. We've noticed a return to lighter stories from the heavier problem novels of recent years. Attend a writer's workshop or critique group in order to study the structure of successful novels." Publishing "more middle grade fiction, less young adult fiction, because paperback originals seem to have covered that market. More paperback reprints from our backlist because bookstores like them."

■**CLOVERDALE PRESS INC., (II)**, 109 West 17th St., New York NY 10011. (212)727-3370. Editorial Director: Jane Thornton. Estab. 1980. Book packager.
Needs: "Needs vary greatly and frequently, depending on publishers' requirements." Currently producing *Sweet Dreams*, YA romances, *Nowhere High*, YA fiction, and adult nonfiction and how-to.
How to Contact: Does *not* accept unsolicited mss. Contact Marion Vaarn for guidelines. Include SASE.

CONTEMPORARY BOOKS, 180 N. Michigan Ave., Chicago IL 60601. Declined listing (mostly nonfiction).

‡**DAVID C. COOK PUBLISHING COMPANY**, 850 N. Grove, Elgin IL 60120. (312)741-2400. Imprints: Chariot Books, Life Journey Books. Executive Editor: Catherine L. Davis. Estab. 1875. Publishes hardcover and paperback originals. Published new writers within the last year. Number of fiction titles: 35-40 juvenile, 4-6 adult. Encourages new writers.
Needs: Religious/inspirational, juvenile, young adult and adult; sports, animal, spy/adventure, historical, Biblical, fantasy/science fiction, picture book and easy-to-read. Recently published *With Wings as Eagles*, by Elaine Schulte; *Mystery of the Laughing Cat*, by Elspeth Campbell Murphy; *Mystery Rider at Thunder Ridge*, by David Gillett.
How to Contact: All unsolicited mss are returned unopened. Query with SASE. Simultaneous and photocopied submissions OK. Accepts computer printout submissions. Reports in 3 months.
Terms: Royalties vary ("depending on whether it is trade, mass market or cloth" and whether picture book or novel). Offers advance. Writer's guidelines with SASE.
Advice: "Chariot Books publishes books for toddlers through teens which help children better understand their relationship with God, and/or the message of God's book, the Bible. Interested in seeing contemporary novels (*not* Harlequin-type) adventure, romance, suspense with Christian perspective."

CROSSWAY BOOKS, (II, IV), Division of Good News Publishers, 1300 Crescent, Wheaton IL 60187. Acquisitions Editor: Jennifer Nahrstadt. Estab. 1938. Midsize independent religious publisher with plans to expand. Publishes paperback originals. Average print order 5,000 copies. Buys 5% agented fiction. Averages 35 total titles, 8-10 fiction titles each year.
Needs: Contemporary, adventure, fantasy, juvenile (fantasy), literary, religious/inspirational, science fiction and young adult (fantasy/science fiction). "All fiction published by Crossway Books must be written from the perspective of evangelical Christianity. It need not be *explicitly* Christian, but it must understand and view the world through Christian principle. For example, our books *Taliesin* and *Merlin* take place in a pre-Christian era, but Christian themes (e.g., sin, forgiveness, sacrifice, redemption) are present. We are *eager* to discover and nurture Christian novelists." No sentimental, didactic, "inspirational" religious fiction; heavy-handed allegorical or derivative (of C.S. Lewis or J.R.R. Tolkien) fantasy. Recently published *Brothers for Life* by Keith Wander; *High Places*, by Stephen Bransford; *Home by Another Way*, by Nancy Rue.
How to Contact: Does not accept unsolicited mss. Send query with synopsis and sample chapters only. Accepts computer printout submissions. Reports in 4 months on queries. Publishes ms 1-2 years after acceptance.
Terms: Pays in royalties and negotiates advance. Book catalog for 9 × 12 SAE and $1.25.
Advice: "Publishing a higher quality of writing as we develop a wider reputation for excellent Christian fiction. Christian novelists—you must get your writing *up to standard*. The major reason novels informed by a Christian perspective do not have more presence in the market is because they are inferior. Sad but true. I believe Crossway can successfully publish and market *quality* Christian novelists. Also read John Gardner's *On Moral Fiction*. The market for fantasy/science fiction continues to expand (and genre fiction in general). There are more attempts lately at Christian science fiction and fantasy, though they generally fail from didacticism or from being overly derivative. We have a western adult and youth series, a mystery series."

Listings marked with a solid box [■] are book packagers.
See the introduction to Commercial Publishers for more
information.

THE CROWN PUBLISHING GROUP, (II), 201 E. 50th St., New York NY 10022. (212)572-6190. Imprints include Crown, Harmony Books, Orion Books, Clarkson N. Potter, Inc. Executive Vice Pres., Editor-in-Chief: Betty A. Prashker. Executive Editor, Crown: James O'Shea Wade. Editorial Director, Harmony Books: Peter Guzzardi. Editorial Director, Clarkson N. Potter: Carol Southern, Executive Editor: Lauren Shakely. Editorial Director, Orion Books: James O'Shea Wade. Executive Managing Editor: Laurie Stark. Estab. 1936. Large independent publisher of fiction and nonfiction. Publishes hardcover and paperback originals and reprints. Magazine: 50 lb. paper; offset printing; hardcover binding; sometimes illustrations; average print order: 15,000. Plans 4 first novels this year. Averages 250 total titles, 20 fiction titles each year. Average first novel print order: 15,000 copies. Occasionally critiques rejected mss.
Needs: Adventure, contemporary, historical, horror, humor/satire, literary, mainstream, science, war. Recently published *Plains of Passage*, by Jean Auel; *Dave Barry Talks Back*, by Dave Barry; *Russka*, by Edward Rutherfurd; *Zapp!*, by William Byam with Jeff Cox; and *Martha Stewart's Gardening*, by Martha Stewart.
How to Contact: Does not accept unsolicited mss. "Query letters only addressed to the Editorial Department. Complete mss are returned unread . . ." SASE. Reports in 3-4 months. Photocopied submissions OK.
Terms: Pays advance against royalty; terms vary and are negotiated per book.

DAW BOOKS, INC., (I, IV), 375 Hudson St., New York NY 10014. Publishers: Elizabeth R. Wollheim and Sheila Gilbert. Executive VP/Secretary-Treasurer: Elsie B. Wollheim. Submissions Editor: Peter Stampfel. Estab. 1971. Publishes paperback originals, hardcover reprints and hardcover originals. Books: Illustrations sometimes; average print and first novel order vary widely. May publish as many as 6 or more first novels a year. Averages 36 new titles plus 40 or more reissues, all fiction, each year. Occasionally critiques rejected mss.
Needs: Science fiction and fantasy only. Recently published *Stronghold*, by Melanie Rawn (novel); *Stone of Farewell*, by Tad Williams (novel); *Black Sun Rising*, by C.S. Friedman. Publishes many original and reprint anthologies including *Sword & Sorceress* (edited by Marion Zimmer Bradley); *Horse Fantastic* (edited by Martin H. Greenberg); *Tales From the Twilight Zone* (edited by Carol Serling). "You may write to the editors (after looking at the anthology) for guidelines % DAW."
How to Contact: Submit complete ms with SASE. Usually reports in 3-5 months on mss, but in special cases may take longer. "No agent required."
Terms: Pays an advance against royalties. Sends galleys to author (if there is time).
Advice: "We strongly encourage new writers. We are currently working with more than a dozen additional new authors whose first novels we plan to publish in 1992. We like a close and friendly relationship with authors. We are publishing more fantasy than previously, but we are looking for more *serious* fantasy and especially need science fiction. To unpublished authors: Try to make an educated submission and don't give up."

DEL REY BOOKS, Subsidiary of Ballantine Books, 201 E. 50 St., New York NY 10022. (212)572-2677. Estab. 1977. Publishes hardcover originals and paperback originals and reprints. Plans 6-7 first novels this year. Publishes 60 titles each year, all fiction. Sometimes critiques rejected mss.
Needs: Fantasy and science fiction. Fantasy must have magic as an intrinsic element to the plot. No flying-saucer, Atlantis or occult novels. Recently published *Renegades of Pern*, by Anne McCaffrey (science fiction/hardcover original); *The Diamond Throne*, by David Eddings (fantasy/hardcover original); and *The Metaconcert*, by Julian May (science fiction/paperback reprint).
How to Contact: Accepts unsolicited mss. Submit complete manuscript with cover letter or outline/synopsis and first 3 chapters. Prefers complete ms. Address science fiction to SF editor; fantasy to fantasy editor. Reports in 2 weeks on queries; 10 months on ms. Photocopied submissions OK. Computer printout submissions OK.
Terms: Pays in royalties; "advance is competitive." Sends pre-publication galleys to author. Writer's guidelines for #10 SAE and 1 first class stamp.
Advice: Has been publishing "more fiction and more hardcovers, because the market is there for them. Read a lot of science fiction and fantasy, such as works by Anne McCaffrey, David Eddings, Larry Niven, Arthur C. Clarke, Terry Brooks, Frederik Pohl, Barbara Hambly. When writing, pay

Close-up

C. J. Cherryh
Author

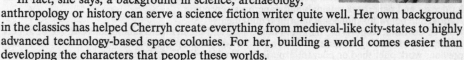

"The creation of an alien world is a lot like the reconstruc-
tion of an ancient city," says science fiction author C.J.
Cherryh. "You ask yourself the same questions about your
society that an archaeologist would ask about an ancient
culture: What did they eat? What did they believe? How
did they bury their dead? What were their trade ties?"

In fact, she says, a background in science, archaeology,
anthropology or history can serve a science fiction writer quite well. Her own background
in the classics has helped Cherryh create everything from medieval-like city-states to highly
advanced technology-based space colonies. For her, building a world comes easier than
developing the characters that people these worlds.

It's the characters, she says, that help readers to identify with strange or different worlds.
"You may want to consider an alien or exotic culture, but it must still be understandable
to the reader. And what usually involves the reader in an alien world is the characters."
Characters, no matter how alien, must behave as readers would expect them to act, she
says. This lends the logic that makes a story believable no matter where it takes place.

Cherryh has written more than 30 books—some are single titles, others are extensive
series. Some of her books were serialized for purely marketing reasons. "A problem with
a lot of genre literature has been publishers' resistance to 'big books.' More and more,
longer books are being broken apart to fit the marketing system. I find that it's hard to
write an intricate plot with complex characters in less than 80,000 words. Many books in
series these days are actually novels that have been broken up for economic reasons."

One of Cherryh's earlier novels, *Cyteen* was published whole in a hardbound edition,
but came out as three volumes in paperback. "My advice to the new writer is for today's
market it's best to keep to under 100,000 words."

A few of Cherryh's series books are actually shared-world novels in which one writer
creates an alternative world and invites others to write separate chapters and create additional characters. "It's a lot of fun," she says, "but writers need a sense of humor about it.
You can't care too much about how others treat your characters."

For a shared-universe book, Cherryh has two rules: No killing or maiming anyone else's
character and all action must take place in a 24-hour period. The one-day rule makes it
easier for her to keep the whole book in sequence, but still Cherryh has to "edit the final
version with a meat cleaver to make stories agree with each other." She finishes each book
by adding connective chapters featuring her original characters.

Cherryh writes for long stretches at a time and admits she hasn't taken a real vacation
in years. "Storytelling is what I do naturally. I go nuts if I'm away from the keyboard too
long—it's harder for me not to work."

—*Robin Gee*

particular attention to plotting (and a satisfactory conclusion) and characters (sympathetic and well-rounded)—because those are what readers look for."

DELACORTE/DELL BOOKS FOR YOUNG READERS/DOUBLEDAY, (II, III, IV), Division of Bantam Doubleday Dell Publishing Group, Inc., 666 5th Ave., New York NY 10103. (212)765-6500. Imprints include Yearling and Laurel-Leaf Books and Yearling Classics. New imprint: Young Yearling Books, for readers 5-8 years old. Vice President/Publisher: George Nicholson. Vice President and Associate Publisher: Craig Virden. Exec. Editor: Michelle Poploff. Large publisher specializing in young adult and middle-age fiction. Occasionally critiques or comments on rejected ms.
Needs: "First chapter books," juvenile, young adult. "We are looking for quality fiction—all categories possible." No romance of the formula type. Published *Fade*, by Robert Cormier; *Beans on the Roof*, by Betsy Byars; *Cal Cameron by Day, Spiderman by Night*, by Ann Cosum (winner of Delacorte fiction contest).
How to Contact: Query first. Unsolicited manuscripts not accepted. Fiction is agented. "Our contest is for first young adult novel. Deadline is December 31. Write for details."
Terms: Pays in royalties; advance is negotiable. Send galleys to author. Book catalog free on request.
Advice: "We are publishing more fiction than in the past. The market is good."

DELL PUBLISHING, 666 Fifth Avenue, New York NY 10103. (212)765-6500. Imprints include Delacorte Press, Delacorte Juvenile, Delta, Dell, Laurel, Laurel-Leaf and Yearling. Estab. 1922. Publishes hardcover and paperback originals and paperback reprints.
Needs: See below for individual imprint requirements.
How to Contact: Reports in 3 months. Photocopied and simultaneous submissions OK. Please adhere strictly to the following procedures: 1. Send *only* a 4-page synopsis or outline with a cover letter stating previous work published or relevant experience. Enclose SASE. 2. *Do not* send ms, sample chapters or artwork. 3. *Do not* register, certify or insure your letter. Dell is comprised of several imprints, each with its own editorial department. Please review the following information and direct your submissions to the appropriate department. Your envelope must be marked: Attention: (One of the following names of imprints), Editorial Department—Proposal.
DELACORTE: Publishes in hardcover; looks for topnotch commercial fiction and nonfiction; 35 titles/year.
DELTA: Publishes trade paperbacks including original fiction and nonfiction; 20 titles/year.
DELL: Publishes mass-market and trade paperbacks; looks for family sagas, historical romances, sexy modern romances, adventure and suspense thrillers, mysteries, psychic/supernatural, horror, war novels, fiction and nonfiction. 200 titles/year.
DELACORTE JUVENILE: Publishes in hardcover for children and young adults, grades K-12. 40 titles/year. "We prefer complete mss for fiction."
LAUREL-LEAF: Publishes originals and reprints in paperback for young adults, grades 7-12. 48 titles/year.
YOUNG YEARLING: pre K to 4th grade. Publishes originals and reprints in paperback for children.
YEARLING: Publishes originals and reprints in paperback for children, grades 1-6. 75 titles/year.
Terms: Pays 6-15% in royalties; offers advance. Sends galleys to author. Book catalog for 8½×11 SAE plus $1.30 postage (Attention: Customer Service).
Advice: "Don't get your hopes up. Query first only with 4-page synopsis plus SASE. Study the paperback racks in your local drugstore. We encourage first novelists. We also encourage all authors to seek agents."

DIAL BOOKS FOR YOUNG READERS, (II), Subsidiary of Penguin Books U.S.A. Inc., 375 Hudson St., New York NY 10014. (212)366-2000. Imprints include Pied Piper Books, Easy-to-Read Books. Editor-in-Chief/Pres./Publisher: Phyllis Fogelman. Estab. 1961. Trade children's book publisher, "looking for picture book mss and novels." Publishes hardcover originals. Plans 1 first novel this year. Averages 50-60 titles, all fiction. Occasionally critiques or comments on rejected ms.
Needs: Juvenile (1-9 yrs.) including: animal, fantasy, spy/adventure, contemporary and easy-to-read; young adult/teen (10-18 years) including: fantasy/science fiction, literary fiction, sports and spy/adventure. Published *Lionel in the Spring*, by Stephen Krensky (easy-to-read); *The Tale of Caliph Stork*, by

Read the Business of Fiction section to learn the correct way to prepare and submit a manuscript.

Close-up

Damaris Rowland
Associate Publisher
Dell Publishing

"The romance market is really happening right now," says Damaris Rowland, Dell associate publisher. "As a result, lots of women want to be involved in it and tell their stories. The mailrooms of publishers across New York City are being flooded with submissions, and, in most cases, it's probably more than we can handle."

That's why Rowland recommends agents. "I always tell people they should get themselves agents. I think it's in their best interest. Good agents are aware of the marketplace and who is doing what kind of book well. They also screen out authors who aren't ready for publication, saving time on this end," she says.

For example, "We're not buying a lot of historical romances right now because we have a very full list of very talented writers," says Rowland. "But we certainly want to find new talent writing contemporaries. I'm particularly looking for books that have a lot of family-oriented issues at their hearts."

Reading submissions, Rowland says, "I'm very open to lots and lots of different kinds of stories from all different kinds of people. I would have to say, however, that what impresses me is the energy in the writing, the conviction the author brings to her prose and to her story, the level of concentration that she's brought to the book."

Next she looks for "the manner in which it is very individual." Many stories are "market-driven" with people trying to duplicate what's become a bestseller, "rather than telling their own stories," says Rowland. "I think everybody learns by imitation—whether we're editors learning how to do our jobs well or authors learning how to write well. But there comes a point, even in a first effort, that an editor senses the way in which an author is being unique to her voice and to her vision of what her story is about.

"To get to that place, you have to spend a lot of time really digging into yourself and getting to where those feelings exist so that those feelings can be put on the page. It's good to do research, it's good to read what others have done and it's good to see how others have done it, but then you really want to make the story absolutely unique," she says.

Rowland advises authors "to read the marketplace." Read all the authors who are doing well, not just the bestsellers, she says. "Then choose those authors you have particularly responded to and decide why you are responding to their writing so much. Ask 'What is it that turns me on about the way this woman writes these stories?' Then discover something similar in yourself as a writer and dare to write it—dare to explore it more fully than the person you've loved has explored it."

You don't have to worry about not writing as well as somebody else, or even writing like somebody else, Rowland says, because "you see what someone's done well, you respond to it, and then, because everybody's different, you ultimately begin to write your very own unique story."

— Christine Martin

Lenny Hort (picture book); and *Bailey's Bones*, by Victor Kelleher (novel).

How to Contact: Accepts unsolicited mss. Submit outline/synopsis and sample chapters or complete ms with cover letter. SASE. Agented fiction 50%. Reports in 3-4 weeks on queries. Simultaneous and photocopied submissions OK. Accepts computer printout submissions.

Terms: Pays in royalties. Writer's guidelines free for #10 SAE and 1 first class stamp. Book catalog for 9×12 SAE and $1.92 postage.

Advice: "We are publishing more fiction books than in the past, and we publish only hardcover originals, most of which are fiction. At this time we are particularly interested in both fiction and nonfiction for the middle grades, and innovative picture book manuscripts. We also are looking for easy-to-reads for first and second graders. Plays, collections of games and riddles, and counting and alphabet books are generally discouraged. Before submitting a manuscript to a publisher, it is a good idea to request a catalog to see what the publisher is currently publishing. As the 'Sweet Valley High' phenomenon has loosened its stranglehold on YA fiction, we are seeing more writers able to translate traditional values of literary excellence and contemporary innovation into the genre. Make your cover letters read like jacket flaps—short and compelling. Don't spend a lot of time apologizing for a lack of qualifications. In fact, don't mention them at all unless you have publishing credits, or your background is directly relevant to the story. 'I found this folktale during a return trip to the Tibetan village where I spent the first ten years of my life.' "

‡*DIANE PUBLISHING CO., (IV), 600 Upland Ave., Upland PA 19015. (215)499-7415. Editorial Contact Person: Herman Baron. Estab. 1987. "Midsize independent publisher." Publishes paperback originals and reprints. Books: 50 lb. paper; offset printing; perfect-bound; average print order: 2,000; first novel print order: 1,000. Published new writers within the last year. Plans 1 first novel this year. Averages 50 total titles, 2-3 fiction titles each year. Sometimes comments on rejected ms.

Needs: Adventure, erotica, spy/adventure, military/war, suspense/mystery. Looking for "law enforcement, adventure, satanism—under 100 pages." No romance.

How to Contact: Accepts unsolicited mss. Query first. Reports in 1 month. Simultaneous, photocopied submissions OK. Accepts computer printout submissions.

Terms: *Subsidy publishes 10% of books.* Pays royalties of 10-12%. Provides 10 author's copies. "Also cooperative and self-publishing arrangements. Authors cover any 'color' work.' " Sends galleys to author. Publishes ms 3 months after acceptance. Writer's guidelines unavailable. Book catalog for $2.

DORCHESTER PUBLISHING CO., INC., (II), Leisure Books, 276 Fifth Ave., New York NY 10001. (212)725-8811. Imprint: Leisure Books. Submissions Editor: Frank Walgren. Estab. 1970. Publisher of mass market paperbacks. Publishes paperback originals and reprints. Books: Photo offset printing; average print order varies. Receptive to first novels. Published new writers within the last year. Averages 150 total titles, mostly fiction. Buys 40% agented fiction.

Needs: "At present, Dorchester publishes an occasional science fiction or nonfiction book, but these are usually agented." Published *Sweet Fury*, by Catherine Hart (historical romance); and *The Devil's Auction*, by Robert Weinberg. No juvenile, young adult, contemporary romance, romantic suspense, or original mysteries. Romance (historical, 90,000 words; futuristic, timeswept, gothic, 75,000 words), horror (80,000 words).

How to Contact: Query first or submit outline/synopsis and 3 sample chapters with SASE. Nothing will be returned without SASE. Reports in 3 weeks on queries; 8-10 weeks on mss. No simultaneous submissions accepted. Letter-quality computer printouts only. Publishes ms usually within 2 years after acceptance.

Terms: Pays in royalties of 4%. Advance is negotiable. Sends galleys to author.

Advice: "We are concentrating on romance. Learn to spell and know your grammar! Most importantly, don't get discouraged by all those rejection slips—if you're good, you'll get published sooner or later. We encourage first novelists. Our relationship with authors is 'a limited partnership with limitless possibilities.' "

DOUBLEDAY, (III), a division of Bantam Doubleday Dell Publishing Group, Inc., 666 Fifth Ave., New York NY 10103. (212)765-6500. Estab. 1897. Publishes hardcover and paperback originals and paperback reprints.

Needs: "Doubleday is not able to consider unsolicited queries, proposals or manuscripts unless submitted through a bona fide literary agent, except that we will consider fiction for Perfect Crime line, romance and western imprints."

How to Contact: Send copy of complete ms (60,000-80,000 words) to Perfect Crime Editor, Loveswept Editor or Western Editor as appropriate. Sufficient postage for return via fourth class mail must accompany ms. Reports in 2-6 months.
Terms: Pays in royalties; offers advance.

DOUBLEDAY CANADA LIMITED, 105 Bond St., Toronto, Ontario M5B 1Y3 Canada. Declined listing. No unsolicited submissions.

EAKIN PRESS, (II, IV), Box 90159, Austin TX 78709-0159. (512)288-1771. Imprint: Nortex. Editor: Edwin M. Eakin. Estab. 1978. Publishes hardcover originals. Books: Old style (acid-free); offset printing; case binding; illustrations; average print order 2,000; first novel print order 5,000. Plans 2 first novels this year. Averages 80 total titles each year.
Needs: Juvenile. Specifically needs historical fiction for school market, juveniles set in Texas for Texas grade schoolers. Published *Wall Street Wives*, by Ande Ellen Winkler; *Jericho Day*, by Warren Murphy; and *Blood Red Sun*, by Stephen Mertz. Published new writers within the last year.
How to Contact: Accepts unsolicited mss. First send query or submit outline/synopsis and 2 sample chapters. SASE. Agented fiction 5%. Simultaneous and photocopied submissions OK. Accepts computer printout submissions. Reports in 3 months on queries.
Terms: Pays royalties; average advance: $1,000. Sends galleys to author. Publishes ms 1-1½ years after acceptance. Writers guidelines for #10 SAE and 1 first class stamp. Book catalog for 75¢.
Advice: "Juvenile fiction only with strong Texas theme. Just beginning category of adult fiction. We receive around 600 queries or unsolicited mss a year."

ECLIPSE BOOKS/ECLIPSE COMICS, (II, IV), P.O. Box 1099, Forestville CA 95460. (707)887-1521. Editor-in-Chief: Catherine Yronwode. Estab. 1978. Books: White or coated stock, up to 200 pages, every page illustrated. "Publishes 10-20 titles—comics and graphic novels each month."
Needs: Comics and graphic novels: adventure, condensed/excerpted novel, contemporary, ethnic, experimental, fantasy, feminist, gay, historical, horror, juvenile, lesbian, literary, mainstream, psychic/supernatural/occult, romance, science fiction, serialized novel, suspense/mystery, translations, westerns, young adult. "No religious, nationalistic, racist material." Receives "hundreds" of unsolicited fiction mss/year. Published *The Hobbit*, by J.R.R. Tolkien, adapted by Chuck Dixon, Sean Deming and David Wenzel; *The Complete Alec*, by Eddie Campbell; *The Magic Flute*, by W.A. Mozart, adapted by P. Craig Russell.
How to Contact: Send a cover letter, proposal, sample of script for artist to draw from. Reports in 3 months. SASE. Simultaneous, photocopied and reprint submissions (especially adaptations of well-known prose fiction). Sample copy for $3. Fiction guidelines for #10 SAE.
Terms: Pays $35-50/page (for a screenplay type of comics script, not a page of prose); advance against royalties (royalties are about 8%, but must be shared with the artist). Also pays 2-5 contributor's copies and discount on extras.
Advice: Looks for "interesting, original stories with in-depth characterization. We are developing a detective fiction 'comics noir' line."

PAUL S. ERIKSSON, PUBLISHER, (II), Suite 208, Battell-on-the-Otter, Middlebury VT 05753. (802)388-7303. Editor: Paul S. Eriksson. Estab. 1960. Publishes hardcover and paperback originals.
Needs: Mainstream. Published *Zachary*, by Ernest Pintoff; and *A Season of Dreams*, by Laurence Dean Hill.
How to Contact: Query first. Photocopied submissions OK. Publishes ms an average of 6 months after acceptance.
Terms: Pays 10-15% in royalties; advance offered if necessary. Free book catalog.
Advice: "Our taste runs to serious fiction."

M. EVANS & CO., INC., (II), 216 E. 49th St., New York NY 10017. (212)688-2810. Contact: Editors. Westerns Editor: Patrick La Brutto. Publishes hardcover and trade paper fiction and nonfiction. Publishes 40-50 titles each year.
Needs: Western, young adult/teen (10-18 years).
How to Contact: Accepts unsolicited mss. Query first with outline/synopsis and 3 sample chapters. SASE. Agented fiction: 100%. Reports on queries in 3-5 weeks. Simultaneous and photocopied submissions OK. Accepts computer printout submissions.
Terms: Pays in royalties and offers advance; amounts vary. Sends galleys to author. Publishes ms 6-12 months after acceptance.

FANTAGRAPHICS BOOKS, (II, IV), 7563 Lake City Way, Seattle WA 98115. (206)524-1967. Publisher: Gary Groth. Estab. 1976. Publishes comic books, comics series and graphic novels. Books: Offset printing, saddle-stitched periodicals and smythe-sewn books; heavily illustrated. Publishes originals and reprints. Publishes 10 titles per month.
Needs: Comic books and graphic novels (adventure, fantasy, romance, mystery, horror, science, social parodies). "We look for subject matter that is more or less the same as you would find in mainstream fiction." Recently published *Blood of Palomar*, by Gilbert Hernandez; *The Dragon Bellows Saga*, by Stan Sakai; *Death of Speedy*; *Housebound With Rick Geary*; *Little Nemo in Slumberland*.
How to Contact: Send a plot summary, pages of completed art (photocopies only) and character sketches. May send completed script if the author is willing to work with an artist of the publisher's choosing. Include cover letter and SASE. Reports in 1 month.
Terms: Pays in royalties of 8% (but must be split with artist) and advance.

FARRAR, STRAUS & GIROUX, (III), 19 Union Sq. W., New York NY 10003. (212)741-6900. Imprints include Michael di Capua Books, Hill & Wang, The Noonday Press. Editor-in-Chief: Jonathan Galassi. Midsized, independent publisher of fiction, nonfiction, poetry. Publishes hardcover originals. Published new writers within the last year. Plans 2 first novels this year. Averages 100 total titles, 30 fiction titles each year. No genre material. Published *The Mambo Kings Play Songs of Love*, by Oscar Hijuelos; *My Son's Story*, by Nadine Gordimer; *The Burden of Proof*, by Scott Turow.
How to Contact: Does not accept unsolicited mss. Query first. "Vast majority of fiction is agented." Reports in 2 months. Simultaneous and photocopied submissions OK. Accepts computer printout submissions.
Terms: Pays royalties (standard, subject to negotiation). Advance. Sends galleys to author. Publishes ms one year after acceptance. Writer's guidelines for #10 SAE and 1 first class stamp.

FARRAR, STRAUS & GIROUX/CHILDREN'S BOOKS, (II), 19 Union Sq. W., New York NY 10003. Imprint is Sunburst Books. Children's Books Publisher: Stephen Roxburgh. Editor-in-Chief: Margaret Ferguson. Number of titles: 40. Published new writers within the last year. Buys juvenile mss with illustrations. Buys 25% agented fiction.
Needs: Children's picture books, juvenile novels, nonfiction. Recently published *Celine*, by Brock Cole; *Carl's Afternoon in the Park*, by Alexandra Day; *Predator*, by Bruce Brooks.
How to Contact: Submit outline/synopsis and 3 sample chapters, summary of ms and any pertinent information about author, author's writing, etc. No simultaneous submissions; photocopied submissions OK. No unsolicited submissions during the month of August. Reports in 1 month on queries, 3 months on mss. Publishes ms 18 months to 2 years after acceptance.
Terms: Pays in royalties; offers advance. Book catalog with 6½ × 9½ SASE.
Advice: "Study our list before sending something inappropriate. Publishing more titles—our list has expanded."

FAWCETT, 201 E. 50th St., New York NY 10022. Unable to obtain information.

FEARON/JANUS, (II), (formerly Fearon/Janus/Quercus), Subsidiary of Simon & Schuster, Supplementary Education Group, 500 Harbor Blvd., Belmont CA 94002. (415)592-7810. Publisher and Editorial Director: Kate Wilson. Estab. 1954. Special-education publishers with a junior high, high school, and adult basic education audience—publishing program includes high interest/low level fiction, vocational and life skills materials, and low reading level secondary textbooks in all academic areas. Publishes paperback originals and reprints. Books: 3 lb. book set paper; offset printing; perfect or saddle-wired binding; line art illustrations; average print order: 5,000.
Needs: Adventure, contemporary, ethnic, historical, regional, romance, science fiction, short story collections, suspense/mystery, western, young adult/teen. "Our fiction appears in series of short novellas, aimed at new literates and high school students reading no higher than a fifth-grade level. All are

Market conditions are constantly changing! If you're still using this book and it is 1993 or later, buy the newest edition of Novel & Short Story Writer's Market at your favorite bookstore or order directly from Writer's Digest Books.

written to specification. It's a hard market to crack without some experience writing at low reading levels. Manuscripts for specific series of fiction are solicited from time to time, and unsolicited manuscripts are accepted occasionally." Published *A Question of Freedom*, by Lucy Jane Bledsoe (adventure novella—one of series of eight); *Just for Today*, by Tana Reiff (one novella of series of seven life-issues stories); and *The Everett Eyes*, by Bernard Jackson & Susie Quintanilla (one of twenty in a series of extra-short thrillers).

How to Contact: Submit outline/synopsis and sample chapters. SASE. Reports in 1 month. Simultaneous and photocopied submissions OK.

Terms: Authors usually receive a predetermined project fee. Book catalog for 9×12 SAE with 4 first class stamps.

FLARE BOOKS, (II), Imprint of Avon Books, Div. of the Hearst Corp., 1350 Avenue of the Americas, New York NY 10019. (212)261-6816. Editorial Director: Ellen Krieger. Estab. 1981. Small, young adult line. Publishes paperback originals and reprints. Plans 2-3 first novels this year. Averages 30 titles, all fiction each year.

Needs: Young adult (easy-to-read [hi-lo], problem novels, romance, spy/adventure) "very selective." Looking for contemporary fiction. No historical, science fiction/fantasy, heavy problem novels. Published *Show Me the Evidence*, by Alane Ferguson; *One Step Short*, by Jane McFann; and *So Long at the Fair*, by Hadley Irwin.

How to Contact: Accepts unsolicited mss. Submit complete ms with cover letter (preferred) or outline/synopsis and 3 sample chapters. Agented fiction 75%. Reports in 3-4 weeks on queries; 6-10 weeks on mss. Simultaneous and photocopied submissions OK. Accepts computer printout submissions.

Terms: Royalties and advance negotiable. Sends galleys to author. Writer's guidelines for #10 SAE and 1 first class stamp. Book catalog for 9×12 SAE with 98¢ postage. "We run a young adult novel competition each year."

FOUR WINDS PRESS, (II), Imprint of Macmillan Children's Book Group, 866 Third Ave., New York NY 10022. Editor-in-Chief: Virginia Duncan. Estab. 1966. A children's trade book imprint. Publishes hardcover originals. Books: 3 piece binding for older reading books, 1 piece binding for picture books. Books for children ages 3-12 usually illustrated; average print order 6,000-10,000; first novel print order: 6,000. Published new writers within the last year. Publishes 18 total titles each year, 10 fiction titles. No longer publishing young adult fiction.

Needs: Picture book manuscripts for ages 2-4 and 5-8. Recently published *Mrs. Toggle's Zipper*, by Robin Pulver and *Crow Moon, Worm Moon*, by James Skofield (picture books).

How to Contact: Accepts unsolicited mss. SASE required. Reports in 8-12 weeks. Photocopied submissions OK. Accepts computer printout submissions. No simultaneous submissions.

Terms: Pays royalties, negotiable advance and author's copies. Book catalogs *not* available. Manuscript guidelines and portfolio guidelines are available on request with #10 SAE and 1 first class stamp. "No calls, please."

Advice: "The majority of the fiction manuscripts accepted by Four Winds Press are picture book texts; we publish very little older fiction. Due to volume of submissions received, we cannot guarantee a quick response time or answer queries about manuscript status."

GARETH STEVENS, INC., (II, IV), 1555 N. River Center Dr., Milwaukee WI 53212. (414)225-0333. Creative Director: Paul Humphrey. Estab. 1986. "Midsize independent children's book publisher determined to expand." Publishes hardcover originals. Books: Matte paper; sheet feed printing; reinforced binding; several 4-color illustrations; average print order: 6,000; first novel print order: 4,000-5,000. Published new writers within the last year. Plans 3 first novels this year. Publishes total of 120 titles, 30 fiction titles/year.

Needs: Juvenile (animal, easy-to-read, fantasy, historical, sports, spy/adventure, contemporary). Especially needs picture books and very juvenile fiction.

How to Contact: Accepts unsolicited mss. Send outline/synopsis and sample chapters or complete ms with cover letter. SASE. Reports in 3 weeks on queries; 6 months on mss. Simultaneous, photocopied, computer printout submissions OK. Accepts electronic submissions.

Read the Business of Fiction section to learn the correct way to prepare and submit a manuscript.

Terms: Pays royalties of 3-7% maximum. Average advance: $750. Advance is negotiable. Sends pre-publication galleys to author. Publishes ms 1 year to 18 months after acceptance. Book catalog for 9×12 SAE and 1 first class stamp.

GESSLER PUBLISHING COMPANY, 55 W. 13th St., New York NY 10011. (212)627-0099. Editorial Contact Person: Seth C. Levin. Estab. 1932. "Publisher/distributor of foreign language educational materials (primary/secondary schools)." Publishes paperback originals and reprints. Averages 75 total titles each year. Sometimes comments on rejected ms.
Needs: "Foreign language or English as a Second Language." Needs juvenile, literary, preschool/picture book, short story collections, translations. Published *Don Quixote de la Mancha, (cartoon version of classic, in Spanish); El Cid,* (prose and poetry version of the classic in Spanish); and *Les Miserables* (simplified versions of Victor Hugo classic, in French).
How to Contact: Query first, then send outline/synopsis and 2-3 sample chapters; complete ms with cover letter. Agented fiction 40%. Reports on queries in 4 weeks; on mss in 6 weeks. Simultaneous and photocopied submissions OK. Accepts computer printout submissions.
Terms: Pay varies with each author and contract. Sends galleys to author. "Varies on time of submissions and acceptance relating to our catalogue publication date." Writer's guidelines not available. Book catalog free on request.
Advice: "We specialize in the foreign language market directed to teachers and schools—a book that would interest us has to be attractive to that market—a teacher would be most likely to create a book for us."

DAVID R. GODINE, PUBLISHER, INC., 300 Massachusetts Ave., Boston MA 02115. Declined listing. Presently overstocked.

GROSSET & DUNLAP, INC., (III), A Division of the Putnam & Grosset Group, 11th Floor, 200 Madison Ave., New York NY 10016. (212)951-8700. Publisher/Vice President: Jane O'Connor. Editor-in-Chief: Craig Walker.
Needs: Juvenile, preschool/picture book.
How to Contact: Queries only. "Include such details as length and intended age group and any other information that you think will help us to understand the nature of your material. Be sure to enclose a stamped, self-addressed envelope for our reply. We can no longer review manuscripts that we have not asked to see, and they will be returned unread."

HARCOURT BRACE JOVANOVICH, (III), 1250 Sixth Ave., San Diego CA 92101. (619)699-6810. FAX: (619)699-6777. Imprints include HBJ Children's Books, Gulliver Books and Jane Yolen Books. Director: Louise Howton. Executive Editor: Bonnie V. Ingber. Senior Editors: Diane D'Andrade, Elizabeth Van Doren and Allyn Johnston. Editor: Karen Grove. Publishes hardcover originals and paperback reprints. Averages 75 titles/year. Published new writers within the last year.
Needs: Young adult fiction, nonfiction for all ages, picture books for very young children, mystery. Recently published *Baseball in April,* by Gary Soto; *Dixie Storms,* by Barbara Hall; *Aida,* by Leontyne Price; *On the Day You Were Born,* by Debra Frasier.
How to Contact: Unsolicited mss currently accepted *only* by HBJ Children's Books, not by Gulliver Books, Jane Yolen Books or Voyager Books. Send to "Manuscript Submissions, HBJ Children's Books." SASE. For picture books, send complete ms; for novels, send outline/synopsis and 2-4 sample chapters. Photocopied submissions OK. No simultaneous submissions. No phone calls. Responds in 6-8 weeks.
Terms: Terms vary according to individual books; pays on royalty basis. Writers' guidelines for #10 SASE; catalog for 9×12 SASE.
Advice: "Familiarize yourself with the type of book published by a company before submitting a manuscript; make sure your work is in line with the style of the publishing house. Research the market your work will reach; make yourself familiar with the current children's book field." New line: Environmental series "Gulliver Green Books."

HARLEQUIN ENTERPRISES, LTD., (II, IV), 225 Duncan Mill Rd., Don Mills, Ontario M3B 3K9 Canada. (416)445-5860. Imprints include Harlequin Romances, Harlequin Presents, Harlequin American Romances, Superromances, Temptation, Intrigue and Regency, Silhouette, Worldwide Mysteries, Gold Eagle. Editorial Manager Harlequin: Karin Stoecker; Silhouette: Isabel Swift; Editorial Director, Gold Eagle: Randall Toye. Estab. 1949. Publishes paperback originals and reprints. Books: Newsprint paper; web printing; perfect-bound. Published new writers within the last year. Number of titles: Averages 700/year. Buys agented and unagented fiction.

Needs: Romance and heroic adventure. Will accept nothing that is not related to the desired categories. Recently published *The Hidden Years*, by Penny Jordan; *Silhouette Summer Sizzlers: Three Stories*, by Kathleen Eagle, Marilyn Pappano, Patricia Gardner Evans; *My Valentine 1991*, stories by Katherine Arthur, Debbie Macomber, Leigh Michaels, Peggy Nicholson.

How to Contact: Send query letter or send outline and first 50 pages (2 or 3 chapters) or submit through agent with SAE and IRC or SASE (Canadian). Absolutely no simultaneous submissions; photocopied submissions OK. Reports in 1 month on queries; 2 months on mss.

Terms: Offers royalties, advance. Must return advance if book is not completed or is unacceptable. Sends galleys to author. Guidelines available.

Advice: "The quickest route to success is to follow directions for submissions: Query first. We encourage first novelists. Before sending a manuscript, read as many Harlequin titles as you can get your hands on. It's very important to know the genre and the series most appropriate for your submission." Authors may send manuscript for Romances and Presents to Paula Eykelhof, editor; Superromances: Marsha Zinberg, senior editor; Temptation: Birgit Davis-Todd, senior editor; Regencys: Marmie Charndoff, editor. American Romances and Intrigue: Debra Matteucci, senior editor and editorial coordinator, Harlequin Books, 6th Floor, 300 E. 42 Street, New York, NY 10017. Silhouette submissions should also be sent to the New York office, attention Isabel Swift. Gold Eagle query letters should be addressed to Feroze Mohammed, senior editor, at the Canada address. "The relationship between the novelist and editor is regarded highly and treated with professionalism."

HARMONY BOOKS, (II), Subsidiary of Crown Publishers, 201 E. 50th St., New York NY 10022. (212)572-6121. Contact: General Editorial Department. Publishes hardcover and paperback originals.
Needs: Literary fiction. Also publishes in serious nonfiction, history, biography, personal growth, media and music fields.
How to Contact: Accepts unsolicited mss. Query first with outline/synopsis and 2-3 sample chapters. SASE. Agented fiction: 75%. Simultaneous and photocopied submissions OK. Accepts computer printouts.
Terms: Pays royalties and advance; amounts negotiable. Sends galleys to authors.

HARPERCOLLINS CHILDREN'S BOOKS, (II), 10 E. 53rd St., New York NY 10022. (212)207-7044. Publisher: Marilyn Kriney. Editors: Charlotte Zolotow, Nina Ignatowicz, Barbara Fenton, Laura Geringer, Robert O. Warren, Antonia Markiet, David Allender, Joanna Cotler. Publishes hardcover originals and paperback reprints.
Needs: Picture books, easy-to-read, middle-grade, teenage and young adult novels; fiction, fantasy, animal, sports, spy/adventure, historical, science fiction, problem novels and contemporary. Published Harper/Charlotte Zolotow Books: *Fell Back*, by M.E. Kerr (ages 12 and up); Harper: *My Daniel*, by Pam Conrad (ages 10 and up); Crowell: *Lucie Babbidge's House*, by Sylvia Cassedy (ages 9-12); Lippincott: *Yours Till Forever*, by David Gifaldi (ages 12 and up).
How to Contact: Query; submit complete ms; submit outline/synopsis and sample chapters; submit through agent. SASE for query, ms. Please identify simultaneous submissions; photocopied submissions OK. Reports in 2-3 months.
Terms: Average 10% in royalties. Royalties on picture books shared with illustrators. Offers advance. Book catalog for self-addressed label.
Advice: "Write from your own experience and the child you once were. Read widely in the field of adult and children's literature. Realize that writing for children is a difficult challenge. Read other young adult novelists as well as adult novelists. Pay attention to styles, approaches, topics. Be willing to rewrite, perhaps many times. We have no rules for subject matter, length or vocabulary but look instead for ideas that are fresh and imaginative. Good writing that involves the reader in a story or subject that has appeal for young readers is also essential. One submission is considered by the four imprints."

HARVEST HOUSE PUBLISHERS, (IV), 1075 Arrowsmith, Eugene OR 97402. (503)343-0123. Manuscript Coordinator: LaRae Weikert. Editor-in-Chief: Eileen L. Mason. Estab. 1974. Midsize independent publisher with plans to expand. Publishes hardcover and paperback originals and reprints. Books: 40 lb. ground wood paper; offset printing; perfect binding; average print order: 10,000; first novel print order: 10,000-15,000. Averages 50 total titles, 4 fiction titles each year.

Needs: Christian living, contemporary issues, humor, Christian preschool/picture books, religious/inspirational and Christian romance (contemporary, historical). Especially seeks inspirational, romance/historical and mystery. Recently published *A Gathering of Memories*, by Lori Wick; *From This Time Forth*, by June Masters Bacher; *Shipwreck*, by Brenda Wilbee; and *Moses*, by Ellen Gunderson Traylor.
How to Contact: Accepts unsolicited mss. Query first or submit outline/synopsis and 2 sample chapters with SASE. Reports on queries in 2-8 weeks; on mss in 6-8 weeks. Simultaneous and photocopied submissions OK.
Terms: Pays in royalties of 14-18%; 10 author's copies. Sends galleys to author. Writer's guidelines for SASE. Book catalog for 8½×11 SASE.

HEARTFIRE ROMANCE, (I), Subsidiary of Zebra Books, 475 Park Ave. So., New York NY 10016. (212)889-2299. Senior Director: Carin Ritter. Publishes paperback originals and reprints. Publishes 48 fiction titles each year.
Needs: Romance. Published *Blood Wings*, by Stephen Gresham; *Lovers' Masquerade*, by Robin St. Thomas; and *Last of the California Girls*, by Pamela Jekel. Ms length ranges from 125,000 to 150,000 words.
How to Contact: Submit short (no more than 3 page) synopsis and first several chapters. SASE. Reports on queries in 6 weeks; on mss in 3 months. Simultaneous and photocopied submissions OK. Accepts computer printout submissions.
Terms: Pays royalties and negotiable advance. Writer's guidelines and book catalog for SASE.
Advice: Send for tip sheet. "Don't use all the fancy fonts available to you; we're not impressed and it often works against you. Don't tell me my business in your cover letter; just give me the basic facts and let your manuscript sell itself."

HERALD PRESS, (II), Division of Mennonite Publishing House, 616 Walnut Ave., Scottdale PA 15683. (412)887-8500. Imprints include Congregational Literature Division; Herald Press. Book Editor: S. David Garber. Fiction Editor: Michael A. King. Estab. 1908. "Church-related midsize publisher." Publishes paperback originals. Books: Recycled, acid-free Glatfelter thor paper; offset printing; adhesive binding; illustrations for children; average print order: 4,000; first novel print order: 3,500. Published new writers in the last year. Company publishes 30 titles/year. Number of fiction titles: 5/year. Sometimes critiques rejected mss.
Needs: Adventure, historical, juvenile (historical, spy/adventure, contemporary), literary, religious/inspirational, young adult/teen (historical, problem novels and spy/adventure). "Does not want to see fantasy, picture books." Published *Fear Strikes at Midnight*, by Jones (juvenile); *Leah*, by Schott (adult, biblical); and *The Deserter*, by Koch (historical, peace/Civil War).
How to Contact: Accepts unsolicited mss. Submit outline/synopsis and 2 sample chapters with SASE. Agented fiction 2%. Reports in 1 month on queries, 2 months on mss. Photocopied submissions OK. Accepts computer printout submissions. Accepts electronics submissions (only *with* paper copy).
Terms: Pays 10-12% in royalties; 12 free author's copies. Pays after first 3 months, then once/year. Sends galleys to author. Publishes ms 10 months after acceptance. Writer's guidelines free. Book catalog for 50¢.
Advice: "Need more stories with Christian faith integrated smoothly and not as a tacked-on element."

HOLIDAY HOUSE, INC., (I, II), 425 Madison, New York NY 10017. (212)688-0085. Editor-in-Chief: Margery Cuyler. Estab. 1935. Independent publisher. Books: High quality printing; occasionally reinforced binding; illustrations sometimes. Publishes hardcover originals and paperback reprints. Published new writers within the last year. Number of titles: Approximately 50 hardcovers and 15 paperbacks per year.
Needs: Contemporary, Judaica and holiday, literary, adventure, humor and animal stories for young readers—preschool through middle grade. Recently published *Back in Action*, by Elvira Woodruff; *Seven Long Years Until College*, by Mary Jane Auch. "We're not in a position to be too encouraging, as our list is tight, but we're always open to good 'family' novels and humor."

Market categories: (I) Beginning; (II) General; (III) Prestige; (IV) Specialized.

How to Contact: "We prefer query letters for novels; complete manuscripts for shorter books and picture books." Simultaneous and photocopied submissions OK as long as a cover letter mentions that other publishers are looking at the same material. Accepts computer printout submissions. Reports in 1 month on queries, 6-8 weeks on mss.

Terms: Advance and royalties are flexible, depending upon whether the book is illustrated.

Advice: "We have received an increasing number of manuscripts, but the quality has not improved vastly. This appears to be a decade in which publishers are interested in reviving the type of good, solid story that was popular in the '50s. Certainly there's a trend toward humor, family novels, novels with school settings, biographies and historical novels. Problem-type novels and romances seem to be on the wane. We are always open to well-written manuscripts, whether by a published or nonpublished author. Submit only one project at a time."

HOLLOWAY HOUSE PUBLISHING COMPANY, (II), 8060 Melrose Ave., Los Angeles CA 90046. (213)653-8060. Imprints include Mankind Books, Melrose Square and Heartline Books. Editor: Peter Stone. Estab. 1960. Midsize independent publisher of varying interests, publishes black experience books, history, games and gambling books. Publishes paperback originals and reprints. Book: Offset printing; paper binding; some illustrations; average print order: 20,000 to 30,000; first novel print order: 15,000. Published new writers within last year. Plans 6 first novels this year. Publishes 30-40 titles each year, 6 fiction titles.

Needs: Adventure, contemporary, ethnic, experimental, fantasy, historical, horror, literary, mainstream, romance (historical), suspense/mystery, war, western. "We are looking for more 'literary' type books than in the past; books that appeal to young professionals. Especially interested in young adult contemporaries. Absolutely no books dealing with 'street action' about pimps, whores, dope dealing, prisons, etc." Published *A Mississippi Family*, by Barbara Johnson (fiction); *Diva*, a first novel by the award-winning playright Stanley Bennet Clay; *Secret Music*, by Odie Hawkins (memoirs); also a Jessie Jackson bio, by Eddie Stone.

How to Contact: No unsolicited mss. Query.

Advice: Publishing fewer Heartline Romances "as the contemporary romance market seems to have bottomed out, at least for us. Study the market; we do not publish poetry, short story collections, juvies, etc. but not a week goes by that we don't get at least one submission of each. If you send second-generation copies or dot-matrix check and see if *you* can read it before you expect us to. Neatness, spelling, etc. counts!"

HENRY HOLT & COMPANY, (II), 6th Floor, 115 W. 18th St., New York NY 10011. (212)886-9200. Imprint includes Owl (paper). Publishes hardcover and paperback originals and reprints. Averages 50-60 total original titles, 20% of total is fiction each year.

Needs: Adventure, contemporary, feminist, historical, humor/satire, juvenile (5-9 years, including animal, easy-to-read, fantasy, historical, sports, spy/adventure and contemporary), literary, mainstream, suspense/mystery, translations and young adult/teen (10-18 years including easy-to-read, fantasy/science fiction, historical, problem novels, romance, sports and spy/adventure). Published *Fool's Progress*, by Edward Abbey; *Tracks*, by Louise Erdrich; *Trust*, by George V. Higgins; and *Frank Furbo*, by Wm. Wherton.

How to Contact: Accepts queries; no unsolicited mss. Agented fiction 95%.

Terms: Pays in royalties of 10-15%; advance. Sends galleys to author. Book catalog sent on request.

■**HORIZON PUBLISHERS & DIST., INC., (III, IV),** Box 490, 50 S. 500 West, Bountiful UT 84011-0490. (801)295-9451. President: Duane S. Crowther. Estab. 1971. "Midsize independent publisher with in-house printing facilities, staff of 30+." Publishes hardcover and paperback originals and reprints. Books: 60 lb. offset paper; hardbound, perfect and saddle-stitch binding; illustrations; average print order: 3,000; first novel print order: 3,000. Plans 2 first novels this year. Averages 25-30 total titles; 1-3 fiction titles each year.

Needs: Adventure, historical, humor/satire, juvenile, literary, mainstream, military/war, religious/inspirational, romance (contemporary and historical), science fiction, spiritual and young adult/teen (romance and spy/adventure). "Religious titles are directed only to the LDS (Latter-day Saints) market. General titles are marketed nationwide." Looking for "good quality writing in salable subject areas. Will also consider well-written books on social problems and issues, (divorce, abortion, child abuse, suicide, capital punishment and homosexuality)." Published *The Couchman and the Bells*, by Ted C. Hindmarsh.

Close-up

Sue Grafton
Author

© Carter Blackmar

"My favorite people in the world are writers because we are so brave," mystery writer Sue Grafton tells an audience. "People come in not realizing how hard it is to write." The scene is a reading for a packed house at Brentano's bookstore in New York City, just after *H is for Homicide* was favorably reviewed in *The New York Times*.

By the time Grafton made this appearance, she was already halfway through writing her next title, *I is for Innocent* (Holt, 1992), featuring detective Kinsey Millhone. While she appreciates the kind words, she says she feels removed from reviews of *Homicide*—good or bad. "Reviews give me this out-of-body experience," she says. "I just hate to be criticized. I think I'm like other writers. I'm affected by reviews. But there's usually nothing I can do. I'm done with *H is for Homicide* and I'm on *I is for Innocent*. What good is it to have criticism on *H*?"

Later, Grafton says she's much more attentive to reader feedback on her work. "One person in California asked, 'Couldn't Kinsey have more sex in her life?' The comment filtered down the coast to me, so in *G* I gave her Robert Dietz. I'm very good-natured about that kind of thing."

But she never submits to critiques during the writing process. "I stopped *G is for Gumshoe* and asked my husband to read it and tell me if I was on the right track. He handed it back afterward and said, 'Get on with it.' "

About her detective, Grafton says, "We all know I'm secretly Kinsey." She pauses. "But she'll always be younger and thinner." The two have different backgrounds "but the same sensibility."

I is for Innocent is Grafton's ninth book in her mystery series. She writes a book beginning in November each year and turns in the manuscript to her editor the next August. "I keep a journal for each book," Grafton says. "I open a document on my word processor without any clear notion of what I'm going to do. Each time I log in, I indicate briefly what's going on in my life. In my writing process, the right brain keeps giving me messages. I believe in those messages." She finds this technique invaluable and urges writers to "dare to be stupid when you are in the creative process."

Grafton combines the creative side with solid research. "I cut everything out of the paper that interests me," she says. "As I read articles and notice the law enforcement people mentioned, I make notes. When I feel brave, I call them up and ask questions for the book."

For *H is for Homicide*, Grafton had an idea for infiltration of an insurance fraud ring and wanted to add a Romeo and Juliet theme of a cop and a crook falling in love. For the insurance information, "I had to cultivate all kinds of insurance people," she says. Soon after beginning to write Chapter One, she realized she needed some on-site research to go with her article and phone research, so she went to a local jail and went through the process of being arrested. "There is a wealth of information available to all of us. You just have to know where to get it."

Of her successful series, Grafton says using the "alphabet idea" in titles has been done before, but she has found it works well for her mystery series. "Marketing people love me," she says.

Knowing that she has so many more books left can be overwhelming, but Grafton says all writers have to deal with the doubts of pouring out everything into a book. "Sometimes I have this feeling that if I use it all I'll never have another idea. I have to have confidence that the well will fill up again."

Grafton came to mystery writing after working in Hollywood. "I set about writing mysteries to learn how to plot," she says. But she isn't particularly interested in having Kinsey turned into a TV or movie character, saying that readers would either believe the casting was wrong or would always identify Kinsey with whatever actress portrayed her.

In addition to her own writing, Grafton's also a student of the craft. "Elmore Leonard is one my favorite writers. [In *Killshot*] he scared me so bad. I went back and read it again and noted his methods because he did it so well."

Although she's one of the relatively few prominent women mystery writers, Grafton says she doesn't like to isolate herself as a "woman writer" or feel Kinsey has to be portrayed "correctly."

"I hate having to be politically correct. I don't think propaganda makes for good storytelling."

— Glenda Tennant Neff

How to Contact: Accepts unsolicited mss. Query first. SASE. Include Social Security number with submission. Reports in 2-4 weeks on queries; 10-12 weeks on mss. Simultaneous and photocopied submissions OK if identified as such. Accepts computer printout submissions. Accepts electronic submissions.

Terms: Pays royalties of 6-12%. Provides 10 author's copies. Sends page proofs to author. Publishes ms 3-9 months after acceptance. "We are not a subsidy publisher but we do job printing, book production for private authors and book packaging." Writer's guidelines for #10 SAE and 1 first class stamp.

Advice: Encourages "only those first novelists who write very well, with salable subjects. Please avoid the trite themes which are plaguing LDS fiction such as crossing the plains, conversion stories, and struggling courtships that always end in temple marriage. While these themes are important, they have been used so often that they are now frequently perceived as trite and are often ignored by those shopping for new books. In religious fiction we hope to see a process of moral, spiritual, or emotional growth presented. Some type of conflict is definitely essential for good plot development. Watch your vocabulary too—use appropriate words for the age group for which you are writing. We don't accept elementary children's mss for elementary grades."

‡**HOUGHTON MIFFLIN COMPANY, (III),** 2 Park St., Boston MA 02108. (617)725-5000. Subsidiary: Ticknor and Fields Inc. Contact: Janice Harvey. Publishes hardcover and paperback originals and paperback reprints. Averages 100 total titles, 50 fiction titles each year. Buys virtually 100% agented fiction.

Needs: None at present. Recently published *The Translator*, by Ward Just.

How to Contact: Does not accept unsolicited mss. Contact Janice Harvey with sample chapter and outline/synopsis. SASE. Simultaneous and photocopied submissions OK. Reports in 2 months. Publishes ms an average of 1 year after acceptance.

Terms: Pays in royalties on sliding scale of 10-15%; pays advance. Must return advance if book is not completed or is unacceptable.

INTERLINK PUBLISHING GROUP, INC., (IV), 99 Seventh Ave., Brooklyn NY 11215. (718)797-4292. Imprints include: Interlink Books, Olive Branch Press and Crocodile Books USA. Publisher: Michel Moushabeck. Fiction Editor: Phyllis Bennis. Estab. 1987. "Midsize independent publisher." Publishes hardcover and paperback originals. Books: 55 lb. Warren Sebago Cream white paper; web offset printing; perfect binding; average print order: 5,000; first novel print order: 5,000. Published new writers within the last year. Plans 3-5 first novels this year. Averages 30 total titles, 3-5 fiction titles each year.

Needs: Juvenile (5-9 yrs.), preschool/picture book and translations. Needs adult fiction—relating to the Middle East, Africa or Latin America; translations accepted. Published *Wild Thorns*, by Sahar Khalifeh; *Crocodile, Crocodile*, by Peter Nickl, Binette Shroeder (illus.); and *The Elephant's Child*, by Rudyard Kipling, Jan Mogensen (illus.).

How to Contact: Does not accept unsolicited mss. Submit outline/synopsis only. SASE. Reports in 2 weeks on queries. Photocopied submissions OK. Accepts computer printout submissions.

Terms: Pays royalties of 5-8%. Sends galleys to author. Publishes ms 1-1½ years after acceptance.

JAMESON BOOKS, (I, II, IV), Jameson Books, Inc., The Frontier Library, 722 Columbus St., Ottawa IL 61350. (815)434-7905. Editor: Jameson G. Campaigne, Jr. Estab. 1986. Publishes hardcover and paperback originals and reprints. Books: Free sheet paper; offset printing; average print order: 10,000; first novel print order: 5,000. Plans 6-8 novels this year. Averages 12-16 total titles, 4-8 fiction titles each year. Occasionally critiques or comments on rejected mss.

Needs: Very well-researched western (frontier pre-1850). No romance, sci-fi, mystery, et al. Published *Wister Trace*, by Loren Estelman; *Buckskin Brigades*, by L. Ron Hubbard; *One-Eyed Dream*, by Terry Johnston.

How to Contact: Does not accepted unsolicited mss. Submit outline/synopsis and 3 consecutive sample chapters. SASE. Agented fiction 50%. Reports in 2 weeks on queries; 2-5 months on mss. Simultaneous and photocopied submissions OK. Accepts computer printouts.

Listings marked with a solid box [■] are book packagers. See the introduction to Commercial Publishers for more information.

Terms: Pays royalties of 5-15%. Average advance: $1,500. Sends galleys to author. Book catalog for 6×9 SASE.

JOY STREET BOOKS, 34 Beacon St., Boston MA 02108. (617)227-0730. Imprint of Little, Brown and Co. Children's Books Editor-in-chief: Melanie Kroupa. Publishes hardcover and quality paperback originals. Sometimes buys juvenile mss with illustrations.
Needs: General fiction, juvenile: sports, animal, mystery/adventure, realistic contemporary fiction, picture books and easy-to-read. Published *The Arizona Kid*, by Ron Koertge; *The Girl in the Box*, by Ouida Sebestyen; *Alias Madame Doubtfire*, by Anne Fine. Very interested in first novels.
How to Contact: Prefers query letter with sample chapters. SASE. Accepts simultaneous submissions; photocopied submissions OK.
Terms: Pays variable advances and royalties.

ALFRED A. KNOPF, (II), 201 E. 50th St., New York NY 10022. Senior Editor: Ashbel Green. Estab. 1915. Publishes hardcover originals. Number of titles: 43 in 1990. Buys 75% agented fiction. Published 14 new writers within the last year.
Needs: Contemporary, literary, suspense and spy. No western, gothic, romance, erotica, religious or science fiction. Recently published *Saint Maybe* by Anne Tyler; *A Thousand Acres*, by Jane Smiley; *Sacrifice* by Andrew Vachss; published work by previously unpublished writers within the last year.
How to Contact: Submit complete ms with SASE. Simultaneous and photocopied submissions OK. Reports within 6 weeks on mss. Publishes ms an average of 1 year after acceptance.
Terms: Pays 10-15% in royalties; offers advance. Must return advance if book is not completed or is unacceptable.
Advice: Publishes book-length fiction of literary merit by known and unknown writers. "Don't submit manuscripts with matrix type."

KNOPF BOOKS FOR YOUNG READERS, (II), 225 Park Ave. South, New York NY 10003. Subsidiary of Random House, Inc. Editor-in-Chief: Janet Schulman. Publishes hardcover and paperback originals and reprints. New paperback imprints include Dragonfly Books (picture books), Bullseye (middle-grade fiction) and Borzoi Sprinters (Young Adult fiction). Averages 50 total titles, approximately 20 fiction titles each year.
Needs: "High-quality" contemporary, humor and nonfiction. "Young adult novels, picture books, middle group novels." Published *No Star Nights*, by Anna Smucker; *Mirandy and Brother Wind*, by Patricia McKissoch; *The Boy Who Lost His Face*, by Lewis Sachar.
How to Contact: Query with outline/synopsis and 2 sample chapters with SASE. Simultaneous and photocopied submissions OK. Reports in 6-8 weeks on mss.
Terms: Sends galleys to author.

LEISURE BOOKS, (II), division of Dorchester Publishing Co., Inc., Suite 1008, 276 Fifth Ave., New York NY 10001. (212)725-8811. Address submissions to Frank Walgren, editor. Mass-market paperback publisher—originals and reprints. Books: Newsprint paper; offset printing; perfect-bound; average print order: variable; first novel print order: variable. Plans 25 first novels this year. Averages 150 total titles, 145 fiction titles each year. Comments on rejected ms "only if requested ms requires it."
Needs: Romance (historical, futuristic, gothic, time travel), horror. Looking for "historical romance (115,000 words) and futuristic, gothic and time travel romance (90,000 words). Recently published *Outback Station*, by Aaron Fletcher; *Night Wind's Woman*, by Shirl Henke; and *Prairie Heat*, by Madeline Baker.
How to Contact: Accepts unsolicited mss. Query first. SASE. Agented fiction 70%. Reports in 1 month on queries; 2 months on mss. Photocopied submissions OK. "All mss must be typed, double-spaced on one side and left unbound."
Terms: Offers negotiable advance. Payment depends "on category and track record of author." Sends galleys to author. Publishes ms within 2 years after acceptance. Romance guidelines and book catalog for #10 SASE.
Advice: Encourages first novelists "if they are talented and willing to take direction, *and* write the kind of category fiction we publish. Please include a brief synopsis if sample chapters are requested."

‡LERNER PUBLICATIONS COMPANY, (II, IV), 241 1st Ave. N., Minneapolis MN 55401. Imprints include First Avenue Editions. Editor: Jennifer Martin. Estab. 1959. "Midsize independent *children's* publisher." Publishes hardcover originals and paperback reprints. Books: Offset printing; reinforced library binding; perfect binding; average print order: 5,000-7,500; first novel print order: 5,000. Averages 70 total titles, 4-6 fiction titles each year. Sometimes comments on rejected ms.

Needs: Young adult: Easy-to-read, problem novels, sports, spy/adventure, mystery. Looking for "well-written middle grade and young adult. *No adult fiction.*" Recently published *The Shimmering Ghost of Riversend*, by Norma Lehr (middle grade mystery, age 9-11).

How to Contact: Accepts unsolicited mss. Query first or submit outline/synopsis and 2 sample chapters. Reports in 1 month on queries; 2 months on mss. Simultaneous, photocopied submissions OK. Accepts computer printout submissions.

Terms: Pays royalties. Offers advance. Provides author's copies. Sends galleys to author. Publishes ms 12-18 months after acceptance. Writer's guidelines for #10 SAE and 1 first class stamp. Book catalog for 9×12 SAE with $1.90 postage.

Advice: Would like to see "less gender and racial stereotyping; more protagonists from ethnic minority groups."

LION PUBLISHING CORPORATION, (II), 1705 Hubbard Ave., Batavia IL 60510. (708)879-0707. Subsidiary of Lion Publishing plc, Oxford, England. Editor: R.M. Bittner. Estab. 1971 (Oxford offices); 1984 (US). "Christian book publisher publishing books for the *general* market." Publishes hardcover and paperback originals and paperback reprints. Books: Average print order 7,500; first novel print order 5,000. Plans 1-3 first novels this year. Averages 15 total titles, 2-5 fiction titles each year. Sometimes comments on rejected ms.

Needs: Open. "Because we are a Christian publisher, all books should be written from a Christian perspective." Recently published *The Paradise War*, by Stephen Lawhead (fantasy); *An Ordinary Exodus*, by Roger Bichelberger (literary); *Bury Her Sweetly*, by Linda Amey (mystery).

How to Contact: Accepts unsolicited mss. Submit complete ms with cover letter. SASE. Agented fiction 5%. Reports in 2 weeks on queries; 1-3 months on mss. Photocopied submissions OK. Accepts computer printout submissions.

Terms: Pays negotiable royalties. Sends galleys to author. Publishes ms 1 year after acceptance. Writer's guidelines and book catalog free.

Advice: "Seriously study our author guidelines."

LITTLE, BROWN AND COMPANY CHILDREN'S BOOKS, (II), Trade Division; Children's Books, 34 Beacon St., Boston MA 02108. Editorial Department. Contact: John G. Keller, publisher; Maria Modugno, editor-in-chief; Stephanie Owens Lurie, senior editor. Books: 70 lb. paper; sheet-fed printing; illustrations. Published new writers within the last year. Sometimes buys juvenile mss with illustrations "if by professional artist." Buys 60% agented fiction.

Needs: Middle grade fiction and young adult. Published *Maniac Magee*, by Jerry Spinelli; *The Day that Elvis Came to Town*, by Jan Marino.

How to Contact: Will accept unsolicited mss. "Query letters for novels are not necessary."

Terms: Pays on royalty basis. Sends galleys to author. Publishes ms 1-2 years after acceptance.

Advice: "We are looking for trade books with bookstore appeal. Young adult 'problem' novels are no longer in vogue, but there is now a dearth of good fiction for that age group. We are looking for young children's (ages 3-5) books and first chapter books. We encourage first novelists. New authors should be aware of what is currently being published. I recommend they spend time at the local library familiarizing themselves with new publications."

LITTLE, BROWN AND COMPANY, INC., (II, III), 34 Beacon St., Boston MA 02108. (617)227-0730. Imprints include Little, Brown, Joy Street, Bulfinch Press, Arcade Publishing. Medium-size house. Publishes adult and juvenile hardcover and paperback originals. Averages 200-225 total adult titles/year. Number of fiction titles varies.

Needs: Open. No science fiction. Published *Vineland*, by Thomas Pynchon; *Old Silent*, by Martha Grimes; *The Truth About Lorin Jones*, by Alison Lurie; published new writers within the last year.

How to Contact: Does not accept unsolicited mss. Query editorial department first; "we accept submissions from authors who have published before, in book form, magazines, newspapers or journals. No submissions from unpublished writers." Reports in 4-6 months on queries. Simultaneous and photocopied submissions OK.

Terms: "We publish on a royalty basis, with advance." Writer's guidelines free.

LODESTAR BOOKS, (II), An affiliate of Dutton Children's Books; A division of Penguin Books USA, Inc., 375 Hudson St., New York NY 10014. (212)366-2000. Editorial Director: Virginia Buckley. Senior Editor: Rosemary Brosnan. Books: 50 or 55 lb. antique cream paper; offset printing; hardcover binding; illustrations sometimes; average print order: 5,000-6,500; first novel print order 5,000. Published new writers within the last year. Number of titles: Approximately 30 annually, 12-15 fiction titles annually. Buys 50% agented fiction.

Needs: Contemporary, humorous, sports, mystery, adventure, for middle-grade and young adult. Recently published *Sammy Carducci's Guide to Women*, by Ronald Kidd (ages 8-12 yrs.); *Journey of the Sparrows*, by Fran Leeper Buss; and *Lyddie*, by Katherine Paterson (ages 10-14 yrs.).

How to Contact: "Can query, but prefer complete ms." SASE. Simultaneous and photocopied submissions OK. Accepts computer printout submissions. Reports in 2-4 months. Publishes ms an average of 1 year after acceptance.

Terms: Pays 8-10% in royalties; offers negotiable advance. Sends galleys to author. Free book catalog.

Advice: "We are looking to add to our list more books about black, Hispanic, Native American, and Asian children, in particular. We encourage first novelists. Publishing fewer young adult novels. They are difficult to find and difficult to sell reprint rights. Middle grade does better in terms of subsidiary rights sales."

LOUISIANA STATE UNIVERSITY PRESS, (II), French House, Baton Rouge LA 70893. (504)388-6294. Editor-in-Chief: Margaret Fisher Dalrymple. Fiction Editor: Martha Hall. Estab. 1935. University press—medium size. Publishes hardcover originals. Average print order: 1,500-2,500; first novel print order: 2,000. Averages 60-70 total titles, 4 fiction titles/year.

Needs: Contemporary, literary, mainstream, short story collections. No science fiction and/or juvenile material. Recently published *A Kind of Redemption*, by Stephen Hathaway (stories); *Worry Beads*, by Kay Sloan (novel); *Turbulence*, by Jia Pingwa (novel). Publishes fiction anthologies. Author should submit proposal listing contents.

How to Contact: Does not accept unsolicited mss. Query first. Reports in 2-3 months on queries and mss. Simultaneous and photocopied submissions OK. No computer printouts.

Terms: Pays in royalties, which vary. Sends pre-publication galleys to the author.

LOVESWEPT, (I, II), Bantam Books, 666 5th Ave., New York NY 10103. (212)765-6500. Associate Publisher: Nita Taublib. Consulting Editor: Susann Brailey. Imprint estab. 1982. Publishes paperback originals. Plans several first novels this year. Averages 72 total titles each year.

Needs: "Contemporary romance, highly sensual, believable primary characters, fresh and vibrant approaches to plot. No gothics, regencies or suspense."

How to Contact: Query with SASE; no unsolicited mss or partial mss. "Query letters should be no more than two to three pages. Content should be a brief description of the plot and the two main characters."

Terms: Pays in royalties of 6%; negotiates advance.

Advice: "Read extensively in the genre. Rewrite, polish and edit your own work until it is the best it can be—before submitting."

■LUCAS/EVANS BOOKS, (II), 1123 Broadway, New York NY 10010. (212)929-2583. Editorial Director: Barbara Lucas. Projects Director: Jill Kastner. Estab. 1984. "Book packager—specializes in children's books." Publishes hardcover and paperback originals. Published new writers within the last year. Plans 1 first novel this year. Averages 17 total titles, 11 or 12 fiction titles, all of which are children's picture books. Sometimes comments on rejected ms; sometimes charge for critiques.

Needs: Juvenile (5-9 yrs.) animal, easy-to-read, fantasy, historical, sports, spy/adventure and contemporary; young adult/teen (10-18 years) easy-to-read, fantasy, historical (young adult) and sports and spy/adventure. "Novels are not our specialty. If we come across something really spectacular, we'll try to sell it. Usually publishers handle individual novels themselves." Published *Sing for a Gentle Rain*, by J. Alison James (Atheneum); *The Trouble with Buster*, by Janet Lorimer (Scholastic); and *The Glass Salamander*, by Ann Downer (Atheneum).

How to Contact: No unsolicited mss. Query first or submit outline/synopsis and 1 or 2 sample chapters. SASE. Agented fiction 15 to 25%. Reports in 2 weeks on queries; 4-6 weeks on mss. Photocopied submissions OK. Accepts computer printout submissions.

Terms: Pays royalties; variable advance. Provides 5-10 author's copies. Sends galleys to author. Writer's guidelines for SASE. Brochure available.

Listings marked with a solid box [■] are book packagers. See the introduction to Commercial Publishers for more information.

MARGARET K. McELDERRY BOOKS, (I, II), Imprint of the Macmillan Children's Book Group, 866 3rd Ave., New York NY 10022. (212)702-7855. Publisher: Margaret K. McElderry. Publishes hardcover originals. Books: High quality paper; offset printing; cloth and three-piece bindings; illustrations; average print order: 15,000; first novel print order: 6,000. Published new writers within the last year. Number of titles: 23 for picture books. Buys juvenile and young adult mss, agented or non-agented.

Needs: All categories (fiction and nonfiction) for juvenile and young adult: picture books, early chapter books, contemporary, literary, adventure, mystery, science fiction and fantasy. "We will consider any category. Results depend on the quality of the imagination, the artwork and the writing." Recently published *Matthew's Dragon*, by Susan Cooper and Jos. A. Smith; *What the Dickens!*, by Jane Louise Curry; *Natural History from A to Z*, by Tim Arnold; *Climbing Jacob's Ladder* by John Langstaff, John Andrew Ross and Ashley Bryan.

How to Contact: Accepts unsolicited mss. Prefers complete ms. SASE for queries and mss. Simultaneous submissions OK if so indicated; photocopied submissions must be clear and clean. Accepts computer printout submissions. Reports in 4 weeks on queries, 12-14 weeks on mss. Publishes ms an average of 1 year after acceptance.

Terms: Pays in royalties; offers advance.

Advice: "Imaginative writing of high quality is always in demand; also picture books that are original and unusual. We are looking especially for nonfiction and for easy-to-read books for beginners. Beginning picture-book writers often assume that texts for the very young must be rhymed. This is a misconception and has been overdone. Picture book manuscripts written in prose are totally acceptable. We are trying to publish more beginning chapter books—about 48 pages with text geared toward the 6-9 year old reader."

MACMILLAN CANADA, (II), A Division of Canada Publishing Corporation, 29 Birch Ave., Toronto, Ontario M4V 1E2 Canada. (416)963-8830. Editor-in-Chief: Philippa Campsie. Estab. 1905. Publishes hardcover and trade paperback originals. Published new writers within the last year. Books: Average print order: 4,000-5,000; first novel print order: 1,500. Averages 35 total titles, 5-6 fiction titles each year. Rarely comments on rejected mss.

Needs: Literary, mainstream and suspense/mystery. Recently published *Last Rights*, by David Laing Dawson; *Tall Lives*, by Bill Gaston; *Swimming Toward the Light*, by Joan Clark; *The Nest Egg*, by S.L. Sparling; and *The Jacamar Nest*, by David Parry and Patrick Withrow.

How to Contact: No longer accepts unsolicited mss. Agented material only. SASE for return of ms. Reports in 1-2 months on mss. Simultaneous and photocopied submissions OK. Accepts computer printout submissions.

Terms: Pays royalties of 8-15%; advance negotiable. Provides 10 author's copies. Sends galleys to author. Book catalog for 9 × 12 SASE.

Advice: "Canadian material only."

MACMILLAN CHILDREN'S BOOKS, Macmillan Publishing Co., 866 Third Ave., New York NY 10022. (212)702-4299. Imprint of Macmillan Publishing/Children's Book Group. Contact: Attention Submissions Editor. Estab. 1919. Large children's trade list. Publishes hardcover originals.

Needs: Juvenile submissions. Not interested in series. "We generally are not interested in short stories as such, unless intended as the basis for a picture book. As the YA market is weak, only extremely distinctive and well-written YA novels will be considered (and must be preceded by a query letter)." Published *Weasel*, by Cyntha De Felice; *Dynamite Dinah*, by Claudia Mills; *Borgel*, by Daniel Pinkwater.

How to Contact: Accepts unsolicited mss or for novel send query letter with outline, sample chapter and SASE. Response in 6-8 weeks. No simultaneous submissions; photocopied submissions OK. Accepts computer printout submissions.

Terms: Pays in royalties; negotiates advance. For catalog, send 9 × 12 envelope with 4 oz. postage.

MACMILLAN PUBLISHING CO, INC., 866 3rd Ave., New York NY 10022. Declined listing.

‡METEOR PUBLISHING CORPORATION, (I, II); Kismet Romances, 3369 Progress Dr., Bensalem PA 19020. (215)245-1489. Editor-in-Chief: Kate Duffy. Senior Editor: Catherine Carpenter. "Category romance publisher distributed solely via direct mail." Publishes paperback originals. Published new writers within the last year. Plans 20 first novels this year. Averages 48 total titles, all fiction. Sometimes comments on rejected ms.

Needs: Romance (contemporary). Looking for "65,000-word contemporary romances." Recently published *Always*, by Catherine Sellers; *Silent Enchantment*, by Lacey Dancer; *Daddy's Girl*, by Janice Kaiser.

How to Contact: Accepts unsolicited mss. Submit outline/synopsis and 3 sample chapters, if previously published in same genre or complete ms with cover letter, if unpublished. Agented fiction 50%. Reports in 2 months on queries; 2-3 months on mss. Simultaneous, photocopied submissions OK. Accepts computer printout submissions.
Terms: Pays royalties of 6-8%. Offers negotiable advance. Sends galleys to author. Publishes ms 6-12 months after acceptance.
Advice: "We receive approximately 25 mss/week. Most are previously unpublished. We buy the best that are submitted and promptly return those not of interest. All of our first novels acquired were reviewed as completed mss and all have been published."

MODERN PUBLISHING, A Division of Unisystems, Inc., (II), 155 East 55th St., New York NY 10022. (212)826-0850. Imprint: Honey Bear Books. Editorial Director: Kathy O'Hehir. Fiction Editor: Mandy Rubenstein; Art Director: Harriet Sherman. Estab. 1973. "Mass-market juvenile publisher; list mainly consists of picture, coloring and activity, and novelty books for ages 2-8 and board books." Publishes hardcover and paperback originals, and Americanized hardcover and paperback reprints from foreign markets. Average print order: 50,000-100,000 of each title within a series. "85% of our list first novels this year." Averages 100+ total titles each year. Sometimes comments on rejected mss.
Needs: Juvenile (5-9 yrs, including animal, easy-to-read, fantasy, historical, sports, spy/adventure and contemporary), preschool/picture book, young adult/teen (easy-to-read). Published new writers within the last year.
How to Contact: Accepts unsolicited mss. Submit complete ms. SASE. Agented fiction 5%. Reports in 2 months. Simultaneous and photocopied submissions OK.
Terms: Pays by work-for-hire or royalty arrangements. Advance negotiable. Publishes ms 7-12 months after acceptance.
Advice: "We publish picture storybooks, board books, coloring and activity books, bath books, shape books and any other new and original ideas for the children's publishing arena. We gear our books for the preschool through third-grade market and publish series of four to six books at a time. Presently we are looking for new material as we are expanding our list and would appreciate receiving any new submissions. We will consider manuscripts with accompanying artwork or by themselves, and submissions from illustrators who would like to work in the juvenile books publishing genre and can adapt their style to fit our needs. However, we will only consider those projects that are written and illustrated for series of four to six books. Manuscripts must be neatly typed and submitted either as a synopsis of the series and broken-down plot summaries of the books within the series, or full manuscripts for review with a SASE."

WILLIAM MORROW AND COMPANY, INC., (II), 1350 Avenue of the Americas, New York NY 10019. Imprints include Hearst Books, Hearst Marine Books, Mulberry Books, Tambourine Books, Beech Tree Books, Quill Trade Paperbacks, Perigord, Greenwillow Books, Lothrop, Lee & Shepard and Fielding Publications (travel books), and Morrow Junior Books. Estab. 1926. Approximately one fourth of books published will be fiction.
Needs: "Morrow accepts only the highest quality submissions" in contemporary, literary, experimental, adventure, mystery, spy, historical, war, feminist, gay/lesbian, science fiction, horror, humor/satire and translations. Juvenile and young adult divisions are separate. Recently published *Gate of Rage*, by C.Y. Lee; *The Gold Bug Variations*, by Richard Powers; and *This Earth of Mankind*, by Pramoedya Ananta Toer. Published work by previously unpublished writers within the last year.
How to Contact: Submit through agent. All unsolicited mss are returned unopened. "We will accept queries, proposals or mss only when submitted through a literary agent." Simultaneous and photocopied submissions OK. Accepts double-spaced computer printout submissions. Reports in 2-3 months.
Terms: Pays in royalties; offers advance. Sends galleys to author. Free book catalog.
Advice: "The Morrow divisions of Morrow Junior Books, Greenwillow Books, Tambourine Books, Mulberry Books, Beech Tree Books, and Lothrop, Lee and Shepard handle juvenile books. We do five to ten first novels every year and about one-fourth of the titles are fiction. Having an agent helps to find a publisher."

MORROW JUNIOR BOOKS, (III), 1350 Avenue of the Americas, New York NY 10019. (212)261-6691. Editor-In-Chief: David L. Reuther. Plans 1 first novel this year. Averages 55 total titles each year.
Needs: Juvenile (5-9 years, including animal, easy-to-read, fantasy (little), spy/adventure (very little), preschool/picture book, young adult/teen (10-18 years, including historical, sports).
How to Contact: Does not accept unsolicited fiction mss.
Terms: Authors paid in royalties. Books published 12-18 months after acceptance. Book catalog free on request.
Advice: "Our list is very full at this time. No unsolicited manuscripts."

MULTNOMAH, (II, IV), 10209 SE Division, Portland OR 97266. (503)257-0526. Editor: Al Janssen. Estab. 1969. Midsize publisher of religious and inspirational books. Publishes hardcover and paperback originals. Books: Average print order: 10,000. Averages 25-35 total titles a year. "We are just getting into publishing fiction and our first books will be for children (8-12 yrs.)."
Needs: Juvenile (5-9 yrs.) easy-to-read and fantasy, historical, sports, humorous, spy/adventure and contemporary, preschool/picture book, religious/inspirational and spiritual. Young adult/teen (10-18 years), religious/inspirational, fantasy, historical, problem novels, sports and spy/adventure. "We're looking for children's 8-12 yrs. and short chapter books for 7-9 year olds—both in series. No adult romance, science fiction."
How to Contact: Accepts unsolicited mss. Submit outline/synopsis and 3 sample chapters. SASE. Simultaneous and photocopied submissions OK. Accepts computer printout submissions.
Terms: Pays royalties of 8-12% net with possible escalation depending on type of children's book, amount of illustrations and stature of author; offers negotiable advance. Provides 15 author's copies. Sends galleys to author. Publishes ms 9-12 months after acceptance. Writer's guidelines free. Book catalog for 9×12 SASE.

THE MYSTERIOUS PRESS, (III), 666 5th Ave., New York NY 10103. (212)484-2900. Imprint: Penzler Books. Publisher: Otto Penzler. Editor-in-Chief: William Malloy. Editor: Sara Ann Freed. Estab. 1976. Small independent publisher, publishing only mystery and suspense fiction. Publishes hardcover originals and paperback reprints. Books: Hardcover (some Smythe sewn) and paperback binding; illustrations rarely. Average first novel print order 5,000 copies. Critiques "only those rejected writers we wish particularly to encourage."
Needs: Suspense/mystery. Published *The Fourth Durango*, by Ross Thomas; *The Bridesmaid*, by Ruth Rendell; *Tomorrow's Crimes*, by Donald E. Westlake; published new writers within the last year.
How to Contact: Agented material only.
Terms: Pays in royalties of 10% minimum; offers negotiable advance. Sends galleys to author. Buys hard and softcover rights. Book catalog for SASE.
Advice: "We have a strong belief in the everlasting interest in and strength of mystery fiction. Don't talk about writing, do it. Don't ride bandwagons, create them. Our philosophy about publishing first novels is the same as our philosophy about publishing: The cream rises to the top. We are looking for writers with whom we can have a long-term relationship. A good editor is an angel, assisting according to the writer's needs. My job is to see to it that the writer writes the best book he/she is capable of, *not* to have the writer write *my* book. Don't worry, publishing will catch up to you; the cycles continue as they always have. If your work is good, keep it circulating and begin the next one, and keep the faith. Get an agent."

NAL/DUTTON, (III), (formerly New American Library), a division of Penguin USA, 375 Hudson St., New York NY 10014. (212)366-2000. Imprints include Dutton, Onyx, Signet, Mentor, Signet Classic, Plume, Plume Fiction, DAW, Meridian, Roc. Contact: Michaela Hamilton, editorial director (mass market books); Arnold Dolin, associate publisher, Plume (trade paperback); Kevin Mulroy, editorial director, Dutton; John Silbersack, editorial director, Roc. Estab. 1948. Publishes hardcover and paperback originals and paperback reprints.
Needs: "All kinds of commercial and literary fiction, including mainstream, historical, Regency, New Age, western, thriller, science fiction, fantasy, gay. Full length novels and collections." Recently published *Four Past Midnight*, by Stephen King; *Beloved*, by Toni Morrison; and *Impulse*, by Catherine Coulter; published new writers within the last year.
How to Contact: Queries accepted with SASE. "State type of book and past publishing projects." Agented mss only. Simultaneous and photocopied submissions OK. Reports in 3 months.
Terms: Pays in royalties and author's copies; offers advance. Sends galleys to author. Free book catalog.
Advice: "Write the complete manuscript and submit it to an agent or agents. We publish The Destroyer, The Trailsman, Canyon O'Grady and Medal of Honor series—all by ongoing authors. Would be receptive to ideas for new series in commercial fiction."

NEW READERS PRESS, (IV), Publishing division of Laubach Literacy International, Box 131, Syracuse NY 13210. (315)422-9121. Editor-in-Chief: Laura Martin. Estab. 1959. Publishes paperback originals. Books: 55A Warner's Old Style paper; offset printing; paper binding; 6-12 illustrations per fiction book; average print order: 7,500; first novel print order: 5,000. Fiction titles may be published both in book form and as read-along audio tapes. Averages 30 total titles, 4-8 fiction titles each year.

Needs: High-interest, low-reading-level materials for adults with limited reading skills. Short novels of 12,000-15,000 words, written on 3rd-grade level. "Can be mystery, romance, adventure, science fiction, sports or humor. Characters are well-developed, situations realistic, and plot developments believable." Accepts short stories only in collections of 8-20 very short stories of same genre. Will accept collections of one-act plays that can be performed in a single class period (45-50 min.) with settings than can be created within a classroom. Short stories and plays can be at 3rd-5th grade reading level. All material must be suitable for classroom use in public education, i.e., little violence and no explicit sex. "We will not accept anything at all for readers under 18 years of age." Recently published *Kaleidoscope* (8 short story books); *Fitting In* (8 short story books).
How to Contact: Accepts unsolicited mss. Query first or submit outline/synopsis and 3 sample chapters. SASE. Reports in 1 month on queries; 3 months on mss. Photocopied submissions OK. Accepts computer printout submissions.
Terms: Pays royalties of 5-7.5% on gross sales. Average advance: $200. "We may offer authors a choice of a royalty or flat fee. The fee would vary depending on the type of work." Book catalog, authors' brochure and guidelines for short novels free.
Advice: "Many of our fiction authors are being published for the first time. It is necessary to have a sympathetic attitude toward adults with limited reading skills and an understanding of their life situation. Direct experience with them is helpful."

W.W. NORTON & COMPANY, INC., (II), 500 5th Ave., New York NY 10110. (212)354-5500. For unsolicited mss contact: Liz Malcolm. Estab. 1924. Midsize independent publisher of trade books and college textbooks. Publishes hardcover originals. Occasionally comments on rejected mss.
Needs: High-quality fiction (preferably literary). No occult, science fiction, religious, gothic, romances, experimental, confession, erotica, psychic/supernatural, fantasy, horror, juvenile or young adult. Recently published *White Girls*, by Lynn Lawber; *Relative Stranger* by Charles Baxter; *The Perez Family*, by Christine Bell.
How to Contact: Submit outline/synopsis and first 50 pages. Simultaneous and photocopied submissions OK. Accepts computer printout submissions. Reports in 6-8 weeks. Packaging and postage must be enclosed to ensure safe return of materials.
Terms: Graduated royalty scale starting at 7½% or 10% of net invoice price, in addition to 15 author's copies; offers advance. Free book catalog.
Advice: "We will occasionally encourage writers of promise whom we do not immediately publish. We are principally interested in the literary quality of fiction manuscripts. A familiarity with our current list of titles will give you an idea of what we're looking for. Chances are, if your book is good and you have no agent you will eventually succeed; but the road to success will be easier and shorter if you have an agent backing the book. We encourage the submission of first novels."

PANTHEON BOOKS, (III), Subsidiary of Random House, 27th Floor, 201 E. 50th St., New York NY 10022. (212)572-2404. Estab. 1950. "Small but well-established imprint of well-known large house." Publishes hardcover and trade paperback originals and trade paperback reprints. Plans 3-5 first novels this year. Averages 90 total titles, 25 fiction titles each year.
Needs: Pantheon no longer accepts unsolicited fiction. Recently published *Dogeaters*, by Jessica Hagedorn; *We are the Stories We Tell*, edited by Wendy Martin; and *The Great World*, by David Malouf.
How to Contact: Agented fiction 100%.
Advice: "We are beginning to publish more American fiction and fewer translations. We are also publishing more first novels."

PELICAN PUBLISHING COMPANY, (IV), Box 189, 1101 Monroe St., Gretna LA 70053. Editor: Nina Kooij. Estab. 1926. Publishes hardcover reprints and originals. Books: Hardcover and paperback binding; illustrations sometimes. Published new juvenile writers within the last year. Buys juvenile mss with illustrations. Comments on rejected mss "infrequently."
Needs: Juvenile fiction, especially with a regional focus. "Our adult fiction is *very* limited." Recently published *Lipstick Like Lindsay's and Other Christmas Stories*, by Gerald R. Toner; and *Henry Hamilton in Outer Space*, by Marilyn Redmond.

Market categories: (I) Beginning; (II) General; (III) Prestige; (IV) Specialized.

How to Contact: Prefers query. May submit outline/synopsis and 2 sample chapters with SASE. No simultaneous submissions; photocopied submissions only. "Not responsible if writer's only copy is sent." Reports in 1 month on queries; 3 months on mss. Publishes ms 12-18 months after acceptance.
Terms: Pays 10% in royalties; 10 contributor's copies; advance considered. Sends galleys to author. Catalog of titles and writer's guidelines for SASE.
Advice: "Research the market carefully. Order and look through publishing catalogs to see if your work is consistent with their lists."

‡PHILOMEL BOOKS, (II), The Putnam & Grosset Book Group, 200 Madison Ave., New York NY 10016. (212)951-8712. Editor-in-Chief: Paula Wiseman. Editorial Assistant: Laura Walsh. "A high-quality oriented imprint focused on stimulating picture books and young adult novels." Publishes hardcover originals and paperback reprints. Published new writers within the last year. Averages 50 total titles, 45 fiction titles/year. Sometimes comments on rejected ms.
Needs: Adventure, ethnic, fantasy, historical, juvenile (5-9 years), literary, preschool/picture book, regional, short story collections, translations, young adult/teen (10-18 years). Looking for "ethnic novels with a strong cultural voice but which speak universally." No "generic, mass-market oriented fiction." Recently published *I Am Regina*, by Sally Keehn (young adult); *Flight*, by Robert Burleigh and Mike Wimmer (historical picture book); and *Bear*, by John Schoenherr (fiction picture book).
How to Contact: Accepts unsolicited mss. Query first or submit outline/synopsis and 3 sample chapters. SASE. Agented fiction 40%. Reports in 6-8 weeks on queries; 6-10 weeks on mss. Simultaneous and photocopied submissions OK. Accepts computer printout submissions.
Terms: Pays royalties, negotiable advance and author's copies. Sends galleys to author. Publishes ms anywhere from 1-3 years after acceptance. Writer's guidelines for #10 SAE and 1 first class stamp. Book catalog for 9×12 SASE.

POCKET BOOKS, (II), Division of Simon & Schuster, 1230 Avenue of the Americas, New York NY 10020. (212)698-7000. Imprints include Washington Square Press and Star Trek. Senior Vice President/Editorial Director: William Grose. Publishes paperback and hardcover originals and reprints. Averages 300 titles each year. Buys 90% agented fiction. Sometimes critiques rejected mss.
Needs: Contemporary, literary, faction, adventure, spy, historical, western, gothic, romance, military/war, mainstream, suspense/mystery, feminist, ethnic, erotica, psychic/supernatural, fantasy, horror and humor/satire. Recently published *To Dance with the White Dog*, by Terry Kay; *Boy's Life*, by Robert McCammon (hardcover); *Rules of Evidence*, by Jay Brandon (hardcover); published new writers within the last year.
How to Contact: Query with SASE. No unsolicited mss. Reports in 6 months on queries only. Publishes ms 12-18 months after acceptance.
Terms: Pays in royalties and offers advance. Sends galleys to author. Writer must return advance if book is not completed or is not acceptable. Free book catalog.

POINT BOOKS, Scholastic, Inc., 730 Broadway, New York NY 10003. (212)505-3000. Senior Editor: Regina Griffin. Estab. 1984. Young adult imprint. Publishes paperback originals and reprints.
Needs: Young adult/teen (12-18 years). Published *Fallen Angels*, by Walter Dean Myers; *Born into Light*, by Paul Samuel Jacobs; *The Babysitter*, by R.L. Stine; and *April Fools*, by Richard Cusick.
How to Contact: Query first. SASE.
Advice: "Query letters should describe the genre of the book (mystery, sci-fi, etc.), give a brief plot description, and tell about the writer's background (i.e. have they published anything; taken writing courses, etc.). One common mistake I see is that I get letters that go on and on about the marketing possibilities, but neglect to describe the book at all. That makes me feel I'm dealing with someone who wants to be a 'writer,' but doesn't really take writing seriously enough. We like to publish fiction by previously unpublished writers, if we can. We are expanding our hardcover program and our paperback middle-reader line."

POSEIDON PRESS, (II), 1230 Avenue of the Americas, New York NY 10020. (212)698-7290. Distributed by Simon & Schuster. Publisher: Ann E. Patty. Executive Editor: Elaine Pfefferbilt. Estab. 1981. Hardcover and quality trade paper. Books: Paper varies; offset printing; illustrations; average print order varies; first novel print order: 5,000-7,500. Averages 20 total titles, 10-12 fiction titles (3 first novels) each year. Does "not critique rejected ms by unsolicited authors unless work merits it."

Needs: General fiction and nonfiction, commercial and literary. Published *Inheritance*, by Judith Michael; and *Bad Behavin*, by Mary Gaitskill.
How to Contact: Query first. No unsolicited manuscripts or sample chapters. Photocopied submissions OK. Reports in 2 months.
Terms: Payment varies, according to content of book.

CLARKSON N. POTTER, INC., 201 E. 50th St., New York NY 10022. (212)572-6160. Distributed by Crown Publishers, Inc. Vice President/Editor-in-Chief: Carol Southern.
Needs: Illustrated fiction, biography, style and juvenile. Published *Black Water: The Book of Fantastic Literature*, by Alberto Manguel.
How to Contact: Submissions through agent only.
Terms: Pays 6-12% in royalties on hardcover; 6-7½% in royalties on paperback; offers $5,000 up in advance.

PRENTICE-HALL BOOKS FOR YOUNG READERS, 1230 Avenue of the Americas, New York NY 10020. Company no longer publishes children's books.

PRICE STERN SLOAN, INC., (II), Suite 650, 11150 Olympic Blvd., Los Angeles CA 90064. Subsidiaries/ Divisions are Wonder Books, Troubador, Serendipity, Doodle Art and HPBooks. Contact: Editorial Dept. Estab. 1962. Midsize independent, expanding. Publishes hardcover originals, paperback originals and reprints. Books: Perfect or saddle-stitched binding; illustrations. Averages 200 total titles each year.
Needs: Humor/satire, juvenile (series, easy-to-read, humor, educational) and adult trade nonfiction. No adult fiction. Published *Shopaholics* (adult trade); *My Grandmother's Cookie Jar* (juvenile fiction); and *Where Fish Go in Winter*, (juvenile nonfiction). Also publishes "self-help, cookbooks, automotive books, photography and gardening."
How to Contact: Query only. Submit outline/synopsis and sample pages. SASE required. Reports in 2 months on queries. Simultaneous and photocopied submissions OK. Accepts computer printouts.
Terms: Terms vary.

‡PULPHOUSE PUBLISHING, INC., (II, IV), Box 1227, Eugene OR 97440. (503)344-6742. Senior Books Editor: Kristine Kathryn Rusch. Estab. 1987. Midsize publisher with 4 book lines. "We are *only* a short fiction house." Publishes hardcover and paperback originals and reprints. Published new writers within the last year. Averages 120 total titles, all fiction. Sometimes comments on rejected ms.
Needs: Adventure, fantasy, horror, humor/satire, science fiction, short story collections. "No novels." Recently published *Yours Truly, Jack the Ripper*, by Robert Bloch (short story paper); and *The Collected Short Fiction of Robert Sheckley* (a 5-volume set).
How to Contact: Accepts unsolicited mss. Submit complete ms with cover letter. "Short stories only." SASE for return of ms. Agented fiction 10%. Reports in 1 month. Photocopied submissions OK. Accepts computer printout submissions.
Terms: Pays 3-6¢/word. "We buy short fiction for all types of projects. We send contracts for one time use." Sends galleys to author. Publishes ms 6-18 months after acceptance. Writer's guidelines for #10 SASE. Book catalog free.
Advice: "We publish about 25 new authors every year. Be professional. We would like to see more original ideas and good writing."

G.P. PUTNAM'S SONS, (III), The Putnam Publishing Group, 200 Madison Ave., New York NY 10016. (212)951-8400. Imprints include Perigee, Philomel, Platt and Munk, Coward McCann, Grosset and Dunlap Pacer. Publishes hardcover originals.
Needs: Published fiction by Stephen King, Lawrence Sanders, Alice Hoffman; published new writers within the last year.
How to Contact: Does not accept unsolicited mss. Query.

The double dagger before a listing indicates that the listing is new in this edition. New markets are often the most receptive to freelance contributions.

RANDOM HOUSE, INC., 201 E. 50th St., New York NY 10022. (212)751-2600. Imprints include Pantheon Books, Panache Press at Random House, Vintage Books, Times Books, Villard Books and Knopf. Contact: Adult Trade Division. Publishes hardcover and paperback originals. Encourages new writers. Rarely comments on rejected mss.
Needs: Adventure, contemporary, historical, literary, mainstream, short story collections, suspense/mystery. "We publish fiction of the highest standards." Authors include James Michener, Robert Ludlum, Mary Gordon.
How to Contact: Query with SASE. Simultaneous and photocopied submissions OK. Reports in 4-6 weeks on queries, 2 months on mss.
Terms: Payment as per standard minimum book contracts. Free writer's guidelines.
Advice: "Please try to get an agent because of the large volume of manuscripts received, agented work is looked at first."

RESOURCE PUBLICATIONS, INC., (I, IV), Suite 290, 160 E. Virginia St., San Jose CA 95112. (408)286-8505. Book Editor: Kenneth Guentert. Estab. 1973. "Independent book and magazine publisher focusing on imaginative resources for professionals in ministry, education and counseling." Publishes paperback originals. Averages 12-14 total titles, 2-3 fiction titles each year.
Needs: Story collections for storytellers, "not short stories in the usual literary sense." No novels. Published *Jesus on the Mend: Healing Stories for Ordinary People*, by Andre Papineau; and *The Magic Stone: Stories for Your Faith Journey*, by James Henderschedt.
How to Contact: Query first or submit outline/synopsis and 1 sample chapter with SASE. Reports in 2 weeks on queries; 6 weeks on mss. Photocopied submissions OK "if specified as *not* simultaneous." Accepts computer printout submissions. Accepts disk submissions compatible with CP/M, IBM system. Prefers hard copy with disk submissions.
Terms: Pays in royalties of 8-10%; 10 author's copies. "We require first-time authors purchase a small portion of the press-run, but we do not subsidy publish under the Resource Publications imprint. However, our graphics department will help author's self-publish for a fee."

ST. MARTIN'S PRESS, 175 5th Ave., New York NY 10010. (212)674-5151. Imprint: Thomas Dunne. Chairman and CEO: Thomas J. McCormack. President: Roy Gainsburg. Publishes hardcover and paperback reprints and originals.
Needs: Contemporary, literary, experimental, faction, adventure, mystery, spy, historical, war, gothic, romance, confession, feminist, gay, lesbian, ethnic, erotica, psychic/supernatural, religious/inspirational, science fiction, fantasy, horror and humor/satire. No plays, children's literature or short fiction. Published *The Silence of the Lambs*, by Thomas Harris; *The Shell Seekers* and *September* by Rosamunde Pilcher.
How to Contact: Query or submit complete ms with SASE. Simultaneous (if declared as such) and photocopied submissions OK. Reports in 2-3 weeks on queries, 4-6 weeks on mss.
Terms: Pays standard advance and royalties.

ST. PAUL BOOKS AND MEDIA, (I), Subsidiary of Daughters of St. Paul, 50 St. Paul's Ave., Jamaica Plain, Boston MA 02130. (617)522-8911. Children's Editor: Sister Anne Joan, fsp. Estab. 1934. Roman Catholic publishing house. Publishes hardcover and paperback originals. Averages 20 total titles, 5 fiction titles each year.
Needs: Juvenile (animal, easy-to-read, fantasy, historical, religion, contemporary), preschool/picture book and young adult/teen (historical, religion, problem novels). All fiction must communicate high moral and family values. "Our fiction needs are entirely in the area of children's literature. We are looking for bedtime stories, historical and contemporary novels for children. Would like to see characters who manifest faith and trust in God." Does not want "characters whose lifestyles are not in conformity with Catholic teachings."
How to Contact: Does not accept unsolicited mss. Query first. SASE. Reports in 2 weeks.
Terms: Pays royalties of 8-12%. Provides negotiable number of author's copies. Publishes ms approx 2 or 3 years after acceptance. Writer's guidelines for #10 SAE and 1 first class stamp.
Advice: "There is a dearth of juvenile fiction appropriate for Catholics and other Christians."

SCHOLASTIC, Scholastic, Inc., 730 Broadway, New York NY 10003. (212)505-3000. Publishes a variety of books (hardcovers, paperback originals and reprints) for children and young adults under the following imprints:
SCHOLASTIC HARDCOVER: Senior Editor: Regina Griffin. Estab. 1985. A hardcover line of high quality fiction. No multiple submissions. Include SASE.

POINT BOOKS: Senior Editor: Regina Griffin. Estab. 1984. A paperback line of young adult fiction for readers aged 12-up. Most Point novels have contemporary settings and take as their central characters young adults between the ages of 13-18. No multiple submissions.

APPLE BOOKS: Senior Editor: Regina Griffin. Estab. 1981. A paperback line of juvenile fiction for readers aged 8-12. No multiple submissions. Include SASE.

How to Contact: Query first or submit outline/synopsis and 3 sample chapters with SASE. Accepts computer printout submissions.

CHARLES SCRIBNER'S SONS, 866 3rd Ave., New York NY 10022. Declined listing. "Swamped."

CHARLES SCRIBNER'S SONS, BOOKS FOR YOUNG READERS, Division of Macmillan Publishing Co., 866 Third Ave., New York NY 10022. (212)702-7885. Editorial Director: Clare Costello. Publishes hardcover originals. Averages 20-25 total titles, 8-13 fiction titles each year.

Needs: Juvenile (animal, easy-to-read, fantasy, historical, picture book, sports, spy/adventure, contemporary, ethnic and science fiction) and young adult (fantasy/science fiction, romance, historical, problem novels, sports and spy/adventure). Recently published *The Irish Piper*, by Jim Latimar (picture book); *Around the Table*, by Sholom Aleichem, translated by Aliza Shevrin (ages 10-13); *Cleaver & Company*, by James Duffy (ages 9-11).

How to Contact: Submit complete ms with SASE. Simultaneous and photocopied submissions OK. Reports in 8-10 weeks on mss.

Terms: Free book catalog free on request. Sends galleys to author.

SIERRA CLUB BOOKS, 100 Bush St., San Francisco CA 94104. (415)291-1617. FAX: (415)291-1602. Editor-in-Chief: D. Moses. Estab. 1892. Midsize independent publisher. Publishes hardcover and paperback originals and paperback reprints. Averages 20-25 titles, 1-2 fiction titles each year.

Needs: Contemporary (conservation, environment).

How to Contact: Query only with SASE. "We will only deal with queries; we are not staffed to deal with mss." Simultaneous and photocopied submissions OK. Accepts computer printout submissions. Reports in 6 weeks on queries.

Terms: Pays in royalties. Book catalog for SASE.

Advice: "Only rarely do we publish fiction. We will consider novels on their quality and on the basis of their relevance to our organization's environmentalist aims."

SILHOUETTE BOOKS, (II, IV), 6th Floor, 300 E. 42nd St., New York NY 10017. (212)682-6080. Imprints include Silhouette Romance, Silhouette Special Edition, Silhouette Desire, Silhouette Intimate Moments, Harlequin Historicals; also Silhouette Christmas Stories, Silhouette Summer Sizzlers, Harlequin Historical Christmas Stories. Editorial Manager: Isabel Swift. Senior Editor & Editorial Coordinator (SIM): Leslie J. Wainger. Seniors Editors: (SE) Tara Hughes Gavin, (SD) Lucia Macro, (SR) Valerie Hayward. Editor: Mary Clare Kersten, Gail Chasen. Historicals: Senior Editor: Tracy Farrell. Estab. 1979. Publishes paperback originals. Published 10-20 new writers within the last year. Buys agented and unagented adult romances. Number of titles: 316/year. Occasionally comments on rejected mss.

Needs: Contemporary romances, historical romances. Recently published *Rookie Dad*, by Pepper Adams (SR); *Best Man for the Job*, by Dixie Browning (SD); *Marriage of Inconvenience*, by Debbie Macomber (SE); *Better Than Before*, by Judith Duncan (IM); *The Prisoner*, by Cheryl Reavis (HH).

How to Contact: Submit query letter with brief synopsis and SASE. No unsolicited or simultaneous submissions; photocopied submissions OK. Accepts computer printout submissions. Publishes ms 9-24 months after acceptance.

Terms: Pays in royalties; offers advance (negotiated on an individual basis). Must return advance if book is not completed or is unacceptable.

Advice: "Study our published books before submitting to make sure that the submission is a potential Silhouette. Developing new line of women in jeopardy—gothic, suspense, horror. Looking for new authors in all lines. Interested in fresh, original ideas and new directions within the romance genre."

Read the Business of Fiction section to learn the correct way to prepare and submit a manuscript.

SIMON & SCHUSTER, 1230 Avenue of the Americas, New York NY 10020. (212)698-7000. Imprints include Pocket Books, Linden Press.
Needs: General adult fiction, mostly commercial fiction.
How to Contact: Agented material 100%.

GIBBS SMITH, PUBLISHER, (II), Box 667, Layton UT 84041. (801)544-9800. FAX: (801)544-5582. Imprints: Peregrine Smith Books. Editorial Director: Madge Baird. Fiction Editor: Steve Chapman. Estab. 1969. Publishes hardcover and paperback originals and reprints. Books: Illustrations as needed; average print order 5,000. Publishes 25+ total titles each year, 5-6 fiction titles.
Needs: Contemporary, experimental, humor/satire, literary, short story collections, translations and nature. "Literary works exhibiting the social consciousness of our times." Published *Relative Distances*, by Victoria Jenkins; *The Tennessee Waltz and Other Stories*, by Alan Cheuse; and *The Light Possessed*, by Alan Cheuse.
How to Contact: Query first. SASE. 60% of fiction is agented. Reports in 3 weeks on queries; 10 weeks on mss. Simultaneous and photocopied submissions OK. Accepts computer printout submissions.
Terms: Pays 7-15% royalties. Sends galleys to author. Writer's guidelines for #10 SASE; book catalog for 9×6 SAE and 56¢ postage.
Advice: "Our foremost criteria is the literary merit of the work."

STANDARD PUBLISHING, (II, IV), 8121 Hamilton Ave., Cincinnati OH 45231. (513)931-4050. Director: Mark Plunkett. Estab. 1866. Independent religious publisher. Publishes paperback originals and reprints. Books: Offset printing; paper binding; b&w line art; average print order: 7,500; first novel print order: 5,000-7,500. Number of titles: 18/year. Rarely buys juvenile mss with illustrations. Occasionally comments on rejected mss.
Needs: Religious/inspirational and easy-to-read. "Should have some relation to moral values or Biblical concepts and principles." Katie Hooper Series, by Jane Sorenson; Julie McGregor Series, by Kristi Holl. Recently published *A Change of Heart* and *A Tangled Webb*, by Kristi Holl; *Jaws of Terror*, by Dayle Courtney.
How to Contact: Query or submit outline/synopsis and 2-3 sample chapters with SASE. "Query should include synopsis and general description of perceived market." Accepts computer printout submissions. Reports in 1 month on queries, 3 months on mss. Publishes ms 1-2 years after acceptance.
Terms: Pays varied royalties and by outright purchase; offers varied advance. Sends galleys to author. Catalog with SASE.
Advice: Publishes fiction with "strong moral and ethical implications." First novels "should be appropriate, fitting into new or existing series. We're dealing more with issues."

STODDART, (III), Subsidiary of General Publishing, 34 Lesmill Rd., Toronto, Ontario M3B 2T6 Canada. (416)445-3333. Managing Editor: Donald G. Bastian. "Largest Canadian-owned publisher in Canada, with a list that features nonfiction primarily." Publishes hardcover and paperback originals and reprints. Plans 2 first novels this year. Averages 50-60 total titles, 8 fiction each year.
Needs: Adventure, suspense/mystery, young adult/teen (10-18 years). Looking for "quality commercial fiction with international potential." Published *A Man Wanders Sometimes*, by Kent Baker; *The First Garden*, by Anne Hebert; and *The Leaving*, by Budge Wilson.
How to Contact: Submit outline/synopsis and 2-3 sample chapters. SASE. Agented fiction 50%. Reports in 4-6 weeks on queries; 2-3 months on mss. Simultaneous and photocopied submissions OK. Accepts computer printout submissions, including dot-matrix.
Terms: Pays royalties of 10-25% for hardcover. Advance is negotiable. Sends galleys to author. Publishes ms up to 2 years after acceptance.
Advice: "Fiction accounts for about 10% of the list. The amount we do depends on quality and marketability, co-publishing arrangements in US etc., and foreign language sales potential." Encourages first novelists, "but they should be realistic. Don't expect to make a living on it. Presentation is very important. Clear-typed, open spacing. Typos can easily turn readers away from a potentially good book."

‡SUMMIT BOOKS, (II, III), Division of Simon & Schuster, 1230 Avenue of the Americas, New York NY 10020. President and Editor-in-Chief: James Silberman. Estab. 1976. Midsize independent publisher with plans to expand. Publishes hardcover originals. Books: Average print order: 3,000-200,000. Plans 3 first novels this year. Averages 50 total titles each year.

Needs: Contemporary, feminist, historical (occasionally), satire, literary, mainstream, suspense/mystery, translations. Recently published *The Pursuit of Happiness*, by Anne Roiphe; *1492*, by Homero Aridjis; *Evenings at Mongini's*, by Russell Lucas.
How to Contact: Does not accept unsolicited mss. Unagented authors should query first. SASE. Agented fiction: 99%. Reports on queries in 2-3 months. Simultaneous, photocopied submissions OK.
Terms: Pays in royalties and negotiable advance. Sends galleys to author. Publication time after ms is accepted varies.
Advice: "Our editorial staff is too small to critique writers, and it is sometimes hard to tell exactly what is wrong (or right) with a novel in the time we would have to do it. Get an agent."

TAB BOOK CLUB (TEEN AGE BOOK CLUB), (II), Scholastic Inc., 730 Broadway, New York NY 10003. Contact: Greg Holch. See listing for Scholastic Inc. Published new writers within the last year.
Needs: "Scholastic and the TAB Book Club publish novels for young teenagers in seventh through ninth grades. We do not publish short stories or standard teenage romances. A book has to be unique, different, and of high literary quality."
How to Contact: Send "a query letter and the first 20 pages of the manuscript."
Advice: "I personally prefer humorous, light novels that revolve around a unique premise, such as *A Royal Pain*, by Ellen Conford. We publish mass-market entertainment reading, not educational books."

THORNDIKE PRESS, (IV), Division of Macmillan, Inc., Box 159, Thorndike ME 04986. (800)223-6121. Editorial Assistant: Barbara Libby. Estab. 1979. Midsize publisher of hardcover and paperback large print *reprints*. Books: Alkaline paper; offset printing; Smythe-sewn library binding; average print order: 4,000. Publishes 175 total titles each year, 150 fiction titles.
Needs: *No fiction that has not been previously published*. Recently published *Plains of Passage*, by Jean Auel; *Sum of All Fears*, by Tom Clancy.
How to Contact: Does not accept unsolicited mss. Query.
Terms: Pays 10% in royalties.

TICKNOR & FIELDS, (I, II), Affiliate of Houghton-Mifflin, 215 Park Ave. South, New York NY 10003. (212)420-5800. Estab. 1979. Publishes hardcover originals.
Needs: Open to all categories, but selective list of only 30 titles a year. Recently published *Closing Arguments*, by Frederich Busch; *Forms of Shelter*, by Angela Davis-Gardner; *Afghanistan*, by Alex Ullmann; *Mister Touch*, by Malcolm Bosse.
How to Contact: Query letters only; no unsolicited mss accepted. No simultaneous submissions (unless very special); photocopied submissions OK. Reports in 2 months on ms.
Terms: Pays standard royalties. Offers advance depending on the book.

TOR BOOKS, (II), 175 Fifth Ave., New York NY 10010. Editor-in-Chief: Robert Gleason. Estab. 1980. Publishes hardcover and paperback originals, plus some paperback reprints. Books: 5 point Dombook paper; offset printing; Bursel and perfect binding; few illustrations. Averages 200 total titles, all fiction, each year. Some nonfiction titles.
Needs: Fantasy, mainstream, science fiction, suspense and westerns. Recently published *Xenocide*, by Orson Scott Card; *Midnight Sun*, by Ramsey Campbell; *The Nemesis Mission*, by Dean Ing; and *The Dragon Reborn*, by Robert Jordan.
How to Contact: Agented mss preferred. Buys 90% agented fiction. Photocopied submissions OK. No simultaneous submissions. Address manuscripts to "editorial," *not* to the Managing Editor's office.
Terms: Pays in royalties and advance. Writer must return advance if book is not completed or is unacceptable. Sends galleys to author. Free book catalog on request.

TRILLIUM PRESS, (I, II), First Avenue, Unionville NY 10988. (914)726-4444. Vice President: Thomas Holland. Fiction Editor: William Neumann. Estab. 1978. "Independent educational publisher." Publishes hardcover and paperback originals and paperback reprints. Published new writers within the last year. Plans 40 first novels this year. Averages 150 total titles, 70 fiction titles each year.
Needs: Young adult/teen (10-18 years), fantasy/science fiction, historical, problem novels, romance (ya), sports and mystery/adventure, middle school/young adult (10-18) series. Recently published the following young adult series: Mystery & Adventure (including historical novels); Growing Up Right (values, relationships, adult development); science fiction. Also published *The Journal of Jenny September*, by Isaacsen-Bright; *The T-206 Honus Wagner Caper*, by Janet Amann; *A Matter of Choice*, by H. Henry Williams.

How to Contact: Accepts unsolicited mss. SASE. Reports in 3 months on mss. Photocopied submissions OK. Accepts computer printouts.

Terms: Negotiated "as appropriate." Sends galleys to author. Writer's guidelines for #10 SAE and 1 first class stamp. Book catalog for 9 × 12 SAE and 3 first class stamps.

TROLL ASSOCIATES, (II), Watermill Press, 100 Corporate Drive, Mahwah NJ 07430. (201)529-4000. Editorial Contact Person: M. Frances. Estab. 1968. Midsize independent publisher. Publishes hardcover originals, paperback originals and reprints. Averages 100-300 total titles each year.

Needs: Adventure, historical, juvenile (5-9 yrs. including: animal, easy-to-read, fantasy), preschool/picture book, young adult/teen (10-18 years) including: easy-to-read, fantasy/science fiction, historical, romance (ya), sports, spy/adventure. Published new writers within the last year.

How to Contact: Accepts and returns unsolicited mss. Query first. Submit outline/synopsis and sample chapters. Reports in 2-3 weeks on queries. Accepts dot-matrix computer printout submissions.

Terms: Pays royalties. Sometimes sends galleys to author. Publishes ms 6-18 months after acceptance.

TSR, INC., Box 756, Lake Geneva WI 53147. (414)248-3625. Imprints include the Dragonlance® series, Forgotten Realms® series, Buck Rogers® Books, TSR® Books, Ravenloft® Books. Contact: Mary Kirchoff, Managing Editor. Estab. 1974. "We publish original paperback novels and 'shared world' books." TSR publishes games as well, including the Dungeons & Dragons® role-playing game. Books: Standard paperbacks; offset printing; perfect binding; b&w (usually) illustrations; average first novel print order: 75,000. Averages 20-30 fiction titles each year.

Needs: "We most often publish character-oriented fantasy and science fiction, and some horror. We work with authors who can deal in a serious fashion with the genres we concentrate on and can be creative within the confines of our work-for-hire contracts." Recently published *Sojourn*, by R.A. Salvatore; *The Kinslayer Wars*, by Douglas Niles; and *Sorcerer's Stone*, by L. Dean James.

How to Contact: "Because most of our books are strongly tied to our game products, we expect our writers to be very familiar with those products."

Terms: Pays royalties of 4% of cover price. Offers advances. Always sends galleys to authors. "Commissioned works, with the exception of our TSR® Books line, are written as work-for-hire, with TSR, Inc., holding all copyrights."

Advice: "With the huge success of our Dragonlance® series and Forgotten Realms® books, we expect to be working even more closely with TSR-owned fantasy worlds. Be familiar with our line and query us regarding a proposal."

TYNDALE HOUSE PUBLISHERS, (II, IV), P.O. Box 80, 351 Executive Drive, Wheaton IL 60189. (708)668-8300. Vice President of Editorial: Ron Beers. Estab. 1960. Privately owned religious press. Publishes hardcover and mass paperback originals and paperback reprints. Plans 6 first novels this year. Averages 100 total titles, 6 fiction titles each year. Average first novel print order: 5,000-10,000 copies.

Needs: Religious/inspirational. Published *Grace Livingston Hill Series* and *Mark: Eyewitness*, by Ellen Traylor (biblical novel).

How to Contact: Accepts unsolicited mss. Submit complete ms. Reports in 6-10 weeks. Simultaneous and photocopied submissions OK. Publishes ms an average of 18 months after acceptance.

Terms: Pays in royalties of 10% minimum; negotiable advance. Must return advance if book is not completed or is unacceptable. Writer's guidelines and book catalog for 9 × 12 SAE and $2 for postage.

Market conditions are constantly changing! If you're still using this book and it is 1993 or later, buy the newest edition of Novel & Short Story Writer's Market at your favorite bookstore or order directly from Writer's Digest Books.

*VESTA PUBLICATIONS, LTD, (II), Box 1641, Cornwall, Ontario K6H 5V6 Canada. (613)932-2135. Editor: Stephen Gill. Estab. 1974. Midsize publisher with plans to expand. Publishes hardcover and paperback originals. Books: Bond paper; offset printing; paperback and sewn hardcover binding; illustrations; average print order: 1,200; first novel print order: 1,000. Plans 7 first novels this year. Averages 18 total titles, 5 fiction titles each year. Negotiable charge for critiquing rejected mss.
Needs: Adventure, contemporary, ethnic, experimental, faction, fantasy, feminist, historical, humor/ satire, juvenile, literary, mainstream, preschool/picture book, psychic/supernatural/occult, regional, religious/inspirational, romance, science fiction, short story collections, suspense/mystery, translations, war and young adult/teen. Published *Sodom in her Heart*, by Donna Nevling (religious); *The Blessings of a Bird*, by Stephen Gill (juvenile); and *Whistle Stop and Other Stories*, by Ordrach.
How to Contact: Accepts unsolicited mss. Submit complete ms with SASE or SAE and IRC. Reports in 1 month. Simultaneous and photocopied submissions OK. Accepts computer printout submissions. Disk submissions OK with CPM/Kaypro 2 system.
Terms: Pays in royalties of 10% minimum. Sends galleys to author. "For first novel we usually ask authors from outside of Canada to pay half of our printing cost." Free book catalog.

VILLARD BOOKS, (II, III), Random House, Inc., 201 E. 50th St., New York NY 10022. (212)572-2720. Editorial Director: Peter Gethers. Fiction Editors: Diane Reverand, Stephanie Long, Emily Bestler. Estab. 1983. Imprint specializes in commercial fiction and nonfiction. Publishes hardcover and trade paperback originals. Published new writers within the last year. Plans 2 first novels this year. Averages 40-45 total titles, approx. 10 fiction titles each year. Sometimes critiques rejected mss.
Needs: Strong commercial fiction and nonfiction. Adventure, contemporary, historical, horror, humor/satire, literary, mainstream, romance (contemporary and historical), suspense/mystery. Special interest in mystery, thriller, and literary novels. Recently published *How to Make an American Quilt*, by Whitney Otto (bestseller); *Domestic Pleasure*, by Beth Eutcheon; *First Hubby*, by Roy Blount.
How to Contact: Does not accept unsolicited mss. Submit outline/synopsis and 1-2 sample chapters to a specific editor. Agented fiction: 95%. Reports in 2-3 weeks. Simultaneous and photocopied submissions OK. Accepts electronic submissions.
Terms: "Depends upon contract negotiated." Sends galleys to author. Writer's guidelines for 8½×11 SAE with 1 first class stamp. Book catalog free on request.
Advice: "Most fiction published in hardcover."

WALKER AND COMPANY, (II), 720 5th Ave., New York NY 10019. Editors: Michael Seidman, J. Johnson, Mary Elizabeth Allen, Peter Rubie, Amy Shields, Mary Kennan Herbert. Midsize independent publisher with plans to expand. Publishes hardcover and trade paperback. Average first novel print order: 4,000-5,000. Number of titles: 120/year. Published many new writers within the last year. Occasionally comments on rejected mss.
Needs: Nonfiction, sophisticated, quality mystery, regency romance, quality thrillers and adventure, traditional western and children's and young adult nonfiction.
How to Contact: Submit outline and chapters as preliminary. Query letter should include "a concise description of the story line, including its outcome, word length of story, writing experience, publishing credits, particular expertise on this subject and in this genre. Common mistakes: Sounding unprofessional (i.e. too chatty, too braggardly). Forgetting SASE." Buys 50% agented fiction. Photocopied submissions OK, "but must notify if multiple submissions." Accepts computer printout submissions. Reports in 1-2 months. Publishes ms an average of 1 year after acceptance.
Terms: Negotiable (usually advance against royalty). Must return advance if book is not completed or is unacceptable.
Advice: Publishing more fiction than previously, "exclusively hardcover. Manuscripts should be sophisticated. As for mysteries, we are open to all types, including suspense novels and offbeat, cross genre books. We are always looking for well-written western novels and thrillers that are offbeat and

 The asterisk indicates a publisher who sometimes offers subsidy arrangements. Authors are asked to subsidize part of the cost of book production. See the introduction to Commercial Publishers for more information.

strong on characterization. Character development is most important in all Walker fiction. We have been actively soliciting submissions to all divisions."

WARNER BOOKS, (II), Subsidiary of Warner Publishing, Inc., 666 Fifth Ave., New York NY 10103. (212)484-2900. Imprints include Questor Science Fiction/Fantasy, Mysterious Press. Contact: Editorial dept. for specific editors. Estab. 1961. Publishes hardcover and paperback originals. Published new writers within the last year. Averages approx. 500 titles/year. Sometimes critiques rejected mss.
Needs: Adventure, contemporary, fantasy, horror, mainstream, preschool/picture book, romance (contemporary, historical, regency), science fiction, suspense/mystery, war, western, "We are continuing to publish romances, mainstream novels, science fiction, men's adventure, etc. No historicals that are not romances, Civil War novels, young adult." Recently published *Red Phoenix*, by Larry Bond (military thriller); *Mirror Image*, by Sandra Brown (commercial women's fiction).
How to Contact: Does not accept unsolicited mss. Query first. Agented fiction 85-90%. Reports in 6-8 weeks on mss. Simultaneous submissions accepted "but we prefer exclusive submissions"; and photocopied submissions "of high quality" OK.
Terms: Varies for each book.
Advice: "Continuing a strong, varied list of fiction titles. We encourage first novelists we feel have potential for more books and whose writing is extremely polished. Be able to explain your work clearly and succinctly in query or cover letter. Read books a publisher has done already—best way to get a feel for publisher's strengths. Read *Publishers Weekly* to keep in touch with trends and industry news."

WASHINGTON SQUARE PRESS, (III), Subsidiary of Pocket Books/Simon & Schuster, 1230 Ave. of the Americas, New York NY 10020. Senior Fiction Editor: Jane Rosenman. Estab. 1962. Quality imprint of mass-market publisher. Publishes paperback originals and reprints. Averages 26 titles, mostly fiction, each year.
Needs: Literary, high quality novels; serious nonfiction, journalistic nonfiction. Recently published *The Woman Lit by Fireflies*, by Jim Harrison; *Men Under Water*, by Ralph Lombreglia (short stories); *Up Through the Water*, by Darcey Steinke (first novel).
How to Contact: Accepts unsolicited mss. Query first. Agented fiction nearly all. Reports in 2 months on queries. Simultaneous and photocopied submissions OK.

■**DANIEL WEISS ASSOCIATES, INC., (II)**, 33 W. 17th St., New York NY 10011. Editor-in-Chief: Elise Howard. Estab. 1987. "Packager of 75 titles a year including juvenile and adult fiction as well as nonfiction titles. We package for a range of publishers within their specifications." Publishes hardcover and paperback originals. All titles by first-time writers are commissioned for established series. Averages 120 total titles, 100 fiction titles each year. Sometimes critiques rejected mss.
Needs: Juvenile (animal, easy-to-read, historical, sports, spy/adventure, contemporary), mainstream, preschool/picture book, young adult (easy-to-read, fantasy/science fiction, historical, problem novels, romance, sports, spy/adventure). "We cannot acquire single-title manuscripts that are not part of a series the author is proposing or submitted specifically according to our guidelines for an established series." Published *Sweet Valley High*, by Francine Pascal (young adult series); *Hollywood Daughters*, by Joan Lowery Nixon (young adult historical trilogy); *Pets, Inc.*, by Jennifer Armstrong (elementary fiction series).
How to Contact: Accepts unsolicited mss. Query first with outline and 3-5 sample chapters. SASE. Agented fiction 75%. Reports in 2 months. Simultaneous and photocopied submissions OK. Accepts computer printout submissions.
Terms: Pays flat fee plus royalty. Advance is negotiable. Sends galleys to author. Publishes ms 1 year after acceptance. Writer's guidelines for #10 SAE and 1 first class stamp.
Advice: "We are always happy to work with and encourage first time novelists. Being packagers, we often create and outline books by committee. This system is quite beneficial to writers who may be less experienced. Usually we are contacted by agent rather than writer directly. Occasionally, however, we do work with writers who send in unsolicited material. I think that a professionally presented manuscript is of great importance."

WESTERN PUBLISHING COMPANY, INC., 850 3rd Ave., New York NY 10022. (212)753-8500. Imprint: Golden Books. Juvenile Editors-in-Chief: Selma Lanes and Margo Lundell. Estab. 1907. High-volume mass market and trade publisher. Publishes hardcover and paperback originals. Number of titles: Averages 160/year. Buys 20-30% agented fiction.

Needs: Juvenile: Adventure, mystery, humor, sports, animal, easy-to-read picture books, and "a few" nonfiction titles. Published *Little Critter's Bedtime Story*, by Mercer Mayer; *Cyndy Szekeres' Mother Goose Rhymes*; and *Spaghetti Manners*, by Stephanie Calmenson, illustrated by Lisa MaCue Karsten.
How to Contact: Send a query letter with a description of the story and SASE. Unsolicited mss are returned unread. Publishes ms an average of 1 year after acceptance.
Terms: Pays by outright purchase or royalty.
Advice: "Read our books to see what we do. Call for appointment if you do illustrations, to show your work. Do not send illustrations. Illustrations are not necessary; if your book is what we are looking for, we can use one of our artists."

ALBERT WHITMAN & COMPANY, (II), 6340 Oakton St., Morton Grove IL 60053. (708)581-0033. Associate Editor: Judith Mathews. Senior Editor: Abby Levine. Editor-in-Chief: Kathleen Tucker. Estab. 1919. Small independent juvenile publisher. Publishes hardcover originals and paperback reprints. Books: Paper varies; printing varies; library binding; most books illustrated; average print order: 7,500. Average 30 total titles/year. Number of fiction titles varies.
Needs: Juvenile (2-12 years including easy-to-read, fantasy, historical, adventure, contemporary, mysteries, picture-book stories). Primarily interested in picture book manuscripts and preschool nonfiction. Published *All About Asthma*, by William Ostrow and Vivian Ostrow; *You Push, I Ride*, by Abby Levine; published new writers within the last year.
How to Contact: Accepts unsolicited mss. Submit complete ms, if not possible—3 sample chapters and outline; complete ms for picture books. "Queries don't seem to work for us." SASE. "Half or more fiction is not agented." Reports in 3 weeks on outline; 2 months average on mss. Simultaneous and photocopied submissions OK. ("We prefer to be told.") Accepts computer printouts including dot-matrix.
Terms: Payment varies. Royalties, advance; number of author's copies varies. Some flat fees. Sends galleys to author. Writer's guidelines for SASE. Book catalog for 9 × 12 SAE and 85¢ postage.

■**WILDSTAR BOOKS/EMPIRE BOOKS, (II, IV)**, Subsidiary of The Holy Grail Co., Inc., 26 Nantucket Pl., Scarsdale NY 10583. (914)961-2965. Vice President: Ralph Leone. Estab. 1986. Packager of Empire Books. Imprint: Wildstar (with Lynx Communications). Publishes paperback originals. Averages 40 fiction titles each year. Sometimes critiques rejected mss.
Needs: Horror, biography, psychic/supernatural/occult, romance (contemporary, historical), suspense/mystery, western. Especially interested in romance, horror, New Age, occult, western, mystery and thriller. Published 22-book series *American Regency*; *Wildstar* for Warner Books (romance); 12-book series, *Americans Abroad, Empire* for St. Martin's (romance); 18-book series, *Horror, Empire* for Pageant Books (horror).
How to Contact: Accepts unsolicited mss. Query first. SASE. Agented fiction 80%. Reports in 3 weeks on queries; 3 months on mss. Photocopied submissions OK. Accepts computer printout submissions, including dot-matrix.
Terms: Pays in royalties: "depends on deal we make with publisher." Advance negotiable. Provides author's copies. Sends galleys to author. Publishes ms generally within 18 months after acceptance.
Advice: "Short and to the point—not cute or paranoid—is best tone in a query letter."

WINDSONG BOOKS, (II, IV), Subsidiary of St. Paul Books and Media, 50 St. Paul's Ave., Boston MA 02130. Children's Editor: Sister Anne Joan, fsp. Estab. 1932. "Midsize Roman Catholic publishing house." Publishes paperback originals. Plans 2 first novels this year. Publishes 20 total titles/year.
Needs: Juvenile (contemporary, religious/inspirational) and young adult (historical, problem novels, romance (Christian), religious/inspirational). Especially needs "young adult/teen novels with a Christian (and Catholic) focus. Religion should be vital in the plot and outcome."
How to Contact: Does not accept unsolicited mss. Send an outline/synopsis with 3 sample chapters. SASE. Reports in up to 2 months. Photocopied submissions OK.
Terms: Pays in royalties of 4-8%. Also pays author's copies (amount varies). Publishes ms 2 years after acceptance. Writer's guidelines for #10 SAE and 1 first class stamp. Catalog for 9 × 12 SAE and 1 first class stamp.
Advice: Looks for "characters and plots in which religion, faith, convictions are not just written in, but essential to the person or story."

*****WINSTON-DEREK PUBLISHERS, (II)**, Box 90883, Nashville TN 37209. (615)321-0535, 329-1319. Imprints include Scythe Books. Senior Editor: Marjorie Staton. Estab. 1978. Midsize publisher. Publishes hardcover and paperback originals and reprints. Books: 60 lb. old Warren style paper; litho press;

perfect and/or sewn binding; illustrations sometimes; average print order: 3,000-5,000 copies; first novel print order: 2,000 copies. Published new writers within the last year. Plans 10 first novels this year. Averages 55-65 total titles, 20 fiction titles each year; "90% of material is from freelance writers; each year we add 15 more titles."

Needs: Gothic, historical, juvenile (historical), psychic, religious/inspirational, and young adult (easy-to-read, historical, romance) and programmed reading material for middle and high school students. "Must be 65,000 words or less. Novels strong with human interest. Characters overcoming a weakness or working through a difficulty. Prefer plots related to a historical event but not necessary. No science fiction, explicit eroticism, minorities in conflict without working out a solution to the problem. Downplay on religious ideal and values." Published *A Gentle Wind Came with Us*, by George T. McGuire, Jr.; *The Mengele Hoax*, by Ray V. Waymire; and *From Kathmandu to Timbuctu*, by Juanita Owen Fleming.

How to Contact: Submit outline/synopsis and 3-4 sample chapters with SASE. Simultaneous and photocopied submissions OK. Accepts computer printout submissions. Reports in 4-6 weeks on queries; 6-8 weeks on mss. Must query first. Do not send complete ms.

Terms: Pays in royalties of 10-15%; negotiates advance. *Offers some subsidy arrangements.* Book catalog on request for $1 postage.

Advice: "Stay in the mainstream of writing. The public is reading serene and contemplative literature. Authors should strive for originality and a clear writing style, depicting universal themes which portray character building and are beneficial to mankind. Consider the historical novel; there is always room for one more."

WORLDWIDE LIBRARY, (II), Division of Harlequin Books, 225 Duncan Mill Rd., Don Mills, Ontario M3B 3K9 Canada. (416)445-5860. Imprints are Worldwide Library Mystery; Gold Eagle Books. Senior Editor: Feroze Mohammed. Estab. 1979. Large commercial category line. Publishes paperback originals and reprints. Published new writers within the last year. Averages 60 titles, all fiction, each year. Sometimes critiques rejected ms. "Mystery program is largely reprint; no originals please."

Needs: "We are looking for action-adventure series and writers; future fiction." Recently published *Survival 2000; Soldiers of War; Time Warriors; Agents* – all action series. Soon to be published: *Hatchet, Code Zero, Time Raider, Cade, Nomad, Warkeep 2030*.

How to Contact: Query first or submit outline/synopsis/series concept or overview and sample chapters. SAE. U.S. stamps do not work in Canada; use International Reply Coupons or money order. Agented fiction 95%. Reports in 10 weeks on queries. Simultaneous submissions OK.

Terms: Advance and sometimes royalties; copyright buyout. Publishes ms 1-2 years after acceptance.

Advice: "Publishing fiction in very selective areas. As a genre publisher we are always on the lookout for new writing talent and innovative series ideas, especially in the men's adventure area."

YEARLING, (II, III), 666 5th Ave., New York NY 10103. (212)765-6500. Division of Doubleday, Dell Publishing Co., Inc. Publishes originals and reprints for children grades K-6. Most interested in humorous upbeat novels, mysteries and family stories. 60 titles a year. "Will, regrettably, no longer consider unsolicited material at this time."

ZEBRA BOOKS, (II), 475 Park Ave. S, New York NY 10016. (212)889-2299. Contact: Editorial Director. Estab. 1975. Publishes hardcover reprints and paperback originals. Averages 400 total titles/year.

Needs: Contemporary, adventure, English-style mysteries, historical, war, gothic, saga, romance, true crime, nonfiction, women's, erotica, thrillers and horror. No science fiction. Published *Missing Beauty*, by Teresa Carpenter; *Kiss of the Night Wind*, by Janelle Taylor; *Stardust*, by Nan Ryan; and *Wolf Time*, by Joe Gores.

How to Contact: Query or submit complete ms or outline/synopsis and sample chapters with SASE. Simultaneous and photocopied submissions OK. Address women's mss to Carin Cohen Ritter and male adventure mss to Editorial Director. Reports in 3-5 months.

Terms: Pays royalties and advances. Free book catalog.

Advice: "Put aside your literary ideals and be commercial. We like big contemporary women's fiction; glitzy career novels, high-tech espionage and horror. Work fast and on assignment. Keep your cover letter simple and to the point. Too many times, 'cutesy' letters about category or content turn us off some fine mss. We are more involved with family and historical sagas. But please do research. We buy many unsolicited manuscripts, but we're slow readers. Have patience."

ZONDERVAN, 1415 Lake Dr. SE, Grand Rapids MI 49506. (616)698-6900. Imprints include Academie Books, Daybreak Books, Francis Asbury Press, Lamplighter Books, Ministry Resources Library, Pyranee Books, Regency Reference Library, Youth Specialties and Zondervan Books. Publishers: Stan Gundry, Scott Bolinder. Estab. 1931. Large evangelical Christian publishing house. Publishes hardcover and paperback originals and reprints, though fiction is generally in paper only. Published new writers in the last year. Averages 150 total titles, 5-10 fiction titles each year. Average first novel: 5,000 copies.
Needs: Adult fiction, (mainstream, biblical, historical, adventure, sci-fi, fantasy, mystery), "Inklings-style" fiction of high literary quality and juvenile fiction (primarily mystery/adventure novels for 8-12-year-olds). Christian relevance necessary in all cases. Will *not* consider collections of short stories or inspirational romances. Published *Men of Kent*, by Elizabeth Gibson; *Nightwatch*, by John Leax; and *Morning Morning True*, by Ernest Herndon.
How to Contact: Accepts unsolicited mss. Write for writer's guidelines first. Include #10 SASE. Query or submit outline/synopsis and 2 sample chapters. Reports in 4-6 weeks on queries; 3-4 months on mss. Photocopied submissions OK. Accepts computer printout submissions.
Terms: "Standard contract provides for a percentage of the net price received by publisher for each copy sold, usually 14-17% of net."
Advice: "There has been a revival of Christian fiction in last year. The renewed reader interest is exciting. There is great room for improvement of writing quality, however. Send plot outline and one or two sample chapters. Most editors will *not* read entire mss. Your proposal and opening chapter will make or break you."

International commercial publishers

The following commercial publishers, all located outside the United States and Canada, also accept work from fiction writers. The majority are from England, a few are from India and one each is from Scotland and Ghana. As with other publishers, obtain catalogs and writer's guidelines from those that interest you to determine the types of fiction published and how well your work might fit alongside other offerings.

Remember to use self-addressed envelopes (SAEs) with International Reply Coupons (IRCs) in all correspondence with publishers outside your own country. IRCs may be purchased at the main branch of your local post office. In general, send IRCs in amounts roughly equivalent to return postage. When submitting work to international publishers, you may want to send a disposable copy of your manuscript and only one IRC along with a self-addressed postcard for a reply. This saves you the cost of having work returned.

‡**MARION BOYARS PUBLISHERS INC.**, Editorial Office: 24 Lacy Road, London SW15 1NL England. Fiction Editor: Marion Boyars. Publishes 15 novels or story collections/year. "A lot of American fiction. Authors include Ken Kesey, Eudora Welty, Stephen Koch, Samuel Charters, Page Edwards, Kenneth Gangemi, Tim O'Brien, Julian Green. British and Irish fiction. Translations from the French, German, Turkish, Arabic, Italian, Spanish." Send cover letter and entire manuscript "always with sufficient return postage by check." Pays advance against royalties. "Most fiction working *well* in one country does well in another. We usually have world rights, i.e. world English plus translation rights." Enclose return postage by check, minimum $3, for catalog.

‡**GHANA PUBLISHING CORPORATION, PUBLISHING DIVISION**, Private Post Bag, Tema, Accra, 1001 Ghana. Fiction Editor: Muhammed, Amuda. Ghana Publishing "is the largest publishing house in Ghana; owned by the government, but run independently in the main. We publish all types of fiction but with a bias towards classics, the sort that the Ministry of Education may prescribe to students. In general, the merit of a book lends itself to publication with us." Length: 40,000-80,000 words. Send cover letter, synopsis, brief summary, 3 sample chapters or entire manuscript. Pays royalties of 10-15% based on fictional impact and possible saleability or marketability. "Research the area of concern and market. Material must be contemporary or relevent. Technique must be clear and accessible to target readership. We prefer novels to short stories, which must be around 60 to 80,000 words. Novella's should be about 40,000. Materials must deal with relations affecting Ghanaian (African) culture under transition—clash of cultures, clash of old and new, personalities, old and aged, socio-economic conventions and morals. Treatment must be humorous bent. Ghanaians love to be relaxed and enter-

tained; and they admire adventure and success worn through hard work—against corruption and indirection." Write for guidelines.

ROBERT HALE LIMITED, (II), Clerkenwell House, 45/47 Clerkenwell Green, London EC1R 0HT England. Publishes hardcover and trade paperback originals and hardcover reprints. Historical, mainstream, romance and western. Length: 40,000-150,000 words. Send cover letter, synopsis or brief summary and 2 sample chapters. Submission policies available on romances only.

*HARSHA BOOK AGENCY, Hallmark Publishing Ltd., T.D. East Sannidhi Road, P.O. Box 3541, Kochi-682 035, Kerala, India. Managing and Editorial Director: C. I. Oommen. Publishers of trade paperbacks and educational books. Looking for adventure, novel and short fiction. Accepts unsolicited mss, simultaneous and photocopied submissions and computer printouts. Reports in 2 months. Pays in royalties of 10% maximum. No advance. "We also produce books for self publishers and small press with marketing and distribution support." No SASE/IRC required.

HEADLINE BOOK PUBLISHING PLC, 79 Great Titchfield St., London W1P 7FN England. Editorial Director: Susan J. Fletcher. Averages approximately 300 titles/year. Mainstream publisher of popular fiction and nonfiction in hardcover and mass-market paperback. Length: 120,000-200,000 words. "Study UK publishers' catalogs to see what is published in both the USA and the UK. Read the UK trade press: *The Bookseller* and *Publishing News* to get a feel for our market. *The Writers' & Artists' Yearbook* is useful." Pays advance against royalties. "Send a synopsis/5 consecutive chapters and *curriculum vitae* first, and return postage." Catalog and *very* brief guidelines available.

HODDER & STOUGHTON PUBLISHERS, 47 Bedford Square, London WC1B 3DP, England, U.K. Imprints: Coronet, NEL, Sceptre. Editorial Director: Nick Sayers. Fiction Editors: Humphrey Price (NEL); Anna Powell (Coronet); Carole Welch (Sceptre). Coronet: intelligent, mainstream romantic fiction; humour; historical novels/crime; Sceptre: literary—fiction and nonfiction; NEL: horror, SF, fantasy, humour, serious nonfiction. "We do not consider short stories." Length: 70,000-120,000 words. Payment is made "usually by an advance and then final payment on publication." Send a cover letter, synopsis and sample chapters. "If you can't get an agent to represent you, then do make enquiries to the editorial departments first, before sending off complete manuscripts."

‡JULIA MACRAE BOOKS, Random Century House, 20 Vauxhall Bridge Road, London SW1V 2SA England. Editors: Julia MacRae, Delia Huddy, Susan Reid. Children's books: Board books, picture books, fiction for juniors and teenagers, nonfiction. *Adult titles*: biography, history, music, religion. Send cover letter and entire manuscript. Writers are paid by royalties. Julia MacRae Books is an imprint of the Random Century Group.

MY WEEKLY STORY LIBRARY, D.C. Thomson and Co., Ltd., 22 Meadowside, Dundee DD19QJ, Scotland. Fiction Editor: Mrs. D. Hunter. Publishes 48, 35,000-word romantic novels/year. "Cheap paperback story library with full-colour cover. Material should not be violent, controversial or sexually explicit." Length: 35,000-45,000 words. Writers are paid on acceptance. "Send the opening 3 chapters and a synopsis. Avoid too many colloquialisms/Americanisms. Stories can be set anywhere but local colour not too "local" as to be alien." Guidelines available on request.

ORIENT PAPERBACKS, A division of Vision Books Pvt Ltd., Madarsa Rd., Kashmere Gate, Delhi 110 006 India. Editor: Sudhir Malhotra. Publishes 10-15 novels or story collections/year. "We are one of the largest paperback publishers in S.E. Asia and publish English fiction by authors from this part of the world." Length: 40,000 words minimum. Pays royalty on copies sold. Send cover letter, brief summary, 1 sample chapter and author's bio data. "We send writers' guidelines on accepting a proposal."

‡PICADOR, Pan MacMillan Ltd., 18-21 Cavaye Place, London SW10 9PO England. Publishing Director: Peter Straus. Publishes hardbound and paperback titles. "Picador is a literary imprint specializing in the best international fiction and nonfiction in recent years. Its authors include G. Garcia Marquez, Umberto Eco, Julian Barnes, Graham Swift, Ian McEwan, Toni Morrison, Tom Wolfe." Length: 50,000-150,000 words. Send cover letter, synopsis, brief summary and 2 sample chapters. For catalog, send large addressed envelope and IRCs.

‡POPULAR PUBLICATIONS, P.O. Box 5592, Limbe, Malawi. Fiction Editor: Joseph-Claude Simwaka. Averages between 3-5 titles/year. "Popular Publications is probably the biggest publisher of Malawian fiction in the country. In order to boost and promote Malawian literary writers (creative works) the publishing house launched the Malawian Writers Series in 1974 to cater to fiction, short story collections and poetry. We also publish children's books on fiction." Length: 5,000-25,000 words. Send cover letter and entire manuscript. We pay 10% royalties by 31st December every year. "Submit a typewritten manuscript, double-spaced on A4 paper. It is also advisable for the writer to submit two copies of the same manuscript, one for us and the other for the Government Censorship Board. Writer too, should keep a triplicate copy." Write for catalog or guidelines.

QUARTET BOOKS LIMITED, 27-29 Goodge Street, London W1P1FD England. Fiction Editor: Stephen Pickles. Publishes 50 stories/year. "Middle East fiction, European classics in translation, original novels." Payment is: advance—half on signature, half on delivery and publication. "Send brief synopsis and sample chapters. *No* romantic fiction, historical fiction, crime, science fiction or thrillers."

VISION BOOKS PVT LTD., Madarsa Rd., Kashmere Gate, Delhi 110006 India. Fiction Editor: Sudhir Malhotra. Publishes 25 titles/year. "We are a large multilingual publishing house publishing fiction and other trade books." Pays royalties. "A brief synopsis should be submitted initially. Subsequently, upon hearing from the editor, a typescript may be sent."

WEIDENFELD AND NICOLSON LTD., 91, Clapham High St., London SW4 7TA England. Fiction Editor: Allegra Huston. Publishes approx. 10 titles/year. "We are an independent publisher with a small fiction list. Authors include, or have included, V. Nabokov, J.G. Farrell, Olivia Manning, Edna O'Brien, Margaret Drabble, Richard Powers, John Hersey, Penelope Gilliatt, Charlotte Vale Allen. We publish literary and commercial fiction: sagas, historicals, crime." Pays by advance. Royalties are set against advances. "Send a covering letter, a detailed synopsis and some sample pages such as the first chapter. Do not send the whole typescript unless invited. Please enclose return postage and retain photocopies of all material sent. Very rare that we would publish a work by an author which had not previously been published in their own country."

Other commercial publishers

The following commercial publishers appeared in the 1991 edition of *Novel & Short Story Writer's Market* but do not appear in the 1992 edition. Those listings that did not respond to our request for an update are listed without further explanation below. There are several reasons why a publisher did not return an update—they could be overstocked, no longer taking fiction or have been recently sold—or they may have responded too late for inclusion. If a reason for the omission is known, it is included next to the publisher's name. Additional international commercial publishers appear at the end of the list.

Abingdon Press (no longer publishes fiction)
Ballantine/Epiphany Books (line no longer open)
Children's Press (no novels, asked to be deleted)
Dembner Books (no longer publishing fiction)
Doubleday-Foundation Books
(asked to be deleted)
Gemstone Books
Iron Crown Enterprises (asked to be deleted)
Larksdale (asked to be left out this year)
Navel Institute Press (overstocked)
Presidio Press
University of Georgia Press (submit through contest only)
University of Minnesota Press (asked to be deleted)
Western Producer Prairie Books
Charlotte Zolotow Books (see HarperCollins)

Other international commercial publishers
The Blackstaff Press
Hamish Hamilton Ltd.
Michael Joseph Ltd.
Mills & Boon
The Women's Press

Contests and Awards

Contests and awards programs offer writers a number of benefits. In addition to honors and quite often cash awards, contests also offer writers the opportunity to be judged on the basis of quality alone without the outside factors that sometimes influence publishing decisions. New writers who win contests may receive their first publications, while more experienced writers may gain public recognition of an entire body of work.

This year a number of state-sponsored awards programs were slashed along with the budgets of state art councils. The Massachusetts Artists Fellowship Program, the Creative Artist Grant of the Michigan Council for the Arts and the New Jersey Author Awards are all missing this year because of budget cuts.

In addition, we've removed the listings for a number of retreat programs offered previously in this section. We've created a new section, Retreats and Colonies, leaving only contests, grants, awards and a few fellowships in this section. Even with these cuts, however, the section continues to grow.

There are contests for almost every type fiction writing. Some focus on form, such as the World's Best Short Short Story Contest, for stories under 250 words, and the National Writers Club Annual Novel Writing Contest, for full-length novels. Others feature writing on particular themes or topics including the *Japanophile* Short Story Contest, the Stephen Leacock Medal for Humor and the *Military Lifestyle* Short Story Contest. Still others are prestigious prizes or awards for work that must be nominated such as The Hugo Awards and Pulitzer Prize in Fiction. Chances are no matter what type of fiction you write, there is a contest or award program that may interest you.

Selecting and submitting to a contest

Use the same care in submitting to contests as you would sending your manuscript to a publication or book publisher. Deadlines are very important and where possible we've included this information. At times contest deadlines were only approximate at our press deadline, so be sure to write or call for complete information and additional rules.

Follow the rules to the letter. If, for instance, contest rules require you to put your name on a cover sheet only, you will be disqualified if you ignore this and put your name on every page. Find out how many copies to send. If you don't send the correct amount, by the time you are contacted to send more it may be past the submission deadline.

As with publishers, of course, your submission must be clean, neatly typed and professionally presented. Do not cost yourself points by sending a manuscript no one cares to handle or read.

One note of caution: Beware of contests that charge entry fees that are disproportionate to the amount of the prize. Contests offering a $10 prize, but charging $7 in entry fees, are a waste of your time and money.

If you are interested in a contest or award that requires your publisher to nominate your work, it's acceptable to make your interest known. Be sure to leave them plenty of time, however, to make the nomination deadline.

The Roman numeral coding we use to rank listings in this section is different than that used in previous sections. A new or unpublished writer is eligible to enter those marked I (and some IVs), while a writer with a published book (usually including self-published) may enter most contests ranked II (and, again, some IVs). Entrants for contests ranked III must be nominated by someone who is not the writer (usually the publisher or editor). The following is our ranking system:

I **Contest for unpublished fiction, usually open to both new and experienced writers.**

II **Contest for published (usually including self-published) fiction, which may be entered by the author.**

III **Contest for published fiction, which must be nominated by an editor, publisher or other nominating body.**

IV **Contest limited to residents of a certain region, of a certain age or to writing on certain themes or subjects.**

AIM MAGAZINE SHORT STORY CONTEST, (I), Box 20554, Chicago IL 60620. (312)874-6184. Contact: Ruth Apilado and Mark Boone, publisher and fiction editor. Estab. 1984. Contest offered annually if money available. "To encourage and reward good writing in the short story form. The contest is particularly for new writers." Award: $100 plus publication in fall issue. "Judged by *Aim*'s editorial staff." Sample copy for $3.50. Contest rules for SASE. Unpublished submissions. "We're looking for compelling, well-written stories with lasting social significance."

ALABAMA STATE COUNCIL ON THE ARTS INDIVIDUAL ARTIST FELLOWSHIP, (II, IV), #1 Dexter Ave., Montgomery AL 36130. (205)242-4076. Contact: Randy Shoults. "To provide assistance to an individual artist." Semiannual awards: $5,000 and $10,000 grants. Competition receives approximately 30 submissions annually. Judges: Independent peer panel. Entry forms or rules for SASE. Deadline: May 1. Two-year Alabama residency required.

ALASKA STATE COUNCIL ON THE ARTS LITERARY ARTS FELLOWSHIPS, (I, IV), Alaska State Council on the Arts, Suite 1E, 411 West 4th Ave., Anchorage AK 99501-2343. (907)279-1558. Contact: Christine D'Arcy. "Open-ended grant award, non-matching, to enable creative writers to advance their careers as they see it." Biennial. Award: $5,000. Judges: Peer panel review. Deadline: October 1. Alaskan writers only.

THE NELSON ALGREN AWARD FOR SHORT FICTION, (I), *Chicago Tribune*, 435 N. Michigan Ave., Chicago IL 60611. (312)222-3232. Annual award to recognize an outstanding, unpublished short story, minimum 2,500 words, maximum 10,000 words. Awards: $5,000 first prize; three runners-up receive $1,000 awards. Publication of four winning stories in the *Chicago Tribune*. No entry fee. "All entries must be typed, double spaced and accompanied by SASE." A brochure bearing the rules of the contest will be sent to writers who inquire in writing. Deadline: Entries are accepted only from November 30-February 1.

ALLEGHENY REVIEW AWARDS, (I, IV)), Box 32, Allegheny College, Meadville PA 16335. Contact: John Burns and Vern Maczuzak, editors. Annual award for unpublished short stories. U.S. undergraduate students only. SASE for rules. Deadline: January 31.

AMBERGRIS ANNUAL FICTION AWARD, (I, IV), *Ambergris* Magazine, P.O. Box 29919, Cincinnati OH 45229. Editor: Mark Kissling. Award "to recognize and reward excellence in fiction writing." Annual competition for short stories. Award: $100 and nomination to *The Pushcart Prize*. Competition receives 300 mss/contest. Judges: Editorial staff. Guidelines for #10 SASE. Unpublished submissions. "We give special but not exclusive consideration to works by Ohio writers or about the Midwest in general. Winner is chosen from all works submitted during the year. We prefer works under 5,000 words. Writers may want to review the results of previous contests. Sample copies are $4 and back issues are available for $3."

AMELIA MAGAZINE AWARDS, (I), 329 "E" St., Bakersfield CA 93304. (805)323-4064. Contact: Frederick A. Raborg, Jr., editor. The Reed Smith Fiction Prize; The Willie Lee Martin Short Story Award; The Cassie Wade Short Fiction Award; The Patrick T. T. Bradshaw Fiction Award; and four annual genre awards in science fiction, romance, western and fantasy/horror. Estab. 1984. Annually. "To publish the finest fiction possible and reward the writer; to allow good writers to earn some money in small press publication. *Amelia* strives to fill that gap between major circulation magazines and quality university journals." Unpublished submissions. Length: The Reed Smith—3,000 words max.; The Willie Lee Martin—3,500-5,000 words; The Cassie Wade—4,500 words max.; The Patrick T. T. Bradshaw—10,000 words; the genre awards—science fiction, 5,000 words; romance, 3,000 words; western, 5,000 words; fantasy/horror, 5,000 words. Award: "Each prize consists of $200 plus publication and two copies of issue containing winner's work." The Reed Smith Fiction Prize offers two additional awards of $100 and $50, and publication; Bradshaw Book Award: $300 plus publication, 2 copies. Deadlines: The Reed Smith Prize—September 1; The Willie Lee Martin—March 1; The Cassie Wade—June 1; The Patrick T. T. Bradshaw—February 15; Amelia fantasy/horror—February 1; Amelia western—April 1; Amelia romance—October 1; Amelia science fiction—December 15. Entry fee: $5. Bradshaw Award fee: $7.50. Contest rules for SASE. Looking for "high quality work equal to finest fiction being published today."

AMERICAN ACADEMY AND INSTITUTE OF ARTS AND LETTERS LITERARY AWARDS, (III), 633 W. 155th St., New York NY 10032. (212)368-5900. Contact: Betsey Feeley, assistant to the executive director. Annual awards for previously published books. To honor authors for excellence in literature and encourage them in their creative work. Selection is by members of the Academy-Institute. *Applications not accepted.* Award: Prizes vary. Eight $7,500 Academy-Institute awards. Special awards include: The Richard & Hinda Rosenthal Foundation Award: $5,000 for "an American work of fiction published during the preceding 12 months"; The Sue Kaufman Prize for First Fiction: $2,500; and The William Dean Howells Medal for Fiction (every 5 years). Also the Award of Merit Medal for the Novel and $5,000 prize (every 6 years); the Award of Merit Medal for The Short Story and $5,000 prize (every 6 years); and The Gold Medal for Fiction (every 6 years). The Harold D. Vursell Memorial Award: $5,000 to single out recent writing in book form that merits recognition for the quality of its prose style. The Morton Dauwen Zabel Award: $2,500 for a writer of fiction of progressive, original and experimental tendencies (every 3 years). The Rome Fellowship in Literature (periodically) for a year's residence at the American Academy in Rome. The E.M. Forster Award ($12,500) for a young English writer to stay in the U.S. The Jean Stein Award ($5,000) given to a writer (nonfiction, fiction, poetry in succession) whose work takes risks expressing its commitment to the author's values and vision.

AMERICAN FICTION VOL II, (I), Birch Lane Press/American Fiction, English Dept., Springfield College, 263 Alden St., Springfield MA 01109. (413)788-3000. Editors: Michael C. White and Alan Davis. To "recognize unpublished stories by both *known* and *unknown* writers." Annual competition for short stories. Award: $1,000 first prize; $500 second; $250 third; publication, 2 copies. Entry fee: $7.50. Guidelines in *AWP Newsletter* and in *Poets & Writers.* Deadline: April 1. Unpublished submissions. 10,000-word limit.

ANALECTA COLLEGE FICTION CONTEST, (I, IV), The Liberal Arts Council, FAC 19, Austin TX 78712. (512)471-6563. Awards Coordinator: Isabel Ramirez. Award to "give student writers, at the Univ. of Texas and universities across the country, a forum for publication. We believe that publication in a magazine with the quality and reputation of *Analecta* will benefit student writers." Annual competition for short stories. Award: $100. Competition receives approx. 80 submissions. Judges: Student editiorial board of approx. 15 people. No entry fee. Guidelines for SASE. Deadline: October 28. Unpublished submissions. Limited to college students. Length: 15 pages or less. "We also accept poetry, drama and art submissions."

SHERWOOD ANDERSON SHORT FICTION PRIZE, (I), *Mid-American Review,* Dept. of English, Bowling Green State University, Bowling Green OH 43403. (419)372-2725. Contact: Ellen Behrens, fiction editor. Award frequency is subject to availability of funds. "To encourage the writer of quality short fiction." No entry fee. No deadline. Unpublished material. "Winners are selected from stories published by the magazine, so submission for publication is the first step."

THE ANNUAL/ATLANTIC WRITING COMPETITIONS, (I, IV), Writers' Federation of Nova Scotia, Suite 203, 5516 Spring Garden Rd., Halifax, Nova Scotia B3J 1G6 Canada. (902)423-8116. "To recognize and encourage unpublished writers in the region of Atlantic Canada. (Competition only open to residents of Nova Scotia, Newfoundland, Prince Edward Island and New Brunswick, the four Atlantic Provinces.)" Annual competition for short stories, novels, poetry, nonfiction, children's writing, drama, magazine feature/essay. Award: Various cash awards. Competition receives approximately 10-12 submissions for novels; 75 for poetry; 75 for children's; 75 for short stories; 10 for nonfiction. Judges: Professional writers, librarians, booksellers. Entry fee $15/entry. Guidelines for SASE. Unpublished submissions.

ANTIETAM REVIEW LITERARY AWARD, (I, IV), *Antietam Review*, 82 W. Washington St., Hagerstown MD 21740. (301)791-3132. Executive Editor: Susanne Kass. Annual award to encourage and give recognition to excellence in short fiction. Open to writers from Maryland, Pennsylvania, Virginia, West Virginia, Washington DC and Delaware. "We consider only previously unpublished work. We read manuscripts between October 1 and March 1." Award: $100 plus $100 for the story; the story is printed as lead in the magazine. "We consider all fiction mss sent to *Antietam Review* as entries for the prize. We look for well crafted, serious literary prose fiction under 5,000 words."

‡ANVIL PRESS 3-DAY NOVEL WRITING CONTEST, (I), Anvil Press, Box 1575, Station A, Vancouver, British Columbia V6C 2P7 Canada. (604)876-8700. Contact: Editor. Contest to write the best novel in 3 days, held every Labor Day weekend. Annually, for unpublished novels. "Prize is publication." Receives approximately 500 entries for each award. Judged by Anvil Press editorial board. Entry fee $10. Guidelines for SASE or SAE and IRC. Deadline: Friday before Labor Day weekend. "Entrants must register with Anvil Press. Winner is announced October 31."

ARIZONA AUTHORS' ASSOCIATION ANNUAL LITERARY CONTEST, (I), Suite 117, 3509 E. Shea Blvd., Phoenix AZ 85028. (602)996-9706. Contact: Cynthia Greening. Estab. 1981. Annually. "To encourage AAA members and all other writers in the country to write regularly for competition and publication." Award: "Cash prizes totalling $1,000 for winners and honorable mentions in short stories, essays and poetry. Winning entries are published in the *Arizona Literary Magazine*." Entry fee: $4 for poetry, $6 for essays and short stories. Contest rules for SASE. Deadline: July 29. Unpublished submissions. Looking for "strong concept; good, effective writing, with emphasis on the subject/story."

ARIZONA COMMISSION ON THE ARTS CREATIVE WRITING FELLOWSHIPS, (I, IV), 417 West Roosevelt St., Phoenix AZ 85003. (602)255-5882. Literature Director: Tonda Gorton. Fellowships awarded in alternate years to fiction writers and poets. Four awards of $5,000-7,500. Judges: Out-of-state writers/editors. Next deadline for fiction writers: September 1992. Arizona resident poets and writers over 18 years of age only.

ARTIST TRUST ARTIST FELLOWSHIPS; GAP GRANTS, (I, II, IV), Artist Trust, #512, 1331 3rd Ave., Seattle WA 98101. (206)467-8734. Awards Coordinator: Gabrielle Dean. Awards to "offer direct support to individual artists in all disciplines in Washington state: The Fellowship Program and the GAP (Grants for Artist Projects) Program. Our goal is to offer financial support for an artist's creative process, therefore grants are made to generative, rather than interpretive, artists." Annual fellowships and biannual grants for short stories, novels and story collections. Awards: $5,000 fellowship; up to $1,000 GAP. Competition receives approx. 200-300 submissions. Judges: Fellowship: Peer panel of 3 professional artists and arts professionals in each discipline. GAP: Interdisciplinary peer panel of 6-8 artists and arts professionals. Guidelines available for SASE. Deadlines: Fellowship:Winter 1992. GAP: Spring and Fall 1992. Limited to Washington state artists only. Students not eligible.

ASF TRANSLATION PRIZE, (I, IV), American-Scandinavian Foundation, 725 Park Ave., New York NY 10021. Contact: Publishing office. Estab. 1980. Annual award "to encourage the translation and publication of the best of contemporary Scandinavian poetry and fiction and to make it available to a wider American audience." Competition includes submissions of poetry, drama, literary prose and fiction translations. Award: $2,000, a bronze medallion and publication in *Scandinavian Review*. Competition rules and entry forms available with SASE. Deadline: June 1. Submissions must have been previously published in the original Scandinavian language. No previously translated material. Original authors should have been born within past 100 years.

 The double dagger before a listing indicates that the listing is new in this edition. New markets are often the most receptive to freelance contributions.

ASTED/GRAND PRIX DE LITTERATURE JEUNESSE DU QUEBEC-ALVINE-BELISLE, (III, IV), Association pour l'avancement des sciences et des techniques de la documentation, 1030 rue Cherrier, Bureau 505, Montréal, Québec Canada. (514)521-9561. President: Johanne Petel. "Prize granted for the best work in youth literature edited in French in the Quebec Province. Authors and editors can participate in the contest." Annual competition for fiction and nonfiction for children and young adults. Award: $500. Deadline: June 1. Contest entry limited to editors of books published during the preceding year. French translations of other languages are not accepted.

THE ATHENAEUM LITERARY AWARD, (II, IV), The Athenaeum of Philadelphia, 219 S. 6th St., Philadelphia PA 19106. Contact: Literary Award Committee. Annual award to recognize and encourage outstanding literary achievement in Philadelphia and its vicinity. Award: A bronze medal bearing the name of the award, the seal of the Athenaeum, the title of the book, the name of the author and the year. Judged by committee appointed by Board of Directors. Deadline: December. Submissions must have been published during the preceding year. Nominations shall be made in writing to the Literary Award Committee by the author, the publisher or a member of the Athenaeum, accompanied by a copy of the book. The Athenaeum Literary Award is granted for a work of general literature, not exclusively for fiction. Juvenile fiction is not included.

AWP AWARD SERIES IN THE NOVEL AND SHORT FICTION, (I), The Associated Writing Programs, c/o Old Dominion University, Norfolk VA 23529-0079. Annual award. The AWP Award Series was established in cooperation with several university presses in order to publish and make fine fiction available to a wide audience. Awards: $1,500 honorarium and publication with a university press. In addition, AWP tries to place mss of finalists with participating presses. Judges: Distinguished writers in each genre. Entry fee $10. Contest/award rules available for SASE. Deadlines: Manuscript postmarked between January 1-February 29. Only book-length mss in the novel and short story collections are eligible. Manuscripts previously published in their entirety, including self-publishing, are not eligible. No mss returned.

AWP INTRO JOURNALS PROJECT, (IV), Old Dominion University, Norfolk VA 23529-0079. (804)683-3840. Contact: Tony Ardizonne. "This is a prize for students in AWP member university creative writing programs only. Authors are nominated by the head of the creative writing department. Each school may send 2 nominated short stories." Annual competition for short stories. Award: $25 plus publication in participating journal. 1992 journals include *New England Review, Puerto del Sol, Indiana Review, Quarterly West, Mid-American Review, Willow Springs* and *Black Warrior Review*. Judges: AWP. Deadline: December 15. Unpublished submissions.

EMILY CLARK BALCH AWARDS, (I), *The Virginia Quarterly Review*, One West Range, Charlottesville VA 22903. Editor: Staige D. Blackford. Annual award "to recognize distinguished short fiction by American writers." For stories published in *The Virginia Quarterly Review* during the calendar year. Award: $500.

MILDRED L. BATCHELDER AWARD, (II), Association for Library Service to Children/American Library Association, 50 E. Huron St., Chicago IL 60611. (312)944-6780. To encourage international exchange of quality children's books by recognizing U.S. publishers of such books in translation. Annual competition for translations. Award: Citation. Judge: Mildred L. Batchelder award committee. Guidelines for SASE. Deadline: December. Books should be U.S. trade publications for which children, up to and including age 14, are potential audience.

GEORGE BENNETT FELLOWSHIP, (I), Phillips Exeter Academy, Exeter NH 03833. (603)772-4311. Coordinator, Selection Committee: Charles Pratt. "To provide time and freedom from monetary concerns to a person contemplating or pursuing a career as a professional writer." Annual award for writing residency. Award: A stipend ($5,000 at present), plus room and board for academic year. Competition receives approximately 100 submissions. Judges are a committee of the English department. Entry fee $5. SASE for application form and guidelines. Deadline: December 1.

BEST FIRST MALICE DOMESTIC NOVEL, (I, IV), Thomas Dunne Books, St. Martin's Press and Macmillan London Ltd., St. Martin's Press, 175 Fifth Ave., New York NY 10010. "To publish a writer's first 'malice domestic novel.' " Annual competition for novels. Award: Publication by St. Martin's Press in the US and Macmillan London in the UK. Advance: $10,000 (and standard royalties). Judges are selected by sponsors. Guidelines for SASE. Deadline: November 1. Unpublished submissions.

"Open to any professional or nonprofessional writer who has never published a malice domestic novel and who is not under contract with a publisher to publish one. Malice domestic is a traditional mystery novel that is not hardboiled; emphasis is on the solution rather than the details of the crime. Suspects and victims know one another. In marginal cases, judges will decide whether entry qualifies."

BEST FIRST PRIVATE EYE NOVEL CONTEST, (I, IV), Private Eye Writers of America, St. Martin's Press and Macmillan London Ltd., Thomas Dunne Books, St. Martin's Press, 175 Fifth Ave., New York NY 10010. Annual award. To publish a writer's first "private eye" novel. Award: Publication of novel by St. Martin's Press in the US and Macmillan London in the UK. Advance: $10,000 against royalties (standard contract). Judges are selected by sponsors. Guidelines for SASE. Deadline: August 30. Unpublished submissions. "Open to any professional or nonprofessional writer who has never published a 'private eye' novel and who is not under contract with a publisher for the publication of a 'private eye' novel. As used in the rules, private eye novel means: a novel in which the main character is an independent investigator who is not a member of any law enforcement or government agency."

‡BEST SHORT STORY REJECTED BY REDBOOK (or other large market), (I), Housewife-Writer's Forum, P.O. Box 780, Lyman WY 82937. (307)786-4513. "To give new fiction writers a chance to have their work recognized." Annual contest for short stories. Award: $30, $20, $10. Competition receives approx. 50 submissions. Judges: Fiction Editor Bob Haynie and Editor Diane Wolverton. Entry fee: $4. Guidelines for SASE. Unpublished submissions. Any genre except risqué; 2,000 words max. "The title of the contest is just to encourage writers who have found it difficult to break into large markets. Your story doesn't actually have to have been rejected."

IRMA S. AND JAMES H. BLACK CHILDREN'S BOOK AWARD, (II), Bank Street College, 610 W. 112th St., New York NY 10025. (212)663-7200, ext. 587. Children's Librarian: Linda Greengrass. Annual award "to honor the young children's book published in the preceding year judged the most outstanding in text as well as in art. Book must be published the year preceding the May award." Award: Press luncheon at Harvard Club, a scroll and seals by Maurice Sendak for attaching to award book's run. No entry fee. Deadline: January 15. "Write to address above. Usually publishers submit books they want considered, but individuals can too. No entries are returned."

JAMES TAIT BLACK MEMORIAL PRIZES, (III, IV), Department of English Literature, University of Edinburgh, Edinburgh EH8 9JX Scotland. Contact: Professor R.D.S. Jack. "Two prizes are awarded: one for the best work of fiction, one for the best biography or work of that nature, published during the calendar year." Annual competition for short stories, novels and story collections. Award: £1,500 each. Competition receives approx. 200 submissions. Judge: Professor R.D.S. Jack, Chairman, Dept. of English Literature. Guidelines for SASE. Deadline: November 30. Previously published submissions. "Eligible works are those written in English, originating with a British publisher, and first published in Britain in the year of the award. Works should be submitted by publishers."

THE BLACK WARRIOR REVIEW LITERARY AWARD, (II, III), Box 2936, Tuscaloosa AL 35486. (205)348-4518. Editor: Glenn Mott. "Award is to recognize the best fiction published in *BWR* in a volume year. Only fiction accepted for publication is considered for the award." Competition is for short stories and novel chapters. Award: $500. Competition receives approximately 1,500 submissions. Prize awarded by an outside judge.

BOARDMAN TASKER PRIZE, (III, IV), 14 Pine Lodge, Dairyground Rd., Bramhall, Stockport, Cheshire SK7 2HS United Kingdom. Contact: Mrs. D. Boardman. "To reward a book which has made an outstanding contribution to mountain literature. A memorial to Peter Boardman and Joe Tasker, who disappeared on Everest in 1982." Award: £1,000. Competition receives approx. 15 submissions. Judges: A panel of 3 judges elected by trustees. Guidelines for SASE. Deadline: August 1. Limited to works published or distributed in the UK for the first time between November 1, 1991 and October 31, 1992. Publisher's entry only. "May be fiction, nonfiction, poetry or drama. Not an anthology. The prize is not primarily for fiction though that is not excluded. Subject must be concerned with mountain environment. Previous winners have been books on expeditions, Himalayan experiences; a biography of a mountaineer; a novel."

BOOTS ROMANTIC NOVEL OF THE YEAR, (II, IV), 38 Stanhope Rd., Reading, Berks RG2 7HN England. Contact: Mrs. Betty O'Rourke, Award Organiser, Romantic Novelists' Association. "To publish good romantic fiction and therefore raise the prestige of the genre." Annual competition for novels. Award: £5,000. Competition receives approx. 100 submissions. Judges: A panel of experienced writers. Deadline: September 1-December 1. Previously published submissions. For novels "published in the U.K. only. A modern or historical (before 1950) romantic novel. Three copies of each entry are required. They may be hardback or paperback. Only novels written in English and published in the U.K. during the relevant year are eligible. Authors must be domiciled in U.K. or temporarily living abroad whilst in possession of British passport."

BOSTON GLOBE-HORN BOOK AWARDS, (II), *Boston Globe* Newspaper, Horn Book Awards, *Horn Book* Magazine, 14 Beacon St., Boston MA 02108. Annual award. "To honor most outstanding children's fiction or poetry, picture and nonfiction books published within the U.S." Award: $500 first prize in each category; silver plate for the 2 honor books in each category. No entry fee. Entry forms or rules for SASE. Deadline: May 15. Previously published material from June 30-May 31 of previous year.

BRANDEIS UNIVERSITY CREATIVE ARTS AWARDS, (III), Brandeis University, Irving Enclave, Commission Office, Waltham MA 02254-9110. (617)736-3007. Special Assistants to the President: Mary R. Anderson and Suzanne Yates. Awards "medal to an established artist in celebration of a lifetime of achievement, and a citation to an individual in an earlier stage of his or her career. From time to time the Creative Arts Awards Commission bestows the Notable Achievement Award, when in the Commission's judgment there is someone whose accomplishments so transcend the normal categories that special recognition is due." Awards are made by internal selection only.

BRAZOS BOOKSTORE (HOUSTON) AWARD (SINGLE SHORT STORY), (II, IV), The Texas Institute of Letters, P.O. Box 9032, Wichita Falls TX 76308. (817)692-6611 ext. 4123. Awards Coordinator: James Hoggard. Award to "honor the writer of the best short story published for the first time during the calendar year before the award is given." Annual competition for short stories. Award: $500. Competition receives approx. 40-50 submissions. Judges: Panel selected by TIL Council. Guidelines for SASE. Deadline: January 4. Previously published submissions. Published entries must have appeared in print between January 1 and December 31 of the year prior to the award. "Award available to writers who, at some time, have lived in Texas at least two years consecutively or whose work has a significant Texas theme. Entries must be sent directly to the three judges. Their names and addresses are available from the TIL office. Include SASE."

‡BREVILOQUENCE, (I, IV), *Writer's NW,* 24450 NW Hansen Rd., Hillsboro OR 97124. (503)621-3911. Contact: L. Stovall. "To create—with 99 words or less—a story with all the important elements of the form. Only open to writers in NW—OR, WA, AK, ID, MT and British Columbia." Annual competition for short stories. Award: Books—usually reference. Judges: Editors of newspaper. Entry fee $1. Deadline: May 1. Unpublished submissions.

BUMBERSHOOT WRITTEN WORKS COMPETITION, (I), Seattle's Arts Festival, Box 9750, Seattle WA 98109-0750. (206)622-5123. Annual award for short stories. Award: Six awards of $150 for poetry or literary prose. Winners published in Bumbershoot arts magazine, *Ergo*! and invited to read at Bumbershoot Festival. Judges are professional writers/publishers. Entry forms or rules for SASE. Deadline: Late February.

BUNTING INSTITUTE FELLOWSHIP, (I), Mary Ingraham Bunting Institute of Radcliffe College, 34 Concord Ave., Cambridge MA 02138. (617)495-8212. Deadline: October 15. Women scholars, creative writers, and visual and performing artists are eligible. Scholars must have held the Ph.D. or appropriate terminal degree at least two years prior to appointment (September 1). Non-academic applicants, such as artists, writers, social workers, lawyers, journalists, etc., need to have a significant record of accomplishment and professional experience equivalent to a doctorate and some post-doctoral work. For example, artists must have participated in some group and/or one-person shows; writers must have some published work; other professionals must have some years of work in their respective fields after the appropriate degree. Award: $28,500 stipend for a one-year appointment, September 1-August 31. Private office or studio space is provided, along with access to most Harvard/Radcliffe resources. Fellows are required to present a public lecture or reading in the Institute Colloquium Series or an exhibition in the Institute gallery. Bunting fellows are required to be in residence in the Cambridge/Boston area for the entire term of appointment. "We do not provide housing." Number of fellowships awarded: 6-8. Applications go through three-stage selection process. In the first stage applications are reviewed by an individual reader in the applicant's field. (Creative writing and visual arts applications go to a relevant first stage committee—i.e., fiction, sculpture, etc.) All applications then go to a second stage committee in the applicant's field (i.e., psychology, literature, etc.), which chooses a small number of finalists. Fellows are chosen from the finalist group by an interdisciplinary final selection committee. Applications are judged on the significance and quality of the project proposal, the applicant's record of accomplishment, and on the difference the fellowship might make in advancing the applicant's career. Rejection letters are sent on a rolling basis, but should be received no later than the beginning of April. Finalists will be notified during the months of January and February. Fellows and alternates will be notified in the beginning of April. "We request that you provide us with the names of your three intended recommenders on the Summary Application Information sheet. We will send you the required forms with your letter of notification and you are requested to have your recommenders send their letters directly to us. We will not contact your recommenders."

BURNABY WRITERS' SOCIETY ANNUAL COMPETITION, (I, IV), 6450 Gilpin St., Burnaby, British Columbia V5G 2J3 Canada. (604)435-6500. Annual competition to encourage creative writing in British Columbia. "Category varies from year to year." Award: $100, $50 and $25 prizes. Receives 400-600 entries for each award. Judge: "Independent recognized professional in the field." Entry fee $5. Contest requirements for SASE. Deadline: May 31. Open to British Columbia authors only.

BUSH ARTIST FELLOWSHIPS, (I, IV), The Bush Foundation, E-900 First Nat'l Bank Building, 332 Minnesota St., St. Paul MN 55101. (612)227-5222. Contact: Sally Dixon, Program Director. "To provide artists of exemplary talent time to work in their chosen art forms." Annual grant. Award: Stipend maximum of $26,000 for 6-18 months, plus a production and travel allowance of $7,000. Competition receives approximately 550 submissions. Judges are writers, critics and editors from outside MN, SD, ND or WI. Applicants must be at least 25 years old, and Minnesota, South Dakota, North Dakota or Western Wisconsin residents. Students not eligible.

***BYLINE* MAGAZINE LITERARY AWARDS, (I, IV),** Box 130596, Edmond OK 73013. (405)348-5591. Exec. Editor/Publisher: Marcia Preston. "To encourage our subscribers in striving for high quality writing." Annual awards for short stories and poetry. Award: $250 in each category. Judges are published writers not on the *Byline* staff. Entry fee $5 for stories; $2 for poems. Postmark deadline: December 1. "Entries should be unpublished and not have won money in any previous contest. Winners announced in February issue and published in March issue with photo and short bio. Open to subscribers only."

CALIFORNIA WRITERS' CLUB CONTEST, (I, IV), California Writers' Club, 2214 Derby St., Berkeley CA 94705. (415)841-1217. Awards "to encourage writing." Prizes are free tuition to biennial writers' conference and cash. Competition receives varying number of submissions. Judges: Professional writers, members of California Writers' Club. Entry fee $5. For the contest rules, write to the Secretary. Deadline is mid-April. Next conference will be July 1993. Unpublished submissions. "Open to anyone who is not, nor has ever been, a member of California Writers' Club."

JOHN W. CAMPBELL MEMORIAL AWARD FOR THE BEST SCIENCE-FICTION NOVEL OF THE YEAR; THEODORE STURGEON MEMORIAL AWARD FOR THE BEST SF SHORT FICTION, (II, III), Center for the Study of Science Fiction, English Dept., University of Kansas, Lawrence KS 66045. (913)864-3380. Professor and Director: James Gunn. "To honor the best novel and short science fiction of the year." Annual competition for short stories and novels. Award: Certificate. "Winners' names are engraved on a trophy." Competition receives approx. 50-100 submissions. Judges: 2 separate juries. Deadline: May 1. For previously published submissions. "Ordinarily publishers should submit work, but authors have done so when publishers would not. Send for list of jurors."

CANADA COUNCIL AWARDS, (III, IV), Canada Council, Box 1047, 99 Metcalfe St., Ottawa, Ontario K1P 5V8 Canada. (613)598-4365. The Canada Council sponsors the following awards, for which no applications are accepted. *Canada-Australia Literary Prize*: 1 prize of $3,000, awarded in alternate years

Market categories: (I) Unpublished entries; (II) Published entries nominated by the author; (III) Published entries, nominated by the editor, publisher or nominating body; (IV) Specialized entries.

to an Australian or Canadian writer for the author's complete work; *Canada-French Community of Belgium Literary Prize*: 1 prize of $2,500, awarded in alternate years to a Canadian or Belgian writer on the basis of the complete works of the writer; *Canada-Switzerland Literary Prize*: 1 prize of $2,500, awarded in alternate years to a Canadian or Swiss writer for a work published in French during the preceding 8 years.

CANADA COUNCIL GOVERNOR GENERAL'S LITERARY AWARDS, (IV), Canada Council, Box 1047, 99 Metcalfe St., Ottawa, Ontario K1P 5V8 Canada. (613)598-4376. Contact: Writing and publishing section. "Awards of $10,000 each are given annually to the best English-language and best French-language Canadian work in each of six categories: children's literature (text and illustration), drama, fiction, poetry, nonfiction and translation." All literary works published by Canadians between December 30, 1991 and October 1, 1992 are considered. Canadian authors, illustrators and translators only.

CANADIAN AUTHOR & BOOKMAN STUDENT'S CREATIVE WRITING CONTEST, (I, IV), Suite 500, 275 Slater St., Ottawa, Ontario K1P 5H9 Canada. (613)233-2846. FAX: (613)235-8237. "To encourage writing among secondary school students." Annual competition for short stories. Award: $100 plus $100 to the nominating teacher; $500 to pay for undergraduate education to a worthy student enrolled at a college. Receives 100-120 submissions. Judges: Magazine editors. "Entry form in Winter and Spring issues." Deadline: March. Unpublished submissions. Length: 2,500 words. Writer must be nominated by teacher.

CANADIAN AUTHORS ASSOCIATION LITERARY AWARDS (FICTION), (II, IV), Canadian Authors Association, Suite 500, 275 Slater St., Ottawa, Ontario K1P 5H9 Canada. (613)233-2846. FAX: (613)235-8237. Contact: Executive Director. Annual award "to honor writing that achieves literary excellence without sacrificing popular appeal." For novels published during the previous calendar year. Award: $5,000 plus silver medal. No entry fee. Entry forms or rules for SASE. Deadline: December 15. Restricted to full-length English language novels. Author must be Canadian or Canadian landed immigrant. CAA also sponsors the Air Canada Award, literary awards as above in poetry, nonfiction and drama, and the Vicky Metcalf Awards for children's literature.

CANADIAN FICTION MAGAZINE **CONTRIBUTOR'S PRIZE, (IV),** Box 946, Station F, Toronto, Ontario M4Y 2N9 Canada. Contact: Geoffrey Hancock, editor-in-chief. Annual award to celebrate the best story published by *CFM* in either French or English during the preceding year. Contributors must reside in Canada or be Canadians living abroad. Award: $500, public announcement, photograph. All manuscripts published in *CFM* are eligible. Deadline: August 15. "Looking for contemporary creative writing of the highest possible literary standards."

CANADIAN LIBRARY ASSOCIATION BOOK OF THE YEAR FOR CHILDREN AWARD, (III, IV), Canadian Library Association, 200 Elgin St., Ottawa, Ontario K2P 1L5 Canada. (613)232-9625. "To encourage the writing in Canada of good books for children up to and including age 14." Annual competition for short stories and novels for children. Award: A specially designed medal. Competition receives approx. 10-20 submissions/year. Judges: CLA Book of the Year Award Committee. Guidelines for SASE. Deadline: February 1. Book must have been published in Canada during the last year and its author must be Canadian citizen or landed immigrant. Nominations are generally made by CLA membership – a call for nominations is posted in the Association's newsletter in October. "Although the award is sponsored by the Canadian Library Association, it is the Canadian Association of Children's Librarians (a section of Canadian Association of Public Libraries which in turn is a division of CLA) which staffs the Award Committee, selects the winner and administers the award."

RAYMOND CARVER SHORT STORY CONTEST, (I), Dept. of English, Humboldt State University, Arcata CA 95521-4957. Contact: Coordinator. Annual award for previously unpublished short stories. First prize: $500 and publication in *Toyon 91*. Second Prize: $250. Entry fee $7.50/story. SASE for rules. Deadline: November. For authors living in United States only. Send 2 copies of story; author's name, address, phone number and title of story on separate cover page only. Story must be no more than 25 pages. Title must appear on first page. For notification of receipt of ms, include self-addressed stamped postcard. For Winners List include SASE.

‡**THE** *CHELSEA* **AWARDS, (I),** Box 5880, Grand Central Station, New York NY 10163. *Mail entries to:* Richard Foerster, Associate Editor, P.O. Box 1040, York Beach ME 03910. Annual competition for short stories. Prize: $500 and publication in *Chelsea* (all entries are considered for publication). Judges:

The editors. Entry fee: $10 (for which entrants also receive a subscription). Guidelines for SASE. Deadline: June 15. Unpublished submissions. Manuscripts may not exceed 30 typed pages or about 7,500 words. The stories must not be under consideration elsewhere or scheduled for book publication within 6 months of the competition deadline.

THE CHILDREN'S BOOK AWARD, (II), Federation of Children's Book Groups, 30 Senneleys Park Rd., Northfield, Birmingham B31 1AL England. Award "to promote the publication of good quality books for children." Annual award for short stories, novels, story collections and translations. Award: "Portfolio of children's writing and drawings and a magnificent trophy of silver and oak." Judges: Thousands of children from all over the United Kingdom. Guidelines for SASE. Deadline: December 31. Published and previously unpublished submissions (first publication in UK). "The book should be suitable for children."

THE CHRISTOPHER AWARD, (II), The Christophers, 12 E. 48th St., New York NY 10017. (212)759-4050. Contact: Ms. Peggy Flanagan, awards coordinator. Annual award "to encourage creative people to continue to produce works which affirm the highest values of the human spirit in adult and children's books." Published submissions only. Award: Bronze medallion. "Award judged by a grassroots panel and a final panel of experts. Juvenile works are 'children tested.' " Examples of books awarded: *Dear Mr. Henshaw,* by Beverly Cleary (ages 8-10); *Sarah, Plain and Tall,* by Patricia MacLachlan (ages 10-12).

CINTAS FELLOWSHIP, (I, IV), Cintas Foundation/Arts International Program of I.I.E., 809 U.N. Plaza, New York NY 10017. (212)984-5564. Contact: Vanessa Palmer. "To foster and encourage the professional development and recognition of talented Cuban creative artists. *Not* intended for furtherance of academic or professional study, nor for research or writings of a scholarly nature." Annual competition for authors of short stories, novels, story collections and poetry. 12 awards of $10,000 each. Fellowship receives approx. 40 literature applicants/year. Judges: Selection committee. Guidelines for SASE. Deadline: March 2. Previously published or unpublished submissions. Limited to artists of Cuban lineage *only.* "Awards are given to artists in the following fields: visual arts, literature, music composition and architecture."

CITY OF REGINA WRITING AWARD, (I, IV), City of Regina Arts Commission, Saskatchewan Writers Guild, Box 3986, Regina, Saskatchewan S4P 3R9 Canada. (306)757-6310. "To enable a writer to work for 3 months on a specific writing project; to reward merit in writing." Annual competition for short stories, novels and story collections. Award: $3,300. Competition receives approx. 21 submissions. Judges: Selection committee of SWG. Guidelines for SASE. Deadline: Mid-March. Unpublished submissions. "Grant available only to residents of Regina for previous year."

COLORADO COUNCIL ON THE ARTS & HUMANITIES CREATIVE FELLOWSHIP, (I, II, IV), 770 Pennsylvania St., Denver CO 80203. (303)866-2617. Director, Individual Artist Programs: Daniel Salazar. "To provide both recognition and financial support to Colorado's outstanding individual artists and to provide a forum and secure an audience for the promotion of their work." Award presented on rotating basis (in 1992, 1995 and 1998). Award: 16 fellowships of $4,000 each. Competition receives 350 entries/year. Judges: Peer panels. Guidelines for SASE. For either previously published or unpublished manuscripts. Colorado residents only.

COLUMBIA MAGAZINE **EDITORS AWARDS, (I),** *Columbia; A Magazine of Poetry and Prose,* Writing Division, 404 Dodge Hall, Columbia University NY 10027. Contact: Fiction Editors. Semiannual awards for short stories and sections of novels, unpublished. First prize is $350; second prize is $150; both include publication. Entry fee $6, made payable to *Columbia Magazine.* SASE for rules/entry forms. Deadlines: Spring: December 15; Fall: April 15. "Submissions can be no more than 25 pages; include SASE."

COMMONWEALTH CLUB OF CALIFORNIA, (II, IV), California Book Awards, 595 Market St., San Francisco CA 94105. (415)543-3353. Contact: James D. Rosenthal, Executive Director. Main contest established in 1931. Annually. Purpose: "To encourage California writers and honor literary merit." Awards: Gold and silver medals. Judges: Jury of literary experts. For books published during the year preceding the particular contest. Three copies of book and a completed entry form required. "Write or phone asking for the forms. Either an author or publisher may enter a book. We usually receive over 200 entries."

CONNECTICUT COMMISSION ON THE ARTS ARTIST GRANTS, (I, II, IV), 227 Lawrence St., Hartford CT 06106. (203)566-4770. Senior Program Associate: Linda Dente. "To support the creation of new work by a creative artist *living in Connecticut.*" Biannual competition for the creation or completion of new works in literature, i.e. short stories, novels, story collections, poetry and playwriting. Award: $5,000. Judges: Peer professionals (writers, editors). Guidelines available in August. Deadline: January. Writers may send either previously published or unpublished submissions—up to 25 pages of material. Connecticut residents only.

CONSEIL DE LA VIE FRANCAISE EN AMÉRIQUE/PRIX CHAMPLAIN (The Champlain Prize), (II, IV), Conseil de la vie française en amérique, Bureau 301, 56 rue St-Pierre Étage, Québec, Québec G1K 4A1 Canada. Prix Champlain estab. 1957. Annual award to encourage literary work in novel or short story in French by Francophiles living outside Québec and in the US or Canada. "There is no restriction as to the subject matter. If the author lives in Quebec, the subject matter must be related to French-speaking people living outside of Quebec." Award: $1,500 in Canadian currency. The prize will be given alternately; one year for fiction, the next for nonfiction. Next fiction award in 1993. Judges: 3 different judges each year. Deadline: December 31. For previously published or contracted submissions, published no more than 3 years prior to award. Author must furnish 4 examples of work, curriculum vitae, address and phone number.

CRIME WRITERS' ASSOCIATION AWARDS, (III, IV), Box 172, Tring Herts HP23 5LP England. Six awards. Annual award for crime novels. Competition receives varied amount of submissions. Deadline: October 1. Published submissions in UK in current year. Book must be nominated by UK publishers.

‡THE *CRUCIBLE* POETRY AND FICTION COMPETITION, *Crucible,* Barton College, College Station, Wilson NC 27893. Annual competition for short stories. Award: $150 for first prize; $100 for second prize and publication in *Crucible.* Judges: The editors. Guidelines for SASE. Deadline April. Unpublished submissions. Fiction should be 8,000 words or less.

‡DALY CITY POETRY AND SHORT STORY CONTEST, (I), Daly City History, Arts, and Science Commission, % Serramonte Library, 40 Wembley Dr., Daly City CA 94015. (415)991-8025. Contest coordinator: Ruth Hoppin. "To encourage poets and writers and to recognize and reward excellence." Annual competition for short stories. Awards: $35, $20, $10 and $5. Competition receives 50 submissions. Judges are usually teachers of creative writing. Entry fee: $2/story. Guidelines for SASE. Deadline Jan. 2. Unpublished submissions. Length: 3,000 words maximum. "No profanity."

DEEP SOUTH WRITERS CONFERENCE ANNUAL COMPETITION, (I), DSWC Inc., English Dept., University of Southwestern Louisiana, Box 44691, Lafayette LA 70504. (318)231-6908. Contact: John Fiero, director. Annual awards "to encourage aspiring, unpublished writers." Awards: Certificates and cash plus possible publication of shorter works. Contest rules for SASE and addition to mailing list. Deadline: July 15. Unpublished submissions.

DELACORTE PRESS ANNUAL PRIZE FOR A FIRST YOUNG ADULT NOVEL (I), Delacorte Press, Department BFYR, 666 Fifth Ave., New York NY 10103. (212)765-6500. Contact: Lisa Oldenburg. Estab. 1983. Annual award "to encourage the writing of contemporary young adult fiction." Award: Contract for publication of book; $1,500 cash prize and a $6,000 advance against royalties. Judges are the editors of Delacorte Press Books for Young Readers. Contest rules for SASE. Unpublished submissions; fiction with a contemporary setting in the United States or Canada that will be suitable for ages 12-18. Deadline: December 31 (no submissions accepted prior to Labor Day).

DELAWARE STATE ARTS COUNCIL, (I, IV), 820 N. French St., Wilmington DE 19801. (302)577-3540. Coordinator: Barbara R. King. "To help further careers of emerging and established professional artists." Annual awards for Delaware residents only. Awards: $5,000 for established professionals; $2,000 for emerging professionals. Judges are out-of-state professionals in each division. Entry forms or rules for SASE. Deadline: March 2.

JOHN DOS PASSOS PRIZE FOR LITERATURE, (III, IV), Longwood College, Farmville VA 23901. (804)395-2155. "The John Dos Passos Prize for Literature annually commemorates one of the greatest of 20th-century American authors by honoring other writers in his name." Award: A medal and $1,000. "The winner, announced each fall in ceremonies at the college, is chosen by an independent jury charged especially to seek out American creative writers in the middle stages of their careers—men

GET YOUR WORK INTO THE RIGHT BUYERS' HANDS!

You work hard... and your hard work deserves to be seen by the right buyers. But with the constant changes in the industry, it's not always easy to know who those buyers are. That's why you'll want to keep up-to-date and on top with the most current edition of this indispensable market guide.

Keep ahead of the changes by ordering *1993 Novel & Short Story Writer's Market* today. You'll save the frustration of getting manuscripts returned in the mail, stamped MOVED: ADDRESS UNKNOWN. And of NOT submitting your work to new listings because you don't know they exist. All you have to do to order the upcoming 1993 edition is complete the attched post card and return it with your payment or charge card information. Order now, and here's one thing that won't change from your *1993 Novel & Short Story Writer's Market* - the price! That's right, we'll send you the 1993 edition for just $19.95. *1993 Novel & Short Story Writer's Market* will be published and ready for shipment in February 1993.

Don't let another opportunity slip by…get a jump on the industry with the help of *1993 Novel & Short Story Writer's Market*. Order today!
You deserve it!

(See other side for more books to help you get published)

More Books to Help You Get Published!

SAVE 15% ON THESE NEW WRITING BOOKS!

1992 Guide to Literary Agents & Art/Photo Reps
edited by Robin Gee
This new directory lists agents and reps across North America, plus answers the most-often asked questions in 12 articles by industry professionals. 400 listings are organized into literary agents, script agents and art/photo reps. 240 pages/$15.95 $13.55/hardcover

The Fiction Writer's Silent Partner
by Martin Roth
How would you like a collaborator who doesn't want a cent? This new book provides thousands of idea-sparkers, facts, possibilities and "what ifs" on topics from believable characters to vivid locales and unusual themes. 320 pages/$19.95 $16.95/hardcover

The Writer's Essential Desk Reference
edited by Glenda Tennant Neff
This practical, hands-on reference tool for writers covers virtually every aspect of the writing business and the writing life, from legal services to tax laws to how to self-publish. 368 pages/$19.95 $16.95/hardcover

Use coupon on otherside to order today!

and women who have established a substantial body of significant publication, and particularly those whose work demonstrates one or more of the following qualities, all characteristics of the art of the man for whom the prize is named: an intense and original exploration of specifically American themes; an experimental tone; and/or writing in a wide range of literature forms." Application for prize is by nomination only.

DREAMS & VISIONS: BEST SHORT STORY OF THE YEAR, (I, IV), Skysong Press, RR1, Washago, Ontario L0K 2B0 Canada. Contact: Steve Stanton. The "competition serves the dual purpose of rewarding literary excellence among the authors published in *Dreams & Visions*, and of providing feedback from subscribers as to the type of literature they prefer." Annual award for short stories. Award: $100. "Only the 2⊘ ⌐ries published in *Dreams & Visions* each year are eligible for the award." Judges: Subscribers to *Dreams & Visions*. Guidelines for SASE. Unpublished submissions.

EATON LITERARY ASSOCIATES' LITERARY AWARDS PROGRAM, (I), Eaton Literary Associates, Box 49795, Sarasota FL 34230. (813)366-6589. Vice President: Richard Lawrence. Biannual award for short stories and novels. Award: $2,500 for best book-length ms, $500 for best short story. Competition receives approximately 2,000 submissions annually. Judges are 2 staff members in conjunction with an independent agency. Entry forms or rules for SASE. Deadline is March 31 for short stories; August 31 for book-length mss.

EDMONTON JOURNAL'S LITERARY AWARDS, (I, IV), *Edmonton Journal*, Box 2421, Edmonton, Alberta T5J 2S6 Canada. (403)429-5174. Contact: Dave Reidie, community relations and promotions, manager. Annual award "to recognize novice writers in our circulation area; promote writing and reading; establish goodwill in the community." Award changes annually. SASE for guidelines. Unpublished submissions.

EYSTER PRIZES, (II), *The New Delta Review*, LSU/Dept. of English, Baton Rouge LA 70803. (504)388-5922. Editor: Janet Wondra. "To honor author and teacher Warren Eyster, who served as advisor to *New Delta Review* predecessors *Manchac* and *Delta*." Semiannual awards for best short story and best poem in each issue. Award: $50 and 2 free copies of publication. Competition receives approximately 400 submissions/issue. Judges are published authors. Deadline: September 30 for fall, March 1 for spring.

ROBERT L. FISH MEMORIAL AWARD, (II), Mystery Writers of America, Inc., 6th Floor, 17 E. 47th St., New York NY 10017. Estab. 1984. Annual award "to encourage new writers in the mystery/detective/suspense short story—and, subsequently, larger work in the genre." Award: $500. Judges: The MWA committee for best short story of the year in the mystery genre. Deadline: December 1. Previously published submissions published the year prior to the award. Looking for "a story with a crime that is central to the plot that is well written and distinctive."

DOROTHY CANFIELD FISHER AWARD, (III), Vermont Congress of Parents and Teachers, % Southwest Regional Library, Pierpoint Avenue, Rutland VT 05701. Contact: Gail Furnas, chairperson. Estab. 1957. Annual award. "To encourage Vermont schoolchildren to become enthusiastic and discriminating readers and to honor the memory of one of Vermont's most distinguished and beloved literary figures." Award: Illuminated scroll. Publishers send the committee review copies of books to consider. Only books of the current publishing year can be considered for next year's award. Master list of titles is drawn up in late February or March each year. Children vote each year in the spring and the award is given before the school year ends. Submissions must be "written by living American authors, be suitable for children in grades 4-8, and have literary merit. Can be nonfiction also."

FLORIDA ARTS COUNCIL/LITERATURE FELLOWSHIPS, (I, IV), Division of Cultural Affairs, Dept. of State, The Capitol, Tallahassee FL 32399-0250. (904)487-2980. Director: Ms. Peyton C. Fearington. "To allow Florida artists time to develop their artistic skills and enhance their careers." Annual award for fiction or poetry. Award: $5,000. Competition receives approximately 100 submissions/year. Judges are review panels made up of individuals with a demonstrated interest in literature. Entry forms for

Read the Business of Fiction section to learn the correct way to prepare and submit a manuscript.

SASE. Deadline: January 17. Entry restricted to practicing, professional writers who are legal residents of Florida and have been living in the state for 12 consecutive months at the time of the deadline.

FLORIDA STATE WRITING COMPETITION, (I), Florida Freelance Writers Association, Box 9844, Fort Lauderdale FL 33310. (305)485-0795. "To offer additional opportunities for writers to earn income from their stories." Annual competition for short stories and novels. Award: Varies from $50-150. Competition receives approx. 300 short stories; 125 novels. Judges: Authors, editors and teachers. Entry fee from $5-15. Guidelines for SASE. Deadline: March 15. Unpublished submissions. Categories include literary, sf/fantasy, genre and novel chapter. Length: 7,500 words maximum. "Guidelines are revised each year and subject to change."

FOUNDATION FOR THE ADVANCEMENT OF CANADIAN LETTERS AUTHOR'S AWARDS, (II, IV), In conjunction with Periodical Marketers of Canada (PMC), Suite 400, 20 Toronto St., Toronto, Ontario M5C 2B8 Canada. (416)363-4549. Award Coordinators: Ray Argyle, Marjory Dunstan. "To recognize outstanding Canadian writing and design." Annual award for short stories, novels. Previous competition judged by an independent panel. Deadline: July 15. "Must be published in a Canadian 'mass market' publication."

‡MILES FRANKLIN LITERARY AWARD, (II, IV), Arts Management Pty. Ltd., 56 Kellett St., Potts Point, NSW 2011 Australia. Awards Coordinator: Kate Gralton. "For the advancement, improvement and betterment of Australian literature." Annual award for novels. Award: AUS $25,000, to the author. Guidelines for SASE. Deadline: Jan. 31. Previously published submissions. "The novel must have been published in the year of competition entry, and must present Australian life in any of its phases."

‡GEORGIA COUNCIL FOR THE ARTS INDIVIDUAL ARTIST GRANTS, (I, IV), Suite 100, 2082 E. Exchange Place, Tucker GA 30084. (404)493-5780. Contact: Martha Evans. Annual award for "artist's option for creation of new work." Award: $5,000 maximum. Competition receives approx. 125 submissions. Judges: Professional advisory panel. Guidelines for SASE. Deadline April 1. "Support material must be current within past two years; application must be for new work. Artist must be resident of Georgia for at least one year prior to application date."

GOLD MEDALLION BOOK AWARDS, (III, IV), Evangelical Christian Publishers Association, Suite 101, 3225 S. Hardy Dr., Tempe AZ 85282. (602)966-3998. Executive Director of ECPA: Doug Ross. Annual award to "encourage excellence in evangelical Christian book publishing in 21 categories." Judges: "At least eight judges for each category chosen from among the ranks of evangelical leaders and book-review editors." Entry fee $75 for ECPA member publishers; $175 for non-member publishers. Deadline: December 1. For books published the previous year: Publishers submit entries.

GOODMAN FIELDER WATTIE BOOK AWARD, (III, IV), Goodman Fielder Wattie Industries/Ltd., Book Publishers Association of New Zealand (BPANZ), Box 386, Auckland, New Zealand. Contact: Paul Greene, Convenor, GFW Committee. "To recognize excellence in writing and publishing books by New Zealanders. This is not a category award. Fiction/nonfiction/children's etc. are all included." Award: 1st: NZ$20,000; 2nd: NZ$10,000; 3rd: NZ$5,000. Competition receives approx. 80-90 submissions. Judges: Panel of 3 selected annually by the BPANZ—1 writer, 1 book trade person and 1 other. Entry fee NZ$65. Guidelines for SASE. Deadline: April 5. "Writer must be New Zealander or resident of New Zealand and its former Pacific territories. Must be submitted by publisher. Fuller details available from BPANZ."

‡THE WILLIAM GOYEN PRIZE FOR FICTION, (I), *TriQuarterly Magazine*, 2020 Ridge Ave., Evanston IL 60208-4302. (708)491-7614. Editorial Assistant: Misty Neal. "To award outstanding fiction; to bring recognition to newer/lesser-known writers." Biennial award for novels. Award: $3,000 and publication by TriQuarterly Books/Another Chicago Press. Competition receives approx. 250 submissions. Entry fee $15, includes 1-year subscription; $5 for current subscribers. Guidelines for SASE. Deadline: June 1-30, 1993 (prize not offered in 1992). "Mss should be 150-400 pages in length, double-spaced. Original works in English and translations into English are eligible. Enclose SASE for return of your manuscript and our reply. Entry fee subject to change."

LES GRANDS PRIX DU *JOURNAL DE MONTRÉAL*, (I, IV), Union des écrivaines et écrivains Québécois, #510, 1030 rue Cherrier, Montréal, Québec H2L 1H9 Canada. (514)526-6653. "To support the development of the literature of Québec and assure the public recognition of its authors." Three annual awards, one each for prose, poetry and theater. Award: $1,500 each (Canadian). Judges: 5 judges, nominated by the *Journal de Montréal*. Guidelines for SASE. Deadline: June 10. For books published within the 12 months preceding June 1. Writers must have published at least 3 books of literary creation including the one already submitted and must submit 6 copies of the work to be considered. Write for rules and entry form (in French).

GREAT LAKES COLLEGES ASSOCIATION NEW WRITERS AWARDS, (III), Great Lakes Colleges Association, Antioch College, Yellow Springs OH 45387. Director: Eric Horsting. Annual award "to recognize new young writers; promote and encourage interest in good literature." For books published "during the year preceding each year's February 28 deadline for entry, or the following spring." Award: "Invited tour of up to 12 Great Lakes Colleges (usually 7 or 8) with honoraria and expenses paid." Award judged by critics and writers in residence at Great Lakes Colleges Association colleges and universities. Entry form or rules for SASE. "Entries in fiction (there is also a poetry section) must be first novels or first volumes of short stories already published, and must be submitted (four copies) *by publishers only*—but this may include privately published books."

GREAT PLAINS STORYTELLING & POETRY READING CONTEST, (I,II), Box 438, Walnut IA 51577. (712)784-3001. Director: Robert Everhart. Estab. 1976. Annual award "to provide an outlet for writers to present not only their works, but also to provide a large audience for their presentation *live* by the writer. Attendance at the event, which takes place annually in Avoca, Iowa, is *required*." Award: 1st prize $75; 2nd prize $50; 3rd prize $25; 4th prize $15; and 5th prize $10. Entry fee: $5. Entry forms or rules for SASE. Deadline: Day of contest, which takes place over Labor Day Weekend. Previously published or unpublished submissions.

THE GREENSBORO REVIEW LITERARY AWARDS, (I), Dept. of English, UNC-Greensboro, Greensboro NC 27412. (919)334-5459. Editor: Jim Clark. Annual award. Award: $250. Contest rules for SASE. Deadline: September 15. Unpublished submissions.

GUARDIAN CHILDREN'S FICTION AWARD, (III, IV), The Guardian, 119 Farringdon Rd., London EC1R 3ER England. Contact: Stephanie Nettell, children's books editor. "To recognize an outstanding work of children's fiction—and gain publicity for the field of children's books." Annual competition for fiction. Award: £500. Competition receives approx. 100 submissions. Judges: 4 eminent children's writers plus children's books editor of the *Guardian*. Deadline: December 31. "British or Commonwealth authors only; published in UK; no picture books. Awarded every March for book published in previous year."

HACKNEY LITERARY AWARDS, (I), Box A-3, Birmingham Southern College, Birmingham AL 35254. (205)226-4921. Contact: Special Events Office. Annual award for previously unpublished short stories, poetry and novels. Rules/entry form for SASE. Deadline for submitting a novel—must be postmarked on or before September 30. Deadline for submitting short stories or poetry—must be postmarked on or before December 31.

‡BAXTER HATHAWAY PRIZE, (I), *Epoch Magazine*, 251 Goldwin Smith, Cornell University, Ithaca NY 14853-3201. (607)255-3385. Contact: Ed Hardy. Award "to honor the memory of Baxter Hathaway, founder of *Epoch*, and to encourage new poets and fiction writers." Biennial award for a novella or long poem, depending on the year (1992, long poem; 1994, novella). Award: $1,000 and publication in *Epoch*. Competition receives 400+ submissions. Judge: A distinguished outsider. Guidelines for SASE. Sample copies with past winners for $4 each. Unpublished submissions. "Limited to writers who have published not more than one book of fiction or poetry (chapbooks excluded)."

DRUE HEINZ LITERATURE PRIZE, (II), University of Pittsburgh Press, 127 N. Bellefield Ave., Pittsburgh PA 15260. (412)624-4110. Annual award "to support the writer of short fiction at a time when the economics of commercial publishing make it more and more difficult for the serious literary artist working in the short story and novella to find publication." Award: $7,500 and publication by the University of Pittsburgh Press. Request complete rules of the competition before submitting a manuscript. Submissions will be received only during the months of July and August. Deadline: August 31. Manuscripts must be unpublished in book form. The award is open to writers who have published a book-length collection of fiction or a minimum of three short stories or novellas in commercial magazines or literary journals of national distribution.

HEMINGWAY DAYS SHORT STORY COMPETITION, (I), Hemingway Days Festival, Box 4045, Key West FL 33041. (305)294-4440. "To honor Nobel laureate Ernest Hemingway, who was often pursued during his lifetime by young writers hoping to learn the secrets of his success." Annual competition for short stories. Award: $1000 – 1st; $500 – 2nd; $500 – 3rd. Competition receives approx. 900 submissions. Judges: Panel lead by Lorian Hemingway, granddaughter of Ernest Hemingway and novelist based out of Seattle, WA. Entry fee $10/story. Guidelines for SASE. Deadline: July 6. "Open to anyone so long as the work is unpublished. No longer than 2,500 words."

ERNEST HEMINGWAY FOUNDATION AWARD, (II), PEN American Center, 568 Broadway, New York NY 10012. Contact: John Morrone, coordinator of programs. Annual award "to give beginning writers recognition and encouragement and to stimulate interest in first novels among publishers and readers." Award: $7,500. Novels or short story collections must have been published during calendar year under consideration. Entry form or rules for SASE. Deadline: December 31. "The Ernest Hemingway Foundation Award is given to an American author of the best first-published book-length work of fiction published by an established publishing house in the US each calendar year."

THE O. HENRY AWARDS, (III), Doubleday, 666 Fifth Ave., New York NY 10103. Assistant Editor: Arabella Meyer. Annual award "to honor the memory of O. Henry with a sampling of outstanding short stories and to make these stories better known to the public." These awards are published by Doubleday in hardcover and by Anchor Books in paperback every spring. Previously published submissions. "All selections are made by the editor of the volume, William Abrahams. No stories may be submitted."

HIGHLIGHTS FOR CHILDREN, (I, IV), 803 Church St., Honesdale PA 18431. Editor: Kent L. Brown, Jr. "To honor quality stories (previously unpublished) for young readers." Three $1,000 awards. Stories: up to 600 words for beginning readers (to age 8) and 900 words for more advanced readers (ages 9 to 12). No minimum word length. No entry form necessary. To be submitted between January 1 and February 28 to "Fiction Contest" at address above. "No violence, crime or derogatory humor." Nonwinning entries returned in June if SASE is included with ms. "This year's category is stories set in a country other than the United States or in an ethnic culture within the United States." Send SASE for information.

THE ALFRED HODDER FELLOWSHIP, (II), The Council of the Humanities, Princeton University, 122 E. Pyne, Princeton NJ 08544. "This fellowship is awarded for the pursuit of independent work in the humanities. The recipient is usually a writer or scholar in the early stages of his or her career, a person 'with more than ordinary learning' and with 'much more than ordinary intellectual and literary gifts.' " Traditionally, the Hodder Fellow has been a humanist outside of academia. Candidates for the Ph.D. are not eligible. Annual competition for short stories, novels, story collections and translations. Award: $38,000. The Hodder fellow spends an academic year in residence at Princeton working independently. Judges: Princeton Committee on Humanistic studies. Guidelines for SASE. Deadline November 15. "Applicants must submit a résumé, a sample of previous work (10 page maximum, not returnable), and a project proposal of 2 to 3 pages. Letters of recommendation are not required."

THEODORE CHRISTIAN HOEPFNER AWARD, (I), *Southern Humanities Review*, 9088 Haley Center, Auburn University AL 36849. Contact: Dan R. Latimer or R.T. Smith, co-editors. Annual award. "To award the authors of the best essay, the best short story and the best poem published in *SHR* each year." Award: $100 for the best short story. Judges: Editorial staff. Unpublished submissions to the magazine only. Only published work in the current volume (4 issues) will be judged.

***HONOLULU* MAGAZINE/PARKER PEN COMPANY FICTION CONTEST, (I, IV)**, *Honolulu* Magazine, 36 Merchant St., Honolulu HI 96813. (808)524-7400. Editor: Ed Cassidy. "We do not accept fiction except during our annual contest, at which time we welcome it." Annual award for short stories. Award: $1,000 and publication in the March issue of *Honolulu* Magazine. Competition receives approximately 400 submissions. Judges: Panel of well-known Hawaii-based writers. Rules for SASE. Deadline: December 9. "Stories must have a Hawaii theme, setting and/or characters. Author should enclose name and address in separate small envelope. Do not put name on story."

L. RON HUBBARD'S WRITERS OF THE FUTURE CONTEST, (I, IV), P.O. Box 1630, Los Angeles CA 90078. Estab. 1984. Quarterly. "To find, reward and publicize new speculative fiction writers, so that they may more easily attain professional writing careers." Competition open to new and amateur writers of short stories or novelettes of science fiction or fantasy. Awards: 1st prize, $1,000; 2nd prize, $750; 3rd prize, $500. Annual grand prize $4,000. SASE for contest rules. Deadline: September 30. Unpublished submissions.

THE 'HUGO' AWARD (Science Fiction Achievement Award), (III, IV), The World Science Fiction Convention, c/o Howard DeVore, 4705 Weddel St., Dearborn Heights MI 48125. Temporary; address changes each year. "To recognize the best writing in various categories related to science fiction and fantasy." Award: Metal spaceship 15 inches high. "Winning the award almost always results in reprints of the original material and increased payment. Winning a 'Hugo' in the novel category frequently results in additional payment of $10,000-20,000 from future publishers." The award is voted on by ballot by the members of the World Science Fiction Convention from previously published material of professional publications. Writers may not nominate their own work.

HUTTON FICTION CONTEST, (I), Hutton Publications, Box 1870, Hayden ID 83835. (208)772-6184. "To encourage beginning short story writers." Granted 5 times/year; more often if interest warrants for short stories. Award: Up to $50; publication of winners. Competition receives no more than 50 submissions. Judge: Linda Hutton, editor of Hutton Publications. Entry fee $1-3. (December contest has no fee.) Guidelines for #10 SASE. Deadlines: First of March, June, August, November and December. Unpublished submissions.

ILLINOIS STATE UNIVERSITY NATIONAL FICTION COMPETITION, (I), Illinois State University/Fiction Collective, English Dept., Illinois State University, Normal IL 61761. (309)438-3025. Curtis White, series editor. Annual award for novels, novellas and story collections. Award: Publication. Competition receives approximately 150 submissions each year. Judges different each year. Entry fee $10. Entry forms or rules for SASE.

INTERNATIONAL JANUSZ KORCZAK LITERARY COMPETITION, (II, IV), Joseph H. and Belle R. Braun Center for Holocaust Studies Anti-Defamation League of B'nai B'rith, 823 United Nations Plaza, New York NY 10017. (212)490-2525. Contact: Dr. Dennis B. Klein, director. For published novels, novellas, translations, short story collections. "Books for or about children which best reflect the humanitarianism and leadership of Janusz Korczak, a Jewish and Polish physician, educator and author." Deadline: Inquire.

INTERNATIONAL READING ASSOCIATION CHILDREN'S BOOK AWARDS, (II), Sponsored by IRA/Institute for Reading Research, Box 8139, 800 Barksdale Rd., Newark DE 19714-8139. (302)731-1600. Annual award to encourage an author who shows unusual promise in the field of children's books. Two awards will be given for a first or second book in two categories: one for literature for older children, 10-16 years old; one for literature for younger children, 4-10 years old. Award: $1,000 stipend. No entry fee. Contest/award rules and awards flyer available for IRA. Deadline: December 1. Submissions must have been published during the calendar year prior to the year in which the award is given. Send 10 copies of book to Eileen Burke, 48 Bayberry Rd., Trenton NJ 08618.

IOWA LITERARY AWARDS, (I, IV), Iowa Arts Council, Capitol Complex, Des Moines IA 50319. (515)281-4451. Director of Partnership Programs: Julie Bailey. Estab. 1984. "To give exposure to Iowa's fine poets and fiction writers." Award: 1st prize, $1,000; 2nd prize, $500. Contest rules for SASE. Deadline: January 15. Unpublished submissions by legal residents of Iowa only.

IOWA SCHOOL OF LETTERS AWARD FOR SHORT FICTION, THE JOHN SIMMONS SHORT FICTION AWARD, (I), Iowa Writers' Workshop, 436 English-Philosophy Building, The University of Iowa, Iowa City IA 52242. Annual awards for short story collections. To encourage writers of short fiction. Two awards: $1,000 each, plus publication of winning collections by University of Iowa Press the following

Market conditions are constantly changing! If you're still using this book and it is 1993 or later, buy the newest edition of Novel & Short Story Writer's Market at your favorite bookstore or order directly from Writer's Digest Books.

fall. Entries must be at least 150 pages, typewritten, and submitted between Aug. 1 and Sept. 30. Stamped, self-addressed return packaging must accompany manuscript. Rules for SASE. Iowa Writer's Workshop does initial screening of entries; finalists (about 6) sent to outside judge for final selection. "A different well-known writer is chosen each year as judge. Any writer who has not previously published a volume of prose fiction is eligible to enter the competition for these prizes. Revised manuscripts which have been previously entered may be resubmitted."

JOSEPH HENRY JACKSON AWARD, (I, IV), The San Francisco Foundation, Suite 910, 685 Market St., San Francisco CA 94105. Contact: Awards Program Coordinator. Annual competition "to award the author of an unpublished work-in-progress of fiction (novel or short stories), nonfiction or poetry." Award: $2,000 and award certificate. Entry form and rules available after November 1 for SASE. Deadline: January 15. Unpublished submissions only. Applicant must be resident of northern California or Nevada for 3 consecutive years immediately prior to the deadline date. Age of applicant must be 20 through 35.

JAPANOPHILE SHORT STORY CONTEST, (I, IV), *Japanophile*, Box 223, Okemos MI 48864. (517)349-1795. Contact: Earl R. Snodgrass, editor. Estab. 1972. Annual award "to encourage quality writing on Japan-America understanding." Award: $100 plus possible publication. Entry fee: $5. Send $4 for sample copy of magazine. Contest rules for SASE. Deadline: December 31. Prefers unpublished submissions. Stories should involve Japanese and non-Japanese characters.

JAPAN-UNITED STATES FRIENDSHIP COMMISSION PRIZE FOR THE TRANSLATION OF JAPANESE LITERATURE, (I, II, IV), The Donald Keene Center of Japanese Culture, 407 Kent Hall, Columbia University, New York NY 10027. (212)854-5036. Contact: Victoria Lyon-Bestor. "To encourage fine translations of Japanese literature and to award and encourage young translators to develop that craft." Annual competition for translations only. Award: $2,500 each for the best translation of a modern work of literature and for the best classical literary translation. Competition receives approx. 15 submissions. Judges: A jury of writers, literary agents, critics and scholar/translators. Guidelines for SASE. Deadline: December 31 postmark. Previously published or unpublished submissions. "Translators must be American citizens."

JESSE JONES AWARD FOR FICTION (BOOK), (I, IV), The Texas Institute of Letters, P.O. Box 9032, Wichita Falls TX 76308. (817)692-6611 ext. 211. Awards Coordinator: James Hoggard. Award "to honor the writer of the best novel or collection of short fiction published during the calendar year before the award is given." Annual award for novels or story collections. Award: $6,000. Competition receives approx. 30-40 entries per year. Judges: Panel selected by TIL Council. Guidelines for SASE. Deadline: January 4. Previously published fiction, which must have appeared in print between January 1 and December 31 of the prior year. "Award available to writers who, at some time, have lived in Texas at least two years consecutively or whose work has a significant Texas theme."

THE JANET HEIDINGER KAFKA PRIZE, (II, IV), University of Rochester, Susan B. Anthony Center and English Dept., 538 Lattimore Hall, Rochester NY 14627. (716)275-8318. Award for fiction by an American woman. Annual competition for short story collections and novels. Award: $1,000. Judges: Kafka Committee. Guidelines for SASE. Deadline: December 31. Recently published submissions. American women only.

KANSAS QUARTERLY/KANSAS ARTS COMMISSION AWARDS, (I), *Kansas Quarterly*, 122 Denison Hall, Dept. of English, Kansas State University, Manhattan KS 66506-0703. Contact: Editors. Annual awards "to reward and recognize the best fiction published in *Kansas Quarterly* during the year from authors anywhere in the US or abroad. Anyone who submits unpublished material which is then accepted for publication becomes eligible for the awards." Award: Recognition and monetary sums of $250, $200, $100, $50. "Ours are not 'contests'; they are monetary awards and recognition given by persons of national literary stature." Fiction judges recently have included David Bradley, James B. Hall, Gordon Weaver and Mary Morris. No deadline; material simply may be submitted for consideration at any time. Include SASE.

ROBERT F. KENNEDY BOOK AWARDS, (II, IV), 1031 31st St. NW, Washington DC 20007. (202)333-1880. Endowed by Arthur Schlesinger, Jr., from proceeds of his biography, *Robert Kennedy and His Times*. Annual award. "To award the author of a book which most faithfully and forcefully reflects Robert Kennedy's purposes." For books published during the calendar year. Award: $2,500 cash prize awarded in the spring. Deadline: January 7. Looking for "a work of literary merit in fact or fiction that shows compassion for the poor or powerless or those suffering from injustice."

KENTUCKY ARTS COUNCIL, AL SMITH ARTISTS FELLOWSHIPS, (I, IV), 31 Fountain Place, Frankfort KY 40601. (502)564-3757. "To encourage and support the professional development of Kentucky artists." Writing fellowships offered every other year in fiction, poetry, playwriting. Award: $5,000. Competition received approximately "110 submissions in 1991 in all writing categories." Judges are out-of-state panelists (writers, editors, playwrights, etc.) of distinction. Open only to Kentucky residents (minimum one year). Entry forms or rules "even without SASE." Check for next appropriate deadline.

JACK KEROUAC LITERARY PRIZE, (I), Lowell Historic Preservation Commission, 222 Merrimack St., Lowell MA 01852. (508)458-7653. Award "to promote cultural activities in Lowell, a pivotal event in annual 'Lowell Celebrates Kerouac' festival." Annual award for short stories, poems and essays. Award: $500 and plaque. Competition receives approximately 200 submissions. Judges: Local authors. Guidelines available for SASE. Deadline is May 1. Unpublished submissions. Limited to: fiction—30 pages or less; nonfiction—30 pages or less; poetry—15 pages or less.

AGA KHAN PRIZE, (I), Address entry to Aga Khan Prize, *Paris Review*, 541 E. 72nd St., New York NY 10021. Annual award. For the best short story received during the preceding year. Award $1,000 and publication. Award judged by the editors. Work should be submitted between May 1-June 1. Unpublished short story submissions (1,000-10,000 words). One submission per envelope. Translations acceptable.

KILLER FROG CONTEST, (I, II), *Scavenger's Newsletter*, 519 Ellinwood, Osage City KS 66523. (913)528-3538. Contact: Janet Fox. Competition "to see who can write the funniest/most overdone horror story, or poem, or produce the most outrageous artwork on a horror theme." Annual award for short stories, poems and art. Award: $25 for each of 4 categories and "coveted froggie statuette." Winners also receive complimentary copies of newsletter. Judge: Editor of Scavenger: Janet Fox. Guidelines available for SASE. Deadline is April 1 to July 31 (postmarked). Published or previously unpublished submissions. Limited to horror/humor. Length: up to 4,000 words.

LATINO LITERATURE PRIZE, (II,IV), The Latin American Writers Institute, Division of Humanities NAC6293, The City College of New York, New York NY 10031. (212)650-7382/7383. Competition "to promote the work of Latino writers who write in Spanish or English and live in the United States." Awarded every year for books of poetry and fiction. Award: $1,000, each category. Competition receives approximately 35 submissions. Judges: 3 prominent Latin American writers and/or critics. Guidelines available for SASE. Deadline: Jan. 31. Length: Open.

LAWRENCE FELLOWSHIP, (I), Dept. of English Language and Literature, University of New Mexico, Albuquerque NM 87131. (505)277-6347. Contact: Prof. Gene Frumkin, chairperson. Annual award. Fellowship for writers of unpublished or previously published fiction, poetry, drama. (June-August residency at D.H. Lawrence Ranch, $2,100 stipend). $10 processing fee. Deadline: January 31. Write for rules, application form. SASE for return of materials.

STEPHEN LEACOCK MEDAL FOR HUMOUR, (II, IV), Stephen Leacock Associates, Box 854, Orillia, Ontario L3V 6K8 Canada. (705)325-6546. Award "to encourage writing of humour by Canadians." Annual competition for short stories, novels and story collections. Award: Stephen Leacock (silver) medal for humour and J.P. Wiser cash award of $3,500 (Canadian). Receives 25-40 entries. Five judges selected across Canada. Entry fee $25 (Canadian). Guidelines for SASE. Deadline: December 30. Submissions should have been published in the previous year. Open to Canadian citizens or landed immigrants only.

THE LEADING EDGE **FICTION CONTEST, (I, IV),** 3163 JKHB, Provo UT 84602. (801)378-2456. Competition "to generate interest in the magazine; to increase the quality of submissions to the magazine; to reward excellence in storytelling among new and upcoming authors." Annual award for short stories. Award: $100 first prize, $60 second prize, $40 third prize. Competition receives approximately 900 submissions each year. Judges: Editorial staff of *The Leading Edge*. Guidelines for SASE. Deadline: December 1. Previously unpublished fiction. "The contest is open to all writers of science fiction and fantasy, whether they be pro, semipro, or first timer. Word length should be under 20,000 words unless story absolutely requires more—whatever it takes to tell the story right. No novels. *The Leading Edge* is a semiprofessional magazine of science fiction and fantasy that caters to the new and upcoming author, artist and poet. It is our goal to be the magazine that the professionals look to to find the next generation of writers."

LETRAS DE ORO SPANISH LITERARY PRIZES, (I, IV), The Graduate School of International Studies, University of Miami, Box 248123, Coral Gables FL 33124. (305)284-3266. "The *Letras de Oro* Spanish Literary Prizes were created in order to reward creative excellence in the Spanish language and to promote Spanish literary production in this country. *Letras de Oro* also serves to recognize the importance of Hispanic culture in the United States." Annual award for novels, story collections, drama, essays and poetry. The prizes are $2,500 cash. Deadline: October 12.

LITERATURE AND BELIEF WRITING CONTEST, (I, IV), Center for the Study of Christian Values in Literature, 3134 JKHB, Brigham Young University, Provo UT 84602. (801)378-2304. Director: Jay Fox. Award to "encourage affirmative literature in the Judeo-Christian tradition." Annual competition for short stories. Award $150 (1st place); $100 (2nd place). Competition receives 200-300 entries. Judges: BYU faculty. Guidelines for SASE. Deadline: May 15. Unpublished submissions, up to 30 pages. All winning entries are considered for publication in the annual journal *Literature and Belief*.

LOFT-MCKNIGHT WRITERS AWARDS, (I, IV), The Loft, Pratt Community Center, 66 Malcolm Ave. SE, Minneapolis MN 55414. (612)379-8999. Program Director: Carolyn Holbrook-Montgomery. "To give Minnesota writers of demonstrated ability an opportunity to work for a concentrated period of time on their writing." Annual award for creative prose. $7,500/award; four awards. Competition receives approximately 275 submissions/year. Judges are out-of-state judges. Entry forms or rules for SASE. "Applicants must be Minnesota residents and must send for and observe guidelines."

LOUISIANA LITERARY AWARD, (II, IV), Louisiana Library Association (LLA), Box 3058, Baton Rouge LA 70821. (504)342-4928. Contact: Chair, Louisiana Literary Award Committee. Annual award "to promote interest in books related to Louisiana and to encourage their production." Submissions must have been published during the calendar year prior to presentation of the award. (The award is presented in March or April.) Award: Bronze medallion and $250. No entry fee. Deadline: publication by December 31. "All Louisiana-related books which committee members can locate are considered, whether submitted or not. Interested parties may correspond with the committee chair at the address above. All books considered *must* be on subject(s) related to Louisiana or be written by a Louisiana author. Each year, there may be a fiction *and/or* nonfiction award. Most often, however, there is only one award recipient, and he or she is the author of a work of nonfiction."

THE JOHN H. MCGINNIS MEMORIAL AWARD, (I), *Southwest Review*, Box 4374, 307 Fondren Library West, Southern Methodist University, Dallas TX 75275. (214)373-7440. Contact: Elizabeth Mills, associate editor. Annual awards (fiction and nonfiction). Stories or essays must have been published in the *Southwest Review* prior to the announcement of the award. Awards: $1,000. Pieces are not submitted directly for the award, but simply for publication in the magazine.

THE ENID MCLEOD LITERARY PRIZE, (II, IV), Franco-British Society, Room 636, Linen Hall, 162-168 Regent St., London W1R 5TB England. Executive Secretary: Mrs. Marian Clarke. "To recognize the work of the author published in the UK which in the opinion of the judges has contributed most to Franco-British understanding." Annual competition for short stories, novels and story collections. Award: Cheque and copy of Enid McLeod's memoirs. Competition receives approx. 6-12 submissions. Judges: The Marquis of Lansdowne (FBS President), Martyn Goff and Terence Kilmartin. Guidelines for SASE. Deadline: December 31. Previously published submissions. "Writers, or their publishers, may submit 4 copies to the London Office. No nominations are necessary."

MADEMOISELLE FICTION WRITERS CONTEST, (I), *Mademoiselle Magazine*, 350 Madison Ave., New York NY 10017. Send entries to Fiction Writers Contest. Each entry must be accompanied by the entry coupon or a 3×5 card with name, age, home address. Award: 1st prize: $2,500 and publication in *Mademoiselle*; 2nd prize: $500. Deadline: Manuscripts will be accepted from January 1 to March

15. Open to all short story writers, male and female, age 18-30, who have not published fiction in a magazine with a circulation over 25,000. Entries will not be returned.

MAGGIE AWARD, (I, IV), Georgia Romance Writers, Inc., Box 142, Acworth GA 30101. (404)974-6678. "To encourage and instruct unpublished writers in the romance genre." Annual competition for novels. Award: Silver pendant (1st place), certificates (2nd-4th). 4 categories—short contemporary romance, long contemporary romance, historical, mainstream. Judges: Published romance authors. Entry fee $25. Guidelines for SASE. Deadline: On or about June 1 (deadline not yet final). Unpublished submissions. Writers must be members of Romance Writers of America. Entries consist of 3 chapters plus synopsis. "We welcome a variety of fiction types in our mainstream category, since romance has achieved such a broad and sophisticated scope."

MANITOBA ARTS COUNCIL SUPPORT TO INDIVIDUAL ARTISTS, (II, IV), Manitoba Arts Council, 525-93 Lombard Ave., Winnipeg, Manitoba R3B 3B1 Canada. (204)945-2237. Grants "to encourage and support Manitoba writers." Two awards: Writer's Grants "A" ($7,500 Canadian) for practicing writers who have had previous work published or produced and are recognized as professionals in their field. Writer's Grants "B" ($4,000 Canadian) for emerging writers who have had some previous work published or produced. Deadlines: May 1 and October 1. Open only to Manitoba writers.

‡THE MARTEN BEQUEST AWARD, (I, IV), Arts Management Pty. Ltd., 56 Kellett St., Potts Point NSW 2011 Australia. Awards Coordinator: Kate Gralton. "For the furtherance of culture and the advancement of education in Australia by means of the provision of travelling scholarships as numerous as income will permit, to be awarded entrants who have been born in Australia, and awarded to candidates of either sex between the ages of 21 years and 35 years, who shall be adjudged of outstanding ability and promise." Award granted to writers every 2 years (next in 1994). Competition for writers of short stories, novels or story collections. Award: AUS $15,000 payable in two installments of $7,500 per annum. Guidelines for SASE. Deadline: Oct. 31, 1993.

WALTER RUMSEY MARVIN GRANT, (I, IV), Ohioana Library Association, 1105 State Department Building, 65 S. Front St., Columbus OH 43215. (614)466-3831. Contact: Linda Hengst. "To encourage young unpublished writers (under age 30)." Biennial competition for short stories. Award: $1,000. Guidelines for SASE. Deadline: January 31, 1994. Unpublished submissions. Open to unpublished authors born in Ohio or who have lived in Ohio for a minimum of five years. Must be under 30 years of age. Up to six pieces of prose may be submitted; maximum 60 pages, minimum 10 pages.

MARYLAND STATE ARTS COUNCIL FELLOWSHIP, (I, IV), 15 West Mulberry St., Baltimore MD 21201. (301)333-8232. Fellowships given to reward artistic excellence and to promote career development. Annual grant for writers of stories, novels, novellas and story collections. Several awards of $1,000, $3,000 and $6,000 given each year. Competition receives 200 applications for fellowships. Judge: Out-of-state selection panel. Further information available for SASE. Deadline: December 1. Applicants must be Maryland residents over 18. Students are not eligible. Writers are required to submit a body of work demonstrating artistic accomplishment and skill.

THE VICKY METCALF BODY OF WORK AWARD (II, IV), Canadian Authors Association, 275 Slater St., Ottowa, Ontario K1P 5H9 Canada. (613)233-2846. National Director: Jeffrey Holmes. Annual award. "The prize is given solely to stimulate writing for children, written by Canadians, for a *number* of strictly children's books—fiction, nonfiction or even picture books. No set formula." To be considered, a writer must have published at least 4 books. Award: $2,000 for a body of work inspirational to Canadian youth. Deadline: December 31. No entry fee. "Nominations may be made by any individual or association by letter *in triplicate* listing the published works of the nominee and providing biographical information. The books are usually considered in regard to their inspirational value for children. Entry forms or rules for SASE."

Market categories: (I) Unpublished entries; (II) Published entries nominated by the author; (III) Published entries, nominated by the editor, publisher or nominating body; (IV) Specialized entries.

VICKY METCALF SHORT STORY AWARD, (II, IV), Canadian Authors Association, Suite 500, 275 Slater St., Ottawa, Ontario K1P 5H9 Canada. (613)233-2846. FAX: (613)235-8237. Contact: Executive Director. "To encourage Canadian writing for children (open only to Canadian citizens)." Submissions must have been published during previous calendar year in Canadian children's magazine or anthology. Award: $3,000 (Canadian). Award of $1,000 to editor of winning story if published in a Canadian journal or anthology. No entry fee. Entry forms or rules for #10 SASE. Deadline: December 15. Looking for "stories with originality, literary quality for ages 7-17."

MIDLAND AUTHORS' AWARD, (II, IV), Society of Midland Authors, % Jim Bowman, 152 North Scoville, Oak Park IL 60302. (708)383-7568. "To honor outstanding works published during the previous year by Midwestern authors." Award: Monetary sum and plaque. Competition receives approximately 30-50 submissions. Judges are usually members of Society of Midland Authors. Entry forms or rules for SASE. Authors must be residents of IL, IN, IA, KS, MI, MN, MO, NE, OH, SD or WI. Send for entry form.

MILITARY LIFESTYLE SHORT STORY CONTEST, (I, IV), Suite 710, 4800 Montgomery Lane, Bethesda MD 20814-5341. (301)718-7600. "To publish the work of previously unpublished writers; to encourage those of our readers who are military to send us short stories about a lifestyle they know very well." Annual competition for short stories. First Prize: $500; Second Prize: $300; Third Prize: $200. "Also, all three are published in the July/August issue of *Military Lifestyle*." Competition receives 700 submissions. Judges: Editorial staff of *Military Lifestyle*. Guidelines for SASE. Deadline: March 31. Unpublished submissions. "Theme of contest changes annually. Contact magazine for details and contest rules."

MILKWEED EDITIONS NATIONAL FICTION PRIZE, (I), Milkweed Editions, Suite 505, 528 Hennepin Ave., Minneapolis MN 55403. (612)332-3192. Editor: Emilie Buchwald. Annual award for a novel, a short story collection, one or more novellas, or a combination of short stories and novellas. Award: Publication, $3,000 advance against royalties. Reading fee $5. Guidelines for SASE. Deadline: August 15. "Please look at *Ganado Red*, by Susan Lowell, our first winning NFP book, or at *Backbone*, by Carol Bly, or *The Country I Come From*, by Maura Stanton—this is the caliber of fiction we are searching for. Catalog available for 3 first class stamps, if people need a sense of our list."

THE MILNER AWARD, (III), Friends of the Atlanta-Fulton Public Library, 1 Margaret Mitchell Square, Atlanta GA 30303. (404)730-1710. Executive Director: Rennie Davant. Award to a living American author of children's books. Annual competition for novels and story collections. Award: $1,000 honorarium and specially commissioned glass sculpture by Hans Frabel. Judges: Children of Atlanta vote during children's book week. Prior winners not eligible. Children vote at will—no list from which to select. Winner must be able to appear personally in Atlanta to receive the award at a formal program.

MIND BOOK OF THE YEAR—THE ALLEN LANE AWARD, (II, IV), MIND, 22 Harley St., London W1N 2ED England. Contact: Ms. A. Brackx. "To award a prize to the work of fiction or nonfiction which outstandingly furthers public understanding of the causes, experience or treatment of mental health problems." Annual competition for novels and works of nonfiction. Award: £1,000. Competition receives approx. 50-100 submissions. Judges: A panel drawn from MIND's Council of Management. Deadline: December. Previously published submissions. Author's nomination is accepted.

MINNESOTA STATE ARTS BOARD/ARTISTS ASSISTANCE FELLOWSHIP, (I, IV), 432 Summit Ave., St. Paul MN 55102-2624. (612)297-2603. Artist Assistance Program Associate: Karen Mueller. "To provide support and recognition to Minnesota's outstanding literary artists." Annual award for fiction writers, creative nonfiction writers and poets. Award: Up to $6,000. Competition receives approx. 150 submissions/year. Deadline: January. Previously published or unpublished submissions. Send request or call the above number for application guidelines. *Minnesota residents only.*

MINNESOTA VOICES PROJECT, (IV), New Rivers Press, #910, 420 N. 5th St., Minneapolis MN 55401. Contact: C.W. Truesdale, editor/publisher. Annual award "to foster and encourage new and emerging regional writers of short fiction, novellas, personal essays and poetry." Requires bibliography of previous publications and residency statement. Awards: $500 to each author published in the series plus "a generous royalty agreement if book goes into second printing." No entry fee. Send request with SASE for guidelines in December. Deadline: April 1. Send two copies of each manuscript of 125-200 pages; restricted to writers from Minnesota, Wisconsin, North and South Dakota, and Iowa.

MISSISSIPPI ARTS COMMISSION ARTIST FELLOWSHIP GRANT, (I, IV), Suite 207, 239 N. Lamar St., Jackson MS 39201. (601)359-6030. Contact: Program Administrator. "To encourage and support the creation of new artwork, and to recognize the contribution that artists of exceptional talent make to the vitality of our environment. Awards are based upon the quality of previously created work." Award granted every 3 years on a rotating basis. Award for writers of short stories, novels and story collections. Grant: Up to $5,000. Judges: Peer panel. Guidelines for SASE. "The next available grants for creative writing, including fiction, nonfiction and poetry will be in 1993-94." Deadline: March 1. Applicants must be Mississippi residents. "The Mississippi Arts Commission's Art in Education Program contains a creative writing component. For more information, contact the AIE Coordinator. The Mississippi Touring Arts program offers writers the opportunity to give readings and workshops and have the Arts Commission pay part of the fee." For more information, contact the Program Administrator.

MISSOURI WRITERS' BIENNIAL, (I, IV), Missouri Arts Council, Suite 105, 111 N. 7th St., St. Louis MO 63101-2188. (314)340-6845. Award to support and promote Missouri writers. Every 2 years competition for short stories, essays and poetry. Award: $5,000 each to 5 writers. Competition receives approx. 400 submissions. Judges: Panel of national judges. Guidelines for SASE. Deadline "approx." July 30. Unpublished submissions. "Writers must have lived in Missouri for at least 2 years immediately preceding submission. Writers *must* request complete written guidelines."

MONTANA ARTS COUNCIL FIRST BOOK AWARD, (IV), New York Block, 48 North Last Chance Gulch, Helena MT 59620. (406)444-6430. Director of Artists Services: Julia Smith. Biannual award for publication of a book of poetry or fiction—the best work in Montana. Submissions may be short stories, novellas, story collections or poetry. Award: Publication. Competition receives about 35 submissions/year. Judges are professional writers. Entry forms or rules for SASE. Deadline: Early April (1992). Restricted to residents of Montana; not open to degree-seeking students.

MONTANA ARTS COUNCIL INDIVIDUAL ARTIST FELLOWSHIP, (IV), New York Block, 48 North Last Chance Gulch, Helena MT 59620. (406)444-6430. Director of Artists Services: Julia Smith. Biannual award of $2,000. Competition receives about 35 submissions/year. Panelists are professional writers. Contest requirements available for SASE. Deadline: Spring, 1993. Restricted to residents of Montana; not open to degree-seeking students.

‡JENNY MOORE WRITER-IN-WASHINGTON, Jenny Moore Fund, English Department, George Washington University, Washington DC 20052. (202)994-8223. To provide a teaching residency. Annual competition. Award: $36,500 plus benefits. Receives approximately 150 applications. Judges: Committees from English department and board members of fund. Guidelines for SASE. Deadline: November 15. "Genre varies from year to year." Length: 25 pages.

NATIONAL BOOK COUNCIL/BANJO AWARDS, (III, IV), National Book Council, Suite 3, 21 Drummond Place, Carlton, Victoria 3053 Australia. "For a book of highest literary merit which makes an outstanding contribution to Australian literature." Annual competition for creative writing. Award: $15,000 each for a work of fiction and nonfiction. Competition receives approx. 100-140 submissions. Judges: 4 judges chosen by the National Book Council. Entry fee $30. Guidelines for SASE. Deadline: Mid-April. Previously published submissions. For works "written by Australian citizens or permanent residents and first published in Australia during the qualifying period." Books must be nominated by the publisher.

‡NATIONAL BOOK COUNCIL/QANTAS NEW WRITERS AWARD, (III, IV), Qantas Airways Ltd., National Book Council, 21 Drummond Place, Carlton, Victoria 3053 Australia. "To encourage new writers. It is open to writers under 35 or to a writer of any age who has not had a book published previously." Judges: 2 judges chosen by the National Book Council. Entry fee $20. Guidelines for SASE. "The books shall have been written by Australian citizens or permanent residents and first published in Australia during the qualifying period. Books must be nominated by the publisher."

 The double dagger before a listing indicates that the listing is new in this edition. New markets are often the most receptive to freelance contributions.

NATIONAL BOOK FOUNDATION, INC., (III), Rm. 904, 260 5th Ave., New York NY 10001. (212)685-0261. Executive Director: Neil Baldwin. Assistant: Liddy Detar. Annual award to honor distinguished literary achievement in three categories: nonfiction, fiction and poetry. Books published Dec. 1 through Nov. 30 are eligible. Award: $10,000 to each winner; $1,000 to four runners-up in each category. Awards judged by panels of critics and writers. Entry fee $100. Deadline: July 15. November ceremony. Selections are submitted by publishers only, or may be called in by judges. Read *Publishers Weekly* for additional information.

NATIONAL ENDOWMENT FOR THE ARTS FELLOWSHIP, (I), Literature Program, Room 723, 1100 Pennsylvania Ave. NW, Washington DC 20506. (202)682-5451. Program Specialist, Literature Program: Kristin Kelly. "The mission of the NEA is to foster the excellence, diversity and vitality of the arts in the United States, and to help broaden the availability and appreciation of such excellence, diversity and vitality." The purpose of the fellowship is to enable creative writers "to set aside time for writing, research or travel and generally to advance their careers." Competition open to fiction writers who have published a novel or novella, a collection of stories or at least 5 stories in 2 or more magazines since Jan. 1, 1982. Annual award: $20,000. All mss are judged anonymously. Application and guidelines available upon request. Deadline: March 5.

NATIONAL FOUNDATION FOR ADVANCEMENT IN THE ARTS, ARTS RECOGNITION AND TALENT SEARCH (ARTS), (I, IV), 3915 Biscayne Blvd., Miami FL 33137. (305)573-0490. President: William H. Banchs. "To encourage 17- and 18-year-old writers and put them in touch with institutions which offer scholarships." Annual award for short stories, novels, "fiction, essay, poetry, scriptwriting." Awards: $3,000, $1,500, $500, and $100. Judges: Nationally selected panel. Entry fee $25 by May 15; $35 until October 1. Guidelines for SASE. 17- and 18-year-old writers only.

‡NATIONAL JEWISH BOOK AWARDS, (II, IV), JWB Jewish Book Council, 15 E. 26th St., New York NY 10010. Contact: Paula Gottlieb, director. Annual awards "to promote greater awareness of Jewish-American literary creativity." Previously published submissions in English only by a US or Canadian author/translator. Awards judged by authors/scholars. Award: $750 to the author/translator plus citation to publisher. Over 100 entries received for each award. Contest requirements available for SASE. Awards made in these categories: Autobiography/Memoir (autobiography or memoir of life of Jewish person); Children's Literature (children's book on Jewish theme); Children's Picture Book (author and illustrator of a picture book on Jewish theme); Fiction (fiction of Jewish interest); Yiddish Literature (book of literary merit in Yiddish language); also nonfiction awards in Jewish Thought, Jewish History, the Holocaust, Israel, Scholarship, Shepardic Studies and Visual Arts.

NATIONAL WRITERS CLUB ANNUAL NOVEL WRITING CONTEST, (I), National Writers Club, Suite 620, 1450 S. Havana, Aurora CO 80012. (303)751-7844. Contact: James L. Young, director. Annual award to "recognize and reward outstanding ability and to increase the opportunity for publication." Award: $500 first prize; $300 second prize; $100 third prize. Award judged by successful writers. Charges $25 entry fee. Contest/award rules and entry forms available with SASE. Opens December 1. Entry deadline: April 29. Unpublished submissions, any genre or category. Length: 20,000-100,000 words.

NATIONAL WRITERS CLUB ANNUAL SHORT STORY CONTEST, (I), National Writers Club, 1450 S. Havana, Aurora CO 80012. (303)751-7844. Contact: James L. Young, director. Annual award to encourage and recognize writing by freelancers in the short story field. Award: $200 first prize; $100 second prize; $50 third prize. Opens March 1. Charges $10 entry fee. Write for entry form and rule sheet. All entries must be postmarked by July 1. Unpublished submissions. Length: No more than 5,000 words.

THE NATIONAL WRITTEN & ILLUSTRATED BY . . . AWARDS CONTEST FOR STUDENTS, (I, IV), Landmark Editions, Inc., Box 4469, Kansas City MO 64127. (816)241-4919. Contact: Nan Thatch. "Contest initiated to encourage students to write and illustrate original books and to inspire them to become published authors and illustrators." Annual competition. "Each student whose book is selected for publication will be offered a complete publishing contract. To insure that students benefit from the proceeds, royalties from the sale of their books will be placed in an individual trust fund, set up for each student by his or her parents or legal guardians, at a bank of their choice. Funds may be withdrawn when a student becomes of age, or withdrawn earlier (either in whole or in part) for educational purposes or in case of proof of specific needs due to unusual hardship. Reports of book sales and royalties will be sent to the student and the parents or guardians annually." Winners also receive an all-expense-paid trip to Kansas City to oversee final reproduction phases of their books. Books by students may be entered in one of three age categories: A—6 to 9 years old; B—10 to 13 years old; C—14 to 19 years old. Each book submitted must be both written and illustrated by the same student. "Any books that are written by one student and illustrated by another will be automatically disqualified." Book entries must be submitted by a teacher or librarian. Entry fee: $1. For rules and guidelines, send a #10 SAE stamped with 58¢ postge. Deadline: May 1 of each year.

NEBULA® AWARDS, (III, IV), Science Fiction Writers of America, Inc., Box 4335, Spartanburg SC 23305-4335. Executive Secretary: Peter Dennis Pautz. Annual awards for previously published short stories, novels, novellas, novelettes. SF/fantasy only. "No submissions; nominees upon recommendation of members only." Deadline: December 31. "Works are nominated throughout the year by active members of the SFWA."

***NEGATIVE CAPABILITY* SHORT FICTION COMPETITION, (I),** *Negative Capability,* 62 Ridgelawn Dr. E., Mobile AL 36608. (205)343-6163. Contact: Sue Walker. "To promote and publish excellent fiction and to promote the ideals of human rights and dignity." Annual award for short stories. Award: $1,000 best story award. Judge: Leon Driskell. Reading fee $10, "includes copy of journal publishing the award." Guidelines for SASE. Deadline: December 15. Length: 1,500-4,500 words. "Award honors an outstanding author each year, and the award is given his or her name."

THE NENE AWARD, (II), School Library Services, Dept. of Education, 641 18th Ave., Honolulu HI 96816. Chairperson: Reva Dacanay (changes annually). Annual award "to help the children of Hawaii become acquainted with the best contemporary writers of fiction for children; to become aware of the qualities that make a good book; to choose the best rather than the mediocre; and to honor an author whose book has been enjoyed by the children of Hawaii." Award: Koa plaque. Judged by the children of Hawaii. No entry fee.

NEUSTADT INTERNATIONAL PRIZE FOR LITERATURE, (III), *World Literature Today,* 110 Monnet Hall, University of Oklahoma, Norman OK 73019-0375. Contact: Dr. Djelal Kadir, director. Biennial award to recognize distinguished and continuing achievement in fiction, poetry or drama. Awards: $40,000, an eagle feather cast in silver, an award certificate and a special issue of *WLT.* "We are looking for outstanding accomplishment in world literature. The Neustadt Prize is not open to application. Nominations are made only by members of the international jury, which changes for each award. Jury meetings are held in February of even-numbered years. Unsolicited manuscripts, whether published or unpublished, cannot be considered."

THE NEW ERA WRITING, ART, PHOTOGRAPHY AND MUSIC CONTEST, (I, IV), *New Era Magazine* (LDS Church), 50 E. North Temple, Salt Lake City UT 84150. (801)240-2951. "To encourage young Mormon writers and artists." Annual competition for short stories. Award: Scholarship to Brigham Young University or Ricks College or cash awards. Competition receives approx. 300 submissions. Judges: *New Era* editors. Guidelines for SASE. Deadline: January 3. Unpublished submissions. Contest open only to members of the Church of Jesus Christ of Latter-Day Saints.

NEW HAMPSHIRE STATE COUNCIL ON THE ARTS INDIVIDUAL ARTIST FELLOWSHIP, (I, IV), 40 N. Main St., Concord NH 03301-4974. (603)271-2789. Artist Services Coordinator: Audrey V. Sylvester. Fellowship "for career development to professional artists who are legal/permanent residents of the state of New Hampshire." Annual award: Up to $3,000. Competition receives 150 entries for 15 awards in all disciplines. Judges: 7 panels of in-state and out-of-state experts (music, theater, dance, literature, film, etc.). Guidelines for SASE. Deadline: May 1. Submissions may be either previously published or unpublished. Applicants must be over 18 years of age; not enrolled as fulltime students; permanent, legal residents of New Hampshire 1 year prior to application. Application form required.

NEW JERSEY STATE COUNCIL ON THE ARTS PROSE FELLOWSHIP, (I, IV), 4 North Broad St., Trenton NJ 08625. (609)292-6130. Annual award for writers of short stories, novels, story collections. Award: Maximum is $15,000; other awards are $5,000, $7,000 and $12,000. Judges: Peer panel. Guidelines for SASE. Deadline Jan. 31. For either previously published or unpublished submissions. "Previously published work must be submitted as a manuscript." Applicants must be New Jersey residents. Submit several copies of short fiction, short stories or prose not exceeding 15 pages and no less than 10 pages. For novels in progress, a synopsis and first chapter should be submitted.

NEW LETTERS LITERARY AWARD, (I), *New Letters,* UMKC 5100 Rockhill, Kansas City MO 64110. (816)235-1168. Adm. Assistant: Glenda McCrary. Award to "discover and reward good writing." Annual competition for short stories. Award: $750. Competition receives 350 entries/year. Entry fee $10. Guidelines for SASE. Deadline May 15. Submissions must be unpublished. Length requirement: 5,000 words or less.

‡NEW VOICES IN POETRY AND PROSE SPRING AND FALL COMPETITION, (I), *New Voices in Poetry and Prose Magazine,* P.O. Box 52196, Shreveport LA 71135. (318)797-8243. Publisher: Cheryl White. "To recognize and publish a previously unpublished work of outstanding short fiction." Biannual award for short stories. Award: $100 (first place) and publication in *New Voices.* ("Cash award may increase in 1992 if number of entries increases.") Competition receives approx. 50 submissions. Judges: Panel. Entry fee $10/short story. Guidelines for SASE. Deadlines: April 30 and September 30. Unpublished submissions. "All writers welcome. There is no line limit, but as a general rule, works under 5,000 words are preferred." Contact: Cheryl White, Publisher.

NEW WRITING AWARD, (I), *New Writing Magazine,* 165 Calvin Ct. S., Tonawanda NY 14150. "To seek out and reward *new* writing. We want to see originality in form and content. Awarding those who find the current literary scene a hard market because it is too confining." Annual competition for stories. Award: Varies, but should be $1,000 or more. Additional awards for finalists. Possible publication. Judges: Panel of editors. Entry fee $10, $5 for additional. Guidelines for SASE. Unpublished submissions.

NEW YORK FOUNDATION FOR THE ARTS FELLOWSHIP, (I, IV), New York Foundation for the Arts, #600, 5 Beekman St., New York NY 10038. (212)233-3900. Contact: D. Green. Biennial competition for short stories and novels. Award: $7,000. Competition receives approx. 450 submissions. Judges: Fiction writers. Call for guidelines or send SASE. Deadline: September 1993. Previously published or unpublished submissions. "Applicants must have lived in New York state at least 2 years immediately prior to application deadline."

NEW YORK STATE EDITH WHARTON CITATION OF MERIT (State Author), (III, IV), NYS Writers Institute, Humanities 355, University at Albany/SUNY, Albany NY 12222. (518)442-5620. Contact: Thomas Smith, associate director. Awarded biennially to honor a New York State fiction writer for a lifetime of works of distinction. Fiction writers living in New York State are nominated by an advisory panel. Recipients receive an honorarium of $10,000 and must give two public readings a year.

JOHN NEWBERY AWARD, (III), American Library Association (ALA) Awards and Citations Program, Association for Library Service to Children, 50 E. Huron St., Chicago IL 60611. Annual award. Only books for children published during the preceding year are eligible. Award: Medal. Entry restricted to US citizens-residents.

CHARLES H. AND N. MILDRED NILON EXCELLENCE IN MINORITY FICTION AWARD, (I, IV), University of Colorado at Boulder and the Fiction Collective Two, English Dept. Publications Center, Campus Box 494, University of Colorado, Boulder CO 80309-0494. "We recognize excellence in new minority fiction." Annual competition for novels, story collections and novellas. Award: $1,000 cash prize; joint publications of mss by CU-Boulder and Fiction Collective Two. Competition receives approx. 50 submissions. Judges: Well-known minority writers. Guidelines for SASE. Deadline: November 30. Unpublished submissions. "Only specific recognized U.S. racial and ethnic minorities are eligible. The definitions are in the submission guidelines. The ms must be book length (a minimum of 250 pages)."

‡THE NOMA AWARD FOR PUBLISHING IN AFRICA, (III, IV), % Hans Zell Associates, P.O. Box 56, Oxford OX1 2SJ England. Sponsored by Kodansha Ltd. Administered by *The African Book Publishing Record.* Award "to encourage publications of works by African writers and scholars in Africa, instead of abroad as is still too often the case at present." Annual competition for a new book in any of these categories: Scholarly or academic; books for children; literature and creative writing, including fiction, drama and poetry. Award: $5,000. Competition receives approx. 100 submissions. Judges: A committee of African scholars and book experts and representatives of the international book community. Chairman: Professor Abiola Irele. Guidelines for SASE. Previously published submissions. Submissions are through publishers only.

‡NORDMANNS-FORBUNDET TRANSLATION GRANT, (II, IV), Nordmann-Forbundet, Rädhusgt 23B, N-0158 Oslo 1 Norway. FAX: (02)425163. Contact: Dina Tolfsby, information officer. Annual award for translation of Norwegian poetry or fiction, preferably contemporary. Award: Maximum NOK 15,000. Competition receives approx. 10 submissions. Judges: A committee of three members. Deadline March 1. "The grants are awarded to foreign publishing houses that want to publish Norwegian literature in translation." Payment is made at the time of publication.

NORTH CAROLINA ARTS COUNCIL FELLOWSHIP, (IV), 221 E. Lane St., Raleigh NC 27611. (919)733-2111. Literature Director: Deborah McGill. Grants program "to recognize and encourage North Carolina's finest creative writers." Annual award: Up to $8,000 each for 5 writers. Council receives approximately 200 submissions. Judges are a panel of editors and published writers from outside the state. Writers must be over 18 years old, not currently enrolled in degree-granting program on undergraduate or graduate level, and must have been a resident of North Carolina for 1 full year prior to applying. Writers may apply in either poetry or fiction. Deadline: February 1.

NORTH CAROLINA ARTS COUNCIL RESIDENCIES, (IV), 221 E. Lane St., Raleigh NC 27611. (919)733-2111. Literature Director: Deborah McGill. "To recognize and encourage North Carolina's finest creative writers." Annual award. "We offer a three-month residency at the LaNapoule Foundation in southern France and a two- to three-month residency at Headlands Center in Northern California." Judges: Editors and published writers from outside the state. Deadline for France, February 1; for California, mid-August. Writers must be over 18 years old, not currently enrolled in degree-granting program on undergraduate or graduate level and must have been a resident of North Carolina for 1 full year prior to applying.

NORTH CAROLINA ARTS COUNCIL SCHOLARSHIPS, (IV), 221 E. Lane St., Raleigh NC 27611. (919)733-2111. Literature Director: Deborah McGill. "To provide writers of fiction with opportunities for research or enrichment. Available on a six-weeks basis throughout the year." Award up to $500. "To be eligible writers must have lived in the state for at least a year and must have published at least five works of fiction in two or more literary journals, a volume of short fiction or collection of short stories, a novel or a novella. Self-published or vanity press published work is ineligible."

THE FLANNERY O'CONNOR AWARD FOR SHORT FICTION, (I), The University of Georgia Press, Terrell Hall, Athens GA 30602. (404)542-2830. Contact: Award coordinator. Annual award "to recognize outstanding collections of short fiction. Published and unpublished authors are welcome." Award: $1,000 and publication by the University of Georgia Press. Deadline: June 1-July 31. "Manuscripts cannot be accepted at any other time." Entry fee: $10. Contest rules for SASE. Ms will not be returned.

FRANK O'CONNOR FICTION AWARD, (I), *Descant*, Dept. of English, Texas Christian University, Fort Worth TX 76129. (817)921-7240. Contact: Betsy Colquitt, editor. Estab. 1979 with *Descant*; earlier awarded through *Quartet*. Annual award to honor achievement in short fiction. Submissions must be published in the magazine during its current volume. Award: $500 prize. No entry fee. "About 12 to 15 stories are published annually in *Descant*. Winning story is selected from this group."

THE SCOTT O'DELL AWARD FOR HISTORICAL FICTION, (II, IV), Scott O'Dell (personal donation), c/o Houghton Mifflin, 2 Park St., Boston MA 02108. (617)725-5000. Contact: Mrs. Zena Sutherland, professor, 1100 E. 57th St., Chicago IL 60637. Annual award "to encourage the writing of good historical fiction about the New World (Canada, South and Central America, and the United States) for children and young people." Award: $5,000. Entry forms or rules for SASE. Deadline: December 31. For books published during the year preceding the year in which the award is given. To be written in English by a U.S. citizen and published in the U.S. Looking for "accuracy in historical details, and all the standard literary criteria for excellence: style, setting, characterization, etc."

OHIO ARTS COUNCIL AID TO INDIVIDUAL ARTISTS FELLOWSHIP, (I, IV), 727 E. Main St., Columbus OH 43205-1796. (614)466-2613. "To recognize and support Ohio's outstanding creative artists." Annual grant/fellowship. Award: $5,000 or $10,000. Competition receives approx. 200-300 submissions/

Read the Business of Fiction section to learn the correct way to prepare and submit a manuscript.

year. Judges: Panel of experts. Contact the OAC office for guidelines. Writers must be residents of Ohio and must not be students.

OHIOANA AWARD FOR CHILDREN'S LITERATURE, ALICE WOOD MEMORIAL, (IV), Ohioana Library Association, 1105 Ohio Department Bldg., 65 S. Front St., Columbus OH 43215. (614)466-3831. Competition "to honor an individual whose body of work has made, and continues to make, a significant contribution to literature for children or young adults." Annual award for body of work. Award: $1,000. Guidelines for SASE. Deadline: December 31 prior to year award is given. Published fiction. "Open to authors born in Ohio or who have lived in Ohio for a minimum of five years."

OHIOANA BOOK AWARD, (II, IV), Ohioana Library Association, 1105 Ohio Department Bldg., 65 S. Front St., Columbus OH 43266-0334. Contact: Linda R. Hengst, director. Annual award (only if the judges believe a book of sufficiently high quality has been submitted) to bring recognition to outstanding books by Ohioans or about Ohio. Criteria: Book written or edited by a native Ohioan or resident of the state for at least 5 years; two copies of the book MUST be received by the Ohioana Library by December 31 prior to the year the award is given; literary quality of the book must be outstanding. Award: Certificate and glass sculpture. Each spring a jury considers all books received since the previous jury. Award judged by a jury selected from librarians, book reviewers, writers and other knowledgeable people. No entry forms are needed, but they are available. "We will be glad to answer letters asking specific questions."

THE OKANAGAN SHORT FICTION AWARD, (I, IV), *Canadian Author & Bookman*, Suite 500, 275 Slater St., Ottawa, Ontario K1P 5H9 Canada. Contact: Veronica Ross, fiction editor. Award offered 4 times a year. To present good fiction "in which the writing surpasses all else" to an appreciative literary readership, and in turn help Canadian writers retain an interest in good fiction. Award: $125 to each author whose story is accepted for publication. Entries are invited in each issue of the quarterly *CA&B*. Sample copy $5.50; guidelines printed in the magazine. "Our award regulations stipulate that writers must be Canadian, stories must not have been previously published, and be under 3,000 words. Mss should be typed double-spaced on 8½×11 bond. SASE with Canadian postage or mss will not be returned. Looking for superior writing ability, stories with good plot, movement, dialogue and characterization. A selection of winning stories has been anthologized as *Pure Fiction: The Okanagan Award Winners*, and is essential reading for prospective contributors."

OMMATION PRESS BOOK AWARD, (I, II), Ommation Press, 5548 N. Sawyer, Chicago IL 60625. (312)539-5745. Annual competition for short stories, novels, story collections and poetry. Award: Book publication, $50 and 50 copies of book. Competition receives approx. 60 submissions. Judge: Effie Mihopoulos (editor). Entry fee $12, includes copy of former award-winning book. Guidelines for SASE. Deadline: December 30. Either previously published or unpublished submissions. Submit no more than 50 pages.

OPEN VOICE AWARDS, (I, II), Westside YMCA—Writer's Voice, 5 W. 63rd St., New York NY 10023. (212)787-6557. Biannual (twice a year) competition for short stories. Award: $50 honorarium and featured reading. Semiannual deadlines: January 1 and June 1. "Submit 10 double-spaced pages in a single genre. Nonmembers enclose $10 entry fee."

OREGON INDIVIDUAL ARTIST FELLOWSHIP, (I, IV), Oregon Arts Commission, 835 Summer St. NE, Salem OR 97301. (503)387-3625. Artist Services Coordinator: Vincent Dunn. "Award enables professional artists to undertake projects to assist their professional development." Biennial competition for short stories, novels, poetry and story collections. Award: $3,000 and $10,000. (Please note: 8 $3,000 awards and 2 $10,000 Master Fellowship Awards are spread over 5 disciplines—literature, music/opera, media arts, dance and theatre awarded in even-numbered years.) Competition receives approx. 50 entries/year. Judges: Professional advisors from outside the state. Guidelines and application for SASE. Deadline: September 1. Competition limited to Oregon residents.

‡PACIFIC NORTHWEST WRITERS CONFERENCE LITERARY AWARD, Suite 804, 2033 6th Ave., Seattle WA 98121-2526. (206)443-3807. "To encourage writers." Annual competition for short stories and novels (adult and juvenile). Also for nonfiction articles and books, poetry and screenplays/scripts. First prize each category is $300. Entry fee $10 for members, $20 for nonmembers. Guidelines for 3 ounce postage. Deadline: Mid-April. Previously unpublished submissions.

DOBIE PAISANO FELLOWSHIPS, (IV), Office of Graduate Studies, University of Texas at Austin, Austin TX 78712. (512)471-7213. Coordinator: Audrey N. Slate. Annual fellowships for creative writing (includes short stories, novels and story collections). Award: 6 months residence at ranch; $7,200 stipend. Competition receives approx. 100 submissions. Judges: faculty of University of Texas and members of Texas Institute of Letters. Entry fee: $5. Guidelines on request. "Open to writers with a Texas connection—native Texans, people living in Texas now or writers whose work focuses on Texas and Southwest." Deadline: Third week in January.

PALM COUNCIL PHILIPPINE AMERICAN SHORT STORY CONTEST, (I, IV), Philippine Arts, Letters and Media Council, Washington DC, 10829 Split Oak Lane, Burke VA 22015. (703)503-9012. Competition "to encourage and recognize fiction writing talent in the Philippine American community and promote the writing of Philippine American fiction." Annual award for short stories (when money is available). Award: $300 for first prize, $200 for second, $100 for third. Competition receives approximately 25 submissions. Judges: Screening committee selects 10 best entries which are sent to a panel of judges (3) who select the winners. Guidelines available for SASE. Deadline is May 3. Previously unpublished fiction. Limited to Philippine American themes by writers of Philippine American ancestry. No more than 5,000 words.

PAPER BAG **Short, Shorts, (I),** Paper Bag Press, P.O. Box 268805, Chicago IL 60626-8805. (312)285-7972. Award "to find quality short, short works of fiction (under 500 words)." Annual award for short stories (under 500 words). Award: Publication and $25. Competition receives approx. 50 submissions. Judges: Editors of *Paper Bag*. Guidelines for SASE. Deadline is ongoing. Unpublished submissions. Nothing over 500 words.

JUDITH SIEGEL PEARSON AWARD, (I), Wayne State University, Detroit MI 48202. Contact: Chair, English Dept. Competition "to honor writing about women." Annual award. Short stories up to 20 pages considered every third year (poetry and drama/nonfiction in alternate years). Plays and nonfictional prose in 1992. Award: Up to $400. Competition receives up to 100 submissions/year. Submissions are internally screened; then a noted writer does final reading. Entry forms for SASE.

WILLIAM PEDEN PRIZE IN FICTION, (I), *The Missouri Review*, 1507 Hillcrest Hall, University of Missouri, Columbia MO 65211. (314)882-4474. Contact: Speer Morgan, Greg Michalson, editors. Annual award "to honor the best short story published in *The Missouri Review* each year." Submissions are to be previously published in the volume year for which the prize is awarded. Award: $1,000. No entry deadline or fee. No rules; all fiction published in *MR* is automatically entered.

‡PEGASUS PRIZE, (III), Mobil Corporation, 3225 Gallows Rd. (Room 3C916), Fairfax VA 22037-0001. (703)846-2375. Director: Michael Morgan. To recognize distinguished works from literature not normally translated into English. Award for novels. "Prize is given on a country-by-country basis and does not involve submissions."

PEN/BOOK-OF-THE-MONTH CLUB TRANSLATION PRIZE, (II, IV), PEN American Center, 568 Broadway, New York NY 10012. (212)334-1660. Awards Coordinator: John Morrone. Award "to recognize the art of the literary translator." Annual competition for translations. Award: $3,000. Deadline: December 31. Previously published submissions within the calendar year. "Translators may be of any nationality, but book must have been published in the U.S. and must be a book-length literary translation." Books may be submitted by publishers, agents or translators. No application form. Send three copies. "Early submissions are strongly recommended."

THE PEN/FAULKNER AWARD FOR FICTION, (II, III), c/o The Folger Shakespeare Library, 201 E. Capitol St. SE, Washington DC 20003. (202)544-7077. Attention: Janice Delaney, PEN/Faulkner Foundation Executive Director. Annual award. "To award the most distinguished book-length work of fiction published by an American writer." Award: $7,500 for winner; $2,500 for nominees. Judges: Three writers chosen by the Trustees of the Award. Deadline: December 31. Published submissions only. Writers and publishers submit four copies of eligible titles published the current year. No juvenile. Authors must be American citizens.

PENNSYLVANIA COUNCIL ON THE ARTS, FELLOWSHIP PROGRAM, (I, IV), 216 Finance Bldg., Harrisburg PA 17120. (717)787-6883. Annual awards to provide fellowships for creative writers. Award: Up to $5,000. Competition receives approx. 175 submissions for 12 to 15 awards/year. Six judges: Three poetry, three fiction, different each year. Guidelines mailed upon request. Deadline: October 1. Applicants must be Pennsylvania residents.

‡PENNY DREADFUL SHORT STORY CONTEST, (I), *sub-TERRAIN Magazine*, P.O. Box 1575, Station A, Vancouver, British Columbia V6C 2P7 Canada. (604)876-8710. Contact: B. Kaufman. "To inspire writers to get down to it and struggle with a form that is condensed and difficult. To encourage clean, powerful writing." Annual award for short stories. Prize: $50 and publication. Competition receives about 100 submissions. Judges: An editorial collective. Entry fee $8 (includes 4-issue subscription). Guidelines for SASE, or SAE and IRC, in November. "Contest kicks off in mid-November." Deadline: April 15. Unpublished submissions. Length: 1,000 words. "We are looking for work that is trying to do something unique/new in form or content. Radical as opposed to the standard short story format. Experiment, take risks. That excites us. We are looking for work that expresses the experience of urban existence as we approach the closing of the century."

JAMES D. PHELAN AWARD, (I, IV), The San Francisco Foundation, Suite 910, 685 Market St., San Francisco CA 94105. Contact: Awards Program Coordinator. Annual award "to author of an unpublished work-in-progress of fiction (novel or short story), nonfictional prose, poetry or drama." Award: $2,000 and certificate. Rules and entry forms available after November 1 for SASE. Deadline: January 15. Unpublished submissions. Applicant must have been born in the state of California and be 20-35 years old.

PLAYBOY COLLEGE FICTION CONTEST, (I), *Playboy* Magazine, 680 North Lake Shore Dr., Chicago IL 60611. (312)751-8000. Fiction Editor: Alice K. Turner. Award "to foster young writing talent." Annual competition for short stories. Award: $3,000 plus publication in the magazine. Judges: Staff. Guidelines available for SASE. Deadline: January 1. Submissions should be unpublished. No age limit; college affiliation required. Stories should be 25 pages or fewer. "Manuscripts are not returned. Results of the contest will be sent via SASE."

EDGAR ALLAN POE AWARDS, (II), Mystery Writers of America, Inc., 6th Floor, 17 E. 47th St., New York NY 10017. Annual awards to enhance the prestige of the mystery. For mystery works published or produced during the calendar year. Award: Ceramic bust of Poe. Awards for best mystery novel, best first novel by an American author, best softcover original novel, best short story, best critical/biographical work, best fact crime, best young adult, best juvenile novel, best screenplay, best television feature and best episode in a series. Contact above address for specifics. Deadline: December 1.

THE RENATO POGGIOLI TRANSLATION AWARD, (I, IV), PEN American Center, 568 Broadway, New York NY 10012. (212)334-1660. Awards Coordinator: John Morrone. Award "to encourage beginning and promising translator who is working on a book-length translation from Italian to English." Annual competition for translations. Award: $3,000. Competition receives approx. 30-50 submissions. Judges: A panel of three translators. Guidelines for SASE. Deadline: January 15. Unpublished submissions. "Letters of application should be accompanied by a curriculum vitae, including Italian studies and samples of translation-in-progress."

KATHERINE ANNE PORTER PRIZE FOR FICTION, (I), *Nimrod*, Arts and Humanities Council of Tulsa, 2210 S. Main St., Tulsa OK 74114. (918)584-3333. Editor: Francine Ringold. "To award promising young writers and to increase the quality of manuscripts submitted to *Nimrod*." Annual award for short stories. Award: $1,000 first prize; $500 second prize. Receives approx. 650 entries/year. Judge varies each year. Past judges: Rosellen Brown, Alison Lurie, Gordon Lish, George Garrett, Toby Olson, John Leonard and Gladys Swan. Entry fee: $10. Guidelines for #10 SASE. Deadline for submissions: April 15. Previously unpublished manuscripts. Length: 7,500 words maximum. "Must be typed, double-spaced. Our contest is judged anonymously, so we ask that writers take their names off of their manuscripts (need 2 copies total). Include a cover sheet containing your name, full address, phone and the title of your work. Finally, include a SASE for notification of the results."

PRAIRIE SCHOONER THE LAWRENCE FOUNDATION AWARD, (I), 201 Andrews Hall, University of Nebraska, Lincoln NE 68588-0334. (402)472-1812. Contact: Hilda Raz, editor. Annual award "given to the author of the best short story published in *Prairie Schooner* during the preceding year." Award: $500. "Only short fiction published in *Prairie Schooner* is eligible for consideration."

PRISM INTERNATIONAL **SHORT FICTION CONTEST, (I),** *Prism International,* Dept. of Creative Writing, University of British Columbia, E455-1866 Main Mall, Vancouver, British Columbia V6T 1Z1 Canada. (604)822-2514. Contact: Publicity Manager. Award: $2,000 first prize and 5 $200 consolation prizes. Entry fee $10 plus $5 reading fee for each story. SASE for rules/entry forms.

LE PRIX MOLSON DE L'ACADÉMIE CANADIENNE-FRANÇAISE, (II, IV), Union des écrivaines éi écrivains québécois, #510, 1030 rue Cherrier, Montréal, Québec H2L 1H9 Canada. (514)526-6653. Annual prize for a novel in French by a writer from Québec or another province in Canada. Award: $5,000 (Canadian). Judges: 5 persons, members of the Académie canadienne française. Guidelines for SASE. Deadline: June 10. Five copies of the work must be submitted. Write for guidelines and entry forms (in French).

PUBLISHED SHORT-STORY CONTEST, (II), Hutton Publications, P.O. Box 1870, Hayden ID 83835. (208)772-6184. Award "to recognize good literature already published." Annual competition for short stories. Award: Cash/subscriptions/books. Competition receives approx. 50-75 submissions. Judge: Linda Hutton, Editor of Hutton Publications. Guidelines for #10 SASE. Deadline: December 1. Previously published submissions.

PULITZER PRIZE IN FICTION, (III), Graduate School of Journalism, 702 Journalism Bldg., Columbia University, New York NY 10027. Contact: Robert C. Christopher. Annual award for distinguished fiction *first* published in book form during the year by an American author, preferably dealing with American life. Award: $3,000. Deadline: Books published between January 1 and June 30 must be submitted by July 1. Books published between July 1 and December 31 must be submitted by November 1. Submit 4 copies of the book, entry form, biography and photo of author and $20 handling fee. Open to American authors.

PURE BRED DOGS/AMERICAN KENNEL GAZETTE, (I), 51 Madison Ave., New York NY 10010. (212)696-8331. Executive Editor: Elizabeth Bodner, DVM. Annual contest for short stories under 2,000 words. Award: Prizes of $500, $250 and $150 for top three entries. Certificate and complimentary one-year subscription for honorable mention winners. Top entry published in magazine. Judge: Panel. Contest requirements available for SASE. "The *Gazette* sponsors an annual fiction contest for short short stories on some subject relating to pure-bred dogs. Fiction for our magazine needs a slant toward the serious fancier with real insight into the human/dog bond and breed-specific pure-bred behavior."

PUSHCART PRIZE, (III), Pushcart Press, Box 380, Wainscott NY 11975. (516)324-9300. Contact: Bill Henderson, editor. Annual award "to publish and recognize the best of small press literary work." Previously published submissions, short stories, poetry or essays on any subject. Must have been published during the current calendar year. Award: Publication in *Pushcart Prize: Best of the Small Presses.* Deadline: Dec. 1. Nomination by small press publishers/editors only.

QUARTERLY WEST **NOVELLA COMPETITION, (I),** University of Utah, 317 Olpin Union, Salt Lake City UT 84112. (801)581-6168. Biennial award for novellas. Award: 2 prizes of $300 and publication. Send SASE for rules. Deadline: December 31 of even-numbered years.

SIR WALTER RALEIGH AWARD, (II, IV), North Carolina Literary and Historical Association, 109 E. Jones St., Raleigh NC 27601-2807. (919)733-7305. Secretary-Treasurer: Jeffrey J. Crow. Award "to promote among the people of North Carolina an interest in their own literature." Annual award for novels. Award: Statue of Sir Walter Raleigh. Judges: University English and history professors. Guidelines for SASE. Book must be an original work published during the twelve months ending June 30 of the year for which the award is given. Writer must be a legal or physical resident of North

Market conditions are constantly changing! If you're still using this book and it is 1993 or later, buy the newest edition of Novel & Short Story Writer's Market at your favorite bookstore or order directly from Writer's Digest Books.

Carolina for the three years preceding the close of the contest period. Authors or publishers may submit 3 copies of their book to the above address.

RAMBUNCTIOUS REVIEW, ANNUAL FICTION CONTEST, (I), 1221 W. Pratt, Chicago IL 60626. Contact: Nancy Lennon, co-editor. Annual award for short stories. Requirements: Typed, double-spaced, maximum 12 pages. SASE for deadline, rules/entry forms.

RHODE ISLAND STATE ARTS COUNCIL, (I, IV), Individual Artist's Fellowship in Literature, Suite 103, 95 Cedar St., Providence RI 02903-1034. (401)277-3880. Fellowship Program Director: Edward Holgate. Annual fellowship. Award: $3,000. Competition receives approximately 50 submissions. In-state panel makes recommendations to an out-of-state judge, who makes the final award. Entry forms for SASE. Deadline: April 1. Artists must be Rhode Island residents and not undergraduate or graduate students. "Program guidelines may change. Prospective applicants should contact RISCA prior to deadline."

HAROLD U. RIBALOW PRIZE, (II, IV), *Hadassah Magazine*, 50 W. 58th St., New York NY 10019. (212)355-7900. Contact: Alan M. Tigay, Executive Editor. Estab. 1983. Annual award "for a book of fiction on a Jewish theme. Harold U. Ribalow was a noted writer and editor who devoted his time to the discovery and encouragement of young Jewish writers." Book should have been published the year preceding the award. Award: $500 and excerpt of book in *Hadassah Magazine*. Deadline: December 31.

THE MARY ROBERTS RINEHART FUND, (III), *George Mason University*, 4400 University Dr., Fairfax VA 22030. (703)993-1185. Roger Lathbury, director. Biennial award for short stories, novels, novellas and story collections by unpublished writers (that is, writers ineligible to apply for NEA grants). Award: Two grants whose amount varies depending upon income the fund generates. Competition receives approx. 75-100 submissions annually. Entry forms or rules for SASE. Next fiction deadline: November 30, 1993. Writers must be nominated by a sponsoring writer, writing teacher, editor or agent.

RIVER CITY WRITING AWARDS IN FICTION, (I), *River City*, Dept. of English/Memphis State U., Memphis TN 38152. (901)678-8888. Awards Coordinator: Sharon Bryan. "Annual award to reward the best short stories." Award: $2,000 first prize; $500 second; $300 third. Competition receives approximately 280 submissions. Judge: To be announced. Entry fee $9; waived for subscribers to *River City*. Guidelines available for SASE. Deadline: Dec. 6. Unpublished fiction. Open to all writers. Word length: 7,500 maximum.

SUMMERFIELD G. ROBERTS AWARD, (IV), The Sons of the Republic of Texas, Suite 222, 5942 Abrams Rd., Dallas TX 75231. "Given for the best book or manuscript of biography, essay, fiction, nonfiction, novel, poetry or short story that describes or represents the Republic of Texas, 1836-1846." Annual award of $2,500. Deadline: January 31. "The manuscripts must be written or published during the calendar year for which the award is given. Entries are to be submitted in quintuplicate and will not be returned."

ROBERTS WRITING AWARDS, (I), H. G. Roberts Foundation, Box 1868, Pittsburg KS 66762. (316)231-2998. Awards Coordinator: Stephen E. Meats. "To reward and recognize exceptional fiction writers with money and publication." Annual competition for short stories. Award: $500 (first place); $200 (second place); $100 (third place); publication for prize winners and honorable mention receipts. Competition receives approx. 600 submissions. Judge: Established fiction writer, different each year. Entry fee $6/story. Guidelines and entry form for SASE. Deadline: September 15. Previously unpublished submissions. "Open to any type of fiction, up to 15 typed pages."

ROCKY MOUNTAIN WOMEN'S INSTITUTE ASSOCIATESHIP, (I, II), Foote Hall 317, 7150 Montview Blvd., Denver CO 80220. (303)871-6923. "Each year RMWI receives project proposals, selects those most promising and invites seven to ten to become Associates. These are artists, writers and scholars who are given office/studio space, stipends, support services and promotional events for one year." Competition receives approx. 150 submissions with selection based on excellence, project feasibility, group dynamics and need. Selection committees are composed of experts in arts/humanities. Entry fee $5. SASE for returns. Deadline: March 15 of each year for following September. Located at the

University of Denver law campus, work space provided but not residence. Part-time commitment per week and Associates meet as group once each week.

ROMANCE WRITERS OF AMERICA GOLDEN HEART AND THE RITA AWARDS, (I, II, IV), #315, 13700 Veterans Memorial, Houston TX 77014. (713)440-6885. "To recognize best work in romantic fiction in 7 categories by members of RWA, both published and not-published." Annual award for novels. Golden Heart Award: Heart and certificate; The Rita Award: Etched plaque. Golden Heart Award receives 600+ submissions/year; The Rita Award receives 250+ submissions/year. Judges: Published writers, editors. Entry fee for Golden Heart is $25; The Rita fee is $15. Guidelines for SASE. Deadline: January 15. Previously published submissions for The Rita; unpublished for Golden Heart. Categories are "traditional, short and long contemporary, historical, single title (historical and contemporary), young adult."

SACRAMENTO PUBLIC LIBRARY FOCUS ON WRITERS CONTEST, (I, IV), 828 I St., Sacramento CA 95814. (916)440-5926. Contact: Debbie Runnels. Award "to support and encourage aspiring writers." Annual competition for short stories and novels. Awards: $100 (first place); $50 (second place); $25 (third place). Competition receives approx. 147 short story; 78 novel chapters; 71 children's stories. Judges: Local teachers of English, authors and librarians. Entry fee $5/entry. Guidelines for SASE. Deadline: February 1. Unpublished submissions. Length: 2,500-word short story; 1,000-word story for children. Open to all writers in northern California.

***SAN JOSE STUDIES* BEST STORY AWARD, (I),** Bill Casey Memorial Fund, 1 Washington Square, San Jose CA 95192. Contact: Fauneil J. Rinn. Winning author receives a year's complimentary subscription to journal, which prints notice of award, and is also considered for the Bill Casey Memorial Award of $100 for the best contribution in each year's volume of *San José Studies* in essay, fiction or poetry.

CARL SANDBURG AWARDS, (I, IV), Friends of the Chicago Public Library, Harold Washington Library Center, 400 S. State St., Chicago IL 60605. (312)269-2922. Annual. To honor excellence in Chicago or Chicago area authors (including 6 counties). Books published between May 31 and June 1 (the following year). $1,000 honorarium for fiction, nonfiction, poetry and children's literature. Medal awarded also. Deadline: September 1. All entries become the property of the Friends.

SASSY FICTION CONTEST, (I, IV), *Sassy*, 7th Floor, 230 Park Ave., New York NY 10169. (212)551-9500. Competition "to recognize promise in fiction writers aged 13-19 and to encourage teenagers to write." Annual award for short stories. Award: 1st prize: $1,000, a Smith Corona PWP 2100, and the story printed. 2nd prize: $500, a Smith Corona 1XO7700. Competition receives approximately 5,000 submissions. Judges: Christina Kelly, Mary Kay Schilling, Jane Pratt. No entry fee. Guidelines available for SASE. Deadline is November 30. Unpublished fiction. Only for writers aged 13-19.

SCHOLASTIC WRITING AWARDS, (I, IV), Scholastic Inc., 730 Broadway, New York NY 10003. (212)505-3566. Awards Coordinator: Lori Maccione. To provide opportunity for recognition of young writers. Annual award for short stories and other categories. Award: Cash awards, scholarships and grants. Competition receives 22,000 submissions/year. Judges vary each year. Deadline: January 17. Unpublished submissions. Contest limited to junior high and senior high students; grades 7-12. Entry blank must be signed by teacher. "Program is run through school and is only open to students in grades 7 through 12, regularly and currently enrolled in public and non-public schools in the United States and its territories, U.S.-sponsored schools abroad or any schools in Canada."

SCIENCE FICTION WRITERS OF EARTH (SFWoE) SHORT STORY CONTEST, (I, IV), Science Fiction Writers of Earth, Box 121293, Fort Worth TX 76121. (817)451-8674. SFWoE Administrator: Gilbert Gordon Reis. Purpose "to promote the art of science fiction/fantasy short story writing." Annual award for short stories. Award: $100 (1st prize); $50 (2nd prize); $25 (3rd prize). Competition receives approx. 75 submissions/year. Judge: Author Edward Bryant. Entry fee: $5 for 1st entry; $2 for additional entries. Guidelines for SASE. Deadline: October 30. Submissions must be unpublished. Stories should be science fiction or fantasy, 2,000-7,500 words. "Although many of our past winners are now published authors, there is still room for improvement. The odds are good for a well-written story."

***SE LA VIE WRITER'S JOURNAL* CONTEST, (I, IV),** Rio Grande Press, P.O. Box 371371, El Paso TX 79937. (915)595-2625. Contact: Rosalie Avara, editor. Competition offered quarterly for short stories. Award: Publication in the *Se La Vie Writer's Journal* plus up to $10 and contributor's copy. Judge:

Editor. Entry fee $4 for each or $7 for two. Guidelines for SASE. Deadlines: March 31, June 30, September 30, December 31. Unpublished submissions. Theme is "life" or "the writing life." Length: 500 words maximum.

THE SEATON AWARDS, (I, IV), *Kansas Quarterly*, 122 Denison Hall, Kansas State University KS 66506-0703. Annual awards to reward and recognize the best fiction published in *KQ* during the year from authors native to or resident in Kansas. Submissions must be previously unpublished. Anyone who submits unpublished material which is then accepted for publication becomes eligible for the awards. Award: Recognition and monetary sums of $250, $150, $100 and $50. No deadline. Material simply may be submitted for consideration at any time with SASE. "Ours are not contests. We give monetary awards and recognition to Kansas writers of national literary stature."

SEVENTEEN MAGAZINE FICTION CONTEST, (I, IV), *Seventeen Magazine*, 850 3rd Ave., New York NY 10022. Contact: Adrian Nicole LeBlanc. To honor best short fiction by a young writer. Rules are found in the November and December issues. Contest for 13-21 year olds. Deadline: April 31. Submissions judged by a panel of outside readers and *Seventeen*'s editors.

‡SHORT GRAIN CONTEST, (I), Box 1154, Regina, Saskatchewan S4P 3B4 Canada. Contact: Geoffrey Ursell. Annual competition for postcard stories and prose poems. Awards: $250 (1st prize), $150 (2nd prize) and $100 (third prize) in each category. "All winners and Honourable Mentions will also receive regular payment for publication in *Grain*." Competition receives approximately 400 submissions. Judges: Canadian writers with national and international reputations. First entry fee $15 (includes one-year subscription); each additional entry $5. Guidelines for SASE or SAE and IRC. Deadline: April 30. Unpublished submissions. Contest entries must be either an original postcard story (a work of narrative fiction written in 500 words or less) or a prose poem (a lyric poem written as a prose paragraph or paragraphs in 500 words or less).

‡SIDE SHOW ANNUAL SHORT STORY CONTEST, (I), Somersault Press, P.O. Box 1428, El Cerrito CA 94530-1428. (510)215-2207. "To attract quality writers for our 300-odd page paperback fiction annual." Awards: 1st: $30; 2nd: $25; 3rd: $20; $5/printed page paid to all accepted writers (on publication). Judges: The editors of *Side Show*. Entry fee $10 (includes subscription) for *first* submission *only*. Leaflet available. Sample copy for $10 plus $2.50 postage. Deadline: July 15. Multiple submissions encouraged. All mss with SASE critiqued.

CHARLIE MAY SIMON BOOK AWARD, (III, IV), Arkansas Department of Education, Elementary School Council, State Education Building, Capitol Mall, Division of Instruction, Room 301-B, Little Rock AR 72201. (501)682-4371. Contact: James A. Hester, Secretary/Treasurer, Arkansas Elementary School Council. Annual award "to encourage reading by children in quality children's literature." Award: Medallion. No entry fee. Previously published submissions. "The committee doesn't accept requests from authors. They will look at booklists of books produced during the previous year and check recommendations from the following sources: *Booklist, Bulletin of the Center for Children's Books, Children's Catalog, Elementary School Library Collection, Hornbook, Library of Congress Children's Books, School Library Journal.*"

W.H. SMITH/BOOKS IN CANADA FIRST NOVELS (III, IV), Books in Canada, 33 Draper St., Toronto, Ontario M5V 2M3 Canada. (416)340-9809. Contact: Paul Stuewe, editor. Annual award "to promote and recognize Canadian writing." Award: $5,000. No entry fee. Submissions are made by publishers. Contest is restricted to first novels in English, intended for adults, published in Canada in the previous calendar year.

‡SNAKE NATION PRESS ANNUAL SUMMER CONTEST, (I, II), 110-#2 W. Force St., Valdosta GA 31601. (912)249-8334. Contact: Janice Daugharty. "Because we pay only in contributor's copy, this contest allows us to give some financial compensation." Annual award for short stories. Awards: $300, $200, $100. Competition receives approx. 500 submissions. Judge: Independent ("it varies"). Entry fee $5 (includes contest issue). Guidelines for SASE. Deadline: February (for annual summer issue). Previously published or unpublished submissions. Length: 5,000 words maximum.

‡KAY SNOW CONTEST, (I, IV), Willamette Writers, Suite 5-A, 9045 SW Barbur Blvd., Portland OR 97219. (503)452-1592. Contact: Contest Coordinator. Award "to create a showcase for writers of all fields of literature." Annual competition for short stories; also poetry (structured and nonstructured), nonfiction, juvenile, script and student writers. Award: $100 1st prize in each category, 2nd and 3rd prizes, honorable mentions. Competition receives approx. 500-1,000 submissions. Judges: Nationally recognized writers and teachers. Entry fee $10 nonmembers; $7 members. Guidelines for #10 SASE. Deadline: July 1 postmark. Unpublished submissions. Maximum 1,500 words. "This contest is held in association with our annual conference. Prizes are awarded at the banquet held during the conference in early August."

SOCIETY OF CHILDREN'S BOOK WRITERS WORK-IN-PROGRESS GRANTS, (I, IV), Box 66296, Mar Vista, Los Angeles CA 90066. (818)347-2849. Contact: SCBW. Annual grant for contemporary novel for young people; also nonfiction research grant and grant for work whose author has never been published. Award: 1st-$1,000; 2nd-$500 (work-in-progress). 1st-$1,000; 2nd-$400 (Judy Blume/SCBW contemporary novel grant). Competition receives approx. 80 submissions. Judges: Members of children's book field—editors, authors, etc. Guidelines for SASE. Deadline: Feb. 1-May 1. Unpublished submissions. Applicants must be SCBW members only.

***SONORA REVIEW* FICTION CONTEST, (I),** Dept. of English, University of Arizona, Tucson AZ 85721. (602)621-8077. Contact: fiction editor. Annual award "to encourage and support quality short fiction." Award: $150 first prize; $50 second prize; plus publication in *Sonora*. Contest rules for SASE. Unpublished submissions. "We accept manuscripts all year, but manuscripts received during the summer (May-August) will not be read until fall."

SOUTH CAROLINA ARTS COMMISSION AND *THE STATE NEWSPAPER* SOUTH CAROLINA FICTION PROJECT, (I, IV), 1800 Gervais St., Columbia SC 29201. (803)734-8696. Steve Lewis, director, Literary Arts Program. The purpose of the award is "to get money to fiction writers and to get their work published and read." Annual award for short stories. Award: $500 and publication in *The State Newspaper*. Competition receives approximately 400 submissions for 12 awards (up to 12 stories chosen). Judges are a panel of professional writers and senior writer for *The State Newspaper*. Entry forms or rules for SASE. Deadline November 19. South Carolina residents only.

SOUTH CAROLINA ARTS COMMISSION LITERATURE FELLOWSHIP AND LITERATURE GRANTS, (I, IV), 1800 Gervais St., Columbia SC 29201. (803)734-8696. Steve Lewis, director, Literary Arts Program. "The purpose of the fellowships is to give a cash award to two deserving writers (one in poetry, one in creative prose) whose works are of the highest caliber." Award: $7,500 fellowship. Matching grants up to $7,500. Competition receives approximately 40 submissions/fellowship. Judges are out-of-state panel of professional writers and editors for fellowships, and in-state panels and SCAC staff for grants. Entry forms or rules for SASE. Fellowship deadline September 15. Grants deadline January 15. South Carolina residents only.

SOUTH DAKOTA ARTS COUNCIL, ARTIST FELLOWSHIP, (IV), 108 West 11th, Sioux Falls SD 57102-0788. (605)339-6646. Award "to assist artists with career development. Grant can be used for supplies or to set aside time to work, but cannot be used for academic research or formal study toward a degree." Annual competition for writers. Award: $1,000 for emerging artists; $5,000 for established artists. Competition receives approx. 80 submissions. "Grants are awarded on artists' work and *not* on financial need." Judges: Panels of in-state and out-of-state experts in each discipline. Guidelines for SASE. Deadline: February 1. Previously published or unpublished submissions. Fellowships are open only to residents of South Dakota. "SD writers with specific projects may apply for a Project Grant. They would not be eligible for fellowship grants in that case. Deadline is Feb. 1 and guidelines are available by writing SDAC."

***THE SOUTHERN REVIEW*/LOUISIANA STATE UNIVERSITY ANNUAL SHORT FICTION AWARD, (II),** *The Southern Review*, 43 Allen Hall, Louisiana State University, Baton Rouge LA 70803. (504)388-5108. Contact: Editors, *The Southern Review*. Annual award "to encourage publication of good fiction." For a first collection of short stories by an American writer appearing during calendar year. Award: $500 to author. Possible campus reading. Deadline: A month after close of each calendar year. The book of short stories must be released by a U.S. publisher. Two copies to be submitted by publisher or author. Looking for "style, sense of craft, plot, in-depth characters."

SPUR AWARD CONTEST, (II, IV), Western Writers of America, P.O. Box 823, Sheridan WY 82801. Secretary-treasurer: Barb Ketcham. Annual award to encourage excellence in western writing. A spur is awarded for Best Historical Fiction, Best Juvenile Fiction and Best Short Fiction works. Entries are accepted only from the current calendar year for each year's award; that is, books can only be entered in the year they are published. Award: A wooden plaque shaped like a W with a bronze spur attached. Judges: A panel of experienced authors appointed by the current Spur Awards Chairman. Contest/award rules and entry forms available with SASE. Deadline: December 31. "A special Medicine Pipe Bearer Award, is offered in the Best First Western Novel competition. First novels may be entered in both Spur and Medicine Pipe Bearer competition. Books must be of the traditional or historical western theme, set anywhere west of the Mississippi River before the 20th century, ideally from 1850 to 1900."

STAND MAGAZINE SHORT STORY COMPETITION, (I), *Stand Magazine,* 179 Wingrove Road, Newcastle upon Tyne NE4 9DA England. Biennial award for short stories. Award: 1st prize £1,250; 2nd prize £500; 3rd prize £250; 4th prize £150; 5th prize £100; 6th prize £75 (or U.S. $ equivalent). Judges are Susan Hill and David Hughes. Entry fee $7. Guidelines for SAE and 2 IRCs. Deadline: March 31, 1993.

WALLACE E. STEGNER FELLOWSHIP, (I, IV), Creative Writing Program, Stanford University, Stanford CA 94305-2087. (415)723-2637. Contact: Gay Pierce, program coordinator. Annual award. Four two-year fellowships in fiction ($10,000 stipend plus required tuition or $3,800 annually). Entry fee $20. Deadline: January 2. For unpublished or previously published fiction writers. Residency required.

STORY TIME SHORT-STORY CONTEST, (I), Hutton Publications, Box 1870, Hayden ID 83835. (208)772-6184. Contact: Linda Hutton, editor. Estab. 1982. "To encourage short-story writers." Award: $15 first prize; $10 second prize; $7.50 third prize. Send #10 SASE for rules. Deadlines: March 1, June 1, August 1, December 1. Previously published or unpublished submissions. Looking for "tightly written plot and well developed characters."

SWG LITERARY AWARDS, (I, IV), Saskatchewan Writers Guild, Box 3986, Regina, Saskatchewan S4P 3R9 Canada. (306)757-6310. Awards "to recognize excellence in work by Saskatchewan writers." Annual competition for short stories, poetry, nonfiction and children's literature. Also a long manuscript category that rotates through poetry, nonfiction, drama and fiction. The 1992 Long Manuscript competition is in nonfiction. Awards: Manuscript awards (3) are $1,000; 3 awards of $150 in each of the short categories. Judges: Writers from outside the Province. Entry fee: $15 (one ms allowed); $4 for other categories (multiple submissions allowed). Guidelines for SASE. Deadline: February 28. Unpublished submissions. Available only to Saskatchewan citizens.

TEXAS-WIDE WRITERS CONTEST, (I, IV), Byliners, P.O. Box 6218, Corpus Christi TX 78413. (512)991-1442. Awards Coordinator: Deborah Ferguson. "Award to fund a scholarship in journalism or creative writing." Annual award for adult and children's short stories, novels and poems. Award: Novels—1st $100, 2nd $75, 3rd $50; short stories—1st $75, 2nd $50, 3rd $25. Competition receives approximately 50 novel, 125 short story and 62 children's story submissions. Judges: Varies each year. Entry fee $5/story, $10/novel. Guidelines available for SASE. Deadline is March 1 (date remains same each year). Unpublished submissions. Limited to Texas residents and winter Texans. Length: Children's story limit 2,000 words; short story limit 3,000 words; novel 3 page synopsis plus chapter one. "Contest also has nostalgia, article and nonfiction book categories."

THURBER HOUSE RESIDENCIES, (II), The Thurber House, 77 Jefferson Ave., Columbus OH 43215. (614)464-1032. Literary Director: Michael J. Rosen. "Four writers/year are chosen as writers-in-residence, one for each quarter." Award for writers of novels and story collections. $5,000 stipend and housing for a quarter in the furnished third-floor apartment of James Thurber's boyhood home. Judges: Advisory panel. Guidelines for SASE. Deadline: January 1. "The James Thurber Writer-in-Residence will teach a class in the Creative Writing Program at The Ohio State University in either fiction or poetry, and will offer one public reading and a short workshop for writers in the community.

Market categories: (I) Unpublished entries; (II) Published entries nominated by the author; (III) Published entries, nominated by the editor, publisher or nominating body; (IV) Specialized entries.

Significant time outside of teaching is reserved for the writer's own work in progress. Candidates should have published at least one book with a major publisher, in any area of fiction, nonfiction or poetry, and should possess some experience in teaching."

TOWSON STATE UNIVERSITY PRIZE FOR LITERATURE, (II, IV), Towson State University Foundation, Towson State University, Towson MD 21204. (301)830-2128. Contact: Annette Chappell, dean, College of Liberal Arts. Annual award for novels or short story collections, previously published. Requirements: Writer must not be over 40; must be a Maryland resident. SASE for rules/entry forms. Deadline: May 15.

JOHN TRAIN HUMOR PRIZE, (I), *The Paris Review*, 541 E. 72nd St., New York NY 10021. Fiction Editor: George Plimpton. Award for the best previously unpublished work of humorous fiction, nonfiction or poetry. One submission per envelope. Award: $1,500 and publication in *The Paris Review*. Guidelines for SASE. Deadline: March 31. Manuscripts must be less than 10,000 words. No formal application form is required; regular submissions guidelines apply. For samples, send $7.50 to *The Paris Review*, 45-39171 Place, Flushing NY 11358.

TRANSLATION CENTER AWARDS, (I, II, IV), The Translation Center, 412 Dodge Hall, Columbia University, New York NY 10027. (212)854-2305. Contact: Award Secretary. Over a dozen annual awards "for outstanding translation of a substantial part of a book-length *literary* work." Award: Cash grant (varies). No entry fee. Write for application form. Deadline: January 15.

TRANSLATORS ASSOCIATION AWARDS, (III, IV), 84 Drayton Gardens, London SW10 9SB England. Scott Moncrieff Prize for best translation into English of 20th century French work; Schlegel-Tieck Prize for translations from German; John Florio Prize for translations from Italian into English; Bernard Shaw Prize for translations from Swedish; Portuguese Prize for translations, published or unpublished, from Portuguese (originals must be by Portuguese nationals). Award: Scott Moncrieff Prize: £1,500; Schlegel-Tieck Prize: £2,000; John Florio Prize (biannual): £900; Bernard Shaw Prize (every 3 years): £ 1,000; Portuguese Prize (every 3 years): £3,000. Judges: 3 translators. Deadline: December 31. Previously published submissions. Awards for translations published in U.K. during year of award. U.K. publishers submit books for consideration.

‡TRI-STATE FAIR LITERARY AWARDS, (I), P.O. Box 31087, Amarillo TX 79120-1087. For rules, contact: Marianne McNeil, 7003 Amarillo Blvd. E., Amarillo TX 79107. Annual competition for short stories. Award: $5-$3-$2 and $25 Best of Show Awards for Prose and Poetry. Judges: Different judges each year. Entry fee $7. Guidelines for SASE. Deadline: August 1. Unpublished submissions. Length: 3,000 words max. "Categories may change a bit from year to year. Guidelines required. At present: Prose—1. Humor, 2. Nostalgia, 3. Short Story, 4. Inspirational, 5. Story for Children. Entries are displayed at Literary Booth at Tri-State Fair during fair week."

‡MARK TWAIN AWARD, (III, IV), Missouri Association of School Librarians, P.O. Box 22476, Kansas City MO 647113-2476. Estab. 1970. Annual award to introduce children to the best of current literature for children and to stimulate reading. Award: A bronze bust of Mark Twain, created by Barbara Shanklin, a Missouri sculptor. A committee selects pre-list of the books nominated for the award; statewide reader/selectors review and rate the books, and then children throughout the state vote to choose a winner from the final list. Books must be published two years prior to nomination for the award list. Publishers may send books they wish to nominate for the list to the committee members. 1) Books should be of interest to children in grades 4 through 8; 2) written by an author living in the U.S.; 3) of literary value which may enrich children's personal lives.

UTAH ORIGINAL WRITING COMPETITION, (I,IV), Utah Arts Council, 617 East South Temple, Salt Lake City UT 84102. (801)533-5895. Literary Arts Coordinator: G. Barnes. Annual competition for poetry, essays, nonfiction books, short stories, novels and story collections. Awards: Vary; last year between $200-$1,000. Competition receives 700 entries. Judges: "Published and award-winning judges from across America." Guidelines available, no SASE necessary. Deadline: Mid-June or later. Submissions should be unpublished. *Limited to Utah residents.* "Some limitation on word-length. See guidelines for details."

VERMONT COUNCIL ON THE ARTS FELLOWSHIP, (I, II, IV), Vermont Council on the Arts, 133 State St., Montpelier VT 05633-6001. (802)828-3291. "To support creative development." Annual competition for short stories, novels, story collections and translations. Award: $3,500 with $500 Finalist Awards. The VCA awards approximately 17-20 Fellowships annually. There is no predetermined number of Fellowships by discipline. Judges: A peer panel makes recommendations to the VCA Board of Trustees. Guidelines for SASE after December 1. Deadline: March 2. Previously published and unpublished submissions. Applicants must be legal residents of Vermont and must have lived in VT at least 6 months prior to date of application. Word length: 10-15 pages poetry, 10-20 pages fiction. Applicants may include a synopsis or summary of longer works in addition to submitted excerpts. Applicants must be 18 or older, may not be enrolled as fulltime students, and must have submitted all reports on past council grants. Grant money may not be used for foreign travel, tuition applied to academic programs, or purchase of permanent equipment. *Manuscripts should be unsigned and should indicate completion date.* Manuscripts must be sent with completed application.

VICTORIAN FELLOWSHIP OF AUSTRALIAN WRITERS ANNUAL NATIONAL LITERARY AWARDS, (I, II, IV), 1/317 Barkers Rd., Kew (Melbourne) Victoria 3101 Australia. Contact: J.S. Hamilton, president, Victorian FAW. Sponsors 20 awards for Australian writers, both published and unpublished. Annual competitions for poetry, short stories, novels, nonfiction books and story collections. Awards vary: Largest award is $1,200. Competition receives over 200 entries for books, at least 100 for manuscripts. Judges: Writers and critics appointed by the organizer. Guidelines for SASE. Deadline: December 31. Published or previously unpublished submissions, depending on award. Awards offered to Australians (including those living overseas) or residents of Australia. Send for guidelines, but only from October each year.

VOGELSTEIN FOUNDATION GRANTS, (II), The Ludwig Vogelstein Foundation, Inc., Box 4924, Brooklyn NY 11240-4924. Executive Director: Frances Pishny. "A small foundation awarding grants to individuals in the arts and humanities. Criteria are merit and need. No student aid given." Send SASE for complete information after Jan. 31.

HAROLD D. VURSELL MEMORIAL AWARD, (III), American Academy and Institute of Arts and Letters, 633 W. 155th St., New York NY 10032. (212)368-5900. Annual award "to single out recent writing in book form that merits recognition for the quality of its prose style. It may be given for a work of fiction, biography, history, criticism, belles lettres, memoir, journal or a work of translation." Award: $5,000. Judged by 7-member jury composed of members of the Department of Literature of the American Academy and Institute of Arts and Letters. *No applications accepted.*

EDWARD LEWIS WALLANT MEMORIAL BOOK AWARD, (II, IV), 3 Brighton Rd., West Hartford CT 06117. Sponsored by Dr. and Mrs. Irving Waltman. Contact: Mrs. Irving Waltman. Annual award. Memorial to Edward Lewis Wallant, which offers incentive and encouragement to beginning writers, for books published the year before the award is conferred in the spring. Award: $250 plus award certificate. Books may be submitted for consideration to Dr. Sanford Pinsker, Department of English, Franklin & Marshall College, P.O. Box 3003, Lancaster PA 17604-3003. "Looking for creative work of fiction by an American which has significance for the American Jew. The novel (or collection of short stories) should preferably bear a kinship to the writing of Wallant. The award will seek out the writer who has not yet achieved literary prominence."

WASHINGTON PRIZE FOR FICTION, (I), 1301 S. Scott St., Arlington VA 22204. (703)920-3771. Director: Larry Kaltman. Awards: $1,000 (1st prize), $500 (2nd prize), $250 (3rd prize). Judges: Dr. Hans Bergmann (George Mason University), J.R. Salamanca (University of Maryland), Dr. Joseph M. Sendry (Catholic University). Entry fee $25. Deadline: November 30 annually. Unpublished novels or short story collections. Length: 65,000 words minimum.

WASHINGTON STATE ARTS COMMISSION ARTIST FELLOWSHIP AWARD, (I, IV), 110 9th and Columbia, Olympia WA 97504-4111. (206)753-3860. Arts Program Manager: Mary Frye. "Unrestricted award to a mid-career artist." Biannual award for writers of short stories, novels and literary criticism. Award: $5,000. Competition receives 100 entries. Judges: Peer panel. Guidelines upon request. Deadline: Spring/Summer. Literary arts award made in even-numbered years. Submissions can be either previously published or unpublished. Washington residents only. "Applicant must be 5 years out of school in field they're applying to and have 5 years of professional experience. No emerging artists."

WESTERN CANADIAN MAGAZINE AWARDS, (II, IV), 3898 Hillcrest Ave., North Vancouver, British Columbia V7R 4B6 Canada. (604)984-7525. "To honour and encourage excellence." Annual competition for short stories (fiction articles in magazines). Award: $500. Entry fee: $18-24 (depending on circulation of magazine). Deadline: January. Previously published submissions (between January and December). "Must be Canadian or have earned immigrant status and the fiction article must have appeared in a publication (magazine) that has its main editorial offices located in the 4 Western provinces, the Yukon or NW territories."

WESTERN HERITAGE AWARDS, (II, IV), National Cowboy Hall of Fame, 1700 NE 63rd St., Oklahoma City OK 73111. (405)478-2250. Contact: Dana Sullivant, public relations director. Annual award "to honor outstanding quality in fiction, nonfiction and art literature." Submissions are to have been published during the previous calendar year. Award: The Wrangler, a replica of a C.M. Russell Bronze. No entry fee. Entry forms and rules available November 1 for SASE. Deadline: December 31. Looking for "stories that best capture the spirit of the West."

WESTERN STATES BOOK AWARDS, Western States Arts Federation, 236 Montezuma, Santa Fe NM 87501. (505)988-1166. Literature Coordinator: Robert Sheldon. Estab. 1984. Biannual award. "Recognition for writers living in the West; encouragement of effective production and marketing of quality books published in the West; increase of sales and critical attention." For unpublished manuscripts submitted by publisher. Award: $2,500 for authors; $5,000 for publishers. Contest rules for SASE. Write for information on deadline.

WILLIAM ALLEN WHITE CHILDREN'S BOOK AWARD, (III), Emporia State University, 1200 Commercial, Emporia KS 66801. Contact: Mary E. Bogan, executive secretary. Estab. 1952. Annual award to honor the memory of one of the state's most distinguished citizens by encouraging the boys and girls of Kansas to read and enjoy good books. "We do not accept submissions from authors or publishers." Award: Bronze medal. The White Award Book Selection Committee looks for excellence of literary quality in fiction, poetry and nonfiction appropriate for 4th through 8th graders. All nominations to the annual White Award master list must be made by a member of the White Award Book Selection Committee.

WHITING WRITER'S AWARDS, (III), Mrs. Giles Whiting Foundation, Rm 3500, 30 Rockefeller Pl., New York NY 10112. Director: Dr. Gerald Freund. To encourage the work of emergent writers and to recognize the work of older, proven writers. Annual award for writers of fiction, poetry, nonfiction and plays. Award: $30,000 (10 awards). Writers are submitted by appointed nominators and chosen for awards by an appointed selection committee. Direct applications and informal nominations not accepted by the foundation.

LAURA INGALLS WILDER AWARD, (III), American Library Association/Association for Library Service to Children, 50 E. Huron St., Chicago IL 60611. Award offered every 3 years; next year 1992. "To honor a significant body of work for children, for illustration, fiction or nonfiction." Award: Bronze medal.

LAURENCE L. WINSHIP BOOK AWARD, (III, IV), *The Boston Globe*, Boston MA 02107. (617)929-2649. Contact: Marianne Callahan, public affairs department. Annual award "to honor *The Globe*'s late editor who did much to encourage young talented New England authors." Award: $2,000. Contest rules for SASE. Deadline: June 30. Previously published submissions from July 1 to July 1 each year. Book must have some relation to New England—author, theme, plot or locale. To be submitted by publishers.

WISCONSIN ARTS BOARD INDIVIDUAL ARTIST PROGRAM, (II, IV), Suite 301, 131 W. Wilson St., Madison WI 53703. (608)266-0190. Contact: Elizabeth Malner. Annual awards for short stories, poetry, novels, novellas, drama, essay/criticism. Awards: 3 awards of $5,000; 4 awards of $3,500; 6 awards of $1,000. Competition receives approx. 175 submissions. Judges are 3 out-of-state jurors. Entry forms or rules for SASE. Deadline: September 15. Wisconsin residents only. Students are ineligible.

WISCONSIN INSTITUTE FOR CREATIVE WRITING FELLOWSHIP, (I, II, IV), University of Wisconsin—Creative Writing, English Department, Madison WI 53705. Competition "to provide time, space and an intellectual community for writers working on first books." Annual award for short stories, novels and story collections. Award: $20,000/9-month appointment. Competition receives approximately 300 submissions. Judges: English Department faculty. Guidelines available for SASE; write to Ron Kuka. Deadline is month of February. Published or unpublished submissions. Published submissions must

548 *Novel & Short Story Writer's Market '92*

be typed. Applicants must have received an M.F.A. or comparable graduate degree in creative writing. Limit one story up to 30 pages in length.

WORLD'S BEST SHORT SHORT STORY CONTEST, (I), English Department Writing Program, Florida State University, Tallahassee FL 32306. (904)644-4230. Contact: Jerome Stern, director. Annual award for short-short stories, unpublished, under 250 words. Prizewinning story gets $100, a box of Florida oranges and broadside publication; winner and finalists are published in *Sun Dog: The Southeast Review*. SASE for rules. Deadline: February 15. Open to all.

WRITER'S DIGEST **ANNUAL WRITING COMPETITION (Short Story Division), (I),** *Writer's Digest*, 1507 Dana Ave., Cincinnati OH 45207. (513)531-2222. Grand Prize is a trip to New York City with arrangements to meet editors in writer's field. Other awards include cash, reference books, plaques and certificates of recognition. Names of grand prize winner and top 100 winners are announced in the October issue of *Writer's Digest*. Top two entries published in booklet ($4.50). Send SASE to *WD* Writing Competition for rules or see January-May issues of *Writer's Digest*. Deadline: May 31. All entries must be original, unpublished and not previously submitted to a *Writer's Digest* contest. Length: 2,000 words maximum, one entry only. No acknowledgment will be made of receipt of mss nor will mss be returned.

WRITERS GUILD OF ALBERTA LITERARY AWARD, (II, IV), Writers Guild of Alberta, 10523-100 Avenue, Edmonton, Alberta T5J 0A8 Canada. (403)426-5892. "To recognize, reward and foster writing excellence." Annual competition for novels and story collections. Award: $500, plus leather-bound copy of winning work. Short story competition receives 5-10 submissions; novel competition receives about 20; children's literature category up to 40. Judges: 3 published writers. Guidelines for SASE. Deadline: December 31. Previously published submissions (between January and December). Open to Alberta authors, resident for previous 18 months. Entries must be book-length and published within the current year.

WRITERS' JOURNAL **ANNUAL FICTION CONTEST, (I),** 27 Empire Dr., St. Paul MN 55103. (612)225-1306. Publisher/Managing Editor: Valerie Hockert. Annual award for short stories. Award: 1st place: $200; 2nd place: $75; 3rd place: $25. Also gives honorable mentions. Competition receives approximately 400 submissions/year. Judges are Valerie Hockert, Steven Petsch and others. Entry fee $5 each. Maximum of 3 entries/person. Entry forms or rules for SASE. Maximum length is 3,000 words. Two copies of each entry are required—one *without* name or address of writer.

‡THE WRITERS' WORKSHOP INTERNATIONAL FICTION CONTEST, (I), The Writers' Workshop, P.O. Box 696, Asheville NC 28802. (704)254-8111. Executive Director: Karen Tager. Annual award for short stories. Awards: $500 and submission to *The Paris Review* (1st prize), $250 (2nd prize), $100 (3rd prize). "Winners will also receive an autographed copy of E.L. Doctorow's highly acclaimed novel, *Billy Bathgate*; and one year's membership to The Writers' Workshop." Competition receives approximately 350 submissions. Final judge: E.L. Doctorow. Entry fee $15/$12 members. Guidelines for SASE. Deadline: February. Unpublished submissions. Length: 30 typed, double-spaced pages per story. Multiple submissions are accepted.

WYOMING COUNCIL ON THE ARTS, LITERARY FELLOWSHIPS, (I, IV), Wyoming Council on the Arts, 2320 Capitol Ave., Cheyenne WY 82002. (307)777-7742. Contact: Literature consultant. Award to "honor the most outstanding new work of Wyoming writers—fiction, nonfiction, drama, poetry." Annual competition for short stories, novels, story collections, translations, poetry. Award: 4 awards of $2,500 each. Competition receives approx. 120 submissions. Judges: Panel of writers selected each year from outside Wyoming. Guidelines for SASE. Deadline: Fall. Applicants "must be Wyoming resident for one year prior to application deadline. Must not be a fulltime student *or* a fulltime tenured faculty member." No genre exclusions; combined genres acceptable. 25 pages double-spaced maximum; 10 pages maximum for poetry. Winners may not apply for 4 years after receiving fellowships.

YOUNG ADULT CANADIAN BOOK AWARD, (II, IV), Young Adult Services Interest Group, c/o Unionville Library, 15 Library Lane, Unionville, Ontario L3R 5C4 Canada. Contact: Nancy E. Black, convener of book award committee. Established 1980 by the Young Adult Caucus of the Saskatchewan Library Association. Transfered to YASIG 1988. Annual award given when merited. To recognize an outstanding Canadian work of fiction written for young adults. Submissions should have been published during the previous calendar year. Award: Recognition through media press releases; leather-bound copy of book; "usually an author tour." Judged by Young Adult Services Group of the Canadian Library Association.

YOUNG READER'S CHOICE AWARD, (III), Pacific Northwest Library Association, Graduate School of Library and Information Sciences, 133 Suzzallo Lib., FM-30 University of Washington, Seattle WA 98195. (206)543-1897. Contact: Carol A. Doll. Annual award "to promote reading as an enjoyable activity and to provide children an opportunity to endorse a book they consider an excellent story." Award: Silver medal. Judges: Children's librarians and teachers nominate; children in grades 4-8 vote for their favorite book on the list. Guidelines for SASE. Deadline: February 1. Previously published submissions. Writers must be nominated by children's librarians and teachers.

Other contests

The following contests, grants and awards appeared in the 1991 edition of *Novel & Short Story Writer's Market* but do not appear in the 1992 edition. Those contests, grants and awards that did not respond to our request for an update appear below without further explanation. If a reason for the omission was available, it was included next to the listing name. There are several reasons why a contest may not appear—the contest may not be an annual event, for example, or last year's listing might have resulted in too many unsuitable manuscripts. Some retreats previously listed in this section have been moved to the new Retreats and Colonies section.

Jane Addams Children's Book Award
Edward F. Albee Foundation
Alberta New Fiction Competition
The Alberta Writing for Young People Competition
Animal Tales Holiday Contest
Avon Flare Young Adult Novel Competition
Banff Writing Residency
H.E. Bates Short Story Competition (responded late)
CCL Student Writing Contest
Child Study Children's Book Award
Council for Wisconsin Writers Annual Writing Contest
Creative Artist Grant/Michigan Council for the Arts (funds cut)
Foster City Annual Writers Contest
Friends of American Writers Awards

Gestalt Magazine Fiction Award (out of business)
Gulfshore Life Fiction Writer's Contest (discontinued)
Georgette Heyer Historical Novel Prize
Houghton Mifflin Literary Fellowship (asked to be deleted)
Iowa Woman Contest, International Writing Contest
JAB Publishing Fiction Contest
Language Bridges Contest (discontinued)
Los Angeles Times Book Prizes
Massachusetts Artists Fellowship Program (funds cut, temporarily suspended)
Money for Women
Mythopoeic Fantasy Award
National Novella Award (discontinued)
New Jersey Author Award (discontinued, budget cuts)
Nuts to Us (asked to be

deleted)
The Other Side Short Fiction Contest (discontinued)
Regina Medal Award
Rockland Center for the Arts Writer-in-Residence (discontinued)
Short Story Science Fiction/Fantasy Competition
Society of Children's Book Writers Golden Kite Awards
Southern Arts Literature Prize (asked to be left out this year)
Tennessee Arts Commission Individual Artists Fellowship (asked to be left out this year)
The Virginia Prize for Fiction (asked to be left out this year)
Writers at Work Fellowship Competition

Resources

Conferences and Workshops

Welcome to the first of four new sections for *Novel & Short Story Writer's Market*: Conferences and Workshops. Over the years, it has become increasingly apparent that workshops and conferences can be an integral part of a writer's life. Indeed, the number of these events alone attests to their popularity. Today's writers are also spending time at retreats and colonies, joining various writers' organizations and reading publications specific to their writing interests. Sections devoted to all of these activities follow.

In this section, however, you will find a wide variety of both conferences and workshops for fiction writers — and even more are out there. A "typical" conference may have a number of workshop sessions, keynote speakers and perhaps even a panel or two. Topics may include everything from writing fiction, poetry or books for children to marketing work and locating an agent. Sometimes a theme will be the connecting factor.

Other conferences and workshops are more specific, catering to a certain type of writer or aspect of writing. The Appalachian Writers Conference at Radford University, for example, is for writers with a connection to the Appalachian region. Mount Hermon Christian Writers Conference includes all aspects of Christian writing, and the Writers Workshop in Science Fiction focuses on the writing and marketing of science fiction work.

Each of the listings here includes information about the specific focuses of an event as well as the planned panels or speakers. It is important to note, though, that some conference and workshop directors were still in the organizing stages when contacted. Consequently, some listings include last year's speakers and/or panels to simply give you an idea of what to expect. This holds true for the costs of many of these events as well. For more current information, it's best to send a self-addressed, stamped envelope to the director in question about three months before the date(s) listed.

Learning and networking

First and foremost, conferences and workshops provide writers with opportunities to learn more about their craft, whether it be the business or the writing side. Some even feature individual sessions with workshop leaders, allowing writers to specifically discuss their works-in-progress with people respected in their field. If these one-on-one sessions include critiques (generally for an additional fee), that, too, is included in the listings.

Besides learning from workshop leaders in formal sessions, writers may also benefit from conversations with other attendees. Writers on all levels enjoy sharing insights. Often a conversation over lunch can reveal a new market for your work or let you know which editors have changed houses. A casual chat while waiting for a session to begin can acquaint you with a new resource in your area or one available nationwide.

Another reason writers find conferences and workshops worthwhile is the opportunity to meet editors and agents. In fact, *The Writer's Book of Checklists* (Writer's Digest Books) indicates the best way to make business contacts is through workshops and conferences, followed by special-interest conventions, such as mystery or science fiction "cons." Be careful, however. Although some writers have been fortunate to sell manuscripts at such events, the availability of editors and agents does not usually mean these folks will want to read your six best short stories (unless, of course, you've scheduled an individual meeting with them). While editors and agents are glad to meet writers and discuss work in general terms, they cannot give extensive attention to everyone they meet.

To get the most out of your brief contact with an editor or agent, treat him or her as you would anyone you were meeting for the first time—be courteous and friendly. Ask specific questions about his or her job or, better yet, some point of his or her presentation. Let the conversation turn toward your writing naturally. If your time is up before you get the chance to mention your craft, don't worry. You can follow up later with a letter making reference to having met at such-and-such a conference.

Selecting a conference

To narrow down your options when it comes to finally selecting the right conference or workshop to attend, keep your goals in mind. If your goal is to learn how to improve your writing, for example, then consider the level of writers toward which the event is geared. A workshop focusing on the best ways to market work may hold valuable insight, but it may not help you learn how to determine what constitutes a good first chapter for a novel. If your goal is to network, then choose events where editors who focus on your type of writing will be in attendance.

Of course, writers should also take into consideration their own resources. If both your time and funds are limited, you may want to search for a conference or workshop in your city, state or province. Some conferences are actually regional events sponsored by branches of large organizations, such as the International Women's Writing Guild (IWWG) and the Society of Children's Book Writers (SCBW). Many events are held during weekends and may be close enough that you can commute, so you don't have to take time off work and/or spend more than your budget allows.

On the other hand, you may want to combine your vacation with time spent meeting other writers and working on your craft. If this is the case, there are events such as the Summer in France Writing Workshops or, if that's a little too far from home, The Vancouver International Writers Festival. It is important to at least consider the conference location and be aware of other activities to enjoy in the area. The listings in these pages describe both the location of the conference and the events or attractions available nearby.

Still other factors may influence your decision when selecting a certain workshop or conference. Those with contests allow writers to gain recognition and recoup some of their expenses. Similarly, some conferences and workshops have financial assistance or scholarships available. Finally, many are associated with colleges and/or universities and may offer continuing education credits. You will find all of these options included in the listings here. Again, send a self-addressed, stamped envelope for more details.

For more information about the wide range of conferences and workshops, you may want to consult *The Guide to Writers Conferences* (Shaw Associates, publishers, Suite 1406, 625 Biltmore Way, Coral Gables FL 33134) and the May issue of *Writer's Digest* magazine. Other sources include *Writers Conferences* and *Author & Audience: A Readings and Workshops Guide*, both available from Poets & Writers, Inc. (72 Spring St., New York NY 10012).

ALABAMA WRITERS' CONCLAVE, 3225 Burning Tree Dr., Birmingham AL 35226. First Vice President Programs: Ann Moon Rabb. Estab. 1923. Annual. Conference held August 5 to August 7. Average attendance: 85-120. Conference to promote "all phases" of writing. Held at the Ramsey Conference Center (University of Montevallo). "We attempt to contain all workshops under this roof. Some functions take place at other campus buildings."
Costs: In 1991 fees for 3 days were $35 for members; $45 for nonmembers. Lower rates for one- or two-day attendence.
Accommodations: Accommodations available on campus (charged separately).
Additional Information: "We have had a works-in-progress group with members helping members." Sponsors a contest. Conference brochures/guidelines available for SASE. Membership dues are $15. Membership information from Harriette Dawkins, 117 Hanover Rd., Homewood AL 35209.

ANTIOCH WRITERS' WORKSHOP, 135 North Walnut, Yellow Springs OH 45387. Director: Sandra Love. Estab. 1984. Annual. Conference held July 5 to July 11. Average attendance: 80. Conference concentration: Fiction. Conference located on "a lovely ivy-covered college campus." Plans for next conference include a memorial for Judson Jerome. Mark Strand, Joe David Bellamy, Mary Grimm, Ralph Keys will speak at the next conference.
Costs: Tuition is $425 — lower for local and repeat — plus meals.
Accommodations: "We pick up free at airport." Accommodations made at dorms and area hotels. Cost is $10-17/night (for dorms).
Additional Information: Offers free critique sessions. Conference brochures/guidelines are available for SASE.

APPALACHIAN WRITERS CONFERENCE, Box 6935, Radford University, Radford VA 24142-6935. (703)831-5269; 639-0812. AWA President: Dr. R. Parks Lanier, Jr. Estab. 1980. Annual. Conference held from July 10 to July 12. Average attendance: 60. "Fiction, nonfiction, poetry, drama, story telling and grants writing are some of the topics discussed at each AWA Conference. Writers have some form of identification with the Appalachian region, either as the place from which they come, the place in which they live or the place about which they write." Radford University is located just off I-81 on the banks of the historic New River, 40 miles Southwest of Roanoke in Radford, Virginia. Participants may stay "in a newly renovated air-conditioned dormitory at very reasonable rates, cool, quiet, comfortable." The AWA is now regularly inviting editors to speak. Guest speakers. "Most of the AWA members are themselves authors with a national reputation."
Costs: AWA annual dues are $10. Meals in university cafeteria cost $5 or less.
Accommodations: Rooms are less than $50 for two nights, single occupancy.
Additional Information: There are contests for fiction, poetry, nonfiction and younger writers. AWA members are judges. Conference brochures/guidelines available for SASE.

ARIZONA CHRISTIAN WRITERS CONFERENCE, P.O. Box 5168, Phoenix AZ 85010. (602)838-4919. Director: Reg Forder. Estab. 1981. Annual. Conference held November 5 to November 7, 1992. Average attendance: 200. To promote all forms of Christian writing. Conference held in new Holiday Inn Hotel near airport in Phoenix. Panels planned for next conference include "Writing as a Ministry." Representatives from several publishing houses: Tyndale; Harvest House; Regal Books; *Christian Parenting Today Magazine,* are scheduled to speak at next conference.
Costs: Approx. $100 plus meals and accommodation.
Accommodations: Special price in our host hotel (Holiday Inn) $45 per night for 1 or 2 persons.
Additional Information: Conference brochures/guidelines are available for SASE. "This annual conference is held in Phoenix always on the first weekend in November."

ARTS AT MENUCHA, P.O. Box 4958, Portland OR 97208. (503)234-6827. Board Member: Connie Cheifetz. Estab. 1966. Annual. Conference held August 2 to August 15. Conference duration: Each class lasts 1 week. Average attendance: 60 overall (6-10 per class). Conference held at a "residential private estate with dorm rooms, most with private bath. 100-acre wooded grounds overlooking the Columbia River. A beautiful, relaxing place with pool, tennis, volleyball and walking trails. Meals provided (family-style). 1992 will see us offering Katherine Dunn, fiction and Winnifred Morris, writing children's books, possibly others. Also we offer visual arts class including story illustration."
Costs: '91 Rates $425/1 week; $750/2 weeks; includes room and board ('92 rates 3-5% higher).
Accommodations: "We will pick folks up from Portland Airport, bus or train depot." Everyone, including instructors, stays at "Menucha" overnight Sun.-Sat. a.m.
Additional Information: Conference brochures/guidelines are available (no SASE needed).

AUBURN WRITERS CONFERENCE, 25 West Main, Auburn WA 98001. (206)931-3043. Cultural Programs Manager: Josie Emmons Vine. Estab. 1988. Annual. Conference held 1st weekend of November. Conference duration: 2 days. Average attendance: 100. Conference "to give writers the opportunity to have their work critiqued by experienced authors; to meet and discuss the art of writing with other writers." Conference held at Auburn Parks facilities. 1991 conference included Joyce Thompson, Jim Heynen, Jack Cady. 1992 schedule not yet planned at press time.
Costs: $25 including lunch.
Accommodations: There are several motels in Auburn. Information is provided on request.
Additional Information: "Writers are encouraged to submit their work for critique at least 3 weeks before the conference. The amount of work submitted by each writer is limited by the author leading the workshop. Brochures for 1992 conference will be available in August 1992."

AUSTIN WRITERS' LEAGUE FALL AND SPRING WORKSHOPS, E-2, 1501 W. 5th, Austin TX 78703. (512)499-8914. Executive Director: Angela Smith. Estab. 1982. Held each fall and spring (March, April, October, November). Conference duration: 1-day; Saturdays. Average attendance: at least 14 workshops in each series, each drawing from 15 to 150. To promote "all genres, fiction and nonfiction, poetry, writing for children, screenwriting, playwriting, legal and tax information for writers, also writing workshops for children and youth." Conference held at "St. Edward's University – classroom space and auditoriums. Located at 3001 S. Congress, Austin, Texas 78704." Workshops planned include: Finding and working with agents and publishers; writing and publishing short fiction; dialogue; characterization; voice of the fiction writer; basic and advanced fiction writing; book marketing and promotion; also workshops for genres. "Spring '92 series now being planned. Past speakers have included Dwight Swain, Natalie Goldberg, David Lindsey, D.F. Mills, Shelby Heron."
Costs: Each three-hour workshop is $35-45 (members); $25 more for nonmembers. Six-hour labs are $75 (members); $25 more for nonmembers.
Accommodations: Austin Writers' League will provide assistance with transportation arrangements on request. List of hotels is available with SASE. Special rates given at some hotels for workshop participants.
Additional Information: Critique sessions offered. Individual presenters determine critique requirements. Those requirements are then made available through Austin Writers' League office and in workshop promotion. Contests and awards programs are offered separately from workshops. Conference brochures/guidelines are available on request. "In addition to regular series of workshops, Austin Writers' League sponsors ongoing informal classes in writing, plus weekend seminars and retreats during the spring and summer."

AUTUMN AUTHORS' AFFAIR, 1507 Burnham Ave., Calumet City IL 60409. (708)862-9797. President: Nancy McCann. Estab. 1983. Annual. Conference held October 23-25. Begins with Friday night buffet and ends with Sunday brunch. Average attendence: 300. "Focused on romance, contemporary and historical, but also features poetry, short story, mystery, young adult, childrens, screenplay writing and journalism." Site: Hyatt Regency, Oak Brook. Includes indoor parking, conference center, 425 guest rooms, 14 suites, indoor pool, exercise equipment, jacuzzi, and shopping center right across the street. Panels planned include "everything from the basics, to getting started, to how to handle the business aspects of your writing. Out of 25 workshops, 23 focus on 'fiction' writing."
Costs: 1991 costs were $95, which included Friday night buffet, Saturday continental breakfast and luncheon and Sunday brunch. "Prices may be higher in 1992."
Accommodations: Information on overnight accommodations is made available with a "special" room rate for those attending conference. "Last year the rate for single, double or quad was $77. This year, this price may be slightly higher."
Additional Information: Brochures/guidelines available for SASE.

BAY AREA WRITERS WORKSHOP, P.O. Box 620327, Woodside CA 94062. (415)430-3127. Co-Director: Laura Jason. Estab. 1988. Annual. Offers 4-5 separate weekend workshops and a 1-day conference, "Literary Publishing Day." Average attendance for 1-day conference: 200; each weekend workshop: 12-15. Workshops promote fiction and poetry, "both with literary bent." Site: the Mills College campus in Oakland, CA. "Founded in 1852, Mills is the oldest women's college in the western United States and home to a flourishing creative writing department, the Eucalyptus Press, and the renowned Center for Contemporary Music. Its 127 acres of tree-shaded seclusion in the hills east of San Francisco Bay offer an atmosphere free of distraction yet only 30 minutes from San Francisco and 20 minutes from the Oakland Airport. Recreational facilities on campus include a swimming pool, tennis courts and jogging trail." Literary Publishing Day features "agents and editors from around the nation. Last year's workshop leaders included Clarence Major, Olga Broumas, Li-Young Lee, Larry Heinemann and Joy Williams."
Costs: $225/weekend workshop plus $15 application fee. Four full-tuition scholarships are available for fiction writers based on the quality of the application manuscript. Cost for Literary Publishing Day: $75.
Accommodations: On-campus housing is available for approximately $35/day (single room rate), including meals. Information on area hotels is also available, and participants residing off-campus have the option of purchasing boxed lunches, meals in the Mills dining room or lunches at the Mills Grill.
Additional Information: "Our weekend intensives are manuscript evaluation en masse. In most workshops, manuscripts submitted will be the focus of discussion and evaluation. No individual consultations." Conference brochures/guidelines are available for SASE.

BE THE WRITER YOU WANT TO BE MANUSCRIPT CLINIC, 877 Northampton Dr., Palo Alto CA 94303. (415)322-0063. Contact: Louise Purwin Zobel. Estab. 1969. Workshop held irregularly—usually semiannually at several locations. Workshop duration: 1-2 days. Average attendence: 30-50. "This manuscript clinic enables writers of any type of material to turn in their work-in-progress—at any stage of development—to receive help with structure and style, as well as marketing advice." It is held on about 40 campuses at different times, including University of California and other university and college campuses throughout the west.
Costs: Usually $45-65/day, "depending on campus."
Additional Information: Brochures/guidelines available for SASE.

BLUE RIDGE WRITERS CONFERENCE, (NC), P.O. Box 188, Black Mountain NC 28711. (704)669-8421. Director: Yvonne Lehman. Estab. 1975. Annual. Conference held from June 1 to June 5. Conference duration: 3½ days. Average attendance: 70. Conference to promote "all" forms of writing. Conference held at Montreat Conference Center in the mountains of North Carolina. Guest speakers *for 1991* were Thomas Clark, Virginia Muir, Frank Weimann, Dennis Hensley, Keith Bellows, Louise Shivers.
Costs: 1991 fees: $190 for full time tuition plus $10 Program/Facilities fee; part-time fees $15-50 plus $5 Program/Facilities fee.
Accommodations: On-site facilities at Montreat Center. Rates: $188.25 (in 1991) included meals and banquet.
Additional Information: Critique service available. Cost: $30. Work must be submitted by May 1. Conference brochures/guidelines are available for SASE.

BLUE RIDGE WRITERS CONFERENCE, (VA), 2840-C Hershberger Rd., Roanoke VA 24017. Chairman: Dr. Norman Peets. Estab. 1984. Annual. One-day conference held in October ("usually first Saturday, but this may change depending upon availability of speakers."). Average attendence: 120. Conference "to make available an opportunity for networking and exchange of ideas between writers, both aspiring and professional, in Virginia's Blue Ridge area. Also, to enhance the status of writers and writing in this part of Virginia and to bring this artistic endeavor to the same level of public recognition, appreciation and pride in performance that is already enjoyed by music, the theater, dance and the fine arts." Site: Roanoke College, Salem, VA. Special bookstore features publications of speakers and books on writing. "Plans are incomplete for 1992, but we plan to include a session on poetry and another on screenwriting. We will also have fiction writing." Keynote not yet confirmed. Poet John Stone will participate in workshops.
Costs: $40; $20 for fulltime students. Includes luncheon and reception.
Additional Information: Brochures available for SASE.

CANADIAN AUTHORS ASSOCIATION CONFERENCE, Suite 500, 275 Slater St., Ottawa, Ontario K1P 5H9 Canada. (613)233-2846. FAX: (613)235-8237. National Director: Jeffrey Holmes. Estab. 1921. Annual. Conference held June 27 to June 29. Average attendance: 150. To promote "all genres—varies from year to year." 1992 conference to be held at McMaster University in Hamilton, Ontario. "University dormitory, air-conditioned—beautiful campus. On city bus line route." Topic for 1992 conference is "Reach the WRITE Market."
Costs: Approx. $130 (Canadian); accommodation and meals extra, except for keynote breakfast and awards banquet. Special early-bird discounts.
Accommodations: Special conference attendee accommodations can be made on-site. Cost is: $24-29 (Canadian) per night.
Additional Information: Conference brochures/registration forms are available for SAE and IRC.

‡CHRISTOPHER NEWPORT COLLEGE WRITERS' CONFERENCE, 50 Shoe Lane, Newport News VA 23606-2998. (804)594-7158. Coordinator: Doris Gwaltney. Estab. 1981. Annual. Conference held April 3-4. Average attendance: 100. "Our workshop is for both published and unpublished writers in all genres. It provides a network for area writers, connecting them with markets, literary agents, editors and printers." The conference is held on the campus of Christopher Newport College in Newport News, Va. "We have a good food service, a bookstore, adequate meeting rooms and total access for the handicapped." Panels planned for next conference include "Publishing in Virginia," "What if the Editor Wants Pictures?" and "But Will it Play?" Eugenia Panettieri and Mary Wakefield Buxton are scheduled to speak.

Costs: $65, includes wine-and-cheese reception, coffee and pastries, and lunch.
Accommodations: Adequate parking available. "Our staff could help with arrangements for overnight accommodations."
Additional Information: "We have a literary contest in four areas: poetry, fiction, nonfiction and juvenile fiction. Each entry is critiqued by a judge who is a published writer in the field." Conference brochures/guidelines available for SASE.

COPYRIGHT WORKSHOP, 610 Langdon St., Madison WI 53703. (608)262-3447. Director: Christine DeSmet. Offered 2 times/year. Conference held March 23 (check with director for further dates). Average attendance: 50. "Copyright law for writers, publishers, teachers, designers." Conference held at Wisconsin Center, University of Wisconsin—Madison.
Costs: $85.
Additional Information: Conference brochures/guidelines are available.

CRAFT OF WRITING, UTD Box 839688, CN 1.1, Richardson TX 75083. (214)690-2204. Director: Janet Harris. Estab. 1983. Annual. Conference held September (check for exact dates). Average attendance: 150. "To provide information to accomplished and aspiring writers on how to write and how to get published. All genres are included. Areas of writing covered include characterization and dialogue to working with an agent." Conference held at the University of Texas-Dallas. The UTD Conference Center has an auditorium which seats 500, two lecture halls seating 160 each and several smaller classrooms. Workshops in 1991 included a panel of editors and agents (both national and local), "Fiction—What You Should Know About Genres," and "Nonfiction—The Most Important Decision in a Writing Career." 1991 speakers included Michalann Perry, Denise Marcil, Mark Donald.
Costs: $160; includes 2 lunches and a banquet.
Accommodations: A block of rooms is held at the Richardson Hilton for $49/night. Call (214)644-4000 for reservations.
Additional Information: Critiques available. "There are no requirements. Participants may have manuscripts critiqued by members of the Greater Dallas Writers Association. Two manuscript critique sessions are scheduled. A manuscript contest is held prior to the conference. The deadline for submissions is August 1. Judges are specialists in the areas they are critiquing. There are seven categories with several cash prizes. Conference brochures/guidelines are available. Twenty-eight workshops are scheduled on a wide range of topics. Presenters include nationally known authors, agents, editors and publishers."

‡DEEP SOUTH WRITERS CONFERENCE, P.O. Drawer 44691, Lafayette LA 70504. (318)231-6918. Director: John W. Fiero. Estab. 1960. Annual. Conference held September 18-20. Average attendance: 200 ("but in 1991 approached 300"). Conference focuses on "workshops and readings with an emphasis on poetry and fiction, secondarily on drama and nonfiction. Workshops may be how-to-do-it craft lectures, but they have varied tremendously over the years. The site has been a building housing the English department on the University of Southwestern Louisiana campus. Plans in the works may change the site beginning this year to a large Holidome (Holiday Inn) in Lafayette. Lafayette is the center of Acadiana, that area of Louisiana noted for its Cajun heritage and cuisine." Readers and workshop leaders have not yet been finalized. "Last year's conference featured Ellen Gilchrist and Ernest Gaines as the most recognized writers in a group of five."
Costs: Pre-registration is $15; registration at the conference is $25. "The fee may increase if plans to move in 1992 are realized."
Accommodations: "We have provided a shuttle service for participants in the past. Some information about lodging is provided in our annual flyer. Information regarding local restaurants and local attractions is given out at the conference. Local per diem expenses in Lafayette for room and board range between $50 and $150."
Additional Information: Sponsors contest. Write for rules and entry requirements. Conference brochures/guidelines available for SASE.

DUKE UNIVERSITY WRITERS' WORKSHOP, The Bishop's House, Durham NC 27708. (919)684-6259. Director: Marilyn Hartman. Estab. 1978. Annual. Conference held June 22 to June 26. Average attendance: 50. To promote "creative writing: beginning, intermediate and advanced fiction; short story; scriptwriting; children's writing; mystery; poetry; creative nonfiction." Conference held at "Duke University campus classrooms and meeting facilities. Gothic architecture, rolling green hills. Nationally recognized for its beauty and academic excellence, Duke sponsors this workshop annually for creative writers of various genres." Theme is creative writing ("that's our only song!").

Costs: $345 for conference (most meals not included).
Accommodations: On-campus hotel is $45/night, single occupancy (double occupancy @ $22.50). Includes "elegant service, afternoon tea, indoor pool and sauna, van transportation; writing desks in rooms."
Additional Information: Critiques available. "Works-in-progress requested 3 weeks before workshop. Each participant gets *private* consult plus small-group in-class critiques." Conference brochures/guidelines are available. "No 'big' names, no mammoth lectures; simply *excellent*, concentrated instruction plus time to work. No glitz. Hard work. Great results."

‡**EASTERN KENTUCKY UNIVERSITY CREATIVE WRITING CONFERENCE,** Eastern Kentucky University, Richmond KY 40475. (606)622-5861. Conference Director: Dorothy Sutton. Estab. 1962. Annual. Conference held June 15-19 (usually 3rd week in June). Average attendance: 12-15. Conference to promote poetry, fiction and creative nonfiction, including lectures, workshops, private conferences and peer group manuscript evaluation. The conference is held on the campus of Eastern Kentucky University "in the rolling hills of Eastern Kentucky, between the horse farms of the Bluegrass and the scenic mountains of the Appalachian chain." Gregory Orr, Karen Osborne and Betty Receveur are scheduled to speak at the next conference. Also helping with workshops will be EKU faculty William Sutton, Harry Brown, Hal Blythe, Charlie Sweet.
Costs: $55 for undergraduates ($153 if out-of-state); $79 for graduates ($224 if out-of-state). Cost includes 1 hour of credit in creative writing and is subject to change. Auditors welcome at same price. Dining in the cafeteria is approximately $6-8/day.
Accommodations: Air-conditioned dormitory rooms are available for $32 (double) or $46 (single) per week. "Linens furnished. Bring your own blankets, pillow and telephone."
Additional Information: "Participants are asked to submit manuscript in late May to be approved before June 1. A $10 nonrefundable reading fee will be applied to registration." For conference brochure, send SASE to English Department (attn: Creative Writing Conference).

EASTERN WRITERS' CONFERENCE, English Dept., Salem State College, Salem MA 01970. (508)741-6270. Conference Director: Rod Kessler. Estab. 1977. Annual. Conference held June 19-20. Average attendance: 60. Conferece to "provide a sense of community and support for area poets and fiction writers. We try to present speakers and programs of interest, changing our format from time to time. Conference-goers usually have an opportunity to read to an audience or have manuscripts professionally critiqued. We tend to draw regionally." Plans for next conference include "Breaking into Print: A Former Conference-Goer's Success Story." Previous speakers have included Marge Piercy, Audre Dubus and Dianne Benedict.
Costs: "under $100."
Accommodations: Information on overnight accommodations is made available.
Additional Information: "Optional ms critiques are available for an additional fee." Conference brochures/guidelines available for SASE.

THE FESTIVAL OF THE WRITTEN ARTS, Box 2299, Sechelt, British Columbia V0N 3A0 Canada. (604)885-9631. FAX: (604)885-3967. Producer: Betty C. Keller. Estab. 1983. Annual. Festival held: August 13 to August 16. Average attendance: 2,500. To promote "all writing genres." Festival held at the Rockwood Centre. "The Centre overlooks the town of Sechelt on the Sunshine Coast. The lodge around which the Centre was organized was built in 1937 as a destination for holidayers arriving on the old Union Steamship Line; it has been preserved very much as it was in its heyday." A new twelve bedroom annex was added in 1982, and in 1989 the Festival of the Written Arts constructed a Pavilion for outdoor performances next to the annex. "The festival does not have a theme. Instead, it showcases 15 or more Canadian writers in a wide variety of genres each year."
Costs: $6.50 per event or $65 (Canadian) for a pass to 15 events.
Accommodations: Lists of hotels and bed/breakfast available.
Additional Information: The festival runs contests during the 4 days of the event. Prizes are books donated by publishers. Brochures/guidelines are available. "The FWA will celebrate its 10th Anniversary in 1992 with 24 writers showcased during the 4 days."

FLIGHT OF THE MIND—SUMMER WRITING WORKSHOP FOR WOMEN, 622 SE 29th Ave., Portland OR 97214. (503)236-9862. Director: Judith Barrington. Estab. 1984. Annual. Workshops held July 26 to August 2 and August 31 to September 7. Conference duration: Each workshop lasts 1 week. Average attendance: 65. "Conference held at an old retreat center on the Mackenzie River in the foothills of the Oregon Cascades. Right on the river—hiking trails, hot springs nearby. Most students accommo-

dated in single dorm rooms; a few private cabins available. We have our own cooks and provide spectacular food." Five classes—topics vary year to year. 1992 will include "Short Fiction" taught by Ursula LeGuin; "Memory, History and Imagination" taught by Michelle Cliff; "Poetry" taught by Judith Barrington, etc. Also planning to include Barbara Wilson, Andrea Carlisle and Evelyn White.
Costs: Approx. $500 for tuition, board and single dorm room. Extra for private cabin.
Accommodations: Special arrangements for transportation: "We charter a bus to pick up participants in Eugene, OR, at airport, train station and bus station." Accommodations are included in cost.
Additional Information: "Critiquing is part of most classes; no individual critiques. We require manuscript submissions for acceptance into workshop. (Receive about twice as many applications as spaces)." Workshop brochures/guidelines are available for 1 first class stamp (no envelope). "This is a feminist-oriented workshop with an emphasis on the work, literature and problems of women writers."

FLORIDA CHRISTIAN WRITERS CONFERENCE, 2600 Park Ave., Titusville FL 32780. (407)269-6702. Conference Director: Billie Wilson. Estab. 1988. Annual. Conference is held: January 23 to January 27. Average attendance: 130. To promote "all areas of writing." Conference held at Park Avenue Retreat Center, a conference complex at a large church near Kennedy Space Center. Gloria Gaither and Sally Stuart are scheduled to speak at next conference.
Costs: Tuition $200.
Accommodations: "We provide shuttle from the airport and from the Best Western Motel to retreat center. We make reservations at Best Western." Cost for private room and meals is $395.
Additional Information: Critiques available. "Each writer may submit 3 works for critique. We have specialists in every area of writing to critique. We also provide line by line, written critique for a $30 fee." Conference brochures/guidelines are available for SASE.

FLORIDA INTERNATIONAL UNIVERSITY SOUTH BEACH WRITERS WORKSHOP, North Miami Campus, Florida International University, North Miami FL 33181. (305)940-5645. Coordinator: Betty Bailey. Estab. 1988. Annual. Workshop held January 16 to January 19. Average attendance: 45. To promote fiction, poetry, writing for children, screenwriting. Also "how agents view publishing" plus manuscript conference. Conference held at the Ritz Plaza Hotel in Miami Beach. Core themes—fiction/poetry/screenwriting. Carolyn Forché and David Kranes are scheduled for next conference.
Costs: $400, includes coffee and 1 luncheon.
Accommodations: Cost of Ritz Hotel is $75/night.
Additional Information: Critiques available. Submissions by Dec. 1. Workshop brochures/guidelines available for SASE.

FLORIDA ROMANCE WRITERS, #102, 417 Lakeview Dr., Ft. Lauderdale FL 33326. (305)384-7967. President: Barbara J. Parker. Estab. 1986. Annual. Conference held February 28-March 1. Average attendance: 160. Conference to promote women's fiction and romance, held at hotel with conference facilities. Panels planned for next conference include how to write and sell commercial fiction and romance. Author Linda Howard is the keynote speaker. Editors from major publishers of women's fiction will also attend, along with agents who are seeking new clients.
Costs: Approximately $110.
Accommodations: Rooms at Sheraton Design Center Hotel. Conference rates ($90/night).

FLORIDA ROMANCE WRITERS' FUN-IN-THE-SUN CONFERENCE, 1821 NW 111 Ave., Plantation FL 33322. (305)452-0712. Corresponding Secretary: Debbie St. Amand. Estab. 1987. Annual. Conference held February 28-March 1, 1992; February 26, 27 and 28, 1993. Average attendence: 150. "Predominately romance fiction, long and short, historical and contemporary, but each year we also emphasize another area—e.g. screenwriting, mystery-suspense, science fiction." Conference site is a large hotel convenient to the airport. "We feature a variety of published romance authors as well as agents and editors in the field. Recent keynote speaker was Linda Howard."
Costs: Under $100. Includes continental breakfast Saturday, lunch Saturday and welcome party Friday. Optional activities available at additional cost include Saturday dinner and Sunday "Brunch with the Experts."

Accommodations: "A special conference room rate is available at the hotel where the conference is held. 1992's room rate: $90/night.
Additional Information: "Some of our workshops involve critiques. The requirements are set by the individual speakers. For the last 2 years an optional critique by professional reader Nalini Milne has been available. Requirements are publishd with conference information." Conference brochures/ guidelines are available for SASE.

FLORIDA SUNCOAST WRITERS' CONFERENCE, University of South Florida—St. Petersburg Campus, 140 7th Ave. South, St. Petersburg FL 33701. (813)974-2421. Associate Director: Steve Rubin. Estab. 1970. Annual. Three-day conference held in late January/early February. Average attendance: 400. Conference "to provide a 'hands-on' experience for both would-be writers and professional writers. We offer workshops and seminars in poetry, short story, novel, science fiction, detective, travel writing, nonfiction, drama, TV scripts, photojournalism and juvenile." The conference is held on "the picturesque university campus fronting on the bay of St. Petersburg, Fl. We do not focus on any one particular aspect of the writing profession; we have panels with agents and editors every year."
Costs: $95, early registration.
Accommodations: "Special rates are available at area motels. All information is contained in our brochure."
Additional Information: "Participants may submit work for critiquing. Extra fee charged for this service." Conference brochures/guidelines available for SASE.

FORT CONCHO MUSEUM PRESS LITERARY FESTIVAL, 213 East Ave. D, San Angelo TX 76903. (915)657-4441. Contact: Cora Pugmire. Estab. 1988. Annual. Conference held August 7-8. Average attendence: 450. "The purposes of the festival are to showcase writers—from beginners to professionals—of Texas and the southwest through public readings, book displays and informal gatherings; to offer help for writers through writing workshops and informal gatherings with other writers, editors and publishers; and, generally, to support and encourage the literary arts in Texas and the Southwest." Location: A 22-building, 40-acre historic site. The festival is held in the oldest, fully restored building (1865). Several of the other buildings are also used for workshops. Free tours are offered to all participants. "Current festival plans include no special topic, but we will have at least one fiction workshop. Guest speakers will be published Texas writers and publishers/editors of Texas journals of books."
Costs: All events except the banquet are free. Banquet fee is between $8-12.
Accommodations: Transportation arrangements are made on an informal basis only. ("That is, people who need a ride can always find one.") Special accommodations are made at our motel; a list of other area motels and hotels is available.
Additional Information: Current contests are "literary performance" contests. Of those who read from their works during the festival, one poet and one prose writer receive an award. Conference brochures/guidelines are available for SASE.

FRANCIS MARION WRITERS' CONFERENCE, Francis Marion College, Florence SC 29501. (803)661-1500. Director: Robert Parham. Estab. 1982. Conference held annually in May. Conference duration: 3 days. Average attendence: 40-50. Conference for "fiction, poetry, nonfiction." Held in classrooms/ college auditorium (at Francis Marion College).
Costs: $85.
Accommodations: Information on overnight accommodations made available through director.
Additional Information: Some workshops for fiction writers are included. Sponsors a chapbook competition. Brochures or guidelines available for SASE.

GREEN LAKE CHRISTIAN WRITERS CONFERENCE, American Baptist Assembly, Green Lake WI 54941-9300. (800)558-8898. Vice President of Program: Dr. Arlo R. Reichter. Estab. 1948. Annual. Conference held July 11 to July 18. Average attendance: 80. "The mission of the conference is to provide a setting and appropriate resource persons so Christian writers can further develop their writing skills—whether a beginner or seasoned writer. Held annually at the American Baptist Assembly which is a 1,000-acre conference center on Green Lake. The center offers lodging and meals as well as wide range of recreational opportunities. The Assembly is the national training center for American Baptist Churches. The conference is ecumenical." Gianfranco Pagnucci, Susan Pagnucci, Lenore Coberly, Jeri McCormick, Jan White, Jeanne Donovan and others to be named are scheduled to speak at next conference.

Costs: Tuition is $80/person.

Accommodations: "We can provide ground transportation from Appleton and Oshkosh, Wisconsin airports; the Columbus, WI Amtrak station and Ripon, WI Greyhound Bus Stop—there is a charge and advance reservation is required." On-site facilities available. Costs: Rooms range (double occupancy) from $20 to $32/night; meals $17.75/day. Campground available as well as cottages, cabins and homes.

Additional Information: "Personal critique sessions with leaders may be scheduled. Major seminars include group critique. No advance submissions." Conference brochures/guidelines are available for SASE. "Once a person has attended the writers conference they may return during specified fall, winter and spring weeks at a special low cost of $10/night—no instruction."

HEART OF AMERICA WRITERS' CONFERENCE, Johnson County Community College, 12345 College Blvd., Overland Park KS 66213. Program Coordinator: Judith Choice. Estab. 1984. Annual. Conference held last weekend in October or 1st weekend in November. Conference duration: 2 days. Average attendance: 150-200. "The conference features a choice of 12-20 sessions focusing on poetry, nonfiction, children's market, fiction, journaling, essay and genre writing." Conference held at the Cultural Education Center. "The new Cultural Education Center is a 163,000 sq. ft. facility featuring a large theater and concert hall, a recital hall, art gallery and multiple conference spaces. This site is located on the Johnson County Community College campus which serves suburban Kansas City, Missouri. Each year we offer 7-10 sessions of interest to fiction writers." Past guest speakers or panelists have included Natalie Goldberg, Linda Hogan, David Ray, Stanley Elkin.

Costs: $70 for 1-day; $90 for 2-days.

Accommodations: "We provide lists of area hotels."

Additional Information: Manuscript critiques are offered for $20. First chapter for fiction; 5 pages for poetry. Conference brochures/guidelines are available for SASE.

HEMINGWAY DAYS WRITER'S WORKSHOP AND CONFERENCE, P.O. Box 4045, Key West FL 33041. (305)294-4440. Director of Workshop: Dr. James Plath. Festival Director: Michael Whalton. Estab. 1988. Annual. Conference/workshop held July 20 to July 23. Average attendance: 50. "The Hemingway Days Writer's Workshop and Conference focuses on fiction, poetry, stage and screenwriting, with one session per day concentrating on the craft as it relates to Ernest Hemingway and his work. Sessions are held in the oceanfront Café at Louie's Backyard, an intimate upstairs restaurant which easily accommodates 70 participants; and in the Caribbean Spa Grand Cayman Room at the Pier House Resort, which has excellent audio visual facilities and seats 100." All sessions on day one deal with fiction writing; day two—poetry writing; day three—screen and playwriting; day four—round-up (mixture of genres).

Costs: $60. Guaranteed admission on a space-available basis includes admission to all sessions, workshop t-shirt and complementary snacks each day.

Accommodations: "As the time draws nearer, Hemingway Days packages will be available through Ocean Key House and Pier House Hotels. Last year the cost at Ocean Key House was 3 nights: $60/2 in room per night plus tax; $120/3 in room per night suite, plus tax."

Additional Information: "We solicit material from the audience for a public, oral editor's critique—no charge." Brochures/guidelines are available for SASE. "The conference/workshop is unique in its daily emphasis on a different genre, but since it celebrates Hemingway the writer, the workshop will also uniquely include scholarly/critical sessions dealing with Hemingway's work."

HIGHLAND SUMMER CONFERENCE, Box 6935, Radford University, Radford VA 24142. (703)831-5366. Chair, Appalachian Studies Program: Dr. Grace Toney Edwards. Estab. 1978. Annual. Conference held June 15-26. Average attendence: 25. "The HSC features one (two weeks) or two (one week each) guest leaders each year. As a rule, our leaders are well known writers who have connections, either thematic, or personal, or both, to the Appalachian region. The genre(s) of emphasis depends upon the workshop leader(s). In 1991 we had as our leaders, for one week each: David Huddle, poet, essayist and short story writer, and Denise Giardina, a novelist who also writes nonfiction about the Appalachian region. The Highland Summer Conference is held at Radford University, a school of about 9,000 students. Radford is in the Blue Ridge Mountain of southwest Virginia about 45 miles west of Roanoke, VA."

Costs: "The cost is based on current Radford tuition for 3 credit hours plus an additional conference fee. On-campus meals and housing are available at additional cost. In 1991 conference tuition was $298 for undergraduates, $310 for graduate student."

Accommodations: We do not have special rate arrangements with local hotels. We do offer accommodations on the Radford University Campus in a recently refurbished residence hall. (In 1991 cost was $14.75-24 per night.)
Additional Information: "Conference leaders do typically critique work done during the two-week conference, but do not ask to have any writing submitted prior to the conference beginning." Conference brochures/guidelines are available for SASE.

HIGHLIGHTS FOUNDATION WRITERS WORKSHOP AT CHAUTAUQUA, Dept. NM, 711 Court St., Honesdale PA 18431. (717)253-1192. Conference Director: Jan Keen. Estab. 1985. Annual. Workshop held July 18 to July 25. Average attendance: 100. "Writer workshops geared toward beginner, intermediate, advanced levels. Small group workshops, one-to-one interaction between faculty and participants plus panel sessions, lectures and large group meetings. Workshop site is the picturesque community of Chautauqua, New York." Classes offered include Children's Interests, Writing Dialogue, Outline for the Novel, Conflict and Developing Plot. Faculty includes James Cross Giblin, Chris Demarest, Laurence Pringle, Dayton Hyde, Eve Bunting, Pam Conrad.
Accommodations: "We coordinate ground transportation to and from airports, trains and bus stations in the Erie, PA and Jamestown/Buffalo, NY area. We also coordinate accommodations for conference attendees."
Additional Information: "We offer the opportunity for attendees to submit a manuscript for review at the conference." Workshop brochures/guidelines are available for SASE.

HOFSTRA UNIVERSITY SUMMER WRITERS' CONFERENCE, Hofstra UCCE, 205 Davison Hall, Hempstead NY 11550. (516)463-5016. Director, Liberal Arts: Lewis Shena. Estab. 1972. Annual (Every summer starting week after July 4). Conference held July 6 to July 17, 1992. Average attendance: 50. Conference offers workshops in fiction, nonfiction, poetry, juvenile fiction and stage/screenwriting. Site is the university campus, a suburban setting, 25 miles from NYC. Guest speakers are not yet known. "We have had the likes of Oscar Hijuelos, Clive Barnes, Hilma and Meg Wolitzer, Budd Schulberg and Cynthia Ozick."
Costs: Non-credit (no meals, no room): approximately $535 for 3 workshops. Credit: Approximately $640/workshop (2 credits) plus $75 fee.
Accommodations: Free bus operates between Hempstead Train Station and campus for those commuting from NYC. Dormitory rooms are available for approximately $275. Those who request area hotels will receive a list. Hotels are approximately $75 and above/night.
Additional Information: "All workshops include critiquing. Each participant is given one-on-one time of ½ hour with workshop leader. Only credit students must submit manuscripts when registering. We submit work to the *Paris Review* when appropriate."

INTERNATIONAL BLACK WRITERS, P.O. Box 1030, Chicago IL 60690. (312)924-3818. President: Mable Terrell. Estab. 1970. Annual. Conference held June 26-28. Average attendence: 500. Conference to promote fiction, poetry and writing for children, held at the Powell Building, New York, NY. Fiction workshop will introduce successful fiction writers. Speakers not yet decided.
Costs: $85 for all activities.
Accommodations: Special buses transport people from hotel to conference site. Information on overnight accommodations and special conference rates is made available.
Additional Information: Submit work for critique 1 week prior to conference date. Organization sponsors annual writing competition. Deadline for submission: May 30. Contest judged by publishing company. Brochures/guidelines available for SASE.

THE INTERNATIONAL FILM WORKSHOPS, 2 Central St., Rockport ME 04856. (207)236-8581. Director: David Lyman. Estab. 1973. Workshops held weekly throughout each summer. Summer workshop series begins June 8. Workshops last one and two weeks. Average attendance: Maximum of 16/work-

Market conditions are constantly changing! If you're still using this book and it is 1993 or later, buy the newest edition of Novel & Short Story Writer's Market at your favorite bookstore or order directly from Writer's Digest Books.

shop. Conference promotes screenwriting, feature film scripts, television documentaries, TV episodes, novels, short stories and nonfiction writing. "The workshop is located in old Town Hall in the small harbor village of Rockport, Maine—facilities include library, gallery, theater, darkrooms, studios, feature film production center, accommodations for 150 dining room and campground." Themes planned for next workshops include: The feature film script, the TV doc script, writing drama, the mystery writer, the scene writing workshop, comedy writing, writing horror, the first novel. Guest speakers include Christopher Keane, Jurgen Wolff, Syd Fields, Stanley Ralph Ross.
Costs: Course tuition, one week: $500-1,600. Meals and accommodations: $300-500.
Accommodations: Discount airline ticket, airport van service. "Our lodging department can make appointments on campus ($250-500/week).
Additional Information: "Writing samples or a professional resumé must accompany application. Scripts must be submitted 3 weeks prior to the first day of class. Critiques are written and verbal." Workshop brochures/guidelines are available. "But no SASE—it's too big!"

IOWA SUMMER WRITING FESTIVAL, 116 International Center, University of Iowa, Iowa City IA 52242. (319)335-2534. Director: Peggy Houston. Assistant Director: Karen Burgus. Estab. 1987. Annual. Festival held June 7 to July 24. Workshops are one week, two weeks or a weekend. Average attendance: limited to 12/class—over 650 participants throughout the summer. "We offer courses in most areas of writing: novel, fiction, essay, poetry, playwriting, screenwriting, freelance, nonfiction, writing for children, comedy, memoirs, women's writing and science fiction." Site is the University of Iowa campus. Guest speakers are undetermined at this time. Last year's guest readers were W.P. Kinsella, Gerald Stern, Susan Allen Toth, Robley Wilson, Susan Dodd and Marilynne Robinson.
Costs: $245, one-week course; $490, two-week course and $100, weekend course (1991 rates). Housing and meals are separate.
Accommodations: Shuttle service from the Cedar Rapids airport to the university is available for a reasonable fee. "We offer participants a choice of accommodations, which we will book for them: Dormitory, $17.50/night; Iowa House, $43/night; Holiday Inn, $60/night (rates subject to changes)."
Additional Information: Brochure/guidelines are available.

I'VE ALWAYS WANTED TO WRITE BUT . . ., 877 Northampton Dr., Palo Alto CA 94303. (415)322-0063. Contact: Louise Purwin Zobel. Estab. 1969. Workshop held irregularly, several times a year at different locations. Workshop duration: 1-2 days. Average attendence: 30-50. Workshop "encourages real beginners to get started on a lifelong dream. Focuses on the basics of writing." Workshops held at about 40 college and university campuses in the west, including University of California.
Costs: Usually $45-65/day "depending on college or university."
Additional Information: Brochures/guidelines available for SASE.

IWWG EARLY SPRING IN CALIFORNIA CONFERENCE, International Women's Writing Guild, P.O. Box 810, Gracie Station, New York NY 10028. (212)737-7536. Executive Director: Hannelore Hahn. Estab. 1982. Annual. Conference held March 13 to March 15. Average attendance: 50. Conference to promote "creative writing, personal growth and empowerment." Site is "a 150-acre oasis located an hour from San Francisco in the wine country. Originally an Indian healing ground, it features tranquil meadows and streams, clear water springs, ancient oaks, almond trees, wood violets and decorative folk art. Nouvelle health cuisine is served in an original adobe dining room."
Costs: $100 for weekend program, plus room and board.
Accommodations: Accommodations are all at conference site; $110 for room and board.
Additional Information: Conference brochures/guidelines are available for SASE.

IWWG MEET THE AGENTS AND EDITORS: THE BIG APPLE WORKSHOPS, % International Women's Writing Guild, P.O. Box 810, Gracie Station, New York NY 10028. (212)737-7536. Executive Director: Hannelore Hahn. Estab. 1980. Biannual. Workshops held April 25 to April 26 and October 17 to October 18. Average attendance: 200. Workshops to promote creative writing and professional success. Site: Private meeting space of the New York Genealogical Society, mid-town New York City.
Costs: $100.
Accommodations: Information on transportation arrangements and overnight accommodations made available.
Additional Information: Workshop brochures/guidelines are available for SASE.

IWWG MIDWESTERN CONFERENCE, % International Women's Writing Guild, P.O. Box 810, Gracie Station, New York NY 10028. (212)737-7536. Executive Director: Hannelore Hahn. Estab. 1990. Annual. Conference held May 9. Average attendance: 75. Conference to promote creative writing, personal growth and professional success. Site: "Elegant private Women's Athletic Club of Chicago." **Costs:** $75, includes lunch.
Additional Information: Conference brochures/guidelines are available for SASE.

IWWG NEW JERSEY CONFERENCE, % International Women's Writing Guild, P.O. Box 810, Gracie Station, New York NY 10028. (212)737-7536. Executive Director: Hannelore Hahn. Estab. 1988. Annual. Conference held November 10. Average attendance: 75. Conference to promote creative writing, personal growth and professional success. Site: "Former private mansion in residential part of Morristown, NJ."
Costs: $75, includes lunch.
Additional Information: Conference brochures/guidelines are available for SASE.

IWWG SUMMER CONFERENCE, % International Women's Writing Guild, P.O. Box 810, Gracie Station, New York NY 10028. (212)737-7536. Execuive Director: Hannelore Hahn. Estab. 1977. Annual. Conference held August 14 to August 21. Average attendance: 350. Conference to promote writing in all genres, personal growth and professional success. Conference is held "on the tranquil campus of Skidmore College in Saratoga Springs, NY, where the serene Hudson Valley meets the North Country of the Adirondacks." Fifty different workshops are offered. Overall theme: "Writing Towards Wholeness." Guest speakers are Anne Wilson Shaef and Sallie Bingham.
Costs: $300 for week-long program, plus room and board.
Accommodations: Transportation by air to Albany, New York or Amtrak train available from New York City. Conference attendees stay on campus.
Additional Information: "Lots of critiquing sessions. Contacts with literary agents." Conference brochures/guidelines available for SASE. "International attendance."

IWWG WASHINGTON STATE/TACOMA CONFERENCE, International Women's Writing Guild, P.O. Box 810, Gracie Station, New York NY 10028. (212)737-7536. Executive Director: Hannelore Hahn. Estab. 1990. Annual. Conference held September 19 to September 20. Average attendance: 75. Conference to promote all types of creative writing. Site: Annie Wright School, Tacoma; tudor-style private school in residential neighborhood.
Costs: $130, includes program and two lunches; or $70/day.
Accommodations: Information on overnight accommodations is available.
Additional Information: "We include critiques as often as possible." Conference brochures/guidelines are available for SASE.

KINGSTON SCHOOL OF WRITING SUMMER WORKSHOP, P.O. Box 1061, Kingston, Ontario K7L 4Y5 Canada. (613)548-1556. Director: Bob Hilderley. Estab. 1983. Annual. Conference held in July. Conference duration: 1 week. Average attendance: 100. "The workshop has held sessions in fiction, script, children's, poetry and nonfiction writing. It offers emerging and experienced writers the opportunity to work intensively for one week with a faculty of professional editors and authors. Situated in Kingston, the School is enriched by the literary heritage of this community. The Writers Union of Canada was conceived here during the Kingston Writers Conference in 1955. The extensive Lorne Piece collection of Canadian Literature, endowed by the former literary editor of Ryerson Press, is housed here on the Queen's University campus. Kingston is indeed a vital centre for Canadian writing. The Summer Workshop features seminars and lectures by prominent authors and editors. The Speakers for next year have not, however, been finalized."
Costs: Tuition fees are $250 Canadian. Meals and other services are not included in this fee.
Accommodations: Single room bed, breakfast and lunch accommodation packages are available for $35 per day on the Queen's University campus. Participants are responsible for their own dinners on or off campus. Lunch tickets are available for local residents.
Additional Information: Critiques offered. "Admission is *open* to all writers with the desire to improve their craft, regardless of age or experience. Upon registration, a 5-10 page sample of writing will be requested. Workshop administrators will use this work to place registrants in the section best suited to their style and accomplishment. Instructors will use this sample to prepare for one-to-one tutorials with registrants." Conference brochures/guidelines are available for SASE.

MANHATTANVILLE COLLEGE WRITERS' WEEK, 125 Purchase St., Purchase NY 10577. (914)694-3425. Dean of Adult and Special Programs: Ruth Dowd, R.S.C.J. Estab. 1982. Annual. Conference held June 29 to July 3. Average attendance: 50. "The Conference is designed not only for writers but for teachers of writing. Each workshop is attended by a Master teacher who works with the writers/teachers in the afternoon to help them to translate their writing skills for classroom use. For children's literature, journal writing, personal essay, poetry and fiction. Manhanttanville is a suburban campus 30 miles from New York City. The campus centers around Reid Castle, the administration building, the former home of Whitelaw Reid. Workshops are conducted in Reid Castle. We usually feature a major author as guest lecturer during the Conference. We have had such authors as Toni Morrison, Mary Gordon, Gail Godwin and Elizabeth Janeway.
Costs: Conference cost was $500 in 1991 which included 2 graduate credits.
Accommodations: Students may rent rooms in the college residence halls. More luxurious accommodations are available at neighboring hotels. In the summer of 1991 the cost of renting a room in the residence halls was: $25 per night (single); $20 per night (double).
Additional Information: Conference brochures/guidelines are available for SASE.

MIDLAND WRITERS CONFERENCE, Grace A. Dow Memorial Library, 1710 W. St. Andrews, Midland MI 48640. (517)835-7151. Conference Co-Chairs: Eileen Finzel, Margaret Allen. Estab. 1980. Annual. Conference held May 30. Average attendance: 100. "The Conference is composed of a well-known keynote speaker and then, six workshops on a variety of subjects ranging from poetry, children's writing, freelancing, agents, etc. The attendees are both published and unpublished authors. The Conference is held at the Grace A. Dow Memorial Library in the auditorium and conference rooms. Keynoters in the past have included Andrew Greeley, Kurt Vonnegut, David Halberstam."
Costs: Adult - $45 before May 15, after May 15 the fee is $55; student, senior citizen and handicapped - $35 before May 15, after May 15 the fee is $45. A box lunch is available for $7.
Accommodations: A list of area hotels is available.
Additional Information: Conference brochures/guidelines are available for SASE.

MIDWEST WRITERS' CONFERENCE, 6000 Frank Ave. NW, Canton OH 44720 (216)499-9600. Conference Coordinator: Debbie Ruhe. Estab. 1968. Annual. Conference held October 2 and October 3. Average attendance: 250. "The conference provides an atmosphere in which aspiring writers can meet with and learn from experienced and established writers through lectures, workshops, competitive contest, personal interviews and informal group discussions. The areas of concentration include fiction, nonfiction, juvenile literature, poetry and journalism: newswriting. The Midwest Writers' Conference is held on Kent State University Stark Campus in Canton, Ohio. This two-day conference is held in Main Hall, a four-story building and wheel chair accessible." Past topics have included: Writing For Children: Don't Be Juvenile; Fiction Techniques: What They Are, How To Find Them, How To Use Them; Why It's Harder To Find An Agent Than a Publisher. 1991 presenters included: Roger Snell, *Akron Beacon Journal*; Marilyn Apseloff, professor at Kent State University; Douglas Glover, author; Edward Novak III, literary agent.
Costs: $65 includes Friday workshops, keynote address, Saturday workshops, box luncheon and manuscript entry fee (limited to two submissions); $40 for contest only (includes two manuscripts).
Accommodations: Arrangements are made with the Sheraton-Belden Inn. The Sheraton is nearest Kent Stark, and offers a special reduced rate for conference attendees. Conferees must make their own reservations three weeks before the conference to be guaranteed this special conference rate.
Additional Information: Each manuscript entered in the contest will receive a critique. If the manuscript is selected for final judging, it will receive an additional critique from the final judge. Conference attendees are not required to submit manuscripts to the writing contest. Manuscript deadline is early August. For contest: A maximum of one entry for each category is permitted. Entries must be typed on 8½ × 11 paper, double-spaced. A separate page must accompany each entry bearing the author's name, address, phone, category and title of the work. Entries are not to exceed 3,000 words in length. Work must be original, unpublished and not a winner in any contest at the time of entry. Conference brochures and guideliens are available for SASE.

MIDWEST WRITERS WORKSHOP, Dept. of Journalism, Ball State University, Muncie IN 47306. (317)285-8200. Co-Director: Earl H. Conn. Estab. 1974. Annual. Workshop held July 29 to August 1. Average attendance: 125. For fiction, nonfiction, poetry. Conference held at Hotel Roberts in downtown Muncie.

Costs: In 1991, cost was $160 including opening reception, hospitality room and closing banquet.
Accommodations: Special hotel rates offered.
Additional Information: Critiques available. $25 for individual critiquing. Conference brochures/guidelines are available for SASE.

MISSISSIPPI VALLEY WRITERS CONFERENCE, Augustana College, Rock Island IL 61265. (309)762-8985. Conference Founder/Director: David R. Collins. Estab. 1973. Annual. Conference held June 7 to June 12. Average attendance: 80. "Conference for all areas of writing for publication." Conference held at Augustana College, a liberal arts school along the Mississippi River. 1991 guest speakers included Evelyn Witter, Mel Boring, Max Collins, David McFarland, Elizabeth Kary, Karl Largent, Jim Elledge, Roald Tweet, Rich Johnson.
Costs: In 1991 fees were $25 for registration; $35 for 1 workshop; $60 for two; plus $30 for each additional workshops; $20 to audit.
Accommodations: On-campus facitilites available. Accommodations are available at Westerlin Hall on the Augustana College campus. Cost for 6 nights is $75; cost for 15 meals is $75.
Additional Information: Conferees may submit manuscripts to workshop leaders for personal conferences during the week. Cash awards are given at the end of the conference week by workshop leaders based on manuscripts submitted. Conference brochures/guidelines are available for SASE. "Conference is open to the beginner as well as the polished professional—all are welcome."

MISSISSIPPI WRITERS' CLUB CONFERENCE, Box 1278, Jackson MS 39215-1278. (601)366-8151. Vice President: Ms. Jo Barksdale. Estab. 1988. Annual. Conference/workshop held: June 12 and 13, 1992. Average attendence: 200. Conference for "education in all areas, marketing assistance, critiquing." Facilities vary each year. 1992 tentatively to be held on Millsaps College campus. "Always have a wide variety of 1-hour workshops, along with a few especially high profile keynote speakers for the entire group."
Costs: About $100.
Accommodations: "Holiday Inn next door to Millsaps and dormitory space will be recommended, if held at Millsaps."
Additional Information: Workshops require pre-submission and small fee. Sponsors a contest (details not settled yet). Brochures/guidelines available for SASE. "We will add a 4-day, pre-conference summer workshop in novel, poetry and a few other topics to the '92 conference. Twelve writers per workshop to be accepted."

MOUNT HERMON CHRISTIAN WRITERS CONFERENCE, P.O. Box 413, Mount Hermon CA 95041. (408)335-4466. Director of Public Affairs David R. Talbott. Estab. 1970. Annual. Conference held April 10 to April 14. Average attendance: 175. "We are a broad-ranging conference for all areas of Christian writing, including fiction, children's, poetry, nonfiction, magazines, books, educational curriculum and radio and TV script writing. This is a working, how-to conference, with many workshops within the conference involving on-site writing assignments. The Conference is sponsored by and held at the 440-acre Mount Hermon Christian Conference Center near San Jose, California, in the heart of the coastal redwoods. Registrants stay in hotel-style accommodations, and full board is provided as part of conference fees. Meals are taken family style, with faculty joining registrants. The faculty/student ratio is about 1:6 or 7. The bulk of our faculty are editors and publisher representatives from major Christian publishing houses nationwide."
Costs: Registration fees include tuition, conference sessions, resource notebook, refreshment breaks, room and board and vary from $420 economy to $520 deluxe, double occupancy.
Accommodations: Airport shuttles are available from the San Jose International Airport or San Francisco International Airport. Housing is not required of registrants, but about 95% of our registrants use Mount Hermon's own housing facilities (hotel style double-occupancy rooms). Meals with the conference are required, and are included in all fees.
Additional Information: Registrants may submit work for critique (2 works) in advance of the conference, then have personal interviews with critiquers during the conference. No advance work is required, however. Conference brochures/guidelines are available for SASE. "The residential nature of our conference makes this a unique setting for one-on-one interaction with faculty/staff. There is also a decided inspirational flavor to the conference, and general sessions with well-known speakers are a highlight."

NAPA VALLEY WRITERS' CONFERENCE, Napa Valley College, 2277 Napa-Vallejo Hwy., Napa CA 94558. (707)253-3070. Program Director: John Leggett. Managing Director: Sherri Hallgren. Estab. 1980. Annual. Conference held from July 26 to July 31. Average attendance: 70-80. Conference to promote literary fiction and poetry. "No real work in genres and an emphasis on craft rather than marketing." Also promotes new poetry. "Emphasis is on generating new poems, though there is also a critique of already finished work." Workshops are held on the campus of Napa Valley College, in the heart of the famed wine growing region of California. Evenings feature readings hosted by valley wineries. "We have visiting agents and publishers on panels. Each faculty writer gives a craft talk and a public reading."
Costs: $425. Scholarships available.
Accommodations: "We mail schedules for airport shuttles, and we recommend that local (bay area) participants carpool." Attendees are mailed a list of Napa Valley motels, many of which offer a package rate. "We also offer some community housing (guest rooms or spare sofas in the homes of Napa residents) for a charge of $20 for the week."
Additional Information: "We require a qualifying manuscript of 10 pages of fiction or 5 pages of poetry as well as a letter describing applicant's background as a writer. In workshops we critique a 25-page ms of fiction." Conference brochures/guidelines are available for SASE.

NATIONAL LEAGUE OF AMERICAN PEN WOMEN CONFERENCE, P.O. Box 1707, Midlothian VA 23112. (804)744-6503. Conference Director: T.R. Hollingsworth. Estab. 1983. Conference held every two years. Conference duration: One day. Average attendance: 50-100. "For fiction, nonfiction, travel, regional, writing for children. Conference is usually held in a Richmond, Virginia hotel with banquet facilities. The day includes continental breakfast, lunch, book sales, autographing with well-known, published speakers." 1991 theme: Writing to Sell. 1991 guest speaker: Dr. Dennis Hensley.
Costs: $49.50 fee includes lunch, continental breakfast; $15 contest entry; $10 critique of contest entry.
Accommodations: Special rates for overnight stay the night before conference.
Additional Information: Critiques available. Sponsors contest: fiction or nonfiction, 1,500 word maximum, fee charged. Judges are professional writers in NLAPW. Conference brochures/guidelines are available for SASE.

NATIONAL WOMEN'S MUSIC FESTIVAL WRITERS CONFERENCE, P.O. Box 1427, Indianapolis IN 46206-1427. (317)636-7382. Estab. 1985. Annual. Conference held from May 28 to May 31. Average attendance: 2,500-3,000. To promote "feminist writing and publishing—fiction, poetry, journalism, drama." Conference held at Indiana University, Bloomington, IN.
Costs: Approx. $120 for program including all music performances.
Accommodations: Dorm housing available. Costs: Approx. $20/night/person double occupancy dorm room. Approx. $50 food for Fri.-Sun.
Additional Information: Conference brochures/guidelines are available for SASE. "Some workshops are open to women only."

NORTH CAROLINA WRITERS' NETWORK FALL CONFERENCE, P.O. Box 954, Carrboro NC 27510. (919)967-9540. Executive Director: Marsha Warren. Estab. 1985. Annual. Conference held from November 6 to November 8 in Wilmington, NC. Average attendance: 350. "We try to have *all* genres represented. In the past we have had novelists, poets, journalists, editors, children's writers, YA writers, storytellers, puppetry, etc. We take the conference to a different location in North Carolina each year in order to best serve our entire state. We hold the conference at a conference center with hotel rooms available."
Costs: "We try to keep conference cost at just under $100. This does not include hotel accommodations."
Accommodations: "We try to charter buses from far parts of the state to the particular location of the conference. Special conference hotel rates are obtained, but the individual makes his/her own reservations."
Additional Information: Conference brochures/guidelines are available for 2 first class stamps.

OWFI ANNUAL CONFERENCE, 1304 McKinley Ave., Norman OK 73072. (405)321-4982. President: Joye R. Swain. Estab. 1969. Annual. Conference held May 1-2 (always the first weekend in May). Average attendance: 200-250. "The OWFI Annual Conference focuses on the nuts and bolts of writing to sell. Speakers include writers of genre fiction (both book length and short), agents, publishers and editors. This is a 'how to' program offering specific information for beginning writers and those who are already selling. Friday night informal 'buzz sessions' are offered in hotel rooms where participants discuss specialized and limited areas of writing." The conference is held at Days Inn South, in Oklahoma City. "We will have two large conference rooms with simultaneous presentations: one aimed at beginning writers and one aimed at selling writers. In a book room we offer a wide variety of handouts and guidelines as well as material written, edited or published by participants in the conference. A director's suite is available for smaller groups which are organized spontaneously during the conference. A final awards banquet is held in a large dining area. We will have authors in the field speaking on: mystery, science fiction, male action/adventure, women's mainstream, international intrigue. Other topics are: What do agents do?; what happens to your baby (ms) when it gets to New York?; New York markets; local markets; self-promotion—how to do it?; getting started as a writer; changing with the changing markets during a writing career; what you need to know about contracts; plotting a novel; developing characters." Guest speakers and panelists include Mel Odom and Jim Adair, authors, male action/adventure; Michael Seidman, editor at Walker Books; Emma Merritt, past president, Romance Writers of America; Dwight V. Swain, author of fact and fiction and nationally recognized teacher of writing; Jyd Wall, mainstream author; Alice Orr, author and editor; and Robert L. Duncan, author, international intrigue.

Costs: $50, including Friday dinner and Saturday night Awards Banquet. One day (not including dinner): $35. Dinner tickets for spouses and guests: $15 for each evening.

Accommodations: Airport limousine service available for approximately $7. Rooms in the motel are available for a special rate of $38 for conference attendees. The cost remains the same regardless of the number of people in the room. Participants are welcome to make any other arrangements they want on their own.

Additional Information: "Critique sessions are arranged at the conference between participants. Speakers do not agree to critique manuscripts as a part of their appearance at the conference." Organization sponsors annual contest. Send SASE for information. Conference brochures/guidelines also available for SASE.

THE OZARKS WRITERS CONFERENCE, University of Missouri-Kansas City College of Arts and Sciences, Continuing Ed. Division, 5100 Rockhill Rd., Kansas City MO 64110-2499. (816)235-2736. Noncredit Manager: Caryl Neinas. Cosponsored with the University of Arkansas-Fayetteville Continuing Education Division. Estab. in the mid-70s as The Longboat Key Writers Conference. Annual. "Exact dates yet to be established." Conference duration is 4 days, plus a one-day preconference. Average attendance: 75. "The Ozarks Writers Conference brings together talented writers in many genres for lectures, seminars, readings, workshops and individual conferences. Special emphasis is given to fiction and poetry. The emphasis is on craft and the creative process, but the program also deals with matters of psychology, publications and marketing. The conference is appropriate for both advanced and beginning writers. The conference meets on the beautiful campus of The College of the Ozarks, just outside of Branson, Missouri. The rolling hills of southern Missouri provide a relaxed environment sufficiently secluded so that the community of writers can focus on creative concerns without urban distractions. However, just across the ridge Branson presents the brightest lights in the country music industry along with a variety of family attractions such as Silver Dollar City and the Shepherd of the Hills."

Costs: Several options are available. Participants may choose to attend as a non-credit student or they may attend for 3 hours of college credit from the University of Missouri. Conference registration includes continental breakfasts, lunches and a banquet. For complete information, contact the University of Missouri-Kansas City.

Accommodations: Registrants are responsible for their own transportation, but information on area accommodations is made available. Also, special arrangements are made with the hotel and dormitory located on the College of the Ozarks campus. "On-campus rates are very reasonable."

Additional Information: Those registering for college credit are required to submit a manuscript in advance. Manuscript reading and critique is included in the credit fee. Those attending the conference for non-credit also have the option of having their manuscript critiqued for an additional fee. Conference brochures/guidelines are available for SASE.

PACIFIC NORTHWEST WRITERS SUMMER CONFERENCE, #804, United Airlines Building, 2033 6th Ave., Seattle WA 98121. (206)443-3807. Contact: Shirley Bishop. Estab. 1955. Annual. Conference held the last weekend in July. Average attendance: 500. Conference focuses on "fiction, nonfiction, poetry, film, drama, self-publishing, the creative process, critiques, core groups, advice from pros and networking." Site: the campus of Pacific Lutheran University in Tacoma. "Editors and agents come from both coasts. They bring lore from the world of publishing. The PNWC provides opportunities

for writers to get to know editors and agents. The literary contest provides feedback from professionals and possible fame for the winners. The 1991 guest speaker was Elizabeth George, mystery writer.
Costs: $75-85/day. Meals and lodging are available nearby, at minimal cost. Meal of the day is a box lunch ordered with the registration packet.
Accommodations: Buses take attendees to the ferry for a cruise. Lodging is available. "Conference rates are offered at local motels. On-site dorm rooms are quite reasonable."
Additional Information: On-site critiques are available in small groups. Literary contest in these categories: nonfiction books and articles, novels and short stories, playwriting. Send SASE for guidelines.

PACIFIC NORTHWEST WRITERS WINTER CONFERENCE, #804, United Airlines Building, 2033 6th Ave., Seattle WA 98121. (206)443-3807. Contact: Shirley Bishop. Estab. 1981. Annual. Weekend conference held in February. Average attendance: 200. "The conference is mostly hands-on workshops: novel, short story, nonfiction, film, poetry, getting started, keeping going." Site is the Greenwood Hotel, Bellevue, WA. "The winter conference is a good place to get started. Or a good place to recharge your batteries if your writing is stalled. If you're new in town, it's a good place to meet other writers." The 1991 guest speaker was Charles Johnson, author of *Middle Passage*, which won the National Book Award.
Costs: $85/day. Two days for $135. Meals are not included.
Accommodations: Lodging is available at the hotel or at surrounding motels.
Additional Information: On-site critiques are available in small groups. Literary contest in these categories: nonfiction books and articles, novels and short stories, playwriting. Brochures are available.

PALM SPRINGS WRITERS GUILD ANNUAL CONFERENCE, P.O. Box 2385, Palm Springs CA 92263. (619)346-1852 or 328-0970. President: Dr. Stanley S. Reyburn. Conference Chair: Sally Brown. Annual. Conference held May 16th. Average attendance: approx. 100. Conference to promote writing in all genres. Site: Palm Springs area hotel with conference facilities. "Geared in 1992 toward publishers and product they are seeking. Speakers in morning, workshops in afternoon (fiction and nonfiction). Panelists are representatives of major New York publishing houses."
Costs: $75 range, including luncheon.
Accommodations: Possible transportation from airport to conference site. Overnight accommodations and rates to be announced.
Additional Information: Organization sponsors separate annual writing contest during summer months. Brochures/guidelines available for SASE.

PENNWRITERS CONFERENCE, 360 W. Main St., Dallastown PA 17313. Conference Coordinator: Nancy Springer. Estab. 1988. Annual. Conference held third Saturday in May. Average attendance: 150. Conference to promote popular fiction—all sorts. Agents and editors are present as guests/speakers as well as writers. Site: Hilton Hotel, Harrisburg, PA.
Additional Information: Sponsors contest: Categories: 1st chapter of novel, 10 page limit; short story, 3,000 word limit; nonfiction article, 1,500 word limit. Conference brochures/guidelines are available for SASE.

PHILADELPHIA WRITERS' CONFERENCE, P.O. Box 7171, Philadelphia PA 19117-0171. (215)782-1059. President: Gloria Delamar. Estab. 1948. Annual. Conference held June 5-7. Average attendence: 160. Conference to promote fiction, nonfiction, poetry, playwriting and juvenile writing. Site: Holiday Inn, Independence Mall; self-contained wing in the historic section of Philadelphia. "Wing includes writers' 'coffee and conversation' lounge. Restaurants at site and in surrounding area. The hotel caters to writers. We have a long relationship with them. It's a happy and productive atmosphere. It is a block away from Independence Mall—including Independence Hall, The Liberty Bell, etc. Lots to see and experience." Workshops include "mind mapping for writers, basic short story, uses of dialogue in the short story, interweaving multiple plots in the novel, fantasy, basic magazine article, fiction technique in articles writing, nonfiction book, photojournalism, poetry, juveniles, genealogy, business of being a writer (includes record keeping, marketing, goal setting/time management, negotiations/contracts, legalities), and, finally, a closing workshop called charting your course. There will be editors and agents, a forum dinner speaker, and a banquet speaker. The forum dinner speaker will be Paul Norton, a local radio personality. The banquet speaker will be Shere Hite (of Hite Report Fame)."

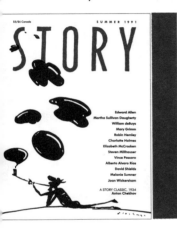

ONE OF THE MOST TALKED-ABOUT REVIVALS IN MAGAZINE PUBLISHING.....

STORY

The first issues of STORY were cranked out on an old mimeograph machine in 1931 by two America newspaper correspondents in Vienna. Editors Whit Burnett and his wife Martha Foley had money—just a vision to create a forum for outstanding short stories, regardless of their commerci appeal. The magazine was an instant literary success, and was hailed "the most distinguished sho story magazine in the world."

Now STORY returns with the same commitment to publishing the best new fiction written today will also provide a workshop for new material from today's more established writers, as well feature at least one piece reprinted from an original issue of STORY. Printed on heavy premiu paper, each issue is meant to be read and cherished for years to come. (Those first mimeograph copies of STORY are collectors' items today!)

Share in the rebirth of a literary legend. Become a subscriber to STORY today!

BUSINESS REPLY MAIL
FIRST CLASS MAIL   PERMIT NO. 125   MT. MORRIS, IL

POSTAGE WILL BE PAID BY ADDRESSEE

STORY
PO BOX 396
MOUNT MORRIS IL 61054-7910

No Postage
Necessary
If Mailed
In The
United States

Costs: Advance registration: $130 (5 workshops features); after May 1: $140; Forum buffet: $25; banquet: $25. Conferences are on their own for breakfasts and lunches.
Accommodations: The Holiday Inn reserves a block of rooms at reduced rates for the conference. "This past year the rates were $85, single; $95, double; plus 11% room tax.
Additional Information: "We have critiques for most workshops. The deadline for mss for critique is May 1. There are also contests for each workshop. The individual must be registered int he particular workshops. The work must be unpublished and meet length requirements. Judges are professionals — not on the conference board or faculty." Brochures/guidelines available for SASE.

PLOUGHSHARES INTERNATIONAL FICTION WRITING SEMINAR, Emerson College, Division of Continuing Education, 100 Beacon St., Boston MA 02116. (617)578-8615. Contact person: Hank Zappala. Estab. 1990. Annual. Conference/workshop held: August 16-28, 1992. Conference duration: 2 weeks. Average attendance: 25. "Castle Well is not a classroom, but a community of practicing writers who breathe, think, discuss and debate fiction with their peers and a group of professional authors." Castle Well is a Renaissance Castle. Located in the Village of Well on the river Maas in southeastern Holland. Co-Directors are James Carroll and Robie Macauley.
Costs: In 1991, cost was $1,650 plus transportation. Tuition includes room and board, special events, workshops and excursions.
Accommodations: On-site accommodations.
Additional Information: Sample work required — 1 short story or short segment of a longer work, no more than 15 pages. Brochures/guidelines available for SASE. "Seminar members may earn four credits toward graduate or undergraduate degrees."

PORT TOWNSEND WRITERS' CONFERENCE, Centrum, Box 1158, Port Townsend WA 98368. (206)385-3102. Director: Carol Jane Bangs. Estab. 1974. Annual. Conference held July 9-19. Average attendance: 180. Conference to promote poetry, fiction, creative nonfiction and writing for children. The conference is held at a 700-acre state park on the strait of Juan de Fuca. "The site is a Victorian-era military fort with miles of beaches, wooded trails and recreation facilities. The park is within the limits of Port Townsend, a historic seaport and arts community, approximately 80 miles northwest of Seattle, on the Olympic Peninsula." Panels include "Writing About Nature," "Journal Writing," "Literary Translation." There will be 5-10 guest speakers including Robert Michael Pyle and Tree Swenson.
Costs: $350 approx. tuition and $200 approx. room and board.
Accommodations: City bus transports ferry passengers to site. "Modest room and board facilities on site." Also list of hotels/motels/inns/bed & breakfasts/private rentals available.
Additional Information: "Admission to workshops is selective, based on manuscript submissions." Brochures/guidelines available for SASE. "The conference focus is on the craft of writing and the writing life, not on marketing."

PORTLAND STATE UNIVERSITY HAYSTACK PROGRAM IN THE ARTS & SCIENCES, PSU Summer Session, P.O. Box 751, Portland OR 97207. (503)725-4081. Contact: Maggie Herrington or Robert Mercer. Estab. 1968. Annual. Conference held from June 29 to August 7, generally in one-week sessions, meeting Monday through Friday. Average attendance: 15/class, 300 total. Conference offers "a varied selection of writing courses including fiction, nonfiction, poetry, essay and memoir — taught by well-known writers in small-group sessions, 6 hours/day." Classes are held in the local school with supplemental activities at the beach, pubs, lecture hall and other areas of the resort town.
Costs: $260-295 (1991 price). Participants provide their own housing and meals.
Accommodations: "We send a listing of available housing options after the participant has signed up. Housing costs are $50-400/week. Camping, bed and breakfasts and hotels are available."
Additional Information: "Some instructors request advance copies of student work. This is handled on a per instructor basis." Brochure is free.

PUBLISHING AND WRITING: CHILDREN'S BOOKS IN THE MARKETPLACE, Vassar College, Poughkeepsie NY 12601. (914)437-5903. Associate Director of College Relations: Maryann Bruno. Estab. 1984. Annual. Week-long conference held in June (most likely June 14-21). Average attendance: 40-50. Conference to promote the writing, illustrating, and publishing of children's book. Site: a 1,000-acre campus in the mid-Hudson Valley, 75 miles north of New York City, known for its beauty. Outdoor tennis courts, indoor pool and golf course available. Panels planned for next conference include all aspects of getting a children's book published — contracts, printers, publishers, magazine

Close-up

Ploughshares International
Fiction Writing Seminar

While writing conferences have always flourished both here and abroad, few, if any, are as exotic as Emerson College's Ploughshares International Fiction Writing Seminar, named after the school's respected literary magazine and held in July at the college's 16th century Castle Well in Holland.

Students from Europe and abroad, selected on the basis of their manuscripts, live for two weeks in airy rooms overlooking a double moat with black and white swans skimming the water. Writers rise at daybreak to a rooster's crowing, then breakfast on pastries and fruit served on white linens and china.

"One of Shirley Jackson's titles is 'We Have Always Lived In The Castle,' " Conference Leader Robie Macauley says. "If you went to sleep and dreamed about being a writer for two weeks of your life, living in the luxury of a castle surrounded by congenial spirits with nothing to do except write and talk about writing, that dream would be Castle Well," he says.

Macauley is a 25-year veteran of the publishing world, formerly Houghton Mifflin executive editor, *Kenyon Review* and *Playboy* fiction editor. He's published many of the world's greatest contemporary writers including John Updike, John Cheever, Graham Greene and Doris Lessing. He's currently advisory board member of *Story* magazine and the *Kenyon Review*, a novelist and short story writer.

Macauley describes the work of the seminar as "the laying on of hands that comes from the love of good writing. There is some kind of mysterious handing on of this fascination, this tradition, this passion that moves from one writer to another," he explains.

"Practically speaking, seminar workshops provide a better, closer reading than apprentice writers ever get at this stage of their career," Macauley explains. "And participants earn undergraduate or graduate credits."

The Ploughshares seminar is unique in other respects — attendance is limited to 25, and Emerson tries to provide each student with a private room. The ratio of students to teachers promotes close interraction. At Castle Well, contact with teachers and talk of writing continues at meals, evening readings, strolls on the grounds, as well as in scheduled conferences and workshops.

Students range in ability; some are published and some are not. Three stories are discussed in each session, with each story the result of weeks, months and sometimes years of labor. Writers attend to receive tough, honest, critical feedback — at times brutal, but still loving.

"One learns by being ruthlessly told the truth," Jim Carroll, conference coleader and bestselling author agrees. "It's like learning a golf swing from someone who knows to tell you what you're doing wrong."

The beautiful Castle Well in Holland is home to the Ploughshares International Fiction Writing Seminar.

Pamela Painter is a short story writer whose work has appeared in *The Atlantic*, *Harper's* and *Ploughshares*. She was a workshop leader at the 1991 conference. Coauthor of *What If?*, an exercise book for writers, Painter helps students into revision by asking questions, noticing "word packages" or a lack of tension in the story. She focuses on the mechanics of language and style.

"The conference serves to underscore the importance of revision," Painter explains. "The difference between a good manuscript and publication may be one or many careful rewrites."

David Applefield, editor of the Paris-based *Frank* magazine, also led a conference workshop in 1991. He's a "literary fix-it man" who likes to push the class slightly toward therapy. He feels that deeper self-knowledge is often more important to a rewrite than technical modification.

Seminar applicants are judged by both Macauley and Carroll, on the basis of a 15-page short story or segment of a novel. "We're looking for a good level of experience and skill," Macauley says. "Somebody who has some practice in writing and who shows some ability in fiction. It isn't necessary to be a polished professional; we might accept a young writer early in his or her career."

Cost for the conference in 1991 was $1,650. Included in this price was room and board, workshop fees, special events, excursions and academic credits. Students pay for transportation separately.

—Roberta Coffey

and story and book writing. Panelists "not known now, but always well-known professionals in the field."

Costs: About $675, including tuition, room and full board.

Accommodations: Airport in Newburgh, NY is 25 minutes away and van service to Vassar is available. Accommodations are in college residence halls.

Additional Information: Writers submit manuscript in advance; illustrators bring portfolios for critique. Brochures/guidelines available for SASE.

ROBERT QUACKENBUSH'S CHILDREN'S BOOK WRITING & ILLUSTRATING WORKSHOPS, 460 East 79th St., New York NY 10021. (212)744-3822. Instructor: Robert Quackenbush. Estab. 1982. Annual. Workshop held the second week in July. Average attendance: limited to 8. Workshops to promote writing and illustrating books for children. Held at the Manhattan studio of Robert Quackenbush, author and illustrator of over 150 books for young readers. "Focus is generally on picture books. All classes led by Robert Quackenbush."

Costs: $550 tuition covers all costs of the workshop, but does not include housing and meals. A $100 nonrefundable deposit is required with the $450 balance due two weeks prior to attendance.

Accommodations: A list of recommended hotels and restaurants is sent upon receipt of deposit.

Additional Information: Class is for beginners and professionals. Work submission not required. Critiques during workshop. Conference brochures/guidelines are available for SASE.

S.U.N.Y. COLLEGE FALL WRITING ARTS FESTIVAL, State University of New York at Oswego, Oswego NY 13126. (315)341-2602. Director of the Program in Writing Arts: Lewis Turco. Estab. 1968. Annual. Conference held October. Conference duration: 5 days, Monday-Thursday. Average attendance: 40-60. For fiction, poetry, drama writing. Conference held at the Student Union facilities. Past themes have included gay and lesbian writing, black writing.

Costs: All sessions free and open to public.

Accommodations: Attendees must make their own arrangements for board and accommodations. May be given information through the Office of Continuing Education at Swetmen Hall, State University College, Oswego NY 13126.

Additional Information: Information poster available for SASE.

SAN DIEGO STATE UNIVERSITY WRITERS CONFERENCE, SDSU-Aztec Center, San Diego CA 92182. (619)594-5152. Assistant to Director of Extension: Erin Alcaraz. Estab. 1984. Annual. Conference held on weekend in January. Average attendance: Approx. 350. "This conference is held on the San Diego State University campus at the Aztec Center. The Aztec Center is conveniently located near parking. The meeting rooms are spacious and comfortable. All sessions meet in the same general area. Each year the SDSU Writers Conference offers a variety of workshops for the beginner and the advanced writer. This conference allows the individual writer to choose which workshop best suits his/her needs. In addition, office hours are provided so that attendees may meet with speakers, editors and agents in small, personal groups to discuss specific questions. Also, a wine-and-cheese reception is offered Saturday immediately following the workshops where attendees may socialize with the faculty in a relaxed atmosphere. Keynote speaker is to be determined."

Costs: Not to exceed $185. This includes all conference workshops and office hours, coffee and pastries in the morning, lunch and wine-and-cheese reception Saturday evening.

Accommodations: The Howard Johnson offers conference attendees a reduced rate, $45/night. Attendees must say they are with the SDSU Writers Conference.

Additional Information: A critique session will be offered. To receive a brochure, call or send a postcard with address to: SDSU Writers Conference, College of Extended Studies, San Diego State University, San Diego CA 92182. No SASE required.

SCBW CONFERENCE IN CHILDREN'S LITERATURE, NYC, P.O. Box 20233, Park West Finance Station, New York NY 10025-1511. Chairman: Kimberly Colen. Estab. 1975. Annual. Conference held "usually" 1st (or 2nd) Saturday in November. Average attendance: 350-400. Conference is to promote writing for children: Picture books, fiction, nonfiction, middle grade and young adult. "The past 3 years it has been at 3 different schools. In 1991 it was held at the Fashion Institute of Technology."

Costs: $45, members; $50 nonmembers; $5 additional on day of conference.

Accommodations: No accommodations available. Write for information; hotel names will be supplied.

Additional Information: Conference brochures/guidelines are available for SASE.

SCBW/DRURY COLLEGE WRITING FOR CHILDREN WORKSHOP, 900 N. Benton, Springfield MO 65802. (417)865-8731. Directors: Lynn Doke or Sandy Asher. Estab. 1986. Annual. One-day workshop held in November. Average attendance: 60. Workshop to promote writing and illustrating fiction and nonfiction for young readers, held at Drury College. Panels planned for next workshop include Writing and Illustrating Picture Books, Marketing Your Work, and Writing for Middle Grade and Young Adult Readers. Faculty includes an editor from a major publishing house (i.e. Bantam, Scholastic) and invited authors.

Costs: $45, includes continental breakfast and luncheon. Discount for SCBW members and early registrants.

Accommodations: Hotel information is made available.

Additional Information: Faculty will meet with individuals to discuss manuscripts and/or illustrations, $25 fee. Workshop brochures/guidelines are available for SASE.

SCBW/HOFSTRA CHILDREN'S LITERATURE CONFERENCE, Hofstra University, University College of Continuing Education, 205 Davison Hall, Hempstead NY 11550. (516)463-5993. Co-organizers: Connie C. Epstein, Adrienne Betz, Lewis Shena. Estab. 1985. Annual. Conference held April 11. Average attendance: 160. Conference to promote writing for children. "Purpose is to bring together various professional groups—writers, illustrators, librarians, teachers—who are interested in writing for children. Each year we organize program around a theme. Last year it was The Global Connection, and this year it will the The American Experience." The conference takes place at the Student Center Building of Hofstra University, located in Hempstead, Long Island. "We have two general sessions and break-out groups we hold in rooms in the Center or classrooms in nearby buildings. Lunch is provided." This year's conference will offer "break-out groups in young-adult fiction (M.E. Kerr), humorous writing (Kate McMullan), picture books (Dilys Evans), nonfiction (Larry Pringle), book reviewing (Leonard Marcus) and submission procedures (Stephanie Lurie). Panel topic not yet decided; may be 'what editors look for.'" Jean Fritz and Joseph Bruchac will be general speakers.

Cost: $47 for SCBW members; $52 for nonmembers. Lunch and end-of-day reception included.

SCBW/ROCKY MOUNTAIN CHAPTER, 8600 Firethorn Dr., Loveland CO 80538. (303)669-3755. Regional Advisor: Vivian Dubrovin. Annual. Fall Conference held 3rd Saturday of Sept.; Winter Workshop held in Feb.; Illustrators Workshop held in May. All last 1 day. Average attendance: 100-175. Fall conference features authors, editors and agents for children's work (picture book—YA). Winter workshop features headline authors. "Emphasis on small-group workshops on characterization, plotting, second level of writing, publishing etc." Illustrators workshop features illustrators of children's books and workshops on writing/illustrating and technical aspects particular to children's books. Conferences rotate between college facilities, hotels and other meeting spaces. Brochures available approximately 3-4 weeks prior to event.

Costs: Generally around $50/day, less for SCBW members. Lunch and snacks plus handouts included.

SHENANDOAH VALLEY WRITERS GUILD, P.O. Box 47, Middletown VA 22645. (703)869-1120. Faculty Liaison: Felicia Cogan, assoc. professor at Lord Fairfax Community College. Estab. 1978. Conferences/workshops held in May and November. Duration: November, 1 day; May, weekend. Average attendance: 60. Conferences to promote fiction, poetry, writing for children and articles. November conference held at Lord Fairfax Community College. May conference held at North Virginia 4H Conference Center. Theme of May conference is "Marketing Your Work." Panelists are husband and wife team of professional writers: Donna Acquavira and Robert Naylor.

Costs: Fee not set yet.

Accommodations: Accommodations for May are at the Center, as are meals.

Additional Information: Workshops for fiction writers include critiques and may require writers to submit for critique prior to the conference/workshop. Conference brochures/guidelines are available for SASE.

SINCLAIR COMMUNITY COLLEGE'S ANNUAL WRITERS' CONFERENCE, 444 W. 3rd St., Dayton OH 45402-1460. (513)226-2594. Professor/Director: Gary Mitchner. Estab. 1967. Annual. Conference held April 3-4. Average attendance: 150. Conference to promote fiction, poetry, and nonfiction freelance writing. Site: David Ponitz Center at the downtown Dayton campus of Sinclair Community College. Guest speakers or panelists not planned yet. "In the past we have had Toni Morrison, John Gardner, Stanley Kunitz, Jessica Mitford, Richard Selzer and Richard Howard."

Costs: $25; luncheon extra.
Additional Information: Contest includes adult and high school categories in poetry, fiction and essay. Sinclair faculty serve as judges. Conference brochures/guidelines available for SASE.

SINIPEE WRITERS' WORKSHOP, P.O. Box 902, Dubuque IA 52004-0902. (319)556-0366. Director: John Tigges. Estab. 1985. Annual. Conference held April 25, 1992. Average attendance: 40-50. To promote "primarily fiction although we do include a poet and a nonfiction writer on each program. The two mentioned areas are treated in such a way that fiction writers can learn new ways to expand their abilities and writing techniques." The workshop is held on the campus of Clarke College in Dubuque. "This campus holds a unique atmosphere and everyone seems to love the relaxed and restful mood it inspires. This in turn carries over to the workshop and friendships are made that last in addition to learning and experiencing what other writers have gone through to attain success in their chosen field." 1992 guest speakers include Mary Mayer Holmes (best-selling romance novelist); Ben Logan (Emmy award winner and best selling novelist); Pam Schuster (poet/novelist); Rebecca Christian (award-winning playwright and newspaper columnist).
Costs: $60 early registration/$65 at the door. Includes all handouts, necessary materials for the workshop, coffee/snack break, lunch, drinks and snacks at autograph party following workshop.
Accommodations: Information is available for out-of-town participants, concerning motels etc. even though the workshop is one day long.
Additional Information: May add critique service in 1992. Fiction contest: Limit 1,500 words. In each category: 1st prize $50 plus publication in an area newspaper or magazine; 2nd prize 50% scholarship; 3rd 25% scholarship (scholarships for following year). Conference brochures/guidelines are available for SASE. "We offer a 50% scholarship to full-time college and high school students as well as to Senior citizens 65 and older."

SOCIETY OF SOUTHWESTERN AUTHORS WRITERS' CONFERENCE, P.O. Box 35220, Tucson AZ 85740. (602)296-5996. Conference Chair: Michael Munday. Estab. 1972. Annual. Conference held the last Saturday in January. Average attendance: 150-250. Conference "covers a spectrum of practical topics for writers. Each year varies, but there is a minimum of 12 different classes during the day, plus the keynote speaker and the free-for-all after lunch." Conference held at Student Union Building of the University of Arizona. "We take over a lounge and five classrooms."
Costs: $35 for the entire day including lunch.
Additional Information: Conference brochures/guidelines are available for SASE.

SOUTHWEST CHRISTIAN WRITERS ASSOCIATION, P.O. Box 2635, Farmington NM 87499. (505)327-1962. President: Pat Burke. Estab. 1980. Annual. Conference held September 19. Average attendance: 27. For "fiction (novel), short stories, writing for teens." Conference held at the First Presbyterian Church, 865 N. Dustin, Farmington, NM 87401. Panels include: Writing the teen novel; Marketing and dealing with editors; Writing for children. Guest speaker Carole Gift Page.
Costs: $39 (meals are "Dutch" at a local restaurant).
Additional Information: Sponsors a contest. "One additional speaker invited (not decided yet). Freebies and a booktable available (authors may bring books to sell if attending conference)."

SOUTHWEST FLORIDA WRITERS' CONFERENCE, P.O. Box 06210, Ft. Myers FL 33906-6210. (813)489-9226. Conference Director: Joanne Hartke. Estab. 1980. Annual. Conference held Feb. 21-22 (always the 4th Friday night and Saturday of February). Average attendance: 150. "This year's conference will include fiction, poetry, screenwriting, children's nonfiction and travel writing. The purpose is to serve the local writing community, whether they are novice or published writers." The conference is held on the Edison Community College campus. "We will have one final panel that will include several presenters from earlier in the day. It will be an open forum to ask questions, share ideas, say what works (and doesn't) for each. The featured keynote address will be given by Peter Matthiessen."
Costs: Friday, February 21—reception and keynote address: $15. Saturday February 22—full-day conference: $45 (continental breakfast and lunch included).
Additional Information: "We do sponsor a contest annually, with the prizes being gift certificates to local bookstores. Local, published writers offer volunteer critique/judging services." Conference brochures or guidelines available for SASE. "Every odd year the conference format is writing intensive rather than mainly presentations, with verbal and written critiques."

STEAMBOAT SPRINGS WRITERS GROUP, P.O. Box 774284, Steamboat Springs CO 80477. (303)879-9008. Chairperson: Harriet Freiberger. Estab. 1982. Annual. Conference held in Summer. Conference duration: 1 day. Average attendance: 45. "Our conference emphasizes instruction within the seminar format. Novices and polished professionals benefit from the individual attention and the camaraderie which can be established within small groups. A pleasurable and memorable learning experience is guaranteed by the relaxed and friendly atmosphere of the old train depot." Steamboat Arts Council sponsors the group at the restored Train Depot.
Costs: In 1991, tuition was $40 for members; $50 for nonmembers. Fee covers all conference activities, including opening reception, continental breakfast and lunch. Lodging available at Steamboat Resorts; 10% discount for participants."
Additional Information: "We are in the process of changing our format and will be featuring one instructor for a limited number of participants."

SUMMER IN FRANCE WRITING WORKSHOPS, HCOI, Box 102, Plainview TX 79072. (806)889-3533. Director: Bettye Givens. Estab. 1966. Annual. Conference: 27 days. Average attendance: 10-15. For fiction, poetry. The classrooms are in the Val de Grace 277 Rue St. Jacques in the heart of the Latin Quarter near Luxeumbourg Park in Paris. Guest speakers include Paris poets, professors and editors (sometimes lecture in English).
Costs: 1,300 French francs—about $800 U.S. and includes French classes, art history and the writing workshop.
Accommodations: Apartments are available (about $300 with a roommate—each) or accommodations with a French family.
Additional Information: Conference brochures/guidelines are available for SASE. "Enroll early. Side trips out of Paris are planned as are poetry readings at the Paris American Academy and at Shakespeare & Co."

TEXAS WRITERS ASSOCIATION FALL, SPRING AND SUMMER WORKSHOPS, 219 Preston Royal, Shopping Center #3, Dallas TX 75230. (214)363-9979. Executive Director: Jheri Fleet. Estab. 1989. Held 3 times/year. Conference held March/April, June and September/October. Conference duration: ½ day—all day—2days (varies). Average attendance: From 15-200 depending on limitation. To promote all types of writing. "All workshop and conference speakers are successful published writers, agents, editors or producers who are lively, informative and congenial with attendees. The locations are selected with handicapped considered. No theme plan. Generally, about ½ our workshops are fiction related."
Costs: "Cost is for members/nonmembers. Meals include *only* lunch *only* on particular all-day workshops. Most half-day workshops are $60 or less for nonmembers. All day workshops generally are $100 for nonmembers."
Accommodations: Accommodations made available usually with discounts. Special hotel and airfare rates, on-site facility, in some cases rooms range from $45 a night to $90.
Additional Information: Critiques available. "Some critique sessions require prior submission, some do not. Must be no more than 20 pages—no poetry. TWA is one of the fastest growing statewide writers association with workshops and conferences in seven to ten Texas cities. TWA is the present home of the National Magazine Editors Conference which brings 20-40 major national magazines to Texas to meet with writers from all over the county."

THIRD COAST WRITERS CONFERENCE, % English Dept., Western Michigan University, Kalamazoo MI 49007. (616)387-2570. Director: Stuart Dybek. Estab. 1987. Annual. Conference held May 7-9. Average attendance: 120. Conference to promote fiction, poetry, nonfiction and drama. Site: The campus of Western Michigan University. "A staff of 15 professional writers will be available to run workshops, and panels on craft issues. Included is a panel on publishing and marketing one's work. Li-Young Lee is our featured poet. Patrick Meyers, our dramatist. A feature fiction writer is still to be decided."
Costs: $120, which includes housing and one meal.
Accommodations: There is university dorm housing. Local motels are also available.
Additional Information: Work for workshops must be submitted in advance. Brochures/guidelines available for SASE.

THUNDER BAY LITERARY CONFERENCE, 211 N. First, Alpena MI 49707. (517)356-6188. Assistant Director: Judi Stillion. Estab. 1990. Annual. Two-day conference held in September. Average attendance: 100-150. "Our current area of concentration is Michigan writers. One objective is to heighten

awareness and understanding of the heritage and current status of literature in the state." The conference is held at the Holiday Inn.
Costs: $15 (nonrefundable).
Accommodations: Information on overnight accommodations is made available. Special rates are available at the Holiday Inn for those who specify the conference.
Additional Information: Sponsors contest for adult short fiction and poetry. Michigan residents only. A panel of University of Michigan faculty will judge entries. Write for more information. Conference brochures/guidelines available for SASE.

UNIVERSITY OF MASSACHUSETTS AT LOWELL WRITERS' CONFERENCE, One University Ave., Lowell MA 01824. (508)934-2405. Program Coordinator: John Hurtado. Assistant Director: Dirk Messelaar. Estab. 1988. Annual. Conference held March 6-8. Average attendance: 85. Conference covers fiction, short stories, children's literature, essays. Conference held at the University of Massachusetts at Lowell (formerly University of Lowell). The conference features readings and lectures in the O'Leary Library lecture room and seminars in the adjacent break-out rooms located in the library. Speakers, include David Rivard (poet), David Huddle (poet/story writer), Valerie Martin (novelist), Loretta Fidel (agent), David R. Godine (publisher).
Costs: In 1991, $125/$75 full-time students plus $35 fee for individual conferences included light lunch and breaks.
Accommodations: Lists of hotels and special rates are available.
Additional Information: For a small additional fee, individual conferences with published authors are available on a limited basis. Ms must be submitted 3 weeks prior to the conference. Brochures/guidelines are available—no SASE required.

UNIVERSITY OF MASSACHUSETTS AT LOWELL WRITING PROGRAM, One University Ave., Lowell MA 01854. (508)934-2405. Program Coordinator: John Hurtado. Estab. 1989. Annual. Conference held July to mid-August. Conference duration: 6 weeks. Average attendance: 250 in 15 courses. Conference includes "credit courses in expository writing, fiction, poetry, playwriting, journalism, arts reporting, in addition to free readings by nationally-known, award-winning, local writers. Courses are held at the University's Mogan Cultural Center, a renovated Millgirl Boardinghouse within the Lowell National Park and in various classrooms on both the North and South campuses."
Costs: In 1991, $285 per 3 credit undergraduate course, plus a one-time $25 registration fee.
Accommodations: Dormitory accommodations available on campus include board option.
Additional Information: Brochures available. "Audit option available at full tuition (pass/fall not available due to nature of courses and requirements)."

UNIVERSITY OF WISCONSIN AT MADISON SCHOOL OF THE ARTS AT RHINELANDER, 727 Lowell Hall, 610 Langdon St., Madison WI 53703. Administrative Coordinator: Kathy Berigan. Estab. 1964. Annual. Conference held from July 20 to July 24. Average attendance: 280. Courses offered in writing, visual arts, drama, photography, music, folkarts, folk dancing. Conference held in junior high school in the city of Rhinelander in northern Wisconsin (James Williams Junior High School).
Costs: Tuition only—approximately $155. Some courses require materials or lab fee.
Accommodations: Information on overnight accommodations made available.
Additional Information: Ms critique workshop available. Request to be put on mailing list. "Courses offered in other 'arts' areas during week."

UNIVERSITY OF WISCONSIN AT MADISON WRITERS INSTITUTE, 610 Langdon St., Madison WI 53703. (608)262-3447. Director: Christine DeSmet. Estab. 1990. Annual. Conference held July 16 to July 17. Average attendance: 175. "Day 2 is fiction—genre writing; Day 1 is nonfiction—journalism freelance writing." Conference held at Wisconsin Center, University of Wisconsin at Madison. Themes: Mystery, suspense, sci fi, romance, mainstream for 1992 fiction. Guest speakers are published authors and editors.
Costs: $75/day or $125 for 2 days; $15 critique fee.
Accommodations: Info on accommodations sent with registration confirmation. Critiques available Conference brochures/guidelines are available for SASE.

THE VANCOUVER INTERNATIONAL WRITERS FESTIVAL, 1243 Cartwright St., Vancouver, British Columbia V6H 4B7 Canada. (604)681-6330. Estab. 1988. Annual. Conference held from October 21 to October 25. Average attendance: 6,600. "This is a festival for readers and writers. The program of events is diverse and includes readings, panel discussions, workshops. Lots of opportunities to interact

with the writers who attend." Conference held at Granville Island—in the heart of Vancouver. Three professional theaters are used as well as space in the Community Centre. "We try to avoid specific themes. The focus in 1991 was Latin American Writers and writing. Programming takes place between February and June each year."
Costs: Tickets are $8 and $12 (Canadian); some special events are a little more.
Accommodations: Local tourist info can be provided when necessary and requested.
Additional Information: Brochures/guidelines are available for SASE. "Only a reminder that this is a festival, a celebration, not a conference or workshop."

WELLS WRITERS WORKSHOPS, 69 Broadway, Concord NH 03301. (603)225-9162. Director: Vic Levine. Estab. 1988. Held: 2 times/year in Wells, Maine. Conferences held from May 17 to May 22; September 13 to September 18. Average attendance: 6. "Workshop concentrates on short and long fiction, especially the novel. Focus is on the rational structuring of a story, using Aristotelian and scriptwriting insights. Throughout, the workshop balances direct instruction with the actual plotting and writing of the basic scenes of a novel." Conference located in a "large, airy and light house overlooking the ocean with ample individual space for writers and group conferences. While the purposes of the workshop is to teach the process of plotting as it applies across the board—to all kinds of fiction, including novels, short stories, movies—it strives to meet the specific needs of participants, especially through individual conferences with the instructor."
Costs: "The cost of $1,085 covers tuition, room and board. Registration cost is $75 (nonrefundable). Payment may be in two or three installments."
Accommodations: Workshop supplies transportation from/to Portland International Airport—or other places, by arrangement. Workshop supplies accommodations.
Additional Information: Conference brochures/guidelines available for SASE. "Workshop has a scholarship fund which can, as it has in the past, defray part of the total expense of $1,085."

WESLEYAN WRITERS CONFERENCE, Wesleyan University, Middletown CT 06457. (203)347-9411, ext. 2448. Director: Anne Greene. Estab. 1956. Annual. 1992 Conference held from June 28 to July 3. Average attendance: 100. For fiction, poetry, nonfiction, literary journalism. The Conference is held on the campus of Wesleyan University, in the hills overlooking the Connecticut River. Meals and lodging are provided on campus. Readings of new fiction. Guest lectures on a range of topics including the art of memoir.
Costs: In 1991, tuition $415; meals $165; room $85.
Accommodations: "Participants can fly to Hartford or take Amtrak to Meriden, CT. We are happy to help participants make travel arrangements." Overnight participants stay on campus.
Additional Information: Ms critiques are available as part of the program but are not required. "We sponsor several scholarship competitions and award teaching fellowships. Application info is in conference brochure." Brochures/guidelines are available for SASE.

WESTCHESTER WRITERS' CONFERENCE, 16 Lawrence Dr., N. White Plains NY 10603. (914)682-1574. Conference Director: Sarah White. Estab. 1985. Annual. Conference held April 11. Average attendance: 200. Conference includes fiction, journalism, poetry, writing for children, enhancing creativity, writers and computers; writers' rights. Conference held on private college campus. Panels include: fictional characters; the young adult market; the short story.
Costs: $65 includes all workshops and luncheon.
Additional Information: Conference brochures/guidelines are available for SASE.

WRITE YOUR LIFE STORY FOR PAY, 877 Northampton Dr., Palo Alto CA 94303. (415)322-0063. Contact: Louise Purwin Zobel. Estab. 1969. Workshop held irregularly, usually semiannually at several locations. Workshop duration: 1-2 days. Average attendance: 30-50. "Because every adult has a story worth telling, this conference helps participants to write fiction and nonfiction in books and short forms, using their own life stories as a base." This workshop is held on about 40 campuses at different times, inluding University of California and other university and college campuses in the west.
Costs: Usually $45-65/day, "depending on campus."
Additional Information: Brochures/guidelines available for SASE.

WRITERS IN RESIDENCE PROGRAMS, Festival of the Written Arts, Box 2299, Sechelt, British Columbia V0N 3A0 Canada. (604)885-9631. FAX: (604)885-3967. Producer: Betty C. Keller. Estab. 1986. Workshops held: April 10 to April 12/92 (short story writing); April 24-April 26/92 (songwriting); April 28 to April 30/92 (romance writing); May 15 to May 17/92 (crime writing); August 8 to August 12/92

(fiction writing, writing for children); August 18 to August 22/92 (nonfiction writing and poetry). Average attendance: 12-20 per workshop. "The Rockwood Centre overlooks the town of Sechelt on the Sunshine Coast. The Lodge around which the Centre was organized was built in 1937 as a destination for holidayers arriving on the old Union Steamship Line; it has been preserved very much as it was in its heyday. A new twelve bedroom annex was added in 1982, and in 1989 the Festival of the Written Arts constructed a Pavilion for outdoor performances next to the annex. The whole complex is managed by the Rockwood Society and reserved exclusively for the arts, recreation and learning. Writers-in-Residence participants are accommodated two (and in a few cases three) to a room with a private bathroom."
Costs: 3 days for $225 (Canadian) includes: Tuition $100, accommodations $60, meals $65. 5 days for $295 (Canadian) includes: Tuition: $140, accommodations $75, meals $80.
Additional Information: Each workshop participant is required to send a manuscript with his/her application so that the instructor can ascertain the level of competency and be prepared to assist improvement. Brochures/guidelines are available for SASE.

WRITERS WORKSHOP IN SCIENCE FICTION, English Department/University of Kansas, Lawrence KS 66045. (913)864-3380. Professor: James Gunn. Estab. 1985. Annual. Conference held from July 18 to July 31; or July 25 to August 7. Average attendance: 8-10. Conference for writing and marketing science fiction. "Housing is provided and classes meet in Jayhawker Towers, an apartment complex on the University of Kansas campus. Workshop sessions operate informally in an apartment living room." Guest speaker: Frederik Pohl, SF writer and former editor and agent. We also expect to have an editor from Tor Books as critiquer.
Costs: Tuition: $400. Housing and meals are additional.
Accommodations: Several airport shuttle services offer reasonable transportation from the Kansas City International Airport to Lawrence. Apartments with cooking facilities are available in Jayhawker Towers; in 1991 the cost for two weeks was $157 per person.
Additional Information: "Admission to the workshop is by submission of an acceptable story. Two additional stories should be submitted by the end of June. These three stories are copied and distributed to other participants for critiquing and are the basis for the first week of the workshop; one story is rewritten for the second week." Brochures/guidelines are available for SASE. "The Writers Workshop in Science Fiction is intended for writers who have just started to sell their work or need that extra bit of understanding or skill to become a published writer."

WRITING BY THE SEA, 1511 New York Ave., Cape May NJ 08204. (609)884-7117, ext. 15. CMI Managing Director: Natalie Newton. Estab. 1990. Annual. Conference held November 4 to November 7. Conference duration: 4 days. Average attendance: 70. Conference offers "about 30 seminars on fiction and nonfiction writing in a retreat atmosphere at the Virginia Hotel." Conference held at "the Cape May Institute, an adult continuing education, nonprofit organization located in Victorian Cape May. Our modern facilities include a comfortable lecture hall and world class b&w photographic darkrooms. The Institute is noted for its support of the arts and hosts annual music and theater performances." Panels include "finding an agent" and "self-publishing." Guest speakers have included James Allen (agent), Esta Cassway (author), Page Edwards (author), Norma Leone (publisher), Margaret Mangum (author), David Poyer (author), Richard Rashke (author).
Costs: $295 for 4 days or $125/day—conference fee only.
Accommodations: For 1992, we have the entire Virginia Hotel, a luxuriously refurbished Victorian Inn from November 3-7. Cost is $65 (single) or $75 (double occupancy) per night.
Additional Information: Conference brochures/guidelines are available for SASE.

WRITING FOR PUBLICATION, Villanova University, Villanova PA 19085. (215)645-4620. Director: Wm. Ray Heitzmann, Ph.D. Estab. 1975. Semiannual. Conference dates vary, held fall, spring. Average attendance: 15-20 (seminar style). Conference covers marketing one's manuscript (fiction, nonfiction, book, article, etc.); strong emphasis on effective component of writing. Conference held in a seminar room at a university (easy access, parking, etc.). Panels include "Advanced Writing for Publication," "Part-time Writing," "Working With Editors." Panelists include Ray Heitzman, and others.
Costs: $270 (graduate credit); $195 (undergraduate credit); $100 (non-credit) plus $10 registration fee.
Accommodations: List of motels/hotels available, but most people live in area and commute. Special arrangements made on an individual basis.
Additional Information: Critiques available. Voluntary submission of manuscripts. Brochures/guidelines are available. "Workshop graduates have been very successful."

WRITING WORKSHOP FOR PEOPLE OVER 57, % Donovan Scholars Program/University of Kentucky, Ligon House, 658 S. Limestone, Lexington KY 40506-0442. (606)257-8314. Director: Roberta H. James. Estab. 1967. Annual. Conference held from June 21 to June 26. Average attendance: 35-50. Conference includes fiction, nonfiction, poetry, children's literature/young adult novel. "Carnahan House Conference Center is a lovely mansion, once the main residence of Coldstream Farm, a Bluegrass estate internationally known for its magnificient horses. It is now owned by the University of Kentucky."
Costs: Workshop registration: $125/person. Lunches are catered at Carnahan House, including an opening day picnic and an evening banquet. All other evening meals are not included. The cost of the 5 lunches, picnic and banquet is $47.50/person.
Accommodations: Shuttle bus service is provided to/from the airport by the Ramada Hotel, one of the hotels offered to our out-of-town registrants. Carnahan House provides a shuttle between the Ramada Hotel and La Quinta Motor Inn and Carnahan House. We offer registrants a choice of four hotels, all within close distance to Carnahan House. Rates range from $31-55.
Additional Information: "Registrants can apply for either full-student or audit status. Under full-student status, registrants must submit a manuscript prior to the workshop, which is submitted to the instructor of the particular genre which they have chosen." Brochures/guidelines are available for SASE. "This workshop is open only to adults age 57 and older."

YELLOW BAY WRITERS' WORKSHOP, Center for Continuing Education, University of Montana, Missoula MT 59812. (406)243-6486. Program Manager: Judy Jones. Estab. 1988. Annual. Conference held from mid to late August. Average attendance: 50-60. Includes four faculty: 2 fiction; 1 poetry; 1 creative nonfiction/personal essay. Conference "held at the University of Montana's Flathead Lake Biological Station, a research station with informal educational facilities and rustic cabin living. Located in northwestern Montana on Flathead Lake, the largest of any natural freshwater lake west of the Mississippi River. All faculty are requested to present a craft lecture—usually also have an editor leading a panel discussion." Past faculty: Carolyn Kizer, Thomas McGuane, Marilynne Robinson, Geoffrey Wolff, Mona Simpson, Blanche Boyd, James Tate, James Welch, Joy Williams, James Crumley, Carolyn Forche, William Kittredge.
Costs: In 1991 $350 for tuition.
Accommodations: Shuttle is available from Missoula to Yellow Bay for those flying to Montana. Cost of shuttle is $36 (1991). On-site rates are $225 for room and board for the week (in 1991); commuter meal plans are available.
Additional Information: "We require a five-page writing sample to accompany the workshop application." Brochures/guidelines are available for SASE.

Other conferences and workshops

The following conferences and workshops responded to our questionnaire too late to receive a full listing in this edition. We've included contact names and addresses, however, so you may write for details. Remember to include self-addressed, stamped envelopes (or SAE with International Reply Coupons) with all requests for information.

Arkansas Writers' Conference: Clovita Rice, director, 1115 Gillette Dr., Little Rock AR 72207.

Baltimore Science Fiction Society Writer's Workshops: Steve Lubs, P.O. Box 686, Baltimore MD 21203-0686.

Cape Cod Writers Conference/Cape Literary Arts Workshop: Marion Vuilleumier, executive director, c/o Cape Cod Conservatory, Route 132, West Barustable MA 02668.

Canyonlands Field Institute Desert Writers Workshop: David Williams, special program coordinator, P.O. Box 68, Moab UT 84532.

Cuyahoga Writers' Conference: Margo Bohanon, 4250 Richmond Rd., Highland Hills Village OH 44122-6195.

Key West Literary Seminar: Monica Haskell, executive director, P.O. Box 391, Sugarloaf Shores FL 33044.

LDS Writers' Market (next held in 1993): Chris Crowe, director, Box 1869, Brigham Young University-Hawaii, Laie HI 96762. (inquire after Sept.)

Maple Woods Community College Writers Conference: Pattie Smith, coordinator, continuing education, 2601 NE Barry Rd., Kansas City MO 64056.

Pasadena Writers' Forum: Meredith Brucker, coordinator, Pasadena City College, 1570 E. Colorado Blvd., Pasadena CA 91106-2003.

Sage Hill Writing Experience, summer writing workshops: Steven Smith, administrator, Box 1731, Saskatoon, Saskatchewan S7K 3S1 Canada.

Santa Fe Writers' Conference: Rae Taylor, seminar coordinator, 826 Camino de Monte Rey, Santa Fe NM 87501.

Saskatchewan Writers Guild Common Ground-Voices Gathering: Paul Wilson, program director, Box 3988, Regina, Saskatchewan S4T 3R9 Canada.

Seattle Pacific University Christian Writers Conference: Linda Wagner, director, School of Humanities, Seattle Pacific University, Seattle WA 98119.

Sewanee Writers' Conference: Cheri Peters, administrator, 310 St. Luke's Hall, Sewanee TN 37375.

Southern California Writers Conference—San Diego: Betty Abell Jurus, director, 3745 Mt. Augustus Ave., San Diego CA 92111.

State of Maine Writers' Conference: Richard F. Burns, chairman, P.O. Box 296, Ocean Park ME 04063.

University of North Dakota Writers Conference in Children's Literature, cosponsored by the Big Sky Chapter of SCBW: Ursula Hovet or Faythe Thureen, codirectors, Department of English, UND, Grand Forks ND 58202-8237.

Woodstock Publishing Conference at Byrdcliffe: Michael Perkins, program director, 34 Tinker St., Woodstock NY 12498.

Write for Success Workshop, children's books: Theo Carroll, speaker/ coordinator, 3748 Harbor Heights Dr., Largo FL 34644.

Write to Sell Writer's Conference: Diane Dunaway, director, 8465 Jane St., San Diego CA 92129.

Retreats and Colonies

Retreats and colonies deserve a section all their own because they function quite differently from conferences and workshops. Whereas the latter events are bustling with people meeting people and attending scheduled activities, folks at the former places don't "bustle" at all. Retreats and colonies are places for writers to find solitude and concentrated time to focus solely on their writing. Communal meals may be the only scheduled activities. Also, a writer's stay at a retreat or colony is typically anywhere from one to 12 weeks (sometimes longer), while time spent at a conference or workshop is generally anywhere from one day to two weeks (perhaps a month at most).

Like conferences and workshops, however, retreats and colonies span a wide range. Some, such as the Bellagio Study and Conference Center, are open only to individuals "with significant publications, exhibitions or shows to their credit" while others, such as the Fine Arts Work Center in Provincetown, Massachusetts, are open to "emerging" writers and visual artists. The Syvenna Foundation Writers-in-Residence program and Wolf Pen Women Writers Colony are two examples of places only for women writers. And you'll find retreats and colonies everywhere from the shore of Green Bay, Wisconsin, to rural Hawaii to a national park in Burgundy, France.

Despite different focuses and/or locations, all retreats and colonies have one thing in common: They are places where writers may work undisturbed, usually in very nature-oriented and secluded settings. A retreat or colony serves as a place for rejuvenation; a writer can find new ideas, rework old ones or put the finishing touches to works-in-progress. Author Allan Gurganus, for example, developed the idea for his book *The Oldest Living Confederate Widow Tells All* while in residence at the Yaddo artist's colony.

Determine your work habits

Arrangements at retreats and colonies differ dramatically so it may help to determine your own work habits before you begin your search. While some retreats house writers in one main building, others provide separate cottages. In both cases, residents are generally given private work space, although they usually must bring along their own typewriters or personal computers. Meals are another factor. Some colonies offer communal, family-style meals at set times, some prepare meals for each resident individually and still others require residents to prepare meals themselves. If you tend to work straight through meals now, you might want to consider a retreat or colony that offers the last option.

A related consideration for most folks is cost. Again, the types of arrangements vary. A good number of residencies are available at no cost or only a minimal daily cost, sometimes including the cost of meals, sometimes not. The MacDowell Colony, for example, asks artists to contribute "according to their financial resources." Other residencies, such as those through the Ucross Foundation, are "awards," resulting from competitive applications. Some retreats and colonies provide residencies as well as stipends for personal expenses. Finally, for those residencies that are fairly expensive, scholarships or fee waivers are often available.

Plan ahead

In general, residencies at retreats and colonies are competitive because only a handful of spots are available at each place. Writers must often apply at least six months in advance for the time period they desire. While some locations are open year-round, others are available only during certain seasons. Planning to go during the "off-season" may lessen your competition. Also, most places will want to see a writing sample with your application, so be prepared to show your best work—whether you are a beginning writer or an established one. In addition, it will help to have an idea of the project you'll work on while in residence, since some places request this information with their applications as well.

Each listing in this section provides information about the type of writers the retreats or colony accepts; the location, accommodations and meal plan available; the costs; and, finally, the application process. As with markets and conferences and workshops, changes in policies may be made after this edition has gone to press. Send a self-addressed, stamped envelope to the places that interest you to receive the most up-to-date details.

For other listings of retreats and colonies, you may want to see *The Guide to Writers Conferences* (Shaw Associates, publishers, Suite 1406, 625 Biltmore Way, Coral Gables FL 33134), which not only provides information on conferences, workshops and seminars but also residencies, retreats and organizations. Another resource is *100 Havens for Creatives*, from ACTS Institute, Inc. (P.O. Box 10153, Kansas City MO 64111). The institute plans an anthology of works produced at or inspired by such residencies.

ACT I CREATIVITY CENTER, #1201, % Plotsky, 4550 Warwick Blvd., Kansas City MO 64111. (816)753-0208. Administrator: Char Plotsky. Estab. 1984. For all disciplines *on an invitational basis only* as of this summer. "We lease spring and fall at Lake of the Ozarks and now summer and winter in Kansas City." Time offered each year varies.
Costs: Costs vary.
To Apply: Invitation only. Send SASE to get on list for next invitation notice.

ATLANTIC CENTER FOR THE ARTS, 1414 Art Center Ave., New Smyrna Beach FL 32168. (904)427-6975. Program Director: James J. Murphy. Estab. 1980. "Residencies at Atlantic Center are open to all who meet selection requirements. Master Artists, who are selected in consultation with the Advisory Council, set the structure of the residency, determine what will be accomplished and set criteria for selection of Associates. Associates, who are typically artists at mid-career, are selected by Master Artists through portfolio review (in this case, examples of writing résumés, etc.) Atlantic Center is located on 67-acres of hammockland on Turnbull Bay, a tidal estuary in New Smyrna Beach, Florida. Buildings include the Administration Building, Workshop, Fieldhouse, 3 Master Artists' Cottages and 28 units of Associate Housing. All buildings are air-conditioned and connected by raised wooden walkways. Associate units have private bath, desk and refrigerator. Writers often meet in Fieldhouse, which has copy machine, kitchen, bath, typewriters, tables and chairs." The Center usually offers 6 residencies each year, usually three weeks in length. Residencies occur throughout the year, but may not always offer opportunities to writers. Accommodates up to 28 Associates (including all disciplines).
Costs: $600 including private room/bath; $200, tuition only and Associates provide their own accommodations, and transportation. Depending on the many factors involved, costs for the 3-week residency may vary from $900 to $1,500. Scholarships are available in selected disciplines for some residencies.
To Apply: Application requirements are different for each residency. Send for information. Application deadlines are generally 4-5 months before start of a residency; notification usually occurs 3-4 weeks after application deadline. Brochure/guidelines available for SASE. Some college credit available.

BELLAGIO STUDY AND CONFERENCE CENTER, Rockefeller Foundation, 1133 Avenue of the Americas, New York NY 10036. (212)869-8500. Manager: Susan Garfield. Estab. 1960. "Scholars and artists from any country and in any discipline are invited to apply. Successful applicants will be individuals of achievement with significant publications, exhibitions or shows to their credit. Bellagio Study and Conference Center, also known as Villa Serbelloni, occupies a wooded promontory . . . Includes main house and seven other buildings. Set in the foothills of the Italian Alps." Residencies are approximately 5 weeks long. Offered February through mid-December. Each scholar and artist is provided with a private room and bath and with a study in which to work. IBM and Apple PCs and printers available on sign-up basis. Accommodates 145 residents chosen annually.

Costs: "The Center does not provide financial assistance to scholars in residence nor does it ordinarily contribute to travel expenses. Once at the center, all scholars and spouses are guests of the foundation."

To Apply: Send for application. Application includes form, half-page abstract describing purpose of project, detailed project description, brief curriculum vitae, one sample of published work, reviews. Brochure/guidelines available for SASE.

THE BLUE MOUNTAIN CENTER, Blue Mountain Lake, New York NY 12812. (518)352-7391. Director: Harriet Barlow. Residencies for established writers. "Provides a peaceful environment where residents may work free from distractions and demands of normal daily life." Residencies awarded for 1 month between June 15 and October 15. For provisions, costs, other information, send SASE for brochure.

To Apply: Application deadline: February 1.

CENTRUM ARTIST-IN-RESIDENCE, P.O. Box 1158, Port Townsend WA 98368. (206)385-3102. Program Coordinator: Sarah Muirhead. Estab. 1978. Open to writers, visual artists, composers, performers. "Artists stay in private 2-3 bedroom cottages on the grounds of Fort Worden State Park, a former military fort. Located on Admiralty Inlet with beaches, woods, trails, turn-of-the century buildings." Month-long residencies, September-May. Stipend of $75 per week. Accommodates approximately 4/month. There is handicapped access.

Costs: No cost.

To Apply: Call or send SASE for brochure.

CHÂTEAU DE LESVAULT, Onlay, 58370 Villapourçon France, Director: Bibbi Lee. Estab. 1984. Open to writers of fiction and nonfiction, poets, playwrights, researchers. Located in "Burgundy within the National Park 'Le Morvan,' the Château de Lesvault is a classic French manor with fully furnished rooms including a salon, dining room and library. The château is surrounded by a large private park and there is a lake on the property." Available in 4-week sessions from October through April. Provisions for the writer include a large private room for sleeping and working, three meals a day (5 days a week), complete use of the château facility. Accommodates 6.

Costs: Cost for a 4-week session is 4,000 French francs. Included is all lodging and all meals.

To Apply: Send a letter to the Selection Committee briefly describing the writing project, two references and a sample of work (max. 3 pages). Specify the 4-week session requested. No application fee required. Brochure/guidelines available for SASE.

THE CLEARING, P.O. Box 65, Ellison Bay WI 54210. (414)854-4088. Resident Manager: Louise or Don Buchholz. Estab. 1935. Open to "any adult 18 to 81 (and we'll relax the 81 requirement)." Located in "historic native log and stone buildings on 128-acres of native forest on the shore of Green Bay. Hiking trails, beach swimming, enjoyable countryside for bicycling. Housed in twin bedded private bath facility. Meals served family style. Classroom is large hall in wooded setting. Clearing open mid-May to mid-Oct. for week-long sessions beginning Sunday night with supper, ending Saturday morning with breakfast—usually 2 or 3 writing weeks per year." Provisions for the writer include options of sharing a twin bedroom or 6-bed dorm, meals furnished, workspace in bedroom, living room, school building or quiet nooks on the grounds. Accommodates 20-24 writers.

Costs: $425-465/person per week includes board, room and tuition. (No Thursday night supper.) Scholarships are available. Brochure/guidelines available.

COTTAGES AT HEDGEBROOK, 2197 E. Millman Rd., Langley WA 98260. (206)321-4786. Director: Linda Haverfield. Estab. 1988. For "women who write—we seek a culturally diverse group." Located on "30-acres on Whidbey Island one hour north of Seattle, WA. Six new individual cottages; a bathhouse for showers and a farmhouse where meals are cooked and dinner is served. The cottages are modern—wood heat, electricity, no TV, limited phone use." Applicants request a stay of 1 week to 3 months (may attend only once). Two application periods a year Jan. 10-June 19; July 1-Dec. 10. "Writers must provide their writing equipment. Very good writing space and relaxing space in each cottage; sleeping loft, down comforters. Lunch delivered, small kitchen facility—dinner in the farmhouse." Accommodates 6 writers.

Costs: No charge for food or housing. Writers provide extras. Meals are nutritious, diet conscious. A fund to help with travel expenses has been started.

To Apply: Deadlines are October 1 and April 1. Application form—5 copies needed for committee review. Approx. 25 writers are invited each of 2 sessions a year. Limited facility for a differently-abled person. Brochure/guidelines available for SASE.

CUMMINGTON COMMUNITY OF THE ARTS, R.R. 1, Box 145, Cummington MA 01026. (413)634-2172. Executive Director: Kirk Stephens. Estab. 1923. Open to all artists. "Land is rural; in Berkshires, western Massachusetts, hilly farmland and forest. Buildings vary from large old-style homes to individual cabins. Private." Offered year-round for 2 weeks to 3 months. Provisions for the writer include private room/studio (one room total), meals included. Accommodates up to 20 writers. Workshop space also available.
Costs: In 1991 $500, all inclusive. Send $15 with application. Brochure/guidelines available for SASE.

CURRY HILL PLANTATION WRITER'S RETREAT, 404 Cresmont Ave., Hattiesburg MS 39401. (601)264-7034. Director: Elizabeth Bowne. Estab. 1977. Open to all fiction and nonfiction writing, except poetry and technical writing. This workshop is held at an antebellum home, located on 400-acres of land. It is limited to only eight guests who live in, all of whom receive individual help with their writing, plus a 3-hour workshop each evening when the group meets together. The location is six miles east of Bainbridge, Georgia. Offered March 29 to April 4. Provisions for the writer include room and board. Accommodates 8 writers.
Costs: $400 for the week; includes room and board and individual help, one hour per guest each day.
To Apply: Interested persons should apply *early* January. Brochure/guidelines available for SASE.

DJERASSI FOUNDATION, 2325 Bear Gulch Rd., Woodside CA 94062. "The Djerassi Foundation appoints approximately 20 artists a year to spend 2 to 6 months working on independent or collaborative projects in a setting of unusual beauty and privacy. We are seeking applications at two levels. One is the level of great promise: artists who have a record of solid achievement but are not yet very well known, for whom appointments as resident artists might make a difference. The other is the level of national or international distinction: artists with established reputations, for whom a change of scene might offer refreshment and inspiration." Residencies scheduled 2-6 months beginning either April 1 or July 1. Provisions for the writer include living and studio accommodations as well as meals. Accommodates 20 writers and other artists/year.
Costs: "The Djerassi Foundation award is strictly a residential grant." All accommodations are provided at no cost.
To Apply: Request application form. Return with $15 application fee, writing sample (short fiction or chapter/s from a book) and publication information on each work. Application period: February 1-March 31. Brochure/guidelines available for SASE.

DORLAND MOUNTAIN ARTS COLONY, P.O. Box #6, Temecula CA 92593. (714)676-5039. Fellows' Liaison: Helén Vigil. Estab. 1980. Open to visual artists, composers, writers, playwrights, theater artists. Provides uninterrupted time in a natural environment. The colony is located on a 300-acre nature preserve. No electricity, rustic single wall constructed cabins; large oak grove; 2 ponds; trails. Available for 2-week to 3-month residencies year round. Provisions for the writer include private cabins with living and work space. Manual (older) typewriters provided. Responsible for own meals. There are a total of 6 cabins.
Costs: $150/month or $5 a day for shorter stays.
To Apply: Application deadlines: March 1 and Sept. 1. $50 nonrefundable processing fee upon acceptance. Brochure/guidelines available for SASE.

FINE ARTS WORK CENTER IN PROVINCETOWN, P.O. Box 565, Provincetown MA 02657. (508)487-9960. Contact: Writing Coordinator. Estab. 1968. Open to emerging writers and visual artists. "Located on the grounds of the former Days Lumberyard complex, the facility has offered studio space to artists and writers since 1914. Renovated coal bins provide artist studios; several houses and a refurbished Victorian Barn offer apartments for writers. The complex encircles the Stanley Kunitz Common Room where fellows and visiting artists offer readings to the public." A seven-month residency offered from October 1st to May 1st each year. "Each writer is awarded his/her own apartment with kitchen and bath. All apartments are furnished and equipped with kitchen supplies. A monthly stipend of $375 is also provided." Accommodates 10 writers (four fiction, four poets).
Costs: No fees other than application fee ($20).
To Apply: Application deadline: February 1. Writing sample: Send 1 or 2 short stories. If novel, excerpt including opening section and synopsis. Limit: 40 pages. Send six copies. Check guidelines for details. Brochure/guidelines available for SASE.

THE TYRONE GUTHRIE CENTRE AT ANNAGHMAKERRIG, New Bliss, County Monaghan, Ireland. Tel: 047-54003. Resident Director: Bernard Loughlin. Estab. 1981. Open to writers, painters, sculptors, composers, directors, artists. There are "11 work rooms in house, generally with private bathroom.

Also 5 new houses which are self-catering. 400-acres, large lake and gardens. Sitting room, library, kitchen, diningroom." Closed for 2-week period at Christmas only. Provisions for the writer include private room and meals. Accommodates 16 writers and other artists.
Costs: IR £1,200/month for big house, meals included. IR £100/week for self-contained houses—also have to pay food, heating, electricity and outgoings.
To Apply: Write for application form. Considered at bimonthly board meeting. Brochure/guidelines available for SASE.

THE HAMBIDGE CENTER, P.O. Box 339, Rabun Gap GA 30568. Estab. 1934. Open to artists from all fields. Includes "600 acres of wooded, rural property serenely set in north Georgia mountains; traversed by streams and waterfalls." 2-week to 2-month stays from May to October. Provisions for writers include private cottages and studios. Accommodates 7 writers.
Costs: $125/week with dinner provided Monday-Friday. Some scholarships available, (very limited and reviewed individually.)
To Apply: Schedule is set during March. Application fee is $10. Application form mailed upon request. Brochure/guidelines available for SASE.

HILAI RESIDENCIES, The Israeli Center for Creative Arts, P.O. Box 53007, Tel-Aviv Israel 61530. Contact: Secretary, Admission Committee. Estab. 1984. "Founded by Tel-Aviv writer Corinna, this grass roots organization provides a common ground in which Jews, Arabs, Israelis and foreign guests can meet through artistic endeavor. Hilai maintains two residential working facilities for published or talented visual artists, poets, fiction writers, playwrights and composers." Provisions for the writer include a studio apartment with kitchen and private bathroom. Residencies of two weeks to one month are offered to four artists in Ma'alot-Tarshiha and six artists in Mitzpe Ramon. Spouses may accompany artists at Mitzpe Ramon, where 2-bedroom studios are available. Residents are asked to help plan and participate, up to four hours per week, in such community cultural activities as literary salons, exhibitions, workshops or readings.
Costs: Artists are asked to contribute, according to their ability to defray costs, a minimum of $25/week.
To Apply: Application deadlines are January 1, May 1 and September 1. Requests for application sheets and information must include a $15 cheque to HILAI as application fees. Notification of acceptance takes at least 10 weeks. Brochure/guidelines available for SASE.

KALANI HONUA, RR2, Box 4500, Pahoa HI 96778. (808)965-7828. Director: Richard Koob. Estab. 1980. Open to all education interests. "Kalani Honua, the 'harmony of heaven and earth,' provides an environment where the spirit of aloha flourishes. Located on twenty secluded acres bordered by lush jungle and rugged coastline forged by ancient lava flows, Kalani Honua offers an authentic experience of rural Hawaii. The surrounding area, including sacred sites and state and national parks, is rich with the island's history and magic." Available year-round, although greatest availability is May and June and September, October, November, December. Provisions for the writer include "comfortable, private room and workspace. 3 meals offered/day, beautiful coastal surroundings and recreation facilities (pool, sauna, jacuzzi, tennis, valleyball, biking) near beaches and Volcano National Park. (Qualifying writers receive stipend to help with costs.)" Accommodates usually 1-5 as artists-in-residence.
Costs: $24-80/night depending on choice of lodging (varying from private room with shared bath to private cottage with private bath) and depending on stipend amount. Meals are approx. $24/day or may be self-provided in kitchen available. Scholarships available. Professional career documentation and assurance the residency will be successfully completed.
To Apply: Application fee $10. Brochure/guidelines available for SASE. College credit may be arranged through University of Hawaii.

THE MACDOWELL COLONY, 100 High St., Peterborough NH 03458. (603)924-3886 or (212)966-4860. Admissions Coordinator: Shirley Bewley. Estab. 1907. Open to writers, composers, visual artists, film/video artists, interdisciplinary artists and architects. Includes "main building, library, 3 residence halls and 31 individual studios on over 400 mostly wooded acres, one mile from center of small town in southern New Hampshire." Available up to 8 weeks year-round. Provisions for the writer include meals, private sleeping room, individual secluded studio. Accommodates variable number of writers, averaging 10 at a time.

Costs: Artists are asked to contribute toward the cost of their residency according to their financial resources.
To Apply: Application forms available. Application deadline: January 15 for summer; April 15 for fall/winter. Writing sample required. For novel, send a chapter or section. For short stories, send 2-3. Send 6 copies. Brochure/guidelines available for SASE.

MILLAY COLONY FOR THE ARTS, Steepletop, P.O. Box 3, Austerlitz NY 12017-0003. (518)392-3103. Executive Director: Ann-Ellen Lesser. Estab. 1973. Open to professional writers, composers, visual artists. Includes "600-acres — mostly wooded, fields, old farm. Two buildings house artists — separate studios (14' × 20') and bedrooms." Available year round. Accommodates 5 people at a time.
Costs: No fees.
To Apply: Requires sample of work and 1 professional reference. Application deadlines: February 1 for June-September; May 1 for October-January; September 1 for February-May. Brochure/guidelines available for SASE.

NORTHWOOD INSTITUTE ALDEN B. DOW CREATIVITY CENTER, 3225 Cook Rd., Midland MI 48640-2398. (517)837-4478. Executive Director: Carol B. Coppage. Estab. 1979. "The Fellowship Program welcomes project ideas from all disciplines: the arts, humanities and sciences. Individuals must be able to work independently. Project ideas are evaluated on the basis of uniqueness, creativity and innovation. Northwood Institute is a small business college located in the central part of the lower peninsula. Fellows are in residence on the campus for 10 weeks. The campus is surrounded by lovely woods and is close to lakes." Available 10 weeks during the summer — mid-June-mid-August. Provisions for the writer include large furnished apartments for living quarters and work space. Lunches are provided during the weekday at the Creativity Center. Accommodates 4 Fellows/year.
Costs: No costs. The Creativity Center provides room, a monthly stipend to cover personal costs (gasoline, laundry, etc.) and a one-time stipend of $500 which each Fellow is encouraged to use on a brief "vacation" midway during the program.
To Apply: Send for a brochure/application form to be submitted and postmarked no later than December 31 of the year preceding the summer's program. Brochure/guidelines available for SASE.

PALENVILLE INTERARTS COLONY, P.O. Box 59, Palenville NY 12463. (518)678-3332. Contact: Admissions Director. "Artists residencies for professional/and emerging literary artists." Located at base of Catskill Mountains at an old summer campground. Main house has 8 rooms, kitchen and dining hall. Cabins for studios and some living space. Trails, fields, dance studio, theater. Available June-September. Accommodates up to 12-15 writers or other artists.
Costs: Write for details.
To Apply: Application fee: $10. Writing samples required. Applications are considered on a competition basis; judges are a panel of 8 distinguished artists. Deadline: April 1. Brochure/guidelines available for SASE.

RAGDALE FOUNDATION, 1260 N. Green Bay Rd., Lake Forest IL 60045. (708)234-1063. Director: Michael Wilkerson. Estab. 1976. For qualified writers, artists and composers. Ragdale, located 30 miles north of Chicago near Lake Michigan, is "the grounds of acclaimed Chicago architect Howard Van Doren Shaw's historic family home." Accommodations include the Ragdale House, the Barnhouse and the new Friend's Studio. Available in 2-week to 2-month sessions year-round, except for the last 2 weeks of June and December. Provisions for the writer include room; linens, laundered by Ragdale and meals. "Breakfast and lunch supplies are stocked in communal kitchens, enabling residents to work throughout the day uninterrupted by scheduled meals. The evening meal is the only exception: wholesome, well-prepared dinners are served six nights a week. The Ragdale House and Barnhouse both contain informal libraries, and the property overlooks a large nature preserve." Accommodates 10.
Costs: $10/day. Scholarships based on financial need are available. "Fee waiver application and decision process is separate from artistic admission process."
To Apply: "Residents are chosen by a selection committee composed of professionals in their artistic discipline. Applicants are required to submit an application, project description, slides or a writing sample and three references." Application fee: $20. Deadlines: September 15 for January-April, January 15 for May-August and April 15 for September-December. Brochure/guidelines available for SASE.

SASKATCHEWAN WRITERS'/ARTISTS' COLONIES, Box 3986, Regina, Saskatchewan S4P 3R9 Canada. (306)757-6310. Program Director: Paul Wilson. Estab. 1979. For all writers and artists, "although priority is given to Saskatchewan residents." St. Peter's College is "a Benedictine Abbey in the serene location just outside the village of Muenster. Emma Lake is located in a forest region approximately 25 miles north of Prince Albert." An 8-week summer colony and year-round individual retreats are held at St. Peter's. A 2-week colony is held in August at Emma Lake. St. Peter's provides private rooms and "home-grown meals" served in the college facility. Residents at Emma Lake "are housed in separate cabins or in single rooms in a one-story unit. The dining room and lounge are located in a central building." The 8-week summer colony at St. Peter's accommodates 8 people a week, "but applicants may request as much time as they need." The individual retreats accommodate no more the 3 at one time.
Costs: $75/week, includes meals and accommodation.
To Apply: Applications should be typewritten and include a check for length of stay as well as 10 ms pages or slides of artwork, a brief resume, a project description and 2 references. Deadline for 8-week summer colony: April 1. Deadline for individual retreats: 1 month before preferred date of attendance. Brochure/guidelines available for SASE.

THE SYVENNA FOUNDATION WRITERS-IN-RESIDENCE, Route 1, Box 193, Linden TX 75563. (903)835-8252. Estab. 1987; first resident in 1989. For beginning and intermediate women writers, all genres. "Two private cottages in rural, wooded area of Northeast Texas, 6½ miles from nearest town. Cottages are within walking distance of main house and administrative offices. Cottages are self-sufficient and equipped with all modern conveniences." Available in four 2- or 3-month terms, January through November. Provisions for the writer include rent- and utilities-free private cottage with workspace. "Residents are responsible for their own meals, laundry and other personal needs. Pick-up truck available once a week for residents without their own transportation." Accommodates 2 at one time (1/cottage).
Costs: "No charge for application or residency. Monthly stipend provided to help offset living expenses."
To Apply: Send SASE to Syvenna Foundation for application materials. Deadlines: April 1 for September-November; August 1 for January-March, October 1 for April-May and December 1 for June-August.

UCROSS FOUNDATION, 2836 U.S. Hwy. 14-16 East, Clearmont WY 82835. (307)737-2291. Executive Director: Elizabeth Guheen. Estab. 1983. For "Artists of *all* disciplines. We are in a rural setting of Wyoming, in a town with a population of 25. The facilities are part of a renovated ranch." Available for 2 weeks to 4 months. "Each artist is provided a private studio, private bedroom, common living area and meals. We have the potential of accommodating 4 writers at one time."
Costs: Ucross Foundation awards residencies.
To Apply: Residents are selected through biannual competition, judged by a 3-member committee. Deadlines: March 1 for August-December, October 1 for January-May. Brochure/guidelines available for SASE.

VERMONT STUDIO CENTER, P.O. Box 613, Johnson VT 05656. (608)635-2727. Registrar: Susan Kowalsky. Estab. 1984. For painters, sculptors and writers. "In the Lamoille Valley of Northern Vermont, VSC is located in the village of Johnson. It is nestled among the rivers and woods of Johnson in 17 reclaimed buildings such as the old grain mill, the 150 year-old town hall and the original elementary school. VSC is bordered everywhere with flower, herb and organic vegetable gardens." Available in 4- and 8-week sessions, January-April. Include "room, writing studio, excellent meals and access to local college library and facilities." Writers responsible for their own studio equipment (personal computers, typewriters etc.). Accommodates approximately 5 writers.
Costs: Approximately $1,300/month, includes everything. "Generous financial aid is available based on individual need."
To Apply: Submit completed application with 3 copies of either 3 pieces of short fiction or 2-3 chapters of a book (plus outline or summary). Include recent résumé, 3 references, project description and $25 application fee. Brochure/guidelines available for SASE.

VIRGINIA CENTER FOR THE CREATIVE ARTS, Mt. San Angelo, Box VCCA, Sweet Briar VA 24595. (804)946-7236. Director: William Smart. Estab. 1971. For writers, visual artists and composers. "Located in a rural setting, within sight of the Blue Ridge Mountains. 450-acre estate, with a herd of Holsteins. Fellows live in a 10-year-old residence; there are 22 bedrooms, dining room, living rooms,

library, laundry room, etc. Studios are located some 5 minutes away by foot. There are a few other small buildings, outdoor swimming pool and year-round swimming available across the road at Sweet Briar College." Available year-round for residencies from 2 weeks to 3 months. Provisions for the writer include private bedroom, private soundproof studio and all meals. Accommodates 13 writers.
Costs: "The standard fee is $20/day, which includes everything." Scholarships are available.
To Apply: $15 application fee. Write or call for application form. Deadlines: Jan. 25, May 25, Sept. 25. Brochure/guidelines available for SASE.

WEST VIRGINIA DIVISION OF CULTURE AND HISTORY, ARTS AND HUMANITIES SECTION, ARTIST-IN-RESIDENCE PROGRAM, The Cultural Center, Capitol Complex, Charleston WV 25305. (304)348-0240. Director: Lakin Ray Cook. Open to both in-state and out-of-state writers. Program to "assist with artist-in-residence programs in West Virginia. Residencies are offered all year by various sponsors for periods of less than 8 months." Provisions depend upon sponsor (for residencies).
To Apply: "Writers should contact an organization for support for the residency. The sponsor (must be a 'not for profit' type of organization) then makes application." Brochure/guidelines for SASE.

WOLF PEN WOMEN WRITERS COLONY, % *The American Voice*, Suite 1215, 332 W. Broadway, Louisville KY 40202. Estab. 1988. "Wolf Pen is for women only. Women lack the space both physical and psychological, in which to expand, to relax and to experiment." Includes "comfortable farmhouse in the middle of soybean or cornfields about 15 miles outside Louisville. There are 3 small studios close to the main house; 2 writers work in spaces attached to their bedrooms." Offered during the month of June. Accommodates 5 writers.
Costs: No fee. Room and board are provided.
To Apply: "Colonists are accepted on the basis of need, talent and commitment to feminist goals." Application form available. Send two short stories or novel excerpt, résumé and at least 1 professional letter of reference (sent separately) Deadline: February 1. Brochure/guidelines available for SASE.

THE WOODSTOCK GUILD'S BYRDCLIFFE ARTS COLONY, 34 Tinker St., Woodstock NY 12498. (914)679-2079. Executive Director: Sondra Howell. Estab. 1902. For writers, playwrights, visual artists and craftspeople. "The historic 600-acre Byrdcliffe Arts Colony is in Woodstock, one and a half miles from the village center. The residency program takes place in the Villetta Inn and Annex and includes a large community living room and common kitchen." Available for 15 weeks, beginning June 1. Provisions for writer include a private room and studio space when appropriate. "Meals are not provided; residents share a large fully equipped communal kitchen." Accommodates 16 writers.
Costs: A 3-month residency is $975; 2 months, $775; 1 month, $475. Depending upon availability, shorter periods are considered. Financial aid is available. "Potential residents are asked to include a list of savings and holdings, a list of income from the last two years (photocopied tax forms), and a projection of income and expenses for the current year."
To Apply: Submit application with $5 handling fee. Literary artists must submit no more than 12 pages of poetry, one chapter or story-length prose piece, professional resume, reviews of articles (if available) and 2 references. Residents are selected by a committee of professionals in the arts. Brochure/guidelines available for SASE.

YADDO, Box 395, Saratoga Springs NY 12866-0395. Contact: Admissions Committee. Estab. 1926. "Those qualified for invitations to Yaddo are writers, visual artists and composers who have already published, exhibited or performed works of high artistic merit and now have other projects under way. Sometimes, but not customarily, the novice may be given admittance to Yaddo, if the advisory committee feels candidate shows promise." Includes mansion, garage, three smaller house and several studios. Site includes four small lakes, a rose garden, woodland. Two seasons: large season is mid-May-Labor Day; small season is October-May (stays from 6-8 weeks). Accommodates 35 writers in large season.
Costs: Voluntary payment of $20/day encouraged. "No artist who is deemed qualified for residency will be denied admission because of inability contribute."
To Apply: Filing fee is $20 (checks to Corporation of Yaddo). Applications are considerd by the Advisory Committee and invitations are issued by April (Deadline: January 15) and September (deadline: August).

Organizations and Resources

When you write, you write alone. It's just you and the typewriter or computer screen. Yet the writing life does not need to be a lonely one. Joining a writing group or organization can be an important step in your writing career. By meeting other writers, discussing your common problems and sharing ideas, you can enrich your writing and increase your understanding of this sometimes difficult, but rewarding life.

The variety of writers' organizations seems endless — encompassing every type of writing and writer — from small, informal groups that gather at a local coffeehouse to critique each others' work to regional groups that hold annual conferences to share marketing tips. National organizations and unions fight for writers' rights and higher wages for freelancers and international groups monitor the treatment of writers around the world.

We're pleased this year to include listings for several writers' organizations. In this section you will find state-, province- and region-based groups such as the Arizona Authors Association, the Ozarks Writers League and the Writers' Federation of Nova Scotia. You'll also find national organizations including the National Writers Club and the Canadian Authors Association. The International Association of Crime Writers and the Science Fiction Writers of America are examples of groups devoted to a particular type of writing. Whatever your needs or goals, you're likely to find a group listed here to interest you.

A few organizations helpful to writers are not clubs or groups and they do not fit neatly into any one category. We've included a few of these, too, as "resources." These are gathering places or helpful services available to writers. The Writers Room in New York City and the Just Buffalo Literary Center are two examples of those featured here.

Selecting a writers' organization

To help you make an informed decision, we've provided information on the scope, membership and goals of the organizations listed on these pages. We asked groups to outline the types of memberships available and the benefits members can expect. Most groups will provide additional information for a self-addressed, stamped envelope and you may be able to get a sample copy of their newsletter for a modest fee.

Keep in mind joining a writers' organization is a two-way street. When you join an organization, you become a part of it and, in addition to membership fees, most groups need and want your help. If you want to get involved, opportunities can include everything from chairing a committee to writing for the newsletter to helping set up an annual conference. The level of your involvement is up to you.

The group you select to join depends on a number of factors. First, you must determine what you want from membership in a writers' organization. Then send for more information on the groups that seem to fit your needs. Start, however, by asking yourself:
- Would I like to meet writers in my city? Am I more interested in making contacts with other writers across the country or around the world?
- Am I interested in a group that will critique my work and give me feedback on my work-in-progress?
- Do I want marketing information and tips on dealing with editors?
- Would I like to meet other writers who write the same type of work I do or am I interested in meeting writers from a variety of fields?
- How much time can I devote to meetings and are regular meetings important to me?

How much can I afford to pay in dues?
● Would I like to get involved in running the group, working on the group's newsletters, planning a conference?
● Am I interested in a group devoted to writers' rights and treatment or would I rather concentrate on the business of writing?

For more information

Because they do not usually have the resources or inclination to promote themselves widely, finding a local writers' group is usually a word-of-mouth process. If you think you'd like to join a local writers' group and do not know of any in your area, check notices at your library or contact a local college English department. You might also try contacting a group based in your state, province or region listed here for information on smaller area groups.

For more information on writers' organizations, check *The Writer's Essential Desk Reference* (Writer's Digest Books, 1507 Dana Ave., Cincinnati OH 45207). Other directories listing organizations for writers include the *Literary Market Place* or *International Literary Market Place* (R.R. Bowker, 245 W. 17th St., New York NY 10011) and *The Writer's Yellow Pages* (Steve Davis Publications, P.O. Box 190831, Dallas TX 75219). The National Writers Club also has a list of writers' organizations. Also available is a reprint of an article listing 18 places writers gather, "Living Rooms for Literature: Literary Centers in the U.S.," from *Poets & Writers*, 72 Spring St., New York NY 10012. Send $2 and a SASE.

ARIZONA AUTHORS ASSOCIATION, Suite 117, 3509 E. Shea Blvd., Phoenix AZ 85028. (602)996-9706. President: Cyndi Greening. Estab. 1978. Number of Members: 500. Type of Memberships: Professional, writers with published work; associate, writers working toward publication; affiliate, professionals in the publishing industry. "Primarily an Arizona organization but open to writers nationally." Benefits include bimonthly newsletter, discount rates on seminars, workshops and newsletter ads, use of AAA reference library, discounts on writing books, discounts at bookstores, copy shops, critique groups and networking events. "Sponsors monthly workshops on a variety of topics of interest to writers (e.g. publishing, marketing, structure, genres)." Publishes *Authors Newsletter*, bimonthly ($40/yr.). Dues: Professional and associate, $40/year; affiliate: $45/year; student: $20/year. Holds monthly critique group and quarterly networking events. Send SASE for information.

ASSOCIATED WRITING PROGRAMS, Old Dominion University, Norfolk VA 23529-0079. (804)683-3839. Publications Editor: D.W. Fenza. Estab. 1967. Number of Members: 1,300 (individual members). Types of Membership: Institutional (universities); graduate students; *Chronicle* subscribers. Open to any person interested in writing; most members are students or faculty of university writing programs (worldwide). Benefits include information on creative writing programs; grants and awards to writers; a job placement service for writers in academe and beyond. "We hold an Annual Conference/Meeting in a different U.S. city every spring; also an annual Award Series in poetry, short story collections, novel and creative nonfiction, in which winner receives $1,500 honorarium and automatic publication with a participating press. We act as agent for finalists in Award Series—try to place their manuscript with publishers throughout the year." Manuscripts accepted January 1-February 28. SASE for guidelines. Publishes *AWP Chronicle* 6 times/year; 3 times/academic semester. Available to members for free. Nonmembers may order a subscription $18/yr. Also publishes the *AWP Official Guide to Writing Programs* which lists about 330 creative writing programs in universities across the country and in Canada. *Guide* is updated every 2 years; cost is $10.95 plus $2 for library rate shipping or $4 for 1st class. Dues: $25 for the placement service for 1 year. We keep dossiers on file and send them to school or organization of person's request. You do not have to be a member to be a part of the placement service. Holds two meetings per year for the Board of Directors. Send SASE for information.

AUSTIN WRITERS' LEAGUE RESOURCE CENTER, Austin Writers' League, 1501 W. 5th, E-2, Austin TX 78703. (512)499-8914. Executive Director: Angela Smith. Estab. 1981. Number of Members: 1,500. Types of Memberships: Regular, student/senior citizen, organization, corporate. Monthly meetings and use of resource center/library is open to the public. "Membership includes both aspiring and professional writers, all ages and all ethnic groups." Job bank is also open to the public. Public also has access to technical assistance. Partial and full scholarships offered for some programs. Of 1,500 members, 800 reside in Austin. Remaining 700 live all over the U.S. and in other countries. Benefits include monthly newsletter, monthly meetings, study groups, resource center/library-checkout privileges, discounts on workshops, seminars, classes, job bank, access to insurance information, discounts on books and tapes, participation in awards programs, technical/marketing assistance, copyright forms and information, access to computers and printers. Center has four rooms plus two offices and storage area. Public space includes reception and job bank area; conference/classroom; library/computer room; and copy/mail room. Library includes 400 titles. Two computers and printers are available for member use. Sponsors fall and spring workshops, weekend seminars, informal classes, sponsorships for special events such as readings, production of original plays, media conferences; Violet Crown Book Awards, newsletter writing awards, poetry contest for annual anthology. Publishes *Austin Writer* (monthly newsletter), subscription: $30. Monthly meetings. Study groups set their own regular meeting schedules. Send SASE for information.

THE AUTHORS GUILD, 330 West 42nd St., New York NY 10036. (212)563-5904. Assistant Director: Peggy Randall. Estab. 1921. Number of Members: 6,500. Membership based on income scale from writing. Open to published authors or those with firm contract offers. "The Authors Guild is a national society of professional authors." Benefits through "collective power and voice," achieving many direct economic benefits from improvement of contracts and royalty statement to the protection of authors' First Amendment rights. Other benefits: Contract advice, surveys and reports and assistance, group insurance available. Publishes the *Authors Guild Bulletin*, containing information on matters of interest to writers. Also publishes *Your Book Contract*, a 35-page pamphlet analyzing publishing contracts and *The Authors Guild Recommended Trade Book Contract and Guide*. Dues: $90 for first year; then dues are based on income scale from $90-500, depending on writing income. Send SASE for information.

CALIFORNIA WRITERS' CLUB, 2214 Derby St., Berkeley CA 94705. (415)841-1217. Estab. 1909. Number of Members: 900. Type of Memberships: Associate and active. Open to: "All published writers and those deemed able to publish within five years." Benefits include speakers—authors, editors, agents, anyone connected with writing—heard at monthly meetings, marketing information, workshops, camaraderie of fellow writers. Sponsors workshops, conferences, awards programs/contests. Publishes a monthly newsletter at state level, monthly newsletter at branch level. Available to members only. Dues: $25/year. Meets monthly. Send SASE for information.

CANADIAN AUTHORS ASSOCIATION, #500, 275 Slater St., Ottawa, Ontario K1P 5H9 Canada. (613)233-2846. FAX: (613)235-8237. National Director: Jeffrey Holmes. Estab. 1921. Number of Members: 800. Type of Memberships: Member (voting); associate (non-voting). "Member must have minimum sales to commercial publications. Associates need not have published yet." National scope (Canada) with 18 regional branches. Benefits include networking, marketing advice, legal advice, several publications, annual conference, awards programs. Sponsors workshops, conferences, awards programs/contests. Publishes *Canadian Author & Bookman*, quarterly $15 (Canadian)/year; $20 (Canadian) for foreign and *National Newsline* (to members only). Dues: $90 (Canadian)/year. "Each branch meets monthly." Send SASE for information.

CANADIAN SOCIETY OF CHILDREN'S AUTHORS, ILLUSTRATORS AND PERFORMERS (CANSCAIP), P.O. Box 280, Station L, Toronto, Ontario M6E 4Z2 Canada. (416)654-0903. Executive Secretary: Bernice Bacchus. Estab. 1977. Number of Members: 1,100. Types of membership: Full professional member and friend (associate member). Open to professional active writers, illustrators and performers in the field of children's culture (full members); beginners and all other interested persons and institutions (friends). International scope, but emphasis on Canada. Benefits include quarterly newsletter, marketing opportunities, publicity via our membership directory and our "members available" list, jobs (school visits, readings, workshops, residencies, etc.) through our "members available" list, mutual support through monthly meetings. Sponsors annual workshop, "Packaging Your Imagination," held every October for beginners. Publishes *CANSCAIP News*, quarterly, available to all (free with membership, otherwise $20 Canadian). Dues: professional fees: $50 Canadian/year; friend fees: institutional $25/year; individual $20/year. "Professionals must have written, illustrated or performed work for children commercially, sufficient to satisfy the membership committee (more details on request)." CANSCAIP National has open meetings from September to June, monthly in Toronto. CANSCAIP West holds bimonthly meetings in Vancouver. Send SASE for information.

COUNCIL OF AUTHOR & JOURNALISTS, 1214 Laurel Hill Dr., Decatur GA 30033. (404)320-1076. Co-Chairman: Ann Ritter. Director of Programming: Tamela Thomas. Estab. 1961. Number of Members: 110. Type of Memberships: Regular, sponsor, donor, patron. Open to: "To anyone interested regional slant—southeastern mostly but a few come from elsewhere (i.e. Michigan and Texas)." Benefits include information in newsletter, networking among members. Sponsors Georgia Author of The Year Awards in several categories and annual writing workshop in June. Publishes *CAJ Communique*, quarterly newsletter (one issue available to nonmembers on request). Dues: $15 (regular). Holds periodic readings and receptions for members and guests—no set schedule. Send SASE for information.

FEDERATION OF BRITISH COLUMBIA WRITERS, MPO Box 2206, Vancouver, British Columbia V6B 3W2 Canada. Manager: Corey Van't Haaff. Estab. 1982. Number of members: 865. Types of membership: regular and subsidized for those with limited income. "Open to established and emerging writers in any genre, provincial-wide." Benefits include newsletter, liaison with funding bodies, publications, workshops, readings, literary contest. Sponsors readings and workshops. Publishes a newsletter 4 times/year, included in membership. Dues: $50 Canadian (regional) regular; $25 limited income. Send SASE for information.

HORROR WRITERS OF AMERICA (HWA), executive office, P.O. Box 10901, Greensboro NC 27404. Did not respond to questionnaire, but information available—contact Leanne Johnson, secretary.

INTERNATIONAL ASSOCIATION OF CRIME WRITERS (NORTH AMERICAN BRANCH), JAF Box 1500, New York NY 10116. (212)757-3915. Executive Director: Mary A. Frisque. Estab. 1987. Number of Members: 225. Open to: "Published authors of crime fiction, nonfiction, screenplays and professionals in the mystery field (agents, editors, booksellers). Our branch covers the US and Canada, there are other branches world-wide." Benefits include information about crime-writing world-wide and publishing opportunities in other countries. "We sponsor annual members' receptions during the Edgar awards week in New York and in the spring and in the fall we host a reception at the Bouchercon. We also have occasional receptions for visiting authors/publishers. We publish a quarterly newsletter, *Border Patrol*, available to members only." Dues: $50 year. Send SASE for information.

ISLAND WRITERS ASSOCIATION, P.O. Box 273, Charlottetown, Prince Edward Island C1A 7K4 Canada. (902)569-3913. President: Julie V. Watson. Executive Director: Debbie Gamble-Arsenault. Estab. 1981. Number of Members: 25. Open to: "Anyone who aspires to or does earn all or part of their living by writing." Scope is "province-wide, with informal sub-groups in different locations/towns/ villages." Benefits include marketing advice; use of a central office which holds our reference library; networking with more experienced members. Sponsors workshops, conferences. Publishes a newsletter infrequently; available to members and included in the yearly membership fee. Dues: $10/year. Requirements for membership are an interest in producing marketable material. Send SASE for information.

JUST BUFFALO LITERARY CENTER, INC., 111 Elmwood Ave., Buffalo NY 14201. (716)885-6400. Coordinator of Readings & Workshops: Rachel Moran. Executive Director: Debora Ott. "We're not a membership organization but do have group of supporters, the Friends of Just Buffalo. As a community-based literary center, Just Buffalo presents readings by writers in all genres throughout the year, offers ongoing workshops and workshops by guest artists, interdisciplinary concerts in jazz and poetry, a biweekly radio program of interviews with writers and an extensive program of writers' residencies in schools in Western New York State. Two annual writing competitions are held: a Western New York Writer-in-Residence competition and a Labor in Literature contest (open to union members only). Both contests are limited to residents of the Western NY region of the state. We publish a bimonthly calendar of events, available to members of the Friends of Just Buffalo." For writers of short stories or novels who are seeking to read their work for audiences in the WNY area, Just Buffalo is always willing to receive and consider work samples for possible inclusion in its reading series. Enclosing additional biographical materials, or information about possible travel plans to the area would also be helpful. Dues: Membership in Friends begins at $15 for student/seniors and fixed income, $25 for individuals. Send SASE for information.

MYSTERY WRITERS OF AMERICA (MWA), 236 W. 27th St., New York NY 10001. Did not respond to questionnaire. Write for information.

NATIONAL WRITERS CLUB, Suite 620, 1450 S. Havana, Aurora CO 80012. (303)751-7844. Executive Director: James L. Young. Estab. 1937. Number of Members: 4,000. Types of Memberships: Regular membership for those without published credits; professional membership for those with published credits. Open to: Any interested writer. National/International plus we have 16 chapters in various states. Benefits include critiques, marketing advice, editing, literary agency, complaint service, chapbook publishing service, research reports on various aspects of writing, five contests, National Writers Press — self-publishing operation, computer bulletin board service, regular newsletter with updates on marketing, bimonthly magazine on writing related subjects, discounts on supplies, magazines and some services. Sponsors periodic conferences and workshops: short story contest opens March, closes July 1; novel contest opens November, closes February 28. Publishes *Flash* (market news-monthly publication for professional members only); *NWC Newsletter* (monthly publication for members only); *Authorship Magazine* (bimonthly publication available by subscription $18 to nonmembers). Dues: $50 regular; $60 professional. For professional membership requirement is equivalent of 3 articles or stories in a national or regional magazine; a book published by a royalty publisher, a play, TV script, or movie produced. An initial $15 set up fee is required for first time members. Send SASE for information. Chapters hold meetings on a monthly basis.

THE NATIONAL LEAGUE OF AMERICAN PEN WOMEN, INC., Headquarters: Pen Arts Building, 1300 17th St., NW, Washington DC 20036. (202)785-1997. Contact: National President. Estab. 1897. Number of Members: 5,000. Type of Memberships: Three classifications: Arts, letters, music composition. Open to: Professional women. "Professional to us means our membership is only open to women who sell their art, writings or music compositions. We have 200 branches in the continental U.S., Hawaii and the Republic of Panama. Some branches have as many as 100 members, some as few as 10 or 12. It is necessary to have 5 members to form a new branch." Benefits include marketing advice, use of a facility, critiques and competitions. Our facility is national headquarters which has a few rooms available for Pen Women visiting the D.C. area, and for Board members in session four times a year. Branch and State Association competitions, as well as biennial convention competitions. Offers a research library of books and histories of our organization only. Sponsors $1,000 award biennially to Pen Women in each classification: Art, letters, music and $1,000 award biennially to nonPen Women in each classification for women over 35 years of age who wish to pursue special work in her field. *The Pen Woman* is our membership magazine, published from five to nine times a year, free to members, $7 a year for nonmembers subscribers. Dues: $25/year for national organization, from $5-10/year for branch membership and from $1-5 for state association dues. Branches hold regular meeting each month, September through May except in northern states which meet usually March through September (for travel convenience). Send SASE for information.

THE NEBRASKA WRITERS GUILD, P.O. Box 30341, Lincoln NE 68503-0341. (402)477-3804. President: Diane L. Kirkle. Estab. 1925. Number of Members: 166. Type of Memberships: Active, associate, youth. Open to: Professional and aspiring writers and poets editors, publishers, librarians, educators and others allied to the writing/publishing industry. Statewide scope. Benefits include marketing advice, critiques, moral support. Sponsors 2 conferences/year. Publishes the *NWG Bulletin* once a year; *The Broadside* (newsletter) twice/year for members only. Dues: $10/year (active and associate members); $7/year (youth members). Meets twice/year. Send SASE for information.

NEW HAMPSHIRE WRITERS AND PUBLISHERS PROJECT, P.O. Box 150, Portsmouth NH 03802-0150. (603)436-6331. Executive Director: Barbara Tsairis. Estab. 1988. Number of Members: 395. Type of Memberships: Senior/student; individual; business; benefactor; sponsor. Open to anyone interested in the literary arts — writers (fiction, nonfiction, journalists, poets, scriptwriters, etc.), teachers, librarians, publishers and *readers*. Statewide scope. Benefits include a bimonthly newsletter featuring articles about NH writers and publishers; leads for writers, new books listings; and NH literary news. Also — use of resource library and discounts on workshops, readings, conferences. Publishes *Ex Libris*, a bimonthly publication (included in the cost of membership). Dues: $25 for individuals $15 for seniors, students; $50 for businesses, libraries $250 for sponsor, $500 for benefactor. Board of Directors meets bimonthly and is open to the membership. Send SASE for information.

NORTH CAROLINA WRITERS' NETWORK, P.O. Box 954, Carrboro NC 27510. (919)967-9540. Executive Director: Marsha Warren. Estab. 1985. Number of Members: 1,400. Open to: All writers, all levels of skill and friends of literature. Membership is approximately 1,200 in North Carolina and 250 in 28 other states. Benefits include bimonthly newsletter, reduced rates for fall conference, workshops, etc., use of critiquing service, use of library and resource center, press release and publicity service, information database(s). Sponsors annual Fall Conference, Creative Journalism Competition, statewide workshops, Writers & Readers Series, Randall Jarrell Poetry Prize, Poetry Chapbook Competition, Fiction Competition, One-Act Play Competition. Publishes *The Network News*, 24-pages, bimonthly. Subscription included in dues. Dues: $25/year, $15/year (students to age 23). Meetings held annually in spring; again at fall conference. Send SASE for information.

OZARKS WRITERS LEAGUE, P.O. Box 152, Branson MO 65616. (417)334-6016. Board Member: Debbie Redford. Estab. 1983. Number of Members: 250. Open to: Anyone interested in writing, photography and art. Regional Scope: Missouri, Arkansas, Oklahoma, Kansas—"Greater Ozarks" area. Benefits include mutual inspiration and support; information exchange. Sponsors quarterly seminars/workshops, two annual writing competitions, one annual photography competition, special conferences. Publishes quarterly newsletter, the *Owls Hoot*, available to nonmembers for limited receipt. Dues: $10/year. Meets quarterly—February, May, August, November. Send SASE for information.

PHILADELPHIA WRITERS ORGANIZATION, P.O. Box 42497, Philadelphia PA 19101. (215)387-4950. Administrative Coordinator: Jane Brooks. Estab. 1981. Number of members: 250. Types of membership: full (voting), associate, student. Open to any writer, published or unpublished. Scope is tri-state area—Pennsylvania, Delaware, New Jersey, but mostly Philadelphia area. Benefits include medical insurance (for full members only), disability insurance, monthly meetings with guest panelists, Spring workshop (in full day) plus Editors Marketplace. Sponsors Spring workshop, Writers Meeting Editors Marketplace. Publishes a monthly newsletter for members only. Dues: $50 (full and associate); $25-student. Proof of publication required (minimum of 2,000 words-full members). Meets monthly throughout year except August. Send SASE for information.

ROMANCE WRITERS OF AMERICA (RWA), #315, 13700 Veterans Memorial Drive, Houston TX 77014. Did not respond to questionnaire. Write for information.

SCIENCE FICTION AND FANTASY WORKSHOP, 1193 South 1900 East, Salt Lake City UT 84108. (801)582-2090. Director/Editor: Kathleen D. Woodbury. Estab. 1980. Number of members: 400. Types of membership: "Active" is listed in the membership roster and so is accessible to all other members; "inactive" is not listed in the roster. Open to "anyone, anywhere. Our scope is international although over 96% of our members are in the United States. Benefits include "several different critique groups: short stories, novels, articles, screenplays, poetry, etc. We also offer services such as copyediting, working out the numbers in planet building (give us the kind of planet you want and we'll tell you how for it is from the sun, etc.—or tell us what kind o sun you have and we'll tell you what your planet is like), brainstorming story, fragments or cultures or aliens, a clearing house for information on groups who write/critique science fiction and fantasy in your area, etc. We sponsored a writing contest at a science fiction convention last year and plan to do so this year." Publishes *SF and Fantasy Workshop* (monthly); non-members subscribe for $10/year; samples are $1 and trial subscription: $6/6 issues. "We also publish a fiction booklet on an irregular basis. It contains one short story and three critiques by professional writers. Cost to anyone is $5/5 issues or $8/10 issues." Dues: Members pay a one-time fee of $5 (to cover the cost of the roster and the new-member information packet) and the annual $10 subscription fee. To renew membership, members simply renew their subscriptions. Our organization is strictly by mail. Send SASE for information.

SCIENCE FICTION WRITERS OF AMERICA, INC., P.O. Box 4335, Spartanburg SC 29305. (803)578-8012. Executive Secretary: Peter Dennis Pautz. Estab. 1965. Number of Members: 1,200. Type of Memberships: Active, affiliate, institutional, estate. Open to: "Professional writers, editors, anthologists, artists in the SF/fantasy genres and allied professional individuals and institutions. Our membership is international; we currently have members throughout Europe, Australia, Central and South America, Canada and some in Asia." Benefits include: "We produce a variety of journals for our members, annual membership directory and provide a grievance committee, publicity committee, circulating book plan and access to TEIGIT medical/life/disability insurance. We award the SFWA Nebula Awards each year for outstanding achievement in the genre at novel, novella, novelet and short story lengths." Quarterly *SFWA Bulletin* to members; nonmembers may subscribe at $15/4 issues within U.S./Canada; $18.50 overseas. Bimonthly *SFWA Forum* for active members only. Annual *SFWA Membership Directory* for members; available to professional organizations for $60. Active membership requires professional sale in the U.S. of at least three short stories or one full-length book. Affiliate membership requires at least one professional sale in the U.S. or other professional sale in the U.S. or other professional involvement in the field. Dues are pro-rated quarterly; info available upon request. Business meetings are held during our Annual Nebula Awards weekend and usually during the annual World SF Convention. Send SASE for information.

SMALL PRESS WRITERS AND ARTISTS ORGANIZATION (SPWAO), 309 N. Humphrey Circle, Shawano WI 54166. (715)524-2750. SPWAO President: Mike Olson. Estab. 1977. Number of members: 300-400. Open to all members (anyone who paid dues for current year). Scope is international. Benefits include market news, critiquing services (art, poetry, fiction), grievance arbitration, reviews, nonfiction articles and essays, editor-mentor program, infor-swap/collaboration service, etc. Facilities include SPWAO library/archives. Sponsors awards and contests; have held conventions in conjunction with known cons—NECON, BUBONICON. Publishes *SPWAO Newsletter* (monthly), available to nonmembers upon request and $1 per copy; *Showcase* (yearly or as funding allows), $6 member and nonmember; *Alpha Gallery* (funding allows) $8.95 member and nonmember. Dues: US: $17.50 initial, $15 renew; 2 year new member option $28.50 *rebate available new members after May 1*; Canadian: $20 new, $17.50 renew; International: $20 new and renew. Send SASE for information.

WASHINGTON INDEPENDENT WRITERS, #220, 733 15th St. NW, Washington DC 20005. (202)347-4973. Executive Director: Isolde Chapin. Estab. 1975. Number of Members: 2,200. Type of Memberships: Full, associate, senior, student, dual. Open to any writer or person who has an interest in writing. Regional scope. Benefits include group health insurance, grievance committee, job bank, social events, workshops, small groups, networking, etc. Sponsors monthly workshops, spring conference. Publishes *The Independent Writer* newsletter, published 11 times/year. Newsletter subscription $35/year, must live outside metropolitan area. Dues: $75/year full and associate members; $45 senior and student members; $120 dual members (2 writers living at the same address). Holds monthly workshops and small group meetings. Send SASE for information.

WESTERN WRITERS OF AMERICA, P.O. Box 823, Sheridan WY 82801. Write for information.

WOMEN WRITERS OF COLOR, P.O. Box 1560, Murray Hill Station, New York NY 10156. Write for more information (emphasis on romance).

THE WRITERS ALLIANCE, Box 2014, Setauket NY 11733. Executive Director: Kiel Stuart. Estab. 1979. Number of Members: 125. Open to all writers: Professional, aspiring, those who have to write business memos or brochures; those interested in desktop publishing. National scope. Benefits: Members can run one classified or display ad in each issue of membership newsletter, *Keystrokes*; which also provides software and hardware reviews, how-to articles, market information and general support. Sponsors local writer's workshops; one annual poetry contest (SASE for rules). Publishes *Keystrokes*, quarterly, $15/year (payable to Exec. Dir. Kiel Stuart) covers both the cost of membership and newsletter. Local writer's critique group meets every three weeks. Send SASE for information.

THE WRITER'S CENTER, 7815 Old Georgetown Rd., Bethesda MD 20814. Responded late; write for information.

WRITERS CONNECTION, Suite 180, 1601 Saratoga-Sunnyvale Rd., Cupertino CA 95014. Community Relations: Mardeene Mitchell. Estab. 1983. Number of Members: 1,500. Open to: Anyone interested in writing or publishing. Mainly northern California scope, but we have members nationwide. Benefits include job placement service, seminars, referral network, newsletter, bookstore, resource library, meeting facility, mailing lists, advertising. Offers grammar help-line and research library. Sponsors workshops, conferences. Publishes *Writers Connection* monthly newsletter. One-year subscription is $18. Dues: $40/year. Newsletter/catalog available for 9×12 SAE and 3 first class stamps.

WRITERS' FEDERATION OF NEW BRUNSWICK, P.O. Box 37, Station A, Fredericton, New Brunswick E3B 4Y2 Canada. Project Coordinator: Anna Mae Snider. Estab. 1983. Number of Members: 180. Membership is open to anyone interested in writing. "This a provincial organization. Benefits include promotion of members' works through newsletter announcements and readings and launchings held at fall festival and annual general meeting, participation in a Writers-in-Schools Program, manuscript reading service, workshops held at fall and spring events. The WFNB sponsors a fall festival and an annual general meeting which features workshops, readings and book launchings." There is also an annual literary competition, open to residents of New Brunswick only, which has prizes of $200, $100 and $30 in four categories: Fiction, nonfiction, children's literature and poetry and $400 prize for the best manuscript of poems (48 pgs.) Publishes a quarterly newsletter. Dues: $15/year. Board of Directors meets approximately 5 times a year. Annual General Meeting is held in April of each year. Send SASE for information.

WRITERS' FEDERATION OF NOVA SCOTIA, 203-5516 Spring Garden Rd., Halifax, Nova Scotia B3J 1G6 Canada. Executive Director: Dawn Rae Downton. Estab. 1976. Number of Members: 500. Type of Memberships: General membership, student membership, Nova Scotia Writers' Council membership (professional), Nova Scotia Dramatists' Co-op membership (for playwrights), Honorary Life Membership. Open to: Anyone who writes, and is a resident or native of Nova Scotia. Provincial scope, with a few members living elsewhere in the country or the world. Benefits include advocacy of all kinds for writers, plus regular programs like workshops and regular publications, including directories and a newsletter. Sponsors workshops, two annual conferences (one for general membership, the other for the professional wing), two book awards, one annual competition for unpublished manuscripts in seven categories; a writers in the schools program, a manuscript reading service, reduced photocopying and typing rates, a typing referral service. Publishes *Eastword*, six issues annually, available by subscription for $30 (Canadian) to nonmembers. Dues: $30/year (Canadian). Holds an annual general meeting, an annual meeting of the Nova Scotia Writers' Council, several board meetings annually. Send 5×7 SASE for information.

WRITERS GUILD OF ALBERTA, WordWorks Building, 10523 - 100 Avenue, Edmonton, Alberta T5J 0A8 Canada. (403)426-5892. Executive Director: Lyle Weis. Estab. 1980. Number of Members: 700. Membership open to current and past residents of Alberta. Regional (provincial) scope. Benefits include discounts on programs offered; manuscript evaluation service available; bimonthly newsletter; contacts; use of photocopier at discount; info on workshops, retreats, readings, etc. Sponsors workshops 2/year, retreats 3 times/year, annual conference, annual book awards program (Alberta residents only). Publishes *WestWord* 6/year; available for $15/year (Canadian) to nonmembers. Dues: $55/year for regular membership; $20/year senior/students/limited income; $100/year donating membership— charitable receipt issued (Canadian funds). Organized monthly meetings. Send SASE for information.

THE WRITERS ROOM, INC., 153 Waverly Place, 5th Floor, New York NY 10014. (212)807-9519. Executive Director: Renata Rizzo-Harvi. Estab. 1978. Number of Members: 150. Open to: Any writer who shows a serious commitment to writing. "We serve a diverse population of writers, but most of our residents live in or around the NYC area. We encourage writers from around the country (and world!) to apply for residency if they plan to visit NYC for a while." Benefits include 24-hour access to the facility. "We provide desk space, storage areas for computers, typewriters, etc., a kitchen where coffee and tea are always available, bathrooms, a library and lounge. We also offer in-house workshops on topics of practical importance to writers and readings of work-in-progress. We publish a newsletter for members (once or twice a year), *The Writers Room News*." Dues: $165 per quarter/year. Send SASE for application and background information.

Publications of Interest to Fiction Writers

This new section features listings for magazines and newsletters that focus on writing or the publishing industry. While many of these are not markets for fiction, they do offer articles, marketing advice or other information valuable to the fiction writer. Several magazines in this section offer actual market listings while others feature reviews of books in the field and news on the industry.

Changes in publishing happen very quickly and magazines can help you keep up with the latest news. Some magazines listed here, including *Writer's Digest* and the *Canadian Writer's Journal*, cover the entire field of writing, while others such as *Children's Book Insider* and *Mystery Scene* focus on a particular type of writing.

You will also find information on some publications for writers in the introductions to other sections in this book. Many literary and commercial magazines for writers listed in the markets sections are also helpful to the fiction writer. Keep an eye on the newsstands and library shelves for others and let us know if you've found a publication particularly useful.

CANADIAN WRITER'S JOURNAL, Box 6618, Depot 1, Victoria, British Columbia V8P 5N7 Canada. (604)477-8807. Editor: Gordon M. Smart. Quarterly. "Mainly short how-to and motivational articles related to all types of writing and of interest to both new and established writers. Sponsors occasional short fiction contest." Lists markets for fiction. Sample copies available for $4 ($C for Canadian orders, $US for US orders). Subscription price: $15/year; $25/2 years ($C for Canadian orders, $US for US orders).

CHILDREN'S BOOK INSIDER, 254 E. Mombasha Rd., Monroe NY 10950. (914)782-4936. Editor: Laura Backes. Monthly. "Publication is devoted solely to children's book writers and illustrators. 'At Presstime' section gives current market information each month for submissions to publishers. Other articles include information on the publishing contract and how to negotiate, how to write a cover letter, how to assemble a strong portfolio, writing tips, and interviews with published authors and illustrators. Aimed at people just starting out in publishing." Lists markets for fiction. Reviews novels and short story collections. Review copies should be sent to Laura Backus (only if person has 2 or more books published). Sample copies for SASE (no charge). Single copy price: $2.75. Subscription price: $33/year (US); $38/year (Canadian).

FACTSHEET FIVE, P.O. Box 1163, Cincinnati OH 45201-1163. Bimonthly. "Reviews small press publications including magazines, books." Reviews novels and short story collections. Send review copies to Jon Lebkowski, % 2507 Roehampton, Austin TX 78745. Single copy price: $4 (bulk rate), $5 (first class). Subscription price: $20/6 issues (bulk rate), $30/6 issues (first class) Canada add $10 (bulk), $20 (first class).

GILA QUEEN'S GUIDE TO MARKETS, % Kathy Ptacek, P.O. Box 97, Newton NJ 07860. Write for information.

LOCUS, 34 Ridgewood Lane, Oakland CA 94611. Science fiction field publication. Did not respond to questionnaire. Write for more information.

MYSTERY SCENE, Mystery Enterprises, 3840 Clark Rd., SE, Cedar Rapids IA 52403. Mystery and horror reviews and articles. Write for more information.

THE NIGHTMARE EXPRESS, 275 W. Stevens, St. Paul MN 55107. (612)227-6958. Editor: Donald L. Miller. Bimonthly. *"The Nightmare Express* was established in 1986 as a vehicle for horror writers (both published/unpublished). Its purpose is to give market information, ideas, how-to information to help the author further advance their career." Recent articles included "One Way to Write Your Novel," "Cover Letters and Their Friends." Articles include "Dark Windows," NightTime Selections, etc." Lists markets for horror (6-12 markets) each issue. Reviews novels or short story collections. Sample copies available. Single copy price; $1.50 U.S.; subscription price: $10/year plus *Terror Time Again*; $8 renewals; foreign orders add $4. Please remit in U.S. funds.

THE NOOK NEWS CONFERENCES & KLATCHES BULLETIN, Suite 181, 38114 Third St., Willoughby OH 44094. (216)975-8965. Editor: Brian Sykes; Contributing Editor, Jan May. Quarterly. *"The Nook News Conferences & Klatches Bulletin* is a spin-off from *The Writer's Nook News* column of the same name. It is published for those writers looking for upcoming workshops, conferences, and other in-person events such as local regularly-scheduled writers groups (klatches)." Single copy price: $5. Subscription price: one year, $18; two years, $32 (add 50% if outside U.S. or Canada).

THE NOOK NEWS CONTESTS & AWARDS BULLETIN, Suite 181, 38114 Third St., Willoughby OH 44094. (216)975-8965. Editor: Brian Sykes; Contributing Editor, Deborah Bouziden. Quarterly. *"The Nook News Contests & Awards Bulletin* is a spin-off of *The Writer's Nook News* column of the same name. It is widely recognized that writing competitions help incite writer to continue writing, gives them a deadline to shoot for, and sometimes the added bonus of a free critique, not to mention monetary return and of course publication. *NNCAB* lists complete information and contacts for these competitions." Lists markets for fiction. Single copy price: $5. Subscription price: one year, $18; two years, $32 (add 50% if outside U.S. or Canada).

THE NOOK NEWS MARKET BULLETIN, Suite 181, 38114 Third St., Willoughby OH 44094. (216)975-8965. Editor: Brian Sykes; Contributing Editor: Donna Bocian. Quarterly. *"The Nook News Market Bulletin* is a spin-off of *The Writer's Nook News* column of the same name. It lists up-to-date market information and contacts for writers of fiction, nonfiction and poetry." Lists markets for fiction. Single copy price: $5. Subscription price: one year, $18; two years, $32 (add 50% if outside U.S. or Canada).

THE NOOK NEWS REVIEW OF WRITER'S PUBLICATIONS, Suite 181, 38114 Third St., Willoughby Oh 44094. (216)975-8965. Editor: Brian Sykes; Contributing Editor, Marcella Owens. *"NNRWP* reviews books and magazines, newsletters, etc., useful to freelance writers." Single copy price: $5. Subscription price: one year, $18; two years, $32 (add 50% if outside U.S. or Canada).

POETS & WRITERS, 72 Spring St., New York NY 10012. Covers all types of writing. Write for information.

RISING STAR, 47 Byledge Rd., Manchester NH 03104. (603)623-9796. Editor: Scott E. Green. Published every 5-7 weeks. "A newsletter which covers new markets for writers and artists in the science fiction/fantasy/horror genres." Lists markets for fiction. Reviews novels and short story collections. Send review copies to Scott E. Green. Sample copies available. Single copy price: $1.50. Subscription price: $7.50 for 6 issues (checks payable to Scott E. Green) $10 for overseas subscribers.

SCAVENGER'S NEWSLETTER, 519 Ellinwood, Osage City KS 66523. (913)528-3538. Editor: Janet Fox. Monthly. "A market newsletter for SF/fantasy/horror writers with an interest in the small press. Articles about SF/fantasy/horror writing/marketing." Lists markets for fiction. Sample copies available. Single copy price: $1.50. Subscription price: $11.50/year, $5.75/6 months. Canada: $14, $7; overseas $20, $10 (U.S. funds only).

SCIENCE FICTION CHRONICLE, P.O. Box 2730, Brooklyn NY 11202-0056. Write for information.

SMALL PRESS REVIEW, P.O. Box 100, Paradise CA 95967. (916)877-6110. Editor: Len Fulton. Quarterly. "Publishes news and reviews about small publishers, books, magazines." Lists markets for fiction. Reviews novels and short story collections. Sample copies available. Subscription price: $23/year.

THE WRITER, 120 Boylston St., Boston MA 02116-4615. Editor: Sylvia K. Burack. Monthly. Lists markets for fiction (March and October issues have special fiction lists annually. July lists book publishers). Single copy price: $2. Subscription price: $27/year, $50/2 years. Special introductory offer: 5 issues $10. Canadian and foreign at additional $8 (US) per year.

WRITERS CONNECTION, Suite 180, 1601 Saratoga-Sunnyvale Rd., Cupertino CA 95014. (408)973-0227. Editor: Jan Stiles. Monthly. "How-to articles for writers, editors and self-publishers. Topics cover all types of writing, from fiction to technical writing. Columns include markets, contests and writing events and conferences for fiction and nonfiction poetry." Lists markets for fiction. Sample copies available. Single copy price: $2. Subscription price: $18 ($24 in Canada/U.S. dollars).

WRITER'S DIGEST, 1507 Dana Ave., Cincinnati OH 45207. (513)531-2222. Editor: Bruce Woods. Monthly. "*Writer's Digest* is a magazine of techniques and markets. We *inspire* the writer to write, *instruct* him or her on how to improve that work, and *direct* it toward appropriate markets." Lists markets for fiction, nonfiction, poetry. Single copy price: $2.75. Subscription price: $18.

WRITER'S GUIDELINES, Box 608, Pittsburg MO 65724. Editor: Susan Salaki. Bimonthly. "Short stories published in *Writer's Guidelines* are considered by the editors of *Street Songs* for inclusion in the annual anthology of the best twenty stories published in small press during a given year. Fiction writers are welcome to submit material for our Roundtable Discussions, a section devoted to the grassroots approach of revealing and/or developing a workable submission and acceptance system for writers. Our magazine also assists writers in obtaining guidelines from over two hundred different magazine and book editors through our Guidelines Service. We also offer a Adopt-A-Writer program whereby the managing editor of WGM 'adopts' up to 10 writers and works with each writer on a one-on-one basis for six months." Lists markets for fiction. Reviews novels and short story collections. Sample copies available. Send SASE with 52¢ postage for guidelines. Single copy price: $4. Subscription price: $18; Canada, $30; Overseas, $42.

WRITER'S INFO, P.O. Box 1870, Hayden ID 83835. (208)772-6184. Editor: Linda Hutton. Monthly. "*WI* provides helpful hints to beginning writers, covering the basics of writing and submitting one's work." Lists markets for fiction. Sample copies available. Single copy for #10 SAE plus 2 first-class stamps. Subscription price: $12/year.

WRITERS' JOURNAL, (Minnesota Ink section), 27 Empire Dr., St. Paul MN 55103. (612)225-1306. Managing Editor: Valerie Hockert. Bimonthly. "Provides a creative outlet for writers of fiction." Sample copies available. Single copy price: $3; 3.75 (Canadian). Subscription price: $18; $23 Canada.

WRITERS NEWS, Hainault Road, Little Heath, Romford RM6 5NP England. Covers all genres of writing in England. Did not respond to questionnaire. Write for information.

THE WRITER'S NOOK NEWS, Suite 181, 38114 Third St., Willoughby OH 44094. (216)975-8965. Editor: Eugene Ortiz. Quarterly. "*The Writer's Nook News* is a national quarterly publication dedicated to giving freelance writers specific information for their immediate practical use in getting published and staying published. It contains news; writing tips; books; reviews; legislative/tax updates; conference, contest, and market listings; and various other topics." Lists markets for fiction. Single copy price: $5. Subscription price: $18/year; 2 years/$32 (add 50% if outside U.S. or Canada).

WRITER'S YEARBOOK, 1507 Dana Ave., Cincinnati OH 45207. (513)531-2222. Editor: Bruce Woods. Annual. "An annual collection of the best writing *about* writing, with a survey of the year's 100 top markets for freelancers." Single copy price: $3.95.

Glossary

Advance. Payment by a publisher to an author prior to the publication of a book, to be deducted from the author's future royalties.

All rights. The rights contracted to a publisher permitting a manuscript's use anywhere and in any form, including movie and book-club sales, without additional payment to the writer.

Anthology. A collection of selected writings by various authors.

Auction. Publishers sometimes bid against each other for the acquisition of a manuscript that has excellent sales prospects.

Backlist. A publisher's books not published during the current season but still in print.

Belles lettres. A term used to describe fine or literary writing more to entertain than to inform or instruct.

Book producer/packager. An organization that may develop a book for a publisher based upon the publisher's idea or may plan all elements of a book, from its initial concept to writing and marketing strategies, and then sell the package to a book publisher and/or movie producer.

Category fiction. See Genre.

Chapbook. A booklet of 15-30 pages of fiction or poetry.

Cliffhanger. Fictional event in which the reader is left in suspense at the end of a chapter or episode, so that interest in the story's outcome will be sustained.

Clip. Sample, usually from newspaper or magazine, of a writer's published work.

Cloak-and-dagger. A melodramatic, romantic type of fiction dealing with espionage and intrigue.

Commercial. Publishers whose concern is salability, profit and success with a large readership.

Contemporary. Material dealing with popular current trends, themes or topics.

Contributor's copy. Copy of an issue of a magazine or published book sent to an author whose work is included.

Copublishing. An arrangement in which the author and publisher share costs and profits.

Copyediting. Editing a manuscript for writing style, grammar, punctuation and factual accuracy.

Copyright. The legal right to exclusive publication, sale or distribution of a literary work.

Cover letter. A brief letter sent with a complete manuscript submitted to an editor.

"Cozy" (or "teacup") mystery. Mystery usually set in a small British town, in a bygone era, featuring a somewhat genteel, intellectual protagonist.

Cyberpunk. Type of science fiction, usually concerned with computer networks and human-computer combinations, involving young, sophisticated protagonists.

Division. An unincorporated branch of a company (e.g. Viking Penguin, a division of Penguin USA).

Experimental fiction. Fiction that is innovative in subject matter and style; avant-garde, non-formulaic, usually literary material.

Exposition. The portion of the storyline, usually the beginning, where background information about character and setting is related.

Fair use. A provision in the copyright law that says short passages from copyrighted material may be used without infringing on the owner's rights.

Fanzine. A noncommercial, small-circulation magazine usually dealing with fantasy, horror or science-fiction literature and art.

First North American serial rights. The right to publish material in a periodical before it appears in book form, for the first time, in the United States or Canada.

Formula. A fixed and conventional method of plot development, which varies little from one book to another in a particular genre.

Frontier novel. Novel that has all the basic elements of a traditional western but is based upon the frontier history of "unwestern" places like Florida or East Tennessee.

Galleys. The first typeset version of a manuscript that has not yet been divided into pages.

Genre. A formulaic type of fiction such as romance, western or horror.

Gothic. A genre in which the central character is usually a beautiful young woman and the setting an old mansion or castle, involving a handsome hero and real danger, either natural or supernatural.

Graphic novel. An adaptation of a novel into a long comic strip or heavily illustrated story of 40 pages or more, produced in paperback.

Hard-boiled detective novel. Mystery novel featuring a private eye or police detective as the protagonist; usually involves a murder. The emphasis is on the details of the crime.

Honorarium. A small, token payment for published work.

Horror. A genre stressing fear, death and other aspects of the macabre.

Imprint. Name applied to a publisher's specific line (e.g. Owl, an imprint of Henry Holt).

Interactive fiction. Fiction in book or computer-software format where the reader determines the path the story will take by choosing from several alternatives at the end of each chapter or episode.

International Reply Coupon (IRC). A form purchased at a post office and enclosed with a letter or manuscript to a international publisher, to cover return postage costs.

Juvenile. Fiction intended for children 2-12.

Libel. Written or printed words that defame, malign or damagingly misrepresent a living person.

Literary. The general category of serious, non-formulaic, intelligent fiction, sometimes experimental, that most frequently appears in little magazines.

Literary agent. A person who acts for an author in finding a publisher or arranging contract terms on a literary project.

Mainstream. Traditionally written fiction on subjects or trends that transcend experimental or genre fiction categories.

Malice domestic novel. A traditional mystery novel that is not hard-boiled; emphasis is on the solution. Suspects and victims know one another.

Manuscript. The author's unpublished copy of a work, usually typewritten, used as the basis for typesetting.

Mass market paperback. Softcover book on a popular subject, usually around 4×7, directed to a general audience and sold in drugstores and groceries as well as in bookstores.

Ms(s). Abbreviation for manuscript(s).

Multiple submission. Submission of more than one short story at a time to the same editor. Do not make a multiple submission unless requested.

Narration. The account of events in a story's plot as related by the speaker or the voice of the author.

Narrator. The person who tells the story, either someone involved in the action or the voice of the writer.

New Age. A term including categories such as astrology, psychic phenomena, spiritual healing, UFOs, mysticism and other aspects of the occult.

Nom de plume. French for "pen name"; a pseudonym.

Novella (also novelette). A short novel or long story, approximately 7,000-15,000 words.

#10 envelope. $4 \times 9\frac{1}{2}$ envelope, used for queries and other business letters.

Novels of the West. Novels that have elements of the western but contain more complex characters and subjects such as fur trading, cattle raising and coal mining.

Offprint. Copy of a story taken from a magazine before it is bound.

One-time rights. Permission to publish a story in periodical or book form one time only.

Outline. A summary of a book's contents, often in the form of chapter headings with a few sentences outlining the action of the story under each one; sometimes part of a book proposal.

Over the transom. Slang for the path of an unsolicited manuscript into the slush pile.

Page rate. A fixed rate paid to an author per published page of fiction.

Payment on acceptance. Payment from the magazine or publishing house as soon as the decision to print a manuscript is made.

Payment on publication. Payment from the publisher after a manuscript is printed.

Pen name. A pseudonym used to conceal a writer's real name.

Periodical. A magazine or journal published at regular intervals.

Plot. The carefully devised series of events through which the characters progress in a work of fiction.

Proofreading. Close reading and correction of a manuscript's typographical errors.

Proofs. A typeset version of a manuscript used for correcting errors and making changes, often a photocopy of the galleys.

Proposal. An offer to write a specific work, usually consisting of an outline of the work and one or two completed chapters.

Prose poem. Short piece of prose with the language and expression of poetry.

Protagonist. The principal or leading character in a literary work.

Public domain. Material that either was never copyrighted or whose copyright term has expired.

Pulp magazine. A periodical printed on inexpensive paper, usually containing lurid, sensational stories or articles.

Purple prose. Ornate writing using exaggerated and excessive literary devices.

Query. A letter written to an editor to elicit interest in a story the writer wants to submit.

Reader. A person hired by a publisher to read unsolicited manuscripts.

Reading fee. An arbitrary amount of money charged by some agents and publishers to read a submitted manuscript.

Regency romance. A genre romance, usually set in England between 1811-1820.

Remainders. Leftover copies of an out-of-print book, sold by the publisher at a reduced price.

Reporting time. The number of weeks or months it takes an editor to report back on an author's query or manuscript.

Reprint rights. Permission to print an already published work whose rights have been sold to another magazine or book publisher.

Roman à clef. French "novel with a key." A novel that represents actual living or historical characters and events in fictionalized form.

Romance. The genre relating accounts of passionate love and fictional heroic achievements.

Royalties. A percentage of the retail price paid to an author for each copy of the book that is sold.

SASE. Self-addressed stamped envelope.

Science fiction. Genre in which scientific facts and hypotheses form the basis of actions and events.

Second serial rights. Permission for the reprinting of a work in another periodical after its first publication in book or magazine form.

Self-publishing. In this arrangement, the author keeps all income derived from the book, but he pays for its manufacturing, production and marketing.

Sequel. A literary work that continues the narrative of a previous, related story or novel.

Serial rights. The rights given by an author to a publisher to print a piece in one or more periodicals.

Serialized novel. A book-length work of fiction published in sequential issues of a periodical.

Setting. The environment and time period during which the action of a story takes place.

Short short story. A condensed piece of fiction, usually under 700 words.

Simultaneous submission. The practice of sending copies of the same manuscript to several editors or publishers at the same time. Some people refuse to consider such submissions.

Slant. A story's particular approach or style, designed to appeal to the readers of a specific magazine.

Slice of life. A presentation of characters in a seemingly mundane situation which offers the reader a flash of illumination about the characters or their situation.

Slush pile. A stack of unsolicited manuscripts in the editorial offices of a publisher.

Speculation (or Spec). An editor's agreement to look at an author's manuscript with no promise to purchase.

Splatterpunk. Type of horror fiction known for its very violent and graphic content.

Subsidiary. An incorporated branch of a company or conglomerate (e.g. Alfred Knopf, Inc., a subsidiary of Random House, Inc.).

Subsidiary rights. All rights other than book publishing rights included in a book contract, such as paperback, book-club and movie rights.

Subsidy publisher. A book publisher who charges the author for the cost of typesetting, printing and promoting a book. Also Vanity publisher.

Suspense. A genre of fiction where the plot's primary function is to build a feeling of anticipation and fear in the reader over its possible outcome.

Synopsis. A brief summary of a story, novel or play. As part of a book proposal, it is a comprehensive summary condensed in a page or page and a half.

Tabloid. Publication printed on paper about half the size of a regular newspaper page (e.g. *The National Enquirer*).

Tearsheet. Page from a magazine containing a published story.

Theme. The dominant or central idea in a literary work; its message, moral or main thread.

Trade paperback. A softbound volume, usually around 5×8, published and designed for the general public, available mainly in bookstores.

Unsolicited manuscript. A story or novel manuscript that an editor did not specifically ask to see.

Vanity publisher. See Subsidy publisher.

Viewpoint. The position or attitude of the first- or third-person narrator or multiple narrators, which determines how a story's action is seen and evaluated.

Western. Genre with a setting in the West, usually between 1860-1890, with a formula plot about cowboys or other aspects of frontier life.

Whodunit. Genre dealing with murder, suspense and the detection of criminals.

Work-for-hire. Work that another party commissions you to do, generally for a flat fee. The creator does not own the copyright and therefore can not sell any rights.

Young adult. The general classification of books written for readers 12-18.

Category Index

The category index is a good place to begin searching for a market for your fiction. Below is an alphabetical list of subjects of particular interest to the editors listed in *Novel and Short Story Writer's Market*. The index is divided into sections: literary and small circulation magazines, commercial periodicals, small press and commercial publishers.

Some of the markets listed in the book do not appear in the Category Index, because they have not indicated specific subject preferences. Most of these said they accept "all categories." Listings that were very specific also do not appear here. An example of this might be a magazine accepting "fiction about coal mining only."

If you'd like to market your romance novel, check the Commercial Publishers subhead under Romance. There you will find a list of those publishers interested in the subject. To find the page numbers for the ones you select, check the Markets Index. Then read the listings *carefully* to find the romance publishers best suited to your work.

Literary and Small Circulation Magazines

Adventure. Abyss Magazine; Advocate, The; Amateur Writers Journal; Amelia; Amherst Review, The; Arnazella; Arts Indiana Literary Supplement; Atalantik; Being; Belletrist Review, The; Black Jack; Blind Iguana Press; Blueline; Breakthrough!; Carousel Literary Arts Magazine; Chapter One; Chrysalis; City Scriptum; Cochran's Corner; Crime Club; Dagger of the Mind; Dan River Anthology; Dead Tree Product; Dream International/Quarterly; Ecphorizer, The; Eldritch Science; 11th Street Ruse; Elf: Eclectic Literary Forum; Escapist, The; Event; Fighting Woman News; Gotta Write Network Litmag; Grasslands Review; Green Mountains Review; Green's Magazine; Hawaii Pacific Review; Helter Skelter; Hippo; Hobo Jungle; Hyperbole; Imagine!; Indian Youth of America Newsletter; Innisfree; ipsissima verba/the very words; Jeopardy; Journal of Regional Criticism; Lactuca; Leading Edge, The; Left-Footed Wombat; Legend; Lighthouse; Llamas Magazine; Long Shot; MacGuffin, The; Merlyn's Pen; Mindscapes; Minnesota Ink; Monocacy Valley Review, The; Monthly Independent Tribune . . . , The; Nahant Bay; Negative Capability; New Methods; New Press, The; Nimrod; No Idea Magazine; No Newz; Northern Arizona Mandala; Oak, The; Ouroboros; Oxalis; P.I. Magazine; Palace Corbie; Paper Bag, The; Perceptions; Plowman, The; Portable Wall, The; Post, The; Potpourri; Prisoners of the Night; Pub, The; Queen's Quarterly; Rag Mag; Re Arts & Letters; Renegade; Renovated Lighthouse Publications; Review La Booche; Riverwind; Salome; Samisdat; San Gabriel Valley Magazine; Sensations; Shawnee Silhouette; Short Story Digest, The; Short Stuff Magazine for Grown-ups; Slate and Style; South Hill Gazette, The; Sozoryoku; SPIT Magazine; SPSM&H; Thema; Thumbprints; Tickled By Thunder; Tucumcari Literary Review; Ultimate Writer, The; Very Small Magazine, A; Villager, The; Vincent Brothers Review, The; Vintage Northwest; Virginia Quarterly Review; Wisconsin Restaurateur, The; Words of Wisdom; Wordsmith; Writers' Bar-B-Q, The; Writer's Guidelines

Canadian. Antigonish Review, The; Atlantis (Nova Scotia); Bardic Runes; Breakthrough!; Canadian Author & Bookman; Canadian Fiction Magazine; Capilano Review, The; Carousel Literary Arts Magazine; Chalk Talk; Champagne Horror; Dalhousie Review, The; Dance Connection; Dandelion Magazine; Dead Tree Product; Descant (Ontario); Dreams & Visions; Event; Fiddlehead, The; Grain; Green's Magazine; Herspectives; K; Legend; Lost; Malahat Review, The; New Quarterly, The; Plowman, The; Poetry Halifax Dartmouth; Pottersfield Portfolio, The; Prairie Fire; Prairie Journal of Canadian Literature, The; Prism International; Quarry; Queen's Quarterly; Scrivener; Sidetrekked; This Magazine; Tickled By Thunder; Underpass; Wascana Review; Whetstone; White Wall Review; Writ

Comics. Fat Tuesday; Processed World; Rag Mag; Sign of the Times

Condensed Novel. Alabama Literary Review; Ararat Quarterly; Art:Mag; Arts Indiana Literary Supplement; Atalantik; Bahlasti Paper; Brownbag Press; Chakra; Chaminade Literary Review; Chapter One; Cimmerian Journal; City Scriptum; Forbidden Lines; G.W. Review, The; Gulf Coast; Humerus; Hyperbole; Immanent Face Magazine; Indian Youth of America Newsletter; K; Kenyon Review, The; Lactuca; Language Bridges Quarterly; Libido; Limestone: A Literary Journal; Manoa; Moody Street Review, The;

Nahant Bay; NCASA News; New Methods; Night Owl's Newsletter; Northern Arizona Mandala; Notes From The Southwest; Oxalis; Painted Hills Review; Perceptions; Poetry Motel; Primal Voices; Psychotrain; Pub, The; Renegade; River Styx; Ruby's Pearls; Salmon Magazine; Snake Nation Review; SPIT Magazine; Story; Tandava; Toad Hiway; Tucumcari Literary Review; Two-Ton Santa; Underground Forest; Vincent Brothers Review, The; Vintage Northwest; Witness (Michigan); Wordsmith; Writer's Guidelines

Confession. Amherst Review, The; Art:Mag; Bakunin; City Scriptum; D.C.; Deuterium; Dream International/Quarterly; Epiphany; Hippo; Imagine!; K; Lactuca; Ledge Poetry and Fiction Magazine, The; Libido; Long Shot; New Press, The; Painted Hills Review; Perceptions; Plowman, The; Poetry Forum Short Stories; Processed World; Shattered Wig Review; SPSM&H; Ultimate Writer, The; Very Small Magazine, A; Village Idiot, The; Writer's Guidelines; Zero Hour

Contemporary. ACM, (Another Chicago Magazine); Adrift; Advocate, The; Alabama Literary Review; Alaska Quarterly Review; Amaranth Review, The; Amateur Writers Journal; Ambergris; Amelia; American Fiction; Americas Review, The; Amherst Review, The; Antaeus; Antietam Review; Antigonish Review, The; Antioch Review; Ararat Quarterly; Archae; Arnazella; Artemis; Art:Mag; Arts Indiana Literary Supplement; Asylum; Atalantik; Aura Literary/Arts Review; Azorean Express, The; Belletrist Review, The; Bellowing Ark; Beloit Fiction Journal; Black Jack; Black River Review; Black Scholar, The; Black Warrior Review; Blatant Artifice; Blind Iguana Press; Blue Ryder; Blueline; Blur; Boulevard; Brownbag Press; Callaloo; Calliope; Canadian Author & Bookman; Capilano Review, The; Caribbean Writer, The; Carousel Literary Arts Magazine; Cathedral of Insanity; Center Magazine; Central Park; Changing Men; Chapter One; Chariton Review, The; Chattahoochee Review, The; Chicago Review; Chiron Review; Chrysalis; Cimarron Review; Cipher; City Scriptum; Clifton Magazine; Clockwatch Review; Coe Review, The; Colorado Review; Colorado-North Review; Concho River Review; Confrontation; Corona; Crazyquilt; Crucible; Dan River Anthology; Dead Tree Product; Descant (Ontario); Descant (Texas); Deuterium; Dream International/Quarterly; Ecphorizer, The; 11th Street Ruse; Elf: Eclectic Literary Forum; Emrys Journal; Epiphany; Epoch Magazine; Event; Eyes; Farmer's Market, The; Fiction; Fine Madness; Fish Drum Magazine; Flipside; Florida Review, The; Folio: A Literary Journal; Footwork; Friction; G.W. Review, The; Gamut, The; Gettysburg Review, The; Gotta Write Network Litmag; Grain; Grasslands Review; Great Stream Review; Green Mountains Review; Greensboro Review; Groundswell; Gulf Coast; Gulf Stream Magazine; Habersham Review; Hawaii Pacific Review; Hawaii Review; Hayden's Ferry Review; Helter Skelter; High Plains Literary Review; Hill and Holler; Hippo; Hobo Jungle; Housewife-Writer's Forum; Howling Dog; Hyperbole; Imagine!; Immanent Face Magazine; Indian Youth of America Newsletter; Indiana Review; Inlet; Innisfree; Interim; ipsissima verba/the very words; Jacaranda Review; Jeopardy; Journal of Regional Criticism; K; Karamu; Kenyon Review, The; Lactuca; Lake Effect; Laurel Review, The; Ledge Poetry and Fiction Magazine, The; Left Curve; Left-Footed Wombat; Lighthouse; Limberlost Review, The; Long Shot; Long Story, The; Lost and Found Times; Lost Creek Letters; Louisville Review, The; MacGuffin, The; Manoa; Mark; Maryland Review, The; Mati; Metropolitain; MidCoaster, The; Mindscapes; Minnesota Ink; Mississippi Review; Mississippi Valley Review; Missouri Review, The; Mobius; Monocacy Valley Review, The; Moody Street Review, The; Moon; Nahant Bay; Nassau Review; NCASA News; Nebraska Review, The; Negative Capability; New Delta Review; New Laurel Review; New Letters Magazine; New Methods; New Orleans Review; New Virginia Review; Nexus; Nimrod; No Idea Magazine; North Dakota Quarterly; Northern Arizona Mandala; Northwest Review; Notes From The Southwest; NRG; Oak, The; Ohio Review, The; Old Hickory Review; Onionhead; Other Voices; Ouroboros; Oxalis; Oyez Review; Painted Bride Quarterly; Painted Hills Review; Palace Corbie; Panhandler, The; Paper Bag, The; Partisan Review; Pearl; Pennsylvania English; Perceptions; Pikestaff Forum, The; Pikeville Review; Pinehurst Journal, The; Plowman, The; Poetic Space; Poetry Forum Short Stories; Poetry Magic Publications; Poetry Motel; Pointed Circle, The; Portable Wall, The; Poskisnolt Press; Potato Eyes; Potpourri; Pottersfield Portfolio, The; Prairie Fire; Prairie Journal of Canadian Literature, The; Primavera; Prism International; Prisoners of the Night; Processed World; Puerto Del Sol; Quarterly West; Queen's Quarterly; Rag Mag; Re Arts & Letters; Redneck Review of Literature, The; Renegade; Response; Review La Booche; River Styx; Riverwind; Rohwedder; Salad; Salmon Magazine; Salome; Salt Lick Press; Samisdat; San Gabriel Valley Magazine; Sanskrit; Santa Monica Review; Seattle Review, The; Sensations; Sewanee Review, The; Shattered Wig Review; Shawnee Silhouette; Shockbox; Shooting Star Review; Short Story Digest, The; Short Stuff Magazine for Grown-ups; Side Show; Sing Heavenly Muse!; Sisyphus; Skylark; Slate and Style; Slipstream; Snake Nation Review; Soundings East; South Carolina Review; South Dakota Review; Southern Exposure; Southern Review, The; Spectrum (Massachusetts); Spindrift; Spirit That Moves Us, The; SPIT Magazine; SPSM&H; Story; Stroker Magazine; Struggle; Studio One; Sycamore Review; Tampa Review; Tandava; Texas Review, The; Thema; This Magazine; Tickled By Thunder; Toad Hiway; Triquarterly; Tucumcari Literary Review; Turnstile; Twopenny Porringer, The; Two-Ton Santa; Underpass; University of Portland Review; Unmuzzled Ox; Valley Grapevine; Verve; Village Idiot, The; Vincent Brothers Review, The; Virginia Quarterly Review; Webster Review; Welter; West Branch; Widener

Review, The; Willow Review; Wisconsin Restaurateur, The; Witness (Michigan); Words of Wisdom; Wordsmith; Worm; Writers' Bar-B-Q, The; Writers' Forum; Writer's Guidelines; Xavier Review; Zyzzyva

Erotica. Aberations; Adrift; Alabama Literary Review; Alpha Beat Soup; Amelia; Anything That Moves; Arnazella; Art:Mag; Asylum; Baby Sue; Bahlasti Paper; Bakunin; Belletrist Review, The; Blatant Artifice; Blind Iguana Press; Brownbag Press; Bvi-Pacifica Newsletter; Center Magazine; Central Park; Changing Men; Chattahoochee Review, The; Clifton Magazine; Coe Review, The; Dream International/Quarterly; Ecphorizer, The; Eidos; Erotic Fiction Quarterly; Fat Tuesday; Fish Drum Magazine; Forbidden Lines; Fritz; Hippo; Hobo Jungle; Hyperbole; Joyeux Erotique; K; Kiosk; Lactuca; Ledge Poetry and Fiction Magazine, The; Left-Footed Wombat; Libido; Long Shot; Magic Changes; Metropolitain; Nahant Bay; New Delta Review; No Newz; Oxalis; Palace Corbie; Paper Bag, The; Paper Radio; Pinehurst Journal, The; Poetic Space; Poetry Motel; Poskisnolt Press; Potent Aphrodisiac; Prisoners of the Night; Psychotrain; Rag Mag; Riverwind; Salmon Magazine; Salt Lick Press; Samisdat; Sanskrit; Shattered Wig Review; Sign of the Times; Slipstream; Snake Nation Review; SPIT Magazine; SPSM&H; Starry Nights; Sub-Terrain; Toad Hiway; Two-Ton Santa; Very Small Magazine, A; Village Idiot, The; Words of Wisdom; Worm; Writers' Bar-B-Q, The; Yellow Silk; Zero Hour

Ethnic. ACM, (Another Chicago Magazine); Acorn, The; Adrift; Advocate, The; Alabama Literary Review; Amelia; American Dane; Americas Review, The; Amherst Review, The; Antietam Review; Anything That Moves; Ararat Quarterly; Arnazella; Art:Mag; Arts Indiana Literary Supplement; Atalantik; Aura Literary/Arts Review; Azorean Express, The; Bahlasti Paper; Bakunin; Bamboo Ridge; Being; Bella Figura, La; Belles Lettres; Bilingual Review; Black Jack; Black Scholar, The; Black Warrior Review; Black Writer Magazine; Blatant Artifice; Blind Iguana Press; Blue Light Red Light; Blue Ryder; Bridge, The; Brownbag Press; Callaloo; Caribbean Writer, The; Carousel Literary Arts Magazine; Central Park; Chakra; Chaminade Literary Review; Chapter One; Chiricŭ; Cicada; City Scriptum; Clifton Magazine; Coe Review, The; Collages and Bricolages; Colorado Review; Concho River Review; Crazyquilt; Cream City Review, The; D.C.; Dan River Anthology; Dead Tree Product; Dream International/Quarterly; Elf: Eclectic Literary Forum; Epiphany; Epoch Magazine; Escapist, The; Fish Drum Magazine; Five Fingers Review; Footwork; Fritz; Grasslands Review; Groundswell; Gulf Coast; Gulf Stream Magazine; Hawaii Pacific Review; Hawaii Review; Hayden's Ferry Review; Heartlands Today, The; Hill and Holler; Hobo Jungle; Imagine!; Innisfree; ipsissima verba/the very words; Japanophile; Jeopardy; Jewish Currents Magazine; Journal of Regional Criticism; Kennesaw Review; Kenyon Review, The; Latin American Literary Review; Left Curve; Left-Footed Wombat; Little Magazine, The; Long Shot; Long Story, The; Lost Creek Letters; MacGuffin, The; Mark; Metropolitain; MidCoaster, The; Middle Eastern Dancer; Midland; Miorita; Mobius; Moody Street Review, The; Moon; Mosaic; Nahant Bay; NCASA News; Negative Capability; New Letters Magazine; New Press, The; Nimrod; No Newz; North Dakota Quarterly; North East ARTS Magazine; Notebook/Cnaderno: A Literary Journal; Now & Then; Nuez, La; Onionhead; Oxalis; Oxford Magazine; Painted Bride Quarterly; Painted Hills Review; Palace Corbie; Panhandler, The; Paper Bag, The; Plowman, The; Poetic Space; Poetry Forum Short Stories; Poetry Motel; Pointed Circle, The; Portable Wall, The; Poskisnolt Press; Potpourri; Pottersfield Portfolio, The; Primal Voices; Psychotrain; Puerto Del Sol; Rag Mag; Reconstructionist; Response; River Styx; Riverwind; Rockford Review, The; Rohwedder; Ruby's Pearls; Salmon Magazine; Salt Lick Press; Samisdat; San Jose Studies; Sanskrit; Seattle Review, The; Sequoia; Shattered Wig Review; Side Show; Sing Heavenly Muse!; Sisyphus; Skylark; Slipstream; Snake Nation Review; South Carolina Review; South Dakota Review; South Hill Gazette, The; Southern Exposure; Sozoryoku; Spindrift; SPIT Magazine; Spoofing!; SPSM&H; Struggle; Studio One; Tampa Review; Third Woman; This Magazine; Tributary; Tucumcari Literary Review; Ultimate Writer, The; Underground Forest; Valley Grapevine; Valley Women's Voice; Village Idiot, The; Vincent Brothers Review, The; Willow Review; Words of Wisdom; Wordsmith; Worm; Writers' Bar-B-Q, The; Writers' Forum; Writer's Guidelines; Xavier Review; Zero Hour

Experimental. Aberations; ACM, (Another Chicago Magazine); Adrift; Advocate, The; Alabama Literary Review; Alaska Quarterly Review; Alpha Beat Soup; Amaranth Review, The; Amelia; American Fiction; Amherst Review, The; Antietam Review; Antioch Review; Anything That Moves; Archae; Arnazella; Artful Dodge; Art:Mag; Arts Indiana Literary Supplement; Asylum; Atalantik; Azorean Express, The; Baby Sue; Bad Haircut; Bahlasti Paper; Being; Black River Review; Blind Iguana Press; Blue Light Red Light; Blue Ryder; Bluff City; Blur; Bogg; Bone Saw; Boulevard; Brownbag Press; Bvi-Pacifica Newsletter; Calliope; Capilano Review, The; Carousel Literary Arts Magazine; Cathedral of Insanity; Ceilidh; Center Magazine; Central Park; Chakra; Chaminade Literary Review; Changing Men; Chapter One; Chattahoochee Review, The; Chicago Review; Chiron Review; Chrysalis; Cimmerian Journal; Cipher; City Scriptum; Clockwatch Review; Collages and Bricolages; Colorado Review; Compost Newsletter; Conjunctions; Corona; Cream City Review, The; Crime Club; Crucible; D.C.; Dagger of the Mind; Dan River Anthology; Dead Tree Product; Deathrealm; Denver Quarterly; Deuterium; Dream International/Quarterly; Dreams & Nightmares; Ecphorizer, The; 11th Street Ruse; Eotu; Escapist, The; Explorations '92; Eyes; Fat Tuesday; Fiction; Fine Madness; Fish Drum Magazine; Five Fingers Review; Flipside; Florida Review, The; Footwork; Forbidden Lines; Fritz; G.W. Review, The; Gamut, The; Georgia

Review, The; Gettysburg Review, The; Grain; Grasslands Review; Green Mountains Review; Greensboro Review; Groundswell; Gulf Coast; Gypsy; Habersham Review; Hawaii Pacific Review; Hawaii Review; Hayden's Ferry Review; Heaven Bone; Hippo; Hobo Jungle; Housewife-Writer's Forum; Howling Dog; Humerus; Hyperbole; Imagine!; Immanent Face Magazine; Indiana Review; ipsissima verba/the very words; Iris; Jacaranda Review; Jeopardy; Journal of Regional Criticism; K; Kennesaw Review; Kenyon Review, The; Kings Review; Kiosk; Leading Edge, The; Left Curve; Left-Footed Wombat; Limberlost Review, The; Limestone: A Literary Journal; Lite Magazine; Little Magazine, The; Long Shot; Lost; Lost and Found Times; Lost Creek Letters; Lost Worlds; Louisville Review, The; Lynx; MacGuffin, The; Madison Review, The; Mage, The; Magic Realism; Merlyn's Pen; Metropolitain; Mid-American Review; MidCoaster, The; Midland; Mind in Motion; Mindscapes; Minnesota Ink; Minnesota Review, The; Mississippi Review; Mobius; Monocacy Valley Review, The; Monthly Independent Tribune . . . , The; Moon; Nahant Bay; NCASA News; Negative Capability; New Delta Review; New Letters Magazine; New Methods; New Pathways; New Press, The; new renaissance, the; New Virginia Review; Next Phase; Nexus; Night Owl's Newsletter; Nimrod; No Idea Magazine; No Newz; Nocturnal Lyric, The; North Dakota Quarterly; Northern Arizona Mandala; Northwest Review; NRG; Oak, The; Ohio Review, The; Old Hickory Review; Onionhead; Other Voices; Ouroboros; Oxalis; Oxford Magazine; Oyez Review; Painted Bride Quarterly; Painted Hills Review; Palace Corbie; Panhandler, The; Paper Bag, The; Paper Radio; Partisan Review; Perceptions; Phoebe; Pikeville Review; Pinehurst Journal, The; Poetic Space; Poetry Forum Short Stories; Poetry Halifax Dartmouth; Portable Wall, The; Porter International, Bern; Poskisnolt Press; Potpourri; Pottersfield Portfolio, The; Prairie Fire; Primal Voices; Prisoners of the Night; Psychotrain; Puckerbrush Review; Puerto Del Sol; Pulsar; Quarry; Queen's Quarterly; Rag Mag; Re Arts & Letters; Red Cedar Review; Renegade; Renovated Lighthouse Publications; Response; Review La Booche; River Styx; Rockford Review, The; Rohwedder; Ruby's Pearls; Salad; Salmon Magazine; Salt Lick Press; Samisdat; Sanskrit; Seattle Review, The; Sequoia; Shattered Wig Review; Shockbox; Shooting Star Review; Sign of the Times; Silver Web, The; Sisyphus; Skylark; Slipstream; Small Hours, The; Snake Nation Review; South Dakota Review; Sozoryoku; Spectrum (Massachusetts); Spindrift; SPIT Magazine; SPSM&H; Story; Struggle; Sub-Terrain; Sycamore Review; Syzygy; Tampa Review; Tandava; Thema; Thin Ice; This Magazine; Toad Hiway; Tributary; Turnstile; 2 AM Magazine; Twopenny Porringer, The; Two-Ton Santa; Ultimate Writer, The; Underpass; Unsilenced Voice, The; Verve; Very Small Magazine, A; Videomania; Village Idiot, The; Vincent Brothers Review, The; Westview; Whetstone; Widener Review, The; Willow Review; Wisconsin Academy Review; Witness (Michigan); Wordsmith; Worm; Writers' Bar-B-Q, The; Writer's Guidelines; Xavier Review; Yellow Silk; Zero Hour; Zoiks!; Zyzzyva

Fantasy. Aberations; Abyss Magazine; Advocate, The; Alabama Literary Review; Amateur Writers Journal; Amelia; Amherst Review, The; Anything That Moves; Argonaut; Arnazella; Art:Mag; Bahlasti Paper; Bardic Runes; Being; Beyond; Blue Light Red Light; Bone Saw; Bradley's Fantasy Magazine, Marion Zimmer; Bravo Mundo Nuevo; Bvi-Pacifica Newsletter; Carousel Literary Arts Magazine; Chakra; Chapter One; Cimmerian Journal; City Scriptum; Clifton Magazine; Coe Review, The; Companion in Zeor, A; Compost Newsletter; Corona; Crazyquilt; Crime Club; Dagger of the Mind; Dan River Anthology; Dead Tree Product; Deathrealm; Deuterium; Dream International/Quarterly; Dreams & Nightmares; Ecphorizer, The; Eldritch Science; Elf: Eclectic Literary Forum; Encounters Magazine; Epiphany; Escapist, The; Eyes; Fighting Woman News; Figment Magazine; Fish Drum Magazine; Forbidden Lines; Golden Isis Magazine; Gotta Write Network Litmag; Grasslands Review; Green's Magazine; Groundswell; Haunts; Hawaii Pacific Review; Hayden's Ferry Review; Heaven Bone; Helter Skelter; Hippo; Hobo Jungle; Hobson's Choice; Hor-Tasy; Humerus; Hyperbole; Imagine!; Immanent Face Magazine; Inlet; Innisfree; ipsissima verba/the very words; Jeopardy; Journal of Regional Criticism; Kennesaw Review; Kenyon Review, The; Lake Effect; Language Bridges Quarterly; Leading Edge, The; Left-Footed Wombat; Legend; Lite Magazine; Long Shot; Lost Creek Letters; Lost Worlds; MacGuffin, The; Mage, The; Magic Changes; Magic Realism; Merlyn's Pen; Midnight Zoo; Minas Tirith Evening-Star; Mind in Motion; Minnesota Ink; Minnesota Review, The; Mississippi Review; Mobius; Mythic Circle, The; Nahant Bay; Nassau Review; Negative Capability; New Laurel Review; New Pathways; New Press, The; Next Phase; Night Owl's Newsletter; No Idea Magazine; No Newz; Nocturnal Lyric, The; Northern Arizona Mandala; Nuclear Fiction; Old Hickory Review; Once Upon A World; Ouroboros; Oxalis; Pablo Lennis; Palace Corbie; Pandora; Paper Bag, The; Paper Radio; Perceptions; Poetic Space; Poetry Forum Short Stories; Poetry Motel; Poskisnolt Press; Potpourri; Pottersfield Portfolio, The; Primal Voices; Primavera; Prisoners of the Night; Processed World; Pub, The; Pulphouse; Pulsar; Quarry; Queen's Quarterly; Rag Mag; Renegade; Renovated Lighthouse Publications; Riverside Quarterly; Rockford Review, The; Salmon Magazine; Salome: A Journal for the Performing Arts; Samisdat; Seattle Review, The; Sensations; Short Story Digest, The; Sidetrekked; Silver Web, The; Sing Heavenly Muse!; Sisyphus; Skylark; Slate and Style; Slipstream; Snake Nation Review; Southern Humanities Review; Sozoryoku; SPIT Magazine; SPSM&H; Square One; Starsong; Tampa Review; Tandava; Thin Ice; This Magazine; Tickled By Thunder; Tributary; 2 AM Magazine; Ultimate Writer, The; Verve; Videomania; Village Idiot, The; Vintage Northwest; Weirdbook; Witness (Michigan); Wordsmith; Writers' Bar-B-Q, The; Writer's Guidelines; Yellow Silk

Feminist. ACM, (Another Chicago Magazine); Adrift; Advocate, The; Alabama Literary Review; Amelia; Amherst Review, The; Antietam Review; Anything That Moves; Arnazella; Art:Mag; Arts Indiana Literary Supplement; Atlantis (Nova Scotia); Aura Literary/Arts Review; Bakunin; Bella Figura, La; Belles Lettres; Blatant Artifice; Blue Ryder; Bridge, The; Broomstick; Brownbag Press; Callaloo; Calyx; Carousel Literary Arts Magazine; Central Park; Chakra; Changing Men; Chapter One; Chattahoochee Review, The; City Scriptum; Clifton Magazine; Coe Review, The; Collages and Bricolages; Communities: Journal of Cooperation; Compost Newsletter; Corona; Crucible; Daughters of Sarah; Dead Tree Product; Earth's Daughters; Elf: Eclectic Literary Forum; Emrys Journal; Epiphany; Event; Farmer's Market, The; Fiction; Fighting Woman News; Five Fingers Review; Fritz; Gamut, The; Groundswell; Gulf Coast; Gulf Stream Magazine; Gypsy; Hayden's Ferry Review; Heresies; Herspectives; Hobo Jungle; Hurricane Alice; Iowa Woman; ipsissima verba/the very words; Iris; Jeopardy; K; Kennesaw Review; Kenyon Review, The; Kiosk; Left-Footed Wombat; Limestone: A Literary Journal; Little Magazine, The; Long Shot; Long Story, The; Lost Creek Letters; Mati; Metropolitain; Midland; Minnesota Review, The; Mobius; Moon; Moving Out; Nahant Bay; NCASA News; Negative Capability; No Newz; North Dakota Quarterly; Northwest Review; Notes From The Southwest; Onionhead; Oxalis; Oxford Magazine; Oyez Review; Painted Bride Quarterly; Palace Corbie; Paper Bag, The; Perceptions; Pinehurst Journal, The; Poetic Space; Poetry Forum Short Stories; Poetry Motel; Portable Wall, The; Poskisnolt Press; Pottersfield Portfolio, The; Primal Voices; Primavera; Prisoners of the Night; Psychotrain; Rag Mag; Rainbow City Express; Re Arts & Letters; Red Cedar Review; Renegade; Renovated Lighthouse Publications; Response; River Styx; Riverwind; Rockford Review, The; Rohwedder; Salmon Magazine; Salome; Salt Lick Press; Samisdat; Sanskrit; Seattle Review, The; Shattered Wig Review; Side Show; Sing Heavenly Muse!; Sinister Wisdom; Sisyphus; Skylark; Snake Nation Review; Southern Exposure; Southern Humanities Review; Sozoryoku; SPIT Magazine; SPSM&H; Struggle; Studio One; Third Woman; 13th Moon; Tributary; Two-Ton Santa; Valley Women's Voice; Videomania; Village Idiot, The; Vincent Brothers Review, The; Virginia Quarterly Review; Willow Review; Wisconsin Restaurateur, The; Witness (Michigan); Woman of Power; Words of Wisdom; Writers' Bar-B-Q, The; Writer's Guidelines; Yellow Silk; Zero Hour

Gay. ACM, (Another Chicago Magazine); Adrift; Amelia; Amherst Review, The; Anything That Moves; Arnazella; Art:Mag; Arts Indiana Literary Supplement; Bahlasti Paper; Bakunin; Blatant Artifice; Blue Ryder; Brownbag Press; Carousel Literary Arts Magazine; Central Park; Chakra; Changing Men; Chattahoochee Review, The; City Scriptum; Coe Review, The; Compost Newsletter; Corona; Crazyquilt; Crucible; Dead Tree Product; Deuterium; Evergreen Chronicles, The; Fag Rag; Fish Drum Magazine; Five Fingers Review; Fritz; Groundswell; Gulf Coast; Gulf Stream Magazine; Hayden's Ferry Review; Kennesaw Review; Kenyon Review, The; Kiosk; Left-Footed Wombat; Libido; Little Magazine, The; Long Shot; Metropolitain; Minnesota Review, The; Mobius; Moon; Nahant Bay; NCASA News; No Newz; North East ARTS Magazine; Northwest Gay & Lesbian Reader, The; Onionhead; Oxalis; Oxford Magazine; Painted Bride Quarterly; Palace Corbie; Pinehurst Journal, The; Poetic Space; Poetry Motel; Poskisnolt Press; Pottersfield Portfolio, The; Primal Voices; Primavera; Prisoners of the Night; Psychotrain; Puckerbrush Review; Renovated Lighthouse Publications; River Styx; Salmon Magazine; Salt Lick Press; Samisdat; Sanskrit; Seattle Review, The; Sensations; Shattered Wig Review; Side Show; Sign of the Times; Sisyphus; Snake Nation Review; Southern Exposure; SPIT Magazine; SPSM&H; This Magazine; Two-Ton Santa; Village Idiot, The; White Review, The James; Worm; Writers' Bar-B-Q, The; Yellow Silk; Zero Hour

Historical. Advocate, The; Agora; Alabama Literary Review; Amelia; Amherst Review, The; Anything That Moves; Appalachian Heritage; Archae; Arnazella; Art:Mag; Atalantik; Black Writer Magazine; Blue Ryder; Breakthrough!; Callaloo; Caribbean Writer, The; Central Park; Chapter One; Chrysalis; City Scriptum; Cochran's Corner; Concho River Review; Crazyquilt; Crime Club; Dan River Anthology; Daughters of Sarah; Dead Tree Product; Deuterium; Dream International/Quarterly; Ecphorizer, The; 11th Street Ruse; Elf: Eclectic Literary Forum; Fritz; Gettysburg Review, The; Gotta Write Network Litmag; Hayden's Ferry Review; Hobo Jungle; Housewife-Writer's Forum; Humerus; Hyperbole; Imagine!; Indian Youth of America Newsletter; ipsissima verba/the very words; Journal of Regional Criticism; Kenyon Review, The; Lake Effect; Language Bridges Quarterly; Left Curve; Legend; Lighthouse; Linington Lineup; Lite Magazine; Llamas Magazine; MacGuffin, The; Merlyn's Pen; Midland; Mind Matters Review; Minnesota Review, The; Miorita; Mobius; Monocacy Valley Review, The; Mountain Laurel, The; Nahant Bay; Nassau Review; Negative Capability; New Methods; No Newz; Nomos; North Atlantic Review; North Dakota Quarterly; North East ARTS Magazine; Northern Arizona Mandala; Notebook/Cnaderno: A Literary Journal; Oak, The; Ouroboros; Oxalis; Painted Hills Review; Palace Corbie; Pinehurst Journal, The; Pipe Smoker's Ephemeris, The; Plowman, The; Poetry Forum Short Stories; Portable Wall, The; Potpourri; Primal Voices; Prophetic Voices; Queen's Quarterly; Re Arts & Letters; Renegade; Renovated Lighthouse Publications; Response; Review La Booche; Riverwind; Rockford Review, The; Samisdat; Seattle Review, The; Sensations; Shawnee Silhouette; Short Stuff Magazine for Grown-ups; Sisyphus; South Hill Gazette, The; Sozoryoku; Spectrum (Massachusetts); Spindrift; SPIT Magazine; SPSM&H; Struggle; Sycamore Review; Tampa Review; Thumbprints; Tributary; Tucumcari Literary

Review; Ultimate Writer, The; Village Idiot, The; Villager, The; Vincent Brothers Review, The; Vintage Northwest; Westview; Willow Review; Wisconsin Academy Review; Words of Wisdom; Wordsmith; Worm; Writers' Bar-B-Q, The; Writer's Guidelines; Xavier Review; Yesterday's Magazette

Horror. Aberations; Abyss Magazine; Advocate, The; Amateur Writers Journal; Amherst Review, The; Art:Mag; Arts Indiana Literary Supplement; Bahlasti Paper; Being; Belletrist Review, The; Blind Iguana Press; Bloodreams; Bone Saw; Brownbag Press; Bvi-Pacifica Newsletter; Carousel Literary Arts Magazine; Champagne Horror; Chapter One; Cimmerian Journal; City Scriptum; Clifton Magazine; Cochran's Corner; Crime Club; D.C.; Dagger of the Mind; Dan River Anthology; Dark Tome; Dead Tree Product; Deathrealm; Dream International/Quarterly; Dreams & Nightmares; Encounters Magazine; Event; Eyes; Forbidden Lines; Grasslands Review; Haunts; Hippo; Hor-Tasy; Hyperbole; Imagine!; Journal of Regional Criticism; Kennesaw Review; Left-Footed Wombat; Lite Magazine; Long Shot; Lost; Lost Worlds; Mage, The; Merlyn's Pen; Midland; Midnight Zoo; Miss Lucy Westenra Society of the Undead, The; Mobius; Moon; Nahant Bay; Next Phase; No Idea Magazine; No Newz; Nocturnal Lyric, The; Northern Arizona Mandala; Nuclear Fiction; Ouroboros; Oxalis; Palace Corbie; Paper Bag, The; Pinehurst Journal, The; PLOTS Magazine; Primal Voices; Psychotrain; Pub, The; Pulphouse; Renegade; Riverwind; Salmon Magazine; Seattle Review, The; Sensations; Short Story Digest, The; Silver Web, The; Small Hours, The; Snake Nation Review; Sozoryoku; SPIT Magazine; SPSM&H; Square One; Starsong; Terror Time Again; Thin Ice; 2 AM Magazine; Two-Ton Santa; Ultimate Writer, The; Unsilenced Voice, The; Videomania; Virgin Meat; Weirdbook; Wordsmith; Writers' Bar-B-Q, The; Writer's Guidelines

Humor/Satire. Aberations; ACM, (Another Chicago Magazine); Advocate, The; Agora; Alabama Literary Review; Amateur Writers Journal; Amelia; Amherst Review, The; Anything That Moves; Ararat Quarterly; Archae; Arnazella; Art:Mag; Arts Indiana Literary Supplement; Atalantik; Atrocity; Azorean Express, The; Baby Sue; Bad Haircut; Bahlasti Paper; Belles Lettres; Belletrist Review, The; Black Jack; Black River Review; Blatant Artifice; Blind Iguana Press; Blue Ryder; Blueline; Breakthrough!; Bridge, The; Brownbag Press; Bvi-Pacifica Newsletter; Callaloo; Canadian Author & Bookman; Caribbean Writer, The; Carousel Literary Arts Magazine; Cathedral of Insanity; Center Magazine; Chakra; Chaminade Literary Review; Changing Men; Chapter One; Chattahoochee Review, The; Chiron Review; City Scriptum; Clifton Magazine; Clockwatch Review; Cochran's Corner; Collages and Bricolages; Companion in Zeor, A; Compost Newsletter; Concho River Review; Corona; Crazyquilt; Cream City Review, The; Crime Club; D.C.; Dan River Anthology; Dead Tree Product; Dream International/Quarterly; Dreams & Nightmares; Eidos; 11th Street Ruse; Elf: Eclectic Literary Forum; Escapist, The; Explorations '92; Farmer's Market, The; Fat Tuesday; Fiction; Five Fingers Review; Forbidden Lines; Friction; Fritz; G.W. Review, The; Gamut, The; Gettysburg Review, The; Gotta Write Network Litmag; Grasslands Review; Green Mountains Review; Green's Magazine; Groundswell; Gulf Coast; Gulf Stream Magazine; Hawaii Pacific Review; Hawaii Review; Hayden's Ferry Review; Heartlands Today, The; Helter Skelter; High Plains Literary Review; Hill and Holler; Hippo; Hobo Jungle; Hobson's Choice; Housewife-Writer's Forum; Howling Dog; Humerus; Hyperbole; Imagine!; Inlet; Iowa Woman; ipsissima verba/the very words; Jeopardy; Journal of Polymorphous Perversity; Journal of Regional Criticism; K; Kaleidoscope; Kennesaw Review; Kenyon Review, The; Kiosk; Lake Effect; Language Bridges Quarterly; Leading Edge, The; Ledge Poetry and Fiction Magazine, The; Left Curve; Left-Footed Wombat; Lighthouse; Limestone: A Literary Journal; Lite Magazine; Little Magazine, The; Llamas Magazine; Long Shot; Lost Creek Letters; MacGuffin, The; Mark; Maryland Review, The; Merlyn's Pen; Metropolitain; MidCoaster, The; Mind in Motion; Mindscapes; Minnesota Ink; Mississippi Review; Mobius; Monocacy Valley Review, The; Monthly Independent Tribune . . . , The; Moody Street Review, The; Moon; Mountain Laurel, The; Nahant Bay; NCASA News; Nebraska Review, The; New Delta Review; New Letters Magazine; New Press, The; new renaissance, the; Night Owl's Newsletter; No Idea Magazine; No Newz; Nocturnal Lyric, The; Nomos; North Dakota Quarterly; Northern Arizona Mandala; Notebook/Cnaderno: A Literary Journal; Oak, The; Onionhead; Other Voices; Ouroboros; Oxalis; Oxford Magazine; P.I. Magazine; P.U.N. (Play on Words); Painted Hills Review; Panhandler, The; Pearl; Pegasus Review, The; Pinehurst Journal, The; Pipe Smoker's Ephemeris, The; Poetic Space; Poetry Halifax Dartmouth; Poetry Magic Publications; Poetry Motel; Portable Wall, The; Poskisnolt Press; Potato Eyes; Potpourri; Pottersfield Portfolio, The; Primal Voices; Primavera; Processed World; Psychotrain; Queen's Quarterly; Red Cedar Review; Renegade; Response; River Styx; Riverwind; Rockford Review, The; Ruby's Pearls; Salad; Salome; Samisdat; San Gabriel Valley Magazine; San Jose Studies; Sanskrit; Seattle Review, The; Secret Alameda, The; Sensations; Shattered Wig Review; Shawnee Silhouette; Shockbox; Short Story Digest, The; Short Stuff Magazine for Grown-ups; Side Show; Silver Web, The; Sing Heavenly Muse!; Sisyphus; Skylark; Slate and Style; Slipstream; Snake Nation Review; Snake River Reflections; Sneak Preview, The; South Carolina Review; South Hill Gazette, The; Southern Exposure; Southern Humanities Review; SPIT Magazine; Spoofing!; SPSM&H; Starsong; Struggle; Studio One; Sub-Terrain; Sycamore Review; Syzygy; Tampa Review; Thema; Thin Ice; Thumbprints; Tickled By Thunder; Toad Hiway; Tributary; Tucumcari Literary Review; Turnstile; 2 AM Magazine; Two-Ton Santa; Ultimate Writer, The; Uncle; Unsilenced Voice, The; Verve; Very Small Magazine, A; Videomania; Village Idiot, The; Villager, The;

Vincent Brothers Review, The; Vintage Northwest; Virginia Quarterly Review; Wascana Review; Willow Review; Wisconsin Academy Review; Wisconsin Restaurateur, The; Words of Wisdom; Wordsmith; Worm; Writers' Bar-B-Q, The; Writer's Guidelines; Yellow Silk; Yesterday's Magazette; Zero Hour; Zoiks!

Juvenile. Acorn, The; Advocate, The; Atalantik; Black Scholar, The; Chalk Talk; Chapter One; Cochran's Corner; Creative Kids; Dream International/Quarterly; Lighthouse; Plowman, The; Shattered Wig Review; Spoofing!; Two-Ton Santa; Ultimate Writer, The; Young Judaean; Young Voices Magazine

Lesbian. ACM, (Another Chicago Magazine); Adrift; Amelia; Amherst Review, The; Anything That Moves; Anything That Moves; Arnazella; Art:Mag; Arts Indiana Literary Supplement; Bahlasti Paper; Bakunin; Bella Figura, La; Belles Lettres; Blatant Artifice; Blue Ryder; Brownbag Press; Carousel Literary Arts Magazine; Central Park; Chakra; Changing Men; City Scriptum; Coe Review, The; Common Lives/Lesbian Lives; Compost Newsletter; Corona; Crucible; Dead Tree Product; Evergreen Chronicles, The; Fish Drum Magazine; Five Fingers Review; Fritz; Groundswell; Gulf Coast; Heresies; Herspectives; Hurricane Alice; Iris; Kenyon Review, The; Kiosk; Left-Footed Wombat; Libido; Little Magazine, The; Long Shot; Metropolitain; Minnesota Review, The; Mobius; Moon; Moving Out; Nahant Bay; No Newz; Northwest Gay & Lesbian Reader, The; Onionhead; Oxalis; Oxford Magazine; Painted Bride Quarterly; Palace Corbie; Pinehurst Journal, The; Poetic Space; Poetry Motel; Poskisnolt Press; Pottersfield Portfolio, The; Primavera; Prisoners of the Night; Psychotrain; Renovated Lighthouse Publications; River Styx; Salmon Magazine; Salt Lick Press; Samisdat; Sanskrit; Seattle Review, The; Sensations; Shattered Wig Review; Side Show; Sign of the Times; Sinister Wisdom; Sisyphus; Snake Nation Review; Southern Exposure; SPIT Magazine; SPSM&H; This Magazine; Two-Ton Santa; Valley Women's Voice; Videomania; Village Idiot, The; Visibilities; Worm; Writers' Bar-B-Q, The; Yellow Silk

Literary. Adrift; Advocate, The; Agora; Alabama Literary Review; Alaska Quarterly Review; Alpha Beat Soup; Amaranth Review, The; Amelia; American Fiction; American Literary Review; Americas Review, The; Antaeus; Antietam Review; Antigonish Review, The; Antioch Review; Appalachian Heritage; Ararat Quarterly; Archae; Arnazella; Artemis; Artful Dodge; Art:Mag; Arts Indiana Literary Supplement; Asylum; Aura Literary/Arts Review; Azorean Express, The; Bahlasti Paper; Bakunin; Bamboo Ridge; Being; Bella Figura, La; Belles Lettres; Belletrist Review, The; Bellingham Review, The; Bellowing Ark; Beloit Fiction Journal; Black Jack; Black Mountain Review; Black River Review; Black Warrior Review; Black Writer Magazine; Blind Iguana Press; Blue Light Red Light; Blue Ryder; Blueline; Bluff City; Bone Saw; Breakthrough!; Brownbag Press; Byline; Capilano Review, The; Caribbean Writer, The; Ceilidh; Central Park; Chakra; Chaminade Literary Review; Changing Men; Chapter One; Chariton Review, The; Chattahoochee Review, The; Chicago Review; Chiron Review; Chrysalis; Cimarron Review; Cipher; City Scriptum; Clifton Magazine; Clockwatch Review; Coe Review, The; Collages and Bricolages; Colorado Review; Colorado-North Review; Columbia: A Magazine of Poetry & Prose; Concho River Review; Confrontation; Conjunctions; Corona; Crazyhorse; Crazyquilt; Cream City Review, The; Crime Club; Crosscurrents; Crucible; Dalhousie Review, The; Dan River Anthology; Dandelion Magazine; Dead Tree Product; Denver Quarterly; Descant (Ontario); Descant (Texas); Dream International/Quarterly; Eagle's Flight; Ecphorizer, The; Eldritch Science; Elf: Eclectic Literary Forum; Emrys Journal; Epiphany; Epoch Magazine; Ergo!; Escapist, The; Farmer's Market, The; Fat Tuesday; Fiction; Fiction International; Fiddlehead, The; Fine Madness; Fish Drum Magazine; Five Fingers Review; Flipside; Florida Review, The; Folio: A Literary Journal; Friction; Fritz; G.W. Review, The; Gamut, The; Georgia Review, The; Gettysburg Review, The; Gotta Write Network Litmag; Grasslands Review; Great Stream Review; Green Mountains Review; Green's Magazine; Greensboro Review; Groundswell; Gulf Coast; Gulf Stream Magazine; Gypsy; Habersham Review; Hawaii Pacific Review; Hawaii Review; Hayden's Ferry Review; Heartlands Today, The; Helter Skelter; High Plains Literary Review; Hill and Holler; Hippo; Hobo Jungle; Housewife-Writer's Forum; Howling Dog; Humerus; Hyperbole; Imagine!; Immanent Face Magazine; Indian Youth of America Newsletter; Indiana Review; Inlet; Innisfree; Interim; Iowa Woman; ipsissima verba/the very words; Jacaranda Review; Jeopardy; Journal, The (Ohio); Journal of Regional Criticism; K; Kaleidoscope; Kalliope; Karamu; Kennesaw Review; Kenyon Review, The; Kings Review; Lactuca; Lake Effect; Language Bridges Quarterly; Laurel Review, The; Ledge Poetry and Fiction Magazine, The; Limestone: A Literary Journal; Linington Lineup; Lite Magazine; Literary Review, The; Little Magazine, The; Long Story, The; Lost and Found Times; Lost Creek Letters; Louisiana Literature; Lynx; MacGuffin, The; Magic Changes; Magic Realism; Manoa; Mark; Maryland Review, The; Mati; Merlyn's Pen; Metropolitain; Michigan Quarterly Review; Mid-American Review; MidCoaster, The; Midland; Mind in Motion; Mind Matters Review; Mindscapes; Minnesota Review, The; Miorita; Mississippi Review; Mississippi Valley Review; Missouri Review, The; Mobius; Monocacy Valley Review, The; Moody Street Review, The; Moon; Nahant Bay; Nassau Review; NCASA News; Nebo; Nebraska Review, The; Negative Capability; New Delta Review; New Laurel Review; New Letters Magazine; New Mexico Humanities Review; New Orleans Review; New Press, The; New Quarterly, The; new renaissance, the; New Virginia Review; Nexus; Night Owl's Newsletter; No Newz; North American Review, The; North Dakota Quarterly; North East ARTS Magazine; Northern Arizona Mandala; Notebook/Cnaderno: A Literary Journal;

Notes From The Southwest; Now & Then; NRG; Nuez, La; Ohio Review, The; Old Hickory Review; Old Red Kimono, The; Onionhead; Other Voices; Ouroboros; Outerbridge; Oxalis; Oxford Magazine; Oyez Review; Painted Bride Quarterly; Painted Hills Review; Palace Corbie; Panhandler, The; Paper Bag, The; Paper Radio; Paris Review, The; Partisan Review; Pearl; Pegasus Review, The; Pennsylvania English; Phoebe; Pikestaff Forum, The; Pikeville Review; Pinehurst Journal, The; Pipe Smoker's Ephemeris, The; Ploughshares; Plowman, The; Poetic Space; Poetry Forum Short Stories; Poetry Motel; Pointed Circle, The; Portable Wall, The; Porter International, Bern; Poskisnolt Press; Potato Eyes; Potpourri; Primal Voices; Primavera; Prism International; Prisoners of the Night; Processed World; Psychotrain; Pub, The; Puckerbrush Review; Puerto Del Sol; Quarry; Quarterly West; Queen's Quarterly; Radio Void; Rag Mag; Red Cedar Review; Renegade; Renovated Lighthouse Publications; Response; Review La Booche; Review, Latin American Literature and Arts; River Styx; Rockford Review, The; Rohwedder; Salad; Salmon Magazine; Salome; Salt Lick Press; Samisdat; San Jose Studies; Sanskrit; Santa Monica Review; Secret Alameda, The; Seems; Sensations; Sequoia; Sewanee Review, The; Shawnee Silhouette; Shockbox; Shooting Star Review; Side Show; Signal, The; Silverfish Review; Sing Heavenly Muse!; Sisyphus; Skylark; Slipstream; Snake Nation Review; Snake River Reflections; Sonora Review; South Carolina Review; South Dakota Review; Southern Exposure; Southern Review, The; Sozoryoku; Spirit That Moves Us, The; SPIT Magazine; SPSM&H; Story; Stroker Magazine; Struggle; Studio One; Sub-Terrain; Sycamore Review; Syzygy; Tampa Review; Thema; This Magazine; Tickled By Thunder; Tributary; Tucumcari Literary Review; Turnstile; Twopenny Porringer, The; Underpass; Valley Grapevine; Verve; Villager, The; Vincent Brothers Review, The; Wascana Review; Washington Review; Webster Review; Welter; West Branch; Westview; Widener Review, The; Willow Review; Wind Magazine; Wisconsin Academy Review; Witness (Michigan); Wordsmith; Worm; Writers' Bar-B-Q, The; Writers' Forum; Writer's Guidelines; Yellow Silk; Zyzzyva

Mainstream. Acorn, The; Advocate, The; Amateur Writers Journal; Amelia; American Literary Review; Amherst Review, The; Archae; Arnazella; Art:Mag; Arts Indiana Literary Supplement; Atalantik; Belletrist Review, The; Bellowing Ark; Beloit Fiction Journal; Black Warrior Review; Blind Iguana Press; Bridge, The; Brownbag Press; Caribbean Writer, The; Chapter One; Chattahoochee Review, The; Chrysalis; Cipher; City Scriptum; Clockwatch Review; Collages and Bricolages; Colorado Review; Crazyquilt; Crime Club; Dan River Anthology; Dead Tree Product; Deuterium; Dream International/Quarterly; Eagle's Flight; Ecphorizer, The; 11th Street Ruse; Elf: Eclectic Literary Forum; Emrys Journal; Eyes; Folio: A Literary Journal; G.W. Review, The; Gamut, The; Gettysburg Review, The; Gotta Write Network Litmag; Grain; Great Stream Review; Green Mountains Review; Green's Magazine; Groundswell; Gulf Stream Magazine; Habersham Review; Hawaii Pacific Review; Hayden's Ferry Review; Heartlands Today, The; Helter Skelter; High Plains Literary Review; Hippo; Hobo Jungle; Housewife-Writer's Forum; Howling Dog; Hyperbole; Imagine!; Indiana Review; Inlet; Innisfree; ipsissima verba/the very words; Iris; Jacaranda Review; Jeopardy; Journal, The (Pennsylvania); Journal of Regional Criticism; K; Kennesaw Review; Kenyon Review, The; Lactuca; Lake Effect; Ledge Poetry and Fiction Magazine, The; Lighthouse; Limestone: A Literary Journal; Lost Creek Letters; Louisiana Literature; MacGuffin, The; Manoa; Maryland Review, The; Merlyn's Pen; Metropolitain; Mindscapes; Minnesota Ink; Mobius; Monocacy Valley Review, The; Moody Street Review, The; Nahant Bay; Nassau Review; NCASA News; Nebo; Nebraska Review, The; New Delta Review; New Letters Magazine; New Methods; New Pathways; New Press, The; New Virginia Review; No Newz; North Atlantic Review; Northern Arizona Mandala; Notes From The Southwest; Oak, The; Old Hickory Review; Ouroboros; Oxalis; Panhandler, The; Paper Bag, The; Pearl; Pennsylvania English; Phoebe; Pinehurst Journal, The; Plowman, The; Poetry Forum Short Stories; Portable Wall, The; Poskisnolt Press; Potato Eyes; Potpourri; Pottersfield Portfolio, The; Puerto Del Sol; Queen's Quarterly; Radio Void; Rag Mag; Renegade; Renovated Lighthouse Publications; Review La Booche; River Styx; Riverwind; Ruby's Pearls; Samisdat; Sanskrit; Seattle Review, The; Sensations; Shawnee Silhouette; Short Story Digest, The; Short Stuff Magazine for Grown-ups; Side Show; Sisyphus; Skylark; Slipstream; Snake Nation Review; Sozoryoku; Spectrum (Massachusetts); SPIT Magazine; SPSM&H; Square One; Story; Studio One; Sycamore Review; Tampa Review; Thema; This Magazine; Thumbprints; Tickled By Thunder; Tucumcari Literary Review; Ultimate Writer, The; Verve; Videomania; Village Idiot, The; Vincent Brothers Review, The; Westview; Whetstone; Widener Review, The; Wisconsin Academy Review; Words of Wisdom; Wordsmith; Writers' Bar-B-Q, The; Writer's Guidelines; Yesterday's Magazette

Preschool/Picture Book. Acorn, The; Chapter One; Cochran's Corner; Corona; Plowman, The

Prose Poem. Aberations; ACM, (Another Chicago Magazine); Acorn, The; Advocate, The; Agni; Alabama Literary Review; Alaska Quarterly Review; Alpha Beat Soup; Amelia; Amherst Review, The; Antaeus; Antietam Review; Antigonish Review, The; Archae; Argonaut; Arnazella; Artful Dodge; Art:-Mag; Arts Indiana Literary Supplement; Asylum; Bad Haircut; Bakunin; Being; Bella Figura, La; Beloit Fiction Journal; Black Warrior Review; Black Writer Magazine; Blind Iguana Press; Blue Light Red Light; Blue Ryder; Blueline; Bluff City; Bogg; Bone Saw; Boulevard; Brownbag Press; Callaloo; Capilano Review, The; Caribbean Writer, The; Carousel Literary Arts Magazine; Ceilidh; Center Magazine; Central Park; Chakra; Chapter One; Cipher; City Scriptum; Clifton Magazine; Clockwatch Review; Cochran's Corner; Collages and Bricolages; Colorado-North Review; Companion in Zeor, A; Confrontation; Corona; Cream City Review, The; Crime Club; D.C.; Dan River Anthology; Dead Tree Product; Deuterium; Dream International/Quarterly; Ecphorizer, The; Elf: Eclectic Literary Forum; Eotu; Escapist, The; Explorer Magazine; Eyes; Fat Tuesday; Fine Madness; Fish Drum Magazine; Five Fingers Review; Folio: A Literary Journal; Fritz; G.W. Review, The; Gamut, The; Gotta Write Network Litmag; Grain; Grasslands Review; Hawaii Review; Hayden's Ferry Review; Hippo; Hobo Jungle; Hyperbole; Imagine!; Imminent Face Magazine; ipsissima verba/the very words; Jacaranda Review; Jeopardy; Journal of Regional Criticism; Kaleidoscope; Kenyon Review, The; Kings Review; Kiosk; Lactuca; Language Bridges Quarterly; Leading Edge, The; Ledge Poetry and Fiction Magazine, The; Left Curve; Left-Footed Wombat; Lighthouse; Limestone: A Literary Journal; Little Magazine, The; Long Shot; Lost; Lost and Found Times; Louisville Review, The; Lynx; MacGuffin, The; Madison Review, The; Magic Changes; Metropolitain; Mid-American Review; MidCoaster, The; Midland; Midnight Zoo; Mind in Motion; Mind Matters Review; Mobius; Monocacy Valley Review, The; Moon; Mythic Circle, The; Nahant Bay; NCASA News; Negative Capability; New Delta Review; New Press, The; new renaissance, the; Nimrod; No Newz; North East ARTS Magazine; Northern Arizona Mandala; Now & Then; NRG; Oak, The; Onionhead; Oxalis; Painted Bride Quarterly; Painted Hills Review; Paper Bag, The; Paper Radio; Partisan Review; Pearl; Pegasus Review, The; Perceptions; Phoebe; Pikeville Review; Pinehurst Journal, The; Ploughshares; Plowman, The; Poetic Space; Poetry Forum Short Stories; Poetry Halifax Dartmouth; Poetry Magic Publications; Poetry Motel; Pointed Circle, The; Portable Wall, The; Porter International, Bern; Poskisnolt Press; Potpourri; Pottersfield Portfolio, The; Prairie Fire; Prairie Journal of Canadian Literature, The; Primal Voices; Prism International; Prisoners of the Night; Prophetic Voices; Psychotrain; Puerto Del Sol; Rag Mag; Rainbow City Express; Renegade; Renovated Lighthouse Publications; Response; River Styx; Riverwind; Salmon Magazine; Salome; Samisdat; Sanskrit; Seattle Review, The; Sensations; Shattered Wig Review; Sing Heavenly Muse!; Skylark; Slipstream; Snake Nation Review; Sneak Preview, The; Soundings East; South Hill Gazette, The; Sozoryoku; Spindrift; SPIT Magazine; Starsong; Struggle; Studio One; Syzygy; Tampa Review; Tandava; Thema; This Magazine; Thumbprints; Tickled By Thunder; Toad Hiway; 2 AM Magazine; Twopenny Porringer, The; Two-Ton Santa; Underpass; Unmuzzled Ox; Unsilenced Voice, The; Valley Women's Voice; Verve; Village Idiot, The; Villager, The; Vincent Brothers Review, The; West Branch; Willow Review; Willow Springs; Wisconsin Academy Review; Worcester Review, The; Words of Wisdom; Wordsmith; Wormwood Review, The; Writer's Guidelines; Xavier Review; Zyzzyva

Psychic/Supernatural/Occult. Abyss Magazine; Amherst Review, The; Anything That Moves; Art:Mag; Arts Indiana Literary Supplement; Atalantik; Bahlasti Paper; Being; Bloodreams; Brownbag Press; Bvi-Pacifica Newsletter; Cathedral of Insanity; Chakra; Chapter One; City Scriptum; Coe Review, The; Compost Newsletter; Corona; Crime Club; D.C.; Dan River Anthology; Dark Tome; Dead Tree Product; Deathrealm; Dream International/Quarterly; Ecphorizer, The; Epiphany; Fat Tuesday; Forbidden Lines; Golden Isis Magazine; Haunts; Hayden's Ferry Review; Heaven Bone; Hippo; Humerus; Imagine!; ipsissima verba/the very words; Journal of Regional Criticism; Kennesaw Review; Left-Footed Wombat; Lite Magazine; Long Shot; Lost; Lost Worlds; MacGuffin, The; Midland; Midnight Zoo; Monthly Independent Tribune . . . , The; Moon; Nahant Bay; Negative Capability; No Newz; Nocturnal Lyric, The; Ouroboros; Pablo Lennis; Palace Corbie; Perceptions; PLOTS Magazine; Poskisnolt Press; Prisoners of the Night; Psychotrain; Pub, The; Rainbow City Express; Renegade; Renovated Lighthouse Publications; San Gabriel Valley Magazine; Seattle Review, The; Shattered Wig Review; Short Story Digest, The; Silver Web, The; Snake Nation Review; Sozoryoku; SPIT Magazine; Starsong; Thema; Thin Ice; Tickled By Thunder; 2 AM Magazine; Unsilenced Voice, The; Weirdbook; Wordsmith; Writers' Bar-B-Q, The; Writer's Guidelines; Zero Hour; Zoiks!

Regional. Acorn, The; Advocate, The; Agora; Alabama Literary Review; Amherst Review, The; Appalachian Heritage; Arnazella; Artemis; Art:Mag; Arts Indiana Literary Supplement; Aura Literary/Arts Review; Azorean Express, The; Belletrist Review, The; Blueline; Breakthrough!; Bridge, The; Callaloo; Chapter One; Chattahoochee Review, The; Cicada; Clifton Magazine; Clockwatch Review; Coe Review, The; Concho River Review; Confrontation; Corona; Cream City Review, The; Crime Club; Crucible; Dan River Anthology; Descant (Texas); Deuterium; Ecphorizer, The; Elf: Eclectic Literary Forum; Emrys Journal; Event; Farmer's Market, The; Fish Drum Magazine; Five Fingers Review; Gamut, The; Gettysburg Review, The; Grasslands Review; Great Stream Review; Green Mountains Review; Groundswell; Gulf Coast; Gulf Stream Magazine; Habersham Review; Hawaii Pacific Review; Hawaii Review; Hayden's Ferry Review; Heartlands Today, The; Heaven Bone; High Plains Literary Review; Hill and Holler; Hippo; Hobo Jungle; Imagine!; Innisfree; Iowa Woman; ipsissima verba/the very words; Japanophile; Jeopardy; Journal of Regional Criticism; Kennesaw Review; Lactuca; Lake Effect; Left Curve; Left-Footed Wombat; Lighthouse; Louisiana Literature; Manoa; Mark; Merlyn's Pen; Metropolitain; MidCoaster, The; Middle Eastern Dancer; Midland; Minnesota Ink; Miorita; Monocacy Valley Review, The; Moody Street Review, The; Mountain Laurel, The; Nahant Bay; NCASA News; Negative Capability;

New Methods; New Mexico Humanities Review; Nexus; No Newz; Notebook/Cnaderno: A Literary Journal; Notes From The Southwest; Now & Then; Oak, The; Onionhead; Oxalis; Oyez Review; Painted Hills Review; Partisan Review; Phoebe; Plowman, The; Poetic Space; Pointed Circle, The; Portable Wall, The; Potato Eyes; Pottersfield Portfolio, The; Prairie Journal of Canadian Literature, The; Primal Voices; Rag Mag; Re Arts & Letters; Red Cedar Review; Renovated Lighthouse Publications; Response; River-wind; Rockford Review, The; Rohwedder; Salad; Salmon Magazine; Samisdat; San Jose Studies; Sanskrit; Seattle Review, The; Sensations; Shattered Wig Review; Shawnee Silhouette; Shooting Star Review; Short Stuff Magazine for Grown-ups; Skylark; Snake Nation Review; Snake River Reflections; Sneak Preview, The; South Dakota Review; South Hill Gazette, The; Southern Exposure; Southern Humanities Review; Sozoryoku; Spindrift; SPIT Magazine; Spoofing!; SPSM&H; Struggle; Studio One; Sycamore Review; Thema; This Magazine; Thumbprints; Tributary; Tucumcari Literary Review; Turnstile; Vincent Brothers Review, The; Washington Review; Widener Review, The; Willow Review; Wind Magazine; Wisconsin Academy Review; Words of Wisdom; Writers' Bar-B-Q, The; Writers' Forum; Writer's Guidelines; Xavier Review; Zyzzyva

Religious. Acorn, The; Agora; Amateur Writers Journal; Ararat Quarterly; Arnazella; Being; Beloit Fiction Journal; Black Writer Magazine; Breakthrough!; Carousel Literary Arts Magazine; Chakra; Chaminade Literary Review; Chapter One; Cochran's Corner; Crime Club; Daughters of Sarah; Dreams & Visions; Escapist, The; Explorer Magazine; Heaven Bone; Helter Skelter; Journal of Regional Criti-cism; Language Bridges Quarterly; Left-Footed Wombat; Mosaic; New Press, The; Now & Then; Oak, The; Pablo Lennis; Painted Hills Review; Palace Corbie; Pegasus Review, The; Perceptions; Plowman, The; Poetry Forum Short Stories; Queen of All Hearts; Rainbow City Express; Reconstructionist; Rene-gade; Response; Riverwind; Skylark; Starlight; Tickled By Thunder; Two-Ton Santa; Ultimate Writer, The; Valley Women's Voice; Vintage Northwest; Wordsmith; Writer's Guidelines; Xavier Review; Yes-terday's Magazette; Young Judaean

Romance. Acorn, The; Advocate, The; Amateur Writers Journal; Amherst Review, The; Atalantik; Aura Literary/Arts Review; Breakthrough!; Carousel Literary Arts Magazine; Chapter One; Cochran's Corner; Corona; Dan River Anthology; Deuterium; Dream International/Quarterly; Eagle's Flight; Epiphany; Explorer Magazine; Gotta Write Network Litmag; Hayden's Ferry Review; Helter Skelter; Housewife-Writer's Forum; Imagine!; ipsissima verba/the very words; Jeopardy; Journal of Regional Criticism; Ledge Poetry and Fiction Magazine, The; Lighthouse; Merlyn's Pen; Minnesota Ink; Negative Capability; North-ern Arizona Mandala; Notes From The Southwest; Oak, The; Oxalis; Peoplenet; Plowman, The; Poetry Forum Short Stories; Poskisnolt Press; Post, The; Potpourri; PSI; Renegade; Salome; Sensations; Shaw-nee Silhouette; Short Stuff Magazine for Grown-ups; South Hill Gazette, The; SPSM&H; Thumbprints; Ultimate Writer, The; Village Idiot, The; Villager, The; Virginia Quarterly Review; Wordsmith; Writer's Guidelines

Science Fiction. Aberations; Abyss Magazine; Acorn, The; Advocate, The; Agora; Alabama Literary Review; Amateur Writers Journal; Amelia; Amherst Review, The; Anything That Moves; Argonaut; Arnazella; Art:Mag; Arts Indiana Literary Supplement; Atalantik; Aura Literary/Arts Review; Bahlasti Paper; Being; Belles Lettres; Beyond; Blind Iguana Press; Bone Saw; Bravo Mundo Nuevo; Bvi-Pacifica Newsletter; Callaloo; Carousel Literary Arts Magazine; Ceilidh; Chakra; Chapter One; Chrysalis; Cimme-rian Journal; City Scriptum; Cochran's Corner; Coe Review, The; Collages and Bricolages; Communities: Journal of Cooperation; Companion in Zeor, A; Compost Newsletter; Cosmic Landscapes; Crazyquilt; Crime Club; Dagger of the Mind; Dan River Anthology; Dead Tree Product; Deathrealm; Deuterium; Dream International/Quarterly; Dreams & Nightmares; Ecphorizer, The; Eldritch Science; Elf: Eclectic Literary Forum; Encounters Magazine; Epiphany; Escapist, The; Explorer Magazine; Fighting Woman News; Figment Magazine; Fish Drum Magazine; Forbidden Lines; Gotta Write Network Litmag; Grass-lands Review; Green's Magazine; Hawaii Pacific Review; Hayden's Ferry Review; Helter Skelter; Hippo; Hobo Jungle; Hobson's Choice; Humerus; Hyperbole; Imagine!; Immanent Face Magazine; Innisfree; ipsissima verba/the very words; Jeopardy; Journal of Regional Criticism; K; Leading Edge, The; Left Curve; Left-Footed Wombat; Lite Magazine; Long Shot; Lost Creek Letters; Lost Worlds; MacGuffin, The; Mage, The; Magic Changes; Mark; Mati; Merlyn's Pen; Midland; Midnight Zoo; Mind in Motion; Minnesota Ink; Minnesota Review, The; Mobius; Nahant Bay; Negative Capability; Neophyte; New Methods; New Pathways; Next Phase; Nimrod; No Idea Magazine; No Newz; Nocturnal Lyric, The; Nomos; Northern Arizona Mandala; Nuclear Fiction; Once Upon A World; Other Worlds; Ouroboros; Oxalis; Pablo Lennis; Palace Corbie; Pandora; Paper Radio; Perceptions; Poetry Forum Short Stories; Poetry Motel; Portable Wall, The; Potpourri; Pottersfield Portfolio, The; Primavera; Prisoners of the Night; Processed World; Pulphouse; Pulsar; Quarry; Queen's Quarterly; Re Arts & Letters; Renegade; Renovated Lighthouse Publications; Riverside Quarterly; Salmon Magazine; Salome; Samisdat; Sanskrit; Seattle Review, The; Sensations; Shawnee Silhouette; Short Story Digest, The; Sidetrekked; Silver Web, The; Sisyphus; Skylark; Slipstream; Small Hours, The; Snake Nation Review; South Hill Gazette, The; Sozoryoku; Spindrift; SPIT Magazine; SPSM&H; Square One; Starsong; Struggle; Syzygy; Tandava; Thema; Tickled By Thunder; Toad Hiway; 2 AM Magazine; Ultimate Writer, The; Uncle; Village Idiot,

The; Vincent Brothers Review, The; Vision; Wordsmith; Worm; Writers' Bar-B-Q, The; Writer's Guidelines

Senior Citizen/Retirement. Advocate, The; Amelia; Chapter One; Corona; Dan River Anthology; Dream International/Quarterly; Hayden's Ferry Review; Imagine!; ipsissima verba/the very words; Kenyon Review, The; Left-Footed Wombat; Lighthouse; Minnesota Ink; Moving Out; Negative Capability; Northern Arizona Mandala; Oxalis; Plowman, The; Poetry Forum Short Stories; Portable Wall, The; Poskisnolt Press; Primal Voices; Salmon Magazine; Shattered Wig Review; Snake Nation Review; SPIT Magazine; SPSM&H; Struggle; Thumbprints; Tucumcari Literary Review; Two-Ton Santa; Village Idiot, The; Vincent Brothers Review, The; Vintage Northwest; Wordsmith; Writer's Guidelines; Yesterday's Magazette

Serialized/Excerpted Novel. Agni; Alabama Literary Review; Antaeus; Art:Mag; Arts Indiana Literary Supplement; Bahlasti Paper; Bakunin; Bellowing Ark; Black Jack; Blatant Artifice; Bvi-Pacifica Newsletter; Callaloo; Cathedral of Insanity; Ceilidh; Central Park; Coe Review, The; Compost Newsletter; Crazyquilt; Crime Club; Dream International/Quarterly; Ecphorizer, The; Farmer's Market, The; Fat Tuesday; Forbidden Lines; Gettysburg Review, The; Green Mountains Review; Groundswell; Gulf Stream Magazine; Gypsy; Hobo Jungle; Hyperbole; Imagine!; Immanent Face Magazine; ipsissima verba/the very words; K; Kiosk; Lost Worlds; Madison Review, The; Mid-American Review; Mystery Notebook; Nassau Review; NCASA News; New Press, The; New Virginia Review; Northern Arizona Mandala; Notes From The Southwest; Now & Then; Other Voices; Phoebe; Poetic Space; Prairie Journal of Canadian Literature, The; Pub, The; Puerto Del Sol; Quarry; Salome; Samisdat; Seattle Review, The; Shattered Wig Review; Skylark; South Dakota Review; Spindrift; SPIT Magazine; Virginia Quarterly Review; Widener Review, The; Willow Springs; Wordsmith; Writ Magazine; Writers' Bar-B-Q, The; Writer's Guidelines; Xavier Review

Sports. Advocate, The; Aethlon; Amelia; Beloit Fiction Journal; Carousel Literary Arts Magazine; Changing Men; Chapter One; Chrysalis; Elf: Eclectic Literary Forum; Folio: A Literary Journal; Imagine!; ipsissima verba/the very words; Lighthouse; Magic Changes; New Press, The; Now & Then; Oxalis; Portable Wall, The; Primal Voices; Riverwind; Samisdat; Skylark; SPIT Magazine; Sycamore Review; Thema; Thumbprints; Valley Women's Voice; Witness (Michigan); Wordsmith

Suspense/Mystery. Acorn, The; Advocate, The; Alabama Literary Review; Amateur Writers Journal; Amelia; Amherst Review, The; Armchair Detective, The; Arnazella; Art:Mag; Arts Indiana Literary Supplement; Atalantik; Bahlasti Paper; Belles Lettres; Belletrist Review, The; Blind Iguana Press; Breakthrough!; Bvi-Pacifica Newsletter; Byline; Carousel Literary Arts Magazine; Chapter One; Chrysalis; Cimmerian Journal; City Scriptum; Cochran's Corner; Crazyquilt; Crime Club; Dagger of the Mind; Dan River Anthology; Dead Tree Product; Deuterium; Dream International/Quarterly; Eagle's Flight; Ecphorizer, The; 11th Street Ruse; Epiphany; Escapist, The; Folio: A Literary Journal; Grasslands Review; Green's Magazine; Groundswell; Gulf Stream Magazine; Hardboiled; Hawaii Pacific Review; Helter Skelter; Hobo Jungle; Housewife-Writer's Forum; Hyperbole; Imagine!; Innisfree; ipsissima verba/the very words; Left-Footed Wombat; Lighthouse; Linington Lineup; Lite Magazine; Long Shot; Merlyn's Pen; Minnesota Ink; Monthly Independent Tribune . . . , The; Mystery Notebook; Mystery Time; Nahant Bay; Negative Capability; No Idea Magazine; No Newz; Nocturnal Lyric, The; Nomos; Northern Arizona Mandala; Oak, The; Ouroboros; Oxalis; P.I. Magazine; Paper Bag, The; Perceptions; Pinehurst Journal, The; PLOTS Magazine; Poetry Forum Short Stories; Post, The; Potpourri; Prisoners of the Night; PSI; Pub, The; Renegade; Ruby's Pearls; Salmon Magazine; Salome; Samisdat; Seattle Review, The; Sensations; Shawnee Silhouette; Short Story Digest, The; Short Stuff Magazine for Grown-ups; Sing Heavenly Muse!; Sisyphus; Skylark; Snake Nation Review; Snake River Reflections; South Hill Gazette, The; Sozoryoku; SPIT Magazine; SPSM&H; Square One; Struggle; Thema; Tickled By Thunder; Tucumcari Literary Review; 2 AM Magazine; Ultimate Writer, The; Village Idiot, The; Villager, The; Vincent Brothers Review, The; Vintage Northwest; Wordsmith; Writers' Bar-B-Q, The; Writer's Guidelines

Translations. ACM, (Another Chicago Magazine); Adrift; Agni; Alabama Literary Review; Alaska Quarterly Review; Amelia; Amherst Review, The; Antaeus; Antigonish Review, The; Antioch Review; Ararat Quarterly; Archae; Arnazella; Artful Dodge; Art:Mag; Arts Indiana Literary Supplement; Asylum; Atalantik; Bad Haircut; Bakunin; Bella Figura, La; Belles Lettres; Blatant Artifice; Brownbag Press; Callaloo; Ceilidh; Center Magazine; Central Park; Chakra; Chaminade Literary Review; Chariton Review, The; Chattahoochee Review, The; Cicada; Cipher; Coe Review, The; Colorado Review; Columbia; Confrontation; Conjunctions; Cream City Review, The; Descant (Ontario); Dream International/Quarterly; Ecphorizer, The; Epiphany; Escapist, The; Fiction; Fighting Woman News; Fine Madness; Folio: A Literary Journal; G.W. Review, The; Gamut, The; Green Mountains Review; Groundswell; Gulf Coast; Gypsy; Hawaii Pacific Review; Hawaii Review; Hobo Jungle; Hyperbole; Imagine!; Immanent Face Magazine; ipsissima verba/the very words; Jacaranda Review; Jeopardy; Jewish Currents Magazine; Kenyon Review, The; Kiosk; Language Bridges Quarterly; Left Curve; Left-Footed Wombat; Lynx; MacGuffin, The; Manoa; Mati; Metropolitain; Mid-American Review; MidCoaster, The; Midland; Miorita; Mississippi Review; Moody Street Review, The; Moon; Nahant Bay; NCASA News; Negative Capability; New Delta Review; New Laurel Review; New Letters Magazine; New Orleans Review; New Press, The; new renaissance, the; Nexus; Nimrod; Northern Arizona Mandala; Northwest Review; Oxford Magazine; Painted Bride Quarterly; Painted Hills Review; Palace Corbie; Partisan Review; Phoebe; Pikeville Review; Pinehurst Journal, The; Plowman, The; Poetic Space; Portable Wall, The; Porter International, Bern; Primal Voices; Prism International; Psychotrain; Puerto Del Sol; Quarry; Quarterly West; Renegade; Response; River Styx; Riverwind; Rohwedder; Salmon Magazine; Salome: A Journal for the Performing Arts; Samisdat; Sanskrit; Seattle Review, The; Shattered Wig Review; Shooting Star Review; Signal, The; South Dakota Review; Spindrift; SPIT Magazine; SPSM&H; Story; Struggle; Sycamore Review; Tampa Review; Third Woman; Toad Hiway; Translation; Triquarterly; Twopenny Porringer, The; Underground Forest/La Selve Subterránea; Unmuzzled Ox; Village Idiot, The; Vincent Brothers Review, The; Virginia Quarterly Review; Webster Review; West Branch; Willow Springs; Writ Magazine; Writers' Bar-B-Q, The; Xavier Review; Zero Hour; Zoiks!

Western. Advocate, The; Amelia; Amherst Review, The; Arts Indiana Literary Supplement; Azorean Express, The; Black Jack; Carousel Literary Arts Magazine; Chapter One; City Scriptum; Concho River Review; Dan River Anthology; Dead Tree Product; Dream International/Quarterly; Grasslands Review; Hippo; Imagine!; Indian Youth of America Newsletter; ipsissima verba/the very words; Lighthouse; Long Shot; Merlyn's Pen; Minnesota Ink; New Methods; Northern Arizona Mandala; Oxalis; Painted Hills Review; Paper Bag, The; Plowman, The; Poskisnolt Press; Potpourri; Riverwind; Salmon Magazine; Samisdat; San Gabriel Valley Magazine; Seattle Review, The; Short Story Digest, The; Short Stuff Magazine for Grown-ups; Skylark; Snake River Reflections; South Hill Gazette, The; Sozoryoku; SPIT Magazine; SPSM&H; Thema; Tickled By Thunder; Tucumcari Literary Review; Ultimate Writer, The; Valley Grapevine; Village Idiot, The; Westview; Wordsmith

Young Adult/Teen. Acorn, The; Advocate, The; Amateur Writers Journal; Black Scholar, The; Chapter One; Cochran's Corner; Creative Kids; Dream International/Quarterly; Gotta Write Network Litmag; Language Bridges Quarterly; Lighthouse; Merlyn's Pen; Minnesota Ink; No Newz; Painted Hills Review; Plowman, The; Poetry Forum Short Stories; Poskisnolt Press; Reflections; Shattered Wig Review; Shooting Star Review; Spoofing!; Struggle; Wordsmith

Commercial Periodicals

Adventure. Art Times; Bostonia Magazine; Bowbender; Bowhunter Magazine; Boys' Life; Buffalo Spree Magazine; Caffe, Il; Career Focus; Catholic Forester; Cavalier Magazine; Clubhouse; Companion of Saint Francis and St. Anthony, The; Cosmopolitan Magazine; Crusader Magazine; Florida Wildlife; Flyfishing News, Views and Reviews; Gallery Magazine; Georgia Sportsman; Horse Illustrated; Indian Life Magazine; International Bowhunter; Lethbridge Magazine; Modern Gold Miner and Treasure Hunter; Modern Woodmen, The; New Hampshire Life; Plain Dealer Magazine, The; Pockets; Radiance; Ranger Rick Magazine; Road King Magazine; Shofar; Sporting Times; Sports Afield; Trailer Boats Magazine; Western People

Canadian. Atlantic Advocate, The; Bowbender; Canadian Messenger; Chickadee; Companion of Saint Francis and St. Anthony, The; Lethbridge Magazine; Messenger of the Sacred Heart; Out Magazine; Vancouver Child, The; Vision; Western People

Condensed Novel. Arizona Coast; Bostonia Magazine; Buzzworm; Caffe, Il; Campus Life Magazine; Career Focus; Tikkun; Virtue

Confession. Caffe, Il; Indian Life Magazine; Jive; Lady's Circle; Single Scene, The

Contemporary. American Atheist; Art Times; Associate Reformed Presbyterian, The; Atlantic Monthly; Baby Connection News Journal, The; B'nai B'rith International Jewish Monthly, The; Bomb Magazine; Boston Review; Bostonia Magazine; Buffalo Spree Magazine; Caffe, Il; Career Focus; Catholic Forester; Clubhouse; Cosmopolitan Magazine; Family Magazine; First; Good Housekeeping; Harper's Magazine; Inside; Lady's Circle; Mademoiselle Magazine; Military Lifestyle; Modern Woodmen, The; Moment Magazine; Na'amat Woman; New Hampshire Life; Northeast; Orange Coast Magazine; Organica Quarterly; Other Side, The; Oui Magazine; Plain Dealer Magazine, The; Pockets; Portland Magazine; Radiance; Redbook; St. Anthony Messenger; St. Joseph's Messenger and Advocate of the Blind; Sassy Magazine; Shofar; Single Scene, The; Tikkun; Trailer Boats Magazine; Virtue; Western People; Woman's Day

Erotica. Cavalier Magazine; Chic; Contact Advertising; First Hand; Gallery Magazine; Gent; Guys; Hustler Busty Beauties; Manscape; Nugget; Options; Pillow Talk; Private Letters; Radiance; Screw Magazine; Texas Connection Magazine; Turn-on Letters

Ethnic. American Citizen Italian Press, The; Art Times; Baltimore Jewish Times; B'nai B'rith International Jewish Monthly, The; Bomb Magazine; Boston Review; Bostonia Magazine; Buffalo Spree Magazine; Caffe, Il; Career Focus; Catholic Forester; Christmas; Crusader Magazine; Detroit Jewish News; Emerge Magazine; Hadassah Magazine; India Currents; Indian Life Magazine; Inside; Jive; Lilith Magazine; Midstream; Moment Magazine; Organica Quarterly; Other Side, The; Plain Dealer Magazine, The; Pockets; Radiance; Sassy Magazine; Shofar; Tikkun

Experimental. Boston Review; Bostonia Magazine; Career Focus; College Preview; Direct Aim; Journey; Visions; Modern Gold Miner and Treasure Hunter; Organica Quarterly; Other Side, The; Sassy Magazine; Single Scene, The

Fantasy. AMAZING® Stories; Art Times; Asimov's Science Fiction Magazine, Isaac; Buzzworm; Contact Advertising; Dragon Magazine; Emerge Magazine; New Hampshire Life; Omni; Oui Magazine; Pockets; Radiance; Ranger Rick Magazine; Shofar; Single Scene, The; Trailer Boats Magazine; Weird Tales; Woman's Day

Feminist. American Atheist; Art Times; Buffalo Spree Magazine; Catholic Forester; Contact Advertising; Lilith Magazine; Other Side, The; Radiance; Sassy Magazine; Tikkun; Vancouver Child, The; Women's Glibber

Gay. Art Times; Contact Advertising; Drummer; First Hand; Guide Magazine; Guide, The; Guys; In Touch for Men; Manscape; Options; Out Magazine; Sassy Magazine; Tikkun; Xtra Magazine

Historical. American Atheist; American Citizen Italian Press, The; Arizona Coast; Art Times; Atlantic Advocate, The; Beckett Baseball Card Monthly; B'nai B'rith International Jewish Monthly, The; Career Focus; Christmas; Clubhouse; Flyfishing News, Views and Reviews; Indian Life Magazine; Inside; Juggler's World; Lady's Circle; Lethbridge Magazine; Midstream; Modern Gold Miner and Treasure Hunter; Modern Woodmen, The; Moment Magazine; Montana Senior Citizens News; Plain Dealer Magazine, The; Pockets; Portland Magazine; Purpose; Radiance; Tikkun

Horror. AMAZING® Stories; Bostonia Magazine; Cavalier Magazine; Gorezone; Iniquities; New Mystery; Omni; Weird Tales

Humor/Satire. American Atheist; Art Times; Atlantic Advocate, The; Baby Connection News Journal, The; Beckett Baseball Card Monthly; B'nai B'rith International Jewish Monthly, The; Bostonia Magazine; Boys' Life; Buffalo Spree Magazine; Caffe, Il; Campus Life Magazine; Career Focus; Catholic Forester; Companion of Saint Francis and St. Anthony, The; Emerge Magazine; First; Flyfishing News, Views and Reviews; Freeway; Gallery Magazine; Georgia Sportsman; Golf Journal; Harper's Magazine; Home Life; Horse Illustrated; Ideals Magazine; Juggler's World; Lady's Circle; Lethbridge Magazine; Metro Singles Lifestyles; Midstream; Modern Gold Miner and Treasure Hunter; National Lampoon; New Hampshire Life; Oh! Idaho; Orange Coast Magazine; Other Side, The; Oui Magazine; Outlaw Biker; Plain Dealer Magazine, The; Radiance; Ranger Rick Magazine; Reform Judaism; Road King Magazine; St. Joseph's Messenger and Advocate of the Blind; Sassy Magazine; Shofar; Single Scene, The; Singlelife Magazine; Sports Afield; Sunshine Magazine; Tikkun; Trailer Boats Magazine; Virtue; Vista; Western People; Women's Glibber

Juvenile. Associate Reformed Presbyterian, The; Chickadee; Child Life; Children's Digest; Children's Playmate; Clubhouse; Cricket Magazine; Crusader Magazine; Discoveries; Friend Magazine, The; Highlights for Children; Home Altar, The; Humpty Dumpty's Magazine; Indian Life Magazine; Jack and Jill; Junior Trails; Kid City; Kindergarten Listen; Ladybug; Lollipops Magazine; Modern Woodmen, The; My Friend; On the Line; Pockets; R-A-D-A-R; Ranger Rick Magazine; Shofar; Single Parent, The; Sporting Times; Story Friends; Sunshine Magazine; Touch; Turtle Magazine for Preschool Kids; Vancouver Child, The; Wonder Time; Young Crusader, The

Lesbian. Art Times; Contact Advertising; Guide, The; Lilith Magazine; On Our Backs; Options; Oui Magazine; Tikkun; Women's Glibber; Xtra Magazine

Literary. Art Times; Atlantic Monthly; Boston Review; Bostonia Magazine; Buffalo Spree Magazine; Buzzworm; Christmas; Emerge Magazine; First; Gallery Magazine; Inside; Lethbridge Magazine; Lilith Magazine; Metro Singles Lifestyles; Midstream; Na'amat Woman; New Hampshire Life; New Yorker, The; Organica Quarterly; Other Side, The; PEN Syndicated Fiction Project; Singlelife Magazine; Tikkun; Vancouver Child, The; Woman's Day; Yankee Magazine

Mainstream. American Citizen Italian Press, The; Art Times; Baby Connection News Journal, The; Bostonia Magazine; Catholic Forester; Christmas; Companion of Saint Francis and St. Anthony, The; Country America; First; Gallery Magazine; Good Housekeeping; Ladies' Home Journal; Lady's Circle; Midstream; Modern Woodmen, The; New Hampshire Life; New Yorker, The; Other Side, The; Plain Dealer Magazine, The; Portland Magazine; Radiance; St. Joseph's Messenger and Advocate of the Blind; Sassy Magazine; Single Scene, The; Tikkun; Vancouver Child, The

Prose Poem. Appalachia Journal; Baby Connection News Journal, The; Boston Review; Campus Life Magazine; Career Focus; Church Herald, The; Home Life; Ideals Magazine; Kindergarten Listen; Lilith Magazine; Live; Mature Years; Metro Singles Lifestyles; My Friend; Radiance; Sassy Magazine; Shofar; Student Leadership Journal

Psychic/Supernatural/Occult. Emerge Magazine; Iniquities; Lilith Magazine; Plain Dealer Magazine, The; Weird Tales

Regional. Aloha; Atlantic Advocate, The; Boston Review; Bostonia Magazine; Catholic Forester; Chesapeake Bay Magazine; First; Flyfishing News, Views and Reviews; Georgia Sportsman; Lady's Circle; Lethbridge Magazine; New Hampshire Life; Northeast; Oh! Idaho; Palouse Journal; Plain Dealer Magazine, The; Portland Magazine; Sassy Magazine; Sunday Journal Magazine; Vancouver Child, The; Washingtonian, The; Western People; Wy'East Historical Journal; Yankee Magazine

Religious. Alive Now!; Associate Reformed Presbyterian, The; Baltimore Jewish Times; B'nai B'rith International Jewish Monthly, The; Bread; Campus Life Magazine; Canadian Messenger; Christmas; Church Herald, The; Clubhouse; Companion of Saint Francis and St. Anthony, The; Crusader Magazine; Detroit Jewish News; Discoveries; Evangel; Family, The; Freeway; Friend Magazine, The; Gem, The; Hicall; High Adventure; Home Altar, The; Home Life; I.D.; Ideals Magazine; Indian Life Magazine; Inside; Junior Trails; Kindergarten Listen; Lady's Circle; Liguorian; Lilith Magazine; Live; Living with Teenagers; Lookout, The; Lutheran Journal, The; Lutheran Woman Today; Magazine for Christian Youth!; Mature Living; Mature Years; Messenger of the Sacred Heart; Metro Singles Lifestyles; Midstream; Moment Magazine; My Friend; New Era Magazine; On the Line; Other Side, The; Pockets; Purpose; R-A-D-A-R; Reform Judaism; St. Anthony Messenger; St. Joseph's Messenger and Advocate of the Blind; Seek; Shofar; Standard; Story Friends; Straight; Student Leadership Journal; Student, The; Teen Power; Teens Today; Touch; TQ (Teenquest); Virtue; Vision; Vista; With Magazine; Wonder Time; Young Salvationist/Young Soldier

Romance. Baby Connection News Journal, The; Career Focus; Cosmopolitan Magazine; Good Housekeeping; Jive; Lady's Circle; Metro Singles Lifestyles; St. Anthony Messenger; St. Joseph's Messenger and Advocate of the Blind; Virtue; Woman's World Magazine

Science Fiction. Aboriginal Science Fiction; AMAZING® Stories; Analog Science Fiction & Fact; Art Times; Asimov's Science Fiction Magazine, Isaac; Boys' Life; Career Focus; Crusader Magazine; Emerge Magazine; Iniquities; Juggler's World; New Hampshire Life; Omni; Plain Dealer Magazine, The; Radiance; Ranger Rick Magazine; Trailer Boats Magazine

Senior Citizen/Retirement. Arizona Coast; Catholic Forester; Lady's Circle; Lilith Magazine; Mature Living; Mature Years; Modern Gold Miner and Treasure Hunter; Modern Woodmen, The; Montana Senior Citizens News; New Hampshire Life; St. Anthony Messenger; St. Joseph's Messenger and Advocate of the Blind; Sunshine Magazine; Vista

Serialized/Excerpted Novel. Analog Science Fiction & Fact; Arizona Coast; Bomb Magazine; Bostonia Magazine; Caffe, Il; Capper's; Moment Magazine; New Hampshire Life; Hitchcock's Mystery Magazine, Alfred

Sports. Appalachia Journal; Beckett Baseball Card Monthly; Bike Report; Black Belt; Bowbender; Bowhunter Magazine; Boys' Life; Career Focus; Catholic Forester; Crusader Magazine; Emerge Magazine; Florida Wildlife; Flyfisher, The; Flyfishing News, Views and Reviews; Georgia Sportsman; Golf Journal; Horse Illustrated; Inside Texas Running; Insights; International Bowhunter; New York Running News; Outlaw Biker; Plain Dealer Magazine, The; Radiance; Ranger Rick Magazine; Shofar; Sporting Times; Sports Afield; Surfing Magazine; Student Lawyer

Suspense/Mystery. bePuzzled; Bostonia Magazine; Boys' Life; Buffalo Spree Magazine; Career Focus; Catholic Forester; Cosmopolitan Magazine; Emerge Magazine; Gallery Magazine; Horse Illustrated; Iniquities; Modern Gold Miner and Treasure Hunter; New Hampshire Life; New Mystery; Orange Coast Magazine; Other Side, The; Oui Magazine; Plain Dealer Magazine, The; Pockets; Portland Magazine; Queen's Mystery Magazine, Ellery; Radiance; Ranger Rick Magazine; Road King Magazine; Shofar; Single Scene, The; Trailer Boats Magazine; Woman's World Magazine

Translations. American Citizen Italian Press, The; Boston Review; Caffe, Il; India Currents; Inside; Lilith Magazine; Midstream; Moment Magazine; New Hampshire Life; Shofar; Tikkun; Arizona Coast; Boys' Life; Montana Senior Citizens News; Road King Magazine; Woman's Day

Young Adult/Teen. American Newspaper Carrier, The; Associate Reformed Presbyterian, The; Beckett Baseball Card Monthly; Boys' Life; Bread; Campus Life Magazine; Career Focus; Clubhouse; Hicall; High Adventure; Home Life; I.D.; Indian Life Magazine; Insights; Lilith Magazine; Magazine for Christian Youth!; Modern Woodmen, The; New Era Magazine; On the Line; Radiance; Sassy Magazine; Seventeen; Shofar; Sporting Times; Straight; Student, The; Teen Magazine; Teen Power; Teens Today;

ARE YOU SERIOUS?

About learning to write better? Getting published? Getting paid for what you write? If you're dedicated to your writing, **Writer's Digest School** can put you on the fast track to writing success.

You'll Study With A Professional

Writer's Digest School offers you more than textbooks and assignments. As a student you'll correspond <u>directly with a professional writer</u> who is currently writing **and selling** the kind of material that you want to write. You'll learn from a pro who knows from personal experience, what it takes to get a manuscript written and published. A writer who can guide you as you work to achieve the same thing. A true mentor.

Work On Your Novel, Short Story, Nonfiction Book, Or Article

Writer's Digest School offers six courses: The Novel Writing Workshop, the Nonfiction Book Workshop, Writing to Sell Fiction (Short Stories), Writing to Sell Nonfiction (Articles), the Science Fiction and Fantasy Workshops and the Mystery Writing Workshops. Each course is described on the reverse side.

If you're serious about your writing, you owe it to yourself to check out **Writer's Digest School**. Mail the coupon below today for FREE information! Or call **1-800-759-0963**. (Outside the U.S., call (513) 531-2222.) Writer's Digest School, 1507 Dana Avenue, Cincinnati, Ohio 45207-1005.

Reg. #73-0409H

- -

Yes, I'm Serious!

I want to write and sell with the help of the professionals at **Writer's Digest School**. Send me free information about the course I've checked below:

☐ Novel Writing Workshop   ☐ Writing to Sell Fiction (Short Stories)
☐ Nonfiction Book Workshop   ☐ Writing to Sell Nonfiction (Articles)
☐ Science Fiction & Fantasy Workshops   ☐ Mystery Writing Workshops

Name _____

Address _____

City _____ State _____ Zip + 4 _____

Phone: (Day) (_____) _____ (Eve.) (_____) _____

Mail this card today! No postage needed.
Or Call **1-800-759-0963** for free information today.

IWMXX1X2

Here are six **Writer's Digest School** courses to help you write better and sell more:

Novel Writing Workshop. A professional novelist helps you iron out your plot, develop your main characters, write the background for your novel, and complete the opening scene and a summary of your novel's complete story. You'll even identify potential publishers and write a query letter.

Nonfiction Book Workshop. You'll work with your mentor to create a book proposal that you can send directly to a publisher. You'll develop and refine your book idea, write a chapter-by-chapter outline of your subject, line up your sources of information, write sample chapters, and complete your query letter.

Writing to Sell Fiction. Learn the basics of writing/selling short stories: plotting, characterization, dialogue, theme, conflict, and other elements of a marketable short story. Course includes writing assignments and one complete short story.

Writing to Sell Nonfiction. Master the fundamentals of writing/selling nonfiction articles: finding article ideas, conducting interviews, writing effective query letters and attention-getting leads, targeting your articles to the right publication, and other important elements of a salable article. Course includes writing assignments and one complete article manuscript (and its revision).

Science Fiction and Fantasy Workshops. Explore the exciting world of science fiction and fantasy with one of our professional science fiction writers as your guide. Besides improving your general writing skills, you'll learn the special techniques of creating worlds, science and magic, shaping time and place. And how to get published in this world. Choose Short Story or Novel Writing.

Mystery Writing Workshops. With the personal attention, experience and advice from a professional, published mystery writer, you'll uncover the secrets of writing suspenseful, involving mysteries. In addition to learning the genre's special techniques like how to drop red herrings, when and where to plant critical clues and what to keep hidden from your reader, you'll continue to improve your general writing skills that will lay a critical foundation for your story. Choose Short Story of Novel Writing.

Mail this card today for **FREE** information!

TQ (Teenquest); Vision; With Magazine; Young Salvationist/Young Soldier

Small Press

Adventure. Aegina Press, Inc.; Ariadne Press; Authors Connection Press, The; Authors Unlimited; Barlow Press; Black Heron Press; Borealis Press; British American Publishing, Ltd.; Bryans & Bryans; Council for Indian Education; Dan River Press; Fasa Corporation; Infinite Savant Publishing; Jesperson Press Ltd.; Marron Publishers, Inc.; Mey-House Books; Our Child Press; Pando Publications; Paper Bag Press, The; Read 'n Run Books; Soho Press; Spectrum Press; University Editions; Woodsong Graphics Inc.; Wyrick & Company; Yarrow Press

Canadian. Annick Press Ltd.; Black Moss Press; Borealis Press; Cacanadadada; Coteau Books; Cuff Publications Ltd., Harry; Dundurn Press; Goose Lane Editions; Guernica Editions; Jesperson Press Ltd.; Newest Publishers Ltd.; Orca Book Publishers Ltd.; Polestar Book Publishers; Prairie Journal Press; Prairie Publishing Company, The; Press Gang Publishers; Quarry Press; Red Deer College Press; Reference Press; Simon & Pierre; Thistledown Press; Turnstone Press; Women's Press; York Press

Contemporary. Aegina Press, Inc.; American Atheist Press; Androgyne; Applezaba Press; Ariadne Press; Arrowood Books; Authors Connection Press, The; Authors Unlimited; Barlow Press; Barn Owl Books; Black Heron Press; Black Tie Press; Books for All Times, Inc.; Borealis Press; Bryans & Bryans; Carolina Wren Press; Carpenter Press; Catbird Press; Center Press; Coffee House Press; Confluence Press Inc.; Creative Arts Book Co.; Cross-Cultural Communications; Dan River Press; Dawnwood Press; Dayspring Press, Inc.; Dragonsbreath Press, The; Dundurn Press; Esoterica Press; Feminist Press; Fromm International; Goose Lane Editions; Griffon House Publications; Guernica Editions; Guyasuta Publisher; Haypenny Press; Helicon Nine Editions; Herbooks; Hermes House Press; Marron Publishers, Inc.; Mey-House Books; Milkweed Editions; New Rivers Press; Nightshade Press; Ommation Press; Orca Book Publishers Ltd.; Our Child Press; Paper Bag Press, The; Papier-Mache; Paycock Press; Peachtree Publishers, Ltd.; Pikestaff Publications, Inc.; Pineapple Press; Pocahontas Press, Inc.; Press Gang Publishers; Puckerbrush Press; Read 'n Run Books; Red Deer College Press; Savant Garde Workshop, The; Second Chance Press and the Permanent Press; Seven Buffaloes Press; Simon & Pierre; Southern Methodist University Press; Spectrum Press; Station Hill Press; Tide Book Publishing Company; University Editions; University of Illinois Press; Woman in the Moon Publications; Women's Press; Woodsong Graphics Inc.; Yarrow Press; York Press; Zephyr Press; Zoland Books, Inc.

Erotica. British American Publishing, Ltd.; Center Press; Creative Arts Book Co.; Dragonsbreath Press, The; Guyasuta Publisher; Infinite Savant Publishing; Paper Bag Press, The; Permeable Press; Press Gang Publishers; Red Alder Books; Spectrum Press

Ethnic. Acadia Publishing Co.; Alaska Native Language Center; Arte Publico Press; Authors Unlimited; Bamboo Ridge Press; Barn Owl Books; Bilingual Press/Editorial Bilingüe; Blind Beggar Press; British American Publishing, Ltd.; Carolina Wren Press; China Books; Coffee House Press; Council for Indian Education; Cross-Cultural Communications; Eighth Mt. Press, The; Esoterica Press; Feminist Press; Griffon House Publications; Guernica Editions; Haypenny Press; Helicon Nine Editions; Herbooks; Heritage Press; Island House; Mage Publishers; Mey-House Books; Open Hand Publishing, Inc.; Paper Bag Press, The; Path Press, Inc.; Pocahontas Press, Inc.; Press Gang Publishers; Read 'n Run Books; Sandpiper Press; Seal Press; Seven Buffaloes Press; Soho Press; Soleil Press; Southern Methodist University Press; Spectrum Press; Stone Bridge Press; Third World Press; Three Continents Press; University Editions; Waterfront Press; Woman in the Moon Publications; Wyrick & Company; Zephyr Press

Experimental. Aegina Press, Inc.; Androgyne; Applezaba Press; Black Heron Press; Black Tie Press; Blind Beggar Press; Cacanadadada; Carolina Wren Press; Carpenter Press; Center Press; Clothespin Fever Press; Coffee House Press; Cross-Cultural Communications; Dan River Press; Dragonsbreath Press, The; Feminist Press; Griffon House Publications; Haypenny Press; Helicon Nine Editions; Hermes House Press; Island House; Milkweed Editions; New Directions; New Rivers Press; Ommation Press; Paper Bag Press, The; Paycock Press; Permeable Press; Pikestaff Publications, Inc.; Pineapple Press; Puckerbrush Press; Q.E.D. Press; Quarry Press; Read 'n Run Books; Red Deer College Press; Southern Methodist University Press; Spectrum Press; Station Hill Press; Swamp Press; Textile Bridge Press; Thistledown Press; Turnstone Press; Ultramarine Publishing Co., Inc.; University Editions; University of Illinois Press; Wyrick & Company; York Press; Zephyr Press

Faction. Aegina Press, Inc.; Authors Unlimited; British American Publishing, Ltd.; Fromm International; Island House; Q.E.D. Press

Fantasy. Aegina Press, Inc.; Applezaba Press; Ariadne Press; Authors Unlimited; British American Publishing, Ltd.; Carpenter Press; Clear Light Publishers; Dan River Press; Dragonsbreath Press, The; GMS Publications; Haypenny Press; Infinite Savant Publishing; Jesperson Press Ltd.; Our Child Press; Paper

Bag Press, The; Press of Macdonald and Reinecke, The; Read 'n Run Books; Space and Time; Spectrum Press; Ultramarine Publishing Co., Inc.; University Editions; W.W. Publications; Woman in the Moon Publications; Yith Press

Feminist. Applezaba Press; Ariadne Press; Authors Unlimited; Barn Owl Books; British American Publishing, Ltd.; Calyx Books; Carolina Wren Press; Clothespin Fever Press; Creative Arts Book Co.; Eighth Mt. Press, The; Feminist Press; Firebrand Books; Frog in the Well; Herbooks; Hermes House Press; Infinite Savant Publishing; Mother Courage Press; New Victoria Publishers; Ommation Press; Paper Bag Press; Papier-Mache; Permeable Press; Post-Appolo Press, The; Press Gang Publishers; Quarry Press; Read 'n Run Books; Samisdat; Savant Garde Workshop, The; Seal Press; Silverleaf Press, Inc.; Spectrum Press; Spinsters Book Co.; Tide Book Publishing Company; University Editions; Women's Press; Zephyr Press; Zoland Books, Inc.

Gay. Alyson Publications, Inc.; Applezaba Press; Authors Unlimited; British American Publishing, Ltd.; Carolina Wren Press; Feminist Press; Gay Sunshine Press and Leyland Publications; Infinite Savant Publishing; Knights Press; Los Hombres Press; Permeable Press; Samisdat; Spectrum Press; STARbooks Press; Woman in the Moon Publications; Zephyr Press

Historical. Aegina Press, Inc.; Ariadne Press; Authors Unlimited; Barlow Press; Borealis Press; Bryans & Bryans; Clear Light Publishers; Council for Indian Education; Creative Arts Book Co.; Dan River Press; Esoterica Press; Feminist Press; 1st Amendment Publishers Inc.; GMS Publications; Goose Lane Editions; Herbooks; Jayell Enterprises; Kruza Kaleidoscopix, Inc.; Long Publishing Co., Hendrick; Marron Publishers, Inc.; Mosaic Press; Open Hand Publishing, Inc.; Pando Publications; Paper Bag Press, The; Path Press, Inc.; Permeable Press; Pineapple Press; Pocahontas Press, Inc.; Press of Macdonald and Reinecke, The; Quarry Press; Read 'n Run Books; Simon & Pierre; Soho Press; Southern Methodist University Press; Spectrum Press; Third World Press; Tide Book Publishing Company; University Editions; Woodsong Graphics Inc.; Zephyr Press

Horror. Aegina Press, Inc.; Authors Unlimited; British American Publishing, Ltd.; Bryans & Bryans; Dan River Press; GMS Publications; Infinite Savant Publishing; Paper Bag Press, The; Read 'n Run Books; Scare Ware; Space and Time; University Editions; Yith Press

Humor/Satire. Acadia Publishing Co.; Applezaba Press; Ariadne Press; Authors Unlimited; Barlow Press; Beil, Publisher, Inc., Frederic C.; Black Heron Press; Black Moss Press; Bryans & Bryans; Catbird Press; Center Press; Clear Light Publishers; Coffee House Press; Confluence Press Inc.; Creative with Words Publications; Cross-Cultural Communications; Dan River Press; Dragonsbreath Press, The; Fromm International; Haypenny Press; Homestead Publishing; Jesperson Press Ltd.; Mosaic Press; Nightshade Press; Pando Publications; Paper Bag Press, The; Paycock Press; Press Gang Publishers; Press of Macdonald and Reinecke, The; Read 'n Run Books; Simon & Pierre; Tide Book Publishing Company; University Editions; Woodsong Graphics Inc.; Wyrick & Company; Yarrow Press; Zephyr Press

Juvenile. Acadia Publishing Co.; Advocacy Press; Annick Press Ltd.; Authors Connection Press, The; Black Moss Press; Blind Beggar Press; Borealis Press; British American Publishing, Ltd.; Carolina Wren Press; Council for Indian Education; Creative with Words Publications; Cross-Cultural Communications; Esoterica Press; Homestead Publishing; Jesperson Press Ltd.; Kar-Ben Copies, Inc.; Kruza Kaleidoscopix, Inc.; Lollipop Power Books; Long Publishing Co., Hendrick; Open Hand Publishing, Inc.; Orca Book Publishers Ltd.; Our Child Press; Overlook Press, The; Pando Publications; Permeable Press; Pippin Press; Prairie Publishing Company, The; Read 'n Run Books; Shoe Tree Press; Simon & Pierre; Third World Press; University Editions; Willowisp Press, Inc.; Women's Press; Woodsong Graphics Inc.

Lesbian. Alyson Publications, Inc.; Applezaba Press; Authors Unlimited; Barn Owl Books; British American Publishing, Ltd.; Calyx Books; Carolina Wren Press; Clothespin Fever Press; Eighth Mt. Press, The; Feminist Press; Firebrand Books; Frog in the Well; Herbooks; Infinite Savant Publishing; Los Hombres Press; Madwoman Press; Mother Courage Press; Naiad Press, Inc., The; New Victoria Publishers; Permeable Press; Post-Appolo Press, The; Press Gang Publishers; Rising Tide Press; Samisdat; Seal Press; Silverleaf Press, Inc.; Spectrum Press; Spinsters Book Co.; Woman in the Moon Publications; Women's Press; Zephyr Press

Literary. Aegina Press, Inc.; Androgyne; Another Chicago Press; Applezaba Press; Ariadne Press; Arrowood Books; Authors Unlimited; Bamboo Ridge Press; Barlow Press; Barn Owl Books; Beil, Publisher, Inc., Frederic C.; Bilingual Press/Editorial Bilingüe; Black Heron Press; Books for All Times, Inc.; Borealis Press; Bottom Dog Press; Bryans & Bryans; Burning Books; Cacanadadada; Cadmus Editions; Cane Hill Press; Carolina Wren Press; Carpenter Press; Catbird Press; Chelsea Green Publishing Co.; Coffee House Press; Confluence Press Inc.; Creative Arts Book Co.; Cross-Cultural Communications; Dan River Press; Daniel and Company, Publishers, John; Dragonsbreath Press, The; Ecco Press, The; Esoterica Press; Faber and Faber, Inc.; Feminist Press; 1st Amendment Publishers Inc.; Florida Literary Foundation Press; Four Walls Eight Windows; Fromm International; Goose Lane Editions; Graywolf Press; Griffon House Publications; Guernica Editions; Haypenny Press; Helicon Nine Editions; Hermes House Press; Homestead Publishing; Island House; Longstreet Press; Manic D Press; Marron Publishers, Inc.; Mercury House; Milkweed Editions; Mosaic Press; Moyer Bell Limited; New Rivers Press; Newest Publishers Ltd.; Nightshade Press; Ommation Press; Orca Book Publishers Ltd.; Overlook Press, The; Paper Bag Press, The; Paycock Press; Peachtree Publishers, Ltd.; Permeable Press; Pikestaff Publications, Inc.; Post-Appolo Press, The; Prairie Journal Press; Press Gang Publishers; Press of Macdonald and Reinecke, The; Puckerbrush Press; Q.E.D. Press; Quarry Press; Read 'n Run Books; Red Deer College Press; Rydal Press; Samisdat; Savant Garde Workshop, The; Seal Press; Second Chance Press and the Permanent Press; Shaw Publishers, Harold; Simon & Pierre; Soho Press; Southern Methodist University Press; Spectrum Press; Station Hill Press; Swamp Press; Textile Bridge Press; Thistledown Press; Tide Book Publishing Company; Turnstone Press; University of Arkansas Press, The; University of Illinois Press; Watermark Press, Inc.; Woodsong Graphics Inc.; Yarrow Press; Zephyr Press; Zoland Books, Inc.

Mainstream. Aegina Press, Inc.; Ariadne Press; Arrowood Books; Authors Unlimited; Barlow Press; Bottom Dog Press; Bryans & Bryans; Catbird Press; Confluence Press Inc.; Dan River Press; Daniel and Company, Publishers, John; 1st Amendment Publishers Inc.; Haypenny Press; Longstreet Press; Marron Publishers, Inc.; Nightshade Press; Orca Book Publishers Ltd.; Pando Publications; Paper Bag Press, The; Peachtree Publishers, Ltd.; Press of Macdonald and Reinecke, The; Read 'n Run Books; Seal Press; Soho Press; Southern Methodist University Press; Spectrum Press; Tide Book Publishing Company; Ultramarine Publishing Co., Inc.; University Editions; University of Arkansas Press, The; Woodsong Graphics Inc.; Wyrick & Company; Yarrow Press; Zephyr Press

Novella. Hermes House Press; Rio Grande Press; Samisdat

Preschool/Picture Book. Authors Connection Press, The; Black Moss Press; British American Publishing, Ltd.; Council for Indian Education; Homestead Publishing; Our Child Press; Permeable Press; Read 'n Run Books; Willowisp Press, Inc.; Yarrow Press

Psychic/Supernatural/Occult. Authors Unlimited; Carolina Wren Press; Dan River Press; GMS Publications; Infinite Savant Publishing; Overlook Press, The; Permeable Press; Read 'n Run Books; Scare Ware; Space and Time; Woman in the Moon Publications; Woodsong Graphics Inc.

Regional. Aegina Press, Inc.; Authors Unlimited; Barlow Press; Barn Owl Books; Beil, Publisher, Inc., Frederic C.; Carolina Wren Press; Clear Light Publishers; Confluence Press Inc.; Council for Indian Education; Creative Arts Book Co.; Cuff Publications Ltd., Harry; Dan River Press; Feminist Press; Frog in the Well; Haypenny Press; Long Publishing Co., Hendrick; Mosaic Press; Nightshade Press; Orca Book Publishers Ltd.; Overlook Press, The; Pando Publications; Peachtree Publishers, Ltd.; Pineapple Press; Pocahontas Press, Inc.; Press Gang Publishers; Read 'n Run Books; Rydal Press; Samisdat; Seven Buffaloes Press; Southern Methodist University Press; Three Continents Press; Tide Book Publishing Company; University Editions; University of Idaho Press; Watermark Press, Inc.; Woodley Memorial Press; Wyrick & Company; Zephyr Press

Religious. Authors Unlimited; Bethel Publishing; British American Publishing, Ltd.; GMS Publications; Herbooks; Mosaic Press; Post-Appolo Press, The; Read 'n Run Books; Shaw Publishers, Harold; Star Books, Inc.; Starburst Publishers; Threshold Books

Romance. Authors Unlimited; Bryans & Bryans; Marron Publishers, Inc.; Mosaic Press; Read 'n Run Books; University Editions; Woodsong Graphics Inc.

Science Fiction. Aegina Press, Inc.; Authors Unlimited; Black Heron Press; British American Publishing, Ltd.; Dan River Press; Dayspring Press, Inc.; Dragonsbreath Press, The; Fasa Corporation; Feminist Press; GMS Publications; Haypenny Press; Infinite Savant Publishing; Mey-House Books; Overlook Press, The; Pando Publications; Permeable Press; Press Gang Publishers; Read 'n Run Books; Savant Garde Workshop, The; Space and Time; Spectrum Press; Third World Press; Ultramarine Publishing Co., Inc.; University Editions; W.W. Publications; Woodsong Graphics Inc.

Short Story Collections. Aegina Press, Inc.; Applezaba Press; Authors Connection Press, The; Bamboo Ridge Press; Barlow Press; Beil, Publisher, Inc., Frederic C.; Bilingual Press/Editorial Bilingüe; Black Moss Press; Blind Beggar Press; Books for All Times, Inc.; Calyx Books; Cane Hill Press; Carolina Wren Press; Clothespin Fever Press; Coffee House Press; Confluence Press Inc.; Coteau Books; Creative Arts Book Co.; Cross-Cultural Communications; Dan River Press; Daniel and Company, Publishers, John; Dragonsbreath Press, The; Ecco Press, The; Eighth Mt. Press, The; Esoterica Press; Feminist Press; Frog in the Well; Fromm International; GMS Publications; Goose Lane Editions; Graywolf Press; Guyasuta Publisher; Haypenny Press; Helicon Nine Editions; Hermes House Press; Homestead Publishing; Island House; Longstreet Press; New Rivers Press; Papier-Mache; Path Press, Inc.; Peachtree Publishers, Ltd.; Permeable Press; Post-Appolo Press, The; Press Gang Publishers; Press of Macdonald and Reinecke, The; Quarry Press; Read 'n Run Books; Red Deer College Press; Rio Grande Press; Samisdat;

Seal Press; Seven Buffaloes Press; Silverleaf Press, Inc.; Southern Methodist University Press; Spectrum Press; Swamp Press; Textile Bridge Press; Third World Press; Thistledown Press; Three Continents Press; Ultramarine Publishing Co., Inc.; University Editions; University of Arkansas Press, The; University of Idaho Press; University of Illinois Press; Watermark Press, Inc.; Woman in the Moon Publications; Women's Press; Yarrow Press; Zephyr Press; Zoland Books, Inc.

Sports. Authors Unlimited; Path Press, Inc.; Pocahontas Press, Inc.; Reference Press

Suspense/Mystery. Aegina Press, Inc.; Authors Connection Press, The; Authors Unlimited; Cliffhanger Press; Creative Arts Book Co.; GMS Publications; Infinite Savant Publishing; Marron Publishers, Inc.; Pando Publications; Press Gang Publishers; Q.E.D. Press; Read 'n Run Books; Savant Garde Workshop, The; Second Chance Press and the Permanent Press; Simon & Pierre; Soho Press; Spectrum Press; Woodsong Graphics Inc.

Translations. Applezaba Press; Beil, Publisher, Inc., Frederic C.; Bilingual Press/Editorial Bilingüe; Blind Beggar Press; British American Publishing, Ltd.; Calyx Books; Carolina Wren Press; Catbird Press; Center Press; Creative Arts Book Co.; Cross-Cultural Communications; Esoterica Press; Feminist Press; Fromm International; Griffon House Publications; Helicon Nine Editions; Hermes House Press; Italica Press; Mercury House; New Rivers Press; Overlook Press, The; Paycock Press; Pocahontas Press, Inc.; Post-Appolo Press, The; Q.E.D. Press; Read 'n Run Books; Simon & Pierre; Spectrum Press; Station Hill Press; Stone Bridge Press; Swamp Press; Three Continents Press; Translation Center, The; University Editions; University of Arkansas Press, The; Waterfront Press; Women's Press; York Press; Zoland Books, Inc.

Western. Authors Connection Press, The; Authors Unlimited; British American Publishing, Ltd.; Clear Light Publishers; Coteau Books; Council for Indian Education; Creative Arts Book Co.; Dan River Press; Homestead Publishing; Pocahontas Press, Inc.; Read 'n Run Books; Rydal Press; Spectrum Press; Sunstone Press; Woodsong Graphics Inc.

Young Adult/Teen. Acadia Publishing Co.; Authors Connection Press, The; Bethel Publishing; Blind Beggar Press; Borealis Press; British American Publishing, Ltd.; Council for Indian Education; Cross-Cultural Communications; Davenport Publishers, May; Haypenny Press; Homestead Publishing; Long Publishing Co., Hendrick; Marron Publishers, Inc.; Mosaic Press; Open Hand Publishing, Inc.; Orca Book Publishers Ltd.; Our Child Press; Pando Publications; Pocahontas Press, Inc.; Read 'n Run Books; Seal Press; Shaw Publishers, Harold; Shoe Tree Press; Simon & Pierre; Star Books, Inc.; Third World Press; W.W. Publications; Willowisp Press, Inc.; Women's Press; Woodsong Graphics Inc.

Commercial Publishers

Adventure. Avalon Books; Bethany House Publishers; Books In Motion; Bouregy & Company, Inc., Thomas; Branden Publishing Co.; Broadman Press; Cloverdale Press Inc.; Crown Publishing Group, The; Dell Publishing; Diane Publishing Co.; Fearon/Janus; Harlequin Enterprises, Ltd.; Herald Press; Holiday House, Inc.; Holloway House Publishing Company; Holt & Company, Henry; Horizon Publishers and Dist., Inc.; Morrow and Company, Inc., William; Philomel Books; Pocket Books; Random House, Inc.; St. Martin's Press; Stoddart; Vesta Publications, Ltd; Villard Books; Walker and Company; Warner Books; Worldwide Library; Zebra Books; Zondervan

Canadian. Harlequin Enterprises, Ltd.; Macmillan Canada; Stoddart; Vesta Publications, Ltd; Worldwide Library

Comics. Eclipse Books/Eclipse Comics; Fantagraphics Books

Contemporary. Apple Books; Ballantine Books; Blair, Publisher, John F.; Bookcraft, Inc.; Branden Publishing Co.; Carroll & Graf Publishers, Inc.; Crown Publishing Group, The; Dell Publishing; Fearon/Janus; Harvest House Publishers; Holiday House, Inc.; Holloway House; Holt & Company, Henry; Knopf, Alfred A.; Louisiana State University Press; Morrow and Company, Inc., William; Pocket Books; Random House, Inc.; St. Martin's Press; Sierra Club Books; Smith, Publisher, Gibbs; Summit Books; Vesta Publications, Ltd; Villard Books; Warner Books; Zebra Books

Erotica. Carroll & Graf Publishers, Inc.; Diane Publishing Co.; Pocket Books; St. Martin's Press

Ethnic. Branden Publishing Co.; Fearon/Janus; Holloway House; Philomel Books; Pocket Books; St. Martin's Press; Vesta Publications, Ltd

Experimental. Morrow and Company, Inc., William; St. Martin's Press; Smith, Publisher, Gibbs; Vesta Publications, Ltd

Faction. Pocket Books; Vesta Publications, Ltd

Fantasy. Avon Books; Baen Books; Bantam Spectra Books; Berkley/Ace Science Fiction; Carroll & Graf Publishers, Inc.; Cloverdale Press Inc.; Daw Books, Inc.; Del Rey Books; Delecorte/Dell Books for Young Readers; Holloway House; NAL/Dutton; Philomel Books; Pocket Books; St. Martin's Press; Tor Books; TSR, Inc.; Vesta Publications, Ltd; Warner Books; Zondervan

Feminist. Academy Chicago Publishers; Ballantine Books; Braziller, Inc., George; Holt & Company, Henry; Morrow and Company, Inc., William; Pocket Books; St. Martin's Press; Summit Books; Vesta Publications, Ltd

Historical. Academy Chicago Publishers; Avon Books; Ballantine Books; Bookcraft, Inc.; Branden Publishing Co.; Broadman Press; Cloverdale Press Inc.; Crown Publishing Group, The; Dell Publishing; Fearon/Janus; Harvest House Publishers; Herald Press; Holloway House; Holt & Company, Henry; Horizon Publishers and Dist., Inc.; Morrow and Company, Inc., William; NAL/Dutton; Philomel Books; Pocket Books; Random House, Inc.; Summit Books; Vesta Publications, Ltd; Villard Books; Winston-Derek Publishers; Zebra Books; Zondervan

Horror. Avon Books; Cloverdale Press Inc.; Crown Publishing Group, The; Daw Books, Inc.; Dell Publishing; Dorchester Publishing Co., Inc.; Holloway House; Leisure Books; Morrow and Company, Inc., William; NAL/Dutton; Pocket Books; TSR, Inc.; Villard Books; Walker and Company; Warner Books; Wildstar Books/Empire Books; Zebra Books

Humor/Satire. Books In Motion; Broadman Press; Crown Publishing Group, The; Harvest House Publishers; Holt & Company, Henry; Horizon Publishers and Dist., Inc.; Morrow and Company, Inc., William; Pocket Books; Potter, Inc., Clarkson N.; Price Stern Sloan, Inc.; St. Martin's Press; Smith, Publisher, Gibbs; Summit Books; Vesta Publications, Ltd; Villard Books

Juvenile. Ace Science Fiction; Apple Books; Atheneum Books for Children; Bethany House Publishers; Boyds Mills Press; Bradbury Press, Inc.; Broadman Press; Camelot Books; Clarion Books; Crossway Books; Delecorte/Dell Books for Young Readers; Dell Publishing; Dial Books for Young Readers; Eakin Press; Farrar, Straus & Giroux/Children's Books; Gareth Stevens, Inc.; Gessler Publishing Company; Grosset & Dunlap, Inc.; Harcourt Brace Jovanovich; HarperCollins Children's Books; Herald Press; Holiday House, Inc.; Horizon Publishers and Dist., Inc.; Interlink Publishing Group, Inc.; Joy Street Books; Knopf Books for Young Readers; Little, Brown and Company Children's Books; Lodestar Books; Lucas/Evans Books; McElderry Books, Margaret K.; Macmillan Children's Books; Modern Publishing; Morrow Junior Books; Multnomah; Pelican Publishing Company; Philomel Books; Potter, Inc., Clarkson N.; Price Stern Sloan, Inc.; St. Paul Books and Media; Scribner's Sons Books for Young Readers, Charles; Troll Associates; Vesta Publications, Ltd; Weiss Associates, Inc., Daniel; Western Publishing Company, Inc.; Whitman & Company, Albert; WindSong Books; Winston-Derek Publishers; Yearling

Literary. Bantam Spectra Books; Blair, Publisher, John F.; Branden Publishing Co.; Carroll & Graf Publishers, Inc.; Crown Publishing Group, The; Gessler Publishing Company; Herald Press; Louisiana State University Press; Macmillan Canada; Morrow and Company, Inc., William; Norton & Company, Inc., W.W.; Philomel Books; Pocket Books; Smith, Publisher, Gibbs; Summit Books

Mainstream. Avon Books; Branden Publishing Co.; Carroll & Graf Publishers, Inc.; Crown Publishing Group, The; Eriksson, Publisher, Paul S.; Holloway House; Holt & Company, Henry; Horizon Publishers and Dist., Inc.; Louisiana State University Press; Macmillan Canada; NAL/Dutton; Pocket Books; Random House, Inc.; Summit Books; Tor Books; Vesta Publications, Ltd; Villard Books; Warner Books; Zondervan

Military/War. Avon Books; Branden Publishing Co.; Cloverdale Press Inc.; Crown Publishing Group, The; Dell Publishing; Diane Publishing Co.; Holloway House; Horizon Publishers and Dist., Inc.; Morrow and Company, Inc., William; Pocket Books; Vesta Publications, Ltd; Warner Books; Zebra Books

Preschool/Picture Book. Atheneum Books for Children; Boyds Mills Press; Farrar, Straus & Giroux/Children's Books; Four Winds Press; Gareth Stevens, Inc.; Gessler Publishing Company; Grosset & Dunlap, Inc.; Harcourt Brace Jovanovich; HarperCollins Children's Books; Harvest House Publishers; Holiday House, Inc.; Interlink Publishing Group, Inc.; Joy Street Books; Knopf Books for Young Readers; Little, Brown and Company Children's Books; McElderry Books, Margaret K.; Modern Publishing; Morrow Junior Books; Multnomah; Philomel Books; St. Paul Books and Media; Scribner's Sons Books for Young Readers, Charles; Troll Associates; Vesta Publications, Ltd; Warner Books; Western Publishing Company, Inc.

Psychic/Supernatural/Occult. Avon Books; Cloverdale Press Inc.; Dell Publishing; Pocket Books; St. Martin's Press; Vesta Publications, Ltd; Wildstar Books/Empire Books; Winston-Derek Publishers

Regional. Bethany House Publishers; Blair, Publisher, John F.; Fearon/Janus; Interlink Publishing Group, Inc.; Pelican Publishing Company; Philomel Books; Vesta Publications, Ltd.

Religious. Accent Books; Baker Book House; Bethany House Publishers; Bookcraft, Inc.; Bridge Publishing, Inc.; Broadman Press; Cook Publishing Company, David C.; Crossway Books; Harvest House Publishers; Herald Press; Holiday House, Inc.; Horizon Publishers and Dist., Inc.; Lion Publishing; Multnomah; Resource Publications, Inc.; St. Martin's Press; St. Paul Books and Media; Standard Publishing; Tyndale House Publishers; Vesta Publications, Ltd; WindSong Books; Winston-Derek Publishers; Zondervan

Romance. Avalon Books; Bethany House Publishers; Bookcraft, Inc.; Bouregy & Company, Inc., Thomas; Dorchester Publishing Co., Inc.; Doubleday; Fearon/Janus; Harlequin Enterprises, Ltd.; Harvest House Publishers; Heartfire Romance; Holloway House; Horizon Publishers and Dist., Inc.; Leisure Books; Loveswept; Meteor Publishing Corporation; NAL/Dutton; Pocket Books; St. Martin's Press; Silhouette Books; Vesta Publications, Ltd; Villard Books; Walker and Company; Warner Books; Wildstar Books/Empire Books; Zebra Books

Science Fiction. Avon Books; Baen Books; Bantam Spectra Books; Berkley/Ace Science Fiction; Carroll & Graf Publishers, Inc.; Cloverdale Press Inc.; Crown Publishing Group, The; Daw Books, Inc.; Del Rey Books; Dorchester Publishing Co., Inc.; Fearon/Janus; Horizon Publishers and Dist., Inc.; Morrow and Company, Inc., William; NAL/Dutton; St. Martin's Press; Tor Books; TSR, Inc.; Vesta Publications, Ltd; Warner Books; Zondervan

Short Story Collections. Branden Publishing Co.; Braziller, Inc., George; Fearon/Janus; Gessler Publishing Company; Louisiana State University Press; Philomel Books; Pulphouse Publishing, Inc.; Random House, Inc.; Resource Publications, Inc.; Smith, Publisher, Gibbs; Vesta Publications, Ltd

Suspense/Mystery. Academy Chicago Publishers; Baker Book House; Bethany House Publishers; Books In Motion; Branden Publishing Co.; Carroll & Graf Publishers, Inc.; Cloverdale Press Inc.; Dell Publishing; Diane Publishing Co.; Doubleday; Fearon/Janus; Holloway House; Holt & Company, Henry; Knopf, Alfred A.; Macmillan Canada; Morrow and Company, Inc., William; Mysterious Press, The; NAL/Dutton; Pocket Books; Random House, Inc.; St. Martin's Press; Stoddart; Summit Books; Tor Books; Vesta Publications, Ltd; Villard Books; Walker and Company; Warner Books; Wildstar Books/Empire Books; Zebra Books; Zondervan

Translations. Academy Chicago Publishers; Branden Publishing Co.; Braziller, Inc., George; Gessler Publishing Company; Holt & Company, Henry; Interlink Publishing Group, Inc.; Morrow and Company, Inc., William; Philomel Books; Smith, Publisher, Gibbs; Summit Books; Vesta Publications, Ltd; Vision Books Pvt Ltd.; Washington Square Press; Weidenfeld and Nicolson Ltd.

Western. Avalon Books; Avon Books; Bookcraft, Inc.; Bouregy & Company, Inc., Thomas; Cloverdale Press Inc.; Doubleday; Evans & Co., Inc., M.; Fearon/Janus; Holloway House; Jameson Books; NAL/Dutton; Pocket Books; Tor Books; Walker and Company; Warner Books; Wildstar Books/Empire Books

Young Adult/Teen. Archway Paperbacks; Atheneum Books for Children; Avon Books; Boyds Mills Press; Bradbury Press, Inc.; Broadman Press; Clarion Books; Cloverdale Press Inc.; Crossway Books; Delecorte/Dell Books for Young Readers; Dell Publishing; Evans & Co., Inc., M.; Fearon/Janus; Harcourt Brace Jovanovich; HarperCollins Children's Books; Herald Press; Holiday House, Inc.; Holt & Company, Henry; Horizon Publishers and Dist., Inc.; Knopf Books for Young Readers; Lerner Publications Company; Little, Brown and Company Children's Books; Lodestar Books; Lucas/Evans Books; McElderry Books, Margaret K.; Morrow Junior Books; Multnomah; Philomel Books; Point Books; St. Paul Books and Media; Scribner's Sons Books for Young Readers, Charles; Stoddart; Tab Book Club; Trillium Press; Troll Associates; Vesta Publications, Ltd; Walker and Company; Weiss Associates, Inc., Daniel; WindSong Books; Winston-Derek Publishers

Markets Index

If you can't find a listing in the Markets Index, check pages 312-313 for Other Literary and Small Circulation Magazines, page 393 for Other Commercial Periodicals, page 460 for Other Small Presses, page 509 for Other Commercial Publishers or page 549 for Other Contests.

Other Books of Interest

Annual Market Books
    Artist's Market, edited by Lauri Miller $21.95
    Children's Writer's & Illustrator's Market, edited by Lisa Carpenter (paper) $17.95
    Guide to Literary Agents & Art/Photo Reps, edited by Robin Gee $15.95
    Humor & Cartoon Markets, edited by Bob Staake (paper) $16.95
    Photographer's Market, edited by Sam Marshall $21.95
    Poet's Market, by Judson Jerome $19.95
    Songwriter's Market, edited by Brian Rushing $19.95
    Writer's Market, edited by Mark Kissling $25.95

General Writing Books
    Annable's Treasury of Literary Teasers, by H.D. Annable (paper) $1.99
    Beginning Writer's Answer Book, edited by Kirk Polking (paper) $13.95
    Discovering the Writer Within, by Bruce Ballenger & Barry Lane $17.95
    Freeing Your Creativity, by Marshall Cook $17.95
    Getting the Words Right: How to Rewrite, Edit and Revise, by Theodore A. Rees Cheney (paper) $12.95
    How to Write a Book Proposal, by Michael Larsen (paper) $10.95
    Just Open a Vein, edited by William Brohaugh $15.95
    Knowing Where to Look: The Ultimate Guide to Research, by Lois Horowitz (paper) $16.95
    Make Your Words Work, by Gary Provost $17.95
    Pinckert's Practical Grammar, by Robert C. Pinckert (paper) $11.95
    12 Keys to Writing Books That Sell, by Kathleen Krull (paper) $12.95
    The 28 Biggest Writing Blunders, by William Noble $12.95
    The 29 Most Common Writing Mistakes & How to Avoid Them, by Judy Delton (paper) $9.95
    The Wordwatcher's Guide to Good Writing & Grammar, by Morton S. Freeman (paper) $15.95
    Word Processing Secrets for Writers, by Michael A. Banks & Ansen Dibell (paper) $14.95
    The Writer's Book of Checklists, by Scott Edelstein $16.95
    The Writer's Digest Guide to Manuscript Formats, by Buchman & Groves $18.95
    The Writer's Essential Desk Reference, edited by Glenda Neff $19.95

Fiction Writing
    The Art & Craft of Novel Writing, by Oakley Hall $17.95
    Best Stories from New Writers, edited by Linda Sanders $5.99
    Characters & Viewpoint, by Orson Scott Card $13.95
    The Complete Guide to Writing Fiction, by Barnaby Conrad $17.95
    Cosmic Critiques: How & Why 10 Science Fiction Stories Work, edited by Asimov & Greenberg (paper) $12.95
    Creating Characters: How to Build Story People, by Dwight V. Swain $16.95
    Creating Short Fiction, by Damon Knight (paper) $10.95
    Dialogue, by Lewis Turco $13.95
    The Fiction Writer's Silent Partner, by Martin Roth $19.95
    Handbook of Short Story Writing: Vol. I, by Dickson and Smythe (paper) $10.95
    Handbook of Short Story Writing: Vol. II, edited by Jean Fredette (paper) $12.95
    How to Write & Sell Your First Novel, by Collier & Leighton (paper) $12.95
    Manuscript Submission, by Scott Edelstein $13.95
    Mastering Fiction Writing, by Kit Reed $18.95
    Plot, by Ansen Dibell $13.95
    Spider Spin Me a Web: Lawrence Block on Writing Fiction, by Lawrence Block $16.95
    Theme & Strategy, by Ronald B. Tobias $13.95
    The 38 Most Common Fiction Writing Mistakes, by Jack M. Bickham $12.95
    Writer's Digest Handbook of Novel Writing, $18.95
    Writing the Novel: From Plot to Print, by Lawrence Block (paper) $11.95

Special Interest Writing Books
    Armed & Dangerous: A Writer's Guide to Weapons, by Michael Newton (paper) $14.95
    The Children's Picture Book: How to Write It, How to Sell It, by Ellen E.M. Roberts (paper) $19.95

Comedy Writing Secrets, by Mel Helitzer (paper) $15.95
Creating Poetry, by John Drury $18.95
Deadly Doses: A Writer's Guide to Poisons, by Serita Deborah Stevens with Anne Klarner (paper) $16.95
Families Writing, by Peter Stillman (paper) $12.95
Hillary Waugh's Guide to Mysteries & Mystery Writing, by Hillary Waugh $19.95
How to Write Action/Adventure Novels, by Michael Newton $4.99
How to Write & Sell Greeting Cards, Bumper Stickers, T-Shirts and Other Fun Stuff, by Molly Wigand (paper) $15.95
How to Write Horror Fiction, by William F. Nolan $15.95
How to Write Mysteries, by Shannon OCork $13.95
How to Write Romances, by Phyllis Taylor Pianka $15.95
How to Write Science Fiction & Fantasy, by Orson Scott Card $13.95
How to Write Tales of Horror, Fantasy & Science Fiction, edited by J.N. Williamson (paper) $12.95
How to Write the Story of Your Life, by Frank P. Thomas (paper) $11.95
How to Write Western Novels, by Matt Braun $1.00
Mystery Writer's Handbook, by The Mystery Writers of America (paper) $11.95
The Poet's Handbook, by Judson Jerome (paper) $11.95
Successful Scriptwriting, by Jurgen Wolff & Kerry Cox (paper) $14.95
The Writer's Complete Crime Reference Book, by Martin Roth $19.95
Writing for Children & Teenagers, 3rd Edition, by Lee Wyndham & Arnold Madison (paper) $12.95
Writing Mysteries: A Handbook by the Mystery Writers of America, Edited by Sue Grafton $18.95
Writing the Modern Mystery, by Barbara Norville (paper) $12.95

The Writing Business
A Beginner's Guide to Getting Published, edited by Kirk Polking (paper) $11.95
Business & Legal Forms for Authors & Self-Publishers, by Tad Crawford (paper) $4.99
The Complete Guide to Self-Publishing, by Tom & Marilyn Ross (paper) $16.95
How to Write with a Collaborator, by Hal Bennett with Michael Larsen $1.00
How You Can Make $25,000 a Year Writing, by Nancy Edmonds Hanson (paper) $14.95
This Business of Writing, by Gregg Levoy $19.95
Writer's Guide to Self-Promotion & Publicity, by Elane Feldman $16.95
A Writer's Guide to Contract Negotiations, by Richard Balkin (paper) $4.25
Writing A to Z, edited by Kirk Polking $22.95

To order directly from the publisher, include $3.00 postage and handling for 1 book and $1.00 for each additional book. Allow 30 days for delivery.

Writer's Digest Books
1507 Dana Avenue, Cincinnati, Ohio 45207
Credit card orders call TOLL-FREE
1-800-289-0963
Prices subject to change without notice.

Write to this same address for information on *Writer's Digest* magazine, *Story* magazine, Writer's Digest Book Club, Writer's Digest School, and Writer's Digest Criticism Service.